human sexuality

in a world of diversity

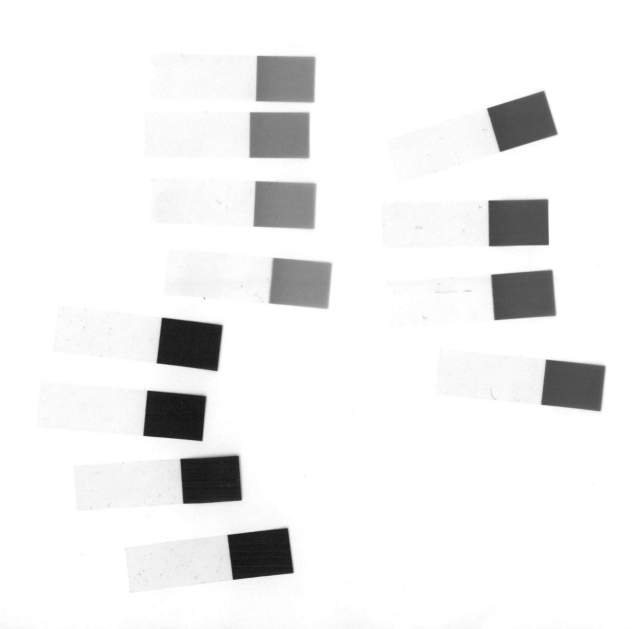

human sexuality

in a world of diversity

fifth canadian edition

Spencer A. Rathus
The College of New Jersey

Jeffrey S. Nevid
St. John's University

Lois Fichner-Rathus
The College of New Jersey

Alexander McKay
Sex Information and Education Council of Canada
Chang School of Continuing Education, Ryerson University

PEARSON

Toronto

Vice-President, CMPS: Gary Bennett
Editorial Director: Claudine O'Donnell
Senior Acquisitions Editor: Matthew Christian
Marketing Manager: Claire Varley
Program Manager: Madhu Ranadive
Project Manager: Marissa Lok
Developmental Editor: Mary Wat and Martina van de Velde
Production Services: Sudip Sinha/Lumina Datamatics, Inc.
Permissions Project Manager: Erica Mojzes
Photo Permissions Research: Marta Johnson/Lumina Datamatics, Inc.
Text Permissions Research: Liz Kincaid/Lumina Datamatics, Inc.
Cover and Interior Designer: Alex Li
Cover Image: Annette Shaff/Shutterstock

Credits and acknowledgments of material borrowed from other sources and reproduced, with permission, in this textbook appear on the appropriate pages within the text.

Library and Archives Canada Cataloguing in Publication

Rathus, Spencer A., author
    Human sexuality in a world of diversity / Spencer A. Rathus (The College of New Jersey), Jeffrey S. Nevid (St. John's University), Lois Fichner-Rathus (The College of New Jersey), Alexander McKay (Sex Information and Education Council of Canada, Chang School of Continuing Education, Ryerson University).—Fifth Canadian edition.

    Revision of: Human sexuality in a world of diversity / Spencer A. Rathus ... [et al.].—4th Canadian ed.— Toronto: Pearson Canada, 2012.
    Includes bibliographical references and index.
    ISBN 978-0-205-96877-0 (pbk.)

    1. Sex—Textbooks.   2. Sex customs—Canada—Textbooks.   I. McKay, Alexander, 1962–, author   II. Nevid, Jeffrey S., author   III. Fichner-Rathus, Lois, 1953–, author   IV. Title.
HQ21.R34 2015
306.7
                                                            C2014-907218-X

KV 08.09.2018 1053

ISBN 978-0-205-96877-0

Dedicated with love to our children, Taylor Lane Rathus and Michael Zev Nevid, who were born at the time the first edition of this book was written.

—S.A.R., L.F.-R., J.S.N.

Dedicated to my parents, Janet and Gerald McKay.

—A.G.M.

Brief Contents

Preface   xv

Chapter One   What Is Human Sexuality?   1

Chapter Two   Using Theory and Research to Understand Human Sexuality   33

Chapter Three   Female and Male Anatomy and Physiology   55

Chapter Four   Sexual Arousal and Response   96

Chapter Five   Gender Identity and Gender Roles   126

Chapter Six   Attraction and Love   152

Chapter Seven   Relationships, Intimacy, and Communication   169

Chapter Eight   Sexual Behaviours and Fantasies   189

Chapter Nine   Sexual Orientation   212

Chapter Ten   Conception, Pregnancy, and Childbirth   239

Chapter Eleven   Contraception and Abortion   266

Chapter Twelve   Sexuality Across the Life Span   292

Chapter Thirteen   Sexual Dysfunction   326

Chapter Fourteen   Sexually Transmitted Infections   356

Chapter Fifteen   Sexual Health Education   386

Chapter Sixteen   Sexual Variations   405

Chapter Seventeen   Sexual Coercion   429

Chapter Eighteen   Commercial Sex   462

Answer Key   489
References   491
Name Index   531
Subject Index   539

Contents

Preface xv

Chapter One
What Is Human Sexuality? 1

Choices, Information, and Decision Making 3

What Is Human Sexuality? 4

INNOVATIVE CANADIAN RESEARCH
What Is This Thing Called Sex? 5

INNOVATIVE CANADIAN RESEARCH
Ethnocultural Communities and Sexuality 6

A WORLD OF DIVERSITY
Sexual Scripts of Young People in Kenya 10

Sexuality and Ethics 13

Sexuality and Spirituality 15

Thinking Critically About Human Sexuality 15

Perspectives on Human Sexuality 16

APPLIED KNOWLEDGE
Thinking Critically About Sexuality Information on the
Internet 18

A WORLD OF DIVERSITY
The History of Desire 25

Multiple Perspectives on Human Sexuality 28

A WORLD OF DIVERSITY
Gender and Sexual Orientation in Aboriginal Culture 29

INNOVATIVE CANADIAN RESEARCH
Canadian Sexuality, Gender, and Other Social Variables 30

Chapter Two
Using Theory and Research to
Understand Human Sexuality 33

Theoretical Approaches to Understanding
Human Sexuality 33

A Scientific Approach to Human Sexuality 39

Quantitative Research Methods 41

Methods of Observation 42

A WORLD OF DIVERSITY
Studying the Sexual Behaviours of Diverse
Populations 46

The Experimental Method 48

A CLOSER LOOK
Measuring Sexual Arousal 49

INNOVATIVE CANADIAN RESEARCH
Using a Thermographic Camera to Measure Sexual
Arousal 50

Qualitative Research Methods 51

Ethics in Sex Research 51

INNOVATIVE CANADIAN RESEARCH
Do Research Consent Forms Affect Findings? 52

Chapter Three
Female and Male Anatomy and
Physiology 55

Female Anatomy and Physiology 55

The External Female Sex Organs 56

A WORLD OF DIVERSITY
Pubic Hair Removal 58

A WORLD OF DIVERSITY
Female Genital Mutilation/Cutting 60

The Internal Female Sex Organs 62

The Female Breasts 68

A WORLD OF DIVERSITY
The Strong Breast Revolution 69

x Contents

The Menstrual Cycle 71

A WORLD OF DIVERSITY
Historical and Cross-Cultural Perspectives on
Menstruation 72

Menstrual Difficulties 75

APPLIED KNOWLEDGE
How to Handle Menstrual Discomfort 77

Male Anatomy and Physiology 78

The External Male Sex Organs 78

A WORLD OF DIVERSITY
Perspectives on Penis Size 81

The Internal Male Sex Organs 82

Diseases of the Male Urogenital System 85

APPLIED KNOWLEDGE
Self-Examination of the Testes 87

Male Sexual Functions 88

Chapter Four
Sexual Arousal and Response 96

The Senses and Sexual Arousal 96

A WORLD OF DIVERSITY
YSEX—The Reasons People Give for Wanting
to Have Sex 100

Aphrodisiacs, Anaphrodisiacs, and
Psychoactive Drugs 101

Sexual Response and the Brain 105

Sex Hormones and Sexual Behaviour 105

Models of Sexual Response 109

INNOVATIVE CANADIAN RESEARCH
Gender, Sexual Orientation, and Arousal 110

INNOVATIVE CANADIAN RESEARCH
Genital Versus Subjective Sexual Arousal 113

INNOVATIVE CANADIAN RESEARCH
The Subjective Experience of Orgasm 115

The Enigmatic Orgasm 116

Sexuality and Disability 118

INNOVATIVE CANADIAN RESEARCH
Improving Sexual Function in Men with Spinal-Cord
Injuries 121

APPLIED KNOWLEDGE
A Comprehensive Guide to Sex and Disability 123

Chapter Five
Gender Identity and Gender Roles 126

Prenatal Sexual Differentiation 126

Gender Identity 129

INNOVATIVE CANADIAN RESEARCH
What Can the Samoan *Fa'afafine* Teach Us about
Western Concepts of Gender Identity? 133

A WORLD OF DIVERSITY
Third Gender/Third Sex 136

INNOVATIVE CANADIAN RESEARCH
The Trans Pulse Project 137

Gender Roles and Stereotypes 137

Sexism 137

Gender Typing 138

Gender Roles and Sexual Behaviour 142

A WORLD OF DIVERSITY
Are There Universal Differences in Sexual
Strategies? 144

INNOVATIVE CANADIAN RESEARCH
Do Young Men Really Prefer Sex Over Romance? 148

Psychological Androgyny 148

Chapter Six
Attraction and Love 152

Attraction 152

INNOVATIVE CANADIAN RESEARCH
What Do Women Want? 157

A WORLD OF DIVERSITY
Sex Differences in Mate Preference Across
37 Cultures 159

A WORLD OF DIVERSITY
Ready, Set, Speed Date 160

Love 160

INNOVATIVE CANADIAN RESEARCH
Obsessive Versus Harmonious Passion   163

Chapter Seven
Relationships, Intimacy, and Communication   169

The ABC(DE)s of Romantic Relationships   169

A CLOSER LOOK
Online Dating—A Revolution in Matchmaking?   171

APPLIED KNOWLEDGE
Sexting and Canadian Youth   172

INNOVATIVE CANADIAN RESEARCH
Obtaining Sexual Consent   178

Communication Skills   182

INNOVATIVE CANADIAN RESEARCH
Keeping the Spark Alive in Romantic Relationships   184

APPLIED KNOWLEDGE
Communicating Sexual Needs   185

Chapter Eight
Sexual Behaviours and Fantasies   189

Solitary Sexual Behaviour   190

INNOVATIVE CANADIAN RESEARCH
Online Masturbation   193

INNOVATIVE CANADIAN RESEARCH
The Depiction of Masturbation in North American Movies   195

A WORLD OF DIVERSITY
Good Vibes   197

Sexual Behaviour with Others   197

INNOVATIVE CANADIAN RESEARCH
Desired Duration of Foreplay   198

Gay and Lesbian Sexual Behaviour   207

A WORLD OF DIVERSITY
Sexual Behaviour in Australia   208

INNOVATIVE CANADIAN RESEARCH
How to Have Great Sex: Advice in Popular Magazines   208

Chapter Nine
Sexual Orientation   212

Getting Oriented to Sexual Orientation   212

INNOVATIVE CANADIAN RESEARCH
Bisexuality and Intimate Relationships   217

A WORLD OF DIVERSITY
Youth Challenging Traditional Concepts of Sexual Orientation and Gender   219

Perspectives on Gay and Lesbian Sexual Orientations   219

INNOVATIVE CANADIAN RESEARCH
Birth Order and Sexual Orientation   224

INNOVATIVE CANADIAN RESEARCH
Measures of Homonegativity   227

The Coming-Out Process   230

APPLIED KNOWLEDGE
Counselling Gays and Lesbians   232

Gay and Lesbian Adjustment   233

APPLIED KNOWLEDGE
Increasing Resilience Among LGBTQ Youth   234

INNOVATIVE CANADIAN RESEARCH
Innovation in Gay Male Relationships   235

Gay and Lesbian Lifestyles   235

Chapter Ten
Conception, Pregnancy, and Childbirth   239

Conception   239

Infertility and Assisted Reproductive Technologies   240

APPLIED KNOWLEDGE
Optimizing the Chances of Conception   241

A WORLD OF DIVERSITY
LGBT Family Building   245

Pregnancy   246

Prenatal Development   248

Childbirth   253

A WORLD OF DIVERSITY
Maternal and Infant Mortality Around the World   257

The Postpartum Period   258

Canadian Birth Rates and Teen
Pregnancy   260

Chapter Eleven
Contraception and Abortion   266

Contraception in Canada   266

A WORLD OF DIVERSITY
A History of Birth Control in Canada   268

Methods of Contraception   268

INNOVATIVE CANADIAN RESEARCH
Emergency Contraception   272

APPLIED KNOWLEDGE
Errors in Using Condoms   279

Abortion   284

APPLIED KNOWLEDGE
Selecting a Method of Contraception   285

INNOVATIVE CANADIAN RESEARCH
Women Who Have Repeat Abortions   289

Chapter Twelve
Sexuality Across the Life Span   292

Childhood Sexuality   292

Adolescent Sexuality   296

A WORLD OF DIVERSITY
The Many Meanings of Menarche   298

A WORLD OF DIVERSITY
Do Sexy TV Shows Encourage Teen Sex and
Pregnancy?   303

Adult Sexuality   304

A WORLD OF DIVERSITY
A Gay Prom Date   305

A WORLD OF DIVERSITY
Mating in Captivity   316

Senior Sexuality   319

Chapter Thirteen
Sexual Dysfunction   326

Prevalence of Sexual Problems and
Dysfunctions   327

Types of Sexual Dysfunction   328

Origins of Sexual Dysfunction   334

Treatments for Sexual Dysfunction   340

APPLIED KNOWLEDGE
How Do You Find a Qualified Sex Therapist?   343

APPLIED KNOWLEDGE
Thinking Critically About Buying Drugs Online   345

APPLIED KNOWLEDGE
Promoting Eroticism in Sex Therapy   347

INNOVATIVE CANADIAN RESEARCH
Treatment for Dyspareunia   351

INNOVATIVE CANADIAN RESEARCH
A Portrait of Great Sex   352

A WORLD OF DIVERSITY
An Alternative Approach to Enhancing Female
Sexuality   353

Chapter Fourteen
Sexually Transmitted Infections   356

STIs in Canada   357

Bacterial Infections   359

Vaginal Infections   363

Viral Infections   364

Ectoparasitic Infestations   373

A WORLD OF DIVERSITY
A School-Based HIV Prevention Education Program for
Youth in Kenya   374

STI Epidemiology: Biological, Psychological,
and Social Factors   375

APPLIED KNOWLEDGE
Reducing Your Risks for STIs and HIV   380

INNOVATIVE CANADIAN RESEARCH
The Male Call Canada Survey of Men Who Have Sex with Men   382

Education and Prevention   383

Chapter Fifteen
Sexual Health Education   386

Sexual Health Education in the Schools:
A Brief History   387

APPLIED KNOWLEDGE
Educating Your Children About Sex   388

INNOVATIVE CANADIAN RESEARCH
Sexual Health Education in Schools Across Canada   389

The Canadian Guidelines for Sexual Health Education   390

Using Theory and Research to Inform Sexual Health Education   391

INNOVATIVE CANADIAN RESEARCH
The Information–Motivation–Behavioural Skills (IMB) Model   392

Attitudes Towards Sexual Health Education   395

Current Sources of Information About Sexuality   397

Innovative Canadian Curricula and Resources   398

Meeting the Sexual Health Education Needs of Diverse Groups   399

INNOVATIVE CANADIAN RESEARCH
Sexual Health Education for Youth with Physical Disabilities   401

Chapter Sixteen
Sexual Variations   405

Normal Versus Deviant Sexual Behaviour   405

The Paraphilias   406

APPLIED KNOWLEDGE
Responding to Exhibitionists and Obscene Phone Callers   412

INNOVATIVE CANADIAN RESEARCH
Normal Voyeurism   413

A WORLD OF DIVERSITY
It Seems Like Voyeurs Are Everywhere!   414

INNOVATIVE CANADIAN RESEARCH
Women's Submissive Desires   417

INNOVATIVE CANADIAN RESEARCH
The Personality Characteristics of Dominant and Submissive BDSM Practitioners   418

Theoretical Perspectives   420

Treatment for Paraphilias   423

Sexual Addiction, Compulsive Sexual Behaviour, and Hypersexuality   426

Chapter Seventeen
Sexual Coercion   429

Sexual Assault   430

A WORLD OF DIVERSITY
Female Sex Offenders   432

A CLOSER LOOK
Anatomy of a Date Rape   434

INNOVATIVE CANADIAN RESEARCH
Sexually Aggressive Behaviour in Bars and Clubs   436

The Complexity of Consent   437

APPLIED KNOWLEDGE
The Date-Rape Drug   439

INNOVATIVE CANADIAN RESEARCH
Male Versus Female Victims of Sexual Coercion   440

APPLIED KNOWLEDGE
If You're Sexually Assaulted   442

Coercive Verbal Pressure Tactics   444

APPLIED KNOWLEDGE
Lowering Your Risk of Sexual Assault   444

Sexual Abuse of Children   445

APPLIED KNOWLEDGE
Helping Children Avoid Sexual Abuse   452

Treatment of Perpetrators   453

Sexual Harassment   454

INNOVATIVE CANADIAN RESEARCH
Trouble Letting Go: Online and Offline Post-Relationship
Contact and Tracking Among Young Adults   456

APPLIED KNOWLEDGE
Resisting Sexual Harassment   459

Chapter Eighteen
Commercial Sex   462

Prostitution   462

A WORLD OF DIVERSITY
"Prostitution" or "Sex Work"?   463

INNOVATIVE CANADIAN RESEARCH
Media Stereotypes   472

A WORLD OF DIVERSITY
Girls on the Streets of American Cities   473

Sexually Explicit Material (SEM)   476

INNOVATIVE CANADIAN RESEARCH
Women Who Visit Sex Shops   482

INNOVATIVE CANADIAN RESEARCH
An Educational Program to Counteract the Effects of
Internet Porn   483

Answer Key 489

References 491

Name Index 531

Subject Index 539

Preface

Canada in the twenty-first century is rapidly evolving with respect to human sexuality. Underlying this change is a growing recognition and acceptance of diversity in regard to many aspects of sexuality. *Human Sexuality in a World of Diversity* fully embraces and affirms this diversity, especially within Canadian society.

Before writing this edition, we searched extensively for new Canadian materials from a number of sources, including Canadian researchers themselves. We've added many new Canadian references to each chapter. In addition to integrating up-to-date Canadian research and statistics, we've addressed key issues in human sexuality within the uniquely Canadian context. A number of new Innovative Canadian Research Boxes featuring the work of leading Canadian researchers in the field of human sexuality have been added, and others have been updated.

This fifth Canadian edition is more concise than most other human sexuality textbooks, because we're aware that many enthusiastic users find other textbooks too long or unnecessarily complex for their courses. We have made every effort to provide a textbook that is clear and succinct but also one that embodies the highest standards of academic rigor. In addition to emphasizing theory and up-to-date research, practical applications that are relevant to students' lives are included.

New to the Fifth Canadian Edition

The fifth Canadian edition of *Human Sexuality in a World of Diversity* includes several important changes that add substantially to its depth and ease of use:

■ Chapter 1 has been revised to place greater emphasis on the theme of diversity and the sociocultural aspects of human sexuality.

■ Chapter 2 now includes a dual focus on theory and research methods, including expanded coverage of different theoretical approaches to the study of human sexuality.

■   A new chapter, Sexual Health Education (Chapter 15), has been added. This chapter introduces students to the theory and practice of sexual health education in a Canadian context.

■ There is a greater emphasis on the impact of new information technologies on human sexuality throughout the book.

■ There is a greater focus on diversity all through the book.

Chapter-by-Chapter Changes

We've added hundreds of new references that reflect the newest research in the field of human sexuality. No part of the textbook has been untouched by change. Following are just a few of the topics we've added, substantially revised, or updated.

Chapter 1

■ Sexuality and ethics
■ The Internet and communication technology
■ Cultural diversity
■ Social and political differences between Canada and the United States with respect to sexuality

Chapter 2
- Theoretical approaches to understanding human sexuality (new sections on Sexual Script Theory and Social Exchange Theory)
- Studying the sexual behaviours of diverse populations

Chapter 3
- Female genital mutilation/cutting
- Pubic hair removal
- Male circumcision
- Cervical, uterine/endometrial, ovarian, breast, testicular, and prostate cancer statistics

Chapter 4
- Effects of recreational drugs on sexual response
- Effects of aphrodisiacs and psychoactive drugs on sexual response
- Female orgasm

Chapter 5
- Gender independent children
- What can the Samoan *Fa'afafine* teach us about Western concepts of gender identity?
- The TransPULSE Project

Chapter 6
- Cross-cultural differences in standards of attractiveness
- Obsessive versus harmonious passion
- Speed dating and attraction

Chapter 7
- Online dating
- Keeping the spark alive in romantic relationships

Chapter 8
- Sexual fantasy
- Masturbation/online sexually explicit material
- Depiction of masturbation in mainstream movies
- Research on vibrator use

Chapter 9
- Estimates of sexual orientation in Canada
- Bisexuality and intimate relationships
- Canadians' changing attitudes towards sexual orientation

Chapter 10
- LGBT family building
- Maternal and infant mortality around the world
- Canadian teen pregnancy statistics

Chapter 11
- Contraceptive use among Canadian university students
- Effectiveness of different methods of contraception
- Emergency contraception

- Errors in condom use
- Canadian abortion rates

Chapter 12

- The meaning of menarche across cultures
- Adolescent sexual behaviour
- Friends with benefits and other new forms of casual sexual relationships
- The percentage of Canadians who are single, cohabiting, and married
- Factors leading to marital satisfaction

Chapter 13

- Chapter revised to incorporate new *DSM-5* classifications and terminology for sexual dysfunctions

Chapter 14

- Updated statistics on sexually transmitted infections in Canada
- Updated statistics in HIV in Canada and female/male risk factors
- STI/HIV risk perceptions
- Gender inequality and STI/HIV risk
- Ethnocultural factors
- The Male Call Canada Survey of MSM

Chapter 15 (New chapter on Sexual Health Education)

- History of sexual health education in Canada
- Sexual health education across Canada
- Sexual health education theory and practice
- *Canadian Guidelines for Sexual Health Education*
- The information–motivation–behavioural skills model
- Attitudes towards sexual health education
- Abstinence versus broadly based approaches
- Innovative Canadian curricular resources
- Meeting the education needs of diverse groups

Chapter 16

- Incorporates new *DSM-5* definitions and classifications of paraphilia and paraphilic disorders
- Personality characteristics of dominant and submissive BDSM practitioners

Chapter 17

- Sexually aggressive behaviour in bars and clubs
- Updated statistics on sexual assault and sexual violations against children in Canada
- Campus sexual assault prevention
- Online and offline post-relationship contact and tracking

Chapter 18

- Legal challenges to Canada's prostitution laws
- Bill C-36: Canada's new prostitution laws
- Human trafficking
- The Internet and sexually explicit material (SEM)
- Gender differences in response to SEM
- Cybersex addiction/compulsivity

Themes in This Edition

The fifth Canadian edition of *Human Sexuality in a World of Diversity* builds upon the strong themes for which previous editions have become known. Four themes are woven throughout the text:

- Human diversity.
- Critical thinking.
- Responsible sexual decision-making.
- Sexual health.

Human Diversity

Colleges and universities undertake the mission of broadening students' perspectives, encouraging them to tolerate and appreciate human diversity. Canada is a nation of hundreds of ethnic and religious groups, many of which endorse culturally distinct beliefs about appropriate gender roles for men and women, as well as distinctive sexual practices and customs. Diversity is even greater within the global village of the world's nearly 200 nations and their subcultures.

Human Sexuality in a World of Diversity incorporates a multicultural, multiethnic perspective that reflects the diversity of sexual experience in Canadian society and around the world. Discussion of diversity encourages respect for people who hold diverse beliefs and attitudes.

Critical Thinking

Colleges and universities also encourage students to become critical thinkers. Today's students are so inundated with information about gender and sexuality that it can be difficult to sort truth from fiction. Critical thinking requires thoughtful analysis and probing of others' claims and arguments in light of evidence. Moreover, it requires a willingness to challenge conventional wisdom and the common knowledge many of us take for granted. Throughout this book we raise issues that call for critical thinking.

Responsible Sexual Decision-Making

We encourage students to make responsible sexual decisions on the basis of accurate information. Responsible decision-making is based not only on acquiring accurate information, but also on carefully evaluating this information in light of your own values.

Sexual Health

Human Sexuality in a World of Diversity emphasizes issues that affect sexual health, with extensive coverage of such topics as HIV/AIDS and other STIs, innovations in contraception and reproductive technologies, breast cancer, menstrual distress, sex and disabilities, and diseases that affect the reproductive tract. The textbook encourages students to take an active—in fact, a proactive—role in health promotion.

Feature Boxes and Additional Learning Aids

This fifth Canadian edition of *Human Sexuality in a World of Diversity* continues to use a variety of features to stimulate interest and enhance understanding.

"Innovative Canadian Research" boxes emphasize significant new research contributions by Canadian scholars. Many new Innovative Canadian Research boxes have been added to the fifth edition, and others have been updated.

"A World of Diversity" boxes highlight the rich variety of human sexual customs and practices, in Canadian society and around the world. They also include opinions that are contrary to commonly held beliefs.

"Applied Knowledge" boxes assist students with personal decisions, providing information and advice.

"A Closer Look" boxes provide in-depth discussions of societal issues and research.

Key terms appear in boldface within the paragraphs, while a running glossary provides definitions in the margins, close to where the key terms appear. At the end of each chapter, a "Summing Up" section organizes and reviews the subject matter according to the headings within the chapter.

The "Test Yourself" section at the end of each chapter contains multiple-choice and critical-thinking questions to facilitate individual study and promote class discussion. "Answer Key," at the end of the book, contains answers to the "Test Yourself" questions.

Student Supplements
CourseSmart for Students

CourseSmart goes beyond traditional expectations–providing instant, online access to the textbooks and course materials students need at an average savings of 50%. With instant access from any computer and the ability to search the text, students will find the content they need quickly, no matter where they are. And with online tools like highlighting and note-taking, they can save time and study efficiently. See all the benefits at www.coursesmart.com/students.

Instructor Supplements
Instructor's Resource Manual

This manual includes a variety of resources, including chapter-at-a-glance tables (which correlate chapter topics and learning objectives with the offered resources), teaching tips, activities, additional lecture material, and recommended readings, videos, and websites.

Test Item File

This test bank in Microsoft Word format includes an extensive set of multiple-choice, true-or-false, and essay questions. This test bank is also available in computerized format (see below).

Computerized Test Bank

Pearson's computerized test banks allow instructors to filter and select questions to create quizzes, tests or homework. Instructors can revise questions or add their own, and may be able to choose print or online options. These questions are also available in Microsoft Word format.

PowerPoint Presentations

Chapter-by-chapter presentations highlight the key points from the text, supported by diagrams and visuals.

The preceding instructor supplements are available for download from a password-protected section of Pearson Canada's online catalogue (http://vig.pearsoned.ca). Navigate to your book's catalogue page to view a list of available supplements. See your local sales representative for details and access.

peerScholar

Firmly grounded in published research, peerScholar is a powerful online pedagogical tool that helps develop your students' critical and creative thinking skills.

peerScholar facilitates this through the process of creation, evaluation and reflection. Working in stages, students begin by submitting a written assignment. peerScholar then circulates their work for others to review, a process that can be anonymous or not, depending on your preference. Students receive peer feedback and evaluations immediately, reinforcing their learning and driving the development of higher-order thinking skills. Students can then re-submit revised work, again depending on your preference. Contact your Pearson Representative to learn more about peerScholar and the research behind it.

CourseSmart for Instructors

CourseSmart goes beyond traditional expectations–providing instant, online access to the textbooks and course materials you need at a lower cost for students. And even as students save money, you can save time and hassle with a digital eTextbook that allows you to search for the most relevant content at the very moment you need it. Whether it's evaluating textbooks or creating lecture notes to help students with difficult concepts, CourseSmart can make life a little easier. See how when you visit www.coursesmart.com/instructors.

Learning Solutions Managers

Pearson's Learning Solutions Managers work with faculty and campus course designers to ensure that Pearson technology products, assessment tools, and online course materials are tailored to meet your specific needs. This highly qualified team is dedicated to helping schools take full advantage of a wide range of educational resources, by assisting in the integration of a variety of instructional materials and media formats. Your local Pearson Canada sales representative can provide you with more details on this service program.

Pearson Custom Library

For enrollments of at least 25 students, you can create your own textbook by choosing the chapters that best suit your own course needs. To begin building your custom text, visit www.pearsoncustomlibrary.com. You may also work with a dedicated Pearson Custom editor to create your ideal text—publishing your own original content or mixing and matching Pearson content. Contact your local Pearson Representative to get started.

Acknowledgments

The authors owe a great debt of gratitude to the many researchers and scholars whose contributions to the body of knowledge of human sexuality are represented in these pages. Underscoring the interdisciplinary nature of this area of study, we've drawn upon the work of scholars in such fields as psychology, sociology, medicine, anthropology, theology, and philosophy, to name a few. We're also indebted to the many researchers who have generously allowed us to quote from their work and reprint tabular material representing their findings.

The authors and publishers wish to thank the many professional colleagues who have provided feedback on this book at various stages in its development. The following people provided invaluable feedback in their reviews:

Krista Carson, Fanshawe College
Judith Grad, Concordia University
Corey R. Isaacs, University of Western Ontario

I'd like to thank Edward S. Herold for setting a standard of excellence in revising previous Canadian editions. His contributions to this textbook remain one of its greatest strengths.

I also wish to thank Mary Bissell of the Sex Information and Education Council of Canada, whose research expertise and critical insights in human sexuality have been invaluable. I appreciate her contributions to the development of this fifth edition. Thanks also to obstetrician/gynaecologist Jonathan Huber for his helpful suggestions about Chapter 10. I especially want to thank Michael Barrett, Executive Director of the Sex Information and Education Council of Canada, for his many years of support and mentorship to me.

I'm grateful to the many people at Pearson Canada for their valuable assistance with this revision. I'm especially indebted to my editors Martina van de Velde and Mary Wat for their exceptional guidance, support, and patience.

~ Alexander McKay, PhD

CHAPTER ONE

What Is Human Sexuality?

Getstock.com

Let's Google two islands; the first is Inis Beag in the North Atlantic Ocean, off the coast of Ireland, and the second, called Mangaia, is in the South Pacific Ocean. If we search Google Maps for these islands, click on the satellite image, and swoop in, we find ourselves visiting two islands that are on opposite sides of the world. From the air, both appear green and fertile. Both islands contain very small populations of people, geographically separated from the outside world. Because of this they have been of particular interest to anthropologists looking to study the customs of unique societies that have developed and existed at least somewhat free of the cultural influences that have shaped personal and social life in the larger, more prominent cultures of the world.

What makes Inis Beag and Mangaia of interest to us is that they provide a vivid example of cultural diversity with respect to sexuality. Values and standards for sexuality are key components of the organization of all cultures, including contemporary Western society. So it is instructive to examine the accepted forms of sexuality and patterns of sexual behaviour in diverse geographical locations and historical time periods not so that we may judge them or marvel at what may seem to us to be their eccentricities. Rather, we learn about diverse cultures so that we can understand the ways in which each culture uniquely shapes and regulates sexuality. Ultimately, the study of sexuality in cultures that are distant from our own enables us to better understand ourselves and the ways in which our own culture shapes our sexuality. In Inis Beag and Mangaia, we see two distinctive cultures that are both different from mainstream North American culture but also quite opposite to each other in the culturally accepted ways that sexuality is expressed.

Inis Beag is a remote island off the coast of Connemara, Ireland. American anthropologist John Messenger visited the island from 1958 to 1966 (Messinger, 1993). The population at the time numbered about 350. The people of Inis Beag were Gaelic speaking Irish Catholics who lived as farmers. At the time of Messenger's visit, there was no electricity, and the primary mode of transportation was horse drawn carriages. In this isolated agrarian culture, the community of Inis Beag evolved beliefs and customs regarding sexuality that, in comparison to mainstream Canadian society, appear as quite restrictive.

From his study of sexuality on the island, here are some of the sexual beliefs, norms, and practices that Messinger (1993) observed among the Inis Beag. The residents of this community did not believe that it was normal for women to experience orgasm. Messinger reported that woman who found sex pleasurable—especially orgasm—were viewed as deviant.

Premarital sex was all but unknown on Inis Beag. Prior to marriage, men and women socialized apart. Marriage came relatively late compared to other cultures—usually in the middle 30s for men and the middle 20s for women. Mothers taught their daughters that they would have to submit to their husbands' animal cravings in order to obey God's injunction to "be fruitful and multiply."

But the women of Inis Beag did not need to be overly concerned about frequent sex, since the men of the island believed that sexual activity would drain their strength. Consequently, men avoided sexual activity on the eve of sporting events or strenuous work. Because of taboos against nudity, married couples had sex with their undergarments on. Intercourse took place in the dark—literally as well as figuratively.

During intercourse, the man was always on top. He was always the initiator. Foreplay was brief or nonexistent. The honourable man ejaculated as fast as he could, in order to spare his wife as much as possible from the unpleasantness of sexual interaction. In sum, rooted in a religious but internally derived and idiosyncratic understanding of human sexuality, the Inis Beag developed into a relatively sex negative culture.

On to Mangaia, which is a lush tropical island in the South Pacific Ocean. Mangaia is the most southerly of the Cook Islands, located about 650 miles southwest of Tahiti. Known for its coconuts, coral reefs, and natural beauty, Mangaia is home to about 500 people, most of whom are of Polynesian descent. As in many other cultures, including the people of Inis Beag, family bonds are of central importance to the people of Mangaia. Like nearly every other place in the world, most of the island's people form romantic attachments, get married, and place a high priority on their families. With respect to beliefs about sexuality and norms for sexual behaviour, however, the Mangaia culture is a stark contrast to that of Inis Beag.

The American anthropologist Donald Marshall conducted field research in the Cook Islands during the 1950s and spent a year living on Mangaia. Marshall's (1971) report on the sexuality of the island's people indicated a relatively sex positive culture. According to his account of sexual life on the island, from an early age, Mangaian boys and girls were encouraged to get in touch with their sexuality through sexual play and masturbation. At about the age of 13, Mangaian boys were given a two-week course of instruction on techniques of sexual behaviour, including how to perform oral sex, which was followed by a socially approved sexual experience with an older woman in the community. Girls also received instruction about sex from an older woman.

Marshall (1971) reported that premarital sex among Mangaia adolescents was culturally approved and frequent. Mangaian parents encouraged their daughters to have sexual relationships with several men so that they would be sure to choose a husband who was compatible. Both males and females emerged from adolescence sexually experienced and skilled. For men, it was important that they were adept in giving their female partners sexual pleasure, including the ability for him to delay ejaculation in order to enhance her experience. Bringing his partner to orgasm was not just expected, it was a principle source of a man's own sense of sexual pleasure. Perhaps not unexpectedly, Marshall reported that regularly experiencing orgasm was a nearly universal experience among women on the island.

So what conclusions can we draw from our brief comparison of sexuality on the islands of Inis Beag and Mangaia? First, although the people living on these two islands belong to the same species (*Homo sapiens*), they have very different, and in some ways opposite, sexual beliefs, attitudes, and behavioural practices. This tells us that while our biology defines us as human, our culture—the group specific beliefs, values, social norms and customs passed down from one generation to the next—plays a central role in shaping human sexuality.

Second, as the title of this book suggests, we can conclude from our brief journey to these two islands that to study human sexuality is to study diversity. As we will see time and time again as we examine and investigate the key dimensions of this fascinating topic, human beings experience and express sexuality in diverse ways. Because our sexuality is a fundamental part of who we are as individuals and communities, this diversity contributes to the uniqueness within each of us.

Choices, Information, and Decision Making

Although sex is a natural function, and our sexuality can be influenced by biological factors, how we voluntarily express our sexuality is a matter of personal choice. We choose how, where, and with whom to become sexually involved. We face a wide array of sexual decisions. What attributes do I look for in a partner? When should my partner and I become sexually intimate? Should I initiate sexual relations, or wait for my partner to approach me? Should my partner and I practise contraception? If so, which method? Should I use a condom to protect against sexually transmitted infections (or insist that my partner do this)? Should I be tested for HIV? Should I insist that my partner be tested for HIV before we engage in sexual relations?

In addition to our biology and our capacity for individual decision making, the expression of our sexuality is also inevitably influenced by the social context in which we live. The contrasting social norms related to sexuality on the islands of Inis Beag and Mangaia described above are a stark example of the powerful influence of culture on human sexuality.

Many aspects of human sexuality are viewed as moral issues, involving questions of right and wrong. Issues such as premarital and extramarital sex, contraception, and abortion, for example, are often subject to moral debate. No single value system defines us all. Each of us has a unique set of moral values—as a Canadian, as a member of one of Canada's hundreds of cultural groups, as an individual. The world of diversity in which we live is a mosaic of different moral codes and cultural traditions and beliefs. Gathering information and weighing the scientific evidence will alert you to what is possible in the contemporary world, but only you can determine which of your options are compatible with your own moral values.

www.melaniegillis.com

Spelling It Out.
In this artistic photo by Hamilton photographer Melanie Gillis, nude people are arranged so their bodies form the word "SEX."

Making decisions involves choosing among various courses of action. The act of not making a formal decision may itself be a tacit decision. For example, we may vacillate about whether to use a particular form of birth control, but continue to engage in unprotected sex. Is this because we haven't made a decision, or because we've decided to accept whatever happens?

Gathering information helps us predict the outcomes of the decisions we make. This textbook provides you with a broad database concerning scientific developments and ways of relating to other people—including people who come from other cultures. We also encourage you to try to understand other people's sexual beliefs and values in light of their cultural backgrounds just as we should reflect on our own beliefs, values, and culture. Understanding is an essential milestone on the pathway to respect, and respect is vital to resolving conflicts and establishing healthy relationships.

CRITICAL THINKING QUESTIONS

Some people don't consider oral–genital contact to be "having sex." What's your opinion?

Erotic Arousing sexual feelings or desires.

Gender The behavioural, cultural, or psychological traits typically associated with one sex.

Gender roles Complex clusters of the ways males and females are expected to behave within a given culture.

Human sexuality The ways we experience and express ourselves as sexual beings.

What Is Human Sexuality?

This is not a trick question. Consider the various meanings of the word "sex." One use of the term refers whether we're anatomically male or female or somewhere in between. The words "sex" and "sexual" also refer to the anatomical structures, called sex organs or sexual organs, that play a role in reproduction and sexual pleasure. We may also speak of sex when referring to physical activities involving our sex organs for purposes of reproduction or pleasure, as in "having sex." Sex also relates to **erotic** feelings, experiences, or desires, such as sexual fantasies and thoughts, sexual urges, and feelings of sexual attraction.

Many researchers reserve the word "sex" for anatomical or biological categories, preferring the word **"gender"** to refer to social or cultural categories. For example, one might say that "reproductive anatomy appears to depend on the sex [not the gender] of the individual, but in some societies, **gender roles** [not sex roles] are often seen as polar opposites and in others they appear more similar or fluid."

The term **"human sexuality"** refers to the ways we experience and express ourselves as sexual beings. Our awareness of ourselves as females or males is part of our sexuality, as is the capacity we have for erotic experiences and responses. Our knowledge of the gender roles in our culture also has a profound influence on us.

Sex as Leisure

Researchers Meaney and Rye (2007), at St. Jerome's University at the University of Waterloo, have conceptualized sex as a fun, healthy activity that can be considered leisure when it is voluntary, is not seen as work, and serves some personal need. According to their definition, sex is not a leisure activity when it is not voluntary, is viewed as work, or is seen as an obligation.

At its most basic level, sex provides physical pleasure. It's a fun activity that can be enjoyed alone or with others. Sexuality can also be a key component of personality development, as we discover which sexual activities are enjoyable, and with whom. Sexuality is an important part of identity. This is certainly true for gay, lesbian, bisexual, or transgender people. It's also true for people who engage in certain sexual variations, such as sadomasochism. Meaney and Rye (2007) argue that learning about one's sexual likes and dislikes through experimentation can lead to sexual self-actualization, a state in which a person is comfortable with his or her sexuality.

The Study of Human Sexuality

The study of human sexuality draws upon the scientific expertise of anthropologists, biologists, medical researchers, sociologists, and psychologists, to name but a few of the professionals involved in the field. These disciplines all make contributions because sexual behaviour reflects our biological capabilities, psychological

Innovative Canadian Research

WHAT IS THIS THING CALLED SEX?

New Brunswick researchers Hilary Randall and Sandra Byers (2003) asked university students to indicate which behaviours they would define as "having sex" with someone if they were the ones engaging in those behaviours. The only behaviours most students defined as sex were penile–vaginal intercourse and penile–anal intercourse. Only about one-fifth defined oral–genital contact as sex, and even fewer (10%) defined the touching of genitals leading to orgasm as sex. Interestingly, there was a slight increase in the percentage of students who defined each behaviour as sex if it resulted in orgasm.

When the researchers modified the question, however, far more students indicated that they would define someone as their "sexual partner" if that person were engaging in those behaviours with the respondent. For example, about two-thirds considered anyone with whom they had oral–genital contact to be a sexual partner, and about one-half considered touching of genitals as an indicator of partnership.

University of Calgary researchers Eileah Trotter and Kevin Alderson (2007) asked university students to define "loss of virginity." The students' definition of "loss of virginity" was more narrow than their definition of "having sex." For example, only about half thought penile–anal intercourse qualified as loss of virginity. Almost all accepted penile–vaginal intercourse as the marker for virginity loss. However, a small percentage indicated that orgasm had to be experienced with penile–vaginal intercourse for it to count as loss of virginity.

The researchers also presented students with a list of behaviours and asked them to define each behaviour as sexual if it was performed by an opposite-sex couple and if it was performed by a same-sex couple. Students were more likely to define most of the behaviours as sexual for opposite-sex couples than for same-sex couples. An exception was oral–genital sex: slightly more of the students classified this behaviour as "having sex" if the couple was same sexed than if it was opposite sexed (Trotter & Alderson, 2007).

characteristics, and social and cultural influences. Biologists inform us about the physiological mechanisms of sexual arousal and response. Medical science teaches us about sexually transmitted infections and the biological bases of sexual dysfunction. Psychologists examine how our sexual behaviours and attitudes are shaped by perception, learning, thought, motivation, emotion, and personality. Sociologists consider the sociocultural contexts of sexual behaviour. For example, they examine relationships between sexual behaviour and religion, race, and social class. Anthropologists focus on cross-cultural similarities and differences in sexual behaviour. Scientists from many disciplines explore parallels between the sexual behaviours of humans and those of other animals.

A number of organizations promote sex research and sexual health education. In Canada, leading organizations include the Sex Information and Education Council of Canada (SIECCAN), which publishes *The Canadian Journal of Human Sexuality*, and the Canadian Sex Research Forum (CSRF). The Canadian Federation for Sexual Health (CFSH), the Society of Obstetricians and Gynaecologists of Canada (SOGC), and the Public Health Agency of Canada (PHAC) also disseminate sexual health information to professionals and the public in Canada. Two major international organizations are the Society for the Scientific Study of Sexuality (SSSS), which publishes *The Journal of Sex Research*, and the World Association for Sexual Health (WAS).

Canadian Society and Sexuality

To understand the complexity of factors influencing sexual attitudes and behaviours in Canada, it's important to be aware of the diverse nature of Canadians. Particularly today, immigration patterns are changing the landscape of Canadian society.

Innovative Canadian Research

ETHNOCULTURAL COMMUNITIES AND SEXUALITY

There has been relatively little research on the sexuality of Canadian ethnic minority groups. Fortunately, some Canadian researchers have begun to study these under-examined groups.

Concerned over the spread of HIV/AIDS, in 1996, Health Canada sponsored a study of diverse ethnic groups in Canada. The study, entitled "Ethnocultural Communities Facing AIDS," was conducted in consultation with representatives of five ethnic communities in Canada: South Asian, Chinese, South African, Caribbean, Latin American, and Arabic.

Most participants reported a double standard for sexual behaviour, with women expected to be virgins before marriage and monogamous after marriage, and men allowed to be sexually permissive before and to some extent after marriage. In the South Asian community, girls were not even allowed to date. In all five communities, many respondents took it for granted that at least some men would have sex with prostitutes and/or women outside their ethnic groups. Homosexuality was treated as if it didn't exist in their communities, and homosexuals were made to feel ashamed. Gender roles were rigidly prescribed, with men considered "bosses" in their families. Women weren't expected to have much interest in or knowledge of sex, and they lacked the power to ask their husbands to use condoms.

Researchers in Vancouver and Montreal, led by Lori A. Brotto of the University of British Columbia, compared the sexuality of Canadian university students from European-Canadian and Asian backgrounds. The Asian students had more conservative sexual attitudes and less sexual experience than the European-Canadian students. The European-Canadian women reported higher rates of sexual desire, arousal, receptivity, and pleasure. The Asian men reported higher rates of erectile dysfunction and less sexual satisfaction than the European-Canadian men.

Brotto et al. (2005) found that degree of acculturation to mainstream Canadian society was significantly related to sexual attitudes and experiences, but that length of residence in Canada was not. In other words, Asian students who kept the strongest ties to their cultural heritage had the most conservative sexual attitudes and experiences. Similarly, a study by Woo and Brotto (2008) found that Asians in Vancouver who identified less with Canadian culture had higher rates of sexual problems and less communication with their partners about sexual issues. They were also more likely to avoid sexual contact, and when they did engage in sexual relations, their encounters were less sensual in nature.

Canadian researcher Yanqui Rachel Zhou (2012) interviewed both male and female Chinese immigrants about their sexual attitudes and experiences during the settlement process in Canada. Zhou noted that while Chinese society has gradually become more open to personal sexual freedom there remains a taboo around

Currently, One in five members of the Canadian population was born outside of Canada, with the majority of immigrants (63%) moving to the metropolitan areas of Toronto, Vancouver, and Montreal. Immigrants constitute 20% of Canadian society and nearly 50% of Toronto's population (Statistics Canada, 2013a). Of course, before the arrival of Europeans in North America, Canada was inhabited by indigenous peoples. Currently, 4.3% of Canada's population is made up of those who identify as First Nations, Metis, or Inuit people, collectively known as Aboriginal peoples (Statistics Canada, 2013a).

The first European explorers in the region were mainly French and British, and for many years those two have been the dominant ethnic groups in Canada. In the latter half of the twentieth century, an increasing number of immigrants came from other European and non-European countries. According to the 2011 National Household Survey, 57% of immigrants who arrived in Canada between 2006 and 2011 were from Asia, and 14% were from Europe (Statistics Canada, 2013a). As a public discourse related to sexuality. In China, silence around sexual issues is often encouraged. When immigrants come to Canada they may be separated from partners and family and experience feelings of loneliness and isolation. Zhou found that many of the men and women she interviewed became involved in sexual relationships in Canada out of a need for intimacy and companionship. The participants often revealed that these relationships were only possible because they were separated from family, friends, and spouses which in turn meant that they experienced a certain amount of liberation from the social and cultural norms of their home country. However, while they tended to be more open to sexual experiences, many still maintained a reluctance to discuss sexual issues with their partners. The cultural tradition of privacy and silence surrounding sexuality persisted even though there was a more open attitude to sexual experiences. Zhou noted that this continued reluctance to talk about sexuality could lead to unsafe sexual behaviours such as unprotected sex and engaging in sex with multiple or risky partners.

Eleanor Maticka-Tyndale at the University of Windsor and two visiting researchers from Iran, Khosro Refaie Shirpak and Maryam Chinichian, conducted research with Iranian immigrants (2007). Like the Health Canada researchers, they found that maintaining virginity prior to marriage was considered essential for girls, to maintain good reputations and the honour of their families. The Iranian adults were fearful of having their children exposed to sexuality from the broader Canadian society, especially by the media. Based on images they saw on Canadian television, the Iranian immigrants believed most Canadian adolescents began having sexual intercourse by age 13 or 14. They also perceived that Canadians didn't seem to care about marital loyalty and engaged in extramarital relationships. The women worried that their husbands would be tempted to engage in affairs, because of the sexual freedoms in Canada. The men worried that in Canada it would be too easy for their wives to walk out of their marriages. Respondents also believed that sex education in Canadian schools emphasized the use of condoms

rather than abstinence before marriage.

Maticka-Tyndale et al. (2007) also studied the sexual health needs of immigrants from Iran. Some of the women expressed concerns that their husbands might want to engage in sexual practices, such as oral sex, that were commonplace in Canada but not acceptable in traditional Muslim culture. The immigrants acknowledged that their own lack of sex education resulted in embarrassment when discussing sexual-health topics with medical professionals. Women who had male physicians avoided having Pap smears taken because of embarrassment. Some women felt it was inappropriate to have Pap smears before marriage, because they worried the procedure might affect their virginity. Both males and females reported that modesty and shyness prevented them from discussing sexual problems and asking questions about sex when talking to health professionals. Maticka-Tyndale et al. recommended that health professionals be more culturally sensitive when interacting with immigrants, especially when talking about sexual-health issues.

result, Canadians of French and British ancestry today make up only about half of the population.

The most notable change in the Canadian mosaic has been the dramatic increase in the proportion of visible minorities. In 2011, 19% of Canadians (6,264,800) were members of visible minorities, with South Asians forming the largest group followed by Chinese and those who identified as Black (Statistics Canada, 2013a).

The **values** of immigrants often differ from those of people born in Canada. In South Asian communities, for example, arranged marriages are still fairly common. Some immigrants from Muslim countries maintain the practice of female circumcision, a procedure usually performed on young girls that involves surgical removal of the clitoris and in some cases parts of the labia. This practice, often referred to as "genital mutilation," is contrary to Canadian values. (The Canadian and American governments have declared female circumcision illegal. Within some

Values The beliefs and qualities in life that are deemed important or unimportant, right or wrong, desirable or undesirable.

Monde Osé Burlesque Ball. Photo: Jo Gorsky.

Sexual Appetites at the Burlesque Ball.
The Burlesque Ball in Montreal, organized by a group called Monde Osé, is meant to encourage people to explore their sexuality. In general, people in Quebec tend to have more permissive sexual attitudes than people in other provinces.

CRITICAL THINKING QUESTIONS

In some cultures, women going topless is seen as sexually provocative and exhibitionist, while in other cultures, it's seen as natural and nonsexual. Can you think of other cultural differences related to human sexuality?

immigrant communities, however, the procedure is still done.) Parents in some groups use gender-selection techniques, such as abortion, to ensure that they have boys rather than girls. In many cultures, sex is a taboo subject, not discussed openly between parents and their children.

For the most part, sexual attitudes and behaviours are more conservative among immigrants than among the rest of Canadian society. This is particularly pronounced in relation to the age of first intercourse. About three-quarters of 20- to 24-year-olds born in Canada report having had sexual intercourse before age 20, compared with less than half of 20- to 24-year-olds born outside of Canada (Maticka-Tyndale et al., 2001).

Children of immigrant parents often get caught in a culture clash between the traditional values of their parents and the more permissive values of Canadian society. A Manitoba study of ethno-racial minority youth found that since sex was a taboo subject within the family setting, young people felt they could not communicate their real thoughts and questions to their parents (Migliardi, 2007). Research also indicates, however, that most bicultural young people successfully adapt to Canadian culture, while still maintaining ties to the cultural identities of their families. Negotiating conflicting cultural norms may prove to be a challenge, especially for issues pertaining to sexuality and relationships, but many young people find a workable balance between the expectations of each culture (Giguère, Lalonde, & Lou, 2010).

COMPARING CANADA WITH OTHER COUNTRIES Tremendous variation in sexual attitudes and behaviours is found among the different countries of the world. Many of these variations are presented throughout this textbook. For example, Laumann et al. (2006) surveyed 27 500 men and women over age 40 from 29 countries, asking about their levels of sexual satisfaction. In general, men reported higher levels of satisfaction than women. Western countries with higher gender equality, such as Canada, had the highest rates of sexual satisfaction. The lowest levels of satisfaction were in Indonesia and Japan. According to Laumann et al., in societies that have greater gender equality, sexual pleasure is considered as important for women as it is for men. However, in male-centred cultures where sex is more reproduction-focused, sexual pleasure for women is not considered important. Not surprisingly, many women in those cultures view sex as a marital duty.

There are also many cross-cultural differences in adolescent sexuality. Eleanor Maticka-Tyndale at the University of Windsor has conducted a groundbreaking study of adolescent sexual practices in Kenya (see "A World of Diversity: Sexual Scripts of Young People in Kenya"). This study shows a sexual "script" for adolescent sexuality that diverges from the scripts with which most Canadians are familiar.

When it comes to sexuality, there are many cultural variations. Consider the issue of women going topless at the beach. In Australia and many European countries, it's commonplace to see topless women at public beaches. In Canada, however, this is not the case. Until the 1990s, in fact, it was illegal in Canada for women to go topless.

On a hot summer day in 1991, University of Guelph student Gwen Jacob caused a sensation in downtown Guelph when she removed her shirt and exposed

THE CANADIAN PRESS IMAGES/Dominic Chan.

Go Topless Day.
At this event in Toronto, topless women marched in protest against the city of Toronto. Toronto denied a group of women permission to bare their breasts and hold a demonstration in a public park, while going topless in the street of Toronto is legal. The event was organized in 2011, in an effort to help women feel comfortable about going topless in public. Many Canadian women are still uncomfortable about going topless.

her breasts. She was arrested and convicted of committing an indecent act in a public place. Jacob brought her case to the Ontario Court of Appeal, arguing that because men had the right to go topless, she had a constitutional right to go topless as well. In 1996, the Ontario Court of Appeal overturned the conviction, stating that her act was not degrading or dehumanizing and that it carried no sexual connotation.

This ruling brought out the central issue in the debate over toplessness: is it or is it not a sexual act? In a study of university students in Australia, Herold, Corbesi, and Collins (1994) found that women who had gone topless at the beach believed this was a "natural" rather than a sexual act when done at the beach. Conversely, women who had never gone topless argued that it was indeed sexual and a type of exhibitionism. Despite the court ruling, few women in Canada go topless in public, even at the beach.

COMPARING CANADA AND THE UNITED STATES   Although there are many similarities between Canadians and Americans, there are also many differences. For example, a much higher proportion of the American population than of the Canadian population comes from a Spanish or African background. Consequently, ethnic comparisons in the United States are often based on three categories: African Americans, Latin Americans, and European Americans. This typology is far too narrow to describe Canada. The more than 5 million Canadians who are members of visible minority groups include significant numbers of South Asians, Chinese, Africans, Filipinos, Latin Americans, Arabs, Southeast Asians, West Asians, Koreans, and Japanese, as well as many who are members of more than one group (Statistics Canada, 2009b). It's important to be aware of social and demographic differences between Canada and the United States, because they account for some major differences in sexual attitudes and behaviours.

The birth rate in Canada is lower than that in the United States, especially for women in their 20s. The teenage pregnancy rate is also almost twice as high in the

A World of Diversity

SEXUAL SCRIPTS OF YOUNG PEOPLE IN KENYA

While most Canadian researchers study the attitudes and behaviours of Canadians, some are conducting important research in other countries. Eleanor Maticka-Tyndale at the University of Windsor has studied sexual practices in a number of countries around the world. Most recently, she conducted several studies in African countries. Her groundbreaking research on the sexual scripts of adolescents in Kenya (Maticka-Tyndale et al., 2005) illustrates the powerful role of culture in influencing sexual behaviour.

A key cultural belief in Kenya is that once puberty is reached, the male sex drive requires release and the female is ready for sex. There is also the belief that delaying the age of engaging in sex has negative consequences. If the male waits to a later age to experience sex, it is believed he may lose the capacity to impregnate his wife and become unable to produce children. Females are concerned that if intercourse is delayed to a later age, their vaginas will become blocked, leaving them unable to engage in sex.

Both boys and girls feel pressure from peer groups to engage in sex at a young age. Having intercourse is referred to as "playing sex." Boys assume girls are easily available for sex. A girl may indicate an interest in a particular boy by acting in a sexually suggestive manner, such as by opening her legs when he looks at her. The actual initiation of a sexual relationship, however, begins with the male.

United States compared to Canada (McKay, 2012). Population growth in Canada depends more on immigration from other countries than it does in the United States.

The American population (which is about 10 times as large as Canada's) is widely spread throughout the various regions of the United States, whereas two out of three Canadians live near the United States border. And since most new immigrants to Canada choose to live in these populated areas, they also have the highest rates of population growth. Canada's population is especially concentrated in southern Ontario, Montreal, the Vancouver region, and the Calgary–Edmonton corridor (Statistics Canada, 2011). Almost two-thirds of Canada's more than 34 million people live in the two largest provinces, Ontario and Quebec.

More Canadians (49%) than Americans (40%) complete some form of post-secondary education. In the United States, income plays a larger role in determining whether someone attends university, with 63% of Americans from the top income quartile attending university, compared with only 15% of those from the bottom income quartile. In Canada, this income gap is lower, with 45% of those from the top income quartile attending university, compared with 24% of those from the bottom income quartile (Statistics Canada, 2005a).

According to a global Gallup poll of 123 countries, more Americans (65%) than Canadians (45%) view religion as an important part of their daily lives (Crabtree & Pelham, 2009). An Ipsos (2010) poll found that 65% of Americans but only 36% of Canadians agreed with the statement, "Religion provides the common values and ethical foundations that diverse societies need to thrive in the twenty-first century." These American–Canadian differences are important, because they may help us understand differences between the two countries that relate to sexuality.

Since 1971, Canada has maintained an official policy of multiculturalism. According to this policy, Canadian society is openly accepting of differing cultural attitudes and traditions as espoused by diverse immigrant groups. The United States, on the other hand, has adhered to the "melting pot" theory, which encourages immigrants to adapt to American ways of thinking and acting. An Angus Reid (2010a) poll of Canadians on multiculturalism, however, points to a possible shift in opinion. While 55% of those surveyed agreed that multiculturalism has been good for Canada, 54% of Canadians preferred the concept of the melting pot, while only 33% preferred multiculturalism.

The boy asks someone who knows the girl he's interested in to tell her he's attracted to her. He gives the go-between a material gift and/or money to give to the chosen girl, to indicate the sincerity of his interest. Along with the gift, the boy may send word that he loves her. Expressions of love don't have the emotional meaning they do in Canada, however; they refer to having sex. Both boys and girls are uncomfortable with talking openly about sex, so much of their communication is nonverbal.

If the girl accepts the gift, she signals that she is open to a dating relationship with the boy. Dating and sex are linked—when a boy and girl begin dating, they also engage in playing sex (having intercourse). There is no intermediate stage, as there is in Canada, where adolescents gradually proceed from kissing and petting to intercourse.

In Kenya, the sexual encounter generally consists of a brief episode of intercourse. Sexual pleasure for the girl is not expected. Rather, sex is seen as something to finish quickly. The objective is to satisfy a basic need for the male. This is an exchange process whereby girls provide sex to obtain material goods.

The girl may delay accepting the boy's advances if she feels the initial material gift is not large enough. Indeed, girls discuss strategies for obtaining more money and more expensive gifts. Many girls prefer to obtain gifts from adult men, because adults can provide more material goods than can younger boys.

Typically, a girl initially refuses to engage in sex. This strategy helps preserve her reputation as a "good" girl and encourages the boy to provide more gifts. If the girl continues to say no to sex, however, it's common practice for the boy to force her to have sex, especially if he feels the amount of his gift is sufficient.

Recently, many Canadians have questioned how far we should go in accommodating immigrant values that conflict with basic Canadian values. In 2007, the Quebec government established a commission to examine the issue of "reasonable accommodation." People expressed a wide range of opinions to the commission. The most heated reactions were to the wearing of the *hijab*, or head scarf, by some Muslim women (Patriquin, 2007). A 2007 national survey conducted by the Institute for Research on Public Policy found that the majority of Canadians wanted limits to the "reasonable accommodation" of immigrants. Quebeckers by far had the strongest feelings on this issue, as many believed Quebec's culture to be threatened by various immigrant and minority groups (Patriquin, 2007).

When it comes to sexuality, Canadians are somewhat more liberal than Americans. For example, more Canadians (80%) than Americans (64%) are accepting of premarital sex (Bibby, 2006). Angus Reid (2010b) polls have found that more Canadians (61%) than Americans (36%) are accepting of same-sex marriage. In other chapters of this textbook, we'll present more comparisons of American and Canadian attitudes and behaviours.

POLITICS AND SEX IN CANADA AND THE UNITED STATES   Christian fundamentalists, known as the "religious right," have a greater presence in the United States than in Canada. They therefore have a much stronger voice in persuading American governments to take a conservative stance on the regulation of sexual values. Since the 1990s, for example, conservative politicians in the United States Congress have voted to spend hundreds of millions of dollars on education programs that teach abstinence from sex but do not teach contraceptive methods to adolescents. During his presidency, Barack Obama has reduced but not eliminated federal government spending on abstinence-only programs, though he has provided relatively more funding for teen pregnancy programs that included contraception.

In general, Canadian governments have taken a more balanced approach to supporting sexual health education for youth. The provincial and territorial ministries of education tend to follow the broadly based approach to providing sexual health information recommended in the Public Health Agency of Canada's (2008) *Canadian Guidelines for Sexual Health Education*. We'll discuss this in Chapter 15.

In general, Canadian politicians have maintained a separation between religion and the state. The *Canadian Charter of Rights and Freedoms* has helped maintain this separation, giving individual rights precedence over religious values. This has been shown in judicial decisions regarding same-sex marriage. Despite protests from various religious groups, Canadian courts have consistently decided that disallowing same-sex marriage is a violation of the individual rights of gays and lesbians. Former Canadian Prime Minister Paul Martin adopted a similar position. Although he was a practising Roman Catholic and received intense pressure from Catholic Church officials to oppose same-sex marriage, Martin stated that his own religious values should not override personal freedoms. While current American President Barack Obama initially defended the rights of gay and lesbian couples to form civil unions, he stopped short of supporting gay marriage, and espoused the traditional definition of marriage as a union between a man and a woman. However, in 2012, saying that his position on the issue had "evolved," President Obama declared his support for the right of gays and lesbians to legally marry.

In 2005, Canada became the fourth country in the world to legalize same-sex marriage. The main political opposition to this legislation came from the Conservative Party of Canada and the Progressive Conservative Alliance of Alberta. Federal Conservative leader Stephen Harper indicated that if his party were to form a government, he would hold another vote in the House of Commons to overturn the law. Here Harper was going against public opinion. A survey conducted by the Strategic Counsel after the passage of same-sex legislation found that 55% of Canadians wanted the next government to leave the legislation in place, and only 39% wanted the law repealed. Shortly after the Conservative Party formed a minority government in 2006, it did introduce a motion to overturn the same-sex law. The motion was defeated by the other parties, which constituted the majority of Parliament. Interestingly, since the Harper government has achieved a majority in the House of Commons it has not attempted to overturn the law even though it has enough votes in Parliament to do so.

Despite the fears of some Canadian religious groups that they would be forced to sanctify same-sex marriages, Bill C-38 governing same-sex marriage specifically states that the legislation is binding only on city officials, and not on religious organizations.

After the Progressive Conservative Party of Canada united with the more socially conservative Canadian Reform Conservative Alliance Party, the new party hinted at introducing restrictive legislation in other areas of sexuality. In 2008, the Harper Conservatives were able to pass legislation that raised the legal age of consent from 14 to 16. Previously, the Progressive Conservatives had followed a middle-of-the-road approach. It was, in fact, the Progressive Conservative government of Brian Mulroney that had lowered the age of sexual consent from 18 to 14 in 1987.

In 2010, Stephen Harper's Conservatives introduced a program to promote maternal health in developing countries, but refused to allow any of the money to fund abortion services. This was widely criticized in Canada and in other countries as endangering the health of women in developing countries and being at odds with the goals of the G8 initiative on maternal and child health.

These examples show that it's not easy to generalize about trends related to sex and politics. While Canada is generally regarded as being more liberal than the United States, recent initiatives by the Harper government (e.g., raising the age of consent, restricting funding for abortion in developing countries) may reflect a Canadian governmental shift toward more conservative values concerning sexuality.

Sexuality and Values

Our society is pluralistic with respect to sexuality. Collectively, we embrace a wide range of sexual attitudes and values. Some readers may be liberal in their sexual views and behaviours. Others may be conservative or traditional. Some

CRITICAL THINKING QUESTIONS

Many of us take pride in the idea that Canadian society welcomes diversity with respect to ethnicity and religion. To what extent do you think Canadian society welcomes diversity when it comes to sexuality?

are staunchly "pro-choice" on abortion, and others adamantly "pro-life." Some approve of sex for couples who are dating casually, others hold the line at emotional commitment, and still others believe people should wait until marriage. While Canadian society has evolved considerably with regard to the rights of gay, lesbian, bisexual, and transgender people, there is still a plurality of views about sexual orientation.

Perhaps one of the defining characteristics of Canadian society is our acceptance of diversity on many levels, including diversity of opinions and values related to sexuality. This acceptance gives us the freedom to adhere to our own distinct values and traditions, while also recognizing that we all have an obligation to respect the rights of others whose beliefs, perspectives, and behaviours are different from our own. The Canadian constitutional framework, particularly the Canadian Charter of Rights and Freedoms, creates an environment in which diverse communities can coexist and flourish, and this acceptance of diversity can and should apply to values and behaviours related to sexuality. The extent to which these ideals actually reflect the current reality in Canada is very much an open question.

People's sexual attitudes, experiences, and behaviours are to a large extent shaped by their cultural traditions and beliefs. Because the world consists of diverse peoples and cultures, the study of human sexuality is really the study of human sexualities. In this book we'll highlight the many ways people experience their sexuality.

Sexuality and Ethics

Some sexual choices can have negative consequences for individuals and society. All societies therefore have restrictions on certain kinds of sex-related behaviours. Sexual ethics govern what societies consider unacceptable sexual behaviours. Glenn Meaney and B. J. Rye (2007) at St. Jerome's University at the University of Waterloo have analyzed three distinct ethical frameworks: the ethics of divinity, community, and autonomy.

The ethics of divinity (which generally have religious roots) are based on a fundamental belief in a divine source for moral judgments of right and wrong. This approach formulates ethical behaviour on the basis of moral laws or pronouncements found in, for example, the Hebrew and Christian Bibles or Quran, which contain many rules pertaining to sexual behaviour, usually in the form of restrictions against behaviours such as adultery, incest, or sexual activity between members of the same sex. The belief that sex should only occur within marriage is often based on an ethics of divinity; all the major religions consider this belief to be a fundamental moral rule that should not be questioned.

Many religious followers accept the moral codes of their religions as a matter of faith and commitment. Some people find it reassuring to be informed by religious authorities or documents that a certain course of action is right or wrong. Others, however, take a more liberal view. They say, for example, that the Bible reflects the social setting of the time in which it was written, not just divine inspiration. Now that population growth is exploding in many parts of the world, religious injunctions to be fruitful and multiply may no longer be socially and environmentally sound. Prohibitions, such as that against sexual relations during menstruation, may have been based on prescientific perceptions of danger. Some people thus view religious teachings as a general framework for decision making rather than as a set of absolute rules.

The ethics of community are based on what is perceived as the greater good for the community. Although different societies vary widely in terms of which sexual behaviours they consider acceptable, they all find some behaviours unethical and intolerable. Laws against sexual assault, for example, are based on the community ethic that no one should force someone else to engage in sex against his or her will. The English philosopher John Stuart Mill (1806–1873) proposed an ethical system based on *utilitarianism*—the view that moral conduct is based on that which will bring about "the greatest good for the greatest number" (Mill, 1863). The utilitarian characterizes behaviour as ethical when it does the greatest good and causes the least harm. This is not the same thing as freedom of action. Utilitarians may come down hard in opposition to sexual behaviours if they believe that they jeopardize a community's health and social fabric.

The ethics of autonomy values the rights and freedoms of individuals. People are allowed to satisfy their own sexual needs, as long as they do not impede the rights of others. The belief that same-sex relationships are acceptable because they cause no harm to others is an example of the ethics of autonomy. This approach to ethical decision making seeks to arrive at moral judgments based on a balancing of individuals' right to exercise their own autonomy to behave as they wish with the responsibility to treat others with respect and not infringe on their autonomy. Sociologist Ira Reiss (1997) has proposed an ethics of "sexual pluralism" in which people have the right to autonomy in making their own decisions about sexual behaviour provided that their sexual interactions with partners are guided by the principles of honesty, equality, and responsibility.

Meaney and Rye's (2007) framework helps us understand the relationship between various ethical positions and sexual decision making. There are, however, many other approaches to understanding this topic. For example, in their national survey of Americans, Laumann et al. (1994) categorized their respondents' moral values into the three categories of traditional, relational, and recreational.

> **CRITICAL THINKING QUESTIONS**
>
> What do you see as the strengths and weakness of the ethics of divinity, community, and autonomy?

Ethics and Sexual Rights

Recent movements based on the ethics of autonomy have been promoting sexual rights and freedoms around the world. The World Association for Sexual Health (WAS) has been at the forefront in promoting sexual rights. At the 2005 World Congress of Sexology meeting in Montreal, participants agreed to urge governments and international agencies to move forward in promoting sexual health, with an emphasis on sexual rights.

To achieve this goal, WAS (2008) issued a declaration consisting of sexual health-related goals for the global community:

- Recognize, promote, ensure, and protect sexual rights for all.
- Advance toward gender equality and equity.
- Condemn, combat, and reduce all forms of sexuality-related violence.
- Provide universal access to comprehensive sexuality education and information.
- Ensure that reproductive health programs recognize the centrality of sexual health.
- Halt and reverse the spread of HIV/AIDS and other sexually transmitted infections (STI).
- Identify, address, and treat sexual concerns, dysfunctions, and disorders.
- Achieve recognition of sexual pleasure as a component of holistic health and well-being.

The validity of these goals may seem self-evident to many Canadians. Some, however, may not be embraced by people from non-Western cultures or some Western religious perspectives. Eleanor Maticka-Tyndale and Lisa Smylie (2008) at the University of Windsor note that the concept of sexual rights is contentious, particularly in cultures with different perspectives toward sexuality. They argue that the goal of sexual rights for all is more likely to be achieved by focusing on broader international human-rights commitments such as the United Nations' Universal Declaration of Human Rights than by trying to convince people from different cultural and religious perspectives to agree on sexual rights per se. Maticka-Tyndale and Smylie also make the case that a more consensus-building approach is needed before global agreements to promote sexual health can be reached.

Sexuality and Spirituality

While researchers have paid considerable attention to the role of religion as a predictor of sexual attitudes and behaviours, research into the spiritual aspects of sexuality has been limited. Peggy Kleinplatz, a researcher and therapist at the University of Ottawa, and Stanley Krippner, a researcher in Israel, believe sexual relationships can be more fulfilling when they extend beyond the purely physical aspects of sex, such as the techniques emphasized in many sex manuals (Kleinplatz & Krippner, 2007). They argue that many people want to transform their sex routines into spiritual experiences that make them "feel utterly alive. . . . Sharing such moments with one's partner feels like a sacred destiny fulfilled" (p. 306). Tantric sex, for example, which is based on tantric yoga that stems from religious practices in India, emphasizes prolonged sexual union as a way to achieve heightened consciousness and enlightenment.

To meet the desire of couples who wish to have spiritually based sexual relationships, workshops on tantric sex are given in many Canadian cities. Kleinplatz and Krippner (2007) are critical of tantric teachers who focus on the sexual techniques but neglect the spiritual foundations of this approach to sexual relationships.

Thinking Critically About Human Sexuality

We're flooded with so much information about sex that it's difficult to separate truth from fiction. Newspapers, television shows, books, magazines, and the Internet contain one feature after another about sex. Many of them contradict one another, contain half-truths, or draw misleading or unsubstantiated conclusions. Taking a scientific approach to human sexuality includes thinking critically about claims and findings that are presented to us as fact or truth.

We tend to assume that information provided by influential or authoritative figures such as television psychologists or government officials must be accurate and valid. But critical thinkers never say, "This is true simply because so-and-so says it's true."

To arrive at a well-thought-out, independently developed point of view, we need to think critically. That is, we need to evaluate the strengths and weaknesses of various claims, arguments, and widely held beliefs. The core of critical thinking is scepticism—not taking things for granted. It means being sceptical of things that are presented in print, uttered by authority figures or celebrities, or passed along by friends. Another aspect of critical thinking is thoughtful analysis and probing of claims and arguments. Critical thinking means scrutinizing definitions of terms and evaluating the premises and logic of arguments. It means basing our own beliefs on careful reasoning, rather than simply accepting what we're told. When we think critically, we maintain open minds. We reach conclusions only after we have obtained and evaluated the evidence.

Principles of Critical Thinking

Following are some suggestions for critical thinking:

- **Be sceptical.** Politicians, religious leaders, and other authority figures attempt to convince you of their points of view. Even researchers and authors may hold certain biases. Accept no opinion as fact—until you have personally weighed the evidence.
- **Examine definitions of terms.** Some statements are true when a term is defined one way, but not true when it's defined another way. Consider the statement

"love is blind," for instance. If love is defined as head-over-heels infatuation, there may be substance to the statement. Infatuated people tend to idealize and overlook the faults of their loved ones. If, however, love is defined as deep caring and commitment involving a more realistic (if still somewhat slanted) appraisal of the loved one, then love is not so much blind as a bit nearsighted.

■ **Examine the assumptions or premises underlying arguments.** For example, consider the statement "abortion is murder." *Webster's New World Dictionary* defines murder as "the unlawful and malicious or premeditated killing of one human being by another." The statement can be true, according to this definition, only if the victim is held to be a human being (and if the act is unlawful and either malicious or premeditated). Most pro-life advocates argue that embryos and foetuses are human beings. Most pro-choice advocates claim that they are not. Hence the argument that abortion is murder would rest in part on the assumption that the embryo or foetus is a human being.

■ **Be cautious in drawing conclusions from evidence.** Recent research has found that teenagers who listen to rap, hip hop, pop, and rock music with lyrics that are sexually explicit or that refer to women as sex objects are more likely to initiate sexual activity at an early age (Martino et al., 2006). The popular media seem obsessed with the idea that sexually explicit songs lead to sex, and lots of it. However, teens who choose to dwell on these songs may have different values than those who don't, leading them not only to spend hours with their iPods blasting sexual lyrics into their ears, but also to choose to have sex at an earlier age. The evidence of a connection between listening to this music and having sex is open to various interpretations, which brings us to our next principle of critical thinking.

■ **Consider alternative interpretations of research evidence.** For example, teens who dwell on sexual song lyrics may also be more open to sexual activity because they are less traditional than teens who (literally) turn off these songs. This example shows that correlations between events do not necessarily reveal cause and effect. Also consider the kinds of evidence upon which conclusions are based. Some conclusions, even seemingly "scientific" conclusions, are based on anecdotes or poorly designed studies. Beware of writers who "cherry pick" research by only mentioning studies that support their own point of view, but ignore studies that don't.

■ **Consider the strengths and weaknesses of different perspectives on sexuality, even ones you don't agree with.** Why do people with other opinions hold their beliefs? Evaluating the strengths and weaknesses of various perspectives can help us arrive at well-thought-out conclusions and effectively communicate our beliefs to others.

■ **Don't oversimplify.** Consider the statement "sexual orientation is inborn." There is some evidence that sexual orientation may involve inborn predispositions, such as genetic influences. However, biology is not destiny in human sexuality. Gay, lesbian, and heterosexual sexual orientations appear to develop as a result of complex interactions of biological and environmental factors.

■ **Don't overgeneralize.** Consider the belief that gay men are effeminate and lesbians are masculine. Yes, some gays and lesbians fit these stereotypes, but many do not. Overgeneralizing makes us vulnerable to accepting stereotypes.

Perspectives on Human Sexuality

Human sexuality is a complex topic. No single perspective can capture all of its nuances. In this book, we explore human sexuality from many perspectives. In Chapter 2 we will look at different theories that can be used to examine human sexuality. But before we get to specific scientific theories, it is important for us to familiarize ourselves with different general perspectives that have informed the ways human sexuality has been perceived and understood. In this section, we introduce a number of perspectives that we'll draw on in subsequent chapters.

The Historical Perspective

History places our sexual behaviour in context. It tells us whether our sexual behaviours reflect trends that have been with us through the millennia, or are customs of a particular culture and era. History shows little evidence of universal sexual trends. Attitudes and behaviours vary extensively from one time and place to another. Contemporary Canadian society may appear permissive when compared with the Victorian and post–World War II eras, yet it looks staid when compared with the sexual norms and customs of some ancient societies. History also shows how religion has been a major influence on sexual values and behaviours.

Let's examine some historical changes in attitudes toward sexuality. We'll begin by turning the clock back 20 000 to 30 000 years, to the days before written records were kept—that is, to prehistory.

SEXUALITY AND ART IN PREHISTORY AND ANTIQUITY   Information about life among our Stone Age ancestors is obtained largely from cave drawings, stone artefacts, and the customs of modern-day preliterate peoples whose existence may have changed little over the millennia.

Art produced in the Stone Age, some 20 000 years ago, suggests the worship of women's ability to bear children and perpetuate the species (Fichner-Rathus, 2010). Primitive statues and cave drawings portray women with large, pendulous breasts, rounded hips, and prominent sex organs. Most theorists regard the figurines as fertility symbols. Emphasis on the female reproductive role may also signify ignorance of the male's contribution to reproduction.

As the ice sheets of the last ice age retreated (about 11000 BCE) and the climate warmed, human societies turned agrarian. Hunters and gatherers became farmers and herders. As people became aware of the male role in reproduction, **phallic worship** sprang into being. Knowledge of paternity is believed to have developed around 9000 BCE, which is about the time people shifted from hunting and gathering to farming and shepherding. The penis was glorified in art as a plough, an axe, or a sword.

Phallic symbols figured in religious ceremonies in ancient Egypt. The ancient Greeks created art that suggests they revered phalluses, rendering them sometimes as rings and sometimes as necklaces. Some phalluses were given wings, suggesting the power ascribed to them. In ancient Rome, a large phallus was carried like a float in a parade honouring Venus, the goddess of love.

The **incest taboo** that discourages sexual intercourse between close blood relatives may have been the first taboo. All human societies apparently have some form of incest taboo, though its strictness may vary from one culture to another. Brother–sister marriages were permitted among the presumably divine rulers of ancient Egypt and the royal families of the Incas and the Hawaiians, even though they were generally prohibited among commoners. Incestuous relationships in these royal bloodlines may have kept wealth, power, and "divinity" in the family.

THE ANCIENT HEBREWS   The ancient Hebrews viewed sex—within marriage, at least—as a fulfilling experience intended to satisfy the divine injunction to "be fruitful and multiply" (Browning et al., 2006). Male–male and female–female sexual behaviours were strongly condemned, because they were thought to threaten perpetuation of the family. Adultery, too, was condemned—at least for women. Although the Hebrew Bible (the Old Testament in the Christian faith) permitted **polygamy**, the vast majority of the Hebrews practised **monogamy**.

CRITICAL THINKING QUESTIONS

What are some examples of things that you have seen or read about sexuality on the Internet that are false or misleading?

Phallic worship Veneration of the penis as a symbol of generative power.

Phallic symbol An object that represents the penis.

Incest taboo The prohibition against intercourse with close blood relatives.

Polygamy The practice of having two or more spouses at the same time.

Monogamy The practice of having only one spouse at a time.

Applied Knowledge

THINKING CRITICALLY ABOUT SEXUALITY INFORMATION ON THE INTERNET

Every day, people surf the Internet in the hope of finding websites that will answer their questions about sexuality and sex-related problems. How can we evaluate the credibility and accuracy of a website?

There are no easy answers. Many of us believe the things we see posted. Anecdotes about how Tyrone increased the size of his penis by 30% and how Maria learned to reach orgasm "every time" can have a powerful allure. Be on guard, because the sexuality information on some websites can do more harm than good.

A price we pay for freedom of speech is that nearly anything can be posted on a website or appear in print. Authors can make extravagant, distorted, or false claims with little fear of punishment. They can lie about the effectiveness of a new sexual cure-all as easily as they can lie about sightings of Elvis Presley or UFOs.

How can you protect yourself?

■ In this instance, do judge the book by its cover. Does the website look well organized? Do the links within the web pages work? A credible website will look professional and well maintained.

■ Ignore websites that make extravagant claims. If it sounds too good to be true, it probably is. No method helps everyone who tries it. Very few methods work overnight. Extravagant claims are clues to look elsewhere.

■ Check the credentials of the people who post the information. Be suspicious if the author's title is "Dr." and is placed before the name. The degree could be a phony doctorate bought through the mail. It's better if the "doctor" has a PhD, PsyD, MD, or EdD after her or his name.

■ Check authors' affiliations. Professionals who are affiliated

discpicture/Shutterstock

Are They Buying It?
Critical thinkers carefully consider the premises of an argument, weigh all the evidence, and arrive at their own conclusions. Critical thinking is important in matters of human sexuality, and valuable in all areas of life.

with colleges, universities, clinics, and hospitals may have more to offer than those who are not.

■ Check out who is responsible for creating the website. Is it a professional association of health care providers or a respected nonprofit organization? Or is it someone with something to sell?

■ Check the evidence reported on the website. Unscientific websites (and books) usually make extensive use of anecdotes. Anecdotes are unsupported stories or case studies about fantastic results with one or a few individuals. Responsible helping professionals check the effectiveness of techniques with large numbers of people. They carefully measure the outcomes.

■ Check the reference citations for the evidence. Legitimate research is reported in the journals and websites you'll find in the References section of this book. These journals report research methods and outcomes that are more likely to be scientifically valid. If there are no links to reference

citations on the website, or if the list of references looks suspicious, you should be suspicious, too.

■ Peer-reviewed academic journals are the gold standard for research on sexuality and other topics. "Peer-reviewed" means the research has been carefully reviewed by experts in the field. Peer-reviewed journals related to sexuality include *Archives of Sexual Behavior, Journal of Sex Research, The Canadian Journal of Human Sexuality, The Journal of Sexual Medicine, Journal of Sex and Marital Therapy, Perspectives on Sexual and Reproductive Health,* and *Culture, Health & Sexuality.* Students at most colleges and universities can access peer-reviewed sexuality journals online through their schools' libraries or library websites. (Hint: Instructors are more likely to be impressed by student assignments that reference peer-reviewed journals than by assignments that reference whatever websites the students have found simply by entering their topics into Internet search engines.)

Scala/Art Resource, NY

Male Sexuality in Ancient Greece.
Many ancient Greek ceramics depict male–male sexual activity. The Greeks believed males were bisexual. In Homer's Iliad, *brought to the silver screen in 2004 as* Troy, *Achilles is spurred to battle by the killing of his lover, Patroclus. The film glossed over this motive, however, emphasizing the pair's family relationship.*

The ancient Hebrews approved of sex within marriage not simply for procreation, but also for mutual pleasure and fulfillment. They believed the expression of sexual needs and desires helped strengthen marital bonds and solidify families. (These points are noteworthy because many people, both Jewish and non-Jewish, believe the traditional Jewish religion held mainly negative attitudes about sexual pleasure. David Ribner at Bar-Ilan University in Israel and Peggy Kleinplatz at the University of Ottawa provide a thorough analysis of myths regarding sexuality and Judaism [2007].)

Among the ancient Hebrews, a wife was considered her husband's property. If she offended him, she could be divorced on a whim. A wife could be stoned to death for adultery. She might also have to share her husband with his secondary wives and concubines. Men who committed adultery by consorting with the wives of other men were considered to have violated the latter's property rights. Although they were subject to harsh penalties for violation of property rights, male adulterers were not put to death.

THE ANCIENT GREEKS   The classical or golden age of ancient Greece lasted about 200 years, from approximately 500 to 300 BCE. Within this relatively short span lived the philosophers Socrates, Plato, and Aristotle. Like the Hebrews, the Greeks valued family life. Greek men admired the well-developed male body and enjoyed nude wrestling among men in the arena. Erotic encounters and off-colour jokes characterized the works of Aristophanes and other playwrights.

The Greeks viewed their gods—Zeus, god of gods; Apollo, who inspired art and music; Aphrodite, the goddess of carnal love, whose name is the basis of the word *aphrodisiac*; and others—as voracious seekers of sexual variety. Not only were they believed to have sexual adventures among themselves, they were also thought to seduce mortals.

Three aspects of Greek sexuality are of particular interest to our study of sexual practices in the ancient world: male–male adult sexual behaviour, **pederasty**, and prostitution. The Greeks viewed men and women as **bisexual**. Male–male adult sex was deemed acceptable so long as it did not threaten the institution of the family.

"Pederasty" means love of boys. Sex between men and prepubescent boys was illegal, but families were generally pleased if their adolescent sons attracted socially prominent mentors. Men in Greece might take on an adolescent male as a lover and

Pederasty Sexual love between a man and a boy.

Bisexual Sexually responsive to either gender.

pupil. Pederasty did not impede the boy's future male–female functioning, because the pederast himself was usually married, and the Greeks believed people equally capable of male–female and male–male sexual activity.

Prostitution flourished at every level of society. Prostitutes ranged from refined **courtesans** to **concubines**, who were usually slaves. Courtesans could play musical instruments, dance, engage in witty repartee, and discuss the latest political crises. They were also skilled in the arts of love. No social stigma was attached to visiting a courtesan. At the lower rungs of society were streetwalkers and prostitutes who lived in tawdry brothels.

The women of Athens had no more legal or political rights than slaves. They were subject to the authority of their male next-of-kin before marriage, and of their husbands afterward. They received no formal education and were consigned most of the time to women's quarters in their homes. They were chaperoned when they ventured out of doors. A husband could divorce his wife without cause and was obligated to do so if she committed adultery.

Courtesan A prostitute, especially the mistress of a noble or wealthy man.

Concubine A secondary wife, usually of inferior legal and social status.

THE ANCIENT ROMANS   Much is made of the sexual excesses of the Roman emperors and ruling families. Emperors such as Caligula sponsored orgies at which guests engaged in a wide variety of sexual practices. These sexual excesses were found more often among the upper classes of palace society than among average Romans.

Unlike their counterparts in ancient Greece, Romans viewed male–male sexual behaviour as a threat to the integrity of the Roman family and to the position of the Roman woman. The family was viewed as the source of the Roman Empire's strength. Although Roman women were more likely than their Greek counterparts to share their husbands' social lives, they were still considered their husbands' property.

Western society traces the roots of many of its sexual terms to Roman culture, as indicated by their Latin roots. "Fellatio," for example, derives from the Latin *fellare*, meaning "to suck." "Cunnilingus" derives from *cunnus*, meaning "vulva," and *lingere*, "to lick." "Fornication" derives from *fornix*, an arch or vault; the term stems from Roman streetwalkers' practice of serving their customers in the shadows of archways near public buildings such as stadiums and theatres.

THE EARLY CHRISTIANS   Christianity emerged within the Roman Empire during the centuries following the death of Jesus. Early Christian views on sexuality were largely shaped by Saint Paul and the Church fathers in the first century and by Saint Augustine in the latter part of the fourth century. Adultery and fornication were rampant among the upper classes of Rome at the time, and early Christian leaders began to associate sexuality with sin (MacCulloch, 2011).

In replacing the pagan values of Rome, the early Christians, like the Hebrews, sought to restrict sex to marriage. They saw temptations of the flesh as distractions from spiritual devotion. Paul preached that celibacy was closer than marriage to the Christian ideal. He recognized that not everyone could achieve celibacy, however, so he said it was "better to marry than to burn" (with passion, that is).

Christians, like Jews before them, demanded virginity of their brides (MacCulloch, 2011). Prostitution was condemned. Christians taught that men should love their wives with restraint, not with passion. The goal of procreation should govern sexual behaviour—the spirit should rule the flesh. Divorce was outlawed. Unhappiness with one's spouse might reflect sexual—thus sinful—restlessness. Dissolving a marriage might also jeopardize the social structure that supported the Church. Masturbation, male–male sexual behaviour, female–female sexual behaviour, oral–genital contact, and anal intercourse were viewed as abominations in the eyes of God.

Saint Augustine (353–430 CE) associated sexual lust with the original sin of Adam and Eve in the Garden of Eden. Lust and shame were passed down through the generations. Lust made any sexual expression inherently evil, even within marriage. According to Augustine, only through celibacy could men and women attain a state of grace.

ISLAM   Now the dominant religion in the Middle East, across North Africa, and into parts of southern Asia, Islam was founded by the prophet Muhammad, who was born in about 570 CE in what is now Saudi Arabia. The Islamic tradition treasures marriage and sexual fulfillment in marriage. Premarital sex invites shame and social condemnation—and, in some fundamentalist Islamic states, harsh penalties.

The family is the backbone of Islamic society (Browning et al., 2006). Muhammad decreed that marriage represented the road to virtue. Islamic tradition permits a sexual double standard, however. Men under most circumstances may take up to four wives, but women are permitted only one husband. Public social interactions between men and women are severely restricted in conservative Islamic societies. Women are expected to keep their heads and faces veiled in public and to avoid all contact with men other than their husbands.

THE HINDUS   Perhaps no culture has cultivated sexual pleasure as a spiritual ideal to the same extent as the ancient Hindus of India did. Temples from the fifth century CE onward show sculptures of gods, nymphs, and ordinary people in erotic poses. Hindu sexual practices were codified in a sex manual, the *Kama Sutra*, which illustrated sexual positions, some of which would challenge a contortionist. It also held recipes for alleged aphrodisiacs. This manual is believed to have been written by the Hindu sage Vatsyayana sometime between the third and fifth centuries CE at about the time Christianity was ascending in the West.

In its graphic representations of sexual positions and practices, the *Kama Sutra* reflected the Hindu belief that sex was a religious duty, not a source of shame or guilt. Hindu deities were often portrayed as engaging in same-sex as well as male–female sexual activities. In the Hindu doctrine of karma (the passage of souls from one place to another), sexual fulfillment was regarded as one way to become reincarnated at a higher level of existence. Indian society grew more restrictive toward sexuality after about 1000 CE.

THE TAOISTS   In the cultures of the Far East, sexuality was akin to spirituality. To the Taoist masters of China, who influenced Chinese culture for millennia, sex was a sacred duty—a form of worship that led toward harmony with nature and immortality.

The Chinese culture was the first to produce a detailed sex manual, which came into use about 200 years before the birth of Jesus. The man was expected to extend intercourse as long as possible, to absorb more of his wife's natural essence, or yin, which enhanced his own masculine essence, or yang. Moreover, he was to help bring his partner to orgasm, so as to increase the flow of energy he might absorb.

Taoists believed it was wasteful for a man to "spill his seed." Masturbation, acceptable

Private Collection/Archives Charmet/The Bridgeman Art Library

An Illustration from the Kama Sutra.
Believed to have been written sometime between the third and fifth centuries CE, the Kama Sutra is an Indian sex manual containing graphic illustrations of sexual techniques and practices.

for women, was ruled out for men. Sexual practices such as anal intercourse and oral–genital contact (fellatio and cunnilingus) were permissible, so long as the man did not squander yang through wasteful ejaculation.

Same-sex activity was not prohibited by Taoist holy writings, though some Taoists frowned on exclusive homosexuality. A parallel to Western cultures was the role accorded women in traditional Chinese society. The "good wife," like her Western counterpart, was limited to a domestic role.

THE MEDIEVAL CHRISTIANS The Middle Ages span the millennium of Western history from about 476 to 1450 CE. The attitudes of the Roman Catholic Church toward sexuality, largely unchanged since the time of Augustine, dominated medieval thought (Crawford et al., 2011). Yet some currents of change crept across medieval Europe in the social standing of women. The Church had long regarded all women as being tainted by the sin of Eve. But in the Eastern Empire of Byzantium, based in Constantinople, the cult of the Virgin Mary flourished. The ideal of womanhood was in the image of Mary: good, gracious, loving, and saintly. Imported by the Crusaders and others who returned from the East, the cult of the Virgin Mary swept European Christendom and helped elevate the status of women.

THE PROTESTANT REFORMERS During the Reformation, Martin Luther (1483–1546) and other Christian reformers such as John Calvin (1509–1564) split off from the Roman Catholic Church and formed their own sects, which led to the development of the modern Protestant denominations of Western Europe (and later, the New World).

Luther disputed many Roman Catholic doctrines on sexuality. He believed priests should be allowed to marry and rear children. To Luther, marriage was as much a part of human nature as eating or drinking. Calvin rejected the Roman Catholic Church's position that sex in marriage was permissible only for the purpose of procreation. He believed sexual expression in marriage fulfilled other legitimate roles, such as strengthening the marriage bond and helping to relieve the stresses of everyday life. Extramarital and premarital sex, however, remained taboo.

THE VICTORIANS The middle and later parts of the nineteenth century are generally called the Victorian period, after Queen Victoria of England. Victoria assumed the throne in 1837 and ruled until her death in 1901. Her name has become virtually synonymous with sexual repression.

Victorian society in Europe and North America, on the surface at least, was prim and proper (Horowitz, 2002). Sex was not discussed in polite society. Many women viewed sex as a marital duty, to be performed for procreation or to satisfy their husbands' cravings. Consider the following often-cited quotation, attributed to Alice, Lady Hillingdon, wife of the second Baron Hillingdon:

> I am happy now that Charles calls on my bed chamber less frequently than of old. As it is, I now endure but two calls a week, and when I hear his steps outside my door, I lie down on my bed, close my eyes, open my legs, and think of England.

Women were assumed not to experience sexual desires or pleasures. "I would say," observed Dr. William Acton (1813–1875), an influential English physician, in 1857, "that the majority of women (happily for them) are not much troubled with sexual feeling of any kind."

It was widely believed among medical authorities that sex drained the man of his natural vitality. Physicians thus recommended that intercourse be practised infrequently. The Reverend Sylvester Graham (1794–1851) preached that ejaculation deprived men of the "vital fluids" they needed to maintain health and vitality. Graham preached against "wasting the seed" by masturbation or frequent marital intercourse (Laqueur, 2003). How frequent was frequent? In Graham's view, intercourse more than once a month could dangerously deplete the man's vital energies. He recommended that young men control their sexual appetites by a diet of simple foods based on whole-grain flours. He invented what we now call the Graham cracker for this purpose.

But the behaviour of Victorians was not as repressed as advertised. Despite Acton's beliefs, Victorian women did experience sexual pleasure and orgasm. Consider an early sex survey conducted in 1892 by a female physician, Clelia Duel Mosher. Although her sample was small and nonrandom, 35 of the 44 women who responded admitted to desiring sexual intercourse. And 34 of them reported experiencing orgasm. Women's diaries of the time also contained accounts of passionate and sexually fulfilling love affairs (Gay, 1984).

Prostitution flourished during the Victorian era. Men apparently thought they were doing their wives a favour by looking elsewhere. Accurate statistics are hard to come by, but there may have been as many as 1 prostitute for every 12 men in London during the nineteenth century; in Vienna, there was perhaps 1 prostitute for every 7 men.

Same-sex sexual behaviour was considered indecent in Victorian society. The celebrated gay Anglo–Irish novelist and playwright Oscar Wilde—author of such famous works as *The Picture of Dorian Gray*, *An Ideal Husband*, and *The Importance of Being Earnest*—was imprisoned after being convicted of gross indecency.

THE SCIENTIFIC STUDY OF SEXUALITY   It was against this backdrop of sexual repression that scientists and scholars first began to approach sexuality as an area of legitimate scientific study. An important early contributor to the science of human sexuality was the English physician Havelock Ellis (1859–1939). Ellis compiled a veritable encyclopaedia of sexuality—a series of volumes published between 1897 and 1910 entitled *Studies in the Psychology of Sex*. Ellis drew information from various sources, including case histories, anthropological findings, and medical knowledge. He challenged the prevailing view, arguing that sexual desires in women were natural and healthful. He promoted the idea that many sexual problems had psychological rather than physical causes. He also argued that a homosexual orientation was a naturally occurring variation within the spectrum of normal sexuality, not an aberration. Ellis treated homosexual orientations as inborn dispositions, rather than vices or character flaws.

Another influential **sexologist**, the German psychiatrist Richard von Krafft-Ebing (1840–1902), described more than 200 case histories of individuals with various sexual deviations in his book *Psychopathia Sexualis: With Especial Reference to the Antipathic Sexual Instinct: A Medico-Forensic Study* (1886). His writings contain vivid descriptions of deviations ranging from sadomasochism (sexual gratification through inflicting or receiving pain) and bestiality (sex with animals) to necrophilia (intercourse with dead people). Krafft-Ebing viewed sexual deviations as mental diseases that could be studied and perhaps treated by medical science.

Sexologist A scientist who studies sexual behaviour.

At about the same time, a Viennese physician, Sigmund Freud (1856–1939), was developing a theory of personality that was to have an enormous influence on modern culture and science. Freud believed the sex drive was our principal motivating force.

Alfred Kinsey (1894–1956), an Indiana University zoologist, conducted the first large-scale studies of sexual behaviour in the 1930s and 1940s. It was then that sex research became recognized as a field of scientific study in its own right. In 1938, Kinsey had been asked to teach a course on marriage. While researching the subject, he had discovered that little was known about sexual practices in American society. He soon embarked on an ambitious research project, conducting detailed personal interviews with nearly 12 000 people across the United States. His survey results were published in two volumes, *Sexual Behavior in the Human Male* (1948) and *Sexual Behavior in the Human Female* (1953). These

George Doyle/ThinkStock

Generational Change.
Are today's young people more or less liberal and sophisticated than people of earlier generations in their expression of sexuality? While most contemporary young people have greater access to information about sexuality and relationships than their parents did, uncertainty and anxiety are common. (Models for illustrative purposes only.)

books represented the first scientific attempts to provide a comprehensive picture of sexual behaviour in the United States.

Filled with statistical tables rather than racy pictures or vignettes, Kinsey's books made for rather dry reading. Nevertheless, they became bestsellers. They exploded on a public that hadn't yet learned to discuss sex openly. Their publication—especially the book on female sexuality—was met with intense criticism. Kinsey's research suffered from methodological flaws (especially by today's standards for scientific research), but much of the criticism branded it immoral and obscene. The *New York Times* refused to run advertisements for the 1948 volume on male sexuality. Many newspapers refused to report the results of his survey on female sexuality. A congressional committee in the 1950s went so far as to claim that Kinsey's work undermined the moral fibre of the nation, rendering it more vulnerable to a Communist takeover (Gebhard, 1976).

Despite the controversy, Kinsey and his colleagues made sex research a scientifically respectable field of study. They helped lay the groundwork for future generations of sexuality researchers and, on a broader societal level, prompted a greater openness to discussing sexual matters among the general public.

THE SEXUAL REVOLUTION   The period of the mid-1960s to the mid-1970s is often referred to as the sexual revolution. Dramatic changes occurred in sexual attitudes and practices during the "swinging sixties." Our society was on the threshold of major social upheaval, not only in sexual behaviour, but also in science, politics, fashion, music, art, and cinema. The so-called Woodstock generation, disheartened by commercialism and the Vietnam War, tuned in (to rock music on the radio), turned on (to drugs), and dropped out (of mainstream society). Films became sexually explicit. Critics seriously contemplated whether the pornography classic *Deep Throat* had profound social implications. Hard rock music bellowed the message of rebellion and revolution.

No single event marked the onset of the sexual revolution. Social movements often gain momentum from timely interplays of scientific, social, political, and economic forces. The Vietnam War, fear of the nuclear bomb, introduction of the birth-control pill, and television were four such forces in the 1960s. The pill greatly reduced the risk of unwanted pregnancy. It permitted young people to engage in recreational or casual sex, rather than procreative sex. Pop psychology movements such as the human-potential movement of the 1960s and 1970s (the latter known as the "Me Decade") spread the message that people should get in touch with and express their genuine feelings, including their sexual feelings. "Do your own thing" became one catchphrase; "If it feels good, do it" became another. Canadian Justice Minister Pierre Trudeau declared in 1967 that "there's no place for the state in the bedrooms of the nation." This often-repeated quote is symbolic of a fundamental change that was taking place in Canadian society. Consensual sexual behaviour was now primarily a matter of personal choice, in the hands of the individual.

A World of Diversity

THE HISTORY OF DESIRE

Much of the historical analysis of sexual practices over various time periods has focused on the roles of religious and cultural traditions. University of Toronto professor Edward Shorter, in his book *Written in the Flesh: A History of Desire* (2005), has also analyzed the role of other influences on sexual behaviour. He argues that past constraints suppressed not only the amount of sex people had, but also

the variety of sexual behaviours they experienced.

According to Shorter, features of everyday life—such as poor hygiene, inadequate diet, periods of hunger, rampant disease, including plagues and sexually transmitted infections, plus lice and scabies infestation—put a damper on sexual desire and decreased the sexual attractiveness of potential partners.

For most people, there was also a lack of privacy. They lived in crowded

conditions, children often sleeping in the same rooms as their parents. Sex was often engaged in quickly, in the dark, and under the bedcovers. And since death in childbirth was common, women's fears made many want to avoid sex. Add religious prohibitions against sex for pleasure to these constraints and it's not surprising that historically, for most people, sex was not seen as a source of adventure.

The sexual revolution was tied to social permissiveness and political liberalism. In part reflecting the times, in part acting as catalyst, the media dealt openly with sex. Popular books encouraged people to explore their sexuality. Film scenes of lovemaking became so commonplace that the movie rating system was introduced to alert parents. Protests against the Vietnam War and racial discrimination spilled over into broader protests against conventional morality and hypocrisy.

FEMINISM   In some respects, the sexual revolution and the feminist movement were intertwined. Although modern feminism traces its roots to the nineteenth century, the 1960s and '70s were periods of significant advancement toward equal rights for women in the social, political, and economic spheres. While the sexual revolution preached sexual freedom more generally, feminism instilled the principle that women were as entitled as men to sexual pleasure and satisfaction. Feminist writers such as Betty Friedan (*The Feminine Mystique*, 1963) and Germaine Greer (*The Female Eunuch*, 1970) wrote bestselling books describing the alienation and repression of the contemporary Western woman, each placing some level of emphasis on sexuality.

The 1976 publication of *The Hite Report: A Nationwide Study of Female Sexuality* provoked an ongoing public discussion and re-examination of stereotypes about female sexual desire and pleasure. Although many questioned author Shere Hite's sampling techniques (just as many had earlier critiqued Kinsey's research methods), the study provided a forum for women to write anonymously about their sexual fantasies, likes, and dislikes in a frank, explicit manner. Among the findings that emerged was the fact that most of the women did not reach orgasm through penile–vaginal intercourse, requiring instead some form of clitoral stimulation. While this observation may seem self-evident in the twenty-first century, public and media discussion of female orgasm and how it was best achieved was highly provocative in the mid-1970s.

The feminist movement played a pivotal role in reconfiguring Western society's conceptualization of female sexuality and the sexual dimensions of the relationship between the sexes.

GAY ACTIVISM   Some say gay activism began in 1969, with the gay "rebellion" against police discrimination at a Manhattan gay bar called the Stonewall Inn. Gay

CRITICAL THINKING
QUESTIONS

How have the feminist
and gay rights movements
transformed the ways we
think about sexuality?

activism mushroomed during the sexual revolution. Gays not only became more vocal in demanding equal rights, they also began staging gay pride parades in major cities. Examples include the annual pride parades in San Francisco, New York's Greenwich Village, Toronto, Montreal, and Vancouver, as well as in many smaller communities.

In the early 1980s, gay people built social institutions to tackle the problem of acquired immunodeficiency syndrome (AIDS), which disproportionately affected gay men in Western societies. The gay community adopted the motto "Silence equals death." Many gay men publicly identified their sexual orientation and spoke up to spur medical research.

The rise of gay activism is an important development in the modern history of sexuality. It not only spurred a grassroots movement that continues to help society progress toward equal rights for gays, lesbians, and bisexuals, it also set an example for sexual minorities in general to speak out for recognition, protection against discrimination, and equal rights in a society that often still thinks of "normal" sexual behaviour as male–female intercourse.

THE INTERNET AND COMMUNICATION TECHNOLOGY   Social developments such as the sexual revolution and the rise of feminism and gay rights transformed societal attitudes towards sexuality in the latter decades of the twentieth century. While the effects of those developments continue, in the beginning of the twenty-first century, however, it is the almost universal penetration of the Internet into modern life and advances in communication technology that have had the greatest impact on sexuality in the Western world. Indeed, it can be argued that the Internet and advanced communication technologies have resulted in a new sexual revolution. Research has shown that men and women of all ages and sexual orientations use the Internet for sexual purposes such as accessing sexually explicit content, finding partners for romance and sex, purchasing sexual aids, and finding sex-related information (Daneback & Ross, 2011). Research-based estimates have indicated that out of the million most popular websites in the world, about 4% contain sexuality content and about 13% of all web searches are for erotic purposes (Ogas & Gaddam, 2012). In October 2013, a Google search using "the word porn" returned 982,000,000 results (Try it now yourself and see if the number has increased).

One of the most significant implications of the Internet for sexuality is that it has made it much easier for a person to explore and express his or her sexuality, and to do so privately and anonymously. Consider that in the not too distant past, for most people, the easiest way to see a sexually explicit film was to make a trip to the video store, browse among the racks of videos, record your rental with the clerk who knew exactly what you were renting, and return home. The Internet has made it possible to quickly and conveniently explore any aspect of sexuality or view innumerable variations in sexual behaviour with almost complete anonymity (provided you delete your search history of course!).

The Internet and other relatively new communication technologies such as cell phones have also revolutionized the ways people in Western society find romantic and sexual partners as well as the ways they communicate sexually. Online dating, for example, has, within the last 20 years, radically altered the way many people seek and find short- and long-term romantic partners (Finkel, Eastwick, Karney, Reis, & Sprecher, 2012), and Canadians have embraced the concept of online dating. Online dating website Plenty of Fish is the 33rd busiest website in Canada (Oliveira, 2010). More and more, people find sexual partners through Internet chat rooms and cell phone apps.

The emergence of the Internet and new communication technologies has both positive and negative implications for sexuality. Among the positives is that the

Internet has allowed disenfranchised individuals or members of sexual minority groups to more easily find information about sexuality that is relevant to their needs and to connect with others. For example, a queer or transgender youth living in a small rural community who feels alienated and alone can use the Internet to communicate with others in the queer and transgender communities. Many people use the Internet for sexuality education, locating information on sexual anatomy and response as well as how to engage in various sexual behaviours (Daneback, Masson, Ross, & Markham, 2012) (See also Applied Knowledge: Thinking Critically About Sexuality Information on the Internet).

However, there have also been negative implications of the Internet for sexuality. The Internet has facilitated and substantially increased the production and distribution of child pornography (Worthy & Smallbone, 2012). There has also been considerable concern about the role of the Internet in the development of sexual addiction/compulsivity among people who are not able to control their use of the web to watch online pornography or seeking of frequent anonymous sex partners (Griffiths, 2012).

The Biological Perspective

The biological perspective focuses on the roles of genes, hormones, the nervous system, and other physiological factors in human sexuality. We're biologically endowed with anatomical structures and physiological capabilities that make sexual behaviour possible and, for most people, pleasurable.

Study of the biology of sex acquaints us with the mechanisms of reproduction. It informs us of the physiological mechanisms of sexual arousal and response. Biology teaches us that erection occurs when the penis becomes engorged with blood. We learn that vaginal lubrication is the result of a "sweating" action of the vaginal walls. We learn that orgasm is a spinal reflex, as well as a psychological event. Researchers have discovered that some sexual dysfunctions originate in anatomical abnormalities or biological processes. In other words, advancements in the scientific understanding of biology have furthered our understanding of sexuality and our ability to help people overcome sexual problems.

The Cross-Species Perspective

The study of other animal species places human behaviour in a broader context. A surprising variety of sexual behaviours exist among animals. There are animal examples, or **analogues**, of human male–male sexual behaviour, female–female sexual behaviour, oral–genital contact, and oral–oral behaviour (kissing). Foreplay is also well known in the animal world. Turtles massage their mates' heads with their claws. Male mice nibble at their partners' necks. Most mammals use only a rear-entry position for **copulation**, but some animals, such as apes, use a variety of coital positions.

Analogue Something that is similar or comparable to something else.

Copulation Sexual intercourse.

Cross-species research reveals an interesting pattern. Sexual behaviour among higher mammals such as primates is less directly controlled by instinct than it is among other species, such as birds, fish, and lower mammals. Experience and learning play more important roles in sexuality as we travel up the evolutionary ladder.

Sociological and Anthropological Perspectives

Sociological and anthropological perspectives, like the historical perspective, provide insight into how cultural beliefs affect sexual behaviour and morality. Interest in cross-cultural perspectives on sexuality was spurred by the early-twentieth-century work of anthropologists Margaret Mead (1901–1978) and Bronisław Malinowski (1884–1942).

In *Sex and Temperament in Three Primitive Societies* (1935), Mead laid the groundwork for later psychological and sociological research challenging gender-role stereotypes. In most cultures characterized by divisions of labour by gender, men typically go to business or to the hunt, and—when necessary—to war. In such cultures, men are perceived as strong, active, independent, and logical. Women are viewed as passive, dependent, nurturant, and emotional. Mead concluded that these stereotypes are not inherent in our genetic heritage. Rather, they are acquired through cultural expectations and socialization. Men and women learn to behave in ways that are expected of them within their particular cultures.

Malinowski lived on the Trobriand Island of Boyowa in the South Pacific during World War I. There he gathered data on two societies of the South Pacific, the Trobrianders and the Amphlett Islanders. The Amphlett Islanders maintained strict sexual prohibitions, whereas the Trobriand Islanders enjoyed greater freedom. Trobrianders, for example, encouraged their children to masturbate. Boys and girls were expected to engage in intercourse when they were biologically old enough. Adolescents were expected to have multiple sex partners until they married. Malinowski found the Trobrianders less anxiety-ridden than the Amphlett Islanders. He attributed this difference to their sexual freedom, thus making an early plea to relax prohibitions in Western societies.

In 1951, anthropologist Clellan S. Ford and psychologist Frank A. Beach reviewed studies of sexual behaviour in preliterate societies around the world. They found great variety in sexual customs and beliefs among the almost 200 societies they studied. They also found some common threads.

Kissing was quite common across the cultures they studied, though not universal. The Thonga of Africa were one group that did not practise kissing. Upon witnessing two European visitors kissing one another, members of the tribe commented that they could not understand why Europeans "ate" one another's saliva and dirt. The frequency of sexual intercourse also varied from culture to culture, but intercourse was relatively more frequent among younger than older people everywhere. Attitudes toward public nudity varied across cultures. Ford and Beach found that where public nudity was accepted, it was not considered sexual. Societies also differed in their attitudes toward childhood masturbation. The Hopi of the southwest United States ignored it, for example, whereas Trobrianders encouraged children to stimulate themselves. Other societies condemned it.

People around the world differ widely in their sexual attitudes, customs, and practices. Members of all human societies, however, share the same anatomical structures and physiological capacities for sexual pleasure. The same hormones flow in their bloodstreams. Yet their sexual practices, and the pleasures they gain or fail to attain, may set some apart from others. Were human sexuality completely or predominantly determined by biology, we would not find such diversity.

Multiple Perspectives on Human Sexuality

Given the complexity and range of human sexual behaviour, we need to consider multiple perspectives to understand sexuality. Each perspective has something to offer in this enterprise. Let's venture a few conclusions based on our overview of these perspectives.

First, human sexuality appears to reflect a combination of biological, social, cultural, sociocultural, and psychological factors that interact in complex ways,

A World of Diversity

GENDER AND SEXUAL ORIENTATION IN ABORIGINAL CULTURE

With the colonization of Canada by the French and British, a European view of sexuality was imposed on indigenous cultures. This view emphasized a Christian perspective that valued heterosexuality and strict gender roles while being intolerant of same-sex and transgendered sexuality. When Europeans first encountered the indigenous people of North America, they observed that some men and women assumed multiple gender roles in their communities. Men might dress as women and adopt traditional female roles associated with childcare, cooking, weaving, and beading. Women might also dress as men and adopt traditionally masculine behaviours such as hunting and participating in warfare. Many gender variant individuals were awarded special status in their communities and acted as shamans, medicine men and women, teachers, and spiritual leaders. Their ability to adopt various gender roles and identities embodied the valued concepts of balance and harmony (DesChamps, 1998). Individual tribes had different names for people whose gender roles were fluid and nonconforming. For example, the Sioux used the term Winkte, the Ojibwe said A-go-ka, the Inuit said Coupan, and the Navajo referred to Nadle. However, each tribe had its unique approach to gender-variant people, and not all were equally accepting of them (Thomas & Jacobs, 1999).

In aboriginal cultures, gender roles did not necessarily reflect sexual orientation, and those who adopted gender roles and behaviour not associated with their biological sex might also have heterosexual relationships. Conversely, individuals might have same-sex relationships without assuming gender-variant behaviour (Mayo & Sheppard, 2012; Meyer-Cook & Labelle, 2004). The European view of sexuality allowed for little ambiguity in gender roles and behaviour, and those people who did not conform to traditional male or female gender roles were labelled as "berdache." This term had its roots in Persian, Italian, and French words associated with male prostitution and sodomy, but was used by Europeans to refer to all those who displayed gender variant behaviour and nonheterosexual tendencies. The term "berdache" has been used by anthropologists and other academics to describe multi- and cross-gendered aboriginal people. However, the term is now considered to be pejorative and representative of a European world view that does not reflect an aboriginal approach to gender and sexual orientation (Thomas & Jacobs, 1999).

Some aboriginal people now adopt the term "Two-Spirited" to describe individuals with different gender roles and sexual identities. This term was originally coined in Winnipeg in 1990 at the annual conference of Native American/First Nation gay and lesbians and was meant to replace the labels of lesbian, gay, bisexual, and transgendered. For aboriginal people, these terms represented the Western preoccupation with sexual orientation rather than a more inclusive consideration of gender and social roles. The term Two-Spirited was also meant to reclaim the special status that traditionally had been given to those with gender variant identities (Meyer-Cook & Labelle, 2004). However, some aboriginal people object to the use of one term to describe the many variations of multi- and cross-gendered identities that have existed in diverse indigenous cultures, and they continue to use traditional terms from their own languages and cultures (Mayo & Sheppard, 2012).

A nonprofit social services organization called 2-Spirited People of the 1st Nations is a nonprofit social services organization whose membership consists of Aboriginal gay, lesbian, bisexual, and transgender people in Toronto.

perhaps in combinations that are unique for each individual. Second, there are few universal patterns of sexual behaviour, and views on what's right and wrong show great diversity. Third, although our own cultural values and beliefs may be deeply meaningful to us, they may not necessarily indicate what sexual behaviours are common, natural, or moral.

Innovative Canadian Research

CANADIAN SEXUALITY, GENDER, AND OTHER SOCIAL VARIABLES

Gender differences are often analyzed in studies of sexuality. Other social variables are usually not considered.

Researchers at the University of Guelph—Dayna Fischstein, Ed Herold, and Serge Demarais (2007)—collected data from a national survey of 1479 Canadian adults over the age of 18 to determine whether gender differences still exist when we take into account other social variables. The researchers examined how gender, age, marital status, education, religiosity, and geographic region affect the sexuality variables of frequency of sexual thoughts, oral sex, age at first intercourse, number of sexual partners, and intentions to engage in casual sex.

The researchers found that the men were more sexually permissive and more sexually active than the women. Some of the gender differences were small or moderate, however, which suggests that the gender gap for differences in sexuality may be narrowing.

Other demographic variables were also significant predictors of sexual attitudes and behaviours. Generally, survey participants who were younger, had more education, or did not attend religious services had more permissive attitudes.

The findings illustrate the value of taking into account other social variables when analyzing gender differences in sexuality.

The most substantial gender differences were seen with intention to engage in casual sex. None of the women reported that they would definitely engage in casual sex, and few reported that they would probably engage in casual sex. Most men, however, reported they would engage in casual sex if given the opportunity.

These findings may be explained by the sexual double standard, which allows greater sexual freedom for men than for women. The strength of the gender effect was demonstrated by the fact that the other social factors were relatively weak predictors of intentions to engage in casual sex. Interestingly, people living in Quebec were more likely than participants from all other regions to report an interest in casual sex.

This study is important because it illuminates the role of gender in relation to social variables in accounting for differences in sexuality among adult Canadians. The survey findings point to the need for large-scale national surveys that use heterogeneous samples, rather than samples of convenience such as university populations.

The complexity of human sexuality—complexity that causes it to remain somewhat baffling to scientists—adds to the wonder and richness of our own uniqueness as individual sexual beings.

Summing Up

Human sexuality concerns the ways we experience and express ourselves as sexual beings. Cross-cultural comparisons of sexual values and beliefs demonstrate that human sexuality is characterized by diversity.

Our values and our knowledge about human sexuality inform our sexual decisions. The ethics of divinity, community, and autonomy represent three different ways of approaching sexual ethics.

Critical thinking is a sceptical approach to evaluating arguments, widely held beliefs, and evidence. Critical thinkers examine definitions of terms and premises of arguments, and are cautious in drawing conclusions from evidence.

The historical perspective suggests that there are few universal sexual trends. Customs and beliefs about sexuality have varied from one historical period to another and from one culture to another.

The sexual revolution, feminism, and the gay rights movement were among the most influential developments impacting on sexuality in the twentieth century.

The Internet and new communication technologies have had both positive and negative effects on sexuality.

The biological perspective focuses on biological sexual processes such as genetic, hormonal, and neural factors.

The cross-species perspective reveals the variety of sexual behaviours among nonhumans.

The sociological perspective shows how cultural beliefs affect sexual behaviours and attitudes.

Test Yourself

Multiple-Choice Questions

1. According to a 2003 study, most students at a Canadian university said they were "having sex" when the behaviour was:
   (a) Oral–genital contact.
   (b) Penile–vaginal intercourse.
   (c) Manual stimulation of the genitals.
   (d) All of the above.

2. Historically, _____ was most likely the first sexual taboo.
   (a) Incest
   (b) Sex before marriage
   (c) Male homosexuality
   (d) Masturbation

3. Critical thinking includes all of the following except:
   (a) Scepticism.
   (b) Getting in touch with our feelings.
   (c) Evaluating the strengths and weaknesses of different perspectives.
   (d) Avoiding oversimplification.

4. Sociologist Ira Reiss has proposed an ethics of "sexual pluralism" that suggests that sexual behaviour should be guided by the principles of:
   (a) Honesty, equality, and responsibility.
   (b) Justice, equality, and responsibility.
   (c) Equity, justice, and compassion.
   (d) Justice, love, and forgiveness.

5. The ancient _____ were the first to produce a detailed sex manual.
   (a) Greeks
   (b) Romans
   (c) Christians
   (d) Hindus

6. Which of the following is not part of the ethical framework presented by Meaney and Rye?
   (a) Autonomy
   (b) Community
   (c) Divinity
   (d) Authority

7. The *New York Times* refused to run advertisements for which of the following books?
   (a) The *Kama Sutra*
   (b) *Sexual Behavior in the Human Male*
   (c) *The Female Eunuch*
   (d) *The Hite Report: A Nationwide Study of Female Sexuality*

8. Ford and Beach's research on preliterate societies found:
   (a) A wide variety of sexual customs and beliefs.
   (b) That intercourse was more common among older than younger people.
   (c) That childhood masturbation was discouraged in all of the societies they studied.
   (d) Kissing in all of the societies they studied.

9. The aboriginal words "Winke" and "A-go-ka" refer to people who:
   (a) Have adopted Anglo-Saxon sexual values and practices.
   (b) Are gay or lesbian.
   (c) Have adopted fluid gender roles.
   (d) Are asexual.

10. In 1967, Canadian Justice Minister Pierre Trudeau declared that,
    (a) "One day Canada will be ready to decriminalize homosexuality but today is not that day."
    (b) "There is no place for the state in the bedrooms of the nation."
    (c) "The problem of prostitution in our country can only be eliminated through harsh legal penalties for all the parties involved."
    (d) "Abortion is murder and should be treated as such in the courts."

You'll find answers to the "Test Yourself" questions on page 489.

Questions for Critical Thinking

1. What are your goals for this course on human sexuality? Do you think what you'll learn here will help you later in life? Why or why not?

2. Religions have historically been major factors influencing human sexual behaviour. Do you think this is still true in Canada today? Why or why not?

3. A friend of yours insists that something is true because she found it on the Internet. As a critical thinker, do you accept your friend's argument as proof? If not, what would you do to determine the truth or falsity of your friend's claim?

4. The Internet has had a significant impact on human sexuality. Some the effects have been positive, and some have been negative. On balance, do you think the positives have outweighed the negatives? Explain the reasoning behind your answer.

CHAPTER TWO

Using Theory and Research to Understand Human Sexuality

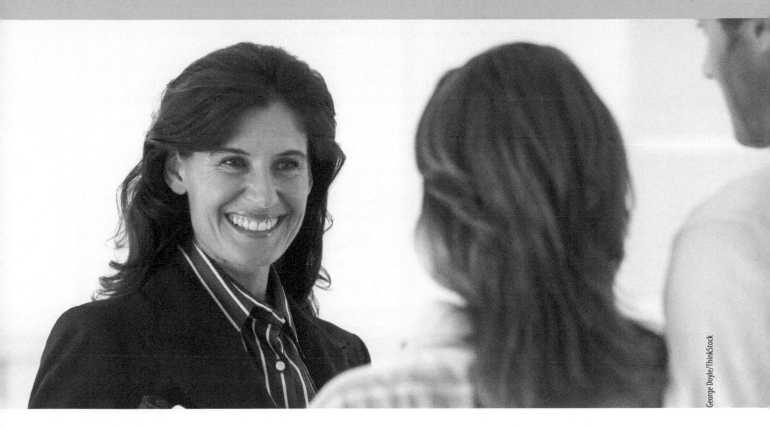

George Doyle/ThinkStock

In this chapter, we look at how scientists use theory and research to study human sexuality. We will begin by summarizing some of the major theories that have been used to examine and explain various aspects of sexuality. Then we look at different research methods that have been employed to search for a scientifically based understanding of sexuality.

Theoretical Approaches to Understanding Human Sexuality

All scientific disciplines use theories to formulate explanations, guide research, and interpret results. A **theory** consists of a set of ideas or concepts that are used to explain a set of observed facts. Put another way, a theory provides us with a conceptual framework for explaining and predicting sexual thoughts, emotions, attitudes, and behaviours.

A basic knowledge of the major theoretical approaches used in the study of human sexuality will be very useful as we examine specific topics such as gender roles, attraction and love, sexual variations, and sexual health promotion. By incorporating theoretical approaches, the study of human sexuality goes beyond the compilation of

Theory A set of ideas or concepts intended to explain something.

random observations about, for example, patterns of sexual behaviour. Theory allows us to organize those observations into meaningful conceptual frameworks that provide possible explanations for why and how those patterns of sexual behaviour occur.

Before we begin our look at a range of different theories, we must note that no single theory can accurately explain all aspects of something as varied and complex as human sexuality. One theory, for example, might propose an explanation for how our biological makeup shapes our sexuality, while another theory might offer an explanation for how the social environment influences the way we learn to behave sexually as we grow up.

Keep in mind that while two theories may offer contrasting explanations, they are not always mutually exclusive. In some cases, you may indeed decide that both cannot be correct. But in other cases you may decide that incorporating multiple theories into your thinking about a particular sexuality topic provides a more nuanced and complete approach to the topic.

Evolutionary Theory

Evolution The development of a species to its present state, which involves adaptations to its environment.

Natural selection The evolutionary process by which adaptive traits enable members of a species to survive to reproductive age and transmit these traits to future generations.

Sociobiology The idea that social behaviour results from evolution.

Species vary not only in their physical characteristics but also in their social behaviour, including their mating behaviour. Scientists look to **evolution** to help explain such variability (Buss & Schmitt, 2011). The English naturalist Charles Darwin (1809–1882) showed that current species of animals and plants evolved from other life-forms through **natural selection**, or "survival of the fittest." In each species, individuals vary, and some are better adapted to their environments than others. Better-adapted members are more likely to survive to reproduce and transmit their traits to succeeding generations. They are not necessarily the strongest or fleetest of foot, although these traits are adaptive for some species and enhance their reproductive success.

Some scientists suggest that there is also a genetic basis to social behaviour, including sexual behaviour, among humans and other animals (Buss & Schmitt, 2011). The hypothesis that evolution has shaped human and animal social behaviours is called **sociobiology**. Sociobiology suggests that human beings today carry traits that helped our prehistoric ancestors survive and reproduce successfully. The idea that sociobiology could explain some aspects of human sexual behaviour gained prominence with the publication of Donald Symons, (1979) book *The Evolution of Human Sexuality*.

The application of evolutionary theory to human sexuality has taken a variety of directions, but a central focus has been on gender differences in mating strategies for reproductive success. According to this theory, because men and women play very different biological roles in reproduction (i.e., women have a limited number of eggs, carry the foetus, and provide breast milk whereas men have millions of sperm and can biologically produce many more offspring than women), they also have different strategies for passing on their genes. Buss and Schmitt (2011) distinguish between short-term mating strategies (e.g., casual sex with multiple partners) and long-term mating strategies (e.g., monogamous relationships over an extended period of time). According to evolutionary theory, while both men and women engage in both short- and long-term mating, men have evolved to have a greater preference than women for a short-term mating strategy because it enables them to father a high number of children which increases the probability that their genes will be passed on. Women, on the other hand, prefer a long-term mating strategy, in which they form a relationship with a male who is willing to commit to the partnership long enough for the women to carry the foetus and nurture the child. In sum, evolutionary theory suggests that men are naturally more promiscuous than women because they are the genetic heirs of ancestors whose reproductive success was related to the number of women they could impregnate (Buss & Schmitt, 2011). Women can produce only a few off-spring in their lifetimes. Thus, the theory goes, they have to be more selective with respect to their mating partners. Women's reproductive success is enhanced by mating with the fittest males—not with any Tom, Dick, or Harry who happens by. From this perspective, the male's "roving eye" and the female's selectivity are embedded in their genes.

Consistent with the proposition that men have evolved a greater preference than women for short-term mating strategies and women have evolved a greater preference for long-term mating strategies than men, evolutionary theory suggests that men and women will also be attracted to different attributes in their mating partners. Specifically, according to this theory, men will be more attracted to women who appear most likely to be fertile (i.e., physically healthy and at an age where they have a high probability of conceiving and bearing children), and women will be more attracted to men who possess the resources (i.e., food, money, etc.) needed for the rearing of their children (Buss & Schmitt, 2011).

EROTIC PLASTICITY   Consider evolutionary theory and the concept of "erotic plasticity" (Baumeister, 2000), which addresses the fact that in response to various social and cultural forces, people show different levels of sex drive and express their sexual desires in various ways. There is evidence that women show greater erotic plasticity than men (Baumeister, 2000; Yost & Thomas, 2011). For example, (1) individual women show greater variation than men in sexual behaviour over time; (2) women seem to be more responsive than men to most specific cultural factors, such as cultural permissiveness or restraint; and (3) men's sexual behaviour is more consistent with their sexual attitudes than women's. Are evolutionary, biological forces an important factor in the greater female erotic plasticity?

Sigmund Freud and Psychoanalytic Theory

Sigmund Freud, a Viennese physician, formulated a grand theory of personality termed **psychoanalysis**. Freud believed that we are all born with biologically based sex drives that must be channelled through socially approved outlets if family and social life are to carry on without undue conflict.

Freud proposed that the mind operates on conscious and unconscious levels. The conscious level corresponds to our state of present awareness. The unconscious mind refers to the darker reaches of the mind that lie outside our direct awareness. The ego shields the conscious mind from awareness of our baser sexual and aggressive urges by means of **defence mechanisms** such as **repression**, or motivated forgetting of traumatic experiences.

Freud introduced us to new and controversial ideas about ourselves as sexual beings. For example, he originated the concept of **erogenous zones**—the idea that many parts of the body, not just the genitals, are responsive to sexual stimulation.

One of Freud's most controversial beliefs was that children normally harbour erotic interests. He believed that suckling by the infant in the oral stage was an erotic act, and he believed the same about the anal bodily experimentation through which two-year-olds find pleasure in the control of their sphincter muscles in the process of elimination. He theorized that it was normal for children to progress through stages of development in which the erotic interest shifts from one erogenous zone to another, as, for example, from the oral cavity to the anal cavity. According to his

Sigmund Freud was among the most influential thinkers of the twentieth century.

Photo Researchers/Alamy

CRITICAL THINKING QUESTIONS

Critics of the evolutionary perspective on human sexuality express concern that the theory may be used to suggest incorrectly that stereotypical male and female patterns of sexual behaviour are inevitable. Do you share this concern? Explain your answer.

Psychoanalysis The theory of personality originated by Sigmund Freud, which proposes that human behaviour represents the outcome of clashing inner forces.

Defence mechanisms In psychoanalytic theory, automatic processes that protect the ego from anxiety by disguising or ejecting unacceptable ideas and urges.

Repression The automatic ejection of anxiety-evoking ideas from consciousness.

Erogenous zones Parts of the body, including but not limited to the sex organs, that are responsive to sexual stimulation.

Psychosexual development In psychoanalytic theory, the process by which sexual feelings shift from one erogenous zone to another.

Oedipus complex In psychoanalytic theory, a conflict of the phallic stage in which the boy wishes to possess his mother sexually and perceives his father as a rival in love.

Behaviourists Learning theorists who argue that a scientific approach to understanding behaviour must refer only to observable and measurable behaviours.

Coitus (co-it-us or co-EET-us) Sexual intercourse.

theory of **psychosexual development**, children undergo five stages of development: oral, anal, phallic, latency, and genital, which are named according to the main erogenous zones of each stage.

Freud believed that it was normal for children to develop erotic feelings toward the parent of the other sex during the phallic stage. These incestuous urges lead to conflict with the parent of the same sex. In later chapters we will see that these developments, which Freud termed the **Oedipus complex**, have implications for the assumption of gender roles and sexual orientation.

Learning Theories

To what extent does sexual behaviour reflect experience? Would you hold the same sexual attitudes and do the same things if you had been reared in another culture? Even within the same society, family and personal experiences can shape unique sexual attitudes and behaviours.

Behaviourists such as John B. Watson (1878–1958) and B. F. Skinner (1904–1990) emphasized the importance of rewards and punishments in the learning process. Children left to explore their bodies without parental condemnation will learn what feels good and tend to repeat it. The Trobriand child who is rewarded for masturbation and premarital **coitus** through parental praise and encouragement will be more likely to repeat these behaviours than a child in a more sexually restrictive culture, who is punished for the same behaviour. When sexual behaviour (like masturbation) feels good, but parents connect it with feelings of guilt and shame, the child is placed in conflict and may vacillate between masturbating and swearing off it, eventually associating sexual stimulation in general with feelings of guilt or anxiety. Can such early learning experiences set the stage for sexual problems or dysfunctions in adulthood?

Acquisition of Gender Roles.
According to social-cognitive theory, children learn gender roles by means of reinforcement of certain behaviour patterns and by observing the gender-related behaviours of their parents, peers, and other role models in media such as TV, films, and books.

Radius Images/Alamy

COGNITIVE THEORY   Cognitive psychologists emphasize the importance of cognitive activity (problem solving, decision making, expectations, and so on). They also recognize that people learn intentionally and by observing others. *Observational learning* refers to acquiring knowledge and skills through observing others. According to **social–cognitive theory**, children acquire the gender roles deemed appropriate in a society through reinforcement of gender-appropriate behaviour and through observing the gender-role behaviour of parents, peers, and other models from television, the Internet, movies, books, and so on.

SEXUAL SCRIPT THEORY   Similar to social-cognitive theory, **sexual script theory** suggests that as we grow up we learn scripts from our social environment for how men and women should behave sexually (Gagnon & Simon, 1973). In other words, sexual scripts are cognitive schema that provide individuals with a learned set of instructions for how to act in sexual situations. According to the theory, sexual scripts influence people on three levels: cultural, interpersonal, and intrapsychic. At the cultural level, the individual learns general social rules for how sexual interactions should unfold. At the interpersonal level, people apply the cultural scripts they have learned to their own sexual interactions with partners and at the intrapsychic level, individuals cognitively internalize the cultural scripts and personalize them according to their own values, preferences, and circumstances (McCormick, 2010).

Sexual script theory stands in stark contrast to evolutionary theory in explaining human sexual behaviour. While evolutionary theory suggests that current patterns of sexual behaviour are embedded in our genes through millions of years of natural selection, sexual script theory argues " . . . that sexual life is like all social life: an activity elicited by social and cultural circumstance and an activity that differs from one historical era to another or from one culture to another" (Gagnon, 1990, p. 3).

Sexual script theory has been used to study different aspects of human sexual behaviour (Laumann, Gagnon, Michael, & Michaels, 1994). In Western culture, mainstream sexual scripts are highly gendered. Researchers refer to the stereotypical heterosexual script for how men and women are expected to behave and interact sexually as the **traditional sexual script** (Byers, 1996), which specifies that men should have a higher sex drive than women, be the initiators of sexual activity, and be responsible for the mutual pleasure of the couple. In contrast, women are expected to be reluctant gatekeepers who accept or reject male advances and play a passive role in sexual interaction. According to the traditional sexual script, men are expected to be relatively more interested in recreational sex, while women are more likely to view sexual activity as a component of a wider relationship. As Western culture has moved towards general gender equality, especially in recent decades, the extent to which the traditional sexual script is still in place has been the subject of a number of studies (e.g., Byers, 1996; Dworkin & O'Sullivan, 2005; Maxwell, 2007). Together, these studies indicate that while elements of the traditional heterosexual sexual script remain, there has been some movement away from them. A recent qualitative study of the gendered sexual scripts of young women and men aged 18 to 25 identified three groups of people: conformers, exception finders, and transformers (Masters, Casey, Wells, & Morrison, 2013). For conformers, their gendered scripts for sexual behaviour were in line with the traditional sexual script. Exception finders accepted the traditional sexual script as a social reality but made exceptions for themselves in their own behaviour. Transformers rejected the acceptability of the traditional sexual script and sought to create their own gender scripts for relationships and sexuality.

Social–cognitive theory A cognitively oriented learning theory in which observational learning, values, and expectations play key roles in determining behaviour.

Sexual script theory A theory that examines sexuality from the standpoint of culturally learned scripts that specify how men and women should behave sexually.

Traditional sexual script A sexual script based on stereotypical standards for sexual behaviour that dictates that males take an assertive and active role in heterosexual interaction while women take a receptive and passive role.

CRITICAL THINKING QUESTIONS

To what extent do you think that the traditional sexual script is still in place today among young people? Can you think of examples that would suggest that college students are increasingly rejecting the traditional sexual script and creating new scripts for sexuality and relationships?

Social Exchange Theory

Based on the concepts of rewards, costs, and reciprocity, social exchange theory has been utilized to study sexuality within relationships (Byers & Wang, 2004). Social exchange theory contains three basic assumptions: "(a) Social behaviour is a series of exchanges; (b) individuals attempt to maximize their rewards and minimize their costs; and (c) when individuals receive rewards from others, they feel obligated to reciprocate" (Sprecher, 1998, p. 32). Based on these theoretical assumptions, Sandra Byers from the University of New Brunswick and her colleagues developed the interpersonal exchange model of sexual satisfaction (Byers & MacNeil, 2006) which focuses on the exchange of specifically sexual resources and the consequences for sexual satisfaction within a relationship. Simply put, sexual satisfaction within the couple is higher the more the partners perceive their sexual rewards to be greater than their sexual costs. If one partner perceives that their sexual costs are higher than the sexual rewards, that partner is likely to experience lower sexual satisfaction and become disenchanted, perhaps to the point of leaving the relationship. Engaging in sexual activities that you dislike but your partner likes or having sex when you are not in the mood are examples of a person's sexual costs within a relationship. Feeling a high degree of emotional closeness or physical pleasure are examples of sexual rewards. **Social exchange theory** has also been used to study a variety of aspects of the sexual component of the couple relationship including extradyadic sex, partner selection, and frequency of sexual activity (Byers & Wang, 2004).

Social exchange theory A theory that examines sexuality within relationships in terms of rewards and costs.

Feminist Theory

The Greek philosopher Aristotle is said to have described a female as a deformed male. We can only guess at the number of objectionable beliefs expressed in this description, such as seeing the male as the ideal, focusing on the differences rather than the similarities between men and women, and the implicit right of men to hold power over women. Feminism and **feminist theory** are born of protest against such ideas—ideas that remain with us today in many, if not most, parts of the world (Chesler, 2006). In general, feminist theory focuses on the subordination of women; analyzing the relationships between sexism, heterosexism (prejudice or discrimination against homosexuals by heterosexuals), racism, and class oppression; and exploring means of resistance—on individual and societal levels (Butler, 1993, 2003).

Just as there are many different types of feminism (e.g., liberal feminism, radical feminism, postmodern feminism, third wave feminism, ecofeminism), there are many different variants of feminist theory, drawing from a wide range of intellectual traditions and methods of analysis. So it is difficult to provide precise generalizations that accurately define or characterize feminist theory. However, many types of feminist theory are based, at least in part, on the following basic assumptions:

Feminist theory A theory that focuses on the subordination of women and the unequal status of girls and women in society.

- There are fundamental distinctions that can be made within society between male and female, men and women, and masculine and feminine.
- These distinctions are mostly or entirely socially constructed. That is, they are not a function of biology or an innate human nature.
- These distinctions function to make women subordinate to men or to disadvantage women in society.
- Women's subordination and/or disadvantage can be effectively addressed through changes in law, social policies, and greater societal awareness and acceptance of the goal of gender equality.

Feminist theories challenge the very concepts of femininity and masculinity because their existence tends to suggest that there is some sort of biological or "actual" basis to the distinction (Shields & Dicicco, 2011). They suggest, instead, that femininity and masculinity might be purely social constructions that have the effect of giving women second-class citizenship—or, in many historic eras and parts of the world, no citizenship whatsoever.

Not surprisingly, many feminist theorists have focused on sexuality but they have viewed it in a variety of different ways and reached very different conclusions about the role of sexuality in oppressing women or, alternatively, liberating them. For example, some feminist scholars have argued that the nature of sexual interaction between men and women in contemporary society, particularly when it is aggressive or violent, is a fundamental instrument of male domination (e.g., Dworkin, 1987; Mackinnon, 1989). Others have focused on the **sexual objectification** of women as an important mechanism to enforce gender inequality (e.g., Barry, 1994).

In contrast, other feminist theorists have focused on the potential of sexuality, particularly the enhancement of women's sexual autonomy and pleasure as well as the acceptance of lesbianism and bisexuality, to play a key role in the liberation of women and the achievement of gender equality (e.g., McElroy, 1995; Queen, 1996; Vance, 1984). This strand of feminist theory is sometimes referred to as "sex-positive" feminism.

Queer Theory

The word *queer* was initially used as an insult to describe nonheterosexual people. However, some people in the gay, lesbian, and bisexual communities have re-appropriated the word as a sign of pride. As one result of this re-appropriation, a widely cited theory of the psychology and sociology of gender roles and sexual orientation is termed **queer theory** (Hegarty, 2011).

Queer theory challenges a number of commonly held assumptions about gender and sexuality, such as the assumptions that heterosexuality is superior to other sexual orientations (Semp, 2011). Queer theory also challenges the assumption that people are accurately categorized as either naturally heterosexual or gay/lesbian (Downing & Gillett, 2011).

According to queer theory, the concepts of heterosexuality and homosexuality are social constructs that ignore commonly experienced mismatches among people's anatomic sex, society's gender roles, and individuals' sexual desires (Downing & Gillett, 2011). Queer theory asserts that human sexuality has always been more varied than those in power—particularly male heterosexuals—are willing to admit. They point to historical examples such as ancient Greek bisexuality and to current **homophobia** as evidence. We will revisit concepts of queer theory in later chapters, particularly the chapters on gender and sexual orientation.

This overview of evolutionary theory, psychoanalytic theory, learning theories, sexual script theory, social exchange theory, feminist theory, and queer theory provides a taste of some of the major theoretical approaches that are applied to the study of human sexuality. We will refer to these theories again at various points in the book where they will help us to deepen our understanding of specific sexuality issues. We will also introduce you to some additional theories such as gender schema theory (Chapter 5), Sternberg's triangular theory of love (Chapter 6), and the information, motivation, behavioural skills (IMB) theoretical model (Chapter 15) at various points in the book.

Let's turn our attention to the methods that researchers use to study sexuality. Because sexuality is so often misunderstood or subject to biased thinking, it's important to use sound research methods.

A Scientific Approach to Human Sexuality

Scientists and researchers who study human sexuality take an **empirical** approach. That is, they base their knowledge on research evidence, rather than on intuition, faith, or superstition.

Sexual objectification Treating a person as an object for the purposes of sexual gratification.

CRITICAL THINKING QUESTIONS

Has the sexual objectification of women decreased in recent years? Has the sexual objectification of men increased?

Queer theory A theory that challenges heteronormativity and heterosexism.

Homophobia Hatred of gays, lesbians, and bisexuals.

Empirical Derived from or based on observation and experimentation.

The Scientific Method

Critical thinking and the scientific approach share the hallmark of scepticism. As sceptics, scientists question prevailing assumptions and theories about sexual behaviour. They are willing to dispute the assertions of authority figures such as political and religious leaders—and even other scientists. Scientists also recognize that they cannot gain perfect knowledge. One era's truths may become another era's ancient myths and fallacies. Scientists recognize that the search for truth is a continuous process, and that a set of final truths, especially those regarding human behaviour, will likely remain elusive.

The scientific method is a systematic way of gathering scientific evidence and testing assumptions through research. It has a number of elements:

1. **Formulating a research question.** Does alcohol inspire or impair sexual response? A scientist formulates a research question on the basis of observation and theory about an event or behaviour. S/he then conducts empirical research to answer these questions.
2. **Framing the research question in the form of a hypothesis.** Experiments are usually undertaken with a hypothesis in mind—a precise prediction about behaviour that is often derived from theory.
3. **Testing the hypothesis.** The scientist then tests the hypothesis through carefully controlled observation and experimentation.
4. **Drawing conclusions.** The scientist then analyzes the results of the test and draws conclusions, or inferences, about whether the hypothesis is correct. If the results of a well-designed research study fail to support a certain hypothesis, the scientist can revise the theory s/he has used as the framework for the hypothesis. Research findings often lead scientists to modify their theories and, in turn, generate new hypotheses that can be tested with further research.

GOALS OF THE SCIENCE OF HUMAN SEXUALITY   The goals of the science of human sexuality are congruent with those of other sciences—to describe, explain, predict, and control the events of interest (in this case, sexual behaviours). Let's discuss some of the general goals of science, and how they relate to the study of human sexuality.

Description is a basic objective of science. To understand a sexual behaviour, for example, we must first be able to describe it. Description precedes understanding. Scientists attempt to be clear, unbiased, and precise in their descriptions of events and behaviours. The scientific approach to human sexuality examines sexual behaviours through techniques as varied as the field study, the survey, the individual case study, and the laboratory experiment.

Researchers attempt to relate their observations to specific factors, or **variables**, that can help explain the observations. For example, researchers may attempt to explain variations in the frequency of different types of sexual behaviours by correlating the behaviours with **demographic** variables such as age, religious or social background, and cultural expectation. The variables that are commonly used to explain sexual behaviour are biological (e.g., age, sex, health status), psychological (e.g., anxiety, self-confidence, knowledge, skills), and demographic or sociological (e.g., educational level, socioeconomic status, ethnicity).

Theories provide frameworks within which scientists can explain and make predictions about what they observe. It's not sufficient for theories to explain only past events. Theories must also enable us to make predictions about what will happen in the future. Some sexuality researchers study factors that may predict the occurrence of specific sexual behaviours (e.g., oral sex, masturbation) or sexuality-related outcomes (e.g., improved sexual functioning, condom use).

The purpose of scientific research into human sexuality is not to dictate how people should behave. Rather, at its best, it can provide information or insights

Variables Quantities or qualities that vary or that may vary.

Demographic Concerning the vital statistics of a human population (e.g., density, race, age, education).

to help people better understand themselves and make decisions about their own behaviour. Sexuality research helps educators, social workers, psychologists, therapists, nurses, doctors, and other professionals improve the sexual health and well-being of individuals and communities. Research will continue to illuminate the many ways gender, sexual identity, sexual orientation, and other factors affect the diversity of human sexuality.

Quantitative Research Methods

Populations and Samples: Representing the World of Diversity

Some researchers try to learn about **populations**. Other researchers focus on specific groups, such as First Nations people or transgender people or adolescents. These are termed the *populations of interest*, or *target populations*.

These target populations are all sizable. It would be all but impossible to study every individual. A scientist therefore selects individuals from the population and studies them. The individuals who participate in the research are collectively called a **sample**. To truly learn about a population of interest, the scientist must ensure that the sample accurately represents the population. A *representative sample* is a research sample of participants who accurately represent the population of interest.

If the sample does not represent the target population, the scientist cannot extend, or **generalize**, the results of his or her research to the population of interest. If we wished to study the sexual behaviour of Asian Canadians, for example, our population would consist of *all* Asian Canadians. If we used only Asian-Canadian college students as our sample, we could not generalize our findings to all Asian Canadians.

Including everyone in Canada in a study of sexual behaviour would be impossible. The government cannot even *find* everyone in Canada when it conducts the census. And incorporating sexuality research into the census would undoubtedly cause many more people to refuse to participate. Sampling a part of a target population makes research possible and practical—if imperfect.

Sampling Methods

Now and then, magazine editors boast that they've surveyed samples of 20 000 or 30 000 readers—but size alone doesn't mean a sample is representative. *Psychology Today* regularly polls readers, for example, but their readers don't represent the general population; they are biased in that they tend to be better educated and more liberal than the population at large (*Psychology Today*, 2006).

One way of acquiring a representative sample is random sampling. A **random sample** is one in which every member of the target population has an equal chance of participating. Researchers overcome biased sampling by drawing random or **stratified random samples** of populations. In a stratified random sample, known subgroups of a population are represented in proportion to their numbers within the population. For instance, about 51% of the Canadian population is female. Researchers could therefore decide that 51% of their sample must be female if the sample is to represent everyone in Canada. The randomness of the sample would be preserved, because the subgroup members would be selected randomly from their particular subgroups.

Another problem is that sexual research is almost invariably conducted with people who volunteer to participate. Volunteers may differ from people who refuse to participate. For example, volunteers may tend to be more open about their sexuality than the general population.

Population A complete group of organisms or events.

Sample Part of a population selected for study.

Generalize Use information from a particular case or sample to draw conclusions about a larger phenomenon or population.

Random sample A sample in which every member of a population has an equal chance of participating.

Stratified random sample A random sample in which known subgroups of a population are represented in proportion to their numbers within the population.

Juice Images/Getty Images

Populations and Samples.
To what populations do you belong? College students? Returning students? What is your gender? What about your ethnic background? How do researchers obtain samples that represent populations such as these? What problems do they encounter in attempting to do so?

The problem of **volunteer bias** is a thorny one for sex researchers, because the refusal of people who have been randomly selected to participate in the survey can ruin the representativeness of the sample. It would be unethical to coerce people to participate in any study, so researchers must use samples of volunteers, rather than truly random samples. A low response rate to a voluntary survey is an indication that the responses probably don't represent everyone the survey has been sent to.

In some cases, samples are samples of convenience. They consist of individuals who happen to be available to the researcher and who share some characteristics with the target population—perhaps religious background or sexual orientation. They may not truly represent the target group. Convenience samples often consist of European-Canadian, middle-class university students who volunteer for studies conducted at their schools.

Volunteer bias   A slanting of research data caused by the characteristics of individuals who volunteer to participate (e.g., their willingness to discuss intimate behaviour).

Methods of Observation

Once scientists have chosen whom they'll study, they observe these people. They use several methods of observation: the case study, the survey, naturalistic observation, ethnographic observation, participant observation, and laboratory observation.

The Case Study Method

Case study   A carefully drawn, in-depth biography of an individual or a small group of individuals. This information may be obtained through interviews, questionnaires, and historical records.

A **case study** is a carefully drawn, in-depth biography of an individual or a small group. The focus is on understanding one or several individuals as fully as possible by unravelling the interplay of various factors in the individual's or group's background. In most case studies, the researcher comes to know the person or group through interviews or other contacts conducted over a prolonged period. The interviewing pattern tends to build upon itself with a good deal of freedom, in contrast to the one-shot, standardized, set of questions used in a survey questionnaire.

Reports of innovative treatments for sexual dysfunctions sometimes appear as well-described case studies. A clinician typically reports the client's background in depth, describes the treatment, reports the apparent outcome(s), and suggests factors that might have contributed to the treatment's success or failure. In writing a treatment case study, the therapist tries to provide information that may be helpful to other therapists who treat clients with similar problems. Case studies or multiple-case studies (reports concerning a few individuals) that hold promise may lead to controlled investigations—ideally, to experimental studies involving treatment groups and control (non-treatment) groups.

Despite the richness of material that may be derived from a case study, it is not as rigorous a research design as an experiment. People often have gaps in memory, especially concerning childhood events. The potential for observer bias is also a prominent concern. Clinicians and interviewers may unintentionally guide people into saying what they expect to hear. Then, too, researchers may inadvertently colour people's reports when they write them down—shaping them subtly in ways that reflect their own views.

The Survey Method

Surveys typically gather information about behaviour through questionnaires or interviews. Researchers may interview or administer questionnaires to thousands of people from particular population groups to learn about their sexual behaviours and attitudes. Interviews such as those used by Kinsey and his colleagues (1948, 1953) have the advantages of allowing face-to-face contact and giving the interviewer the opportunity to probe—that is, to follow up on answers that seem to lead toward useful information.

University of Alberta researcher Melanie Beres (2006) interviewed seasonal workers in Jasper, Alberta, to study casual sex experiences and how the workers perceived potential partners' willingness to engage in casual sex. The interviews were unstructured, allowing the participants to talk about their experiences from their own perspectives, rather than that of the researcher. A skilled interviewer may be able to establish a sense of trust or rapport that encourages self-disclosure (Drucker, 2012).

Questionnaires can be administered to many people at once, and respondents can return them unsigned. Anonymity may encourage respondents to disclose intimate information. Of course, questionnaires can be used only by people who can read and record their responses. Interviews can be used even with people who can't read or write.

Most surveys contribute something to our understanding of human sexuality, but none fully represent the Canadian population at large. Most people think of their sexuality as one of the most intimate, private aspects of their lives. Therefore, many will refuse to participate in surveys about sexual behaviour. Survey results provide, at best, approximations of the sexual attitudes, beliefs, and behaviours of the Canadian population.

Surveys are increasingly conducted through the Internet. An Ontario survey found that research participants were more likely to fully complete an online survey than an equivalent traditional paper-and-pencil survey (Wood et al., 2006).

THE KINSEY REPORTS   The first large-scale modern sex surveys were conducted by Alfred Kinsey and his colleagues (1948, 1953) who interviewed 5300 men and 5940 women in the United States between 1938 and 1949. Kinsey was the first to statistically document the sexual behaviour of the American people. His surveys are of great interest to sexuality researchers because they demonstrate many of the factors and considerations that researchers must take into account in conducting sexuality research.

They asked a wide array of questions about various types of sexual experience, including masturbation, oral sex, and coitus—before, during, and outside of marriage. Kinsey adopted a group sampling approach. He recruited study participants from organizations and community groups such as college fraternities and sororities.

Kinsey's samples did not represent the general population (Drucker, 2012). People of colour, people in rural areas, older people, the poor, Catholics, and Jews were all underrepresented in his samples. There is thus no way of knowing

Survey A detailed study of a sample obtained through such methods as interviews and questionnaires.

Research Interview.
Interviewing is a commonly used survey method.

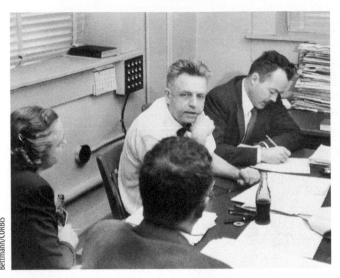

Bettmann/CORBIS

Alfred Kinsey.
Kinsey and his colleagues conducted the first large-scale scientific study of sexual behaviour in the United States.

Reliability The consistency or accuracy of a measure.

Incidence A measure of an event's occurrence.

Validity The degree to which a test measures what it purports to measure.

whether Kinsey's results accurately mirrored the practices of the American population at the time. His estimate that 37% of the male population had reached orgasm at least once through male–male sexual activity was probably too high. But the relationships Kinsey uncovered, such as the positive link between level of education and participation in oral sex, may be more generalizable.

Kinsey took measures to encourage candour in the people he interviewed. He assured study participants that their responses were confidential. He trained his interviewers to ask questions in an objective, matter-of-fact style. To reduce the tendency to slant responses in socially desirable directions, interviewers reassured participants that they would not pass judgment on anything they said. Interviewers were trained to hide any emotional reactions their subjects might interpret as disapproving.

Kinsey also checked the **reliability** of his data by evaluating the consistency of the responses given by several hundred interviewees who were re-examined after at least 18 months. Their reports of the **incidence** of various sexual activities (for example, whether they had ever engaged in premarital or extramarital coitus) were highly reliable. That is, participants tended to give the same answers on both occasions. Kinsey recognized, however, that consistency of responses across time— or retakes, as he called them—did not guarantee their **validity**. That is, the retakes did not show whether the reported behaviours had some basis in fact. One indirect measure was comparison of the reports of husbands and wives—for example, with respect to the incidence of oral–genital sex or the frequency of intercourse. There was a remarkable consistency in the reports of 706 pairs of spouses, lending support to the view that their self-reports were accurate.

The 2004 Hollywood film *Kinsey* gives a realistic portrayal of the interview techniques Kinsey and his colleagues used.

CRITICAL THINKING QUESTIONS

One study conducted at a university found that fewer male than female students volunteered for a sexuality study. Can you think of any reasons to explain this finding?

Social desirability A response bias caused by a subject's tendency to provide a socially acceptable answer to a questionnaire or interview question.

LIMITATIONS OF THE SURVEY METHOD   Many people refuse to participate in surveys. Samples are therefore biased by the inclusion of large numbers of volunteers, who are generally willing to take time to participate. Volunteers for sex surveys also tend to be more sexually permissive and liberal-minded than non-volunteers. At an Ontario university, for example, students who volunteered for a study on human sexuality were more sexually experienced, more interested in sexual variety, and more permissive in their attitudes toward sexuality than were students who did not volunteer (Bogaert, 1996).

Many of the Canadian researchers who study sexuality are based in university social science departments, and for the sake of convenience they frequently obtain samples from students in their departments. Since relatively few men enrol in many social science courses, however, it's difficult to make adequate gender comparisons. Researchers at an Ontario university found that fewer males than females volunteered to take part in a sexuality study, which of course exacerbated the gender-ratio problem (Senn & Demarais, 2001).

Even people who agree to participate in surveys of sexual behaviour may feel pressured to answer questions in the direction of **social desirability**. That is, they give responses they think are socially acceptable. For example, a survey participant who believes masturbation is viewed as a deviant or unacceptable practice may indicate on a survey that he doesn't masturbate, when in fact he does. A married survey respondent who perceives that extramarital sex is looked upon by society with disapproval may be less likely to report that she has engaged in extramarital sex. It's very likely that in the past, when Western culture was more homophobic than it is today, some gay, lesbian, and bisexual people failed to accurately report their sexual orientations when participating in sexuality research. These are all examples of social desirability bias.

It's important to understand that study participants who are influenced by social desirability bias may be responding this way unconsciously, rather than on purpose. Some respondents may consciously or unconsciously exaggerate their sexual behaviour in what they perceive to be socially desirable directions. For example, men may tend to exaggerate their levels of sexual activity, and women may tend to minimize theirs, in accordance with societal expectations (Fisher et al., 2012).

The Naturalistic Observation Method

In **naturalistic observation**, also called the field study, scientists directly observe behaviour where it happens. Anthropologists, for example, live among preliterate societies and report on their social and sexual customs. Scientists in other disciplines also adopt methods of naturalistic observation in their research on human sexuality. For example, sociologists observe the street lives of prostitutes, and psychologists observe patterns of nonverbal communication and body language used by couples in dating situations.

The Ethnographic Observation Method

Ethnographic observation provides data about sexual behaviours and customs within various ethnic groups. This includes groups that are found in many cultures, as well as groups that are limited to just one or a few cultures. Anthropologists are the specialists who typically engage in ethnographic research. They live among societies in the four corners of the earth, observing and studying human diversity. Margaret Mead (1935) reported on the social and sexual customs of various peoples of New Guinea. Bronisław Malinowski (1929) studied the Trobriand Islanders, among others. Even so, ethnographic observation has its limits for the study of sexual behaviour. Sexual activities are most commonly performed away from the watchful gaze of others, especially visitors from other cultures. Ethnographers may therefore have to rely on indirect methods such as interviewing.

The Participant Observation Method

In **participant observation**, the investigators learn about people's behaviour by directly interacting with them. Male–male sexual behaviour and mate swapping has been studied this way. As a graduate student in anthropology, Katherine Frank worked as a stripper at several clubs in a southeastern American city to earn income and pay for graduate school, and as a way to conduct a research study on men's

The Canadian Journal of Human Sexuality

VOLUME 14 - NUMBER 1-2

  PUBLISHED BY SIECCAN
THE SEX INFORMATION & EDUCATION COUNCIL OF CANADA
http://www.sieccan.org

The Canadian Journal of Human Sexuality. Published by the Sex Information and Education Council of Canada, this journal focuses on Canadian sexuality research.

Naturalistic observation A study method in which organisms are observed in their natural environments.

Ethnographic observation A study method in which behaviours and customs are observed within a group's native environment.

Participant observation A study method in which observers interact with their subjects as they collect data.

A World of Diversity

STUDYING THE SEXUAL BEHAVIOURS OF DIVERSE POPULATIONS

Trans Individuals

The Trans PULSE project began in 2004 as a coalition of community activists, academics, and health workers dedicated to improving the services and supports available to trans people across Ontario. A large scale survey was launched in 2009 to help create a profile of trans people and to identify key health issues and social challenges in the community. The Trans PULSE survey was conducted over a 12-month period in 2009–2010, during which time 433 trans individuals who lived, worked, or had received health care in Ontario were questioned about their sexual behaviour and health-related issues (Bauer, Redman, Bradley, & Scheim, 2013). The term *trans* was broadly defined by the study and included those who had medically and socially transitioned to their felt gender, as well as those who had not transitioned. Participants were asked to indicate their current sexual identity and could check off more than one response. Bauer et al. reported on 227 trans men who indicated a wide range of sexual identities including heterosexual (34%), bisexual/pansexual (24%), lesbian (4%), queer (48%), two-spirited (3%), and questioning (12%).

Asian and Euro-Canadians

Most cross-cultural researchers have focused only on ethnic group comparisons or length of residency as predictors of sexual attitudes and behaviours. Brotto et al. (2006, 2007) also considered acculturation to Western society, and found that acculturation was much more powerful than length of residence for predicting sexual attitudes, experiences, and responses.

A study by University of British Columbia researchers (Woo, Morshedian, Brotto, & Gorzalka, 2012) examined the relationship of sex guilt, religiosity, and sexual desire among a sample of Asian and Euro-Canadian female undergraduates. Sex guilt is defined as a negative emotion that occurs after an individual violates or considers violating sexual standards as dictated by religious, cultural, or social norms. The study found that those women who reported that religion played a very important role in their lives also reported higher levels of sex guilt, which were in turn associated with lower levels of sexual desire. This relationship of religiosity, sex guilt, and sexual desire was evident among both Asian Canadian and Euro-Canadian women. However, the study showed that, overall, Euro-Canadian women reported higher levels of sexual desire and lower levels of sex guilt than did Asian-Canadian women.

Sex Workers

University of British Columbia researcher Lisa Lazurus and her colleagues conducted a study of 252 street-based female sex workers in

Courtesy of Katherine Frank

Katherine Frank.
Frank worked as a stripper in graduate school, both to augment her income and to learn about men who frequent strip clubs.

motivations for visiting strip clubs. In reports of her experiences, Frank (2002, 2003) notes that many men told her they attend the clubs because they "just want to relax." She writes that male customers may encounter some stigma for visiting the clubs, but not as much as the strippers do.

The Focus Group Method

Focus group research involves bringing together a group of people to determine their attitudes regarding a specific topic. The researcher guides the discussion by asking questions that are general in nature, with the intent of encouraging interaction and the free flow of ideas.

Focus groups are especially valuable in exploratory research, where there has been limited research on a particular topic. Researchers at the University of Guelph (Humphreys & Herold, 2007) used focus groups in developing scales to measure attitudes and behaviours pertaining to sexual consent. Jocelyn Wentland and Elke Reissing (2011) at the University of Ottawa utilized focus groups to investigate the implicit and explicit rules that guide the initiation, maintenance, and termination of

Vancouver, British Columbia on the subject of social stigma and access to health-related services (Lazarus et al., 2012). Nearly 50% of the sample was Caucasian, 44% was Aboriginal, and 6% identified as visible minorities. Women were considered to have experienced stigma if they hid their sex work from others. The results showed 56% of the women had experienced stigma associated with their work, and almost half of the sample had experienced difficulty accessing health services within the previous six months. The sample also reported high rates of drug use and exposure to past and current violent events. The authors concluded that reported feelings of stigma are associated with increased barriers to health service accessibility. When the women felt compelled to hide the nature of their work because of fear of judgement from health care workers and others in their community, they compromised their personal health. Shannon et al. (2009) suggest that improving

sex worker access to health care should include encouraging non-judgemental delivery of service, provision of clinic services in areas where sex work occurs, extending clinic hours, and involving sex workers and former sex workers in the planning and delivery of health services.

Clients of Sex Workers

Between June 2008 and April 2009, Simon Fraser University sociologist Chris Atchison (2010) conducted a study of men who purchase sex. Over 800 men volunteered to fill out an online questionnaire that asked about their interactions with sex workers, and 24 participated in an in-depth personal interview. The average age of the questionnaire sample was 40 years and the average age of the interview group was 47 years. The majority of men in both groups were heterosexual, Caucasian, well-educated, and employed. Almost half of the men in the larger, questionnaire sample were married or in common-law

relationships, while the men in the smaller interview sample were primarily single. Most participants preferred to frequent massage parlours, escort services, and in-call services, and only a small percentage (3.3%) expressed a preference for street-based services. Only 3.4% of men admitted that they had committed a form of violent assault against sex workers. However, it is unlikely that men who commit violent crimes against sex workers would disclose this information or would even agree to volunteer for this study. Other Canadian studies have shown disturbingly high rates of violence perpetrated by clients against sex workers (Farley, Lynn, & Cotton, 2005; Shannon et al., 2009). Chris Atchison and colleagues have recently launched a national survey, the Sex, Safety & Security project, which continues to explore the attitudes and experiences of Canadians who pay for sex (www.sexsafetysecurity.ca).

different forms of casual sexual relationships such as one-night stands, booty calls, fuck buddies, and friends with benefits.

The Laboratory Observation Method

With the 1966 publication of *Human Sexual Response*, William H. Masters and Virginia E. Johnson became some of the first scientists to report direct laboratory observations of individuals and couples engaged in sexual acts. The women ranged in age from 18 to 78, the men from 21 to 80. There were 276 married couples, 106 single women, and 36 single men. The married couples engaged in intercourse and other forms of mutual stimulation, such as manual and oral stimulation of the genitals. The unmarried people participated in studies that did not require intercourse, such as measurement of female sexual arousal in response to the insertion of a penis-shaped probe, and male ejaculation during masturbation.

Their methods offered the first reliable set of data on what happens to the body during sexual response. Their instruments permitted them to directly measure **vasocongestion** (blood flow to the genitals), myotonia (muscle tension), and other physiological responses.

CRITICAL THINKING QUESTIONS

Which strikes you as the more important measure of sexual arousal—the person's subjective report of arousal or the level of arousal indicated by an instrument such as a vaginal photoplethysmograph?

Vasocongestion Congestion resulting from the flow of blood.

Correlation

What are the relationships between ethnicity and age of coming out among gay, lesbian, and bisexual people? What's the connection between socioeconomic status and teen pregnancy? In each case, we're relating two variables to one another—ethnicity and age of coming out, and socioeconomic status and rate of teen pregnancy. Correlational research describes the relationship between variables such as these.

A **correlation** is a statistical measure of the relationship between two variables. In a correlational study, two or more variables are related, or linked, to one another by statistical means. The strength and direction of the relationship between two variables are expressed with a statistic called a **correlation coefficient**. Correlations can be positive or negative. Two variables are positively correlated if one increases as the other increases, or one decreases as the other decreases. A negative correlation occurs when an opposite relationship exists, such as when one variable increases and the other decreases.

Research has shown relationships (correlations) between sexual satisfaction and a host of variables, including communication skills, marital satisfaction, and general health (see Figure 2.1) Although such research may give us an idea of the factors associated with sexual satisfaction, the experimenters have not manipulated the variables of interest. For this reason, we cannot say which—if any—of the factors is causally related to sexual happiness.

Correlation A statistical measure of the relationship between two variables.

Correlation coefficient A statistic that expresses the strength and direction (positive or negative) of the relationship between two variables.

The Experimental Method

The best (though not always feasible) method for studying cause-and-effect relationships is the **experiment**. Experiments permit scientists to draw conclusions about cause-and-effect relationships, because the experimenters are able to directly manipulate the factors or variables of interest, and observe the effects of this manipulation.

Aspects of the Experimental Method

Experiment A scientific method that seeks to confirm cause-and-effect relationships by manipulating independent variables and observing their effects on dependent variables.

In an experiment on the effects of alcohol on sexual arousal, for example, a group of participants would receive an intervention, called a **treatment**, such as a dose of alcohol. (In other experiments, the intervention or treatment might involve the administration of a drug, exposure to violent sexual material, or a sexual health education program.) They would then be carefully observed to learn whether that treatment made a difference in their behaviour—in this case, their sexual arousal.

Treatment An experimental intervention (such as a test, drug, or sex education program) that's administered to participants so its effects can be observed.

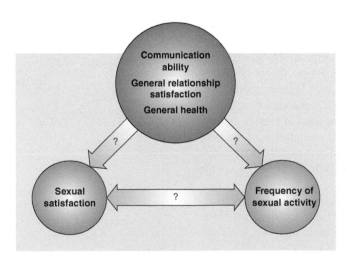

Figure 2.1　What's the relationship between frequency of sexual activity and sexual satisfaction?
Couples who engage in more frequent sexual relations report higher levels of sexual satisfaction—but why? Because researchers have not manipulated the variables, we cannot conclude that sexual satisfaction causes a higher frequency of sexual interaction. Nor can we say that frequent sexual activity causes greater sexual satisfaction. Perhaps both variables are affected by other factors, such as communication skills, general relationship satisfaction, and general health.
Source: Behavioral Technology Inc.

A Closer Look

MEASURING SEXUAL AROUSAL

What sexually excites a man? What sexually excites a woman? Research using a variety of methods suggests that men's sexual responses are more predictable, and that what goes on in men's bodies is more likely to correlate with what they're thinking.

Consider the research of Canadian investigator Meredith Chivers and her colleagues (Chivers & Bailey, 2007; Chivers et al., 2007). She showed erotic videos to men and women, straight and gay. The videos portrayed male–female sex, male–male sex, female–female sex, a man masturbating, a woman masturbating, a muscled man walking nude on a beach, and a well-toned nude woman doing calisthenics. The subjects watched the videos while Chivers measured their arousal objectively and subjectively. The objective measures were made possible by plethysmographs connected to the viewers' genitals. Men wore an apparatus on the penis that gauged its swelling (erection). Women inserted a tampon-shaped probe in the vagina that bounced light off the vaginal walls, providing a gauge of genital blood flow. The participants used a keypad to rate their subjective feelings of arousal.

Self-labelled heterosexual men achieved erection while watching male–female sex, female–female sex, and masturbating and exercising women. They were generally unresponsive when they watched male–male sex and a masturbating man. Gay males showed the opposite pattern of arousal.

Subjective ratings by both the straight and gay males matched the numbers provided by the plethysmograph. The men's thoughts were congruent with their body's responses.

The penile strain gauge (left) and the vaginal photoplethysmograph (right) are used to measure physiological responses to sexual stimuli.

Not so with the women. Regardless of whether the women labelled themselves straight or lesbian, they responded with genital arousal when they viewed male–male sex, female–female sex, and male–female sex. Their genitals were more responsive to the exercising woman than to the nude man.

Their self-reported arousal rates, however, did not particularly match their bodies' responses. Heterosexual women reported less arousal than their bodies indicated when they watched female–female sex and male–male sex. They reported more arousal than their bodies showed when they watched male–female sex. Lesbians showed objective and subjective arousal in response to female–female sex, but reported less arousal than their bodies showed when they viewed male–male sex.

Chivers (in Bergner, 2009) suggests that women are genitally aroused by a wider range of stimuli than men, and that these differences might reflect innate, evolutionary forces. Could female sexuality be divided into two systems, one physiological and the other subjective? According to this view, feminine lust would be a subjective phenomenon, and physiological genital arousal would not tell us much about desire. That is, what a

woman cognitively "wants" might not always be the same as what her body responds to.

Sexologist Lisa M. Diamond suggests that the response of women to a wider range of sexual stimuli allows for quite a bit of plasticity in sexual response. She begins her 2008 book *Sexual Fluidity: Understanding Women's Love and Desire* by noting that " . . . the actress Anne Heche began a widely publicized romantic relationship with the openly lesbian comedian Ellen DeGeneres after having had no prior same-sex attractions or relationships. The relationship with DeGeneres ended after two years, and Heche went on to marry a man." Diamond speculates that for many women, desire may be dictated more by intimacy or emotional connection than by the attractiveness—or even the sex—of a partner.

Penile strain gauge A device for measuring a man's sexual arousal in terms of changes in penis circumference.

Vaginal photoplethysmograph A tampon-shaped probe that is inserted into the vagina to measure the light reflected from the vaginal walls, thereby determining the level of vasocongestion.

Innovative Canadian Research

USING A THERMOGRAPHIC CAMERA TO MEASURE SEXUAL AROUSAL

Researchers at McGill University (Kukkonen et al., 2007) have an alternative method for measuring sexual arousal. In a controlled laboratory experiment, they first showed men and women a neutral film, then randomly assigned the participants to watch either a sexually explicit film, a humorous film, or a neutral film. The researchers used a thermographic camera to measure changes in genital and thigh temperature.

The camera detected significant genital temperature changes during the showing of the erotic film, but not during the showing of the other two films. There were no changes in thigh temperature during the showing of

the sex film, indicating that temperature changes during sexual arousal were specific to the genital region.

There was no difference between men and women in the amount of time it took to reach peak genital temperature. For both men and women, there was a high correlation between temperature change and subjective sexual arousal.

The findings indicate that a thermographic camera is a reliable and useful instrument for measuring sexual arousal. This method is less intrusive than other measures of sexual arousal and can be used with both men and women. Thermography makes it possible to determine whether gender differences in arousal found in previous research are true differences or are results of measurement or instrumentation error.

Independent variable A condition in a scientific study that is manipulated so its effects can be observed.

Dependent variable The condition in a scientific study that is believed to be affected by the independent variable(s). The results of the study are assessed by measuring changes in the dependent variable.

Experimental group A group of study participants who receive the experimental treatment.

Control group A group of study participants who do not receive the experimental treatment. All other conditions are kept the same for the control group as for the experimental group.

Selection factor A research bias that may operate when people are allowed to determine whether they will receive an experimental treatment.

In an experiment, the variable (treatment) that's hypothesized to have a causal effect is manipulated or controlled by the researcher. Consider an experiment designed to determine whether alcohol stimulates sexual arousal. The design might involve giving one group of participants a specified amount of alcohol and then measuring its effects on the participants' sexual arousal. In such an experiment, the dose of alcohol—whose presence and quantity are manipulated by the researchers—is considered the **independent variable**. As they manipulate the independent variable, they watch for changes in the **dependent variable**, which is believed to be affected by (dependent on) the independent variable. In this experiment, the dependent variable is sexual arousal. Changes in the dependent variable are observed and measured, but not manipulated by the researchers. Sexual arousal might be measured in terms of physiological change or self-report.

Experimental and Control Groups

In a well-designed experiment, participants are randomly assigned to the experimental and control groups. Participants in the **experimental group** receive the treatment. Participants in the **control group** do not. Every effort is made to hold all other conditions constant for both groups. By using random assignment and holding other conditions constant, researchers can be reasonably confident that the independent variable (the treatment) has brought about the results, and extraneous factors (e.g., the temperature of the room in which the treatment is administered, or differences between the participants in the experimental and control groups) have not.

Why do experimenters try to assign individuals to experimental and control groups at random? Consider a study about the effects of alcohol on sexual arousal in response to sexually explicit films. If we permit study participants to choose whether they'll drink alcohol, we might not know whether it's the alcohol itself that accounts for the results. Some other factor, called a **selection factor**, might discriminate between people who do and people who do not choose to drink alcohol. Perhaps people who choose to drink have more permissive attitudes toward sexually explicit material. Their permissiveness, rather than the alcohol, might affect their sexual responsiveness to the stimuli. If this is the case, the experimental outcomes might reflect the effects of the selection factor, rather than the alcohol.

Qualitative Research Methods

Most large-scale sexuality studies employ a **quantitative methodology**. Study participants fill out questionnaires that typically consist of multiple-choice questions with a range of answers devised by the researchers. The researchers then determine what percentage of the sample has chosen each of the responses available for each question. Findings from this type of study are presented as statistics. A number of statistical tests can be used to determine whether the results are statistically significant.

A **qualitative methodology** takes a different approach. Rather than forcing them to choose between a set of responses on a multiple-choice questionnaire, a qualitative study uses interviews, focus groups, diaries, or other methods that allow participants to express their thoughts, feelings, emotions, and opinions in their own words and in more detail (Denzin & Lincoln, 2005). Take, for example, the following quote from a male participant in a study investigating the components of "great sex":

> In normal good sex or good relationships, I think there's always some maybe small but detectable barriers, some things held back. In great sex, I think those, for me, disappear, and so that one is quite transparent to the other person, and therefore quite vulnerable, but it feels, it goes with an intensely erotic and good feeling, rather than a scary thing (Kleinplatz et al., 2009, p. 9).

It's unlikely that this nuanced understanding would emerge by having the study participant fill out a multiple-choice questionnaire. Because people's attitudes, feelings, and experiences pertaining to sexuality are often very complex and dependent on social context, qualitative research methods can increase our understanding of sexuality in ways quantitative methods can't.

Ethics in Sex Research

Sex researchers are required to protect the people they study. This ensures that subjects participate of their own free will and are not subjected to physical or psychological harm. In colleges, universities, hospitals, and research institutions, ethics-review committees examine proposed studies in light of ethical guidelines and help researchers weigh the potential harm of administering the independent variables. If a committee finds fault with a proposal, it may advise the researcher about how to modify the research design so it complies with ethical standards and may withhold approval until the proposal has been modified.

Let's consider a number of ethical issues:

- **Exposing participants to harm.** Individuals may be harmed if they're exposed to pain or placed in stressful situations. For this reason, researchers do not expose children to erotic materials in order to determine their effects. Nor do researchers expose human foetuses to male or female sex hormones to learn whether they create predispositions toward tomboyishness, gay or lesbian sexual orientation, or other variables of interest.
- **Confidentiality.** Researchers can do many things to ensure confidentiality for participants. They can make questionnaires anonymous. They can withhold

CRITICAL THINKING QUESTIONS

Can you think of a sexuality research question that might be effectively answered using quantitative research methods? What about using qualitative research methods?

Quantitative methodology The collection of numerical data (e.g., percentages) to produce statistics.

Qualitative methodology The use of interviews, focus groups, diaries, or other methods to record people's attitudes and experiences.

Informed consent
Agreement to participate in research after receiving adequate information about the purposes and nature of the study and about its potential risks and benefits.

subjects' identities from interviewers. In their research reports, they can provide enough information about participants' backgrounds (size of city of origin, region of country, religion, age group, race, educational level, and so on) to make the studies useful without divulging participants' identities. Once the need for follow-up has passed and the results have been fully analyzed, researchers can destroy the participants' records, including names and addresses.

■ **Informed consent.** The principle of **informed consent** requires that people freely agree to participate after being given enough information about the procedures and purposes of the research—and its risks and benefits—to make an informed decision. Once the study has begun, participants must be free to withdraw at any time without penalty.

■ **The use of deception.** Ethical conflicts may emerge when experiments require that participants not know all about their purposes and methods. For example, in an experiment on the effects of violent pornography on aggression against women, participants may be misled into believing they're administering electric shocks to women (who are actually confederates of the experimenter), even though no shocks are actually delivered. The experimenter wants to determine participants' willingness to hurt other women after they've been exposed to aggressive erotic films. Such studies can't be carried out if participants know the shocks are not actually delivered.

Research is the backbone of human sexuality as a science. This textbook focuses on scientific findings that can expand our understanding of human sexuality in all of its varied dimensions.

Innovative Canadian Research

DO RESEARCH CONSENT FORMS AFFECT FINDINGS?

Over the years, research-ethics requirements have become more stringent at universities and other institutions in Canada. Researchers at the University of Windsor and the University of Guelph (Senn & Desmarais, 2006) conducted two studies to determine whether these requirements were affecting findings in sexuality research.

Each participant was given one of three types of consent form. The first described only the research process. The second also described the study's sexuality content. The third form also included a warning about the possible negative effects of involvement in the study.

The first study involved female university students who were randomly assigned to watch one of three types of sexually explicit slides: erotica, nonviolent pornography, and violent pornography. In the second study,

a community sample was asked about sexual experiences, abuse, and assault.

There were no significant differences in the findings for the three different types of consent forms, except for one major difference in the study involving sexually explicit slides. There, the participants who were given detailed information about the explicit slides and the participants who were also warned about possible harm evaluated the slides significantly more negatively than those who were told only about the research process.

A surprising finding in both studies was that students who were given more detail about the content of the studies and warnings about possible harm did not feel they were better informed than those who were told only about the research process. The results raise the question of how best to adequately inform participants about a research study, while at the same time minimizing the possibility that the type of consent form will bias the findings.

Summing Up

A theory consists of a set of ideas or concepts that are used to explain a set of observed facts. Theory provides us with conceptual frameworks for explaining and predicting sexual thoughts, emotions, attitudes, and behaviours.

The application of evolutionary theory to human sexuality has taken a variety of directions, but a central focus has been on gender differences in mating strategies for reproductive success.

The theory of psychoanalysis proposes that biologically based sex drives come into conflict with social codes.

Psychological theories focus on the processes of perception, learning, motivation, emotion, and personality that affect gender and sexual behaviour. Learning theories focus on factors such as rewards and punishments. Social–cognitive theory is a learning theory in which observational learning, values, and expectations play key roles in determining behaviour.

Sexual script theory examines sexuality from the standpoint of culturally learned scripts that specify how men and women should behave sexually.

Social exchange theory examines sexuality within relationships in terms of rewards and costs.

Feminist theory focuses on the subordination of women and the unequal status of women in society.

Queer theory challenges heteronormativity and heterosexism.

The scientific method is a systematic means of gathering scientific evidence and testing assumptions through empirical research. It entails formulating a research question, framing a hypothesis, testing the hypothesis, and drawing conclusions about the hypothesis.

Research samples should accurately represent the populations of interest. Representative samples are usually obtained through random sampling.

Case studies are carefully drawn biographies of individuals or small groups that focus on unravelling the interplay of various factors in individuals' backgrounds.

Surveys typically gather information about behaviour through interviews or questionnaires administered to large samples of people.

In naturalistic observation, scientists directly observe the behaviour of animals and humans where it happens—in the "field." The scientists remain unobtrusive.

Ethnographic research provides data about sexual behaviours and customs that occur widely across cultures.

In participant observation, investigators learn about people's behaviour by interacting with them.

In the laboratory observation method, people engage in the behaviour under study within a laboratory setting.

Correlational studies reveal the strength and direction of relationships between variables. They do not show cause and effect.

Experiments allow scientists to draw conclusions about cause-and-effect relationships, because the scientists directly control or manipulate the variables of interest and observe their effects. Well-designed experiments randomly assign individuals to experimental and control groups.

Ethics concerns the ways researchers protect their research subjects from harm.

Ethical standards require that research be conducted only when the expected benefits of the research outweigh the anticipated risks to participants and experimenters attempt to minimize the expected risks.

The principle of informed consent requires that people agree to participate in research only after being given enough information about the purposes, procedures, risks, and benefits to make informed decisions.

Test Yourself

Multiple-Choice Questions

1. The hypothesis that evolution has shaped human social behaviours, including sexual behaviours, is referred to as:
(a) Social–cognitive theory.
(b) Sociobiology.
(c) The traditional sexual script.
(d) Social exchange theory.

2. A controversial Freudian belief is that:
(a) Children normally harbour erotic interests.
(b) Children ignore unacceptable impulses.
(c) Childhood is an important time of life.
(d) Children seek pain and avoid pleasure.

3. According to _____ theory, children acquire the gender roles deemed appropriate in a society through reinforcement and observational learning.
(a) Evolutionary
(b) Social–cognitive
(c) Feminist
(d) Psychoanalytic

4. According to queer theory,
(a) There is no such thing as lesbian and gay sexual orientations.
(b) All heterosexuals are prejudiced.
(c) Everybody is bisexual.
(d) Current categories of sexual orientation do not adequately describe all people.

5. Researchers use _____ that are often based on theory to predict behaviour.
(a) Hypotheses
(b) Operational definitions
(c) Research questions
(d) Research methods

6. A representative sample:
(a) Consists of at least 75 males and 75 females.
(b) Is a group of people who volunteer to participate in the study.
(c) Is a sample that accurately reflects the composition of the population.
(d) Is a sample in which each member of the population has an equal chance of participating in the study.

7. A random sample:
(a) Consists of at least 75 males and 75 females.
(b) Is a group of people who volunteer to participate in the study.
(c) Is a sample that accurately reflects the composition of the population.
(d) Is a sample in which each member of the population has an equal chance of participating in the study.

8. Masters and Johnson's research on sexual response is an example of:
(a) Participant observation of sexual behaviour.
(b) Laboratory observation of sexual behaviour.
(c) Correlational research on sexual behaviour.
(d) Experimental research on sexual behaviour.

9. Correlational studies provide information about:
(a) Whether a change in one variable causes a change in another.
(b) Statistical relationships between two variables.
(c) The margin of error due to a variable.
(d) The degree of bias in a sample.

10. A basic ethical requirement for all research on human sexuality is the provision of:
(a) Adequate compensation.
(b) Legal permission.
(c) Informed consent.
(d) Parental approval.

You'll find answers to the "Test Yourself" questions on page 489.

Questions for Critical Thinking

1. Evolutionary theory and scripting theory offer very different explanations for human sexual behaviour. In your opinion, is one of these theories more valid than the other? Explain your answer.

2. Have you ever responded to a survey on sexual behaviour, either in a magazine or on the Internet? Looking back on it, do you think your responses were influenced by social desirability bias? Did you answer truthfully? Why or why not?

3. If you were to conduct a study on the psychological impact of sexual assault on its victims, what are some of the ethical issues you would need to take into account?

CHAPTER THREE

Female and Male Anatomy and Physiology

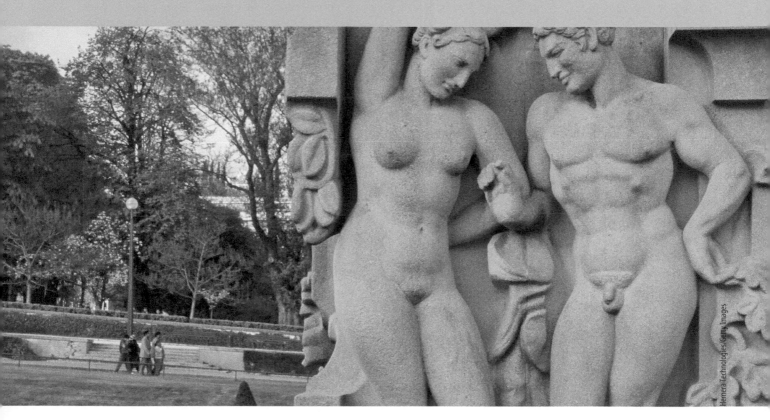

Herrera Technologies/Getty Images

Female Anatomy and Physiology

The French have a saying: *Vive la différence!* (Long live the difference!) It celebrates the differences between men and women. Given the exclusive female possession of a clitoris, some might assert that women in particular have much to celebrate. Only women possess a sex organ—the clitoris—that's solely devoted to producing pleasurable sensations.

In the past, girls were commonly taught to regard their genitals with a sense of shame. As women, they tended to hold negative attitudes about their genitals and sexuality. Fortunately, societal attitudes towards female sexuality have become much more positive in recent decades. Yet, even today, girls may be reprimanded for expressing curiosity about their own anatomy. They may be told to keep their hands off their private parts. This is unfortunate, because knowledge of one's own sexual anatomy contributes to sexual health and pleasure.

The External Female Sex Organs

Vulva The external sexual structures of the female.

Mons veneris A mound of fatty tissue that covers the pubic bone (the joining of the pelvic bones at the front of the body, below the abdomen and above the clitoris). The mons veneris is also known as the mons pubis, or simply the mons.

Labia majora Large folds of skin that run downward from the mons along the sides of the vulva.

Labia minora Hairless, light-coloured membranes located between the labia majora.

Clitoris A female sex organ consisting of a shaft and a glans, located above the urethral opening. It's extremely sensitive to sexual sensation.

Taken collectively, the external sexual structures of the female are termed the **vulva**. The vulva consists of the **mons veneris**, the **labia majora** and **labia minora** (major lips and minor lips), the **clitoris**, and the vaginal opening. (See Figure 3.1.) Figure 3.2 shows variations in the appearance of women's genitals. If you're a female looking at Figure 3.2 and thinking your vulva doesn't look like the ones in the picture, don't be concerned. Each woman is unique, and there are endless variations in the size and appearance of different parts of the vulva.

The Mons Veneris

The mons veneris consists of fatty tissue that covers the public bone, which is the joining of the pelvic bones at the front of the body, below the abdomen and above the clitoris. At puberty the mons becomes covered with pubic hair, which is often thick and curly, but varies from person to person in waviness, texture, and colour.

The mons cushions a woman's body during sexual intercourse, protecting her and her partner from pressure against the pubic bone caused by thrusting motions. There's an ample supply of nerve endings in the mons, so caressing the area can produce pleasurable sexual sensations.

The Labia Majora

The labia majora are large folds of skin that run downward from the mons along the sides of the vulva. The labia majora are thick and bulging in some women, and thinner, flatter, and less noticeable in others. When close together, the labia majora shield the labia minora and the urethral and vaginal openings.

The outer surfaces of the labia majora, next to the thighs, are covered with pubic hair. They're darker than the skin of the thighs and the labia minora. The inner surfaces of the labia majora are hairless and lighter in colour. They're amply supplied with nerve endings that respond to stimulation and can produce sensations of sexual pleasure.

The Labia Minora

The labia minora are two hairless, light-coloured membranes located between the major lips. They surround the urethral and vaginal openings. The outer surfaces of the labia minora merge with the major lips. At the top they join at the prepuce (hood) of the clitoris.

The labia minora differ markedly in appearance from woman to woman. The labia minora of some women form protruding flower shapes that are greatly valued in some cultures, such as the Khoikhoi of Africa. In fact, Khoikhoi women purposely elongate their labia minora by tugging at them.

Rich in blood vessels and nerve endings, the labia minora are highly sensitive to sexual stimulation. When stimulated, they darken and swell, indicating engorgement with blood.

The Clitoris

The clitoris is the female sex organ most sensitive to sexual sensation. It's known by many names around the world, from *bijou* (French

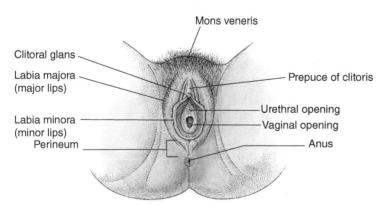

Mons veneris

Clitoral glans

Labia majora
(major lips)

Prepuce of clitoris

Urethral opening

Labia minora
(minor lips)

Vaginal opening

Perineum

Anus

Figure 3.1   The external female sex organs.
This figure shows the vulva with the labia opened to reveal the urethral and vaginal openings.

Figure 3.2   Typical variations in the vulva. The features of the vulva show a great deal of variation. A woman's attitude toward her genitals is likely to reflect her general self-concept and early childhood messages, rather than the appearance of her vulva.

Source: (left) Daniel Sambraus/Science Source; (center) CSMP/Custom Stock Medical Photo; (right) Keith/Custom Medical Stock Photo

for "jewel") to *pokhotnik* (Russian for "lust"). The word "clitoris" derives from the Greek word *kleitoris*, meaning "hill" or "slope." It received its name from the manner in which it slopes upward in the shaft and forms a mound of spongy tissue at the glans (see Figure 3.1).

The body of the clitoris, termed the clitoral shaft, is about 2.5 centimetres long and 0.5 centimetres wide. It consists of erectile tissue, which contains two spongy masses, called **corpora cavernosa** ("cavernous bodies"), that become engorged (filled with blood) and erect in response to sexual stimulation. The stiffening of the clitoris is less apparent than the erection of the penis, because the clitoris does not swing free from the body, as the penis does. The clitoral shaft is covered by the **prepuce** (meaning "before a swelling"), or hood, a sheath of skin formed by the upper part of the labia minora.

The clitoral glans is a smooth, round knob or lump of tissue. It resembles a button and is situated above the urethral opening. The clitoral glans may be covered by the clitoral hood, but it's readily revealed by gently separating the labia minora and retracting the hood. It's highly sensitive to touch, because of its rich supply of nerve endings. Women thus usually prefer to be stroked or stimulated on the mons or the clitoral hood, rather than directly on the glans.

The glans, hood, and shaft of the clitoris are visible from the outside. The clitoral structure, however, extends into the body along the sides of the vagina. The size of the clitoris varies from woman to woman, just as the size of the penis varies from man to man. There is no known connection between clitoris size and sensitivity to sexual stimulation.

In a study, women were asked to rank the areas of their vulva which gave them the most sexual pleasure (Meyer-Bahlburg et al., 2007). The clitoris was ranked highest, followed by the area around the vaginal opening, the sides of the clitoris, the area below the clitoris, the area above the clitoris, the labia majora, and the area around the anus. When the women were asked to rank sources of pleasure within the vagina itself, they ranked the area deep inside the vagina as the highest, followed by the areas just inside and around the opening.

The clitoris and the penis develop from the same embryonic tissue, which makes them similar in structure, or **homologous**. They are not, however, fully similar in function, or **analogous**. Both organs receive and transmit sexual sensations, but the penis is directly involved in reproduction and excretion, serving as a conduit for sperm and urine, respectively.

It's ironic that many cultures—including Victorian culture—have viewed women as unresponsive to sexual stimulation. Women, not men, possess the only

Corpora cavernosa Masses of spongy tissue in the clitoral shaft that become engorged with blood and stiffen in response to sexual stimulation.

Prepuce The fold of skin covering the glans of the clitoris (or of the penis, in a male).

Homologous Similar in structure; developing from the same embryonic tissue.

Analogous Similar in function.

A World of Diversity

PUBIC HAIR REMOVAL

Historical evidence suggests that women in the ancient cultures of Africa, the Middle East, Greece, and Rome practiced some form of pubic hair removal (Ramsey, Sweeney, Fraser, & Oades, 2009). However, pubic hair removal was not common in modern Western culture until the twentieth century. Beginning in the early 1900s, razors were increasingly marketed to women through advertising empha-sizing that body hair removal was feminine and sanitary. Fashion trends, such as the introduction of the bikini in the 1940s, also prompted women to remove hair around the pubic area. More recently, the proliferation of sex-ually explicit media featuring actors, both female and male, with little or no pubic hair has also likely reinforced the message that pubic hair removal is the norm.

A study of 2400 women in the United States found that a majority of women under age 50 practised some form of pubic hair removal in the previous month using various methods (e.g., shaving, waxing), with younger women being more likely to remove some or all of their pubic hair (Herbenick, Schick, Reece, Sanders, & Fortenberry, 2010). In an Australian study (Tiggermann & Hodgson, 2008) of female university students, 61% reported removing pubic hair, but among those women who did remove hair, there was considerable variation in the degree of removal with 20% removing a little hair, 44% removing most hair, and 36% removing all hair. A study in British Columbia found that women's top reasons for removing some or all of their pubic hair included appearance in a bathing suit, feeling attractive, and the idea that pubic hair

removal is cleaner (Riddell, Varto, & Hodgson, 2010).

Although it has been the subject of far less research, pubic hair removal is also common among men. In study of male Australian college students, Martins, Tiggemann, and Churchett (2008) found that about 82% of gay men and 66% of heterosexual men reported engaging in pubic hair removal, primarily because they felt it improved their attractiveness.

Some have expressed the concern that the widespread practice of pubic hair removal has served to increase the sexual objectification of the body, particularly the female body, adding yet another aspect of anatomy which people must monitor and manipulate in order to avoid body shame and conform to societal standards for sex-ual attractiveness (Smoak & Murnen, 2011).

CRITICAL THINKING QUESTIONS

Pubic hair removal has become a common practice. To what extent do you think people feel pressure to remove some or all of their pubic hair in order to measure up to marketing and media influenced standards of sexual attractiveness?

Urethral opening The open-ing through which urine passes from the female's body.

human sex organ whose only known function is the experiencing of pleasure. The clitoris is the woman's most erotically charged organ, which is why they most often masturbate through clitoral stimulation, not through vaginal insertion.

Surgical removal of the clitoral hood is common among Muslims in the Middle East and Africa. As we'll see in "A World of Diversity: Female Genital Mutilation/Cutting," this rite of passage to womanhood leaves many scars, both physical and emotional.

The Vestibule

The word "vestibule" refers to the area within the labia minora that contains the openings to the vagina and the urethra. Richly supplied with nerve endings, the vestibule is very sensitive to tactile and other sexual stimulation.

The Urethral Opening

Urine passes from the female's body through the **urethral opening** (see Figure 3.1), which is connected by a short tube called the urethra to the bladder, where urine collects (see Figure 3.3). The urethral opening lies behind the clitoral glans and in front of the vaginal opening.

The proximity of the urethral opening to the external sex organs may pose hygienic problems for sexually active women. The urinary tract, which includes the urethra, bladder, and kidneys, may become infected by bacteria that are transmitted from the vagina or rectum. Infectious microscopic organisms may pass from the male's sex organs to the female's urethral opening during sexual intercourse. Manual stimulation of the vulva with dirty hands may also transmit bacteria through the urethral opening to the bladder. Anal intercourse followed by vaginal intercourse may transfer microscopic organisms from the rectum to the bladder and cause infection. For similar reasons, women should wipe from front to back, wiping first the vulva and then the anus, when using the bathroom.

Cystitis is a bladder inflammation that may stem from any of these sources. Its primary symptoms are burning and frequent urination (also called urinary urgency). Pus or a bloody discharge is common, and there may be an intermittent or persistent ache just above the pubic bone. These symptoms may disappear after several days, but consultation with a physician is recommended, because untreated cystitis can lead to serious kidney infection.

So-called honeymoon cystitis is caused by the tugging on the bladder and urethral wall that occurs during vaginal intercourse. It may occur upon beginning coital activity (though not necessarily on one's honeymoon) or upon resuming coital activity after lengthy abstinence. Figure 3.3 shows the close proximity of the urethra and the vagina.

The following precautions may help women prevent serious inflammation of the bladder:

- Drink two litres of water a day, to flush the bladder.
- Drink orange or cranberry juice, to maintain an acidic environment that discourages the growth of infectious organisms.
- Reduce the intake of alcohol and caffeine (from coffee, tea, and cola drinks), which may irritate the bladder.
- Wash hands prior to masturbation or self-examination.
- Wash partner's and own genitals before and after intercourse.
- Prevent objects that have touched the anus (fingers, penis, toilet tissue) from subsequently coming into contact with the vulva.
- Cover sex toys with condoms, to prevent possible infection.
- Urinate soon after intercourse, to help wash away bacteria.

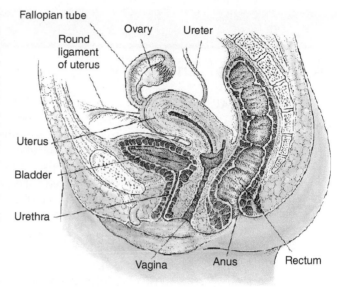

Figure 3.3   The female reproductive system.
This cross-section shows the locations of many of the internal sex organs that constitute the female reproductive system. Note that the uterus is normally tipped forward.

Cystitis An inflammation of the urinary bladder.

The Vaginal Opening

When we part the labia minora, we see the vaginal opening, or **introitus**, rather than the entire vagina. The introitus lies behind the smaller urethral opening. Across the vaginal opening, a fold of tissue called the **hymen** is usually present at birth. The hymen may remain at least partly intact until a woman engages in coitus. For this reason, it has been called the "maidenhead," and its presence has been taken as proof of virginity—and its absence as evidence of coitus. Some females are born with incomplete hymens, however, and other girls' hymens are accidentally torn during such activities as horseback riding, strenuous exercise, gymnastics, and cycling. A punctured hymen therefore doesn't necessarily indicate coital experience. And a flexible hymen may withstand many coital experiences, so its presence is not necessarily proof of virginity. Prior to marriage, some European Muslim women have hymenoplasties—operations that restore their hymens—to provide the illusion of virginity for their wedding nights (Sciolino & Mekhennet, 2008).

Introitus The vaginal opening.

Hymen A fold of tissue across the vaginal opening that's usually present at birth and remains at least partly intact until a woman engages in sexual intercourse.

A World of Diversity

FEMALE GENITAL MUTILATION/CUTTING

According to the World Health Organization, approximately 140 million Muslim women and girls have undergone genital mutilation (World Health Organization, 2012). Despite the fact that people who practice it usually call it circumcision and compare it to male circumcision, social observers assert that female genital mutilation is an attempt by patriarchal societies to control the bodies and behaviour of women (Amnesty International, 2012). In terms of their own perceptions, some groups in Egypt and in the Sudan simply perform clitoridectomies because it is a social custom that has been unchallenged in their own experience (Amnesty International, 2012). Because women tend to adopt the values of the larger cultures in which

they dwell, nearly 80% of procedures are carried out by women who have undergone them themselves (World Health Organization, 2012). Some perceive it as part of their submission to Islam. However, there is no support for it in the Koran—the Islamic bible (Nour, 2000). The typical young woman in this culture—like the typical woman in most patriarchal cultures—does not grasp that she is a victim (Amnesty International, 2012). She assumes that clitoridectomy is part of being female. As one young woman told gynaecologist Nawal M. Nour (2000), the clitoridectomy hurt but was a good thing, because now she was a woman.

Some believe that "female genital cutting" is a more neutral term and that the term "mutilation" is demeaning to the cultures where it is practised, implying that the parents of girls who

undergo the procedure are wilfully harming their daughters.

There are four major types of female genital mutilation (World Health Organization, 2012):

1. **Clitoridectomy**: partial or complete removal of the clitoris
2. Excision: partial or complete removal of the clitoris and the labia minora, with or without removal of the labia majora
3. Infibulation: narrowing of the vaginal opening by creating a seal formed by cutting and repositioning the inner, or outer, labia, with or without removal of the clitoris
4. Other: other procedures on the female genitalia that serve no medical purpose, such as pricking, piercing, scraping, and cauterizing (burning) the genital area

Clitoridectomy Surgical removal of the clitoris.

CRITICAL THINKING QUESTIONS

It has been argued that to be respectful of the cultures where it is practiced, the term "female genital cutting" is more appropriate than "female genital mutilation." Which of these terms do you think is preferable? Why?

Perineum The skin and underlying tissue that lies between the vaginal opening and the anus.

Figure 3.4 illustrates various vaginal openings. The first three show hymen shapes that are frequently found among women who have not had coitus. Now and then a hymen consists of tough, fibrous tissue and is closed, or imperforate, as in the fourth drawing. An imperforate hymen may not be discovered until after puberty, when menstrual discharges begin to accumulate in the vagina. In these rare cases, a simple surgical incision is used to perforate the hymen. The fifth drawing shows a parous ("passed through") vaginal opening, typical of women who have delivered babies.

The skin and underlying tissue between the vaginal opening and the anus (or between the scrotum and the anus, in a male) is called the **perineum**. Because

Figure 3.4 Typical variations in the hymen.
Before first coitus, the hymen can look different in different women. The illustration at far right shows how the introitus generally appears after childbirth.

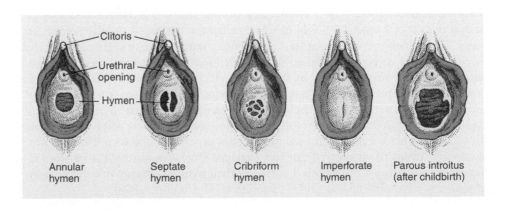

Annular hymen   Septate hymen   Cribriform hymen   Imperforate hymen   Parous introitus (after childbirth)

Clitoris

Urethral opening

Hymen

What effect does female genital mutilation have on women? A study of 250 female patients from the Maternal and Childhood Centres of Ismailia, Egypt, found that those who received the procedures were 80% more likely to complain of painful menstruation, 49% more likely to complain of vaginal dryness during intercourse, 45% more likely to lack sexual desire, 49% less likely to be pleased by sex, and 61% more likely to have difficulty reaching orgasm (El-Defrawi et al., 2001). Complications include severe bleeding, problems urinating, cysts, infections, infertility, complications in childbirth, greater risk of newborn deaths, and psychological and emotional stress (World Health Organization, 2012).

Do not confuse male circumcision with the maiming inflicted on girls in the name of circumcision. Nour (2000) depicts the male equivalent of female genital mutilation as cutting off the penis. The Pulitzer Prize–winning, African American novelist Alice Walker drew attention to the practice in her novel *Possessing the Secret of Joy* and called for its abolition in her book and film *Warrior Marks*.

Many Western countries have outlawed ritual genital mutilation within their borders. Yet, calls from Westerners to ban the practice have sparked arguments that people in one culture cannot dictate the cultural traditions of another. For Alice Walker, however, "Torture is not culture."

The World Health Organization summarizes its stand on the issue as follows:

[Female genital mutilation] is recognized internationally as a violation of the human rights of girls and women. It reflects deep-rooted inequality between the sexes, and constitutes an extreme form of discrimination against women. It is nearly always carried out on minors and is a violation of the rights of children. The practice also violates a person's rights to health, security and physical integrity, the right to be free from torture and cruel, inhuman or degrading treatment, and the right to life when the procedure results in death.

In Canada, female genital mutilation is a criminal offence and it is mandatory for health professionals to report suspected cases or potential cases to child welfare protection services. The Society of Obstetricians and Gynaecologists of Canada advises physicians that after a birth they should not restitch the vaginal opening of an infibulated woman (Perron & Senikas, 2012).

the perineum is rich in nerve endings, stimulating this area may heighten sexual arousal. During labour, many physicians make a routine perineal incision, called an **episiotomy**, to facilitate childbirth.

Structures That Underlie the External Sex Organs

Figure 3.5 shows what lies beneath the skin of the vulva. The vestibular bulbs and Bartholin's glands are active during sexual arousal and are found on both sides (shown on the right in Figure 3.5). Muscular rings (**sphincters**) that constrict

Episiotomy A surgical incision in the perineum that may be made during childbirth, to protect the vagina from tearing.

Sphincters Ring-shaped muscles that surround body openings, which they open or close by expanding or contracting.

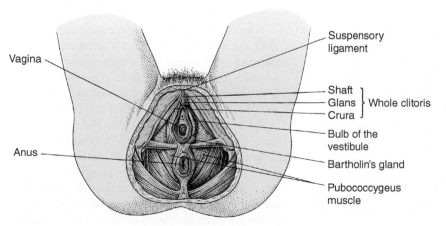

Figure 3.5   The structures that underlie the external female sex organs.
If we could see beneath the vulva, we would find muscle fibres that constrict the various body openings, plus the crura ("legs") of the clitoris, the vestibular bulbs, and Bartholin's glands.

Crura Anatomic structures resembling legs that attach the clitoris to the pubic bone. The singular is "crus."

Vestibular bulbs Cavernous structures that extend downward along the sides of the introitus and swell during sexual arousal.

Vagina The tubular female sex organ that contains the penis during sexual intercourse and through which a baby is born.

Bartholin's glands Glands that lie just inside the minor lips and secrete fluid just before orgasm.

Pubococcygeus muscle The muscle that encircles the entrance to the vagina.

bodily openings, such as the vaginal and anal openings, are also found on both sides.

The clitoral **crura** are wing-shaped, leg-like structures that attach the clitoris to the pubic bone beneath. The crura contain corpora cavernosa, which engorge with blood and stiffen during sexual arousal.

The **vestibular bulbs** are attached to the clitoris at the top and extend downward along the sides of the vaginal opening. Blood congests them during sexual arousal, swelling the vulva and lengthening the **vagina**. This swelling contributes to coital sensations for both partners.

Bartholin's glands lie just inside the minor lips, on each side of the vaginal opening. They secrete a couple of drops of lubrication just before orgasm. This lubrication is not essential for coitus. If the glands become infected and clogged, a woman may notice swelling and local irritation. It's wise to consult a gynaecologist if these symptoms don't fade within a few days. It was once believed that Bartholin's glands were the source of the vaginal lubrication, or wetness, that women experience during sexual arousal. It's now known that engorgement of vaginal tissues during sexual excitement results in a form of "sweating" by the lining of the vaginal wall. During sexual arousal, the pressure from this engorgement causes moisture from the many small blood vessels that lie in the vaginal wall to be forced out and to pass through the vaginal lining, forming the basis of the lubrication. In less time than it takes to read this sentence (generally within 10 to 30 seconds), beads of vaginal lubrication, or "sweat," appear along the interior lining of the vagina in response to sexual stimulation, in much the same way that rising temperature causes water to pass through the skin as perspiration.

Pelvic floor muscles permit women to constrict their vaginal and anal openings. These are the muscles that are used to control urination. They contract automatically, or involuntarily, during orgasm, and toning them may contribute to increased sensation during sexual activity. Repeatedly contracting and relaxing the **pubococcygeal muscle** (these are referred to as Kegel exercises) is sometimes recommended for women who experience sexual response problems.

The Internal Female Sex Organs

The internal sex organs of the female include the innermost parts of the vagina, the cervix, the uterus, and two ovaries, each connected to the uterus by a fallopian tube (see Figures 3.3 and 3.6). These structures make up the female reproductive system.

The Vagina

The **vagina** extends back and up from the vaginal opening (see Figure 3.3). It's usually 7.5 to 12.5 centimetres long when at rest.

The vagina is commonly pictured as a canal or barrel, but when at rest, it's like a collapsed muscular tube whose walls touch. The vagina expands in length and width during sexual arousal. It can also expand to allow insertion of a tampon, as well as passage of a baby's head and shoulders during childbirth.

The vaginal walls have three layers. The inner lining, or vaginal mucosa, can be seen by opening the labia minora. It's a mucous membrane similar to the skin that lines the inside of the mouth. It feels fleshy, soft, and corrugated. It may vary from very dry (especially if the woman is anxious about something, such as exams) to very wet. The middle

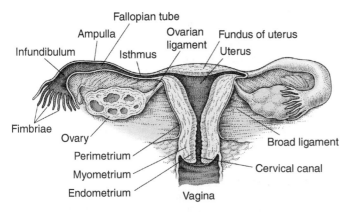

Figure 3.6   The internal female reproductive organs.
This drawing highlights the relationship of the uterus to the fallopian tubes and ovaries. Note the layers of the uterus, the ligaments that attach the ovaries to the uterus, and the relationship of the ovaries to the fimbriae of the fallopian tubes.

layer of the vaginal wall is muscular. The outer or deeper layer is a fibrous covering that connects the vagina to other pelvic structures.

The vaginal walls are rich with blood vessels but poorly supplied with nerve endings. Unlike the sensitive outer one-third of the vaginal barrel, the inner two-thirds are insensitive to touch. The entire vaginal barrel is sensitive to pressure, however, which may be experienced as sexually pleasurable.

The vaginal walls secrete substances that help maintain the vagina's normal acidity (pH 4.0 to 5.0). The secretions normally taste salty, but their odour and taste may vary during the menstrual cycle. Although the evidence is not clear, the secretions are thought to contain substances that may act as sexual attractants. Women who frequently **douche** or use feminine deodorant sprays may thus remove or mask substances that may arouse sex partners. Douching or spraying may also alter the natural chemical balance of the vagina, which can increase the risk of vaginal infections. Feminine deodorant sprays can also irritate the vagina and evoke allergic reactions. The normal, healthy vagina cleanses itself through regular chemical secretions that are evidenced by a mild white or yellowish discharge.

Vaginitis refers to any vaginal inflammation, whether it's caused by an infection, birth control pills, antibiotics that alter natural body chemistry, an allergic reaction, chemical irritation, or lowered resistance due to fatigue or poor diet. Changes in the natural body chemistry or lowered resistance may permit microscopic organisms normally found in the vagina to multiply to infectious levels. Vaginitis may be recognized by abnormal discharge, itching, burning of the vulva, and urinary urgency. Women with vaginitis are advised to seek medical attention.

The following suggestions may help prevent vaginitis:

- Wash your vulva and anus regularly with mild soap. Pat dry, taking care not to touch the vulva after dabbing the anus.
- Wear cotton panties. Nylon underwear retains heat and moisture, which causes harmful bacteria to flourish.
- Avoid pants that are tight in the crotch.
- Be certain your sex partners are well washed. Condoms may also reduce the spread of infection from your partner.
- Use a sterile, water-soluble gel if artificial lubrication is needed for intercourse. Do not use Vaseline. Avoid using flavoured lubricants that contain sugar products, as these can activate yeast infections. Birth-control jellies can be used for lubrication.
- Avoid intercourse that's painful or abrasive to the vagina.
- Avoid diets high in sugar and refined carbohydrates, because they alter the vagina's normal acidity.
- If you're prone to vaginal infections, you may find it helpful to douche occasionally with plain water, a solution of one or two tablespoons of vinegar in a quart of warm water, or a solution of baking soda and water. Douches consisting of unpasteurized plain (unflavoured) yoghurt may help replenish the beneficial bacteria that are normally found in the vagina and that may be destroyed by antibiotics. Be careful when douching, and don't douche if you're pregnant or suspect you may be pregnant. Consult your doctor before deciding to douche or to apply any preparation to the vagina.
- Watch your general health. A poor diet and insufficient rest will reduce your resistance to infection.

The G Spot and Female Ejaculation: Sexual Realities or Gynaecological Myths?

The Gräfenberg spot, or G spot, is a part of the vagina—a bean-shaped area in the anterior (front) wall that may have special erotic significance. The G spot is believed to lie about 2.5 to 5 centimetres from the vaginal entrance and to consist of a soft

Douche Application of a jet of liquid to the vagina as a rinse. From the Italian *doccia*, which means "shower bath."

Vaginitis Vaginal inflammation.

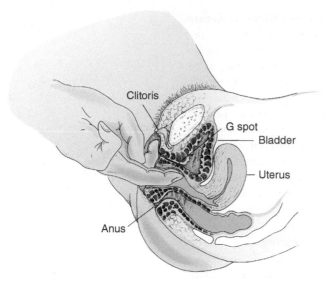

Figure 3.7 The Gräfenberg spot.
It's theorized that the G spot can be stimulated by fingers or by intercourse in the rear-entry or the female-superior position. Does stimulation of the G spot produce intense erotic sensations and a distinct form of orgasm?

mass of tissue that swells from the size of a dime to that of a loonie when stimulated (see Figure 3.7). It's named after gynaecologist Ernst Gräfenberg, who first suggested the area's possible erotic importance.

The spot can be directly stimulated by the woman's or her partner's fingers, or by penile thrusting in the rear entry or the female-superior positions. Some researchers suggest that stimulation of the spot produces intense erotic sensations and that, with prolonged stimulation, a distinct form of orgasm that is characterized by intense pleasure and, in some cases, a biological event formerly thought to be exclusively male: ejaculation. However, these claims are steeped in controversy (Dwyer, 2011; Kilchevsky et al., 2012).

Jannini and her colleagues (2010) summarize much of the research on the G spot as follows: In experiments dating to the 1980s, some researchers claim to have found evidence that many women produce an ejaculate as a result of sexual stimulation. Some researchers believe that this fluid is urine that some women release involuntarily during orgasm. Others believe that it differs from urine and represents a fluid that is released during sex by a system of ducts and glands called *Skene's glands*, in much the same way that semen is released by the prostate gland in men. Some women, on the other hand, may expel urine during sex, perhaps because of urinary stress incontinence.

Even supporters of the existence of the G spot admit that it is difficult to locate because it is not apparent to the eye or touch (Jannini et al., 2010). Most women who are knowledgeable about sexuality in general seem to believe that they have a G spot, even if they cannot locate it with any certainty. Because of difficulties such as these, some researchers wonder whether the notion of a G spot is something of a myth (Dwyer, 2011; Kilchevsky et al., 2012).

The Cervix

Cervix The lower end of the uterus.

Os The opening in the middle of the cervix.

Uterus The hollow, muscular, pear-shaped organ in which a fertilized ovum implants and develops until birth.

The **cervix** is the lower end of the uterus. Its walls, like those of the vagina, produce secretions that contribute to the chemical balance of the vagina. The opening in the middle of the cervix, called the **os**, is typically about the width of a straw, although it expands to permit passage of a baby from the uterus to the vagina during childbirth. Sperm passes from the vagina to the **uterus** through the cervical canal.

CERVICAL CANCER   The incidence of cervical cancer has declined dramatically in Canada since the early 1970s, largely because most women have regular Pap tests. In 2013, there were an estimated 1450 diagnosed cases of cervical cancer and 380 deaths in Canada resulting from this disease (Canadian Cancer Society, 2013a). Cervical cancer is more common among women who've had many sex partners, women who become sexually active at a relatively early age, women of lower socioeconomic status, and women who smoke. All women, however, are at risk.

The greatest risk factor for cervical cancer is infection by the sexually transmitted human papillomavirus (HPV). As we'll discuss in Chapter 14, HPV is extremely common, and in most cases the infection resolves without causing damage. When the cervix is infected with certain strains of HPV, however, the infection can progress to cervical cancer. A vaccine to protect against common strains of HPV has been successfully tested and approved by the Canadian government. The vaccine is most effective if it is administered before a person becomes sexually active.

As discussed in more detail in Chapter 14, all provinces and territories in Canada have school-based programs to vaccinate girls against HPV, but boys are also increasingly being vaccinated.

If detected early, most cases of cervical cancer can be successfully treated by surgery and **radiotherapy** (American Cancer Society, 2012a). Cervical cancer can also be prevented if precancerous changes are detected by a **Pap test**. A Pap test involves smearing a sample of cervical cells on a slide to screen for cervical cancer and other abnormalities. The Canadian Cancer Society (2010a) recommends that once they become sexually active, women should have Pap tests every one to three years, depending on their previous test results and the screening guidelines for their provinces or territories. Not being screened for cervical cancer at the recommended time interval is a major risk factor for developing cervical cancer. Most Canadian women aged 20 to 69 (approximately 70%) have had a pap test within the previous three years (Forte et al., 2012).

Women who are uncomfortable with the Pap test are less likely to be tested. Canadian research has found ethnocultural differences in rates of Pap testing. Brotto, Chou, Singh, and Woo (2008) found that Euro-Canadian women were significantly more likely to have ever had Pap tests than Indo-Canadian or East Asian-Canadian women. Amankwah, Ngwakongnwi, and Quan (2009) found that visible-minority women in Canada were less than half as likely to have had a Pap test.

The Uterus

The uterus, or womb (see Figures 3.3 and 3.6), is the organ in which a fertilized **ovum** implants and develops until birth. The uterus usually slants forward (i.e., it's antroverted), although about 10% of women have uteruses that tip backward (i.e., they're retroverted). In most instances a retroverted uterus causes no problems, but some women with retroverted uteruses find coitus in certain positions painful. (A couple can quickly learn more comfortable positions by trial and error.) The uterus expands to house a foetus during pregnancy and shrinks after pregnancy, although not to its original size. A retroverted uterus normally tips forward during pregnancy.

Like the vagina, the uterus has three layers (also shown in Figure 3.6). The innermost layer, or **endometrium**, is richly supplied with blood vessels and glands. Its structure varies according to a woman's age and the phase of the menstrual cycle. Endometrial tissue is discharged through the cervix and vagina at menstruation. For reasons not entirely understood, in some women endometrial tissue may also grow in the abdominal cavity or elsewhere in the reproductive system. This condition is called **endometriosis**, and its most common symptom is menstrual pain. If left untreated, endometriosis may lead to infertility.

UTERINE/ENDOMETRIAL CANCER   It's estimated that 4600 new cases of uterine cancer were diagnosed in Canada in 2013, and that 890 women died from it that year (Canadian Cancer Society, 2013b). One of the most common forms of uterine cancer is cancer of the endometrial lining. Risk factors for endometrial cancer include high exposure to oestrogen, which is usually the result of early menarche, late menopause, oestrogen replacement therapy, obesity, a high fat diet, and diabetes. Pregnancy, exercise, and hormonal contraceptives appear to lessen the risk.

Endometrial cancer is symptomized by abnormal uterine staining or bleeding, especially after menopause. The most common treatment is surgery (American Cancer Society, 2012b). The five-year survival rate for endometrial cancer is 90% if it's discovered early and limited to the endometrium. (Endometrial cancer is usually diagnosed early because women tend to quickly report postmenopausal bleeding to their doctors.) The survival rate drops when the cancer invades surrounding tissues, or metastasizes.

Radiotherapy Treatment of a disease by X-rays or by emissions from a radioactive substance.

Pap test Examination of a sample of cervical cells for cervical cancer and other abnormalities. Named after the originator of the technique, George Papanicolaou.

Ovum Egg cell. The plural is "ova."

Endometrium The innermost layer of the uterus.

Endometriosis A condition caused by the growth of endometrial tissue in the abdominal cavity, or elsewhere outside the uterus, and characterized by menstrual pain.

Hysterectomy Surgical removal of the uterus.

Complete hysterectomy Surgical removal of the ovaries, fallopian tubes, cervix, and uterus.

HYSTERECTOMY   A **hysterectomy** may be performed when women develop cancer of the uterus, ovaries, or cervix or have other diseases that cause pain or excessive uterine bleeding. An estimated 1.8 million Canadian women have had hysterectomies (Canadian Women's Health Network, 2010). A hysterectomy may be partial or complete. A **complete hysterectomy** involves surgical removal of the ovaries, fallopian tubes, cervix, and uterus. It's usually performed to reduce the risk of cancer's spreading throughout the reproductive system. A partial hysterectomy removes the uterus but not the ovaries and fallopian tubes. Sparing the ovaries allows the woman to continue to ovulate and produce adequate quantities of female sex hormones.

The hysterectomy can relieve symptoms associated with various gynaecological disorders, improving quality of life for many women (Duru et al., 2012). Many gynaecologists, however, believe hysterectomy is often recommended inappropriately, before necessary diagnostic steps are taken or when less radical medical interventions might successfully treat the problems (Belden, 2011; Canadian Women's Health Network, 2010).

Brotto et al. (2008) have conducted research on the sexual difficulties women experience after hysterectomy. About half of those studied reported significant sexual difficulties, and most were highly distressed about these issues. Brotto has developed a brief educational program that is effective in improving the sexual functioning and enjoyment of women who have had hysterectomies.

The Fallopian Tubes

Fallopian tubes Tubes that extend from the upper uterus toward the ovaries, conducting ova to the uterus. Named after the Italian anatomist Gabriel Fallopius, who is credited with their discovery.

The two uterine tubes, called **fallopian tubes**, are about 10 centimetres in length and extend from the upper end of the uterus toward the ovaries. (See Figure 3.6.)

Ova pass through the fallopian tubes on their way to the uterus. The fallopian tubes are not inert passageways; they help nourish and conduct ova. The form of sterilization called tubal ligation ties off the fallopian tubes so ova cannot pass through them to become fertilized.

Ectopic pregnancy A pregnancy in which the fertilized ovum implants outside the uterus, usually in the fallopian tube.

In an **ectopic pregnancy**, the fertilized ovum implants outside the uterus, most often in the fallopian tube, where fertilization has occurred. Ectopic pregnancies can eventually burst fallopian tubes, causing haemorrhaging and death. Ectopic pregnancies are thus terminated before the tube ruptures. They are not easily recognized, however, because their symptoms—a missed menstrual period, abdominal pain, and irregular bleeding—suggest many conditions. Any of these symptoms is an excellent reason to consult a gynaecologist.

The Ovaries

Ovaries Almond-shaped organs that produce ova and the hormones oestrogen and progesterone. These hormones are part of the endocrine system.

Oestrogen A generic term for female sex hormones (including estradiol, estriol, estrone, and others) or synthetic compounds that promote the development of female sex characteristics and regulate the menstrual cycle.

Progesterone A steroid hormone that stimulates proliferation of the endometrium and is involved in regulation of the menstrual cycle. Progesterone is secreted by the corpus luteum or prepared synthetically.

Follicle A capsule within an ovary, containing an ovum.

The two **ovaries** are almond-shaped organs about four centimetres long. They lie on either side of the uterus, which they're attached to by ovarian ligaments. The ovaries produce ova (egg cells) and the female sex hormones **oestrogen** and **progesterone**. Oestrogen is a generic term for several hormones (such as estradiol, estriol, and estrone) that promote the changes of puberty and regulate the menstrual cycle. Progesterone, too, has multiple functions, including regulation of the menstrual cycle and preparation of the uterus for pregnancy by stimulating development of the endometrium (uterine lining). Oestrogen and progesterone levels vary with the phases of the menstrual cycle.

The human female is born with all the ova she will ever have—about two million—but they're immature in form. About 400 000 of these survive into puberty, each contained in the ovary within a thin capsule, or **follicle**. During a woman's reproductive years, from puberty to menopause, only 400 or so ripened ova, typically one per month, are released by their rupturing follicles for possible fertilization.

OVARIAN CANCER   In 2013, about 2600 diagnosed cases of ovarian cancer and 1700 deaths resulting from it occurred in Canada (Canadian Cancer Society, 2013c). Ovarian cancer most often strikes women between the ages of 40 and 70. It ranks as the fourth leading cancer killer of women, behind lung cancer, breast cancer, and colon cancer. Women most at risk are those whose blood relatives, especially first-degree relatives (mothers, sisters, daughters), have had ovarian or breast cancer. Other risk factors are high body weight and never having given birth.

Early detection is the key to fighting ovarian cancer. When it is detected before spreading beyond the ovary, the five-year survival rate is 89% to 99%, depending on how aggressive the cancer is. When it has metastasized, the survival rate drops to as low as 18% (American Cancer Society, 2012c). Unfortunately, ovarian cancer is often silent in its early stages, showing no obvious signs or symptoms. The most common sign is enlargement of the abdomen, which is caused by the accumulation of fluid. Periodic, complete pelvic examinations are important. The Pap test, which is useful in detecting cervical cancer, does not reveal ovarian cancer.

Surgery, radiation therapy, and drug therapy are treatment options. Surgery usually includes the removal of one or both ovaries, the uterus, and the fallopian tubes.

The Pelvic Examination

During a pelvic examination, the physician first examines the woman externally for irritations, swellings, abnormal vaginal discharges, and clitoral adhesions. The physician normally inserts a speculum to help inspect the cervix and vaginal walls for discharges (which can be signs of infection), discolouration, lesions, or growths. This examination is typically followed by a Pap test, to look for cervical cancer. A sample of vaginal discharge may also be taken to test for the sexually transmitted infection gonorrhoea.

To take a Pap smear, the physician holds the vaginal walls open with a plastic or (prewarmed!) metal speculum, then scrapes a sample of cells (a "smear") from the cervix with a wooden spatula (see Figure 3.8). A woman should not douche prior to a Pap test or schedule a test during menstruation, because douche and blood confound analysis of the smear.

The speculum exam is normally followed by a bimanual vaginal exam, in which the physician inserts the index and middle fingers of one hand into the vagina and palpates (touches) the lower part of the abdomen with the other hand from the outside. The physician uses this technique to examine the location, shape, size, and movability of the internal sex organs, searching for abnormal growths and symptoms of other problems. Palpation may be somewhat uncomfortable, but physical discomfort is usually mild. Severe pain is a sign that something is wrong. A woman should not try to be brave and hide such discomfort from the examiner.

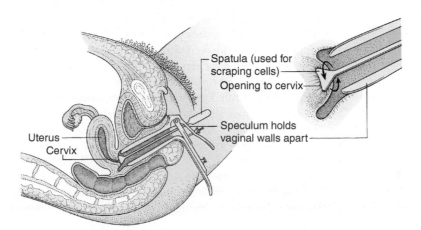

Figure 3.8   Use of the speculum and spatula during a pelvic examination.
The speculum is used to hold the vaginal walls apart, while the spatula is used to gently scrape cells from the cervix. The Pap test screens for cervical cancer and other abnormalities.

It's normal for a woman to be anxious if she's never had a pelvic exam or she's visiting a new doctor. Talking about it with the examiner often relieves psychological discomfort. If the doctor isn't reassuring, the woman should feel free to consult another doctor. She should not forgo the pelvic examination itself—it's essential for early detection of problems.

The Female Breasts

Some college women recall:

> I was very excited about my breast development. It was a big competition to see who was wearing a bra in elementary school. When I began wearing one, I also liked wearing see-through blouses so everyone would know. ...

> My breasts were very late in developing. This brought me a lot of grief from my male peers. I just dreaded situations like going to the beach or showering in the locker room. ...

> All through junior high and high school I felt unhappy about being overendowed. I felt just too uncomfortable in sweaters—there was so much to reveal, and I was always sure that the only reason boys liked me was because of my bustline. ...

> —Morrison et al., 1980, pp. 66–70

In some cultures, the breasts are viewed merely as biological instruments for feeding infants. In our culture, however, breasts have taken on such erotic significance that a woman's self-esteem may become linked to her bustline.

The breasts are **secondary sex characteristics**. That is, like the rounding of the hips, they distinguish women from men but are not directly involved in reproduction. Each breast contains 15 to 20 clusters of milk-producing **mammary glands**. (See Figure 3.9.) Each gland opens through its own duct at the nipple. The mammary glands are separated by soft, fatty tissue. It's the amount of this fatty tissue—not the amount of glandular tissue—that largely determines breast size. Women vary little in their amount of glandular tissue, so breast size does not determine how much milk they can produce.

The nipple, which lies in the centre of the **areola**, contains smooth muscle fibres that contract to make the nipple erect. The areola, or area surrounding the nipple, darkens during pregnancy and remains darker after delivery. Oil-producing glands in the areola help lubricate the nipple during breastfeeding. Milk ducts conduct milk from the mammary glands through the nipple. The nipple is richly endowed with nerve endings, so stimulation heightens sexual arousal for many women.

Figure 3.10 shows typical variations in the size and shape of the adult female breast. The sensitivity of the breasts to sexual stimulation is unrelated to their size. Small breasts may have as many nerve endings as large breasts, but they're more densely packed. The breasts vary in sensitivity with the phases of the menstrual cycle. Some women appear less responsive to breast stimulation than others, though they may learn to enjoy breast stimulation during sexual activity in a relaxed atmosphere.

Secondary sex characteristics Traits that distinguish women from men but are not directly involved in reproduction.

Mammary glands Milk-secreting glands.

Areola The dark ring on the breast that encircles the nipple.

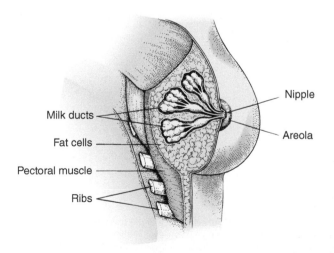

Milk ducts

Fat cells

Pectoral muscle

Ribs

Nipple

Areola

Figure 3.9   The breast of an adult woman.
This drawing reveals the structures underlying the breast, including milk ducts and fat cells.

A World of Diversity

THE STRONG BREAST REVOLUTION

There's a fascination with female breasts in Western society. Among the two most viewed episodes of Discovery Channel Canada's series *The Sex Files* were those on female breasts.

Under the direction of drama professor Kim Renders, female University of Guelph students collectively created a play, largely based on their own experiences, designed to educate and entertain. *The Strong Breast Revolution* explored breastfeeding, breast cancer, breasts and sexuality, and women's anxieties about their breasts, as well as the pleasure they give.

The Strong Breast Revolution

The Strong Breast Revolution.
In a play written by female University of Guelph students, actors went topless to show that women should feel proud of their breasts.

Breast Cancer

Among Canadian women, breast cancer is the most commonly diagnosed cancer and the second-leading cause of cancer-related death (Canadian Cancer Society, 2013d). In 2013, there were an estimated 23 800 new diagnosed cases of breast cancer and 5000 deaths among women in Canada (Canadian Cancer Society, 2013d). The five-year survival rate for women whose breast cancers have not spread beyond the breast is about 93%, up from nearly 80% in the 1950s (American Cancer Society, 2012d). The five-year survival rate drops to about 80% if the cancer has spread to the surrounding region, and drops further to about 15% if it has spread to more distant sites.

CRITICAL THINKING QUESTIONS

The biological function of female breasts is to feed infants. Why do breasts carry such a high degree of erotic significance in Western culture?

Figure 3.10 Typical variations in adult female breasts.
Breast size and shape have little bearing on ability to produce milk or on sensitivity to sexual stimulation. Breasts have become highly eroticized in our culture.

Sources: Left: Dr. P. Marazzi/ Science Source/Middle and right: Custom Medical Stock Photo

RISK FACTORS   According to the U.S. National Cancer Institute (2012a), the following factors increase the risk of breast cancer:

- Family history of breast cancer, especially if a mother, sister, or daughter has been diagnosed with it
- Inherited changes in certain genes, including the BRCA1 and BRCA2 genes (although this risk factor likely accounts for no more than 10% of cases)
- Higher breast density
- First menstrual period before the age of 12, menopause after age 55, delayed childbearing, and never having children—all of which increase lifetime exposure to oestrogen
- Long-term use of menopausal hormone therapy (especially women who have used a combination of oestrogen and progestin for more than five years)

Cysts Saclike structures filled with fluid or diseased material.

Benign Doing little or no harm.

Malignant Lethal; causing or likely to cause death.

Mammography A special type of X-ray test that detects cancerous lumps in the breast.

DETECTION AND TREATMENT   Women with breast cancer have lumps in the breast, but most lumps in the breasts are not cancerous. Most are either **cysts** or **benign** tumours. Breast cancer involves lumps in the breast that are **malignant**.

Breast cancer may be detected in various ways, including, mammography, magnetic resonance imaging (MRI), breast self-examination, and physical examination by a doctor. **Mammography** allows the detection—and treatment—of tiny, highly curable cancers before they can be felt by touch. Mammography and MRI combined is a kind of X-ray technique that detects cancerous lumps in the breast. There is some debate on the value of mammography, but all women should discuss it with their doctors. The Canadian Cancer Society recommends that all 50- to 69-year-old women should have mammograms every two years. Younger and older women should ask their doctors whether this schedule is appropriate for them.

The practice of breast self-examination is also controversial. After reviewing the results of teaching about self-examination, the Canadian Task Force on Preventive Health Care concluded in 2011 that there was no evidence that self-examination benefits women. As of 2007, the Canadian Cancer Society no longer recommended that women conduct monthly breast self-examinations. However, some physicians continue to believe that breast self-examination can play a role in cancer prevention. Women will have to decide, in consultation with their doctors, whether they wish to examine their own breasts for the purpose of detecting possible cancers.

Early detection and treatment reduce the risk of mortality. The sooner cancer is detected, the less likely it is to spread to critical organs. Smaller cancerous lumps can often be removed by **lumpectomy**, which spares the breast. More advanced cancers are likely to be treated by **mastectomy**, which is complete or partial removal of the breast.

Lumpectomy Surgical removal of a (usually cancerous) lump from the breast.

Mastectomy Surgical removal of all or part of a breast.

Many drugs are used to treat breast cancer, and others are in the research pipeline. Tamoxifen, for example, locks into the oestrogen receptors of breast cancer cells, blocking oestrogen's stimulation of the cells to grow and proliferate. Tamoxifen also increases the risks of uterine cancer and of blood clots in the lungs, however, and has other side effects, especially among women over 50. Raloxifene is another drug that's been shown to reduce the risk of breast cancer (Cummings et al., 1999), but apparently without the side effects associated with Tamoxifen.

Many women who undergo mastectomies have surgical breast implants to replace their missing tissue. Others have breast implants to augment their breast sizes. In 2006, after conducting a thorough review of the research evidence, Health Canada concluded that silicone gel implants were safe, and approved their use. These implants had previously been restricted, because of safety concerns. The issue remains controversial.

The Menstrual Cycle

Menstruation is the bleeding that results from the shedding of the uterine lining (endometrium) when a reproductive cycle has not led to fertilization of an ovum. The human menstrual cycle averages 28 days in length.

The cycle is regulated by the hormones oestrogen and progesterone. It can be divided into four phases. The first phase, the proliferative phase, follows menstruation. During this phase, oestrogen levels increase, causing the ripening of perhaps 10 to 20 ova (egg cells) within their follicles and the proliferation of endometrial tissue in the uterus. During the second phase of the cycle, oestrogen reaches peak blood levels, and **ovulation** occurs. Normally only one ovum reaches maturity and is released by an ovary during ovulation.

The third phase of the cycle—the secretory, or luteal, phase—begins right after ovulation, and continues through the beginning of the next cycle. The term "luteal phase" derives from "corpus luteum," the name given to a follicle that has released an ovum. The **corpus luteum** functions as an **endocrine gland**, producing large amounts of progesterone and oestrogen. Progesterone causes the endometrium to thicken, so it can support an embryo if fertilization occurs. If the ovum goes unfertilized, the oestrogen and progesterone levels plummet. These falloffs trigger the fourth phase, the menstrual phase, which leads to the beginning of a new cycle.

Ovulation may not occur in every menstrual cycle. Anovulatory ("without ovulation") cycles are most common in the years just after **menarche**. They may become frequent again in the years prior to menopause, but they may also occur irregularly among women in their twenties and thirties.

Although the menstrual cycle averages 28 days, variations are common from woman to woman, and from month to month in the same woman. Girls' cycles are often irregular for a few years after menarche, but later assume reasonably regular patterns. Variations from cycle to cycle tend to occur during the proliferative phase that precedes ovulation. That is, menstruation tends to follow ovulation reliably by about 14 days. Variations of more than two days in the post-ovulation period are rare. Although hormones regulate the menstrual cycle, psychological factors can influence the secretion of hormones. Stress can delay or halt menstruation.

Regulation of the Menstrual Cycle

The menstrual cycle involves finely tuned relationships between structures in the brain—the **hypothalamus** and the **pituitary gland**—and the ovaries and uterus. All of these structures are parts of the endocrine system, which means they secrete chemicals called **hormones** directly into the bloodstream.

Several hormones play important roles in sexual and reproductive functions. The gonads—the **testes** (or testicles) in the male and the ovaries in the female— secrete sex hormones directly into the bloodstream. The female gonads produce the sex hormones oestrogen and progesterone. The male gonads produce the male sex hormone **testosterone**. Males and females also produce sex hormones characteristic of the other sex, but in relatively small amounts.

The hypothalamus is a pea-sized structure in the front part of the brain. It's involved in regulating many states of motivation, including hunger, thirst, aggression, and sex. The pituitary gland lies below the hypothalamus, at the base of the brain. Because many pituitary secretions regulate other endocrine glands, the pituitary has also been called the master gland. The pituitary gland produces gonadotropins (literally, "that which feeds the gonads"), called follicle-stimulating hormone (FSH) and luteinizing hormone (LH), which stimulate the ovaries and play a key role in regulating the menstrual cycle.

Ovulation The process by which a mature ovarian follicle ruptures and releases an ovum.

Corpus luteum An ovarian follicle that has released an ovum. The corpus luteum remains in existence only if pregnancy begins.

Endocrine gland A gland that secretes a hormone directly into the blood, rather than through a duct. Examples include the thyroid, adrenal, and pituitary glands, as well as the ovaries and testes.

Menarche ("men-AR-kee") The first menstrual period.

Hypothalamus A bundle of neural cell bodies involved in regulating body temperature, motivation, and emotion. It's located near the centre of the brain.

Pituitary gland The gland that secretes growth hormone, prolactin, oxytocin, and other hormones.

Hormone A substance secreted by an endocrine gland to regulate various body functions.

Testes The male gonads.

Testosterone The male sex hormone that fosters development of male sex characteristics and is connected with the sex drive.

A World of Diversity

HISTORICAL AND CROSS-CULTURAL PERSPECTIVES ON MENSTRUATION

In Peru, women speak of a "visit from Uncle Pepe," whereas in Samoa, menstruation is referred to as "the boogie man." One of the more common epithets for menstruation is "the curse." The Fulani of Upper Volta in Africa use a term that translates "to see dirt." Nationalism also rises to the call, with some nations blaming "the curse" on their historical enemies. The French once dubbed menstruation "the English" and its onset "the English are coming."

It is a common folk belief that menstruating women are contaminated. Men may thus avoid contact with menstruating women. To prevent their contaminating others, menstruating women in tribal societies have been dispatched to huts on the fringe of the village. In the traditional Navajo Native American culture, for instance,

menstruating women would be consigned to huts that were set apart from other living quarters. In many Islamic societies, the menstrual flow is considered unclean, and menstruating women are not permitted to pray or to enter a mosque.

Women in industrialized nations are not consigned to special huts, but throughout the history of Western culture, menstruation has been seen as unclean, contaminating, and sometimes even magical.

The ancient Romans believed that menstrual blood soured wine and killed crops. In 77 CE, the Roman Pliny the Elder summed up Roman misbeliefs about menstrual blood in his *Natural History*:

Contact with it turns new wine sour, crops touched by it become barren, grafts die, seeds in gardens are dried up, the fruit of trees falls off . . . [The] edge of steel and the gleam of

ivory are dulled, hives of bees die, even bronze and iron are at once seized by rust, and a horrible smell fills the air; to taste it drives dogs mad and infects their bites with an incurable poison.

Ancient societies—and some contemporary ones—have limited understanding of bodily processes, or else they rely on tradition more than science. Science teaches that there is no medical basis for isolating menstruating women or avoiding sex during menstruation.

We might laugh off these misconceptions as folly and ignorance, if it were not for their profound effect on women. Women who believe the myths about menstruation may see themselves as unclean and endure anxiety, depression, and lowered self-esteem. Negative cultural beliefs concerning menstruation may also exacerbate menstrual distress.

Phases of the Menstrual Cycle

As we've noted, the menstrual cycle has four phases—the proliferative, ovulatory, secretory, and menstrual stages (see Figure 3.11). It might seem logical that a new cycle begins with the first day of menstrual flow, since this is the most clearly identifiable event of the cycle. Many women begin to count the days of the menstrual cycle at the onset of menstruation. Biologically speaking, however, menstruation is really the culmination of the cycle. In fact, the cycle begins with the end of menstruation and the initiation of a series of biological events that lead to maturation of an immature ovum in preparation for ovulation and possible fertilization.

Proliferative phase The first phase of the menstrual cycle, which begins with the end of menstruation and lasts about 9 or 10 days. During this phase, the endometrium proliferates.

THE PROLIFERATIVE PHASE   The first phase, the **proliferative phase**, begins with the end of menstruation and lasts for about 9 or 10 days of an average 28-day cycle (see Figure 3.11). During this phase the endometrium develops, or proliferates. This phase is also known as the pre-ovulatory or follicular phase, because it's when certain ovarian follicles mature and the ovaries prepare for ovulation.

Ovulatory phase The second stage of the menstrual cycle. This is when a follicle ruptures and releases a mature ovum.

THE OVULATORY PHASE   During ovulation, or the **ovulatory phase**, a **Graafian follicle** ruptures and releases a mature ovum near (but not into) a fallopian tube. The other ripening follicles degenerate and are harmlessly reabsorbed

Graafian follicle A mature ovarian follicle that ruptures to discharge an ovum.

Surface of endometrium is sloughed off; bleeding occurs

Menstrual phase 5 days

Proliferative phase 9 days

Estrogens increase

Egg develops and endometrium proliferates

Ovulatory phase

Estrogens reach peak level in blood, causing ovary to release egg

Estrogens and progesterone decrease suddenly

Secretory phase 14 days

Endometrium thickens; secretion and blood supply increase due to follicle's manufacture of progesterone

Figure 3.11 The four phases of the menstrual cycle. The menstrual cycle consists of the proliferative, ovulatory, secretory (luteal), and menstrual phases.

by the body. Occasionally, two ova mature and are released during ovulation, and if both are fertilized, fraternal (non-identical) twins develop. Identical twins develop when one fertilized ovum divides into two separate **zygotes.**

Ovulation is set into motion when oestrogen production reaches a critical level. A woman's basal body temperature, measured by oral or rectal thermometer, dips slightly at ovulation and rises by about 0.5°C on the day following ovulation. Many women use this information to help them conceive or avoid conceiving.

Zygote A fertilized ovum (egg cell).

THE SECRETORY PHASE The phase following ovulation is called the post-ovulatory or **secretory phase.** Some people refer to it as the luteal phase, which reflects the name given to the ruptured Graafian follicle—the corpus luteum.

Levels of progesterone and oestrogen peak at around the twentieth or twenty-first day of an average cycle. These hormones cause the glands in the endometrium to secrete nutrients that will sustain a fertilized ovum implanted in the uterine wall.

If implantation does not occur, the corpus luteum decomposes. After its decomposition, levels of oestrogen and progesterone fall precipitously.

Secretory phase The third phase of the menstrual cycle, following the ovulatory phase. Also referred to as the luteal phase, after the corpus luteum, which begins to secrete large amounts of progesterone and oestrogen after ovulation.

THE MENSTRUAL PHASE During the **menstrual phase,** the uterine lining (endometrium) is sloughed off into a menstrual flow. This occurs when oestrogen and progesterone levels decline to the point where they can no longer sustain the uterine lining, and the lining disintegrates. Menstruation itself is the passing of the lining through the cervix and vagina. Extremely heavy or prolonged (more than a week) menstrual bleeding may reflect health problems and should be discussed with a health care provider.

Prior to 1933, women generally used external sanitary napkins or pads to absorb the menstrual flow. In that year, **tampons** were introduced, altering the habits of millions of women. When they use tampons while menstruating, women can swim without concern, wear more revealing or comfortable apparel, and feel generally less burdened. Questions have arisen about whether tampons cause or exacerbate infections such as toxic shock syndrome (TSS), which is sometimes fatal. Signs of TSS include fever, headache, sore throat, vomiting, diarrhoea, muscle aches, rash, and dizziness. Peeling skin, disorientation, and a plunge in blood pressure may follow. Toxic shock syndrome is caused by the *Staphylococcus aureus* ("staph") bacterium, which is most likely to over breed when highly absorbent tampons are left in place for many hours. As a result, many women now use regular rather than superabsorbent tampons. Others change their tampons three or four times a day, or alternate them with sanitary napkins.

Menstrual phase The fourth phase of the menstrual cycle, when the endometrium is sloughed off in the menstrual flow.

Tampon A cylindrical plug of cotton that's inserted into the vagina and left in place to absorb menstrual fluid. From a French word meaning "plug."

Sex During Menstruation

Many couples continue to engage in sex during menstruation, but others abstain (Schneiderwind-Skibbe et al., 2007). Some people abstain because of religious prohibitions. Others express concern about the "fuss" or the "mess" of the menstrual flow. Despite traditional attitudes that associate menstruation with uncleanliness, there is no evidence that intercourse during menstruation is physically harmful to either partner. Ironically, menstrual coitus may be helpful to the woman. The uterine contractions that occur during orgasm may help relieve cramping by dispelling blood congestion. Orgasm achieved through masturbation may have the same effect.

Women may be sexually aroused at any time during the menstrual cycle. The preponderance of the research evidence, however, points to a peak in sexual desire in women around the time of ovulation.

Sexual behaviour patterns during the phases of the menstrual cycle seem to reflect personal decisions, not hormone fluctuations (although it may be argued that hormonal fluctuations influence sexual decision making). Some couples decide to increase their frequency of coitus at ovulation, to optimize their chances of conceiving; others may abstain during menstruation, because of religious beliefs or beliefs linking menses with uncleanliness. Some may also increase their sexual activity preceding menstruation, to compensate for anticipated abstinence during menses, or increase sexual activity afterward, to make up for deprivation. Among female students at the University of Waterloo, being comfortable with one's sexuality in general was associated with being comfortable with menstruation. Women who engaged in intercourse during menstruation were more likely also to be aroused by a wide diversity of sexual activities (Rempel & Baumgartner, 2003).

Menopause

Menopause The cessation of menstruation.

Perimenopause The years leading up to menopause, between the beginning of the climacteric and the cessation of menstruation.

Climacteric A long-term process, including menopause, that involves the gradual decline in the reproductive capacity of the ovaries.

Menopause, or the "change of life," is the cessation of menstruation. Menopause is a process that most commonly occurs between the ages of 46 and 50 and lasts for about two years, though it may begin at any time between the ages of 35 and 60. There's at least one case of a woman who became pregnant at 61. **Perimenopause** refers to the beginning of menopause and is usually characterized by 3 to 11 months of amenorrhea (lack of menstruation) or irregular periods. Perimenopause ends with menopause.

Menopause is a specific event in a long-term process known as the **climacteric** ("critical period"), the gradual decline in the reproductive capacity of the ovaries. The climacteric generally lasts for about 15 years, from ages 45 to 60 or so. Beginning around the age of 35, many women's menstrual cycles shorten from an average of 28 days to about 25 days by age 40, and to about 23 days by their mid-40s. By the end of their 40s, many women experience erratic cycles, with some periods close together and others missed.

In menopause, the pituitary gland continues to pour normal levels of FSH and LH into the bloodstream, but for reasons that aren't well understood, the ovaries gradually lose their capacity to respond. They no longer ripen egg cells or produce the sex hormones oestrogen and progesterone.

The deficit in oestrogen may lead to a number of unpleasant perimenopausal sensations, including night sweats, hot flashes (suddenly feeling hot), and hot flushes (suddenly looking reddened) (Hunter, 2011). Hot flashes and flushes may alternate with cold sweats, during which a woman feels suddenly cold and clammy. Anyone who has experienced cold feet or hands as a result of anxiety or fear will understand how dramatic the shifting patterns of blood flow can be. Hot flashes and flushes stem largely from waves of blood vessel dilation across the face and upper body. These sensations reflect vasomotor instability, or disruptions in the body mechanisms that dilate and constrict the blood vessels to maintain an even body temperature.

Additional signs of oestrogen deficiency include dizziness, headache, joint pain, tingling in the hands or feet, burning or itchy skin, and heart palpitation. The skin usually becomes drier. There's some loss of breast tissue, as well as a decrease in vaginal lubrication during sexual arousal. Women may also encounter sleep problems, such as awakening more frequently at night and having difficulty falling back to sleep. Many perimenopausal women also experience migraine headaches (Nappi & Nappi, 2012).

HORMONE REPLACEMENT THERAPY (HRT)   Some women who experience severe physical symptoms are helped by **hormone replacement therapy (HRT)**, which typically consists of synthetic (but occasionally naturally sourced) oestrogen and progesterone. These synthetic hormones are used to offset the loss of their naturally occurring counterparts. HRT may help reduce the hot flushes and other symptoms brought about by hormonal deficiencies during menopause (Hunter, 2011).

In 2002, a major controversy over the use of HRT erupted in Canada and many other countries when researchers conducting the Women's Health Initiative study in the United States ended the project after three years instead of eight (the intended length of the study) because they'd found an increase in the incidence of breast cancer among women taking HRT. Currently, the Canadian Cancer Society recommends that women avoid taking HRT unless they're experiencing severe menopausal symptoms that haven't responded to other treatment.

Because of the overall increased health risks, many women may decide not to use HRT. Despite the risks, though, some women use HRT because they feel their quality of life is better, with fewer menopausal symptoms such as hot flashes, night sweats, and vaginal dryness. Women with severe symptoms are therefore advised to explore the health benefits and risks of HRT with their doctors.

Women might also consider alternatives. Selective serotonin reuptake inhibitors (SSRIs) such as Lexapro, Zocor, and Prozac may also help (Utain, 2012). Women using SSRIs to treat hot flashes usually take half the dose used to treat depression, which is their main use. Vaginal dryness can be treated with oestrogens that are used locally—that is, placed in the vagina rather than into the bloodstream, as hormones usually are. Creams (e.g., Estrace), suppositories (e.g., Vagifem), and plastic rings (e.g., Estring) are available for this purpose.

It's important to put the symptoms of menopause into a balanced perspective. Most women cope quite well with menopause, and discover ways of minimizing unpleasant symptoms. Many are quite relieved that they no longer have to worry about the possibility of unplanned pregnancy. Not worrying about contraception can make sexual relationships more enjoyable, and most women continue to have active and pleasurable sex lives after menopause.

Menstrual Difficulties

Although menstruation is a natural biological process, the majority of women experience some discomfort prior to or during menstruation (Studd & Nappi, 2012). About 30% of Canadian women report that they usually experience extremely painful menstrual periods (Fisher, Boroditsky, & Morris, 2004b). The menstrual difficulties we explore in this section include dysmenorrhoea, amenorrhoea, and premenstrual syndrome (PMS).

Dysmenorrhoea

Pain or discomfort during menstruation, known as **dysmenorrhoea**, is the most common type of menstrual difficulty. Most women at some time have at least mild menstrual pain or discomfort. Pelvic cramps are the most common manifestation

Hormone replacement therapy (HRT) Postmenopausal replacement of naturally occurring oestrogen or oestrogen and progesterone with synthetic (or sometimes natural) equivalents.

Dysmenorrhoea Pain or discomfort during menstruation.

Primary dysmenorrhoea
Menstrual pain or discomfort that occurs in the absence of known organic problems.

Secondary dysmenorrhoea
Menstrual pain or discomfort caused by identified organic problems.

Prostaglandins Hormones that cause muscle fibres in the uterine wall to contract, as during labour.

Mastalgia A swelling of the breasts that sometimes causes premenstrual discomfort.

of dysmenorrhoea. They may be accompanied by headache, backache, nausea, and a bloated feeling. Women who develop severe cases usually do so within a few years of menarche. **Primary dysmenorrhoea** is menstrual pain or discomfort in the absence of known organic pathology. **Secondary dysmenorrhoea** is menstrual difficulty caused by (or secondary to) an identified organic problem. Endometriosis, pelvic inflammatory disease, and ovarian cysts are just a few of the organic disorders that can give rise to secondary dysmenorrhoea.

Menstrual cramps appear to result from uterine spasms that may be brought about by copious secretion of hormones called **prostaglandins**. Prostaglandins apparently cause muscle fibres in the uterine wall to contract, as during labour. Most contractions go unnoticed, but powerful, persistent contractions are not only discomfiting in themselves, they may temporarily deprive the uterus of oxygen, which is another source of distress. Women with more intense menstrual discomfort apparently produce higher quantities of prostaglandins than other women. Prostaglandin-inhibiting drugs such as ibuprofen, indomethacin, and aspirin are often helpful. Menstrual pain may also be secondary to endometriosis.

Pelvic pressure and bloating may be traced to pelvic oedema—the congestion of fluid in the pelvic region. Fluid retention can lead to a gain of several pounds, sensations of heaviness, and **mastalgia**, a swelling of the breasts that sometimes causes premenstrual discomfort. Orgasm (through coitus or masturbation) can help relieve menstrual discomfort by reducing the pelvic congestion that spawns bloating and pressure. Orgasm may also increase the menstrual flow and shorten this phase of the cycle.

Amenorrhea

Amenorrhea Absence of menstruation.

Primary amenorrhea
Absence of menstruation in a woman who has never menstruated.

Secondary amenorrhea
Absence of menstruation in a woman who has previously menstruated.

Anorexia nervosa A psychological disorder characterized by a desire to lose weight by refusing to eat.

Premenstrual syndrome (PMS) A combination of physical and psychological symptoms (such as anxiety, depression, irritability, weight gain from fluid retention, and abdominal discomfort) that regularly afflicts many women during the four- to six-day interval that precedes their menses each month.

Amenorrhea, the absence of menstruation, is a primary sign of infertility. **Primary amenorrhea** is the absence of menstruation in a woman who has not menstruated at all by about the age of 16 or 17. **Secondary amenorrhea** is delayed or absent menstruation in a woman who's had regular periods in the past.

Amenorrhea has various causes, including abnormalities in the structures of the reproductive system, hormonal abnormalities, growths such as cysts and tumours, and psychological problems such as stress. Amenorrhea is normal during pregnancy and following menopause. Amenorrhea is also a symptom of the eating disorder **anorexia nervosa**.

Premenstrual Syndrome (PMS)

Premenstrual syndrome (PMS) is the combination of biological and psychological symptoms that may affect a woman during the four- to six-day interval that precedes her menses each month. For many women, premenstrual symptoms persist during menstruation. The great majority of cases involve mild to moderate levels of discomfort. PMS is not unique to our culture.

Although 61% of Canadian women experience premenstrual syndrome (Fisher, Boroditsky, & Morris, 2004b), research on PMS has been limited and concerned only with its psychological aspects. Only a generation ago, PMS was seen as something a woman had to put up with. No longer. Today there are many options to reduce the effects of PMS. These include exercise, dietary control (e.g., eating several small meals a day, rather than two or three large meals, limiting salt and sugar, and taking vitamin supplements), hormone treatments (usually progesterone), and medications that reduce anxiety or increase the amount of serotonin in the nervous system.

Some feminists have objected to the view that PMS and menopause are problems that require medical treatment. Leonore Tiefer (2001), in particular, argues that pharmaceutical companies have overly medicalized various aspects of female sexuality, such as PMS and menopause, for the sake of increasing profits.

Applied Knowledge

HOW TO HANDLE MENSTRUAL DISCOMFORT

Menstrual problems were once erroneously attributed to women's "hysterical" nature. This is nonsense. Menstrual problems largely appear to reflect hormonal variations or chemical fluctuations in the brain during the menstrual cycle. Researchers have not yet fully identified all of the causal elements and patterns, but their lack of knowledge does not mean women who have menstrual problems are "hysterical." Most women experience some degree of menstrual discomfort.

If you experience persistent menstrual distress, you may profit from the suggestions listed below. Researchers are exploring the effectiveness of these techniques in controlled studies. For now, you might consider running a personal experiment. Adopt the techniques that sound right for you—all of them, if you wish.

- Keep a menstrual calendar, so you can systematically track your menstrual symptoms and identify patterns.
- Develop strategies for dealing with days when you experience the greatest distress—strategies that enhance your pleasure and minimize the stress you feel. Activities that distract you from your menstrual discomfort may be helpful. Go see a movie or get into that novel you've been meaning to read.
- Ask yourself whether you harbour any self-defeating attitudes toward menstruation that might be compounding your distress. Do close relatives or friends see menstruation as an illness, a time of "pollution," a "dirty thing"? Have you adopted any of these attitudes—if not verbally, then in ways that affect your behaviour, such as by restricting your social activities during your period?
- See a gynaecologist about your concerns, especially if you have severe symptoms. Severe menstrual symptoms are often secondary to medical disorders such as endometriosis and pelvic inflammatory disease (PID). Check it out.
- Develop healthful eating habits and continue them throughout your entire cycle (that means always). Consider limiting your intake of alcohol, caffeine, fats, salt, and sweets, especially during the days preceding menstruation. Research suggests that a low-fat, vegetarian diet reduces the duration of premenstrual symptoms and the duration and intensity of menstrual pain.
- Eat several smaller meals (or nutritious snacks) throughout the day, rather than a few highly filling meals.
- Try some vigorous exercise, such as jogging, swimming, bicycling, fast walking, dancing, skating, or even jumping rope. Many women find that vigorous exercise helps relieve premenstrual and menstrual discomfort. Evidence suggests that exercise relieves and possibly prevents menstrual discomfort (Daley, 2009).
- Check with your doctor about vitamin and mineral supplements such as calcium and magnesium. Vitamin B6 appears to help some women.
- Try ibuprofen (marketed as Medipren, Advil, and Motrin, for example) and other over-the-counter

Seasonale.
Women who use Seasonale contraceptives have just four periods per year.

Getty Images

medicines for cramping. Prescription drugs such as anti-anxiety medications (e.g., alprazolam) and antidepressants (selective serotonin reuptake inhibitors) may also help. Antidepressants affect neurotransmitter levels in a way that can be helpful for women with PMS. Their benefits do not mean women with PMS are depressed. Ask your doctor for a recommendation.
- Consider using oral contraceptives that reduce the number of menstrual periods. In 2007, Health Canada approved the use of Seasonale, an oral contraceptive that reduces the number of periods to four per year. The idea of eliminating menstruation is very controversial, however, and many health care professionals are worried about the possibility that it may cause unknown long-term health problems.

Male Anatomy and Physiology

Phallic symbols Images of the penis that are usually suggestive of generative power.

From the earliest foundations of Western civilization, male-dominated societies have elevated men and exalted male genitalia. The ancient Greeks carried oversized images of fish as **phallic symbols** in their Dionysian processions, which celebrated the wilder and more frenzied aspects of human sexuality. In the murky predawn light of Western civilization, humankind engaged in phallic worship.

Men held their own genitals in such high esteem that it was common courtroom practice in ancient Rome for them to swear to tell the truth with their hands on their genitals—as we swear to tell the truth in the name of God or by placing our hands on the Bible or other document. The words **"testes"** and **"testicles"** derive from the same Latin word as "testify."

Testes The male sex glands, suspended in the scrotum. They produce sperm cells and male sex hormones. The singular of "testes" is "testis."

Even today, we see evidence of pride in—indeed, veneration of—the male genitalia. Men with large genitals are accorded respect from their male peers, and sometimes adoration from female admirers. Slang describes men with large genitals as "well hung" or "hung like a bull" (or stallion).

Testicles Testes.

Given these cultural attitudes, it's not surprising that some men belittle themselves if they feel, as many do, that they're small—that is, that their penises do not measure up to some ideal. In examining male sexual anatomy and physiology, we'll attempt to sort truth from fiction.

The External Male Sex Organs

The external male sex organs include the penis and the scrotum. (See Figure 3.12.)

The Penis

Penis The male organ of sexual intercourse.

At first glance, the **penis** may seem rather simple and obvious in its structures, particularly when compared with female organs. Yet, as Figure 3.12 shows, the apparent simplicity of the penis is misleading. Much goes on below the surface.

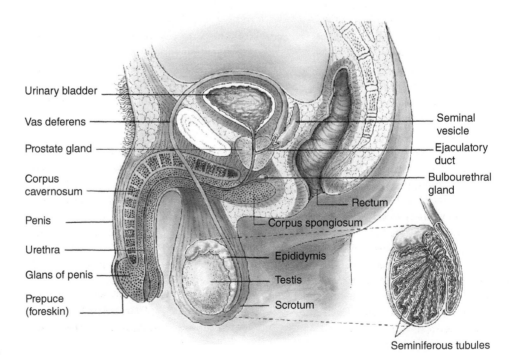

Urinary bladder
Vas deferens
Prostate gland
Corpus cavernosum
Penis
Urethra
Glans of penis
Prepuce (foreskin)

Seminal vesicle
Ejaculatory duct
Bulbourethral gland
Rectum
Corpus spongiosum
Epididymis
Testis
Scrotum

Seminiferous tubules

Figure 3.12 The male reproductive system.
The external male sex organs include the penis and the scrotum.

The penis, like the vagina, is the sex organ used in sexual intercourse. Unlike the vagina, however, the penis also serves as a conduit for urine. Both semen and urine pass out of the penis through the urethral opening. The opening is called the urethral meatus (pronounced me-ATE-us), which means "passage."

Many mammals, including dogs, have penile bones that stiffen their penises to facilitate copulation. Despite the slang term "boner," the human penis contains no bones. Nor, despite another slang term, "muscle," does the penis contain muscle tissue. However, muscles at the base of the penis, like the muscles surrounding the urethral and vaginal openings in the female, are involved in controlling urination and ejaculation.

Rather than bone or muscle, three cylinders of spongy material run the length of the penis. The two larger cylinders, the **corpora cavernosa**, lie side by side and function like the cavernous bodies in the clitoris, filling with blood and stiffening during sexual arousal. The third cylinder, the **corpus spongiosum** (spongy body), runs along the lower (ventral) surface of the penis. It contains the penile urethra, which conducts urine through the penis to the urinary opening (urethral meatus) at the tip, where the spongy body enlarges to become the glans, or head, of the penis. All three cylinders consist of spongy tissue that swells (becomes engorged) with blood during sexual arousal, resulting in erection.

The urethra is connected to the bladder, which is unrelated to reproduction and to those parts of the reproductive system that transport semen.

The glans of the penis, like the clitoral glans, is extremely sensitive to sexual stimulation. Direct, prolonged stimulation can become irritating, even painful. Some men prefer to masturbate by stroking the shaft of the penis rather than the glans. The **corona**, or coronal ridge, separates the glans from the body of the penis. After the glans, the parts of the penis men tend to find most sensitive are the corona and an area on the underside of the penis called the **frenulum**. The frenulum is a thin strip of tissue that connects the underside of the glans to the shaft. Most men find the top part of the penis to be the most sensitive part.

The base of the penis, called the **root**, extends into the pelvis. It's attached to the pelvic bones by leg-like structures, called crura, similar to those that anchor the female's clitoris. The body of the penis is called the penile **shaft**. Unlike the clitoral shaft, the penile shaft is free-swinging. Thus, when sexual excitement engorges the penis with blood, the result—erection—is obvious.

The skin of the penis is hairless and loose, allowing expansion during erection, and fixed to the penile shaft just behind the glans. In an uncircumcised male, some of the skin, like the labia minora in the female, folds over to cover part or all of the glans, just as the clitoral prepuce (hood) covers the clitoral shaft. Known as the prepuce, or **foreskin**, this penile covering consists of loose skin that freely moves over the glans. Smegma—a cheese-like, foul-smelling secretion—may accumulate below the prepuce, causing the foreskin to adhere to the glans.

CIRCUMCISION   Male **circumcision** is the surgical removal of the prepuce. (See Figure 3.13.) It has a long history as a religious rite. Jews traditionally carry out male circumcision shortly after a baby is born. Circumcision is performed as a sign of the covenant between God and the people of Abraham. Muslims also circumcise for religious reasons, although they do so some years after birth. Circumcision became widespread in North America, beginning in the second quarter of the twentieth century, because of its perceived medical benefits.

The circumcision rate for boys in Canada has declined since the 1970s, and currently stands at about 32%, although it varies from province to province (Public Health Agency of Canada, 2009). Male circumcision rates are considerably higher in the United States (57%) (McMillen, 2011). The world's highest circumcision rates are found in countries where the population is largely or exclusively Muslim.

Corpora cavernosa Two cylinders of spongy tissue in the penis that become congested with blood and stiffen during sexual arousal.

Corpus spongiosum The spongy body that runs along the bottom of the penis, contains the penile urethra, and enlarges at the tip of the penis to form the glans.

Corona The ridge that separates the glans from the body of the penis.

Frenulum The sensitive strip of tissue that connects the underside of the penile glans to the shaft.

Root The base of the penis, which extends into the pelvis.

Shaft The body of the penis, which expands as a result of vasocongestion.

Foreskin The loose skin that covers the penile glans in an uncircumcised male. It's also referred to as the "prepuce."

Circumcision Surgical removal of the foreskin of the penis.

CRITICAL THINKING QUESTIONS

Who understands their reproductive anatomy better—men or women?

Figure 3.13 Typical variations in male genitalia. The penis and scrotum vary a good deal from one man to another. The penis in the photo on the right is uncircumcised.

Sources: Left: Publiphoto/Science Source; Middle: Custom Medical Stock; Right: Dr. P. Marazzi/Science Source

In a 1996 report on circumcision, the Canadian Paediatric Society concluded that the procedure is not medically necessary and recommended against circumcision as a routine practice. Still, the Society took the view that parents should have the right to decide whether to have their infants circumcised. In light of recent research on the possible medical benefits of circumcision, the Canadian Paediatric Society began a review of its policy on male circumcision in 2009. As of early 2014, the new policy had not yet been issued.

There is evidence that circumcision has some health benefits (Tobian & Gray, 2011; Wright et al., 2012). Circumcision lessens the risk of infections of the urinary tract, including infections by the human papilloma virus (HPV) and by HIV, and even the risk of prostate cancer, whose development appears to be facilitated by infections. Randomized trials in Africa have shown that men who are circumcised are 51% to 60% less likely to be infected with HIV (Tobian & Gray, 2011). The protective effects of circumcision are likely to reflect a lower incidence of local inflammation and genital ulcers, both of which provide ports of entry for HIV, and the removal of cells in the foreskin—Langerhans cells—that are receptive to infection by HIV. Other studies have found that circumcised males are about 30% less likely to contract genital herpes (Tobian & Gray, 2011). In a study of 4000 men, men who had been circumcised were 15% less likely to develop prostate cancer than those who had not (Wright et al., 2012).

Male circumcision also has potential health benefits for *women*—that is, for the sex partners of circumcised men. Generally speaking, if a woman's male partner is less likely to have sexually transmitted infections, so is she. But more specifically, the female partners of circumcised men are 28% less likely to be infected with HPV, the virus that is connected with cervical cancer, 40% less likely to develop bacterial vaginosis, and 48% less likely to develop trichomoniasis (Tobian & Gray, 2011).

In a study of expecting parents attending prenatal classes in Saskatchewan, the reasons that parents most often gave for supporting male circumcision were hygiene (61.9%), prevention of infection/cancer (44.8%), and the father being circumcised (40.9%). The reasons most commonly given by parents for not supporting circumcision were it not being medically necessary (32.0%), the father being uncircumcised (18.8%), and concerns about bleeding or infection (15.5%) (Rediger & Muller, 2013).

Some people firmly oppose male circumcision, arguing that the procedure is painful and the child has not consented to it. From this perspective, circumcision is a violation of the infant boy's human rights. The Circumcision Information Resource Centre, a Montreal-based lobby group, seeks to ban male circumcision on infants and children in Canada, in the same way female circumcision has been made illegal. Some men are so upset over having been circumcised that they've made efforts to have their foreskins restored.

CRITICAL THINKING QUESTIONS

If you become the mother or father of a newborn baby boy in the near future, would you want him to be circumcised? For you, what would be the most important factors in making this decision?

A World of Diversity

PERSPECTIVES ON PENIS SIZE

The belief that the size of the man's penis determines his sexual prowess is based on the assumption that men with bigger penises are better equipped to satisfy a woman sexually. Some men, particularly younger men, may feel inadequate after watching pornography that often features male actors with abnormally large penises. Some may go so far as to order pills after seeing Internet and magazine ads that claim these products will cause the penis to grow substantially in size. There's no medical evidence that these products work. Moreover, the

available research suggests that many men overestimate the importance of penis size to their female partners.

In an Internet survey of 52 031 men and women, Lever, Frederick, and Peplau (2006) explored perspectives on penis size. Two thirds (66%) of men rated their penis size as average, 22% reported it as large, and 12% reported it as small. While the vast majority (85%) of women said that they were satisfied with their partner's penis size, only 55% of men reported being satisfied with the size of their own penises. In a 1998 national survey of Canadian women, the Compas polling organization asked, "What is

the ideal penis size?" Most women preferred either an average-sized (37%) or somewhat larger than average penis (45%). Hardly any preferred a much larger than average (3%) or a somewhat smaller than average penis (4%). Twelve percent of the women expressed no preference.

The psychiatrist Lawrence Blum (2012) aptly sums up the irony in men's preoccupation about their penis size when he observes that " ... while men are busy imagining that women want them to have bigger penises, the women would prefer that the men be self-confident enough not to be concerned about penis size" (p. 26).

The perception that circumcised men experience less sexual sensation than uncircumcised men is controversial. One study by Canadian and American researchers (Payne et al., 2007) found no difference between these groups in terms of penile sensation. However, there is also some evidence that circumcision may reduce sensation because the foreskin is rich in nerve endings (Smith et al., 2010). In Australia, Richters et al. (2006) found that uncircumcised men were more likely to experience occasional physical pain during intercourse.

Physicians once agreed that circumcision was the treatment of choice for **phimosis**, a condition in which it's difficult to retract the foreskin from the glans. Today, only a small minority of males with phimosis are treated with circumcision.

PENIS SIZE   In our culture, penis size is sometimes seen as a measure of a man's masculinity and ability to please a sex partner. See "A World of Diversity: Perspectives on Penis Size."

Wylie and Eardley (2007) reviewed 12 studies measuring penis size and found that the average flaccid (non-erect) penis was 9 to 10 centimetres in both length and girth, and that the average erect penis ranged from 14 to 16 centimetres in length and 12 to 13 centimetres in girth. There appears to be little relationship between the size of a given penis when flaccid and when erect. Penises that are small when flaccid tend to gain more size when they become erect. Larger flaccid penises gain relatively less size (Jamison & Gebhard, 1988).

Even when flaccid, the same penis can vary in size. Factors such as cold air, cold water, fear, and anxiety can cause the penis (along with the scrotum and testicles) to draw closer to the body, reducing its size.

The Scrotum

The **scrotum** is a pouch of loose skin that becomes lightly covered with hair at puberty. The scrotum consists of two compartments that hold the testes. Each testicle is held in place by a **spermatic cord**, a structure that contains the

CRITICAL THINKING QUESTIONS

Research indicates that the vast majority of women are satisfied with the size of their male partner's penis. Yet, many men wish they had a larger penis. What factors do you think explain the desire of some men to have a larger penis?

Phimosis An abnormal condition in which the foreskin is so tight that it cannot be withdrawn from the glans.

Scrotum The pouch of loose skin that contains the testes. It comes from the same linguistic root as the word "shred," which means "a long, narrow strip," probably referring to the long furrows on the scrotal sac.

Spermatic cord The cord that suspends a testicle within the scrotum and contains a vas deferens, blood vessels, nerves, and the cremaster muscle.

Vas deferens A tube that conducts sperm from the testicle to the ejaculatory duct of the penis. The plural is "vas deferentia."

Cremaster muscle The muscle that raises and lowers the testicle in response to temperature change and sexual stimulation.

vas deferens, blood vessels, nerves, and the **cremaster muscle**. The cremaster muscle raises and lowers the testicle within the scrotum in response to temperature change and sexual stimulation. The testes are drawn closer to the body during sexual arousal.

Sperm production is optimal at a temperature slightly lower than the 37°C that's desirable for most of the body. Typical scrotal temperature is a few degrees lower than body temperature. The scrotum is loose-hanging and flexible. It permits the testes and nearby structures to escape the higher body heat, especially in warm weather. Tightening or constricting of the skin surface helps retain heat and gives the scrotum a wrinkled appearance in the cold.

The scrotum is developed from the same embryonic tissue that becomes the labia majora of the female. Thus, like the labia majora, the scrotum is quite sensitive to sexual stimulation. It's somewhat more sensitive than the top side of the penis, but less sensitive than other areas of the penis.

The Internal Male Sex Organs

The internal male sex organs consist of the testes, which manufacture sperm and testosterone, the system of tubes and ducts that conduct sperm through the male reproductive system, and the organs that help nourish, activate, and enable sperm to neutralize some of the acidity found in the vagina.

The Testes

The testes are the male gonads. In slang, the testes are frequently referred to as "balls" or "nuts." These terms are considered vulgar, but they are reasonably descriptive, and they make it easier for many people to refer to the testes in informal conversation.

Germ cell A cell from which a new organism develops.

The testes serve two functions analogous to those of the ovaries: they secrete sex hormones and they produce mature **germ cells**. The germ cells produced by

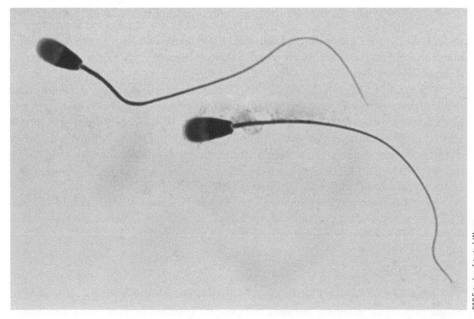

Human Sperm Cells.
This photo shows several spermatozoa, magnified many times. They're actually about 50 microns (0.0005 centimetres) long.

P&R Fotos/age fotostock/Alamy

the testes are called **sperm**, or **spermatozoa**, and the sex hormones are called **androgens**. The most important androgen is **testosterone**.

TESTOSTERONE   Testosterone stimulates the prenatal differentiation of male sex organs, the production of sperm, and the development of **secondary sex characteristics** such as the beard, deep voice, and growth of muscle mass.

In men, several endocrine glands—the hypothalamus, the pituitary gland, and the testes—keep blood testosterone levels at a more or less even level. This contrasts with the peaks and valleys in female sex hormone levels experienced by women during the phases of the menstrual cycle. Testosterone levels vary slightly with stress, time of day or month, and other factors, but a feedback loop among the endocrine glands keeps them relatively stable.

The testes usually range between 2.5 and 4.5 centimetres in length. The left testicle usually hangs lower, because the left spermatic cord tends to be somewhat longer.

SPERM   Each testicle is divided into many lobes. The lobes are filled with winding **seminiferous tubules**. (See Figure 3.12.) Although packed into a tiny space, these tubules, if placed end to end, would span the length of several football fields. Through a process called **spermatogenesis**, these threadlike structures produce and store hundreds of billions of sperm cells through the course of a man's lifetime.

Sperm cells develop through several stages. It takes about 72 days for the testes to manufacture a mature sperm cell. Each sperm cell is about 50 microns (0.0005 centimetres) long, making it one of the smallest cells in the body.

During fertilization, the 23 chromosomes from the father's sperm cell combine with the 23 chromosomes from the mother's ovum, furnishing the standard ensemble of 46 chromosomes in the offspring. Among the 23 chromosomes borne by sperm cells is one sex chromosome—an X sex chromosome or a Y sex chromosome.

Ova contain only X sex chromosomes. The union of an X chromosome and a Y chromosome leads to the development of a male offspring. Two X chromosomes combine to yield a female offspring. Thus, whether the father contributes an X or a Y chromosome determines the baby's gender.

The testes are veritable dynamos of manufacturing power, churning out about 1000 sperm per second, or about 30 billion—yes, *billion*—per year. Mathematically speaking, 10 to 20 ejaculations hold enough sperm to populate the earth.

Sperm proceed from the seminiferous tubules through an intricate maze of ducts that converge in a single tube called the **epididymis**. The epididymis lies against the back wall of the testicle and serves as a storage facility for the sperm.

The Vas Deferentia

Each epididymis empties into a vas deferens. The vas is a thin, cylindrical tube, about 40 centimetres long, that serves as a conduit for mature sperm. In the scrotum, the vas deferens lies near the skin surface within the spermatic cord. A **vasectomy**, an operation in which the right and left vas deferentia are severed, is therefore a convenient means of sterilization. The vas deferens leaves the scrotum and follows a circuitous path up into the abdominal cavity, then it loops back along the rear surface of the bladder. (See Figure 3.14.)

The Seminal Vesicles

The two **seminal vesicles** are small glands, each about five centimetres long. They lie behind the bladder and open into the **ejaculatory ducts**, where the fluids they secrete combine with sperm (see Figure 3.14).

Sperm The male germ cell, which fertilizes the ovum. It's also called "spermatozoon" (singular) and "spermatozoa" (plural).

Spermatozoa Mature male germ cells, which fertilize the ova. The singular is "spermatozoon."

Androgens The male sex hormones.

Testosterone A male steroid sex hormone.

Secondary sex characteristics Traits that distinguish the genders but are not directly involved in reproduction.

Seminiferous tubule A tiny, winding, sperm-producing tube located within the lobe of the testis.

Spermatogenesis The process by which sperm cells are produced and developed.

Epididymis A tube that lies against the back wall of the testicle and serves as a storage facility for the sperm.

Vasectomy A sterilization operation in which the vas deferentia are severed.

Seminal vesicle A small gland that lies behind the bladder and secretes a fluid that combines with sperm in the ejaculatory duct.

Ejaculatory duct A duct formed by the convergence of a vas deferens and a seminal vesicle. Sperm travels via the ejaculatory duct through the prostate gland and into the urethra.

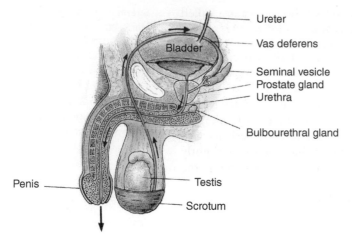

Figure 3.14 Passage of spermatozoa.
Each testicle is divided into lobes that contain threadlike seminiferous tubules. Through spermatogenesis, the tubules produce and store hundreds of billions of sperm over the course of a man's lifetime. During ejaculation, sperm cells travel through the vas deferens, up and over the bladder, into the ejaculatory duct, and through the urethra. Secretions from the seminal vesicles and the bulbourethral glands join with sperm to compose semen.

Andropause The so-called male menopause.

Potent Capable of sexual erection and orgasm.

Human growth hormone (HGH) A hormone that helps maintain muscle strength and that may help prevent fat build up.

Prostate gland The gland that lies beneath the bladder and secretes prostatic fluid, which gives semen its characteristic odour and texture.

At the base of the bladder, each vas deferens joins a seminal vesicle to form a short ejaculatory duct that runs through the middle of the prostate gland (see Figure 3.14). In the prostate, the ejaculatory duct opens into the urethra, which leads to the tip of the penis.

Is There a Male Menopause?

The scientific jury is still out on the existence of a "male menopause," also known as **andropause**. Women encounter relatively sudden age-related declines in sex hormones and fertility during menopause. Men experience gradual declines in testosterone levels as they age, but nothing like the rapid oestrogen drops women experience during menopause. Testosterone levels in men begin to fall at about age 30, and continue to decline thereafter.

The drop in testosterone may be connected to a variety of age-related symptoms, including reduced muscle mass and strength, increased body fat, reduced energy levels, and lowered fertility. Many men in their 50s and 60s experience problems in achieving and maintaining erections. Despite these testosterone declines, most men remain **potent** throughout their lives. Little is known about the critical levels of testosterone needed to maintain erectile ability. Certain age-related changes, such as reduced muscle mass and strength and increased body fat, may be due not to declining testosterone production, but to other factors associated with aging, such as a gradual loss of **human growth hormone (HGH)**, a hormone that helps maintain muscle strength and that may help prevent fat build up.

Some of these changes can be slowed or reversed. Exercise helps maintain muscle tone, keeps the growth of fatty tissue in check, and helps combat osteoporosis. Hormone replacement therapy may help but is controversial. North American physicians write more than one million prescriptions for testosterone and related drugs for men each year, even though it has been suspected that testosterone replacement therapy may heighten the risks of prostate cancer and cardiovascular disorders. However, research that has followed the effects of testosterone replacement has so far shown no clear evidence that testosterone replacement leads to prostate cancer or other major diseases such as heart problems or diabetes (Ginzburg et al., 2010).

The Prostate Gland

The **prostate gland** lies beneath the bladder and is approximately the shape and size of a chestnut (about two centimetres in diameter). It contains muscle fibres and glandular tissue that secrete prostatic fluid. Milky and alkaline, prostatic fluid provides the texture and odour characteristic of the seminal fluid. The alkalinity neutralizes some of the acidity of the vaginal tract, prolonging the lifespan of the sperm as the seminal fluid spreads through the female reproductive system. The prostate is continually active in mature males, though sexual arousal further stimulates secretions. These secretions are conveyed by a sieve-like duct system into the urethra, where they combine with sperm and fluid from the seminal vesicles.

Stimulation of the prostate can heighten sexual arousal and pleasure, making orgasm more intense for some men. Because the prostate is stimulated through the anus, however, many men and their partners are uncomfortable with it.

A vasectomy prevents sperm from reaching the urethra, but does not cut off fluids from the seminal vesicles or the prostate gland. A man who's had a vasectomy emits an ejaculate that appears normal but contains no sperm.

The Cowper's Glands

The **Cowper's glands** lie below the prostate and empty their secretions into the urethra. During sexual arousal, they secrete one or more drops of clear, slippery fluid that appears at the urethral opening.

The functions of this fluid are not entirely understood. It may help buffer the acidity of the male's urethra and lubricate the urethral passageway, easing the passage of seminal fluid. The fluid is not produced in sufficient amounts to play a significant role in lubricating the vagina during intercourse.

Cowper's gland A structure that lies below the prostate and empties its secretions into the urethra during sexual arousal.

Semen

Sperm and the fluids contributed by the seminal vesicles, the prostate gland, and the Cowper's glands make up **semen**, the whitish seminal fluid that is expelled through the tip of the penis during ejaculation. The seminal vesicles secrete about 70% of the fluid that constitutes the ejaculate. The remaining 30% consists of sperm and fluids produced by the prostate gland and the Cowper's glands. Sperm itself accounts for only about 1% of semen volume. This is why men with vasectomies continue to ejaculate about as much semen as before, although their ejaculates are devoid of sperm.

Semen is the medium that carries sperm through much of the male's reproductive system and the female's reproductive tract. Semen contains water, mucus, sugar (fructose), acids, and bases. It activates and nourishes sperm, and the bases help shield sperm from vaginal acidity. The typical ejaculate contains 200 to 400 million sperm cells and ranges from 3 to 5 millilitres in volume. The quantity of semen decreases with age and frequency of ejaculation.

Semen The whitish fluid that constitutes the ejaculate, consisting of sperm and secretions from the seminal vesicles, prostate gland, and Cowper's glands.

Diseases of the Male Urogenital System

Because the organs that make up the urinary and reproductive systems are near one another and share some "piping," they're referred to as the urinogenital or urogenital system. A number of diseases affect the urogenital system. The type of physician who specializes in their diagnosis and treatment is a **urologist**.

Urethritis

Men, like women, are subject to bladder and urethral inflammations, which are generally referred to as **urethritis**. The symptoms include frequent urination (urinary frequency), a strong need to urinate (urinary urgency), burning during urination, and a penile discharge. People with symptoms of urinary frequency and urinary urgency feel the pressing need to urinate repeatedly, even though they may have just done so and have but another drop or two to expel.

Preventive measures for urethritis parallel those suggested for cystitis (bladder infection): drinking more water, drinking cranberry juice (125 millilitres two or three times a day), and lowering intakes of alcohol and caffeine. Cranberry juice is highly acidic, and acid tends to eliminate many of the bacteria that can give rise to urethritis.

Urologist A physician who specializes in the diagnosis and treatment of diseases of the urogenital system.

Urethritis An inflammation of the bladder or urethra.

Testicular Cancer

Cancer of the testicles remains a relatively rare form of cancer. In Canada in 2013, there were 960 new diagnosed cases of testicular cancer, and there were 29 deaths as a result of the disease (Canadian Cancer Society, 2013e). Yet it's the most common

Cryptorchidism A condition in which at least one of the testicles fails to descend from the abdomen into the scrotum.

form of solid-tumour cancer to strike men between the ages of 20 and 34. There's no evidence that testicular cancer results from high levels of sexual activity or frequent masturbation. About 14% of men with testicular cancer had **cryptorchidism** as children, a condition in which one or both testicles fail to descend from the abdomen into the scrotum (American Cancer Society, 2012e). Family history also increases the risk.

Treatments include surgical removal of the diseased testis, radiation, and chemotherapy. The five-year survival rate among cases that are detected before the cancer has spread beyond the testes is about 99% (American Cancer Society, 2012e). If it has spread to nearby lymph nodes, the five-year survival rate is 96%. If it has spread beyond the lymph nodes, the five-year survival rate drops to about 71%.

The surgical removal of a testicle may have profound psychological implications. Some men who have lost a testicle feel less "manly." One option is testicular replacement surgery, which involves implanting a prosthetic testicle into the scrotum. Fears related to sexual performance can engender sexual dysfunctions. From a physiological standpoint, sexual functioning should remain unimpaired, because adequate quantities of testosterone are produced by the remaining testis.

Prostate Disorders

The prostate gland is tiny at birth and grows rapidly at puberty. It may shrink during adulthood but usually becomes enlarged after age 50.

Benign prostatic hyperplasia (BPH) Enlargement of the prostate gland, due to hormonal changes associated with aging. It's characterized by urinary frequency, urinary urgency, and difficulty starting the flow of urine.

BENIGN PROSTATIC HYPERPLASIA   The prostate gland becomes enlarged in about half of men older than 50, and in 80% of men who reach age 80 (ProstateCare.com, 2006). **Benign prostatic hyperplasia (BPH)** is a noncancerous enlargement of the prostate gland resulting from hormonal changes associated with aging, rather than from other causes such as inflammation due to STIs.

Because the prostate surrounds the upper part of the urethra (see Figure 3.12), enlargement constricts the urethra, causing urinary frequency (including increased frequency of nocturnal urination), urinary urgency, and difficulty starting the flow of urine. Several treatments are available to relieve the pressure on the urethra and increase the flow of urine. Part of the prostate is also sometimes surgically removed (ProstateCare.com, 2006).

CANCER OF THE PROSTATE   Prostate cancer is a serious, life-threatening problem among Canadian men. One in seven men will develop prostate cancer during their lifetimes, and 1 in 28 will die from it. About 23 600 Canadian men were diagnosed with prostate cancer in 2013, and an estimated 3900 men died from the disease (Canadian Cancer Society, 2013f). Prostate cancer involves the growth of malignant prostate tumours that can metastasize to bones and lymph nodes if not detected and treated early.

The main risk factors for developing prostate cancer are as follows:

■ Age. Prostate cancer is rare below the age of 45. The risk rises rapidly after the age of 50, and most men with the disorder are 65 or older.

■ Family history. The risk is higher for men who have a father, brother, or son who has had the disease.

■ Mutations of the BRCA1 or BRCA2 genes. Mutations in these genes are why breast and ovarian cancers are significantly more common in some families. It is believed that mutations in these genes may also heighten the risk of prostate cancer in men.

■ Race/ethnicity. Men of African ancestry are at higher risk for prostate cancer than men of European ancestry, and men of Asian origin have lower rates (American Cancer Society, 2012f).

Applied Knowledge

SELF-EXAMINATION OF THE TESTES

Self-examination (see Figure 3.15) is best performed shortly after a warm shower or bath, when the skin of the scrotum is most relaxed. Examine the scrotum for evidence of pea-sized lumps. Gently roll each testicle between your thumb and fingers. Lumps are generally found on the side or front of the testicle.

The presence of a lump is not necessarily a sign of cancer, but it should be promptly reported to a physician for further evaluation. Watch for these warning signals:

■ A slight enlargement of one of the testicles.
■ A change in the consistency of a testicle.

■ A dull ache in the lower abdomen or groin. (Pain may be absent in cancer of the testes, however.)
■ A sensation of dragging and heaviness in a testicle.
■ A lump on a testicle.

Because early detection is crucial to survival, you should examine yourself monthly following puberty, and have regular medical checkups.

Figure 3.15   Self-examination of the testes.
Gently roll each testicle between your thumb and fingers, examining the scrotum for evidence of pea-shaped lumps.

The early symptoms of cancer of the prostate may mimic those of benign prostate enlargement—frequency and difficulty with urination. Later symptoms include blood in the urine, pain or burning during urination, and pain in the lower back, pelvis, or upper thighs. Most cases do not have noticeable symptoms in the early stages.

Early detection is important, because treatment is most effective before the cancer has spread. To test for prostate cancer, the physician inserts a finger into the rectum and feels for abnormalities in the prostate gland. Unfortunately, many men are reluctant to undergo rectal examinations. Avoidance of—or ignorance of the need for—regular exams is a major contributor to the prostate cancer death rate. Another type of test for prostate cancer is the PSA blood test. Prostate-specific antigen (PSA) is a protein that helps transform a gel-like substance in the prostate gland into a liquid that transports sperm when it's ejaculated. In the diseased or enlarged prostate, PSA seeps into the blood at higher levels, giving higher test readings.

Yet the value of PSA testing has been questioned. Two results of two major studies on the effectiveness of PSA screening for prostate cancer were reported in the *New England Journal of Medicine* in 2009. The American study found no statistically significant difference in the death rates due to prostate cancer in men from the experimental group who were screened annually, and in men in the control group who were left to their own judgment as to whether or not to obtain PSA tests (Andriole et al., 2009). The European study found that screening every four years as opposed to screening at the individual's discretion was associated with a 20% lower risk of dying from prostate cancer (Schröder et al., 2009). But if we place the European results in perspective, we find that the average risk of dying from prostate cancer for an unscreened man is about 3%, and the reduced rate for screened men is about 2.4%.

The Canadian Cancer Society (2013g) recommends that men over age 50 talk with their doctors about the potential benefits and risks of PSA testing for prostate cancer. Men at higher risk, especially those with family backgrounds of prostate cancer or African ancestry, should consider being tested earlier.

The most widely used treatment for prostate cancer is surgical removal of the prostate gland. This may damage surrounding nerves, however, leading to problems with urinary and sexual functioning. Recently introduced surgical techniques tend to spare the surrounding nerves and reduce—but not eliminate—the risk of complications. Other treatments include radiation, hormone treatment, and anticancer drugs. Androgen-suppression (testosterone–suppression) therapy and anticancer drugs may shrink the tumour and relieve pain for long periods.

In a large-scale study of men who'd had prostate surgery in Quebec, 75% were found to experience erectile dysfunction and 6.6% to experience severe problems with urination (Karakiewicz et al., 2004). After prostate surgery, many men still feel uncomfortable about seeking help for sexual problems. Those with the highest feelings of distress over their loss of erectile function are most likely to seek medical assistance for this problem (Schover et al., 2004). An interview survey in Toronto concluded that "preservation of manhood" was a central concern for men who had experienced sexual dysfunction after prostate surgery (Fergus et al., 2002). As part of the adjustment process, some of the men refocused their sexual expression away from intercourse to other kinds of sexual activities, and toward more intimate emotional relationships with their partners.

Because of the side effects of prostate surgery, some physicians recommend a period of watchful waiting involving regular PSA tests, rather than aggressive treatment. Toronto urologist Laurence Klotz found in a trial study that only 25% of prostate cancer patients required radical surgery (Dalby, 2007). A large American study found that with watchful waiting, the great majority of prostate cancer patients were more likely to die from other causes than prostate cancer (Marchione, 2008).

Prostatitis Inflammation of the prostate gland.

PROSTATITIS Many infectious agents can inflame the prostate, causing **prostatitis**. The chief symptoms are painful ejaculation and an ache or pain between the scrotum and the anal opening. In a study of men from Canada and several other countries, 19% of those with urinary tract infections reported pain on ejaculation (Nickel et al., 2005). Men whose symptoms were more severe were more likely to experience pain at ejaculation. And 72% of those with painful ejaculation experienced problems with erectile dysfunction.

Prostatitis is usually treated with antibiotics. Although aspirin and ibuprofen may relieve the pain, a man with these symptoms should consult a physician. Painful ejaculation may discourage masturbation or coitus, which is ironic, because regular flushing of the prostate through ejaculation may be helpful in treating prostatitis.

Researchers at Queen's University (Smith et al., 2007) studied the effects of chronic prostatitis on male patients and their partners. These couples experienced more sexual difficulties and psychological depression than the control couples did. The sexual functioning of the males significantly affected the sexual functioning of their partners. Yet the prostatitis did not seem to affect the couples' overall intimate relationships.

Male Sexual Functions

The male sexual functions of erection and ejaculation provide the means for sperm to travel from the male's reproductive tract to the female's. There a sperm cell and an ovum may unite to conceive a new human being. Of course, the natural endowment of reproduction with sensations of pleasure helps ensure that it will take place with or without knowledge of these biological facts.

Erection

Erection is caused by the engorgement of the penis with blood until the penis grows in size and stiffens. The erect penis is an efficient conduit, or funnel, for depositing sperm deep within the vagina.

In mechanical terms, erection is a hydraulic event. The spongy, cavernous masses of the penis are equipped to hold blood. Filling them with blood causes them to enlarge, much as a sponge swells when it absorbs water. This simple description belies the fact that erection is a remarkable feat of biological engineering that involves the cooperation of the vascular (blood) system and the nervous system.

In a few moments—as quickly as 10 or 15 seconds—the penis can double in length, become firm, and shift from a funnel for passing urine to one that expels semen. Moreover, the bladder is closed off when the male becomes sexually aroused, so semen and urine cannot mix.

The corpora cavernosa are surrounded by a tough, fibrous covering. Just as the rubber of a balloon resists the pressure of pumped-in air, this covering resists expansion, stiffening the penis. The corpus spongiosum, which contains the urethra, also engorges with blood during erection. It doesn't become hard, however, because it lacks the fibrous casing. The penile glans, which is formed by the crowning of the spongiosum at the tip of the penis, turns a dark purplish hue as it becomes engorged, but it doesn't stiffen, either.

Erection is reversed when more blood flows out of the erectile tissue than into it, restoring the pre-arousal circulatory balance and shrinking the spongy masses. Loss of erection occurs when sexual stimulation ceases, or when the body returns to a (sexual) resting state after orgasm. Loss of erection can also occur in response to anxiety or perceived threats (Cuzin et al., 2011). Such loss can be abrupt, as when a man in the throes of passion suddenly hears a noise that sounds like an intruder. A man who's afraid he'll be unable to perform successfully may experience **performance anxiety**, which can prevent him from obtaining or maintaining an erection.

Men have nocturnal erections every 90 minutes or so as they sleep. These generally occur during rapid eye movement (REM) sleep. REM sleep is associated with dreaming. It's so named because the sleeper's eyes dart about rapidly under their closed eyelids during this stage.

Spinal Reflexes and Sexual Response

Men may become sexually aroused by a range of stimuli, including tactile stimulation by their partners, visual stimulation (e.g., viewing photos of nudes on the Internet), and sexual fantasies. Regardless of the source of stimulation, men's sexual responses—erection and ejaculation—occur by reflex.

Sexual reflexes are automatic, unlearned responses to sexual stimulation. Examples in women include vaginal lubrication and orgasm. We needn't *try* to become aroused—we need only expose ourselves to sexual stimulation, and allow our reflexes to do the job.

Men cannot will themselves to have erections. People do not control their sexual reflexes voluntarily, the way they might lift their arms, but they can set the stage for these reflexes to occur by seeking sexual stimulation. Efforts to control sexual responses consciously, by force of will, can backfire, making it more difficult to become aroused (e.g., to attain erection or vaginal lubrication).

The reflexes governing erection and ejaculation are controlled within the spinal cord. They're therefore called spinal reflexes. Erectile responses to direct stimulation, such as touching or licking, involve a simple spinal reflex that requires no direct participation by the brain (see Figure 3.16). Erections can be initiated by the brain, such as when a man has sexual fantasies or catches a glimpse of an attractive person; in this case, stimulation from the brain travels to the spinal cord, where the erectile reflex is triggered.

Erection The enlargement and stiffening of the penis as a consequence of its engorgement with blood.

Performance anxiety Feelings of dread and foreboding in connection with sexual activity (or any other activity that might be judged by another person).

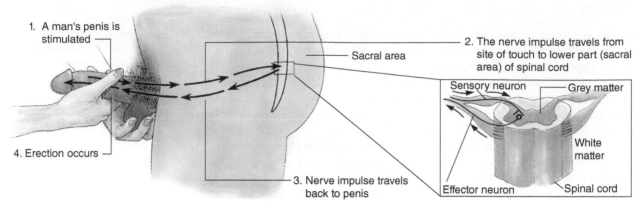

Figure 3.16 The independent nature of reflexes.
Reflexes need not involve the brain, although messages to the brain may make us aware that reflexes are occurring. Reflexes are the products of "local government" in the spine.

Sacrum The thick, triangular bone located near the bottom of the spinal column.

Tactile stimulation (touching) of the penis and nearby areas (lower abdomen, scrotum, inner thighs) causes sensory neurons to transmit nerve messages (signals) to an erection centre in the lower back, in an area of the spinal cord called the **sacrum**. The sacral erection centre controls reflexive erections—that is, erections that occur in response to direct stimulation of the penis and nearby areas. When direct penile stimulation occurs, messages in the form of nerve impulses are received by this erection centre, which in turn sends impulses to the genitalia via nerves that serve the penis. These impulses cause arteries carrying blood to the corpora cavernosa and corpus spongiosum to dilate, so more blood flows into them, causing erection.

The sacral erection centre makes it possible for men whose spinal cords have been injured or severed above the centre to achieve erections (and ejaculate) in response to direct tactile stimulation of the penis. Erection occurs even though their injuries prevent nerve signals from reaching their brains. Because of the lack of communication between the genital organs and the brain, there are no sensations, but many spinal cord injured men report that sex remains psychologically pleasurable because they can observe their partners' responses.

THE ROLE OF THE BRAIN   Direct penile stimulation triggers erection at the spinal level; what's the brain's role? It may seem that the penis has a mind of its own sometimes, but the brain does play an important role in regulating sexual response.

Tactile (touch) stimulation of the penis may trigger erection through the spinal cord, but sexual sensations are then normally relayed to the brain, which generally results in pleasure and perhaps a decision to focus on erotic stimulation. The sight of one's partner, erotic fantasies, memories, and so forth can result in messages being sent by the brain through the spinal cord to the arteries servicing the penis, maintaining or strengthening the erection.

When the brain originates messages that trigger the erectile reflex, it transmits nerve impulses to a second erection centre, located higher than the first, in the lumbar region of the spinal cord in the upper back. This higher spinal erection centre serves as a switchboard between the brain and the penis, allowing perceptual, cognitive, and emotional responses to make contributions. When the nerve pathways between the brain and the upper spinal cord are blocked or severed, men cannot achieve erections solely in response to mental stimulation.

The brain can also stifle sexual response. A man who's highly anxious about his sexual abilities may be unable to achieve an erection, even with intense penile stimulation. Or a man who believes sexual pleasure is sinful or dirty may be filled with anxiety and guilt and be unable to achieve erection with a partner.

In some males, especially adolescents, the erectile reflex is so easily tripped that incidental rubbing of the genitals against their own undergarments, the sight of attractive passersby, or fleeting sexual fantasies produce erections. Spontaneous erections may occur under embarrassing circumstances, such as before classes change in middle or high school, or on a beach. In an effort to distract himself from erotic fantasies and allow an erection to subside, many a male adolescent has desperately renewed his interest in an algebra or language textbook before the class bell has rung. (A well-placed towel may serve in a pinch on the beach.)

As men mature, they need more penile stimulation to achieve full erection. Partners of men in their 30s and 40s shouldn't feel that their attractiveness has waned if their lovers no longer have instant "no-hands" erections when they disrobe. It takes men longer to obtain erection as they age, and direct stimulation becomes more important.

THE ROLE OF THE AUTONOMIC NERVOUS SYSTEM   Although stimulation that brings about an erection can originate in the brain, this doesn't mean erection is a voluntary response, like raising your arm. Whatever the original or dominant source of stimulation—direct penile stimulation or sexual fantasy—erection remains an unlearned, automatic reflex.

Automatic responses such as erections involve the division of the nervous system called the **autonomic nervous system (ANS)**. "Autonomic" means "automatic." The ANS controls automatic bodily processes such as heartbeat, pupil dilation, respiration, and digestion. In contrast, voluntary movement (such as raising an arm) is under the control of the **somatic** division of the nervous system.

The ANS has two branches, the sympathetic and the parasympathetic. These branches have largely opposing effects; when they're activated at the same time, their effects balance out to some degree. In general, the **sympathetic** branch is in command during processes that involve a release of bodily energy from stored reserves, such as running, performing some other athletic task, or being gripped by fear or anxiety. The sympathetic branch also governs general mobilization of the body, by increasing the heart rate and respiration rate in response to threat, for example.

The **parasympathetic** branch is most active during processes that restore reserves of energy, such as digestion. When we experience fear or anxiety, the sympathetic branch of the ANS quickens the heart rate. When we relax, the parasympathetic branch curbs the heart rate. The parasympathetic branch activates digestive processes, but the sympathetic branch inhibits digestive activity. Because the sympathetic branch is in command when we feel fear or anxiety, such emotions can inhibit the activity of the parasympathetic system, thereby slowing down the digestive process and possibly causing indigestion.

The divisions of the autonomic nervous system play different roles in sexual arousal and response. The nerves that cause penile arteries to dilate during erection belong to the parasympathetic branch of the autonomic nervous system. The parasympathetic system therefore largely governs erection. The nerves governing ejaculation, however, belong to the sympathetic branch. One implication of this division of neural responsibility is that intense fear or anxiety, which involves sympathetic nervous system activity, may inhibit erection by counteracting the activity of the parasympathetic nervous system. Because sympathetic arousal is involved in triggering the ejaculatory reflex, anxiety or fear may also accelerate ejaculation, causing **rapid ejaculation** (also known as premature ejaculation). Intense emotions such as fear and anxiety can thus lead to problems in achieving or maintaining erection, as well as causing hasty ejaculation.

Because erection seems spontaneous at times, and because it often occurs when the man would rather it didn't, the penis may seem to have a mind of its own. Despite this common folk belief, however, the penis possesses no guiding intelligence.

Autonomic nervous system (ANS) The division of the nervous system that regulates automatic bodily processes, such as heartbeat, pupil dilation, respiration, and digestion.

Somatic nervous system The division of the nervous system that regulates voluntary movements, such as wiggling a toe or waving an arm.

Sympathetic nervous system The branch of the ANS most active during emotional responses that draw on the body's reserves of energy, such as fear and anxiety. The sympathetic ANS largely controls ejaculation.

Parasympathetic nervous system The branch of the ANS most active during processes that restore the body's reserves of energy, such as digestion. The parasympathetic ANS largely controls erection.

Rapid ejaculation A sexual dysfunction in which the male persistently ejaculates too early to afford the couple adequate sexual gratification. (Yes, what is on time in one relationship may be considered premature—or late—in another.)

ERECTILE ABNORMALITIES Some men find that their erect penises are slightly curved or bent. Some degree of curvature is perfectly normal, but men with **Peyronie's disease** have excessive curvature that can make erection painful and enjoyment of coitus difficult. The condition is caused by a build up of fibrous tissue in the penile shaft. Although some cases of Peyronie's disease appear to clear up on their own, most require medical attention.

Some men experience erections that persist for hours or days. This condition is called **priapism**, after Priapus of Greek myth, the son of Dionysus and Aphrodite who personified male procreative power. Priapism is often caused by leukemia, sickle-cell anaemia, or diseases of the spinal cord, although in some cases the cause remains unknown. Priapism occurs when the mechanisms that drain the blood that makes the penis erect are damaged and cannot return the blood to the circulatory system. Priapism may become a medical emergency, because erection prolonged beyond six hours can starve penile tissues of oxygen, leading to tissue deterioration. Medical intervention in the form of drugs or surgery may be required to reverse the condition and allow blood to drain from the penis.

Ejaculation

Ejaculation, like erection, is a spinal reflex. It's triggered when sexual stimulation reaches a critical point or threshold. Ejaculation generally occurs together with **orgasm**, the sudden muscle contractions that occur at the peak of sexual excitement and result in abrupt release of the sexual tension that has built up during arousal. Orgasm is accompanied by subjective sensations that are generally intensely pleasurable. Ejaculation, however, is simply the expulsion of semen from the tip of the penis. Orgasm and ejaculation are not synonymous, nor do they always occur simultaneously. For example, a **paraplegic** can ejaculate if the area of the lower spinal cord that controls ejaculation is intact. He doesn't experience the subjective aspects of orgasm, however, because the sensations of orgasm don't reach his brain.

Conversely, a prepubescent boy may experience orgasms even though he emits no ejaculate. Orgasms without ejaculate are termed "dry orgasms." Boys do not begin to produce seminal fluid (and sperm) until puberty. A mature man, too, can experience dry orgasms. These can take the form of "little orgasms" preceding a larger orgasm, or they can follow "wet orgasms" when sexual stimulation is continued but seminal fluids have not been replenished.

Ejaculation occurs in two stages. The first stage, often called the **emission stage**, involves contractions of the prostate, the seminal vesicles, and the upper part of the vas deferens (the **ampulla**). The force of these contractions propels seminal fluid into the prostatic part of the urethral tract, a small tube called the **urethral bulb**, which balloons out as muscles close at either end, trapping the semen. At this point, the man perceives that orgasm is inevitable. Masters and Johnson (1966) called this feeling a sense of ejaculatory inevitability. Men might colloquially describe the feeling as being about to "come." The man feels that a point of no return has been passed, and nothing can prevent ejaculation.

The second stage, often referred to as the **expulsion stage**, involves the propulsion of the seminal fluid through the urethra and out of the urethral opening at the tip of the penis. In this stage, muscles at the base of the penis and elsewhere contract rhythmically, forcefully expelling semen. The second stage is generally accompanied by the highly pleasurable sensations of orgasm.

In ejaculation, the seminal fluid is released from the urethral bulb and expelled by forceful contractions of the pelvic muscles that surround the urethral channel and the crura of the penis. During ejaculation, the bladder is closed off so urine cannot escape. The first few contractions are most intense, and occur at 0.8-second intervals. Subsequent contractions lessen in intensity and the intervals between them gradually increase. Seminal fluid is expelled in spurts during the first few

Peyronie's disease An abnormal condition characterized by an excessive curvature of the penis, which can make erection painful.

Priapism Persistent and painful erection of the penis.

Orgasm The climax of sexual excitement.

Paraplegic A person with sensory and motor paralysis of the lower half of the body.

Emission stage The first phase of ejaculation, which involves contractions of the prostate gland, the seminal vesicles, and the upper part of the vas deferens.

Ampulla A sac or dilated part of a tube or canal.

Urethral bulb The small tube that makes up the prostatic part of the urethral tract. It balloons out as muscles close at either end, trapping semen prior to ejaculation.

Expulsion stage The second stage of ejaculation, during which muscles at the base of the penis and elsewhere contract rhythmically, forcefully expelling semen and generally providing pleasurable sensations.

contractions. In younger men the seminal fluid may be propelled 30 centimetres or more. For many men, however, particularly as they grow older, the semen travels a few centimetres, or oozes from the penile opening. The force of the expulsion varies with the condition of the man's prostate, his general health, and his age.

Although ejaculation occurs by reflex, a man can delay ejaculation by maintaining the level of sexual stimulation below the critical threshold, or "point of no return." Men who suffer from rapid ejaculation have been successfully treated in programs that train them to recognize their points of no return and learn how to maintain sexual stimulation below those points.

RETROGRADE EJACULATION   Some men experience **retrograde ejaculation**, in which the ejaculate empties into the bladder rather than being expelled from the body. During normal ejaculation, an external sphincter opens, allowing seminal fluid to pass out of the body, while an internal sphincter closes off the opening to the bladder, preventing seminal fluid from backing up into the bladder. In retrograde ejaculation, the actions of these two sphincters are reversed. The external sphincter remains closed, preventing expulsion of the seminal fluid, while the internal sphincter opens, allowing the ejaculate to empty into the bladder. The result is a dry orgasm. No ejaculate is apparent, because semen has backed up into the bladder.

Retrograde ejaculation may be caused by prostate surgery (though far less often these days), drugs such as tranquillizers, certain illnesses, and accidents.

Retrograde ejaculation is usually harmless in itself, because the seminal fluid is later discharged with urine. Infertility can result, however, and there may be some changes in the sensations associated with orgasm. Persistent dry orgasms should be medically evaluated, since their underlying causes may threaten a man's health.

Retrograde ejaculation
Ejaculation in which the ejaculate empties into the bladder.

Summing Up

The external female sexual structures are collectively known as the vulva. They consist of the mons veneris, the labia majora and minora, the clitoris, the vestibule, and the vaginal opening.

The structures that underlie the external female sex organs include the vestibular bulbs, Bartholin's glands, the sphincters, the clitoral crura, and the pubococcygeus (PC) muscle.

The internal female sex organs—or female reproductive system—include the innermost parts of the vagina, the cervix, the uterus, the ovaries, and the fallopian tubes.

The G spot—an allegedly distinct area of the vagina within the anterior wall—may have special erotic significance. Some researchers suggest that prolonged stimulation of this spot produces an orgasm characterized by intense pleasure and, in some women, a type of ejaculation. The nature of this ejaculate remains uncertain.

Regular pelvic examinations are essential for early detection of problems involving the reproductive tract.

In some cultures, the breasts are viewed merely as biological instruments for feeding infants. In our culture, however, they have taken on erotic significance.

Breast cancer is the second leading cancer killer in women, after lung cancer. Women with breast cancer will have lumps in their breasts, but most breast lumps are benign.

Menstruation is the cyclical bleeding that stems from the shedding of the endometrium when a reproductive cycle has not led to fertilization of an ovum. The menstrual cycle is regulated by oestrogen and progesterone.

The menstrual cycle involves finely tuned relationships among the hypothalamus, pituitary gland, ovaries, and uterus.

The menstrual cycle has four stages, or phases: the proliferative, ovulatory, secretory, and menstrual phases.

Couples are less likely to initiate sexual activity during menstruation than during any other phase of the woman's cycle.

Menopause, the cessation of menstruation, most commonly occurs between the ages of 46 and 50. Oestrogen deficiency in menopause may give rise to night sweats, hot flashes, hot flushes, cold sweats, dry skin, loss of breast tissue, and decreased vaginal lubrication. For most women, menopausal problems are mild.

Most women experience some discomfort prior to or during menstruation. Dysmenorrhoea is the most common menstrual problem, and pelvic cramps are the most common symptom.

Women with persistent menstrual problems may benefit from a number of active coping strategies for handling menstrual distress.

The external male sex organs include the penis and the scrotum.

Semen and urine pass out of the penis through the urethral opening. The penis contains cylinders that fill with blood and stiffen during sexual arousal.

Circumcision—the surgical removal of the prepuce—has historically been carried out for religious and hygienic reasons.

The scrotum is the pouch of loose skin that contains the testes. Each testicle is held in place by a spermatic cord, which contains the vas deferens and the cremaster muscle.

The internal male sex organs consist of the testes, a system of tubes and ducts that conduct sperm, and organs that nourish and activate sperm.

The testes secrete male sex hormones (androgens) and produce germ cells (sperm).

The hypothalamus, pituitary gland, and testes keep blood testosterone at a more or less constant level through a hormonal negative feedback loop.

Sperm is produced by seminiferous tubules. It matures in the epididymis, where it's stored.

Each epididymis empties into a vas deferens that conducts sperm over the bladder.

The seminal vesicles are glands that open into the ejaculatory ducts, where the fluids they secrete combine with and nourish sperm.

The prostate gland secretes fluid that accounts for semen's characteristic texture and odour.

During sexual arousal, the Cowper's glands secrete a drop or so of clear, slippery fluid that appears at the urethral opening.

Sperm and the fluids contributed by the seminal vesicles, the prostate gland, and the Cowper's glands combine to form semen, the whitish fluid that is expelled through the tip of the penis during ejaculation.

Men, like women, are subject to bladder and urethral inflammation, which is generally referred to as urethritis.

Cancer of the testes is the most common form of solid-tumour cancer to strike young men between the ages of 20 and 34.

The prostate gland generally becomes enlarged in men past the age of 50. Prostate cancer involves the growth of malignant prostate tumours that can metastasize to bones and lymph nodes. The chief symptoms of prostatitis are painful ejaculation and an ache or pain between the scrotum and the anal opening.

Erection is the process by which the penis becomes engorged with blood, increases in size, and stiffens.

Erection and ejaculation occur by reflex. Although erection is a reflex, penile sensations are relayed to the brain, where they generally result in pleasure. Erection and ejaculation also involve the autonomic nervous system (ANS). The parasympathetic branch of the ANS largely governs erection, whereas the sympathetic branch largely controls ejaculation.

Ejaculation is triggered when sexual stimulation reaches a critical threshold. Ejaculation usually (though not always) occurs with orgasm, but the terms are not synonymous.

In retrograde ejaculation, the ejaculate empties into the bladder, rather than being expelled from the body.

Test Yourself

Multiple-Choice Questions

1. The female external sex organs are called the:
   (a) Uterus.
   (b) Ovaries.
   (c) Vulva.
   (d) Cervix.

2. The only organ whose sole function is to provide sexual pleasure is the:
   (a) Penis.
   (b) Clitoris.
   (c) Vagina.
   (d) Mons.

3. Which of the following is not a recommended way to prevent vaginitis?
   (a) Wearing pants that fit loosely in the crotch.
   (b) Wearing nylon underwear.
   (c) Washing the vulva with a mild soap.
   (d) Avoiding foods high in sugar and refined carbohydrates.

4. The two pituitary hormones involved in the regulation of the menstrual cycle are:
   (a) GnRH and oestrogen.
   (b) Oxytocin and prolactin.
   (c) FSH and LH.
   (d) LH and testosterone.

5. During menopause, lower levels of _____ may cause hot flashes and other physical symptoms.
   (a) Prolactin
   (b) Oxytocin
   (c) Androgen
   (d) Oestrogen

6. The penis contains:
(a) Bone.
(b) Muscle.
(c) Spongy material.
(d) All of the above.

7. Sperm cells are carried out of the testicles through the:
(a) Seminiferous tubules.
(b) Dartos muscles.
(c) Vas deferentia.
(d) Cremasteric tubes.

8. Surgical removal of the foreskin is known as:
(a) Excision.
(b) Infibulation.

(c) Incision.
(d) Circumcision.

9. The purpose of testicular self-examination is to detect _____ in its early stages.
(a) AIDS
(b) Infertility
(c) Cancer
(d) Erectile dysfunction

10. _____ is the most common form of cancer among Canadian men.
(a) Prostate cancer
(b) Testicular cancer
(c) Penile cancer
(d) Inguinal cancer

Answers to the "Test Yourself" questions in each chapter are found on page 489.

Questions for Critical Thinking

1. Many people grow up with negative perceptions of menstruation. What negative messages did you hear as a child or adolescent? Who did you hear these messages from? Were any of these messages specific to your culture or ethnic group?

2. Female genital cutting or mutilation is a common practice in some countries, but illegal in Canada. To what extent do you think Canadians should try to persuade these countries to ban this practice?

3. Some people seem to be fixated on breast and penis size as measures of sexual attractiveness. Are these people losing sight of more important things? For you, what are the most important things that make a person sexually appealing?

CHAPTER FOUR

Sexual Arousal and Response

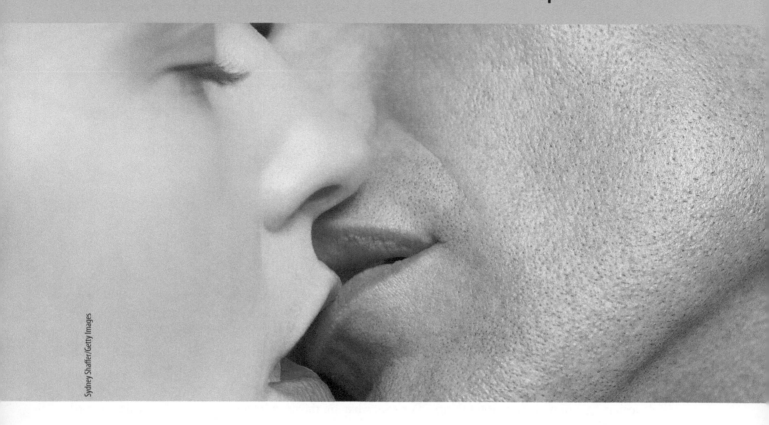

Sydney Shaffer/Getty Images

Judging by media, advertising, and pop culture images of what makes a person sexy, you might assume that human beings are quite uniform in what turns them on. In reality, people vary greatly in the cues that lead them to become sexually aroused and in the frequency with which they experience sexual thoughts and feelings.

In this chapter we look at factors that contribute to sexual arousal and processes related to sexual response. Because we experience the world largely through our senses, we begin the chapter by focusing on the role of the senses in sexual arousal.

The Senses and Sexual Arousal

We experience the world around us through our senses—vision, hearing, smell, taste, and the skin senses, which include that all-important sense of touch. Each of the senses plays some role in sparking sexual arousal.

Vision: The Better to See You With

Visual cues can play an important role in sexual arousal for both men and women. We may be turned on by the sight of a person in the nude, disrobing, or dressed in a way that we find erotically appealing. The physical attributes of a person that we find attractive and potentially arousing are often, but not always, absorbed and interpreted visually. Men appear to be more responsive to visual stimuli than women, although women are also clearly attuned to appealing eyefuls and can be sexually aroused by them (Chivers, 2010; Thompson, 2011).

One study found that women tend to dress and ornament themselves in more appealing ways when they are in the fertile phase of their ovulatory cycle (Haselton et al., 2007). Forty-two judges selected photos of women as "trying to look more attractive" in their fertile (59.5%) phase as compared with their luteal phase (40.5%).

Science has endorsed what lingerie companies have known for centuries—that women seeking male interest might do well to clothe themselves in red. Research shows that men are more likely to consider women dressed in red as more sexually desirable and attractive, although men seem to be unaware of this colourful effect (Elliot & Niesta, 2008; Kayser et al., 2010). Women, interestingly, also find men dressed in red to be more attractive, although men are much less likely to wear this colour (Elliot et al., 2010). But participants in these research studies do not rate people dressed in red as kinder, more intelligent, or more likeable.

Some couples find it arousing to observe themselves having sex in front of a mirror or on a video recording. Some people find sexually explicit media arousing. For others, sexually explicit depictions evoke boredom, feelings of anxiety, or moral disapproval. Although both males and females can be sexually aroused by visually mediated erotica (a technical term for sexually explicit video, also known simply as porn), research suggests that men are more interested in it (Petersen & Hyde, 2011).

Smell: Does the Nose Know Best?

Although the sense of smell plays a lesser role in governing sexual arousal in humans than in lower mammals, our body's natural odours can play a significant role in sexual attraction and arousal. To enhance our allure, perfume

The Canadian Press/AP Photo/Remy de la Mauviniere

Sex as a Traffic Stopper.
A lingerie model at the Galeries Lafayette, a Paris department store, checks out passersby—and vice versa. Scantily clad models used to stop traffic outside the store, until the store received complaints that they were being insensitive to women. Clearly, visual cues can be sexual turn-ons!

Fuse/Getty Images

Subconscious Attraction.
How much sexual communication occurs below the level of conscious awareness? Research suggests that underarm secretions may make people more sexually attractive, even when others are unaware of sensing them. Are they drawn to each other's personal traits or to their pheromones?

Aphrodisiac Any drug or other agent that's sexually arousing or that increases sexual desire.

Pheromones Chemical substances that are secreted externally by certain animals and that convey information to, or produce specific responses in, other members of the same species.

companies bottle fragrances purported to be sexually arousing. Western society has become preoccupied (some would say obsessed) with personal cleanliness. Television commercials continually encourage us to mask bodily scents by using soaps, deodorants, and perfumes or colognes. Indeed, we are told that the artificial scents in a perfume, spray, or soap can make us more sexually appealing. Unilever has been very successful in selling its Axe body spray to young men. Its advertisements unabashedly imply that young men who use the product attract women who are aroused by the scent. Or consider the popular television commercial in which the handsome, towel-clad Isaiah Mustafa says, "Hello, ladies. Look at your man. Now back to me. . . . Sadly, he isn't me. But if he stopped using ladies' scented body wash and switched to Old Spice, he could smell like he's me."

The propensity to find even a whiff of underarm odour or naturally occurring genital smells offensive likely reflects cultural conditioning, rather than biological predisposition. In some societies, genital secretions are considered **aphrodisiacs**.

PHEROMONES   For centuries, people have searched for a love potion—a magical formula that could make others fall in love with or be strongly attracted to them. It has been suggested that such potions may already exist in the form of chemical secretions known as **pheromones**. Pheromones are odourless chemicals that many animals detect through a sixth sense—the vomeronasal organ (VNO). People possess VNOs in the mucous lining of the nose (Touhara & Vosshall, 2009; T. Wyatt, 2009). Infants apparently use pheromones to recognize their mothers, and adults might respond to them in seeking a mate (Martins et al., 2005). Male rodents, such as mice, are extremely sensitive to several kinds of pheromones (Leinders-Zufall et al., 2000).

Until recently, most researchers didn't believe pheromones played a role in human behaviour, but today the issue has attracted new interest. In a typical study, Winnifred Cutler and her colleagues (1998) asked heterosexual men to wear a suspected male pheromone, and a control group to wear a placebo. The men wearing the pheromone increased the frequency of sexual intercourse with their female partners, but did not increase the frequency of masturbation. The researchers concluded that the substance increased the sexual attractiveness of the men to their partners, although they did not claim that it directly stimulated sexual behaviour.

In a double-blind experiment, 36 university women were randomly assigned to wear either a placebo or a perfume laced with a suspected pheromone extracted from their underarm secretions (McCoy & Pitino, 2002). The women recorded their sexual behaviours over three menstrual cycles (12 weeks). Three-quarters (74%) of the women who wore the suspected pheromone showed significant increases in frequency of sexual intercourse, sleeping next to a partner, formal dates, and kissing, petting, and other displays of affection; only one-quarter (23%) of the women who wore the placebo showed such increases. Perhaps the suspected pheromone increased the women's attractiveness to men.

MENSTRUAL SYNCHRONY   Research by several investigators suggests that exposure to other women's sweat can modify a woman's menstrual cycle. In one study, women exposed to other women's underarm secretions, which contained steroids that may function as pheromones, showed converging shifts in their menstrual cycles (Preti et al., 1986). Similar synchronization of menstrual cycles has been observed among women who share dormitory rooms. In another study, 80% of the women who dabbed their upper lips with an extract of perspiration from other women began to menstruate in sync with the cycles of the donors after about three menstrual cycles (Cutler, 1999). A control group, whose members dabbed their lips with alcohol, showed no changes in their menstrual cycles.

BODY ODOURS AND SEXUAL ORIENTATION   There's reason to believe body odours play a role in the selection of sex partners (Moshkin et al., 2011; Preti et al., 2003). Martins et al. (2005) hypothesized that preferences for axillary (underarm) odours would be related to sexual orientation. They collected samples of axillary odours from 24 volunteers—six exclusively male heterosexual and six exclusively female heterosexual, and six exclusively gay male and six exclusively lesbian, according to the Kinsey heterosexuality–homosexuality scale. The study produced a number of interesting findings:

The Nose and Sexual Orientation.
Research by Yolanda Martins, George Preti, Charles J. Wysocki, and their colleagues (2005) suggests that gay men prefer the body odours of other gay men to those of heterosexuals and lesbians. Heterosexual males seem least likely to prefer the body odours of gay males.

- Heterosexual males, heterosexual females, and lesbians preferred axillary odours taken from heterosexual males over those taken from gay males.
- Gay males preferred axillary odours taken from other gay males.
- Heterosexual males, heterosexual females, and lesbians preferred axillary odours taken from lesbians over those taken from gay males.
- Heterosexual males preferred axillary odours taken from lesbians over those taken from gay males.

The researchers suggest that gay males and lesbians may produce axillary odours that can be distinguished from those of heterosexuals. It also appears that gay males may perceive these typical odorants differently than heterosexual males do. The few studies that have investigated the relationships between body odours and sexual orientation indicate that gay males are most likely to be attracted to the body odours of other gay males, and heterosexual males are least likely to be attracted to the body odours of gay males.

Touch: Sex as a Touching Experience

The sense of touch has the most direct effects on sexual arousal and response. Any region of that sensitive layer we refer to as skin can become eroticized. The touch of your lover's hand upon your cheek or your lover's gentle massage of your shoulders or back can be sexually stimulating.

EROGENOUS ZONES   **Erogenous zones** are parts of the body that are especially sensitive to tactile sexual stimulation—to strokes and other caresses. **Primary erogenous zones** are erotically sensitive because they are richly endowed with nerve endings. **Secondary erogenous zones** are parts of the body that become erotically sensitized through experience.

Primary erogenous zones include the genitals; the inner thighs, perineum, buttocks, and anus; the breasts (especially the nipples); the ears (particularly the earlobes); the mouth, lips, and tongue; the neck; the navel; and, yes, the armpits. Preferences vary somewhat from person to person, reflecting possible biological, attitudinal, and experiential differences.

Erogenous zones Parts of the body that are especially sensitive to tactile sexual stimulation. "Erogenous" is derived from roots that mean "giving birth to erotic sensations."

Primary erogenous zones Erogenous zones that are particularly sensitive because they are richly endowed with nerve endings.

Secondary erogenous zones Parts of the body that become erotically sensitized through experience.

A World of Diversity

YSEX—THE REASONS PEOPLE GIVE FOR WANTING TO HAVE SEX

Cindy Meston and David Buss (2007) sought to learn about the most common—and least common—reasons for sex, to see if they were consistent with pervasive gender roles and what they might suggest about theories of human sexuality. To do so, they created a questionnaire with the intriguing title, YSEX ('Why Sex') and administered it to college students.

The researchers had 1549 students take the questionnaire in exchange for course credit. The sample was 62% European American, 15% Asian American, 15% Latin American, 4% African American, and 1% Native American.

The following nine themes characterized the most common reasons among both men and women for having sex: (1) feelings of attraction, (2) desire for physical pleasure, (3) expression of feelings of love, (4) feeling desired by the other person, (5) desire to deepen the relationship, (6) novel experience, (7) celebration of special occasion, (8) opportunity, and (9) seeming to "just happen." People were least likely to have sex to hurt their partners (that is, cheating on them), to get a job or a promotion, to be more popular, to get rid of a headache or cramps, or because of pressure or a sense of duty. Some reasons were unexpected, to put it mildly: "I wanted to feel closer to God."

There were some gender differences: Men were significantly more likely than women to have sex for physical reasons (physical appearance, an attractive face) and because of sheer opportunity. Men's greater emphasis on physical reasons seems to support the view that men are more responsive to visual cues. Men were also more interested in sex for bragging rights, purposes of "conquest," and enhancing their social status among other men. Women exceeded men on having sex to express love. All in all, the responses were consistent with traditional gender roles that portray men as sexual initiators and women as "gate keepers."

Wood, Milhausen, and Maitland (2013) at the University of Guelph administered the YSEX questionnaire to 271 self-identified lesbian, bisexual, queer, and questioning women and found that the women were most likely to engage in sex for reasons related to pleasure, physical desirability, and to express love for their partner.

Areas that are exquisitely sensitive for some people may produce virtually no reaction, or even discomfort, in others. Some women, for example, report little sensation when their breasts are stroked or kissed, while others find it very pleasurable. Many men are uncomfortable when their nipples are caressed. On the other hand (or foot), some people find the areas between their toes sensitive to erotic stimulation, and enjoy keeping toeholds on their partners during sexual activity.

Secondary erogenous zones become eroticized through association with sexual stimulation. For example, a woman might become sexually aroused when her lover gently caresses her shoulders, because such caresses have been incorporated as a regular feature of the couple's lovemaking. A man might become sexually aroused when his partner strokes his chest, because he has come to associate this caress as a prelude to more direct sexual interaction.

Taste: On Savoury Sex

Some people are sexually aroused by the taste of genital secretions, such as vaginal secretions or seminal fluid. We don't know, however, whether these secretions are laced with chemicals that have biologically arousing effects, or whether arousal reflects the meaning these secretions may have for the individuals. That is, we may learn to become aroused by, or to seek out, flavours or odours we have associated with sexual pleasure.

Others are turned off by the taste or odour of these secretions.

Hearing: The Better to Hear You With

The sense of hearing also provides an important medium for sexual arousal and response. Like visual and olfactory cues, sounds can be turn-ons or turn-offs. The sounds of your lover—whether whispers, moans of pleasure, or animated sounds that may attend orgasm—can be arousing during the heat of passion. For some people, key words or vocal intonations may become as arousing as direct stimulation of an erogenous zone. Many people are aroused when their lovers "talk dirty"—sexually explicit talk spurs their sexual arousal. Others find it vulgar.

Music itself can contribute to sexual arousal. Music can relax us and put us in the mood or evoke powerful associations—"They're playing our song!" Many couples find background music atmospheric, a vital accoutrement of lovemaking.

Aphrodisiacs, Anaphrodisiacs, and Psychoactive Drugs

An aphrodisiac is a substance that arouses or increases one's capacity for sexual desire or response. However, the belief that a substance has sexually stimulating effects may itself inspire sexual excitement. In other words, the effects of aphrodisiacs are subject to the **placebo effect** (Downs & Nazario, 2003). That is, a person who consumes a supposed aphrodisiac and feels sexually aroused may attribute the turn-on to the effects of the substance, when in reality it has no direct physiological effect on sexual desire or arousal. In other words, the person anticipates becoming sexually aroused, and it's the expectation of arousal, rather than the substance itself, that results in the perception of increased sexual desire or response.

Foods that in some way resemble genitals have now and then been considered aphrodisiacs. These include oysters, clams, bulls' testicles ("prairie oysters"), tomatoes, and phallic items such as celery stalks, bananas, and even ground-up reindeer antlers, elephant tusks, and rhinoceros horns (which is one derivation of the slang term "horny"). Sadly, myths about the sexually arousing properties of substances extracted from rhinoceroses and elephants are contributing to the rapidly diminishing numbers of these animals.

Drugs and psychoactive substances may have certain effects on sexual arousal and response. The drug arginine, an amino acid extracted from the African yohimbe tree, does stimulate blood flow to the genitals. However, its effects are limited and unreliable (Downs & Nazario, 2003).

Amyl nitrate (in the form of "snappers" or "poppers") is sometimes used, mostly by gay men, but also by some heterosexuals, in the belief that it heightens sensations of arousal and orgasm. Poppers dilate blood vessels in the brain and genitals, producing sensations of warmth in the pelvis and possibly facilitating erection and prolonging orgasm. Amyl nitrate does have some legitimate medical uses, such as helping reduce heart pain (angina) among cardiac patients. It's inhaled from ampoules that pop open for rapid use when heart pain occurs. However, poppers can cause dizziness, fainting, and migraine-type headaches. They should be taken

Placebo effect Perception that consumption of a substance (e.g., a medication) results in an effect (e.g., relief of a headache) even though the substance does not contain properties (e.g., active ingredients that reduce pain) that cause the effect to occur.

only under a doctor's care for a legitimate medical need, not to intensify sexual sensations.

The drug Viagra was originally developed as a treatment for angina (heart pain), because it was thought to increase blood flow to the heart. It does so, modestly. However, it's more effective at dilating blood vessels in the genital organs, thereby facilitating vasocongestion and erection in the male. Viagra and the similar drug Cialis are treatments for male erectile dysfunction. Can Viagra and Cialis be considered aphrodisiacs? If we use a strict definition of "aphrodisiac," the answer is no. Although these drugs facilitate erection, they do not by themselves trigger sexual arousal. If the man is not sexually aroused, Viagra or Cialis will not produce an erection.

But certain drugs do appear to have aphrodisiac effects, apparently because they act on the brain mechanisms controlling the sex drive. Drugs that affect brain receptors for the neurotransmitter dopamine, for example, such as the antidepressant bupropion (sold under the trade name Wellbutrin) and the drug L-dopa, used in the treatment of Parkinson's disease, can increase the sex drive (Saks, 2008).

The scientific literature examining the effects of substances popularly believed to be natural aphrodisiacs suggests that they have little actual effect. Rany Shamloul (2010) at the Department of Pharmacology and Toxicology at Queen's University extensively reviewed the scientific evidence concerning the sexual enhancement effects of such substances as ginseng, Spanish fly, yohimbine, chocolate, saw palmetto, and alcohol, and concluded that "there is little evidence from literature to recommend the usage of natural aphrodisiacs for the enhancement of sexual desire and/or performance" (p. 44).

The most potent chemical aphrodisiac may be a naturally occurring substance in the body—the hormone testosterone. It's the basic fuel of sexual desire in both males and females (Basson, Davis, & Rodenberg, 2009).

Anaphrodisiacs

Anaphrodisiac A drug or other agent whose effects are antagonistic to sexual arousal or sexual desire.

Some people believe aphrodisiacs stimulate sexual response. **Anaphrodisiacs** have the opposite effect. Substances such as saltpetre (potassium nitrate) are considered inhibitors of sexual response. Saltpetre only indirectly dampens sexual arousal, however. As a diuretic that can increase the need for urination, it may make the thought of sex unappealing, but it doesn't directly dampen sexual response.

Other chemicals do dampen sexual arousal and response. Tranquilizers and central nervous system depressants such as barbiturates can lessen sexual desire and impair sexual performance. These drugs may, paradoxically, enhance sexual arousal in some people, by lessening sexual inhibitions and fear of possible repercussions of sexual activity. Antihypertensive drugs, which are used in the treatment of high blood pressure, may produce erectile and ejaculatory difficulties in men and reduction of sexual desire in both men and women. Certain antidepressant drugs, such as fluoxetine (brand name Prozac), amitriptyline (brand name Elavil), and imipramine (brand name Tofranil), appear to dampen the sex drive (Kennedy & Rizvi, 2009). Antidepressants may also impair erectile response and delay ejaculation in men and orgasmic responsiveness in women (Kennedy & Rizvi, 2009). Because they delay ejaculation, some of these drugs are used to treat premature ejaculation.

Nicotine, the stimulant in tobacco smoke, constricts the blood vessels. It can therefore impede sexual arousal, by reducing the capacity of the genitals to become engorged with blood. Several studies have shown that smoking can reduce men's ability to have erections (McKay, 2005). Chronic smoking can also reduce men's blood levels of testosterone, which can in turn lessen sex drive.

Antiandrogen drugs may have anaphrodisiac effects. They have been used in the treatment of deviant behaviour patterns, such as sexual violence and adult sexual interest in children, with some promising results (Roesler & Witztum, 2000).

Antiandrogen A drug that reduces the levels of androgen in the blood system.

Psychoactive Drugs

Psychoactive drugs, including alcohol and cocaine, are widely believed to have aphrodisiac effects. Yet their effects may reflect our expectations of them, or their effects on sexual inhibitions, rather than direct stimulation of sexual response.

ALCOHOL   Small amounts of alcohol can induce feelings of well-being, but large amounts curb sexual response. This fact shouldn't be surprising, because alcohol is a depressant. Alcohol reduces central nervous system activity. Large amounts of alcohol can severely impair sexual function in both men and women.

People who drink moderate amounts of alcohol may feel more sexually aroused because of their expectations about alcohol, not because of its chemical properties (Davis, 2010; Gil-Rivas, 2012). That is, people who expect alcohol to enhance sexual responsiveness may act the part. Moreover, men with problems achieving erection may turn to alcohol in hopes of finding a cure. The fact is that alcohol is a nervous system depressant, and therefore makes getting and keeping an erection more difficult.

Alcohol may also lower sexual inhibitions, because it allows us to ascribe our behaviour to the effects of the alcohol rather than to ourselves. Alcohol is connected with a liberated social role and thus provides an excuse for dubious behaviour. "It was the alcohol," people can say, "not me." When drinking, people may express sexual desires and do things they wouldn't do when sober. For example, those who feel guilty about sex may become sexually active when drinking, because they can later blame the alcohol.

CRITICAL THINKING QUESTIONS

There's evidence that crack cocaine users have more sex partners than nonusers. Is this relationship causal? Does using crack cause multiple partnering? Or could there be other explanations for the association between crack cocaine use and more partners?

Stockbyte/ThinkStock

Alcohol and Sexual Behaviour.
Alcohol can induce feelings of well-being and lower inhibitions, which could be connected with sexual interest and facilitate social and sexual behaviour. However, alcohol reduces fear of the consequences of engaging in risky behaviour—sexual and otherwise. Alcohol is expected to be sexually liberating, and people often live up to social and cultural expectations. Yet as a depressant drug, alcohol in large amounts will biochemically dampen sexual response, and may make sexual response impossible.

Alcohol can also induce feelings of euphoria, which may lead people to believe they're experiencing enhanced sexual arousal and sweep away their qualms about expressing sexual desires. Alcohol appears to impair the ability to weigh information (i.e., information processing) that might otherwise inhibit sexual impulses (Orchowski et al., 2012; Purdie et al., 2011). When people drink, they may be less able to foresee the consequences of inappropriate or illegal behaviour and less likely to stop and think about their own standards of acceptable conduct.

Consuming a small amount of alcohol (e.g., one beer or a glass of wine) is unlikely to have an impact on a person's sexual response. From a physiological perspective, the more alcohol a person consumes, the less able he or she is to respond sexually. A number of studies have shown that consuming large amounts of alcohol reduces the ability of both men and women to become sexually aroused and have orgasms (McKay, 2005).

MARIJUANA (CANNABIS)   Boris Gorzalka at the University of British Columbia and his colleagues reviewed studies on the impact of marijuana on male and female sexuality and the findings can be summarized as follows: (1) marijuana facilitates sexual desire and heightens sexual pleasure among some women; (2) marijuana can facilitate sexual desire and pleasure among men but may hinder erectile functioning; and (3) the effects of marijuana use on both female and male sexuality is dose dependent. That is, smoking a moderate amount of marijuana may have a positive effect on sexual desire and pleasure but consuming a large amount may have the opposite effect (Gorzalka, Hill, & Chang, 2011).

STIMULANTS   Stimulants such as amphetamines ("speed," "uppers," "bennies," "dexies") are reputed to heighten arousal and sensations of orgasm (Frohmader et al., 2010). These drugs can also elevate mood, and sexual pleasure may be heightened by general elation. High doses can give rise to irritability, restlessness, hallucinations, paranoid delusions, insomnia, loss of appetite, and cardiac problems.

Crystal methamphetamine ("crystal meth" or "ice") is used as an aphrodisiac, boosting sexual arousal and lowering sexual inhibitions. It's one of the most addictive street drugs, and its addiction is difficult to treat. Withdrawal typically results in severe pain and depression. It has several negative side effects, including irritability, insomnia, paranoia, and increased aggression. There's concern that it can also damage brain cells, causing memory loss, and can lead to heart attacks and strokes (Ah Shene, 2003). The Canadian AIDS Society has warned that using crystal meth may increase HIV infection, because lowered inhibitions may result in high-risk sexual behaviours.

Cocaine is a natural stimulant extracted from the leaves of the coca plant. It can be ingested in various forms, snorted as a powder, smoked in hardened rock form ("crack" cocaine) or in a freebase form, or injected directly into the bloodstream in liquid form. Cocaine produces a euphoric rush, which tends to ebb quickly. Physically, cocaine constricts blood vessels (reducing the oxygen supply to the heart), elevates blood pressure, and accelerates heart rate.

There's evidence that cocaine enhances sexual arousal in both males and females, in part by increasing levels of the neurotransmitter dopamine (Andersen et al., 2003; Andersen & Tufik, 2005; Festa et al., 2004). Like other stimulants, cocaine use can have negative effects on physical and mental health. The use of crack cocaine is connected with a higher number of sex partners (Maranda et al., 2004).

In a detailed review of the research on recreational drugs and sexuality, Alex McKay (2005) of the Sex Information and Education Council of Canada (SIECCAN) has found that many new users of recreational drugs such as cocaine and methamphetamine report enhanced sexual experiences, but that continued use of these drugs often results in diminished sexual functioning over time, as well as numerous negative general health effects.

Sexual Response and the Brain

The brain may not be an erogenous zone, but it plays a central role in sexual functioning (Fisher, 2000). While genital stimulation without the brain's direct involvement triggers spinal reflexes that produce erection in the male and vaginal lubrication in the female, the same reflexes can be triggered by sexual stimulation that originates in the brain—that is, by erotic memories, fantasies, visual images, and thoughts. The brain may also inhibit sexual responsiveness, as when we experience guilt or anxiety in a sexual situation, or when we suddenly realize, well into a sexual encounter, that we've left the car lights turned on.

Parts of the brain—particularly the **cerebral cortex** and the **limbic system**—play key roles in sexual functioning. Cells in the cerebral cortex fire (transmit messages) when we experience sexual thoughts, images, wishes, and fantasies. These cells interpret sensory information as sexual turn-ons or turn-offs. Seeing your lover disrobe, anticipating a romantic kiss, thinking about a passing sexual fantasy, or viewing an erotic movie can trigger the cortical cells to fire. These cells, in turn, transmit messages through the spinal cord that send blood rushing to the genitals, causing erection or vaginal lubrication. The cortex also provides the conscious sense of self. The cortex judges sexual behaviour as proper or improper, moral or immoral, relaxing or anxiety- or guilt-provoking.

Areas of the brain below the cortex, especially the limbic system (see Figure 4.1), also play roles in sexual processes (Kimble, 1992). For example, when the rear part of a male rat's hypothalamus is stimulated by an electrical probe, the animal mechanically runs through its courting and mounting routine. It nibbles at the ears and back of the neck of a female rat, and mounts her when she responds. Electrical stimulation of the hippocampus and septal nuclei in monkeys produces erections. Klüver and Bucy (1939) found that destruction of areas of the limbic system triggered continuous sexual behaviour in monkeys.

Sex Hormones and Sexual Behaviour

In a television situation comedy, a male adolescent is described as "a hormone with feet." Ask parents why teenagers act the way they do, and you're likely to hear a one-word answer: "Hormones!"

Hormones are chemical substances secreted by the ductless glands of the endocrine system and discharged directly into the bloodstream. Sex hormones released at puberty cause the flowering of **secondary sex characteristics**. In males, these include lengthening of the vocal cords (and consequent lowering of the voice)

Cerebral cortex The wrinkled surface area (grey matter) of the cerebrum (main part of the brain).

Limbic system A group of structures active in memory, motivation, and emotion. These structures form a fringe along the inner edge of the cerebrum.

Hormone A substance, secreted by an endocrine gland, that regulates various body functions.

Secondary sex characteristics Physical traits that differentiate males from females, but are not directly involved in reproduction.

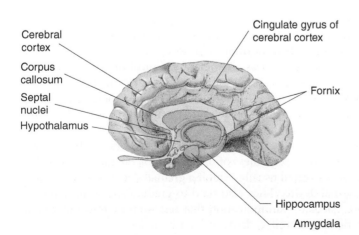

Figure 4.1   Parts of the brain involved in sexual functioning. This is a cross-section of the human brain. When we experience sexual thoughts and mental images, cells in the cerebral cortex interpret this information as sexual turn-ons or turn-offs. The cerebral cortex may then transmit messages through the spinal cord that send blood coursing to the sex organs, leading to erection or vaginal lubrication. The limbic system lies along the inner edge of the cerebrum and is thought to play a role in regulating sexual behaviour.

and growth of facial and pubic hair. In females, they include rounding of the breasts and hips with fatty tissue, and growth of pubic hair.

Organizing and Activating Influences

Sex hormones have organizing and activating effects on behaviour. That is, they influence the type of behaviour that's expressed (an organizing effect), and they influence the frequency or intensity of the drive that motivates the behaviour and the ability to perform the behaviour (activating effects). For example, sex hormones predispose lower animals and possibly people toward stereotypical masculine or feminine mating behaviours (an organizing effect). They also facilitate sexual response and influence sexual desire (activating effects).

The activating effects of testosterone can be clearly observed among male rats. For example, males who are castrated in adulthood and thus deprived of testosterone discontinue sexual behaviour. If they are given injections of testosterone, however, they resume stereotypical male sexual behaviours, such as mounting females.

In rats, testosterone apparently organizes or differentiates the brain in the masculine direction such that adult male rats display stereotypical masculine behaviours—including sniffing (especially sniffing of females) and mounting females—upon activation by testosterone. Male fetuses and newborns normally have sufficient amounts of testosterone in their blood systems to organize their brains in the masculine direction. Female fetuses and newborns normally have lesser amounts of testosterone. Their brains thus become organized in a feminine direction. When female rodents are prenatally exposed to large doses of testosterone, their sexual organs become somewhat masculinized, and they are predisposed toward masculine mating behaviours in adulthood (Banszegi et al., 2010).

Questions remain about the organizing effects of sex hormones on human sexual behaviour. Prenatal sex hormones play a role in the sexual differentiation of the genitalia and of the brain structures, such as the hypothalamus. Their role in patterning sexual behaviour in adulthood remains unclear, however. It has been speculated that prenatal sexual differentiation of the brain may also be connected with sexual orientation.

What of the activating effects of sex hormones on human sex drive and behaviour? Although countless attempts to extract or synthesize aphrodisiacs have failed to produce the real thing, men and women normally produce a genuine aphrodisiac—testosterone. Whatever the early organizing effects of sex hormones in humans, testosterone activates the sex drives of both men and women (Guzick & Hoeger, 2000).

Male Sexual Behaviour

Male sex hormones are known to influence the sex drive and sexual response in men (Maggi, 2012). Evidence of the role of hormones in sex drive is found among men whose testosterone levels have declined as a result of chemical or surgical castration. Surgical castration (removal of the testes) is sometimes performed as a medical treatment for cancer of the prostate or other diseases of the male reproductive tract, such as genital tuberculosis. And some convicted sex offenders have voluntarily undergone castration as a condition of release.

In reviewing the scientific research, Canadian researchers Barbaree and Blanchard (2008) have shown that, regardless of the reason for castration, men who are surgically or chemically castrated usually exhibit a gradual decrease in incidence of sexual fantasies and sexual desire. They also tend to gradually lose the capacity to attain erection and to ejaculate—an indication that testosterone is important in maintaining sexual functioning as well as drive, at least in males.

Castrated men show great variation in sexual interest and functioning, however. Some continue to experience sexual desire and are able to function sexually for years, even decades. Learning appears to play a large role in determining continued sexual response after castration. Men who are sexually experienced before castration show a more gradual decline in sexual activity afterwards. Those who are sexually inexperienced before castration show relatively little or no interest in sex later. Male sexual motivation and functioning thus involve an interplay of hormonal influence and experience.

Further evidence of the relationship between hormonal levels and male sexuality is found in studies of men with **hypogonadism**, a condition marked by abnormally low levels of testosterone production. Hypogonadal men generally experience loss of sexual desire and a decline in sexual activity (Maggi, 2012). Again, hormones don't tell the whole story. Hypogonadal men are capable of erection, at least for a while, even though their sex drives may wane. The role of testosterone as an activator of sex drive in men is further supported by evidence of the effects of testosterone replacement in hypogonadal men. When such men have testosterone injections, their sex drives, fantasies, and activities often return to their former levels (Maggi, 2012).

Hypogonadism A condition marked by abnormally low levels of testosterone production.

Though minimal androgen levels are critical to male sexuality, there's no one-to-one correspondence between hormone levels and sex drive or sexual performance in adults. In men who have ample supplies of testosterone, sexual interest and functioning depend more on learning, fantasies, attitudes, memories, and other psychosocial factors than on hormone levels.

At puberty, however, hormonal variation may play a more direct role in stimulating sexual interest and activity in males. Udry (2001) found, for example, that testosterone levels among teenaged boys predicted sexual interest, masturbation rates, and likelihood of engaging in sexual intercourse. A positive relationship has also been found between testosterone levels in adult men and frequency of sexual intercourse (Maggi, 2012). Moreover, antiandrogens, drugs that reduce androgen levels in the blood system, lead to reductions in sex drive and sexual fantasies (Maggi, 2012).

Female Sexual Behaviour

The female sex hormones estrogen and progesterone play prominent roles in promoting the changes that occur during puberty and in regulating the menstrual cycle. Female sex hormones do not, however, appear to play a direct role in determining sexual motivation or response in human females.

In most mammals, females are sexually receptive only during estrus (when they're "in heat"), a brief period of fertility corresponding to ovulation. Estrus occurs once a year in some species; in others, it occurs periodically during the year, in so-called sexual or mating seasons. Estrogen peaks at the time of ovulation, so there's a close relationship between fertility and sexual receptivity in most female mammals. Women's sexuality, however, is not clearly linked to hormonal fluctuations. Unlike most mammalian females, the human female is sexually responsive during all phases of the reproductive (menstrual) cycle—even during menstruation, when ovarian hormone levels are low—and after menopause.

"Hormones with Feet."
Research shows that androgen levels are connected with sexual interest in both male and female adolescents. Hormone levels are more likely to predict sexual behaviour in adolescent males, however, perhaps because society places greater restraints on female sexuality.

There is some evidence, however, that sexual responsiveness in women is influenced by the presence of circulating androgens, or male sex hormones, in their bodies. Women's adrenal glands, like men's, produce small amounts of androgen (Davis & Braunstein, 2012). The fact that women normally produce smaller amounts of androgen than men doesn't necessarily mean they have weaker sex drives. Rather, women appear to be more sensitive to smaller amounts of androgens. Even so, women's sexual activity increases at points in the menstrual cycle when levels of androgens in the bloodstream are high.

Women who have **ovariectomies**, which are sometimes carried out when a hysterectomy is performed, no longer produce female sex hormones. Nevertheless, they may continue to experience sex drives and interest as before. Loss of the ovarian hormone estradiol may cause vaginal dryness and make sexual activity painful, but it does not necessarily reduce sexual desire. (The dryness can be alleviated by a lubricating jelly or by estrogen-replacement therapy.) However, women whose adrenal glands and ovaries have been removed, so that they no longer produce androgens, gradually lose sexual desire (Davis & Braunstein, 2012). An active and enjoyable sexual history seems to ward off this loss, however, suggestive of the impact of cognitive and experiential factors on human sexual response.

Research provides further evidence on the links between testosterone levels and women's sex drives. Androgen levels predict sexual interest among teenage girls. In contrast to boys, however, girls' androgen levels were unrelated to the likelihood of coital experience. Androgens apparently affect sexual desire in both sexes, but sexual interest may be more likely to be directly translated into sexual activity in men than in women (Carvalho & Nobre, 2010; Petersen & Hyde, 2011). This sex difference may be explained by society's placement of greater restraints on female sexuality.

Androgens thus play a prominent role in activating and maintaining women's sex drives. As with men, however, women's sexuality is too complex to be explained fully by hormone levels. For example, an active and enjoyable sexual history seems to ward off the loss of sexual interest that generally follows the surgical removal of the adrenal glands and ovaries.

Factors Influencing Sexual Arousal

Robin Milhausen (2004) at the University of Guelph has analyzed factors that inhibit or enhance sexual arousal among female and male university students. She's found a number that are common to both sexes.

Both women and men in her study reported that sexual arousal could be enhanced by their partners' positive characteristics (e.g., sense of humour, self-confidence, and ability to make them feel desirable), sex that was varied (e.g., different activities and different settings), and anticipation of sexual encounters. Both sexes also agreed that sexual arousal could be inhibited by a partner's self-consciousness about his or her body, a feeling of giving more than receiving (e.g., always being the one to initiate sex), and worries about various issues (e.g., reputation, STIs, and having to use condoms).

Milhausen (2004) also found gender differences in the importance of certain factors. Women were more inhibited than men about possible sexual violence and exploitation, fear that they weren't good lovers, and fear that they were taking too long to become aroused and/or not having orgasms. They were more aroused than men by their partners' positive characteristics (e.g., relating well to others and doing helpful chores), feeling able to trust their partners, feeling emotionally connected, feeling their partners were sensitive to their needs, and the effects of hormones. Men were more aroused than women by specific sexual stimuli (e.g., seeing their partners' naked bodies, "talking dirty," seeing their partners in sexy outfits, watching erotic films, and quickly advancing to the genitals when starting to have sex).

Ovariectomy Surgical removal of the ovaries.

Models of Sexual Response

Although we may be culturally attuned to focus on gender differences rather than similarities, Masters and Johnson (1966) found that the physiological responses of men and women to sexual stimulation (via intercourse, masturbation, or other sources) are quite alike. The sequence of changes in the body that take place as men and women become progressively more aroused is referred to as the **sexual response cycle.**

Masters and Johnson's Four-Phase Sexual Response Cycle

Masters and Johnson's (1966) four phases of the sexual response cycle consist of excitement, plateau, orgasm, and resolution. Figure 4.2 suggests the levels of sexual arousal associated with each phase.

Both males and females experience **vasocongestion** and **myotonia** early in the response cycle. Vasocongestion is swelling of the genital tissues with blood, which causes erection of the penis and engorgement of the area surrounding the vaginal opening. The testes, nipples, and even earlobes become engorged as blood vessels in these areas dilate. Myotonia is muscle tension. It causes voluntary and involuntary muscle contractions, which produce facial grimaces, spasms in the hands and feet, and eventually, the spasms of orgasm.

THE EXCITEMENT PHASE In younger men, vasocongestion during the **excitement phase** produces penile erection as early as three to eight seconds after stimulation begins. Erection may occur more slowly in older men, but the responses are essentially the same. Erection may subside and return as stimulation varies. The scrotal skin thickens, losing its baggy appearance. The testes increase in size. The testes and scrotum become elevated.

In a woman, vaginal lubrication may start 10 to 30 seconds after stimulation begins. Vasocongestion swells the clitoris, flattens and spreads the labia majora apart, and increases the size of the labia minora. The inner two-thirds of the vagina expands. The vaginal walls thicken and, because of the inflow of blood, turn from

Sexual response cycle Masters and Johnson's model of sexual response, which consists of four phases.

Vasocongestion Swelling of the genital tissues with blood, which causes erection of the penis and engorgement of the area surrounding the vaginal opening.

Myotonia Muscle tension.

Excitement phase The first phase of the sexual response cycle, characterized by erection in the male, vaginal lubrication in the female, and muscle tension and increased heart rate in both the male and the female.

Figure 4.2 Levels of sexual arousal during phases of the sexual response cycle.
Masters and Johnson divide the sexual response cycle into four phases: excitement, plateau, orgasm, and resolution. During the resolution phase, the level of sexual arousal returns to the pre-aroused state. For a man, a refractory period follows orgasm. As shown by the broken line, however, a man can become re-aroused to orgasm once the refractory period is past and his level of sexual arousal has returned to the pre-plateau level. Pattern A for a woman shows a typical response cycle; the broken line indicates multiple orgasms, should they occur. Pattern B shows the cycle for a woman who reaches the plateau phase but for whom arousal is "resolved" without her experiencing orgasm. Pattern C shows the possibility of orgasm in a highly aroused woman who passes quickly through the plateau phase.

Innovative Canadian Research

GENDER, SEXUAL ORIENTATION, AND AROUSAL

Meredith Chivers, a researcher at Queen's University, has conducted groundbreaking research on sexual arousal. In particular, she and her colleagues studied how sexual arousal patterns vary by gender and sexual orientation (Chivers et al., 2007). Participants included both heterosexual and homosexual men and women. The four groups were shown videos depicting men and women engaging in nude exercise, solitary masturbation, same-sex intercourse, and male–female intercourse, as well as copulating chimpanzees. Genital and subjective sexual arousal were recorded.

Arousal was strongest in response to watching the sexual intercourse video, and weakest for the nude exercise one. The gender of the actor was far more important for men than for women, whereas level of sexual activity was more important for women than for men. Heterosexual men were almost exclusively aroused by videos of women, homosexual men were almost exclusively aroused by videos of men, and heterosexual women responded to videos of both men and women.

Chivers and Timmers (2012) conducted a similar study to gauge the sexual responses of heterosexual men and women to sexually explicit audio material. Men were more sexually aroused, both genitally and subjectively, by narratives that described encounters with women rather than encounters with men. Women reported more subjective feelings of arousal when listening to stories involving men; however, they were genitally aroused by material that described sexual situations with either men or women. Women were also more likely to be genitally aroused by stories of encounters between strangers or long-term romantic partners, and less so by encounters with friends. The nature of a relationship had no effect on the degree of male genital sexual response. These findings raise interesting questions for future research about the effect that relationship status might have on female sexual response.

In another study, Chivers and her colleagues (Rieger, Chivers, & Bailey, 2005) compared the sexual responses of bisexual men with those of gay and heterosexual men who were asked to watch either men or women engaging in sexual activity. As expected, the heterosexual men were more aroused by the female actors, and the gay men were more aroused by the male actors. Most of the bisexual men experienced greater genital arousal when watching the male actors; however, they were divided in their subjective feelings of arousal, and were just as likely to say they were aroused by the female as by the male actors.

Chivers and her colleagues (Lawrence, Latty, Chivers, & Bailey, 2005) also studied male-to-female transgender people both before and after gender reassignment surgery. The trans people who were gay before reassignment were more aroused by sexual images of men, while the trans people who were heterosexual before reassignment were more aroused by images of women. The arousal responses after surgery were similar to the arousal responses before surgery.

Sex flush A reddish rash that appears on the chest or breasts late in the excitement phase of the sexual response cycle.

Plateau phase The second phase of the sexual response cycle, characterized by increased vasocongestion, muscle tension, heart rate, and blood pressure, in preparation for orgasm.

their normal pink to a deeper hue. The uterus becomes engorged and elevated. The breasts enlarge, and blood vessels near the surface become more prominent.

Late in this phase, the skin may take on a rosy **sex flush**, which varies with intensity of arousal and is more pronounced in women than in men. The nipples may become erect in both genders, especially in response to direct stimulation. Both men and women show some increase in myotonia, heart rate, and blood pressure.

THE PLATEAU PHASE   The level of arousal remains somewhat constant during the **plateau phase** of sexual response. Nevertheless, it's an advanced state of arousal that precedes orgasm. A man in this phase shows a slight increase in the circumference of the coronal ridge of the penis. The penile glans turns a purplish hue, a sign of vasocongestion. The testes are elevated further into position for ejaculation, and may reach one and a half times their unaroused size. The Cowper's glands secrete a few droplets of fluid that are found at the tip of the penis (see Figure 4.3).

In a woman, vasocongestion swells the tissues of the outer one-third of the vagina, contracting the vaginal opening and building the **orgasmic platform** (see Figure 4.4). The inner part of the vagina expands fully. The uterus becomes fully elevated. The clitoris shortens and withdraws beneath the clitoral hood. The woman (or her partner) may feel that the clitoris has become lost and mistake this as a sign that her sexual arousal is waning, when it's actually increasing.

The labia minora turn red, becoming a deep wine colour in women who have borne children, and bright red in women who have not. This reddened skin is known as **sex skin**. Further engorgement of the areolas of the breasts may make it seem that the nipples have lost part of their erection. The Bartholin's glands secrete a fluid that resembles mucus.

About one man in four—and about three women in four—shows a sex flush, which often appears in the plateau phase. Myotonia may cause facial grimaces and spasmodic contractions in the hands and feet. Breathing becomes rapid, similar to panting, and the heart rate may increase to 100 to 160 beats per minute. Blood pressure continues to rise. The increase in heart rate is usually less dramatic with masturbation than during partnered sexual activity.

THE ORGASMIC PHASE   The orgasmic phase in the male consists of two stages of muscular contraction. In the first stage, contractions of the vas deferens, seminal vesicles, ejaculatory duct, and prostate gland cause seminal fluid to collect in the urethral bulb at the base of the penis (see Figure 4.3). The bulb expands to accommodate the fluid. The internal sphincter of the bladder contracts, preventing seminal fluid from entering the bladder in a backward, retrograde ejaculation and

Orgasmic platform
Thickening of the walls of the outer one-third of the vagina (due to vasocongestion) during the plateau phase of the sexual response cycle.

Sex skin The reddened skin of the labia minora during the plateau phase.

Figure 4.3   The male genitals during the phases of the sexual response cycle.

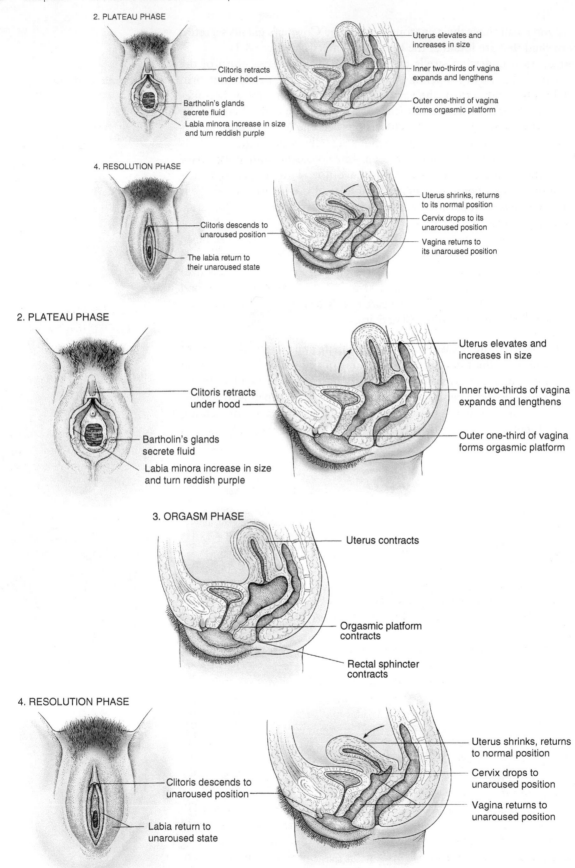

Figure 4.4   The female genitals during the phases of the sexual response cycle.

Innovative Canadian Research

GENITAL VERSUS SUBJECTIVE SEXUAL AROUSAL

Sexual concordance refers to the degree to which actual genital response and self-reported sexual arousal correspond with each other. Studies that explore the differences in sexual concordance between men and women present participants with various forms of sexual stimuli such as erotic audio recordings or videos. In response to the stimuli, male genital arousal is measured by the degree of penile erection, and female genital arousal is measured by genital vasocongestion or vaginal blood flow. Questionnaires or interviews are used to measure perceived (i.e., subjective) levels of sexual arousal.

Canadian researchers have found that men tend to display a higher degree of sexual concordance than women (Chivers, Seto, Lalumiere, Laan & Gimbos, 2010; Suschinsky & Lalumiere, 2012). That is, when men are genitally aroused they're almost always subjectively aware of it. Women, however, vary in their awareness of genital arousal. Huberman, Suschinsky, Lalumiere, and Chivers (2013) raise the possibility from the findings of

their research that some women might underreport feelings of sexual arousal in order to conform to social norms that discourage female sexual responsivity. This bias may be one factor that contributes to the noted differences in sexual concordance between men and women.

Rosemary Basson (2002) at Vancouver General Hospital suggests that sexual arousal is a more complex process for women than for men. According to Basson, when a woman experiences genital vasocongestion, she can experience a range of subjective responses:

- She may not be aware of the physical arousal.
- She may be only vaguely aware of the physical arousal.
- She may be aware of the physical sensations, yet not define them as sexual.
- She may interpret the arousal as sexual but not experience the sensation as enjoyable.

Basson analyzes a number of factors that may account for these responses, such as negative sexual experiences in the past, feelings of inadequacy or guilt, and distractions such as concern over personal appearance, the safety of the situation, and feelings toward her partner.

preventing urine from mixing with semen. Collection of semen in the urethral bulb produces feelings of ejaculatory inevitability—the sensation that nothing will stop the ejaculate from "coming." This sensation lasts for about two to three seconds.

In the second stage, the external sphincter of the bladder relaxes, allowing the passage of semen. Contractions of muscles surrounding the urethra, the urethral bulb, and the base of the penis propel the ejaculate through the urethra and out of the body. Sensations of pleasure tend to be related to the strength of the contractions and the amount of seminal fluid produced. The first three to four contractions are generally most intense, occurring at 0.8-second intervals (five contractions every four seconds). Another two to four contractions occur at a somewhat slower pace. Rates and patterns vary somewhat from man to man.

Orgasm in the female is manifested by 3 to 15 contractions of the pelvic muscles that surround the vaginal barrel. The contractions first occur at 0.8-second intervals, producing, as in the male, a release of sexual tension. Another three to six weaker, slower contractions follow. The spacing of these contractions is generally more variable in women than in men. The uterus and the anal sphincter also contract rhythmically. Uterine contractions occur in waves from the top to the cervix.

In both genders, muscles throughout the body go into spasm. Blood pressure and heart rate peak, with the heart beating up to 180 times per minute. Respiration may increase to 40 breaths per minute.

Resolution phase The fourth phase of the sexual response cycle, during which the body gradually returns to its pre-aroused state.

THE RESOLUTION PHASE The period following orgasm, when the body returns to its pre-aroused state, is called the **resolution phase**. Following ejaculation, the man loses his erection in two stages. The first occurs within about a minute: the erection loses half of its volume as blood from the corpora cavernosa empties into other parts of the body. The second stage occurs over several minutes: the remaining tumescence subsides as the corpus spongiosum empties, the testes and scrotum return to normal size, and the scrotum regains its wrinkled appearance.

In women, orgasm also triggers release of blood from engorged areas. In the absence of continued stimulation, swelling of the areolas decreases and the nipples return to their normal size. The sex flush lightens rapidly. In about 5 to 10 seconds, the clitoris descends to its normal position. The clitoris, vaginal barrel, uterus, and labia gradually shrink to their pre-aroused sizes. The labia minora turn lighter (the sex skin disappears) in about 10 to 15 seconds.

In both men and women, most muscle tension (myotonia) tends to dissipate within five minutes after orgasm. Blood pressure, heart rate, and respiration may also return to pre-arousal levels within a few minutes. About 30% to 40% of men and women find their palms, soles, or entire bodies covered with a sheen of perspiration. Both men and women may feel relaxed and satiated.

Although the processes by which the body returns to its pre-arousal state are similar in men and women, there's an important gender difference during the resolution phase. Unlike women, men enter a **refractory period**, when they're physiologically incapable of experiencing another orgasm or ejaculation. (This is similar to the way a flash on a camera can't be set off again immediately after it's used—it has to be recharged.) The refractory period in adolescent males may last only minutes, whereas in men aged 50 and over it may last from several minutes to a day. Because women don't undergo a refractory period, they can become quickly re-aroused to the point of repeated (multiple) orgasms, if they desire, and can receive continued sexual stimulation (see Figure 4.2).

Myotonia and vasocongestion may take an hour or more to dissipate in people who are aroused but don't reach orgasm. Persistent pelvic vasocongestion in a man may cause "blue balls"—the slang term for a throbbing ache. Some men plead with their partners to have intercourse, on the theory that it's unfair to decline after stimulating them to this point. The ache can be relieved through masturbation or intercourse or allowed to dissipate naturally. Although it may be uncomfortable, it's not dangerous, and it's no excuse to pressure or coerce someone into sexual activity.

"Blue" sensations are not limited to men. Women, too, may experience unpleasant pelvic throbbing if they become highly aroused and don't find release. And women, too, can relieve pelvic throbbing through masturbation.

Refractory period The time following a response (e.g., orgasm) when an individual no longer responds to stimulation (e.g., sexual stimulation).

Kaplan's Three Stages of Sexual Response

Helen Singer Kaplan was a prominent sex therapist and author of several professional books (1974, 1987) on sex therapy. Whereas Masters and Johnson proposed a four-stage model of sexual response, Kaplan developed a three-stage model consisting of desire, excitement, and orgasm.

Kaplan's model was an outgrowth of her clinical experience with people with sexual dysfunctions. She believed their problems could best be classified according to the three stages of sexual response. Her model makes it convenient for clinicians to classify sexual dysfunctions involving desire (e.g., low or absent desire), excitement (e.g., problems with erection in the male or lubrication in the female), and orgasm (e.g., premature ejaculation in the male or orgasmic dysfunction in the female).

CRITICAL THINKING QUESTIONS

Masters and Johnson describe biological processes (i.e., excitement, plateau, orgasm, and resolution) in sexual response. Kaplan and Basson introduce psychological components (e.g., desire, intimacy). Is it important that models of sexual response include both biological and psychological components? Why or why not?

Innovative Canadian Research

THE SUBJECTIVE EXPERIENCE OF ORGASM

Studies suggest that the orgasms of both genders may feel quite similar. In one study, Kenneth Mah of Princess Margaret Hospital in Toronto and Yitzchak Binik at McGill University (2002) developed a scale to measure the subjective experiences of orgasm among men and women. They wanted to determine what characteristics were common to the human experience of orgasm. They asked university students to rate adjectives describing orgasms they experienced both during masturbation and during sex with partners.

The findings supported a two-dimensional model of the psychological experience of orgasm. The first dimension is sensory, with the following components:

- A building sensation
- A flooding sensation
- A flushing sensation
- A spurting sensation
- A throbbing sensation
- General spasms

The second dimension of the orgasm experience is emotional, with the following components:

- Pleasurable satisfaction
- Relaxation
- Emotional intimacy
- Ecstasy

In a subsequent analysis of the data, King, Belsky, Mah, and Binik (2010) found that the women in the study experienced differences in orgasm types, depending on whether they occurred during solitary masturbation or partnered sexual activity. On average, orgasms that occurred as a result of partnered activity included significantly more flushing sensations, general spasms, pleasurable satisfaction, emotional intimacy, and ecstasy. The women reported no differences between orgasms resulting from partnered activity and solitary masturbation with respect to sensations of building, flooding, spurting, and throbbing. Orgasms during solitary masturbation, however, resulted in greater feelings of relaxation than did orgasms from partnered sexual activity.

In a qualitative study of heterosexual undergraduate students, Claire Salisbury and William Fisher (2013) at Western University explored the importance of female orgasm for men and women in a sexual relationship. Many men believed that women needed regular orgasms in order to be satisfied with their sexual interactions, while women often stated that their pleasure during sexual interactions was not dependent on orgasm. Female orgasm was a source of pleasure for men, and lack of orgasm often resulted in feelings of inadequacy as a lover. However, some men also tied this concern with a partner's pleasure to the status of a relationship, with concern being highest in romantic relationships and often lacking in casual encounters. Women were very much aware that their perceived sexual pleasure had a direct effect on the male ego, and this concern led some women to fake orgasms in order to please their partners. As well, many women expressed reluctance to communicate their desire for clitoral stimulation for fear that their partner would feel inadequate.

Kaplan's model is noteworthy for designating desire as a separate phase of sexual response. Lack of sexual interest or desire is one of the problems most commonly brought to sex therapists.

Basson's Intimacy Model of Female Sexual Response

Rosemary Basson (2008) at the British Columbia Centre for Sexual Medicine at Vancouver General Hospital has developed an intimacy-based model of female sexual response that she argues is especially relevant for women in long-term relationships. While Kaplan's model assumes that the process of female sexual response begins with desire, Basson's model suggests that, for many women, the process does not necessarily begin with feelings of desire but rather with feelings of intimacy with their partners. Basson argues that many women in longer-term relationships are motivated to respond to sexual stimuli if they feel that becoming sexually involved will enhance that intimacy.

According to the Basson model, a woman will often begin her sexual encounters with a nonsexual or neutral state of mind. Once she begins to feel sexually aroused for intimacy reasons, she'll continue the experience for sexual reasons. At this point, she's responsive to sexual stimulation, such as breast or genital touching, which increases her arousal and then sexual desire. If she finds the outcome both physically and emotionally satisfying, it increases her feelings of intimacy with her partner, and motivates her to become sexually involved again in the future.

This model allows for the possibility that arousal may precede sexual desire, and that arousal may not lead to orgasm. Basson acknowledges the possibility that spontaneous sexual desire may occur among women outside of the intimacy model, and that this may lead to self-stimulation or partnered sexual activity.

Comparing Models of Female Sexual Response

William Fisher at Western University and his colleague Michael Sand (Sand & Fisher, 2007) conducted a study to see how closely women felt their own sexual experiences corresponded to the Masters and Johnson, Kaplan, and Basson models of sexual response. The research sample consisted of 133 nurses living in the United States.

Interestingly, almost equal proportions of women endorsed each of the three models as best reflecting their own patterns of sexual response. This suggests that none of the models uniformly captures the sexual response patterns of all women. Perhaps there's considerable variability between women in terms of sexual response patterns, and more than one model is required for sexuality research and therapy.

The Enigmatic Orgasm

Orgasm is often thought of as the pinnacle of sexual experience. Some people think a sexual experience is incomplete unless both partners have an orgasm. "Did you come?" the hopeful lover asks his or her partner. With experience, however, many come to realize that achieving orgasm is not the be-all and end-all of a good sexual experience. Indeed, many sex therapists encourage their clients to refrain from making orgasm the goal of sex, emphasizing that it's just one component of the total experience.

Yet there can be no doubt that orgasm provides intensely pleasurable sensations, and biologically speaking, it does represent the peak of sexual excitement. One of the most fascinating things about orgasm is that, while we can easily describe it as a biological process (i.e., a series of involuntary contractions in the pelvic area), we find it much more difficult to describe exactly how it feels. How can we accurately put the sensations of orgasm into words? Do one person's orgasms feel the same as another person's? Do female orgasms feel similar to male orgasms? The answers to these questions are elusive. Although most of us are familiar with it through personal experience, orgasm remains somewhat of an enigma.

Orgasm is also often the subject of myth and misunderstanding. For example, there's long been a social expectation that women should have orgasms through vaginal penetration. In the past, some women have felt inadequate if they couldn't reach orgasm during intercourse. As public awareness of human sexuality has grown in recent years, however, more and more women—and their partners—have learned that many (if not most) women require some form of stimulation of the clitoris before they can have orgasms.

Multiple Orgasms

Kinsey and his colleagues (1953) reported that 14% of his female respondents regularly had **multiple orgasms**. This surprised both his fellow scientists and the community at large. Many people were aghast that women could have more than one orgasm at a time. There were comments that the women in the Kinsey surveys must be "nymphomaniacs" who were incapable of being satisfied with the "normal" complement of one orgasm per occasion. Just 13 years later, Masters and Johnson (1966) reported that most—if not all—women were capable of multiple orgasms.

Although all women may have a biological capability for multiple orgasms, not all women report them. In a survey of 720 nurses, 43% reported experiencing multiple orgasms (Darling et al., 1991)—and nearly half of those occurred when they used vibrators, which they generally applied to their clitorises. The women reported that the orgasms they experienced with vibrators were more intense than other kinds. Two-thirds of those who used vibrators did so in conjunction with sexual activity with their partners.

By Masters and Johnson's definition, men are not capable of achieving multiple orgasms, because they enter a refractory period following ejaculation. Men who want more than one orgasm during one session may have to pause for a while. Women, however, can maintain a high level of arousal between multiple orgasms, and can have them in rapid succession, because they don't have a refractory period. Women can continue to have orgasms if they continue to receive effective stimulation (and, of course, are interested in continuing). Some men thus refrain from reaching orgasm until their partners have had the desired number. The differential capacity for multiple orgasms is one of the major gender differences in sexual response.

Some men have two or more orgasms without ejaculation ("dry orgasms") before a final ejaculatory orgasm. These men may not enter a refractory period following their initial dry orgasms, and may therefore be able to maintain stimulation at near-peak levels.

Masters and Johnson (1966) found that some women experienced 20 or more consecutive orgasms by masturbating. Still, few women have multiple orgasms during most sexual encounters, and many are satisfied with just one per occasion. Some women who have read or heard about female orgasmic capacity wonder what's wrong with them if they're content with just one. Nothing is wrong with them, of course. A biological capacity does not create a behavioural requirement.

How Many Kinds of Orgasms Do Women Have?

Until Masters and Johnson published their laboratory findings, many people believed there were two types of female orgasm, as proposed by psychoanalyst Sigmund Freud: the clitoral orgasm and the vaginal orgasm. Clitoral orgasm was achieved through direct clitoral stimulation such as masturbation. It was seen by psychoanalysts (mostly male psychoanalysts, naturally) as emblematic of a childhood fixation—a throwback to an erogenous pattern acquired during childhood masturbation.

The term "vaginal orgasm" referred to an orgasm achieved through deep penile thrusting during intercourse. It was thought to be a sign of mature sexuality. Freud argued that women achieved sexual maturity when they gave up clitoral stimulation for vaginal stimulation.

This view would be little more than an academic footnote if it weren't for the fact that the many (if not most) adult women who require direct clitoral stimulation

Multiple orgasms One or more additional orgasms following the first, occurring within a short period of time and before the body has returned to its pre-plateau level of arousal.

to reach orgasm, even during vaginal penetration, have been led to believe they're sexually inadequate. There's also an element of heterosexism in the Freudian view of mature female sexuality, since lesbians obviously don't rely on penile thrusting for sexual pleasure or orgasm.

Masters and Johnson (1966) were able to find only one kind of orgasm, physiologically speaking, regardless of whether stimulation was clitoral or vaginal. All orgasms involve spasmodic contractions of the pelvic muscles surrounding the vaginal barrel, leading to a release of sexual tension.

In men, it also doesn't matter how orgasm is achieved. Whether through masturbation, oral sex, or anal or vaginal penetration, orgasm still involves the same physiological processes—involuntary contractions of the pelvic muscles at the base of the penis expel semen and release sexual tension. A woman or a man might prefer one source of orgasm to another (e.g., with a lover or by masturbation, or with one person rather than another), but the biological events that define orgasm remain the same.

The purported distinction between clitoral and vaginal orgasm also rests on the assumption that the clitoris isn't stimulated during vaginal penetration. Masters and Johnson showed this to be false. They found that penile thrusting during intercourse draws the clitoral hood back and forth against the clitoris. Vaginal pressure also heightens blood flow in the clitoris, further setting the stage for orgasm (Cai et al., 2008).

Sexuality and Disability

Millions of Canadians live with physical or intellectual disabilities. Researchers at Trent University who study people with disabilities have found that the disabled are often seen as sexless and childlike (Scott & Humphreys, 2007). Such views are based on misconceptions. Some of these myths and stereotypes may be eroding, in part because of the success of civil and social rights movements of people with disabilities. Films such as *Born on the Fourth of July*, *My Left Foot*, and more recently *The Sessions* have helped to raise awareness of the fact that sexuality is as central to the lives of people living with disabilities as it is to people without them.

A person may be born with or acquire a bodily impairment, or suffer a loss of function or a disfiguring change in appearance. Although the disability may require adjustments before the person can engage in sexual activity, most people with disabilities have the same sexual needs, feelings, and desires as those without disabilities. Their ability to express these needs and feelings depends on the physical limitations imposed by their disabilities, how they adjust to their disabilities, and the availability of partners.

People with intellectual or developmental disabilities also face challenges with respect to sexuality. For example, youth with developmental disabilities may require sex education materials specifically designed to accommodate their levels of comprehension and pace of learning. People with profound intellectual or developmental disabilities may require guidance and education around issues of consent to sexual activity, as they may be sexually exploited by others, and some benefit from learning clear guidelines for appropriate sexual behaviours and relationships.

However, the greatest challenge faced by people with disabilities with respect to sexuality is that they must live in a society where myths, misconceptions, and negative stereotypes about sexuality and disability abound. For example, people with visible physical disabilities are confronted by narrow cultural representations of the "body beautiful" and standards of attractiveness. People with intellectual or developmental disabilities suffer immensely from the belief that they're incapable of healthy sexual and romantic relationships.

Researchers at the University of Alberta (Esmail, Darby, Walter, & Knupp, 2010) have conducted focus groups with service providers, people with disabilities, and the general public to identify societal perceptions and attitudes toward sexuality and disability. To stimulate discussion, they showed participants the documentary film *SexAbility*. Based on their research, the authors concluded that there's a significant stigma attached to the sexuality of people with disabilities. "Stigma can lead individuals to internalize concepts of asexuality," they wrote, "and may impact confidence, desire, and ability to find a partner, while distorting one's overall sexual self-concept, due to these sociocultural barriers" (p. 1154).

For young people, establishing sexual relationships generally demands some distance from parents. People with disabilities who are physically dependent on their parents may find it especially difficult to develop sexual relationships. Parents who acknowledge their children's sexual development can help facilitate dating. Far too often, however, as Cole (1988) reports, parents with adolescent daughters who have a disability may become overprotective:

> In many cases, the families are intensely concerned about the sexual and emotional vulnerability of the daughter and hope that "nothing bad" will happen to her. They may, therefore, encourage her to wear youthful clothing and to stay a safe little girl. The families can mistakenly assume there may be no sexual life ahead of her, and protect her from this perceived bitter reality with youthful clothing and little-girlish ways. The result can be, of course, that the young, emerging woman may become societally handicapped in learning how to conduct herself as a sexual woman. She will be infantilized (pp. 282–283).

In such families, young people with disabilities sometimes get the message that sex is not for them. As they mature, they may need education to help them accept the normality of their sexual feelings and to accept that they have the right to be sexual as much as anyone else does.

Sex education in schools and other sources of information about sexuality have typically neither included nor acknowledged the information needs of people with disabilities (Di Giulio, 2003; Esmail et al., 2010). Fortunately, there are signs of progress. The Public Health Agency of Canada (2012) has published a resource document titled *Questions & Answers – Sexual Health Education for Youth with Physical Disabilities* aimed at assisting in the creation of supportive and healthy learning environments for school-aged youth with physical disabilities and in providing them with sexual health education. Alberta Health Services (2013) provides, on the website teachingsexualhealth.ca, a resource called *Sexuality and Disability: A Guide for Parents* which stresses to parents the importance of fully educating their sons and daughters about sexuality. At the community level, sexuality education programs for people with disabilities are more common today. For example, the Anne Johnston Health Station (www.ajhs.ca) in Toronto offers a program called *SexAbility* that provides sexual health information to youth and adults with mobility disabilities through peer-to-peer education workshops, social events and resources. While information on sexuality and disability was once hard to locate, the Internet now offers a wealth of information on sexuality and disability.

Physical Disabilities

According to Margaret Nosek and her colleagues (2011), sexual wellness for people with disabilities, as for all people, involves five factors:

- A positive sexual self-concept (i.e., seeing oneself as valuable, both sexually and as a person).
- Knowledge about sexuality.
- Positive, productive relationships.
- An ability to cope with social, environmental, physical, and emotional barriers to sexuality.
- Maintenance of good general and sexual health, within personal limitations.

This model applies to all of us, of course. Let's now consider aspects of specific physical disabilities and human sexuality.

MULTIPLE SCLEROSIS   Multiple sclerosis (MS) is a chronic, unpredictable disease that affects the nervous system. The tissue called myelin, which surrounds and protects nerve cells, disintegrates, leaving scar tissue in its place. MS impairs sexual functioning, and people with MS report more sexual problems than people without the disorder (Forbes et al., 2006; McCabe, 2004). There's a good deal of individual variation, however. The disorder's progression and effects don't follow a straight line. Many people with MS in good relationships enjoy fine sex lives for many years.

Researchers at the University of Alberta (Esmail et al., 2007) interviewed couples in which the wives had MS, to find out how it affects sexual relationships. The wives reported that MS negatively affected their sexual functioning and enjoyment, as well as their feelings of sexual desirability. They kept these feelings hidden from their husbands and focused instead on sexually pleasing them, worrying that otherwise their husbands might decide to leave them and find new partners. Because the wives didn't reveal their true sexual status, their husbands thought their wives' sexuality was unaffected by MS.

Cerebral palsy A muscular disorder caused by damage to the central nervous system, usually before or during birth, and characterized by spastic paralysis.

CEREBRAL PALSY   **Cerebral palsy** (CP) doesn't generally impair sexual interest, capacity for orgasm, or fertility. Depending on the nature and degree of muscle spasticity and the lack of voluntary muscle control, however, people with CP may have to adjust sexual activities and positions accordingly (Cho et al., 2004).

People with disabilities such as cerebral palsy often suffer social rejection during adolescence and perceive themselves as unfit for, or unworthy of, intimate sexual relationships, especially with people who aren't disabled. They're often socialized into an asexual role. Sensitive counselling can help them understand and accept themselves as sexual beings, promote a more positive body image, and provide the social skills to establish intimate relationships.

SPINAL CORD INJURIES   People who suffer physical disability as a result of traumatic injury or physical illness must not only learn to cope with their physical limitations but also adjust to a world designed for nondisabled people. Most of those who suffer disabling spinal cord injuries are young, active men and women. Automobile or pedestrian accidents account for about half of these cases. Other common causes include bullet or stab wounds, sports injuries, and falls.

Depending on the location of the injury relative to the spinal cord, a loss of voluntary control (paralysis) can occur in either the legs (paraplegia) or all four limbs (quadriplegia). A loss of sensation may also occur in parts of the body that lie below the site of injury.

The effect of spinal cord injury on sexual response depends on the injury's site and severity. Men have two erection centres in the spinal cord—a higher centre in the lumbar region, which controls psychogenic erections, and a lower one in the sacral region, which controls reflexive erections. When damage occurs at or above the lumbar centre, the man loses the capacity for psychogenic erections, which occur in response to mental stimulation alone (e.g., viewing erotic video or fantasizing). He may still be able to achieve reflexive erections via direct stimulation of the penis, because this type of erection is controlled by the sacral erection centre, which is located in a lower portion of the spinal cord. He can't feel any genital sensations, however, because the nerve connections to the brain are severed. A man with damage to the sacral erection centre loses the capacity for reflexive erections but can still achieve psychogenic erections as long as his upper spinal cord remains intact.

The ability to obtain an erection following spinal cord injury is dependent on the specific site and severity of the injury (Riccardi, Szabo, & Yribarren-Poullos, 2007). Commonly used medications for erectile dysfunction such as Viagra, Cialis,

Innovative Canadian Research

IMPROVING SEXUAL FUNCTION IN MEN WITH SPINAL CORD INJURIES

In an experimental study, researchers in Quebec (Courtois et al., 2007) found that some vibrators are far more successful than others in helping men with spinal cord injuries ejaculate. Some who cannot ejaculate with a vibrator alone can ejaculate when taking the prescription oral drug Midodrine about 30 minutes before using the vibrator. The researchers believe proper instruction and assistance, preferably in a hospital setting, will allow the majority of men with spinal injuries to ejaculate. Courtois and colleagues (2011) have also developed a questionnaire that will help men with spinal cord injuries become more aware of the physiological changes that accompany arousal and ejaculation. These changes include cardiovascular, respiratory, muscular, and autonomic responses, and may occur to varying degrees depending on the nature and location of the injury.

Ejaculation is not the only source of the physical sensations associated with sexual pleasure. Researchers in Vancouver have conducted innovative experiments with spinal cord injured men who lack penile sensation, exploring the use of a sensory substitution device that captures the motion of sexual activity and maps it to an electrotactile stimulation array on the man's tongue (Borisoff, Elliot, Hocaloski, & Birch, 2010). Using this system, they theorized, the men should have been able to perceive rhythmic up-and-down hand stroking of their penises as a flowing motion back and forth on their tongues. Although the men using the system did not report orgasm-like sensations, they did report increased levels of sexual pleasure.

and Levitra can be helpful for men with spinal cord injury, particularly those who are able to have reflexive erections (Elliot, 2006). Overall, researchers have found that about three out of four men with spinal cord injuries are able to achieve erections, but only about one in ten continues to ejaculate naturally. Others can be helped to ejaculate with the aid of vibrators.

Retention of sexual response in women also depends on the site and severity of the injury. Women may lose the ability to experience genital sensations or to lubricate normally during sexual stimulation (Komisaruk & Whipple, 2005). Breast sensations may remain intact, however, making this area even more erotogenic. Most women with spinal cord injuries can engage in intercourse, become impregnated, and deliver vaginally. A survey of 68 spinal cord injuries women showed that about half were able to achieve orgasm as a result of erotic audiovisual material combined with manual genital stimulation (Sipski et al., 2001).

Couples facing the challenge of spinal cord injuries may expand their sexual repertoires to focus less on genital stimulation (except to attain the reflexes of erection and lubrication) and more on parts of the body that retain sensation. Stimulation of some areas, such as the ears, neck, and breasts (in both men and women), can yield pleasurable erotic sensations.

SENSORY DISABILITIES   Sensory disabilities, such as blindness and deafness, do not directly affect genital responsiveness. Still, sexuality may be affected in many ways. A person who has been blind since birth or early childhood may have difficulty understanding a partner's anatomy. Sex education curricula have been designed to enable visually impaired people to learn about sexual anatomy via models.

Deaf people, too, often lack knowledge about sexuality. Their ability to comprehend the social cues involved in forming and maintaining intimate relationships may also be impaired. Sex education programs based on sign language help many hearing-impaired people become more socially perceptive and knowledgeable about the physical aspects of sex.

People with visual and hearing impairments often lack self-esteem and self-confidence, problems that make it difficult for them to establish intimate relationships. Counselling may help them to become more aware of their sexuality and to develop social skills.

OTHER PHYSICAL DISABILITIES AND IMPAIRMENTS   Specific disabilities pose particular challenges and limitations when it comes to sexual functioning. **Arthritis** may make it difficult or painful to bend the arms, knees, and hips. Sexual activities that minimize discomfort may be helpful, and so might applying moist heat to the joints before sexual relations.

For a heterosexual couple, a male amputee may find that he's better balanced in the lateral-entry or female-superior position than in the male-superior position. Gay and lesbian couples can experiment with different positions and techniques for sexual pleasuring that accommodate for limited mobility or function. A woman with limited hand function may find it difficult or impossible to insert a diaphragm and may need to ask for her partner's help or switch to another method of contraception. Sensitivity to one another's needs is vital for couples in which one member has a disability, just as it is for able-bodied couples.

Intellectual and Developmental Disabilities

People with intellectual disabilities (e.g., impaired cognitive functioning), such as developmental disabilities (e.g., mental or physical impairments that begin to occur before age 18), are often stereotyped as incapable of understanding their sexual desires. People with developmental disabilities are sometimes assumed to lack sexuality and to maintain childlike innocence throughout their lives. At the same time, it's widely acknowledged that individuals with limited mental capacity are at higher risk to become the victims of sexual abuse and exploitation and may not be able, in some contexts, to consent to sexual activity with others (Plaut, 2006; Servais, 2006).

Some people stereotype those with developmental disabilities in the opposite direction, as having stronger-than-normal sex drives that they're incapable of controlling. These stereotypes are exaggerated. In cases where people with developmental disabilities have acted inappropriately, it's often because they've never received adequate sexuality education, or they've been forbidden by their families or caregivers to express themselves sexually in any way. Not surprisingly, developmentally disabled people deprived of the opportunity to learn about sexuality and appropriate social conventions—like anyone under these conditions—may behave inappropriately. Appropriate sexual health and relationship education is crucial to the health and well-being of developmentally disabled people.

Although the physical changes of puberty may be delayed in people with developmental disabilities, most develop the same sexual feelings as other youth. Most are capable of learning about their sexuality and can enter into rewarding, responsible intimate relationships (Gross, 2006).

Expanding Sexual Horizons

One of the greatest impediments to sexual fulfillment among people with disabilities is finding a loving and supportive partner. Hopefully, this barrier will decrease as stereotypes that portray disabled people as undesirable erode. Depending on the nature of the disability, a non-disabled partner may need to be open to assuming a more active sexual role, to compensate for the limitations of the partner with the disability. Two partners with disabilities need to be sensitive to one another's needs and physical limitations.

Arthritis A progressive disease characterized by inflammation and pain in the joints.

CRITICAL THINKING QUESTIONS

Should group homes for intellectually or developmentally challenged people have policies about sexual activity between residents? If so, can you think of factors that should be considered in setting such a policy?

Applied Knowledge

A COMPREHENSIVE GUIDE TO SEX AND DISABILITY

Toronto educators Miriam Kaufman, Cory Silverberg, and Fran Odette (2007) conducted a survey of people with disabilities, asking about their beliefs, feelings, and unmet needs around sexuality. The survey responses provided the basis for their book *The Ultimate Guide to Sex and Disability: For All of Us Who Live with Disabilities, Chronic Pain, and Illness.*

This sex guide is aimed at people of all ages and all sexual identities. It's intended to improve readers' sexual self-esteem and sex lives, and to help them become sexually independent. Topics include:

- Where to find partners.
- How to talk to partners about sex and disability.
- How to discuss sex with health care providers.

- Instruction on masturbation, oral sex, vaginal penetration, and anal sex.
- Sexual positions that minimize stress and maximize pleasure.
- How to deal with fatigue, pain, and spasms during sex.
- Adapting sex toys to make them work for you.

The book provides an extensive list of resources.

Living with disabilities can prompt individuals and couples to explore avenues for creative sexual expression. They might expand their sexual repertoires to incorporate ways of pleasuring one another that are not fixated on genital stimulation or conventional standards of sexual activity. Indeed, freeing themselves from conventional standards for what a satisfying sexual experience must include (e.g., vaginal or anal penetration, genital orgasm) can enable disabled people to use their imaginations to expand their sexual horizons in ways that non-disabled people might feel inhibited about. As Penny, a disabled woman, puts it, "If you're a sexually active disabled person, and comfortable with the sexual side of your life, it's remarkable how dull and unimaginative non-disabled people's sex lives can appear" (Shakespeare, 2000, p. 163).

Summing Up

Every sense plays a role in sexual experience, but some are more important than others.

Visual information plays a major role in human sexual attraction. Visual cues can be sexual turn-ons or turn-offs.

Although the sense of smell plays a lesser role in governing sexual arousal in humans than in lower mammals, particular odours can be sexual turn-ons or turn-offs for people. Many organisms are sexually aroused by naturally produced chemicals called pheromones, but their role in human sexual behaviour remains unclear.

The sense of touch has the most direct effects on sexual arousal and response. Erogenous zones are especially sensitive to tactile sexual stimulation.

Taste appears to play only a minor role in sexual arousal and response.

Sounds can be turn-ons or turn-offs.

Alleged aphrodisiacs, such as foods that in some way resemble the genitals, have not been shown to contribute to sexual arousal or response.

Some drugs, such as antidepressants, dampen sexual arousal and response.

The alleged aphrodisiac effects of psychoactive drugs such as alcohol and cocaine may reflect our expectations of them or their effects on sexual inhibitions rather than their direct stimulation of sexual response. Alcohol is also connected with a liberated social role and thereby provides an external excuse for dubious behaviour. Some people report increased sexual pleasure upon initial use of certain drugs, but frequent use can lead to sexual dysfunction.

The brain plays a central role in sexual functioning. The cerebral cortex interprets sensory information as sexual turn-ons or turn-offs.

Sex hormones have organizing and activating effects on behaviour. Both men and women produce one genuine aphrodisiac: testosterone.

Many factors affect the sexual arousal of men and women.

Women show greater flexibility than men in sexual arousal patterns.

Masters and Johnson found that the physiological responses of men and women to sexual stimulation are quite alike.

The excitement phase of sexual response is characterized by erection in the male and vaginal lubrication in the female.

The plateau phase is an advanced state of arousal that precedes orgasm.

The third phase of the sexual response cycle is characterized by orgasmic contractions of the pelvic musculature. Orgasm in the male occurs in two stages of muscular contractions. Orgasm in the female is manifested by contractions of the pelvic muscles that surround the vaginal barrel.

During the resolution phase, the body returns to its pre-aroused state.

Kaplan developed a three-stage model of sexual response: desire, excitement, and orgasm. Kaplan's model makes it more convenient for clinicians to classify and treat sexual dysfunctions.

Basson argues that for women, intimacy plays a key role in sexual response.

Multiple orgasm is the occurrence of one or more additional orgasms following the first, within a short period and before the body has returned to its pre-plateau level of arousal.

Freud theorized the existence of two types of orgasms in women: clitoral and vaginal. Masters and Johnson found only one kind of orgasm among women.

People with disabilities may suffer from prejudice that depicts them as sexless or as lacking the means to express their sexual needs or feelings.

Cerebral palsy (CP) does not usually impair sexual interest, capacity for orgasm, or fertility, but people with CP may be limited to certain types of sexual activity and positions. People with spinal cord injuries may be paralyzed and lose sensation below the waist, but they often respond reflexively to direct genital stimulation.

Most people with developmental disabilities can learn the basics of their own sexuality and develop responsible intimate relationships.

Test Yourself

Multiple-Choice Questions

1. Which of the following statements about the impact of alcohol consumption on sexuality is false?
   (a) For healthy young adults, drinking large amounts of alcohol is unlikely to interfere with the orgasmic phase of sexual response.
   (b) Drinking alcohol can impair judgment and information-processing ability, leading people to engage in sexual behaviours they wouldn't engage in when sober.
   (c) Drinking alcohol can induce feelings of well-being and lower sexual inhibitions.
   (d) Drinking one beer or a glass of wine is unlikely to negatively affect a person's ability to respond sexually.

2. As aphrodisiacs, the effects of chocolate and oysters:
   (a) Are similar to fluoxetine.
   (b) Have been proven in the laboratory.
   (c) Are subject to the placebo effect.
   (d) Are similar to testosterone.

3. Parts of the brain involved in sexual function include:
   (a) The cerebellum and the corpus callosum.
   (b) The cerebral cortex and the limbic system.
   (c) The thalamus and the auditory bulb.
   (d) The medulla and the central sulcus.

4. Prolonged and frequent use of recreational drugs such as cocaine and methamphetamine are likely to:
   (a) Lead to hypersexuality.
   (b) Have little or no impact on sexual function.
   (c) Increase the probability of sexual dysfunction.
   (d) Improve sexual function.

5. According to Masters and Johnson, erection and lubrication occur during the _____ phase of the sexual response cycle.
   (a) excitement
   (b) orgasmic
   (c) plateau
   (d) resolution

continued

6. According to research by King, Belsky, Mah, and Binik, women's orgasms during solitary masturbation are more likely to result in _____ than orgasms during partnered sexual activity.
   (a) feelings of relaxation
   (b) pleasurable satisfaction
   (c) flushing sensations
   (d) throbbing sensations

7. The hormone _____ activates the sex drives of both women and men.
   (a) prolactin
   (b) oxytocin
   (c) progesterone
   (d) testosterone

8. The three stages of Kaplan's model of sexual response are:
   (a) Desire, excitement, and orgasm.
   (b) Plateau, desire, and arousal.
   (c) Desire, resolution, and orgasm.
   (d) Desire, plateau, and orgasm.

9. Basson's female sexual response model puts more emphasis on _____ than Masters and Johnson's or Kaplan's models do.
   (a) desire
   (b) affection
   (c) intimacy
   (d) orgasm

10. Which statement most accurately describes the sexuality of people with disabilities?
    (a) They generally have the same levels of sexual feelings and desires as non-disabled people.
    (b) They generally have lower levels of sexual feelings and desires than non-disabled people.
    (c) They're more likely to be over-sexed than non-disabled people.
    (d) They can easily shrug off the prejudice and ignorance they're subjected to regarding their sexuality.

You'll find answers to the "Test Yourself" questions on page 489.

Questions for Critical Thinking

1. You're a hearing-impaired student who uses a sign-language interpreter in your human sexuality class. The interpreter seemed comfortable earlier in the semester, but now that the topics are getting more personal and the lectures more graphic, he says he's no longer willing to attend the lectures, and that furthermore, he really doesn't think anyone with a disability should even be thinking about sex. How might you deal with this?

2. You're a woman who's read magazine articles telling you how great it is to have multiple orgasms, but you have difficulty having one, let alone several. How does this make you feel? Do you think that just because some women can have multiple orgasms, women who can't or who don't care should feel inadequate?

3. You're a man who's read in magazines that some women can have multiple orgasms, but your partner sometimes has difficulty having just one. How does this make you feel? Is one (or both) of you sexually inadequate? Or is this just another example of the media setting goals for sexual performance that are unrealistic and counterproductive to a couple's sexual enjoyment?

CHAPTER FIVE

Gender Identity and Gender Roles

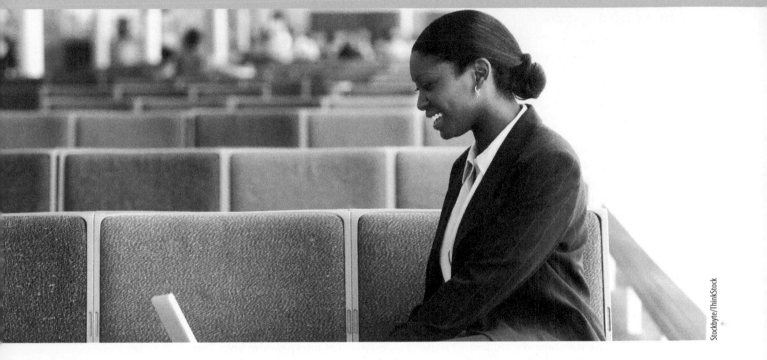

Stockbyte/ThinkStock

In this chapter, we'll address the biological, psychological, and sociological aspects of **gender**. First, we'll define gender as the psychological sense of being female or male, which is influenced by socially ascribed roles. While anatomic sex is based on anatomy, gender is a complex concept, based partly on anatomy, partly on the psychology of the individual, and partly on culture and tradition.

Next, we'll focus on sexual differentiation, or the process by which males and females develop distinct reproductive anatomy. We'll then turn to gender roles, the clusters of behaviour that are deemed masculine or feminine in particular cultures, and examine research findings on sex differences. We'll consider **gender typing**, the processes by which boys and girls come to behave in line with what's expected of men and women (most of the time). We'll also explore the concept of psychological androgyny, which applies to people in our culture who display characteristics associated with both gender roles.

Prenatal Sexual Differentiation

Over the years, many ideas have been proposed to account for **sexual differentiation**. Aristotle mistakenly believed that the anatomical difference between males and females was due to the heat of semen at the time of sexual relations. Hot semen generated males, whereas cold semen made females (National Center for Biotechnology Information, 2006).

Gender The psychological state of being female or male, as influenced by cultural concepts of gender-appropriate behaviour. Gender is distinct from anatomic sex, which is based on the physical differences between females and males.

Gender typing The process by which children acquire behaviours deemed appropriate for their sex.

Sexual differentiation The process by which males and females develop distinct reproductive anatomy.

When a sperm cell fertilizes an ovum, 23 **chromosomes** from the male parent normally combine with 23 chromosomes from the female parent. The **zygote**, the beginning of a new human being, is only 0.04 centimetres long. Yet, on this tiny stage, the stamp of a unique individual has already been ensured—whether the person will have black or blond hair, grow bald or develop a widow's peak, and become male or female.

The chromosomes from each parent combine to form 23 pairs. The twenty-third pair is the sex chromosomes. An ovum carries an X sex chromosome, but a sperm carries either an X or a Y sex chromosome. If a sperm with an X chromosome fertilizes the ovum, the newly conceived embryo will normally develop as a female, with an XX sex chromosomal structure. If the sperm carries a Y chromosome, the child will normally develop as a male, with an XY structure.

After fertilization, the zygote divides repeatedly. Within a few short weeks, one cell becomes billions of cells. At about three weeks, a primitive heart begins to drive blood through the embryonic bloodstream. By about five or six weeks, when the **embryo** is only 0.5 centimetres to 1 centimetre long, it has a pair of sexually undifferentiated gonads, two sets of primitive duct structures called the Müllerian (female) ducts and the Wolffian (male) ducts, and primitive external genitals whose sex cannot be visually distinguished. (See Figures 5.1 and 5.2.)

During the first six weeks or so of prenatal development, embryonic structures of both genders develop along similar lines, resembling primitive female structures. At about the seventh week after conception, the genetic code (XX or XY) begins to assert itself, causing changes in the gonads, genital ducts, and external genitals. Genetic activity on the Y sex chromosome causes the testes to begin to differentiate (National Center for Biotechnology Information, 2006). If the Y chromosome is absent, ovaries begin to differentiate. Those rare embryos that have only one X sex chromosome instead of the typical XY or XX arrangement become female, because they lack the Y chromosome. One could say the basic blueprint of the human embryo is female (De Vries et al., 2002; Steinemann & Steineman, 2005), and the genetic instructions in the Y chromosome cause the embryo to deviate from the female developmental course.

By about the seventh week of prenatal development, strands of tissue begin to organize into seminiferous tubules. Female gonads begin to develop somewhat later than male gonads. The forerunners of follicles that will bear ova are not found until the fetal stage of development, about 10 weeks after conception. Ovaries begin to form at 11 or 12 weeks.

Chromosome A rodlike structure found in the nucleus of every living cell. It carries the genetic code, in the form of genes.

Zygote A fertilized ovum (egg cell).

Embryo The stage of prenatal development that begins with implantation of a fertilized ovum in the uterus and concludes with development of the major organ systems at about two months after conception.

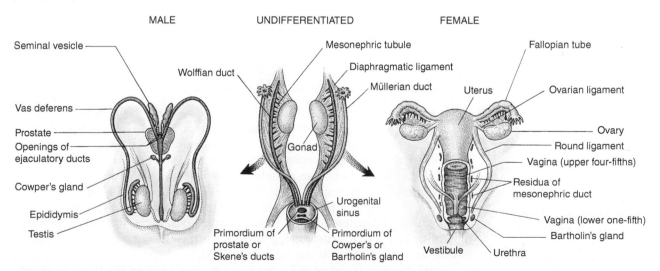

Figure 5.1 Development of the internal sex organs from an undifferentiated stage, about five or six weeks after conception.

UNDIFFERENTIATED

Glans area
Urethral fold
Urethral groove
Lateral buttress
Anal pit
Anal tubercle

Genital tubercle

AT 45–50 MILLIMETRES

MALE

FEMALE

Glans
Site of future origin of prepuce
Urethral fold
Urogenital groove
Lateral buttress (corpus or shaft)
Labioscrotal swelling
Urethral folds partly fused (perineal raph)
Anal tubercle
Anus

FULLY DEVELOPED

MALE

FEMALE

Urethral meatus
Glans penis
Prepuce
Shaft or body of penis (corpus)
Penoscrotal raph
Scrotum

Clitoral shaft
Prepuce
Clitoral glans
Urethral meatus
Labia minora
Labia majora
Vagina

Perineal raph
Perineal tissues including external sphincter

Figure 5.2   Development of the external sex organs from an undifferentiated stage, about five or six weeks after conception.

Sex Hormones and Sexual Differentiation

Once genes have done their work and testes develop in the embryo, they begin to produce male sex hormones, or **androgens**. Without androgens, we'd all develop female external reproductive organs. The most important androgen, **testosterone**, spurs differentiation of the male (Wolffian) duct system (see Figure 5.1). Each Wolffian duct develops into an epididymis, vas deferens, and seminal vesicle. The external genitals, including the penis, begin to take shape at about the eighth week of development, under the influence of another androgen, dihydrotestosterone (DHT). Yet another testicular hormone, secreted during the fetal stage, prevents the Müllerian ducts from developing into the female duct system; it's appropriately termed the Müllerian-inhibiting substance (MIS).

Small amounts of androgen are produced in female fetuses, but they're not normally sufficient to cause male sexual differentiation. In female fetuses, the relative

Androgens Male sex hormones.

Testosterone The male sex hormone that fosters development of male sex characteristics and is connected with the sex drive.

absence of androgens causes degeneration of the Wolffian ducts and prompts development of female sexual organs. The Müllerian ducts evolve into fallopian tubes, the uterus, and the upper two-thirds of the vagina. These developments occur even in the absence of female sex hormones. Although female sex hormones are crucial in puberty, they're not involved in fetal sexual differentiation. If a fetus with an XY sex chromosomal structure failed to produce testosterone, it would develop female sexual organs.

Descent of the Testes and Ovaries

The testes and ovaries develop from slender structures high in the abdominal cavity. By about 10 weeks after conception, they've descended so they're almost even with the upper edge of the pelvis. The ovaries remain there for the rest of the prenatal period, later rotating and further descending to their adult positions in the pelvis. About four months after conception, the testes normally descend into the scrotal sac through the **inguinal canal**, which then closes.

In a small percentage of males, at least one of the testes fails to descend, remaining in the abdomen at birth. The condition is termed **cryptorchidism**. In most cases of cryptorchidism, the testes migrate to the scrotum during infancy. In some cases, they descend by puberty. Men with undescended testes are usually treated through surgery or hormonal therapy, because they're at higher risk for cancer of the testes. Sperm production is also impaired, because the undescended testes are subjected to a higher-than-optimal body temperature, which causes sterility.

Sex Chromosome Abnormalities

Abnormalities of the sex chromosomes can have profound effects on sexual characteristics, physical health, and psychological development. **Klinefelter's syndrome**, a condition that affects about one in 500 males, is caused by an extra X sex chromosome, giving the man an XXY rather than an XY pattern. Men with this pattern fail to develop appropriate secondary sex characteristics. They have enlarged breasts and poor muscular development, and because they fail to produce sperm, they're infertile. They also tend to have mild mental retardation.

Turner's syndrome, which affects about one in 2500 females, is caused by having one rather than two X sex chromosomes. Females with the syndrome may not naturally undergo puberty, so they usually begin hormone treatments when normal pubertal changes would otherwise start to spur the growth of secondary sex characteristics.

The brain, like the genital organs, undergoes prenatal sexual differentiation. Testosterone causes cells in the hypothalamus of a male fetus to become insensitive to the female sex hormone estrogen. In the absence of testosterone, the hypothalamus of a female fetus becomes sensitive to estrogen.

Sensitivity to estrogen is important in regulation of the menstrual cycle after puberty. The hypothalamus detects low levels of estrogen in the blood at the end of each cycle, and initiates a new cycle by stimulating the pituitary gland to secrete follicle-stimulating hormone (FSH). FSH, in turn, stimulates the ovaries to produce estrogen, and stimulates an immature follicle in an ovary to ripen.

Gender Identity

Gender identity is a person's internal psychological sense of being male, female, or any other shade of gender. It's one of the most central aspects of self-concept. **Assigned sex** refers to the classification of anatomic sex given at birth as either male, female, or **intersex.** Most people are **cisgender.** That is, the sex they were

Inguinal canal A fetal canal that connects the scrotum and the testes, allowing the latter to descend.

Cryptorchidism A condition in which at least one of the testes fails to descend.

Klinefelter's syndrome A disorder in which a male has an extra X sex chromosome (an XXY pattern, rather than an XY pattern).

Turner's syndrome A disorder is which a female has just one X sex chromosome (an X pattern, rather than an XX pattern).

Gender identity One's internal and individual sense of being female, male, or other shade of gender.

Assigned sex The classification of anatomic sex assigned to an individual at birth.

Intersex A person who possesses the gonads of one gender and external genitalia that are ambiguous or typical of the other gender.

Cisgender A gender identity that matches assigned sex

assigned at birth matches their gender identity. So, for example, if a newborn baby is labeled as male based on the appearance of external genitalia (i.e., a penis) and grows up with a male gender identity, he is cisgender. Most children become aware of their assigned sex by about 18 months of age. By 36 months, most children have acquired a firm sense of gender identity (Rathus, 2014).

Nature and Nurture

What determines gender identity? Are our brains biologically programmed along masculine or feminine lines by prenatal sex hormones? Does the environment, in the form of postnatal learning experiences, shape our self-concepts as males or females? Or does gender identity reflect an intermingling of biological and environmental influences?

Gender identity is usually consistent with chromosomal gender. Such consistency does not, however, prove that gender identity is biologically determined. In Western culture, children have typically been reared to have either a male or female gender identity, in strict accordance with assigned sex, and with little or no room for variation. This societal rigidity in the classification of gender is referred to as the **gender binary**: a social system that insists that people assume a gender identity that is clearly defined as male or female. It is important to recognize that the gender binary represents a socially prescribed way of classifying gender in our culture, but it does not accurately reflect the diverse range of gender identities that actually exist.

How, then, can we sort out the roles of nature and nurture, of biology and the environment? Researchers have found clues in the experiences of intersex individuals who possess the gonads of one anatomic sex and external genitalia that are ambiguous or typical of the other anatomic sex (Zucker, 2005b). Intersex children are sometimes reared as members of the gender opposite to their chromosomal sex. Researchers wonder whether the gender identity of these children reflects their chromosomal and gonadal sex or the genders they've been reared with. Before going further with this, let's distinguish between hermaphrodites and intersex individuals.

Hormonal factors during prenatal development produce various congenital outcomes. Some individuals are born with both ovarian and testicular tissue. They're called **hermaphrodites**, after the Greek myth of the son of Hermes and Aphrodite, whose body became united with that of a nymph while he was bathing. True hermaphrodites may have one gonad of each gender (a testicle and an ovary) or gonads that combine testicular and ovarian tissue.

Regardless of their genetic sex, hermaphrodites usually assume the identities and roles of the genders they're assigned at birth. The photo in Figure 5.3 shows a genetic female (XX) with a right testicle and a left ovary. This person married and became a stepfather with a firm male identity. The roles of biology and environment remain tangled, however, because true hermaphrodites have gonadal tissue of both genders.

True hermaphroditism is quite rare (Kuhnle et al., 2003). Less rare are intersex conditions, which occur in perhaps one infant in 5000 (Intersex Society of North America, 2012). Intersex people have testes or ovaries, but not both. Unlike hermaphrodites, intersex people's gonads (testes or ovaries) match their chromosomal sex. Because of prenatal hormonal factors, however, their external genitals and sometimes their internal reproductive anatomy are ambiguous or resemble those of the other anatomic sex. Intersex conditions have given researchers an opportunity to examine the roles of nature (biology) and nurture (environmental influences) in shaping gender identity.

The most common female intersex condition is **congenital adrenal hyperplasia** (CAH), in which a genetic (XX) female has female internal sexual structures

---

Gender binary A social system that defines gender as either strictly male or female.

CRITICAL THINKING QUESTIONS

Do your own ideas about gender reflect the gender binary? Have your attitudes changed as the diversity of gender identities has become more visible in Western society?

Hermaphrodite An individual who possesses both ovarian and testicular tissue.

Congenital adrenal hyperplasia An intersex condition in which a genetic female has internal female sexual structures and masculinized external genitals.

(ovaries) and masculinized external genitals. (See the photo in Figure 5.4.) The clitoris is so enlarged that it may resemble a small penis. CAH is caused by high levels of androgens.

Swedish investigator Anna Servin and her colleagues (2003) studied gender-typed behaviours and interests in 26 girls with CAH and 26 girls without CAH. All of the girls were 2 to 10 years of age. Those with CAH showed more interest in masculine-typed toys such as transportation toys and less interest in feminine-typed toys such as dolls. The girls with CAH were more likely to have boys as playmates and to want masculine-typed careers. Parents rated the behaviour of daughters with CAH as more "boylike" in toy choice and aggressiveness.

Another type of intersex condition, **androgen insensitivity syndrome**, affects genetic (XY) males who, as a result of a mutated gene, have experienced lower-than-normal prenatal sensitivity to androgens. Consequently, their genitals do not become normally masculinized. At birth, their testes are undescended and their external genitals are feminized, including small vaginas. Because of androgen insensitivity, their male duct systems (epididymis, vas deferentia, seminal vesicles, and ejaculatory ducts) have failed to develop. Nevertheless, their fetal testes have produced Müllerian-inhibiting substance, preventing the development of uteruses and fallopian tubes. Genetic males with androgen-insensitivity syndrome usually have little or no pubic and axillary (underarm) hair, because development of hair in these locations is dependent on androgens.

Another type of intersex condition is called **Dominican Republic syndrome**, because it was first documented there, in a group of 18 affected boys in two rural villages (Newman, 2012). Dominican Republic syndrome is a genetic enzyme disorder that prevents testosterone from masculinizing the external genitalia. The boys were born with normal testes and internal male reproductive organs, but their external genitals were malformed. Their penises were stunted and resembled clitorises. Their scrotums were incompletely formed and resembled female labia. They also had partially formed vaginas.

The boys with Dominican Republic syndrome resembled girls at birth and were reared as females. At puberty, however, their testes swung into normal testosterone production, causing startling changes: The testes descended, their voices deepened, their musculature filled out, and their "clitorises" expanded into penises. Of the 18 boys who were reared as girls, 17 shifted to male gender identities. Sixteen assumed stereotypical masculine gender roles. Of the remaining two, one adopted a male gender identity but continued to maintain a feminine gender role, including the wearing of dresses, while the other maintained a female gender identity and later sought gender-reassignment surgery to "correct" the pubertal masculinization.

Many scientists conclude that gender identity is influenced by complex interactions among biological and psychosocial factors. Some place relatively greater emphasis on psychosocial factors (Bradley et al., 1998; Money, 1994). Others emphasize the roles of biological factors (Diamond, 2011; Savic et al., 2010), even though they allow that nurture plays a role in gender identity.

Gender Dysphoria

Until recently, the American Psychiatric Association's (APA) *Diagnostic and Statistical Manual of Mental Disorders* (DSM) listed gender identity disorder as a psychiatric diagnosis. In 2013, the new edition of the manual adopted the less pathologizing diagnosis of **gender dysphoria**. According to the APA (2013a), there must be a marked difference between a person's expression and experience of gender and the gender others would assign him or her in order for a person to be diagnosed with gender dysphoria. For children, the desire to be of the other gender should be clearly evident and verbalized by the child before the diagnosis is given. That is, gender dysphoria involves ". . . strong desires to be treated as the other

Figure 5.3 A hermaphrodite. This genetic (XX) female has one testicle and one ovary, and the gender identity of a male.
Source: Liana Zhou, Kinsey Institute for Sex, Gender, and Reproduction

Figure 5.4 Intersex. This genetic (XX) female has female internal sexual structures (ovaries) and masculinized external genitals. This condition has been caused by congenital adrenal hyperplasia.
Source: Liana Zhou, Kinsey Institute for Sex, Gender, and Reproduction

Androgen insensitivity syndrome An intersex condition in which a genetic male is prenatally insensitive to androgens. As a result, his genitals do not become normally masculinized.

Dominican Republic syndrome An intersex condition in which a genetic enzyme disorder prevents testosterone from masculinizing the external genitalia.

Gender dysphoria A sense of incongruity between assigned sex and gender identity that causes significant distress.

gender or to be rid of one's sex characteristics, or a strong conviction that one has feelings and reactions typical of the other gender" (p. 1).

Most importantly, the APA (2013a) is careful to note that gender nonconformity is not in itself a mental disorder and that the diagnosis of gender dysphoria is dependent on the person expressing significant distress about their gender status. In other words, the diagnosis of gender dysphoria is dependent on the condition causing ". . . clinically significant distress or impairment in social, occupational, or other important areas of functioning" (p. 1).

Gender Non-conforming Children

In the past, children whose expression of their gender identity did not conform to traditional societal expectations (e.g., children who indicated that they were or preferred to be a gender different from their assigned sex) were often clinically diagnosed with gender identity disorder. As a result, these children were often given therapy aimed at altering their gender identity to conform with accepted societal standards.

While some clinicians continue to offer interventions aimed, in some circumstances, toward steering gender dysphoric children to adopt a gender identity consistent with their assigned sex (e.g., Zucker et al., 2012), this practice is increasingly being opposed by those who believe that the expression of gender nonconformity by children should be accepted and supported by parents and mental health professionals (Pyne, 2014). For example, the World Professional Association for Transgender Health (2012) states that treatments designed to change gender identity or expression are "no longer considered ethical" (p. 16). It is now more common for interventions and services for gender non-conforming children and their families to take a supportive approach that affirms a child's gender identity rather than attempting to change it (e.g., Hill et al., 2010).

Transgender ("Trans")

Previous editions of this textbook used the terms "transsexualism" and "transgenderism." However, terminology related to transgender identities has changed over time, and although this terminology varies, it is important to use terms that are respectful of the transgender community. For example, the National Center for Transgender Equality (2014) in the United States notes that many people within the transgender community prefer that the term "transsexual" not be used because it sounds overly clinical and perhaps implies that being transgender is a medical condition. Many within the transgender community prefer that "trans" be used as an umbrella term to describe people with diverse gender identities and expressions of gender that do not conform to stereotypical concepts of what it means to be a man or woman. Let us, then, begin this section by defining some relevant terms.

Transgender or **trans** are terms for people whose gender identity, expression, or behaviour is different from those typically associated with their assigned sex at birth. **Transitioning** refers to the activities that some trans people may pursue to begin living as the gender with which they identify rather than the gender they were assigned at birth. This may include changing their name and the way they dress, and possibly having medical treatments such as hormone therapy, gender-reassignment surgery, or other procedures.

In 1953, a former American soldier named George Jorgenson journeyed to Denmark for a "sex-change operation," changed her name to Christine Jorgensen, and made headlines (Michel & Pédinielli, 2005). Since then, thousands of transgender people have undergone gender-reassignment surgery. A trans person who seeks out gender-reassignment surgery wishes to possess the anatomic features of people of the other sex and to live as a person of the other gender.

Transgender/trans A person whose gender identity is different from their assigned sex at birth.

Transitioning The activities that some trans people may use to begin living as the gender with which they identify rather than the gender they were assigned at birth. This may include changing their name and the way they dress, as well as possibly undergoing medical treatments such as hormone therapy and gender-reassignment surgery.

Innovative Canadian Research

WHAT CAN THE SAMOAN *FA'AFAFINE* TEACH US ABOUT WESTERN CONCEPTS OF GENDER IDENTITY?

Canadian researchers Paul Vasey and Nancy Bartlett (2007) have conducted a study in Samoa, where, compared to North America, there's a high level of tolerance for males with feminine characteristics. Most Samoans consider cross-gender behaviour in children an unproblematic variation, not a mental disorder.

Vasey and Bartlett (2007) interviewed males referred to in Samoan culture as *fa'afafine* (feminine males who are sexually attracted to masculine men) who had frequently engaged in cross-gender behaviours during childhood. The authors found that the *fa'afafine* they interviewed did not recall feeling distressed as a direct result of their cross-gendered behaviours and identities. Vasey and Bartlett concluded that the distress felt by North American children who exhibit cross-gender behaviours and identities is not evidence of a disorder. Rather, the distress is caused by the discriminatory and hostile attitudes such children are subjected to by society.

[Text by Paul Vasey]: I first travelled to Samoa, with my colleague Nancy Bartlett, to critically examine a prevailing assumption embedded in the American Psychiatric Association's Diagnostic and Statistical Manual of Mental Disorders, that extreme boyhood femininity (or in clinical parlance at the time, Gender Identity Disorder in Childhood) causes psychological distress. As has often been pointed out to me, Samoa is a long way for a Canadian to commute to work. Although this is certainly true, the reality was that Canada represented a poor location in which to conduct our work because Canadian boys and men alike are censured for feminine behaviour. This situation makes it difficult to disentangle whether any distress that might be present is caused by boyhood femininity itself, or by social condemnation.

Paul Vasey and his fa'afafine friend, Trisha

The tiny Polynesian island nation of Samoa offered a way out of this conundrum. In Samoa, feminine males are generally accepted as unremarkable members of society. They are known locally as *fa'afafine*—a type of "third" gender that are recognized as being neither "men" nor "women." Because *fa'afafine*, (which means "in the manner of a woman") are, by and large, not stigmatized, we reasoned that any distress they might experience in relation to their femininity could not be attributed to societal "sissyphobia." Armed with the telephone number of a single *fa'afafine* contact, Nancy and I headed off to the South Pacific. After two fieldtrips, we had enough data that we could say something definite about our research question. In a nutshell, we found no evidence that the expression of female-typical behaviours in childhood provoked distress in Samoan *fa'afafine*. More often than not, *fa'afafine* recalled that they "loved" engaging in activities that were more typical of girls. Reflecting on "her" childhood, one *fa'afafine* participant told us "With cars, it's just *zoom*…it's no use. I loved playing with dolls. When my sister had a Barbie with long hair, it was like a diamond for me." Because *fa'afafine* don't grow up being constantly bombarded with the message that they're sick, "distress" about their femininity never comes into play.

Many transgender people undergo hormone treatments and surgery to create the appearance of the external genitals typical of the gender they identify themselves with. This can be done more precisely with male-to-female than with female-to-male trans people. After surgery, people can participate in sexual activity and even attain orgasm. One survey found that 85% of transgender women attained orgasm during sexual activity (Lawrence, 2005).

What motivates transgender people to wish to live as people of another anatomic sex? It appears that they experience incongruity between their genital

CRITICAL THINKING QUESTIONS

Does Paul Vasey's research on the childhood experiences of the *fa'afafine* of Samoa change your thinking on childhood gender non-conformity?

anatomy and their gender identity. Although they have the anatomic genitalia of one sex, they feel that they're members of another. The discrepancy motivates them to wish to be rid of their own primary sex characteristics (their external genitals and internal sex organs) and to live as members of an anatomic sex that matches their gender identity.

Some researchers contend that some men who seek to become women tend to fall into other categories—men who are extremely feminine, or men who are sexually aroused by the idea of becoming women. The first category includes very feminine gay men who aren't fully satisfied by sexual activity with other men (Blanchard, 1989; Cantor, 2011). The second category refers to men who are **autogynephilic**, or sexually stimulated by fantasies that their own bodies are female (Moser, 2010; Nuttbrock et al., 2011). However, trans activists have contested the idea that some transgender people are motivated to seek gender reassignment by erotic interests (Dredger, 2008).

Some research suggests that transgender people usually show cross-gender preferences in play and dress during early childhood. Some reported feeling that they've belonged to the other sex for as long as they can remember (Zucker, 2005a, 2005b). Some male-to-female trans people recall that, as children, they preferred playing with dolls, enjoyed wearing frilly dresses, and disliked rough-and-tumble play. They were often perceived by their peers as "sissy boys." Some female-to-male trans people reported that as children they disliked dresses, and acted like "tomboys." They preferred playing with boys and "boys' games."

Autogynephilic Descriptive of transgender men who are sexually stimulated by fantasies that their own bodies are female.

GENDER REASSIGNMENT Surgery is one element of gender reassignment. Because the surgery is irreversible, health professionals conduct careful evaluations to determine that people seeking reassignment are competent to make such decisions and have thought through the consequences (Bockting & Fung, 2006). They usually require that people live openly as members of the other sex for extended trial periods before surgery.

After the decision is reached, a lifetime of hormone treatments is begun. A male-to-female trans person receives estrogen, which fosters the development of female secondary sex characteristics. It causes fatty deposits to develop in the breasts and hips, softens the skin, and inhibits growth of the beard. A female-to-male trans person receives androgens, which promote male secondary sex characteristics. The voice deepens, hair becomes distributed according to the male pattern, muscles enlarge, and the fatty deposits in the breasts and hips are lost. The clitoris may also grow more prominent. For a male-to-female trans person, phonosurgery can raise the pitch of the voice (Bockting & Fung, 2006).

Despite its complexity and intimacy, gender reassignment surgery is largely cosmetic. Medical science cannot construct internal genital organs or gonads. Male-to-female surgery is generally more successful. The penis and testicles are first removed. Tissue from the penis is placed in an artificial vagina, where

Mirek Towski/Contributor/Time & Life Pictures/Getty Images

Chaz Bono's Transition.
Chastity ("Chaz") Bono, 40, daughter of singers Cher (seen here on the left) and the late Sony Bono, announced in 2009 that she was undergoing the initial stages of gender reassignment surgery from female to male. Chaz expressed, through a spokesperson, the hope that this transition would open the "hearts and minds" of people toward transgender people.

sensitive nerve endings will later provide sexual sensations. A penis-shaped plastic or balsa-wood form keeps the vagina distended during healing.

In a female-to-male trans person, the internal sex organs (ovaries, fallopian tubes, uterus) are removed, along with fatty tissue from the breasts. Some female-to-male trans people engage in a series of operations, termed **phalloplasty**, to construct artificial penises, but the penises don't work very well, and the procedures are costly. Most female-to-male trans people are therefore content with hysterectomies, mastectomies, and testosterone treatments.

Phalloplasty Surgical creation of an artificial penis.

Some trans people hesitate to undertake surgery, because they're uncomfortable with the prospect of extreme medical intervention. Others forgo surgery so as not to jeopardize high-status careers or family relationships. Such people continue to think of themselves as members of the other sex, even without surgery.

SURGICAL OUTCOMES   Most reports of trans peoples' postoperative adjustments are positive (Smith et al., 2005). A Canadian follow-up study of 116 trans people at least one year after surgery found that most were content with the results and were reasonably well adjusted (Blanchard et al., 1985). Positive results for surgery were also reported in a study of 141 Dutch trans people (Kuiper & Cohen-Kettenis, 1988).

A study of 326 Dutch candidates for gender reassignment surgery found that about two-thirds (222 individuals) began hormone treatment, whereas 103 did not (Smith et al., 2005). Of the 222, about 15% dropped out before surgery. Generally speaking, after surgery the group was no longer gender-dysphoric, and most individuals functioned well sexually, psychologically, and socially. Only two male-to-female trans people regretted their decisions. Although male-to-female trans people outnumbered female-to-males, postoperative adjustments were more favourable for female-to-male trans people. One reason may be that society is more accepting of women who wish to become men (Smith et al., 2005). Female-to-male trans people tend to be better adjusted socially before surgery, as well, so their superior postoperative adjustment may be nothing more than a selection factor.

Researchers have conducted relatively few studies of societal attitudes toward trans people. B. J. Rye (2001) at the University of Waterloo found that university students were about evenly divided in liking or disliking trans people. The students reported more negative attitudes toward trans people than toward gays and lesbians, however.

More recently, Rye et al. (2007) studied how having a trans person speak to a university class could change perceptions. The researchers found that only 5% of the students in human sexuality classes had knowingly met trans individuals before. They then invited a male-to-female trans person to speak to the students in a personal way about her own experience and about transgender issues in general. The students reported that hearing directly from a trans person was the best way to learn about transgender issues. They also reported that they had better understandings of the issues and greater empathy toward transgender people after hearing the person speak.

There are programs that help trans people come to terms with themselves and adjust to living in a society in which they often feel unwelcome. Central Toronto Youth Services, for example, provides services and resources related to work, school, and other areas for trans youth. Gay and lesbian organizations have expanded their services to include formerly excluded groups, such as trans people. One such program is Supporting Our Youth in Toronto. This program provides cultural, recreational, and employment training opportunities, as well as a mentoring and housing program (Lepischak, 2004). Such programs help create a sense of community for people who feel alienated from the larger society.

CRITICAL THINKING QUESTIONS

In the Rye et al. (2007) study, university students were more likely to report negative attitudes toward trans people than toward gays and lesbians. Can you think of reasons that might explain this difference?

A World of Diversity

THIRD GENDER/THIRD SEX

The terms "third gender" and "third sex" describe people who are considered neither women nor men, as well as a social category in societies that recognize three or more sexes.

Being neither male nor female has ramifications not only in terms of the person's sex, but also in terms of the person's gender role, gender identity, and sexual orientation. In some cultures, or for some individuals, a third sex or gender may represent an intermediate state between man and woman, or it may represent a state of being both, as in the case of someone who has "the spirit of a man in the body of a woman."

It may also represent the state of being neither male nor female (neuter), the ability to cross or swap sexes and gender roles, or another category that's independent of maleness and femaleness. This last definition is favoured by those who argue for a strict interpretation of the third-gender concept.

Thai Ladyboys.
The kathoeys (ladyboys) of Thailand are one example of a third gender.

The Canadian Press/David Longstreath/AP Photo

The Ladyboys of Thailand

The kathoeys (or "ladyboys") of Thailand are an example of a third gender. Although a significant number of Thais—including many kathoeys themselves—perceive kathoeys as belonging to a third gender, some see them as either a kind of man or a kind of woman.

The Two-Spirits of North America

First Nations cultures are also associated with multiple genders. They often contain social gender categories that are collectively known as *berdache*, or "two-spirits." Examples include the *Winkte* of the Lakota culture, the *ninau-poskitzipxpe* (manly-hearted woman) of the North Peigan community, and the *muxe* of the Zapotec people.

Various scholars have debated the nature of such categories, as well as the definition of "third *gender*." Various researchers characterize the *berdaches* as gender crossers, mixed genders, intermediate genders, and distinct third and fourth genders that are not dependent on male and female as primary categories. Those who argue for the last interpretation also point out that mixed-, intermediate-, cross- and non-gender social roles should not be understood as truly representing a third gender.

The Hijras of South-Central Asia

The *hijras* of India, Pakistan, and Bangladesh are probably the most well-known and populous third sex type in the modern world. The Mumbai-based community health organization known as the Humsafar Trust estimates there are five to six million hijras in India. In various areas they're known as aravani, aruvani, and jogappa.

Indian photographer Dayanita Singh writes about her friendship with a hijra named Mona Ahmed, and their two societies' beliefs about gender: "When I once asked her if she would like to go to Singapore for a sex change operation, she told me, 'You really do not understand. I am the third sex, not a man trying to be a woman. It is your society's problem that you only recognize two sexes'" (Singh et al., 1999). Hijra social movements have campaigned for recognition as a third sex, and in 2005, Indian passport application forms were updated with three gender options: M for male, F for female, and E for eunuch.

Source: Adapted from Wikipedia ("Third Gender," http://en.wikipedia.org/wiki/Third_gender), with information from Agrawal (1997), Fausto-Sterling (1993), Goulet (2006), Hester (2005), Murray and Roscoe (1997), Roscoe (2000), Roughgarden (2004), Stockett (2005), Totman (2004), and Winter (2003).

Innovative Canadian Research

THE TRANS PULSE PROJECT

Trans PULSE is a community-based research project designed to examine the impact of social exclusion and discrimination on the health of trans people in Ontario (*transpulseproject.ca*). The project is a partnership among researchers, the trans community, and community organizations committed to improving health outcomes for trans people.

Surveys were completed by 433 trans people aged 16 and over, providing a unique snapshot of the trans community in Ontario. While previous studies in other jurisdictions have suggested that male-to-female trans people outnumber those who are female-to-male by a significant margin, the Trans PULSE survey found that trans people in Ontario are about evenly split between female-to-male (54%) and male-to-female (47%) (Bauer et al., 2010). Participants self-identified a range of sexual orientations including bisexual or pansexual (30%), gay (11%), lesbian (14%), queer (31%), and heterosexual (30%) (participants could identify as more than one sexual orientation). The findings reveal that trans people in Ontario come from a broad range of cultural and ethnoracial groups.

Just under half (48%) of the Trans PULSE participants were living full-time in their felt gender, 30% were doing so part-time, and 22% were not living in their felt gender at all (Coleman et al., 2011). More than half (59%) of participants reported that they became aware that their gender did not match their bodies when they were less than 10 years-old, and 21% said they became aware when they were 10 to 14 years old. The researchers note that "This highlights the importance of teaching about gender identity and trans issues in both primary and secondary school" (p. 2).

About one quarter of participants indicated that they had completed a medical transition process, 24% were in the process of a transition, and 28% were planning but had not yet begun a medical transition.

Experiences of transphobia, including various forms of discrimination, were nearly universal among trans Ontarians, with 98% reporting at least one experience of transphobia and almost all (96%) having heard that trans people aren't normal (Longman et al., 2013). Nearly three quarters reported that they had been made fun of because they are trans, 26% had been beaten up, 39% had been turned down for a job, 32% had to move away, and 24% had been harassed by police.

Gender Roles and Stereotypes

"Why can't a woman be more like a man?" You may recall this lyric from the song Professor Henry Higgins sings in the musical *My Fair Lady*. The song laments that women are emotional and fickle, whereas men are logical and dependable. The emotional woman is a **stereotype**—a fixed, oversimplified, sometimes distorted idea about a group of people. The logical man is also a stereotype, albeit a more generous one. Even emotions are stereotyped. People assume women are more likely to experience feelings of fear, sadness, and sympathy, whereas men are more likely to experience anger and pride (Plant et al., 2000). Gender roles are stereotypes in that they evoke fixed, conventional expectations of men and women.

Stereotype A fixed, conventional idea about a group of people.

Our gender identities—our identification of ourselves according to our concepts of masculinity and femininity—do not determine the roles or behaviours deemed masculine or feminine in our culture. Cultures have broad expectations of men and women that are termed **gender roles**.

Gender roles Complex clusters of ways males and females are expected to behave.

Sexism

We've all encountered **sexism**—the prejudgment that a person will possess certain traits because of gender. These traits are assumed to disqualify the person for certain vocations or to prevent him or her from performing adequately in these jobs or in some social situations.

Sexism The prejudgment that a person will possess certain traits because of gender.

Sexism may even lead us to interpret the same behaviour in different ways, depending on whether it's exhibited by a man or a woman. We may see a man as self-assertive, but a woman as pushy. We may look upon him as flexible, but brand her as fickle and indecisive. He may be rational, whereas she's cold. He's tough when necessary, but she's bitchy.

Children develop stereotypes about the differences between "men's work" and "women's work" (Rathus, 2014). Women have been historically excluded from male-dominated occupations, and stereotypical expectations about men's and women's work filter down to the primary grades. According to traditional stereotypes, for example, girls aren't expected to excel in math. Exposure to such negative expectations may discourage them from pursuing careers in science and technology. Even when they do choose careers in these fields, women are often subject to discrimination when it comes to hiring, promotions, and allocation of research facilities and funds (Loder, 2000). And only recently have men begun to enter occupational domains previously restricted largely to women, such as secretarial work, nursing, and teaching primary grades.

Sexism is psychologically damaging. In one study, women who were led to believe sexism was pervasive reported lower self-esteem than women who were led to believe sexism was rare (Schmitt et al., 2003). In another experiment, men and women were led to believe they'd been prevented from taking a course because of either sexism or personal reasons (Major et al., 2003). Attributing the rejection to prejudice rather than to personal worth ("It's not me; it's society") had the effect of protecting their self-esteem.

How far have we progressed with respect to gender equality in Canadian society? On some basic measures, we've made progress. For example, in 1976, a full-time female worker in Canada earned 59% of what a male full-time worker earned. By 2008, the corresponding figure was 71% (Williams, 2010). It seems likely that this trend toward gender equality in income will continue. Income potential depends to a large degree on educational achievement. In 2008–2009, 57% of students enrolled in Canadian universities were women (Statistics Canada, 2010). This suggests that women will increasingly occupy higher-paying jobs, which should further close the wage gap between men and women in Canada.

Gender Roles and Aggression

In most psychological studies on aggression, males have been found to behave more aggressively than females, and this gender difference emerges early (Hay et al., 2011). Nonetheless, females are likely to act aggressively under certain conditions. The rate of aggression among girls seems to have increased in recent years.

University of Western Ontario researchers Anne Cummings and Alan Leschied (2002) conducted extensive research on aggression among girls and found that aggressive adolescent girls were more likely than aggressive adolescent boys to experience isolation, powerlessness, and depression.

Among both genders, bullying in elementary school is highly predictive of aggression in later dating relationships. An Ontario study found that bullies started dating earlier than non-bullies and were more likely to engage in physical and social aggression with their dating partners (Connolly, Pepler, Craig, & Taradash, 2000).

Gender Typing

Gender typing The process by which a child acquires behaviours deemed appropriate for his or her gender.

We've chronicled the biological process of sexual differentiation and explored some gender differences in cognitive abilities and behaviour. In this section, we'll consider various explanations for **gender typing**, the process by which an individual becomes a man or a woman.

Biological Perspectives

Biological views on gender typing tend to focus on the roles of genetics and prenatal influences in predisposing men and women to gender-linked behaviour patterns. Biological perspectives also focus on the possible roles of hormones in sculpting the brain during prenatal development.

THE EVOLUTIONARY PERSPECTIVE   From an evolutionary perspective, the story of our ancient ancestors' survival is etched in our genes. Those genes that bestow attributes that increase an organism's chances of surviving to produce viable offspring are most likely to be transmitted to future generations. We thus possess the genetic remnants of traits that helped our ancestors survive and reproduce (Buss, 2009).

According to the evolutionary perspective, men's traditional roles as hunters and warriors, and women's roles as caregivers and gatherers of fruits and vegetables, are bequeathed to us in our genes. Men are better suited to war and the hunt because of physical attributes passed along since ancestral times. Upper-body strength, for example, enabled them to throw spears and overpower adversaries. According to this view, men also possess perceptual–cognitive advantages, such as superior visual–motor skills, which enabled them to aim spears or bows and arrows. Personality traits such as aggressiveness also make for effective hunting.

Women, it's argued, are genetically predisposed to be empathic and nurturant, because these traits enabled ancestral women to respond to children's needs and enhanced the likelihood that their children would flourish and eventually reproduce, thereby transmitting their own genetic legacy to future generations.

The evolutionary perspective is steeped in controversy. Although scientists do not dispute the importance of evolution in determining physical attributes, many are reluctant to attribute complex social behaviours, such as aggression and gender roles, to heredity. The evolutionary perspective implies that stereotypical gender roles—men as breadwinners and women as homemakers, for example—reflect the natural order of things. Critics contend that biology is not destiny, that our behaviour is not dictated by our genes. In fact, some feminist and queer theorists argue that the evolutionary explanation for gender differences in behaviour serves as an excuse for rationalizing gender inequality.

PRENATAL BRAIN ORGANIZATION   Researchers have sought the origins of gender-typed behaviours in the organization of the brain. Is it possible that the cornerstone of gender-typed behaviour is laid in the brain before the first breath is taken?

The hemispheres of the brain are specialized to carry out certain functions. In most people, the right hemisphere (right brain) appears to be specialized to perform visual and spatial tasks. The left hemisphere (left brain) appears to be more critical for verbal functions.

We know sex hormones are responsible for prenatal sexual differentiation of the genitals and the gender-related structural differences in the hypothalamus of the prenatal brain. Sexual differentiation of the brain may also partly explain men's (slight!) superiority at spatial-relations tasks, such as interpreting road maps and visualizing objects in space. Testosterone in the brains of male fetuses spurs greater growth of the right hemisphere, and slows the rate of growth of the left hemisphere. This difference may be connected with the ability to accomplish spatial-relations tasks.

Might boys' inclinations toward aggression and rough-and-tumble play also be prenatally imprinted in the brain? Some theorists argue that prenatal sex hormones may masculinize or feminize the brain by creating predispositions that are consistent with gender-role stereotypes, such as rough-and-tumble play and aggressive behaviour in males (Cohen-Bendahen et al., 2005).

CRITICAL THINKING QUESTIONS

Do you agree with feminist and queer theorists who argue that evolutionary theory is little more than a sophisticated excuse for maintaining the status quo in the centres of power in society?

A study investigated the gender-typed visual preferences of human infants at the early ages of three to eight months (Alexander et al., 2009). The researchers hypothesized that preferences for gender-typed toys might be at least in part inborn and should therefore emerge in children before they're self-aware of their gender identities. The researchers assessed interest in a toy truck and a doll among 30 infants, using eye-tracking technology to indicate the direction of visual attention. They did find the hypothesized sex differences in visual interest: girls showed a visual preference for the doll over the truck, and boys showed a higher number of visual fixations on the truck than on the doll. As noted, these sex differences emerge much earlier than self-awareness of one's sex, when there has been relatively little time for social influences to take effect.

Psychological Perspectives

Children become aware of gender-role stereotypes by the tender age of two to three (Rathus, 2014). When asked to describe the differences between the genders, both boys and girls in North America generally agree that boys build things, play with transportation toys such as cars and fire trucks, enjoy helping their fathers, and hit other children. Both boys and girls also agree that girls enjoy playing with dolls and helping their mothers cook and clean, and that they're talkative, dependent on others for help, and nonviolent.

Psychologists have used psychoanalytic, social-cognitive, and cognitive-developmental theories to explain how children acquire such knowledge and adopt stereotypical behaviour patterns.

PSYCHOANALYTIC THEORY Sigmund Freud explained gender typing in terms of identification. Appropriate gender typing, in Freud's view, requires that boys come to identify with their fathers and girls with their mothers. Identification is completed, in Freud's view, as children resolve the **Oedipus complex** (which is sometimes called the Electra complex in girls).

According to Freud, the Oedipus complex occurs during the phallic period of psychosexual development, between the ages of three and five. During this period, the child develops incestuous wishes for the parent of the other gender and comes to perceive the parent of the same gender as a rival. The complex is resolved by the child's forsaking incestuous wishes for the parent of the other gender and identifying with the parent of the same gender. Through identification with the same-gender parent, the child comes to develop behaviours that are typically associated with that gender.

SOCIAL-COGNITIVE THEORY Social-cognitive theorists explain the development of gender-typed behaviour in terms of processes such as observational learning, identification, and socialization (Golombok et al., 2008; Zosuls et al., 2009). In social-cognitive theory, identification is viewed as a continuing and broadly based learning process in which rewards and punishments influence children to imitate adult models of the same gender—especially parents of the same sex. Identification is more than imitation, however. In identification, the child not only imitates the behaviour of the model but also tries to become like the model in broad terms.

Socialization also plays a role in gender typing (Golombok et al., 2008; Zosuls et al., 2009). Almost from the moment a baby comes into the world, it's treated according to its gender. Parents tend to talk more to baby girls, and fathers especially engage in more roughhousing with boys. When children are old enough to speak, parents and other adults—even other children—begin to instruct them in how they're expected to behave. Parents may reward children for behaviour they consider gender-appropriate and punish (or fail to reinforce) them for behaviour they consider gender-inappropriate. Girls are encouraged to practise caretaking behaviours, which are intended to prepare them for traditional feminine adult roles.

Oedipus complex In psychoanalytic theory, a conflict of the phallic stage in which the boy wishes to possess his mother sexually, and perceives his father as a rival for her love.

Socialization The process by which an individual is guided into socially acceptable behaviour patterns through information, rewards, and punishment.

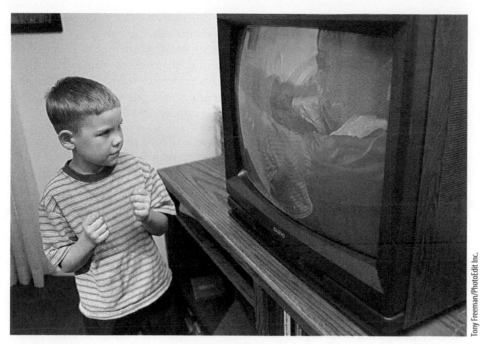

Gender Typing through Observational Learning.
According to social-cognitive theory, children learn about the gender roles available to them—and expected of them—at an early age. Gender schema theory adds that once children learn the expected gender roles (i.e., the gender schema of their cultures), they blend these roles with self-concept. Self-esteem thereby comes to depend on adherence to these gender roles.

Boys are handed Lego or doctor sets, to help prepare them for traditional masculine adult roles.

Parental roles in gender typing are apparently changing. With more mothers working outside the home, girls today are exposed to more career-minded female role models than girls of earlier generations were. More parents today encourage their daughters to focus on careers and engage in strenuous physical activities, such as organized sports. Many boys today have fathers who take larger roles in childcare and household responsibilities than men used to.

Social-cognitive theorists believe that aggression is largely influenced by learning. Boys are permitted, even encouraged, to engage in more aggressive behaviour than girls.

COGNITIVE-DEVELOPMENTAL THEORY   Psychologist Lawrence Kohlberg (1966) proposed a cognitive-developmental view of gender typing. From this perspective, gender typing is not the product of environmental influences that mechanically stamp in gender-appropriate behaviour; rather, children themselves play an active role. They form concepts, or **schemas**, about gender, then exhibit behaviours that conform to their gender concepts. These developments occur in stages and are entwined with general cognitive development.

According to Kohlberg, gender typing entails the emergence of three concepts: gender identity, gender stability, and gender constancy. Gender identity is usually acquired by the age of three. By the age of four or five, most children develop a concept of **gender stability**—the recognition that people retain their genders for a lifetime. Prior to this age, boys may think they'll become mommies when they grow up, and girls may think they'll be daddies.

The more sophisticated concept of **gender constancy** develops in most children by age seven or eight. They recognize that gender doesn't change even when people alter their dress or behaviour; gender remains constant even when

Schema A concept, or a way of interpreting experience or processing information.

Gender stability The concept that people retain their genders for a lifetime.

Gender constancy The concept that people's genders do not change, even if they alter their dress or behaviour.

appearances change. A woman who wears her hair short (or shaves it off) remains a woman. A man who dons an apron and cooks dinner remains a man.

According to cognitive-developmental theory, children are motivated to behave in gender-appropriate ways once they've established the concepts of gender stability and gender constancy. They then make active efforts to learn which behaviour patterns are considered masculine and which are considered feminine. Once they obtain this information, they imitate the gender-appropriate patterns.

GENDER-SCHEMA THEORY Gender-schema theory proposes that children develop **gender schemas** as a means of organizing their perceptions of the world (Bem, 1993). A gender schema is a cluster of mental representations about male and female physical qualities, behaviours, and personality traits. Gender gains prominence as a schema for organizing experience because of society's emphasis on it. Even young children start to mentally group people of the same gender in accordance with the traits that represent that gender.

Once children acquire gender schemas, they begin to judge themselves in accordance with traits considered appropriate to their genders. In doing so, they blend their developing self-concepts with the prominent gender schemas of their culture. The gender schemas furnish standards for comparison. Children with self-concepts that are consistent with the prominent gender schemas of their culture are likely to develop higher self-esteem than children whose self-concepts are inconsistent.

> **Gender schema** A cluster of mental representations about male and female physical qualities, behaviours, and personality traits.

Gender Roles and Sexual Behaviour

Gender roles affect sexual behaviour. While it may be eroding over time as Western society advances towards gender equality, in many respects, the **traditional sexual script** for how heterosexual men and women are expected to behave and interact sexually is still in place (See "Sexual Script Theory" in Chapter 2). Children learn at an early age that men usually approach women and initiate sexual interactions, whereas women usually serve as the gatekeepers in romantic relationships. In their traditional role as gatekeepers, women are expected to wait to be asked out and to screen suitors. Men are expected to make the first (sexual) move, and women to determine how far advances will proceed.

The cultural expectation that men are initiators and women are gatekeepers is embedded within the traditional sexual script that men are sexually aggressive and women are sexually passive. Men are expected to have a higher number of sex partners than women (Fisher et al., 2012; Schmitt et al., 2012). Men are not only expected to initiate, only initiate sexual encounters, they're also expected to dictate all the moves thereafter, just as they're expected to take the lead on the dance floor. According to the traditional sexual script, women are supposed to let men determine the choice, timing, and sequence of sexual positions and techniques. Unfortunately, the stereotype favours men's sexual preferences, denying women the opportunity to give and receive their preferred kinds of stimulation.

The stereotypical masculine role within the traditional sexual script also imposes constraints on men. Men are expected to take the lead in bringing their partners to orgasm, but they shouldn't ask their partners what they like, because men are expected to be natural experts. ("Real men" not only don't eat quiche; they also don't have to ask women how to make love.) Fortunately, more flexible attitudes are emerging. Women are becoming more sexually assertive, and men are becoming more receptive to expressing tenderness and gentleness. Still, the roots of traditional gender roles run deep.

> **Traditional sexual script** A sexual script based on stereotypical standards for sexual behaviour that dictates that males take an assertive and active role in heterosexual interaction while women take a receptive and passive role.

> ## CRITICAL THINKING QUESTIONS
>
> The traditional sexual script suggests that heterosexual men usually make the first move sexually, and it's up to women to determine how far they'll go. In your experience and observations, has this stereotype become increasingly less accurate in recent years?

According to another stereotype, men become sexually aroused at puberty and remain at the ready throughout adulthood. A study conducted at an Ontario university found that 85% of the women believed "it's easy for a woman to sexually arouse a man if she really wants to" (Clements-Schreiber & Rempel, 1995). Women, the stereotype continues, don't share men's natural interest in sex, and a woman discovers her own sexuality only when a man ignites her sexual flame. This stereotype denies that "normal" women have spontaneous sexual desires or are readily aroused (Schmitt et al., 2012).

So far, we've looked at gender roles related to sexuality according to the traditional sexual script. It's clear, however, that gender roles in many aspects of Western life have evolved considerably in recent decades. For example, more and more women are focused on establishing careers and expect male partners to share in domestic chores. Although there are ethnocultural variations in gender roles, it's evident that women increasingly expect and enjoy equality in their relationships with men.

To what extent have changing gender roles in general translated into corresponding changes in gender roles related to sexuality? While the traditional sexual script may in some respects still in place, there's growing evidence that traditional gender role differences related to sexuality may become smaller as we progress toward full gender equality.

Attitude and Behaviour Differences

A common assumption is that gender differences in sexual attitudes and behaviours are quite large. But are men and women that different when it comes to sex?

Jennifer Petersen and Janet Shibley Hyde (2011) examined meta-analytic reviews of previous studies and large sample data sets on heterosexual behaviours, masturbation, use of sexually explicit material, attitudes toward premarital sex, and other variables related to gender differences in sexuality. They found that although men are more likely to have engaged in heterosexual intercourse than women, the gender difference is small and decreasing. Differences in the percentages of men and women who have engaged in oral sex are also small.

The authors cited a large-sample study in the United States in which 77% of men and 68% of women said they'd performed oral on their partners, while 79% of men and 73% of women said they'd received oral sex (Laumann et al., 1994). It's been generally assumed that men are far more sexually permissive in their attitudes than women, but Petersen and Hyde (2011) found that differences in general sexual permissiveness were relatively small, and decreasing over time. Both men's and women's attitudes toward premarital sex have also become more accepting, and gender difference in these attitudes smaller. According to Petersen and Hyde, in large studies of adolescents and adults, while men were more likely to report more lifetime sexual partners than women, the difference was actually quite small.

It appears that common perceptions may overemphasize gender differences. There's usually greater variation within each gender than between the genders (Muehlenhard, 2000), and the differences that do exist seem to be getting smaller. Among older Canadians, for example, men consistently report having had intercourse at much earlier ages than women, but among Canadians in their twenties, there's hardly any difference between men and women (Fischtein & Herold, 2002). In 2009/2010, the percentage of Canadians aged 15 to 24 who reported that they had first sexual intercourse before age 17 was very similar for males (36.2%) and females (33.0%) (Rotermann, 2012).

According to Petersen and Hyde's (2011) review, some significant gender differences in sexual attitudes and behaviours have been maintained. Although men's

A World of Diversity

ARE THERE UNIVERSAL DIFFERENCES IN SEXUAL STRATEGIES?

One of the more controversial theories is the suggestion that males are naturally polygamous and females are naturally monogamous. If this is so, it places a greater burden on societies in which men are expected to remain loyal to their mates. If a man strays, after all, he can take the attitude, "Don't blame me; it's in my genes." Women might wonder how realistic it is to expect their partners to remain faithful.

Evolutionary psychologists have developed a theory of sexual strategies, which holds that men and women differ in their long-term and short-term mating strategies, with men more interested in sexual variety in the short term (Klusmann, 2002). In the long term, according to this theory, both males and females may seek heavy investment in relationships, love, companionship, and resource sharing. Even so, men place more value on signals of fertility and reproductive value, as demonstrated by women's youthfulness and physical appearances. Women place relatively more value on men's social status, maturity, and resources—cues that indicate their ability to provide over the long term. The qualities men and women seek are believed to help solve adaptive problems humans have faced throughout their evolutionary history.

In the short term, according to this theory, men are more interested in one-night stands and relatively brief affairs. By impregnating as many women as possible, they have a greater chance of contributing their genes to future generations. Women, evolutionarily speaking, have little to gain from such encounters. Impregnation requires a long-term commitment to

Sam Edwards/Caiaimage/Getty Images

Roving Males.
In a study of 10 areas of the world, men in every culture surveyed were more likely than women to desire multiple sex partners. According to the sexual-strategies theory, this sex difference reflects human adaptation to environmental forces. Does this research finding mean it's unnatural to expect men to remain faithful to their partners?

child-rearing, and evolutionary forces favour the survival of children whose mothers create long-term, nurturing environments for them.

Because a universal form of behaviour would likely be embedded in our genes, the evolutionary theory of different sexual strategies would find support if males and females in various cultures showed similar sex differences in their short-term mating strategies.

In seeking such evidence, David Schmitt (2003) supervised a survey of 16 288 people across 10 major regions of the world, including North America, South America, western Europe, eastern Europe, southern Europe, the Middle East, Africa, Oceania, south and southeast Asia, and east Asia. He indeed found universal sex differences in the desire for sexual variety.

Table 5.1 and Figure 5.5 reveal some of Schmitt's key findings about the desire for variety in short- and long-term relationships. Men from all

10 areas of the world were significantly more likely than women to say they'd like to have more than one sex partner within the next month. For example, 23.1% of North American men said they'd like more than one partner, compared with just 2.9% of North American women. (See Table 5.1.) And when asked about the mean (average) number of sex partners they'd like over the next 30 years, men from every area wanted significantly more partners than women did. (See Figure 5.5.)

The probability that any sex differences Schmitt (2003) found within a given region were due to chance was less than 1 in 1000 ($p < 0.001$).

Intriguing as they are, we cannot conclude that these research findings prove the validity of the evolutionary approach to understanding differences between men's and women's "sexual strategies." For example, Oceanic women reported that they wanted more sex partners in the long term than African men did. (See Figure 5.5.) We can accept the universality of the findings but consider rival explanations for the data. In a world with common global communication, for instance, it might not be surprising to find worldwide overlap in gender roles. This overlap might affect the ways parents and cultural institutions influence children around the world.

TABLE 5.1

Percentage of Men and Women Who Desire More Than One Sex Partner "In the Next Month" across 10 World Regions

World Region	Percentage of Men Wanting More Than One Sexual Partner	Percentage of Women Wanting More Than One Sexual Partner
North America	23.1%	2.9%
South America	35.0	6.1
Western Europe	22.6	5.5
Eastern Europe	31.7	7.1
Southern Europe	31.0	6.0
Middle East	33.1	5.9
Africa	18.2	4.2
Oceania	25.3	5.8
South/Southeast Asia	32.4	6.4
East Asia	17.9	2.6

Source: Schmitt, D. P. (2003). Universal sex differences in the desire for sexual variety: Tests from 52 nations, 6 continents, and 13 islands. *Journal of Personality and Social Psychology, 85*(1), 85–104.

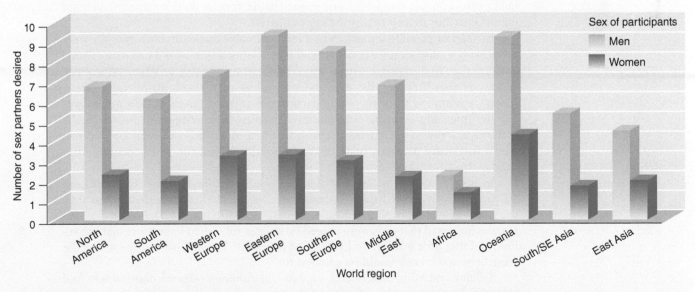

Figure 5.5   Mean number of sex partners desired by men and women "in the next 30 years" across 10 world regions.
Source: Schmitt, D. P. (2003). Universal sex differences in the desire for sexual variety: Tests from 52 nations, 6 continents, and 13 islands. *Journal of Personality and Social Psychology, 85*(1), 85–104.

and women's attitudes toward masturbation are similar, and gender differences in the percentages who report that they've masturbated is somewhat smaller in recent studies, men are still more likely to masturbate than women. In the Laumann et al. (1994) study of 18- to 59-year-old Americans, for example, 63% of the men said they'd masturbated during the previous year, compared to 42% of the women. The largest gender difference Peterson and Hyde found concerned the use of sexually explicit material: men were more likely than women to access magazines, videos, and the Internet for sexual content.

THE SEXUAL DOUBLE STANDARD   Embedded within the traditional sexual script is the concept of the sexual double standard in which men and women are evaluated differently for the same sexual behaviours (Crawford & Popp, 2003).

In a University of Guelph study of university students and singles-bar patrons (Milhausen & Herold, 2001), 79% of the men and 89% of the women reported that women with many sexual partners were more harshly judged than men with many partners. In another study, the majority of women reported that women were more severe than men in judging women's sexual behaviour (Milhausen & Herold, 1999). More recent research (Sakaluk & Milhausen, 2012) has also found evidence of the existence of a sexual double standard among university students.

Of the respondents in Milhausen and Herold's (2001) study, twice as many women (67%) as men (35%) felt that men had greater sexual freedom than women. The women thought it was easier for men to have many partners and to engage in casual sex; the men, on the other hand, felt that women had greater freedom, because they were the ones who decided whether sex would occur. The men typically felt at a disadvantage, because they wanted sex more than women did.

Although most respondents believed a double standard exists in Canada, the majority personally endorsed a single standard for both women and men. This was determined by measuring attitudes toward such behaviours as watching sexually explicit videos and having multiple sex partners. While only a minority of men held a sexual double standard, some women held a reverse double standard, judging men's behaviour more negatively than women's.

In another possible indication of a reverse double standard, both genders were more likely to discourage a female friend from dating a man who'd had many sexual partners than to discourage a male friend from dating a highly experienced woman. It appears that they saw the experienced man as more likely to be exploitative. Indeed, a common term the study participants used to describe such a man was "player," meaning someone who deceived women into having sex. Although the majority of both genders used negative words to describe both men and women who'd had many partners, none of the respondents used the word "player" for a woman.

In a study of 18- to 24-year-olds in Nova Scotia and British Columbia, all 40 participants reported that the sexual double standard was evident when they were adolescents (Shovellor, Johnson, Langille, & Mitchell, 2004). Both males and females indicated that girls were judged by stricter rules than boys for sexual behaviour, and that girls were more likely to be negatively labelled by their peers for the same behaviours boys would be admired for.

Sakaluk and Milhausen (2012), suggest that although research continues to find evidence for the existence of a sexual double standard among university students, their research also indicates that the nature of the double standard is more complex than previously thought and that a range of measures are needed to accurately capture sexual attitudes.

CRITICAL THINKING
QUESTIONS

In your opinion, to what extent is the sexual double standard for young adult men and women still in place today?

Gender and Sex-Advice Literature

Carleton University researchers Erin Connell and Alan Hunt (2006) have analyzed literature containing marital and sexual advice for heterosexuals from the early part of the twentieth century to the present. They've found that throughout the years, gender stereotypes have heavily influenced the type of relational and sexual advice provided to couples.

Throughout the first part of the twentieth century, this literature presented the husband as the wife's tutor and the initiator of sex, and the wife as the passive student. It was the husband's responsibility to arouse his wife and to control the speed of his own orgasm. The assumption was that wives entered marriage as inexperienced virgins who lacked any knowledge of sexual pleasure. In the period between the First and Second World Wars, marriage manuals (as they were called) increasingly emphasized the necessity for the husband to provide his wife with sexual pleasure.

During the sexual revolution of the 1960s, sex was no longer tied to marriage, and marriage manuals were renamed sex manuals. They focused on the need for a couple to master new sexual techniques to maximize sexual pleasure. In the following years, although research shows that many women did have strong sexual desires, the sex manuals continued to focus on gender differences.

Highly Sexual Women

Despite the stereotype that women are undersexed, they're no less arousable than men. Nor do they wait for men to discover their sexuality. Long before they have intimate relationships, children of both genders routinely discover that touching their genitals produces pleasurable sensations.

Jocelyn Wentland and her colleagues (2006; 2009) at the University of Guelph conducted an online survey to compare women who considered themselves highly sexual with women who did not. The sample of 1549 included university students, as well as women from various communities.

More than 80% of the highly sexual women agreed with the following statements:

- I think about sex a lot.
- I enjoy fantasizing about sex.
- When it comes to sex, I'm willing to try almost anything.
- I'm confident about my sexual ability.
- Fantasizing about sex can quickly get me sexually aroused.
- I really enjoy masturbating to orgasm.

Several of the study participants said it was important for society to recognize that many women are highly interested in sex and in obtaining sexual pleasure.

Many women are attempting to change the perception that women are disinterested in sex. In her book *Fearless Sex: A Babe's Guide to Overpowering Your Romantic Obsessions and Getting the Sex Life You Deserve*, sex therapist Joy Davidson (2004) encourages women to:

- Let go of sexual inhibitions and "bad girl" attitudes.
- Electrify their libidos.
- Liberate their most daring fantasies.
- Feel good about their "kinkier" sexual desires, and explore them safely.

Innovative Canadian Research

DO YOUNG MEN REALLY PREFER SEX OVER ROMANCE?

Existing theory and research has generally concluded that men are more sexually motivated than women, and women are more romantically motivated than men. Evolutionary theory suggests that these gender differences are the result of different strategies for reproduction, while social psychology theories explain such differences in terms of differential gender socialization in which boys and men are encouraged to emphasize and seek out sexual opportunities for their own sake while girls and women are socialized to place a greater emphasis on romance and relationships. However, most of the research supporting these assumptions about gender differences has relied on self-report measures which may be subject to social desirability bias (see Chapter 2). That is, men may claim to be more interested in sex than romance when completing study questionnaires because that is what they perceive is expected of them by society, and women may claim the opposite on questionnaires because that is what society expects of them.

Ashley Thompson and Lucia O'Sullivan (2012) at the University of New Brunswick used an implicit association test (IAT) to compensate for social desirability bias in male and female college students' reporting of their attitudes towards sex and relationships. An IAT is designed to assess implicit rather than explicit attitudes. Implicit attitudes are those that occur outside of conscious awareness. In other words, they are gut reactions. This is done by asking participants to very quickly make automatic positive or negative associations in their minds.

Thompson and O'Sullivan used an IAT to assess gender differences in college student's pleasant and unpleasant associations to romantic and sexual stimuli. Based on prevailing assumptions about gender differences, one would expect the female college students would show a stronger automatic preference for romantic stimuli compared to men, and the male college students would show a stronger automatic preference for sexual stimuli compared to women.

Contrary to what we might expect based on prior research, Thompson and O'Sullivan (2012) found that both the male and female students taking the IAT showed a stronger automatic preference for romantic versus sexual stimuli (Although this preference for romantic versus sexual stimuli was more pronounced in the women). According to the authors, these findings suggest that contrary to what men might indicate when filling out traditional questionnaires, where they may be more susceptible to social desirability bias, the IAT method for measuring attitudes appears to be tapping into a stronger preference for romantic stimuli compared to sexual stimuli among men.

Thompson and O'Sullivan (2012) suggest that there are several plausible explanations for their findings. One is that previous research has overstated actual gender differences related to romance and sex and that men and women are actually more similar than different than is typically assumed. Another explanation is that the findings are a reflection of changes in the way that males are socialized in Western culture and that changing masculine gender roles are gradually shifting towards a greater prioritization of romance over sex.

Psychological Androgyny

Most of us think of masculinity and femininity as opposite ends of one continuum. We tend to assume that the more masculine a person is, the less feminine he or she must be, and vice versa. Thus, a man who exhibits the stereotypical feminine traits of nurturance, tenderness, and emotionality is often considered less masculine than other men. Women who compete with men in business are perceived not only as more masculine than other women but also as less feminine than other women.

Some behavioural scientists, including Sandra Bem, argue that masculinity and femininity instead constitute separate personality dimensions (DiDonato & Berenbaum, 2011). Whether male or female, someone who is highly masculine may also possess feminine traits, and vice versa. An individual in Western society who exhibits "masculine" assertiveness and instrumental skills (e.g., abilities in science or business) along with "feminine" nurturance and cooperation fits both masculine and feminine gender-role stereotypes. This person shows **psychological androgyny**. Someone who's high only in assertiveness and instrumental skills fits the masculine stereotype. A person who's high only in traits such as nurturance and cooperation fits the feminine stereotype. Someone who's low in both the stereotypical masculine and the stereotypical feminine patterns is considered undifferentiated in terms of gender-role stereotyping.

People who are psychologically androgynous may be capable of summoning up a wider range of masculine and feminine traits to meet the demands of various situations and to better express their desires and talents (Cooper et al., 2011; Prakash et al., 2010). Researchers have found psychologically androgynous individuals of both genders who show "masculine" independence under group pressures to conform, and "feminine" nurturance during interactions with children (DiDonato & Berenbaum, 2011). Psychologically androgynous adolescents are less likely to stereotype occupations as masculine or feminine (Kulik, 2000).

People who oppose the constraints of traditional gender roles may perceive psychological androgyny as a desirable goal. Some feminist writers, however, criticize the model of psychological androgyny because it's defined in terms of—and thereby perpetuates—masculine and feminine gender roles (Denmark et al., 2008).

Other critics suggest that some benefits of psychological androgyny are actually confounded with masculinity. For example, psychologically androgynous people tend to have higher self-esteem and to be generally better adjusted psychologically than people who are feminine or undifferentiated (DiDonato & Berenbaum, 2011; Parent et al., 2011). Does this mean that masculine traits such as assertiveness and independence may be related to psychological well-being, whether or not they are combined with feminine traits such as warmth, nurturance, and cooperation?

In any event, not all males are extremely "masculine," and not all females are overwhelmingly "feminine." Perhaps it is fortunate that few of us are completely masculine or feminine, despite our anatomic sex.

Psychological androgyny
A state characterized by possession of both stereotypical masculine traits and stereotypical feminine traits.

Summing Up

During the first six weeks or so of prenatal development, embryonic structures in both genders develop along similar lines, and resemble primitive female structures.

At about the seventh week after conception, the genetic code (XX or XY) begins to assert itself, causing changes in the gonads, genital ducts, and external genitals.

Testosterone spurs differentiation of the male (Wolffian) duct system. In the absence of testosterone, the Wolffian ducts degenerate, and female sex organs develop.

Abnormalities of the sex chromosomes can have profound effects on sexual characteristics, physical health, and psychological development. Examples include Klinefelter's syndrome and Turner's syndrome.

Gender-specific changes occur in the hypothalamus during prenatal development. Testosterone causes cells in the hypothalamus of a male fetus to become insensitive to estrogen.

One's gender identity refers to a person's internal and individual sense of being female, male, or other shade of gender.

Gender identity is nearly usually consistent with assigned sex.

Intersex refers to a person who possesses the gonads of one gender and external genitalia that are ambiguous or typical of the other gender.

Transgender or *trans* are terms for people whose gender identity, expression or behaviour is different from those typically associated with their assigned sex at birth.

Transitioning refers to the activities that some trans people may pursue to begin living as the gender with which they identify rather than the gender they were assigned at birth.

Cultures have broad expectations of men and women, which are termed gender roles. In our culture, the stereotypical female is seen as gentle, dependent, kind, helpful, patient, and submissive. The stereotypical male is tough, competitive, gentlemanly, and protective.

Sexism is the prejudgment that simply because of gender, a person will possess certain traits.

Stereotypical gender preferences for toys and play activities are in evidence at an early age. Males are more aggressive than females. The question is why.

Biological views about gender typing focus on the roles of genetics and prenatal influences in predisposing males and females to gender-linked behaviour patterns. Psychologists have attempted to explain gender typing in terms of psychoanalytic, social-cognitive, and cognitive-developmental theories.

Gender-schema theory proposes that children develop gender schemas to organize their perceptions of the world. They then begin to judge themselves in terms of traits considered appropriate for their genders.

Stereotypical gender-role expectations affect dating practices and sexual behaviours.

According to this stereotype, men are sexual initiators, and women are sexual gatekeepers. Men not only initiate sexual encounters; they're also expected to initiate all the moves.

According to another stereotype, women don't share men's interest in sex. Current research, however, suggests that many women do have a strong interest in sexual pleasure.

Gender differences related to sexuality do exist, but many of them appear to be less pronounced than common wisdom suggests. Some gender differences in sexuality appear to be getting smaller.

Masculinity and femininity may be two independent personality dimensions. People who combine stereotypically masculine and feminine behaviour patterns are psychologically androgynous.

Test Yourself

Multiple-Choice Questions

1. The process by which males and females develop distinct sexual anatomies is known as:
   (a) Sexualization.
   (b) Homologous development.
   (c) Sexual differentiation.
   (d) The Müllerian stage.

2. During the first six weeks or so of prenatal development, embryonic structures of both genders develop along similar lines, resembling primitive:
   (a) Male structures.
   (b) Female structures.
   (c) Both male and female structures.
   (d) Neither male nor female structures.

3. In their research with the *fa'afafine* of Samoa, Paul Vasey and Nancy Bartlett found evidence that:
   (a) The *fa'afafine* tended to be victims of "sissyphobia."
   (b) The *fa'afafine* are similar in sexual preference to lesbians.
   (c) The expression of male-typical behaviours among the *fa'afafine* sets them apart from other gay men on the island.
   (d) The expression of female-typical behaviours in childhood did not provoke distress in Samoan *fa'afafine*.

4. *Trans* refers to:
   (a) People whose gender identity, expression, or behaviour is different from those typically associated with their assigned sex at birth.
   (b) People who transition from one sexual orientation to another after puberty.
   (c) People whose gender identity, expression or behaviour is the same as people who are cisgender.
   (d) People whose gender identity is different from their assigned sex but who do not wish to make a full medical transition to a transsexual status.

5. The World Professional Association for Transgender Health states that treatments designed to change gender identity or expression are:
   (a) Acceptable only for children under 5 exhibiting gender dysphoria.
   (b) No longer considered ethical.
   (c) Considered ethical if both parents of a gender dysphoric child under age 16 consent.
   (d) Now considered ethical.

6. A Dutch study found that after gender reassignment surgery, most people:
   (a) Regret their decision.
   (b) Function well sexually, psychologically, and socially.
   (c) Develop psychological disorders they showed no evidence of before.
   (d) Discontinue hormone treatments.

7. According to Kohlberg, gender _____ develops last.
   (a) stability
   (b) identity
   (c) exclusivity
   (d) constancy

8. Social-cognitive theorists explain the development of gender-typed behaviour in terms of processes such as:
   (a) Identification and resolution of the Oedipus complex.
   (b) Evolutionary adaptation and selective imaging.
   (c) Observational learning and socialization.
   (d) Gender schema internalization and genetic programming.

9. Teasing or belittling a woman because she studies engineering is an example of:
   (a) Gender typing.
   (b) Sexism.
   (c) Gender reassignment.
   (d) Homophobia.

10. Research suggests that gender differences in sexual attitudes and behaviours:
   (a) Are uniformly large.
   (b) Do not exist.
   (c) Appear, in many cases, to be getting larger.
   (d) Appear, in many cases, to be getting smaller.

You'll find answers to the "Test Yourself" questions on page 489.

Questions for Critical Thinking

1. In your opinion, will further disruption of the gender binary lead to a healthier society? What is the basis for your opinion?

2. If your friend told you that they had a gender independent child and were unsure about how to handle it, what advice would you give to them?

3. When you were growing up, what messages about traditional gender roles did you receive from your parents? Did you receive different messages from your friends? How did you reconcile any conflicts?

4. Have you ever experienced sexism? What were the circumstances? What effect, if any, did it have on you?

5. Do you think men have stronger sex drives than women? Why or why not?

CHAPTER SIX

Attraction and Love

James Darell/Digital Vision/Getty Images

From ancient philosophers to medieval poets to modern-day advice columnists, many have attempted to unlock the mysteries of attraction and love—with varying degrees of success. Whether William Shakespeare or *Cosmopolitan* magazine better captures the essence of attraction and love we leave to you to decide.

In this chapter, we'll broach these topics from a scientific point of view, using theoretical and research-based approaches to help understand what draws one person to another—and the perhaps indefinable concept of romantic love. We don't claim to have one up on Shakespeare, but we do think it's important for students of human sexuality to grasp the essential elements of a scientific approach to matters of the heart.

Attraction

What attracts one person to another? Can you think of personal attributes that have attracted you to particular individuals? To what extent do you think factors such as looks, personality, age, race or ethnicity, education, and social status have contributed to your personal attractions?

Keep your answers in mind as we explore some of the factors that research suggests govern interpersonal attraction.

The Attraction-Similarity Hypothesis: Who's Right for You?

The **attraction-similarity hypothesis** holds that people tend to develop romantic relationships with those whose levels of physical attractiveness and other traits are similar to their own (Morry et al., 2011; Sprecher & Fehr, 2011). There are some gender differences: Research shows that men are more likely than women to communicate positive feelings and present themselves in a positive light when they are conversing with a woman who is similar in physical attractiveness (van Straaten et al., 2009). Women did not show the same selectivity in talking with men. These findings are consistent with research showing that physical attractiveness is a more important criterion for men than women in partner selection. People are more often than not similar to their partners in height, weight, personality traits, intelligence, and even in use of alcohol and tobacco (DeCuyper et al., 2012; Montoya et al., 2008; van Straaten et al., 2009). Research from the Unites States indicates that people tend to choose partners with similar political perspectives (e.g., liberal vs. conservative) (Klofstad, McDermott, & Hatemi, 2013).

Our partners tend to resemble us in race and ethnicity, age, level of education, and religion. For example, 95% of Canadians choose partners (whether married or common-law) from their own racial backgrounds (Riedmann, Lamanna, & Nelson, 2003). However, romantic pairings between partners of different racial backgrounds are becoming more common in Canada (Milan, Maheux, & Chui, 2010). Perhaps, as our society becomes more racially and ethnically diverse, these characteristics will become less relevant in partner choice.

Attraction-similarity hypothesis The concept that people tend to develop romantic relationships with people who are similar to themselves in factors such as physical attractiveness, cultural background, personality traits, and interests.

CRITICAL THINKING QUESTIONS

How well does the attraction-similarity hypothesis apply to you? For example, do you think you could become attracted to a person who is significantly taller or shorter than you? What about a person with political opinions different from your own?

Propinquity Proximity.

Do Opposites Attract, or Do Birds of a Feather Flock Together?

Contrary to common wisdom, opposites do not attract. We're actually less apt to be attracted to people who disagree with our views and tastes than we are to people who share them.

Why do the great majority of us have partners from our own backgrounds? One reason is **propinquity**. That is, relationships are made in the neighbourhood, and not in heaven. Although mobility has increased in Western society, we tend to live among—and come into contact with—people whose backgrounds are reasonably similar to ours. Another reason is that we're drawn to people whose attitudes are akin to our own. People from similar backgrounds are more likely to hold similar attitudes than people from different backgrounds. Similarity in attitudes and tastes is a key contributor to attraction, friendships, and love relationships (Brown et al., 2003; Morry & Gaines, 2005).

Let's note a sex difference: Evidence shows that women are more likely than men to place greater weight on similar attitudes as a determinant of attraction, whereas men are likely to place more value on physical attractiveness (Furnham, 2008).

We tend to assume that people we find attractive share our attitudes (Montoya et al., 2009). When sexual attraction is strong, perhaps we want to think we can iron out all the kinks in the relationship. Although similarity may be important in determining initial attraction, however, compatibility appears to be a stronger predictor of maintaining an intimate relationship (Amodio & Showers, 2005).

Ancient Alchemy
What's the secret of attraction and love?

Smart-foto/Shutterstock

Reciprocity: If You Like Me, You Must Have Excellent Judgement

Reciprocity Mutual exchange.

When we feel admired and complimented, we tend to return these feelings and behaviours. This is called **reciprocity**. Reciprocity is a potent determinant of attraction (Levine, 2000; Sprecher, 1998). We tend to be much more warm, helpful, and candid when we're with strangers who seem to like us. We even tend to welcome positive comments that we know are inaccurate (Levine, 2000).

The power of reciprocity may enable many couples to become happy with one another and reasonably well adjusted. By reciprocating positive words and actions, a person can sometimes stoke neutral or mild feelings into robust, affirmative feelings of attraction.

Physical Attractiveness: How Important Is It to Look Good?

We might like to think of ourselves as so sophisticated that physical attractiveness doesn't move us. We might like to claim that sensitivity, warmth, and intelligence are more important. However, we may never learn about other people's personalities if we don't find ourselves physically attracted to them in some way. Research shows that physical attractiveness is a major determinant of interpersonal and sexual attraction (Lippa, 2012; Little et al., 2011). Some researchers, in fact, contend that physical appearance is the key factor in consideration of partners for dates, sex, and long-term relationships (Wilson et al., 2005).

IS BEAUTY IN THE EYE OF THE BEHOLDER? What determines physical attractiveness? Research investigating mate preferences has been mostly conducted using samples of North American and European university students, limiting the degree to which we can generalize the findings to other groups and populations. While this research does identify particular preferences with respect to physical attractiveness, we should keep in mind that these preferences are subject to cross-cultural variation. Katarzyna Pisanski and David Feinberg (2013) at McMaster University reviewed research investigating cultural differences in mate preferences. They concluded that there are notable cultural differences in both men's and women's preferences in opposite gender partners. For example, the research reviewed by Pisanski and Feinberg suggests that North American, European, and Japanese men preferred women who are thinner than average, while men in South America and African men generally preferred women who are comparatively heavier. The authors also cite studies indicating cross-cultural differences in women's preferences for facial masculinity. For example, women in Jamaica prefer more masculine male faces (e.g., wider cheek bones and jaws) than do women in Britain (Penton-Voak, Jacobson, & Trivers, 2004).

In general, women around the world consider taller men to be more attractive (Furnham, 2009; Kurzban & Weeden, 2005). Height can play a role in mate choice because it suggests social dominance, status, access to resources, and a positive heritable trait (Salska, 2008). Undergraduate North American women prefer to date men who are about 15 centimetres taller than they are themselves. Undergraduate men, on the average, prefer women who are about 11 centimetres shorter (Furnham, 2009; Kurzban & Weeden, 2005).

"Thin is in" reflects the dominant perspective of North American culture. Some young women are so affected by the cultural ideal that they suffer from the eating disorder anorexia nervosa, in which they literally starve themselves. Both females and males tend to find slenderness (though not anorexic thinness) attractive, especially in females (Furnham, 2009; Glasser et al., 2009; Wilson et al., 2005).

An examination of Internet dating profiles in 5810 personal ads on Yahoo showed that males from various cultures and European-American males and females prefer thin partners (Glasser et al., 2009). European-American males are more likely than African-American and Latino males to want to date slender, physically fit women. African-American and Latino-American men are significantly more likely to be interested in women with large or thick bodies. The study also found that African-American and Latina women are significantly more likely than European-American women to be satisfied with their bodies.

In a study at Dalhousie University (Lalonde et al., 2004), female students rated women of average weight with waist-to-hip ratios of 0.7 as most attractive. Small and medium waists were generally preferred, regardless of body weight. Moderate and heavy figures with large hips received the lower attractiveness ratings; larger figures with more tubular body shapes were considered more attractive. The results indicated that in evaluating physical attractiveness, body weight, waist size, and hip size all interact to influence ratings of women's attractiveness.

Cohen and Tannenbaum (2001) conducted an Internet study in which they posted various women's body shapes and asked lesbian and bisexual women to indicate which they found most sexually attractive. The respondents, like heterosexual men and women, found women with 0.7 waist-to-hip body ratios most attractive. However, they differed from heterosexual women and men in naming *heavy* women with 0.7 waist-to-hip body ratios and large breasts as their first choice. Their second choice was heavy women with the same waist-to-hip body ratio but with small breasts. The authors suggested that the study participants were rejecting what they might have viewed as societal emphasis on excessive slenderness.

Researchers at Queen's University compared the age-based partner preferences of heterosexual men, heterosexual women, gay men, and lesbians (Silverthorne & Quinsey, 2000). They asked adults to rate pictures of 15 male and 15 female faces that were sorted into five age-based categories, ranging from 18 to 60. The lesbians rated 42- to 60-year-old female faces as most attractive, and 19-year-olds as least attractive. Gay and heterosexual men found younger partners more sexually appealing than lesbian and heterosexual women did. Gay men found younger partners more sexually appealing than did heterosexual men, while lesbians found older partners more sexually appealing than heterosexual women did. In another study of gay and bisexual men in three Ontario cities, Barry Adam (2000a) of the University of Windsor found widespread acknowledgment of the ideal of youthfulness in the gay community. In particular, men who preferred their partners to be older than they were noted that they sometimes faced ridicule as a result. Nevertheless, the study showed considerable diversity in the age preferences of gay and bisexual men.

It is often assumed that heterosexual men are uniformly attracted to relatively large female breasts. However, research suggests that although there appears to be a general preference for medium or larger sized breasts, there is also considerable variation in men's breast size preferences. For example, Swami and Tovée (2013) studied White British men's breast size preferences and found that 24% preferred small breasts, 33% medium, 24% large, and 19% very large. In a similar study of men from Papua New Guinea, Samoa, and New Zealand, all three groups of men indicated a preference for medium size or larger breasts, suggesting that there may be some degree of cross-cultural similarity in breast size preferences (Dixson et al., 2011). In their study, Swami and Tovée found that male preference for larger sized breasts was associated with certain sexist attitudes such as the idealization of traditionally feminine women and greater objectification of women's bodies.

People who are attractive know it. In one study, men and women rated both themselves and one another for attractiveness (Marcus & Miller, 2003). By and large, the self-ratings meshed with the ratings of others, both female and male. Women's judgements were most closely related to how men perceived them, suggesting that they were reflecting men's opinions of them more than women's.

An experiment manipulated men's voices and asked women to rate them for attractiveness. Heterosexual women in the fertile (late follicular) phases of their menstrual cycles found men with deeper (more "masculine") voices more attractive than men with higher voices (Feinberg et al., 2006). The study didn't assess possible differences between heterosexual and lesbian women.

At the beginning of this section, we asked how important it is to look good. The research we've reviewed shows that, on average, men and women are attracted to partners with particular physical attributes. But it's important to remember that, just as there's almost endless variation in how people look, there's also a great deal of variation in what people find attractive. Although most women prefer their male partners to be taller than they are themselves, some fall for men who are shorter than they are. Some men are attracted to heavier-set women. Look at it this way: if all heterosexual men were attracted only to relatively thin women with large breasts, and all heterosexual women were attracted only to tall men with deep voices, most heterosexual people would be unable to find partners.

NON-PHYSICAL TRAITS AND ATTRACTIVENESS Although our culture judges beauty by physical standards, our perceptions of beauty are also affected by non-physical traits. For example, how beautiful we find a partner is likely to be enhanced by non-physical traits such as familiarity, liking, respect, and shared values and goals (Morry et al. 2011; Reis et al., 2011; Sprecher & Fehr, 2011). Both females and males rate faces as more attractive when they're smiling than when they're not (O'Doherty et al., 2003).

Gender-role expectations may affect perceptions of attractiveness. Women are more likely to be attracted to socially dominant men than men are to be attracted to socially dominant women (Graziano & Bruce, 2008). In one study, men and women were shown videos of prospective dates. The women found men who acted outgoing and self-expressive more appealing than men who were passive, while the men were put off by outgoing, self-expressive women (Riggio & Woll, 1984). In another study, highly feminine women were more likely than less feminine women to be attracted to dominant, "macho" men (Maybach & Gold, 1994). In yet another study, women rated videos of dominant college men (defined as exhibiting social control over troublesome interactions with instructors) as more appealing than submissive men. Again, male viewers were put off by similarly dominant women (Sadalla et al., 1987). Men are more likely to be jealous of socially dominant men, whereas women are more likely to be jealous of physically attractive women (Dijkstra & Buunk, 2002).

Left: Brand X Pictures/ThinkStock; Right: Piotr & Irena Kolasa/Alamy

Your Ideal Match.
Research shows that people tend to pair off with others who are similar in physical characteristics and personality traits.

Innovative Canadian Research

WHAT DO WOMEN WANT?

Do women who are more open to casual sex differ in their preferences for potential male partners than women who are less open to casual sex? Researchers at Queen's University and the University of Victoria (Provost et al., 2006) conducted two studies to find out. They predicted that women who were more sociosexual—that is, who were more open to short-term sexual relationships—would be more likely to prefer highly masculine male faces and bodies than women who were less sociosexual.

In the first study, they asked women to rate the attractiveness of male faces and various masculine body types. In general, all of the women preferred more masculine faces and more muscular bodies. However, the women who were more sociosexual showed much greater preferences for men with muscular bodies.

In the second study (Provost et al., 2006), a different sample of women met with two equally attractive men (one highly masculinized and one less masculinized) in a "speed dating" setting. After meeting with each man, the women completed a questionnaire that asked about their interest in each man for a short-term or a long-term relationship. A key finding was that the more sociosexual women were more strongly attracted to the highly masculinized man for a short-term relationship than the less sociosexual women were, and the less sociosexual women preferred the less masculinized man for a long-term relationship. Assuming that a higher level of masculinity is associated with "healthier" genes, the researchers theorized that evolutionary theory was supported by the finding that women who were more open to casual sex were more likely to choose more masculine-looking men for casual sex.

In a similar study, researchers at the University of Western Ontario (Wilbur & Campbell, 2010) found that both women who scored high and women who scored low in sociosexuality preferred physically attractive men as short-term sexual partners, though physical attractiveness was far more important to the highly sociosexual women. Interestingly, when it came to long-term romantic partners, both groups of women preferred physical attractiveness to the same extent. They also both preferred long-term romantic partners who were ambitious.

McMaster University researcher Jillian O'Connor and her colleagues (2014) conducted a study of 87 heterosexual, undergraduate women in order to explore how the pitch of a man's voice influences a women's choice of short-term versus long-term romantic partners. In three separate instances, participants were presented with two samples of the same voice, one sample with a raised pitch and the other with a lowered pitch. They were first asked to choose voices that represented partners who would most likely cheat on them. They were then asked to select voices that represented partners most suitable for short-term and long-term relationships.

The study found that, in general, women showed a slight preference for men with lower-pitched voices for both short- and long-term relationships. However, the findings also indicated that women believed men with lower voices were more likely to be unfaithful. Those women who equated lower voices with infidelity showed a stronger preference for men with lower pitched voices for short-term relationships rather than for long-term relationships.

WHAT DO YOU LOOK FOR IN A RELATIONSHIP? In a study at the University of Guelph (Milhausen et al., 2007), women rated responsibility as more important in a future spouse than men did, whereas men rated physical attractiveness as more important than women did. In contrast, when choosing a casual sex partner, women thought physical attractiveness was more important than men did. Both men and women rated responsibility as most important when choosing a future spouse, followed by physical attractiveness, sexual skill, and status or popularity. This was one of the first studies to consider the importance of sexual skill in selecting a partner.

In 2005, a Compas survey asked a national sample of Canadians what they felt were the attributes of the ideal spouse. The men valued only one characteristic more than the women did: "good-looking." Women valued such traits as "manages money well," "is financially successful," "is well-educated and intelligent," and "shares your religion" more highly than the men did.

There have been relatively few studies of mate preference attributes among ethnic groups in Canada. Researchers at York University (Lalonde et al., 2004) found that for second-generation Southeast-Asian Canadians, the strength of connectedness to their own families was the strongest predictor of traditional mate attribute preferences. Despite extensive exposure to Canadian values, most respondents preferred their future spouses to have traditional attributes. Men had more traditional sex-role expectations than women did.

AN EVOLUTIONARY PERSPECTIVE ON MATE PREFERENCE Many people view contemporary gender differences in perception of attractiveness as highly sexist. On one level, most of us would agree that the emphasis on physical beauty for women and economic power and professional status for men as primary indicators of attractiveness is a strong reflection of a patriarchal (male-dominated) society. Some evolutionary psychologists believe evolutionary forces favour the continuation of gender differences in mate preference, because certain preferred traits offer reproductive advantages (Buss, 2005, 2009).

According to this theory, human beings, like all organisms, are genetically motivated to reproduce. (Without this motivation, a species would soon become extinct.) As a result, some physical features—such as cleanliness, good complexion, clear eyes, good teeth, good hair, firm muscle tone, and a steady gait—are universally appealing to both genders, because they're markers of reproductive potential (Buss, 2005). Youth and health may be relatively more important to a woman's appeal because these characteristics tend to be associated with her reproductive capacity—the "biological clock" limits her reproductive potential. Physical characteristics associated with a woman's youthfulness, such as smooth skin, firm muscle tone, and lustrous hair, may have thereby become more closely linked to a woman's appeal (Buss, 1994). A man's reproductive value, however, may depend more on how well he can provide for his family than on his age or physical appeal. From a female perspective, a man's value as a reproducer, therefore, is more intertwined with factors that contribute to a stable environment for child-rearing, such as economic status and reliability. Evolutionary psychologists argue that these gender differences in mate preference may have been passed down through the generations as part of our genetic heritage (Buss, 2009).

CRITICAL THINKING QUESTIONS

Do your own preferences in a romantic partner appear to support or contradict the theory of evolutionary psychology?

Mate preferences that have evolved over millions of years of human evolution are not expressed consciously; they're more like gut-level attractions (Buss & Schmitt, 1993). In other words, from the perspective of evolutionary psychology, having a preference for particular qualities in a mate is similar to having a preference for certain types of food. Over many generations when food was scarce, for example, human beings developed a taste for food that was rich in sugars and fats, because it gave them a greater chance of survival. We don't have a sweet tooth because we choose to, but because it's been bred into us by the forces of evolution. According to evolutionary psychology, these same dynamics influence sexual attraction.

The theory of evolutionary psychology is subject to caveats and criticisms when it comes to mate preference. Among the most prominent caveats is the argument that male-dominated social structures are the main reason so many cultures emphasize female physical beauty and male economic status in their standards of attractiveness. In this view, as cultures develop higher levels of gender equality, male and female standards of attractiveness will gradually change. Some would argue that we're already beginning to see these changes. Are women placing more emphasis on men's physical appearance as they begin to equal men in economic power? Are men increasingly enticed by high-powered professional women? As Western society continues to progress toward gender equality, it will be fascinating to see the extent

A World of Diversity

SEX DIFFERENCES IN MATE PREFERENCE ACROSS 37 CULTURES

What do men in Nigeria, Japan, Brazil, Canada, and the United States have in common? For one thing, men in these countries report that they prefer mates who are younger than themselves. Buss (1994) reviewed survey evidence on the preferred age difference between oneself and one's mate in 37 cultures (representing 33 countries) in Europe, Africa, Asia, Australia, New Zealand, and North and South America. In every culture men preferred younger mates (the range was from 0.38 year to 6.45 years). Women, however, preferred older mates (the range was from 1.82 years to 5.1 years).

Gender differences in the preferred age of mates paralleled actual differences in age of men and women at the time of marriage. Men were between two and five years older, on average, than their wives at the time of marriage. The smallest average age difference at marriage, 2.1 years, was found in Poland. The largest average difference, 4.92 years, was found in Greece. Men in the mainland United States averaged 2.71 years older than women at the time of marriage. In Canada, men were 2.51 years older than their mates, on average.

Buss found that in all 37 cultures, men placed greater value on a prospective partner's "good looks" than did women. On the other hand, women in 36 of 37 cultures placed greater value on "good earning capacity" of prospective mates.

The consistency of Buss's findings lends credence to the notion that there are widespread gender differences in preferences with respect to age, physical characteristics, and financial status of prospective mates. Generally speaking, men place greater value on the physical attractiveness and relative youth of prospective mates. Women place relatively greater value on the earning capacity of prospective mates. Buss interpreted women's preferences for relatively older mates as additional evidence that women appraise future mates on the basis of their ability to provide for a wife and family, because age and income tend to be linked among men.

Despite these gender differences in preferences for mates, Buss found that both men and women placed greater emphasis on personal qualities than on looks or income potential of prospective mates. In all 37 cultures, the characteristics "kind," "understanding," and "intelligent" were rated higher than earning power or physical attractiveness.

(left to right) Peter Foley/Landov; Visage/Getty Images; Jupiterimages/Thinkstock; Digital Vision/Thinkstock

Who Is Mr. or Ms. Right?
Are your judgements of attractiveness based on universal standards or on your cultural experiences? Evolutionary psychologist David Buss found some nearly universal standards for beauty in his study of 37 cultures.

to which standards of attractiveness for men and women also change. Many evolutionary psychologists would contend that while changes in social structure may indeed affect our opinions and choices, we are, at a very basic level, still unavoidably influenced by forces of human evolution.

A World of Diversity

READY, SET, SPEED DATE

The speed-dating phenomenon began in the late 1990s and was originally introduced as a way for Jewish singles in Los Angeles to meet prospective romantic partners. The first speed dating events consisted of 10-minute sessions for couples to meet and then decide if they wanted to see each other again. Subsequent versions have typically used shorter sessions that range from seconds to 5 or 7 minutes. Unlike other social situations such as bars or parties, there is an assumption at a speed dating event that participants are available and interested in meeting others with the goal of forming romantic relationships. Studies that focus on speed-dating events give researchers the opportunity to examine the process of initial attraction in a controlled environment (Finkel, Eastwick, & Matthews, 2007).

A study of 22 speed-dating events in the Netherlands focused on the differences between men's and women's levels of selectivity, as measured by the proportion of *no's* given by participants in assessing their speed dating partners (Overbeek, Nelemans, Karremans, & Engels, 2013). The events took place in two public settings, a popular restaurant and a museum, and involved 546 participants aged 22 to 42 years. Specific characteristics of participants were measured, including educational level, facial attractiveness, and body-mass index (BMI). For 12 of the events, men were told to rotate from one interview to another and in the remaining 10 events women were instructed to rotate between partners. Results showed that when women were in situations characterized as being more competitive they became less selective in their partner preferences. Situations were considered to be more competitive if there were more women than men at an event, or if a woman was less attractive than other women, or if women were

---

CRITICAL THINKING QUESTIONS

Is the concept of "love at first sight" realistic? Or would "infatuation at first sight" be a more accurate term to describe immediate and intense feelings of attraction?

Storge (STORE-gay) Loving attachment and nonsexual affection. This is the type of emotion that binds parents to children.

Agape (AH-gah-pay) Selfless love. This kind of love is similar to generosity and charity.

Philia (FEEL-yuh) Love between friends. This kind of love is based on liking and respect rather than sexual desire.

Eros The kind of love that's closest to our modern-day concept of passion.

Love

Our culture idealizes the concept of romantic love. We readily identify with the plight of the star-crossed lovers in *Romeo and Juliet* and its modern retelling, *West Side Story*, who sacrificed themselves for love. We learn that "love makes the world go round" and "love is everything." A Canadian study found that people who felt they were loved had better health than people who didn't (Nakhaie & Arnold, 2010).

Like other aspects of human sexual and social behaviour, the concept of love must be understood within a cultural context.

A Greek Heritage

The concept of love can be traced back at least as far as the classical age of Greece. The Greeks distinguished four concepts related to the modern meanings of love: **storge**, **agape**, **philia**, and **eros**.

Eros is closest in meaning to our concept of passion. Eros was a character in Greek mythology (transformed in Roman mythology into Cupido, now called Cupid) who would shoot unsuspecting people with his love arrows, causing them to fall madly in love with whoever was nearest to them at the time. Erotic love embraces sudden passionate desire—"love at first sight" and "falling head over heels in love." Younger university students are more likely than older (and wiser?) students to believe in love at first sight and that "love conquers all" (Knox et al., 1999). Passion can be so gripping that you're convinced your life has been changed forever (Aron et al., 2008). Romantic love can also be earthy and sexy. In fact, sexual arousal and desire may be the strongest component of passionate or romantic love. Romantic love begins with a powerful physical attraction or feelings of passion and is associated with strong physiological arousal.

rotating from one partner to another. Men's levels of selectivity were not affected by changes in dating circumstances. Overbeek and colleagues findings suggest that the perception of competition and level of attractiveness may alter the selectivity of female, but not male, speed-dating participants.

Eastwick and Finkel (2008) recruited 163 undergraduate university students to participate in 4-minute speed-dating sessions. Prior to the speed-dating event, the students filled out questionnaires indicating the characteristics of a potential partner they would place the most emphasis on (i.e., physical attractiveness, earning potential, personality). The participants completed an interaction record after each speed date and again after the event to measure their romantic desire for and chemistry with each of their speed-dating partners. They also rated each partner on attractiveness, earning potential, and personality. At a post-event follow-up, participants were asked about their interest in seeing their partners again. When the researchers examined the students' pre-event questionnaires, they found the responses reflected traditional gender stereotypical partner preferences. That is, male students placed more emphasis on physical attractiveness, and female students placed more emphasis on earning potential as the preferred characteristics in potential romantic partners. However, participants, stated partner preferences on the pre-event questionnaire were poor predictors of their actual interest in their speed-dating partners. For example, a participant who placed a high value on physical attractiveness in the pre-event questionnaire was not significantly more likely than other participants to like, feel chemistry with, or want further contact with a partner he or she rated as physically attractive. Based on the results of the study, Eastwick and Finkel suggest that a person's beliefs about his or her own romantic partner preferences may not predict who that individual actually becomes attracted to or pursues for a romantic relationship.

Unlike the Greeks, we tend to use the word "love" to describe everything from feelings of affection toward another to romantic ardour to sexual intercourse ("making love"). Still, different types or styles of love are recognized in our own culture, as we shall see.

Romantic Love

The experience of romantic love, as opposed to loving attachment or sexual arousal per se, occurs within a cultural context that idealizes the concept. Western culture has a long tradition of idealizing romantic love, as represented, for instance, by romantic fairy tales that have been passed down through the generations. Our exposure to the concept of romantic love may begin with the fairy tales of Sleeping Beauty, Cinderella, and Snow White and their respective Princes Charming. Later, perhaps, the concept of romantic love blossoms with exposure to romantic novels, television and film scripts, and the heady tales of friends and relatives.

During adolescence, strong sexual arousal together with idealized images of the objects of our desires leads us to label our feelings "love." We speak of love, rather than lust, because sexual desire in the absence of committed relationships might be viewed as immature. Being "in love" ennobles attraction and sexual arousal—in our own minds, as well as in society's view. Unlike lust, love can be discussed at the dinner table. If others think we're too young to experience "the real thing"—which presumably includes knowledge of and respect for our partners' personality traits—our feelings may be called "puppy love" or "crushes."

A national survey in 2008 found that around half of Canadians (59% of the men and 51% of the women surveyed) believed in love at first sight. Thirty-eight percent said they'd actually experienced it (La Rose, 2008). Overall, 98% said they'd been in love at least once. Romantic love is rated by young people as the single-most important reason for marriage (Reis & Aron, 2008; Hatfield et al., 2012).

When reciprocated, romantic love is usually a source of deep fulfillment and ecstasy (Hatfield et al., 2012). When love is unrequited, however, it can lead to emptiness, anxiety, and despair. Romantic love can thus shift between ecstasy and misery. Perhaps no other feature of our lives can lift us as high or plunge us as low as romantic love.

INFATUATION VERSUS TRUE LOVE   Perhaps you first noticed one another when your eyes met across a crowded room. Or perhaps you met when you were both assigned to the same Bunsen burner in chemistry lab—less romantic, but closer to the flame. However it happened, the meeting triggered such electric charges through your bodies that you couldn't get one another out of your minds. Were you truly in love, however, or was it merely a passing fancy? Was it infatuation or the real thing—a true, lasting, mutual love? How do you tell them apart?

Perhaps you don't, at least not at first. **Infatuation** is a state of intense absorption in or focus on another person. It's usually accompanied by sexual desire, elation, and general physiological arousal or excitement. Some refer to infatuation as "passion." Others dub it a "crush." Both monikers suggest that it's a passing fancy. In infatuation, your heart may pound whenever the other person draws near or enters your fantasies.

For the first month or two, infatuation and the more enduring forms of romantic love are hard to differentiate. At first, both may be characterized by intense focusing or absorption. Infatuated people may become so absorbed that they can't sleep, work, or carry out routine chores. Logic and reason are swept aside. Infatuated people hold idealized images of their love objects, overlooking their faults. They may cast caution to the winds. In some cases, couples in the throes of infatuation rush to get married, only to find, a few weeks or months later, that they're not well suited for each other.

As time goes on, signs that distinguish infatuation from a lasting romantic love begin to emerge. The partners begin to view one another more realistically and are better able to determine whether the relationship should continue. Although the tendency to idealize one's lover is strongest at the outset of a relationship, a so-called "positive illusion" does tend to persist in relationships (Aron et al., 2008). That is, we maintain some tendency to differentiate our partners from the average and to differentiate the value of our relationships from the average.

Infatuation is based on intense feelings of passion but not on the deeper attachment and caring that typify a more lasting mutual love (Hatfield et al., 2012). Infatuation can lead to a more lasting love relationship, but it's not a necessary first step on the path. Some couples develop deep feelings of love without ever experiencing the fireworks of infatuation. And sometimes one partner is infatuated, while the other manages to keep his or her head out of the clouds.

Contemporary Models of Love

Despite the importance of love, scientists have historically paid little attention to it. Some people believe love can't be analyzed scientifically. Love, they maintain, should be left to the poets, philosophers, and theologians. Yet researchers are now applying the scientific method to the study of love. They recognize that love is a complex concept, involving many areas of experience—behavioural, emotional, cognitive, and motivational (Berscheid, 2003). Let's consider some of the views of love that have emerged from modern theory and research.

BIOLOGICAL MECHANISMS   Some researchers focus on the bodily changes that occur when we experience feelings of romantic love. There are many. Some focus on the search for distinct neural pathways (road maps in the brain) that define feelings of love (Marazziti, 2005). Others involve chemistry, with a special focus on the monoamines and neuropeptides involved in the brain's pleasure system (including dopamine and the naturally produced opium look-alikes we call endorphins), as well as the hormones oxytocin and vasopressin.

Infatuation A state of intense absorption in or focus on another person, usually accompanied by sexual desire, elation, and general physiological arousal or excitement. Infatuation is also referred to as passion.

Innovative Canadian Research

OBSESSIVE VERSUS HARMONIOUS PASSION

Passion is often equated with the early part of a romantic relationship when both partners are overwhelmed by intense sexual desire. Some theories of romantic love suggest that as deeper and more committed forms of love evolve, passion may decline or even disappear altogether. Passion is characterized as being a slightly irrational but highly exciting phase of a new relationship which will inevitably subside as time progresses.

However, studies by researchers at Université Laval and Université du Québec à Montréal suggest a more complex model of romantic passion (Ratelle, Carbonneau, Vallerand, & Mageau, 2013; Vallerand, 2008; Vallerand et al., 2003). Catherine Ratelle and colleagues identified two distinct kinds of romantic passion: obsessive and harmonious. Obsessive passion causes individuals to feel controlled by their passions. While they may experience love for their partners, the obsessive nature of their passion usually leads to controlling and selfish behaviour. In contrast, harmonious passion leads individuals to willingly establish relationships, and to feel in control of their emotions and actions. Harmonious passion encourages partners to consider the needs and interests of each other.

Ratelle et al. (2013) conducted studies with undergraduate students and members of the public in Quebec to determine how the different types of passion affected their relationships. Students were asked to fill out in-class questionnaires, and an online questionnaire on the study's Facebook site attracted a broader sample of adults in heterosexual relationships. The questionnaires measured levels of harmonious and obsessive passion, as well as aspects of relationship quality (i.e., intimacy, commitment, trust, sexual passion, love). Harmonious passion was strongly associated with greater levels of sexual passion, intimacy, and relationship satisfaction. Obsessive passion was positively associated with commitment and feelings of love, but did not increase levels of sexual passion, relationship satisfaction, or intimacy. Obsessive passion was also associated with increased levels of distrust in a relationship. Women's levels of sexual passion decreased when a partner exhibited obsessive passion and increased when a partner exhibited harmonious passion. Harmonious passion was also positively associated with greater relationship stability over a three-month period.

Ratelle et al. (2013) concluded that obsessive and harmonious passion affected the quality and experience of romantic relationships differently. Overall, the study's findings suggest that long-lasting high quality relationships tend to be characterized by some degree of harmonious passion. Although relationships characterized by obsessive passion can also last, they tend to have lower degrees of trust and intimacy. The research also supported the conclusion that passion, whether harmonious or obsessive, can persist as long as partners experience feelings of love and commitment for each other and continue to invest time and energy in their relationship.

Let's consider several psychologically oriented views of love. They may touch indirectly on things that happen in the body, but as we'll see, they do so almost apologetically.

LOVE AS APPRAISAL OF AROUSAL   Social psychologists Ellen Berscheid and Elaine Hatfield (Berscheid, 2010; Graham, 2011) defined **romantic love** in terms of a state of intense physiological arousal and the cognitive appraisal of that arousal as love. You may experience a pounding heart, sweaty palms, and butterflies in your stomach when you're in the presence of—or thinking about—your love interest. Cognitive appraisal of the physiological arousal means you attribute it to some cause, such as fear or love.

The perception that you've fallen in love is thus derived from several simultaneous events: a state of intense physiological arousal in connection with an appropriate love object (i.e., a person, not an event such as a rock concert), a cultural

Romantic love Love characterized by feelings of passion and intimacy.

setting that idealizes romantic love, and your attribution of the physiological arousal to feelings of love for the person.

STYLES OF LOVE   Some psychologists talk about styles of love. Susan Hendrick and Clyde Hendrick (2002) speak of love as a positive emotion that contributes to happiness, psychological well-being, and optimism about the future.

They've developed a Love Attitudes Scale that suggests the existence of six styles of love (Hendrick & Hendrick, 2003):

- Romantic love (eros)—"My lover fits my ideal"; "My lover and I were attracted to one another immediately."
- Game-playing love (ludus)—"I keep my lover up in the air about my commitment"; "I get over love affairs pretty easily."
- Friendship (storge, philia)—"The best love grows out of an enduring friendship."
- Logical love (pragma)—"I consider a lover's potential in life before committing myself"; "I consider whether my lover will be a good parent."
- Possessive, excited love (mania)—"I get so excited about my love that I can't sleep"; "When my lover ignores me, I get sick all over."
- Selfless love (agape)—"I'd do anything I could to help my lover"; "My lover's needs and wishes are more important than my own."

CRITICAL THINKING QUESTIONS

If someone asked you what it means to fall in love, how would you respond?

As you can see, these styles of love owe a debt to the Greeks.

Most people who are in love experience a number of these styles, but Hendrick and Hendrick (1986) have found some interesting gender differences. University men are significantly more likely to develop game-playing and romantic love styles. University women are more apt to develop friendly, logical, and possessive love styles. Hendrick and Hendrick (2003) have also found that romantically involved couples tend to experience the same love styles.

STERNBERG'S TRIANGULAR THEORY OF LOVE   Psychologist Robert Sternberg (1988) has offered a triangular theory that organizes the relationships among the different kinds of love discussed by many theorists, including passionate love, romantic love, and companionate love (Gouveia et al., 2009; Hendrick & Hendrick, 2003).

Sternberg's three components of love are

- Intimacy—the experience of warmth toward another person that arises from feelings of closeness, bondedness, and connectedness, including the desire to give and receive emotional support and to share one's innermost thoughts.
- Passion—an intense romantic or sexual desire for another person, accompanied by physiological arousal.
- Commitment—dedication to maintaining the relationship through good times and bad.

According to Sternberg's model, love can be conceptualized in terms of a triangle, with each vertex representing one of these basic elements of love. (See Figure 6.1.) The way the components are balanced can be represented by the shape of the triangle. For example, a love in which all three components are equally balanced—as in a consummate love—is represented by an equilateral triangle, as illustrated in Figure 6.1.

Couples are well matched if they possess corresponding levels of passion, intimacy, and commitment (Drigotas et al., 1999; Sternberg, 1988). Compatibility can be represented visually in terms of the congruence of the love triangles. Figure 6.2(a) shows a perfect match, with the two triangles congruent. Figure 6.2(b) depicts a good match, since the partners are similar in the three dimensions. Figure 6.2(c) shows a mismatch, with major differences between the partners on all three components.

Relationships may run aground when partners are mismatched. A relationship may fizzle, rather than sizzle, if one partner experiences more passion than the other, or if one wants a long-term relationship when the other's idea of commitment is to stay the whole night.

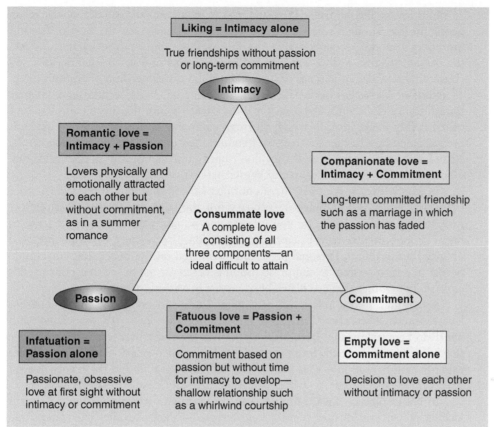

Figure 6.1 The triangular model of love.
According to psychologist Robert Sternberg, love consists of three components, represented by the vertices of this triangle. The various kinds of love consist of different combinations of these components. Romantic love, for example, consists of passion and intimacy. Consummate love—the cultural ideal—consists of all three components.

According to Sternberg's model, various combinations of the three components of love characterize six different types of love relationship (Sternberg, 1986, 1988) (see Figure 6.1): infatuation, liking, romantic love, consummate love, empty love, and fatuous love.

Infatuation (passionate love) is typified by strong sexual desire, but not by intimacy and commitment. Each partner may feel passionate love for the other, or such feelings may go unrequited.

Liking is a basis for friendship. It consists of feelings of closeness and emotional warmth, but without passion or commitment. Liking isn't felt toward passing acquaintances; it's reserved for people to whom we feel close enough to share our innermost feelings and thoughts. We sometimes develop these intimate relationships without committing ourselves to maintaining the long-term relationships that typify other types of love. Liking may develop into passionate love, or into a more committed form of friendship called companionate love according to many writers, including Sternberg (1988), Hendrick and Hendrick (2003), and Hatfield (Hatfield et al., 2008).

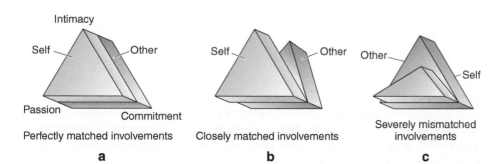

Figure 6.2 Compatibility and incompatibility, according to the triangular model of love.
Compatibility in terms of Sternberg's components of love can be represented as triangles. The first image (a) shows a perfect match, in which the triangles are congruent. The second image (b) shows a good match, since the partners are similar on the three dimensions. The third image (c) is a mismatch—there are major differences between the partners on all three components.

Can lovers also be friends, or shall the twain never meet? There's no reason people in love shouldn't become good friends—perhaps even the best of friends. Sternberg's model recognizes that the intimacy we find in true friendships and the passion we find in love are blended in two forms of love—romantic love and consummate love. These types of love differ along the dimension of commitment.

Romantic love has both passion and intimacy but lacks commitment. It may burn brightly and then flicker out. Or it may develop into the more complete love called consummate love, in which all three components flower—that is, desire is accompanied by a deeper intimacy and commitment. The flames of passion can be stoked across the years, even if they don't burn quite as brightly as they once did. Consummate love is the ideal many Westerners strive for.

In empty love, by contrast, there's nothing *but* commitment. It contains neither the warm, emotional embrace of intimacy nor the flame of passion. With empty love, your partner is someone you tolerate and remain with because of a sense of duty. People often remain in empty-love relationships because of either personal or social prescription. Personal prescription is based on the belief that you should persist in a relationship. Social prescription is based on the belief that your friends and family members believe it's right to persist in a relationship.

Sometimes a love relationship contains both passion and commitment but lacks intimacy. Sternberg calls this fatuous (foolish) love. It's associated with whirlwind courtships that burn brightly but briefly, as the partners come to realize they're not well matched. Intimacy can develop in such relationships, but couples experiencing fatuous love who rush into marriage often find that the reality doesn't match their expectations.

In companionate love, intimacy and commitment are strong, but passion is lacking. This form of love typifies long-term (so-called platonic) friendships and marriages in which passion has ebbed, but deep, abiding friendship remains.

For many of us, a strong dose of all three components—as found in consummate love—typifies the ideal relationship. The balance among Sternberg's three aspects of love, however, is likely to shift through the course of a relationship. At the outset, passion may be strong, but intimacy weak, as a couple is just getting to know one another's innermost thoughts and feelings. Time alone doesn't cause intimacy and commitment to grow. Some couples are able to peer into one another's deeper selves and form meaningful commitments at relatively early stages, while others who've been together for many years may remain distant, or waver in their commitment. Some couples experience only a faint flickering of passion early in their relationships, then it's quickly extinguished. For others, the flames of passion burn ever brightly. Many couples, though, find that passion tends to fade, while intimacy and commitment grow stronger.

Knowing the components of love can help you avoid pitfalls. Couples who recognize that passion exerts a strong pull early in a relationship may be less likely to let passion rush them into premature long-term legal commitments. Couples who recognize that it's normal for passion to fade needn't assume their love is at an end just when it may, in fact, be changing into a deeper, more intimate, committed form of love.

Summing Up

A number of factors determine interpersonal attraction.

Physical attractiveness is a major determinant of sexual attraction. There is considerable cross-cultural diversity in standards of attractiveness. Both genders find smiling faces more attractive than unsmiling faces. Women tend to place greater emphasis on such traits as vocational status and earning potential in potential mates, whereas men tend to give more consideration to physical attractiveness. Evolutionary psychologists believe that evolutionary forces favour such gender differences in preferred traits because these traits offer reproductive advantages.

According to the attraction-similarity hypothesis, we tend to develop romantic relationships with people who are similar to us.

Through reciprocation of positive words and actions, neutral or mild feelings may be stoked into feelings of attraction.

The Greeks had four concepts that relate to our modern definitions of love: storge, agape, philia, and eros.

Western culture has a long tradition of idealizing romantic love. Most people in Canada see romantic love as a prerequisite to marriage. Early in a relationship, infatuation may be indistinguishable from a more enduring form of romantic love.

Researchers are now applying the scientific method to the study of love.

Berscheid and Hatfield define romantic love in terms of intense physiological arousal, and cognitive appraisal of that arousal as love.

Hendrick and Hendrick suggest that there are six styles of love among college students: romantic love, game-playing love, friendship, logical love, possessive love, and selfless love.

Sternberg suggests that there are three distinct components of love: intimacy, passion, and commitment. Various combinations of these components typify different kinds of love. Romantic love is characterized by the combination of passion and intimacy.

Test Yourself

Multiple-Choice Questions

1. According to the research reviewed by Pisanski and Feinberg, compared to men in North America, Europe, and Japan, men in South America and Africa preferred women who were comparatively:
(a) Heavier.
(b) Thinner.
(c) Shorter.
(d) Taller.

2. In his study of sex differences in mate preference across 37 cultures, Buss found that:
(a) Men preferred women who earned more money than they did.
(b) Women preferred men who were older than they were.
(c) Only European men expressed an interest in marriage.
(d) Evolutionary forces contributed to preferences in some cultures, but not in others.

3. A study of age-based partner preferences found that lesbians rated the faces of women age _____ as most attractive.
(a) 18–24
(b) 25–29
(c) 30–41
(d) 42–60

4. A number of studies have shown that:
(a) Men are more attracted to socially dominant women.
(b) Women are more attracted to socially dominant men.
(c) There are no gender differences in attraction.
(d) Social dominance is not important in attraction.

5. Loving attachment, deep friendship, and nonsexual affection describe the ancient Greek concept of:
(a) Agape.
(b) Storge.
(c) Eros.
(d) Philia.

6. People who say, "I keep my lover up in the air about my commitment" or "I get over love affairs pretty easily" appear to be in the _____ style of love.
(a) logical
(b) romantic
(c) game-playing
(d) possessive

7. The idea that people are more likely to look for romantic relationships with those who are similar to themselves is known as the:
(a) Reciprocity theory.
(b) Attraction-similarity hypothesis.
(c) Love profile.
(d) Intimacy theory.

8. Hendrick and Hendrick found that college men were significantly more likely than college women to develop a _____ love style.
(a) friendly
(b) logical
(c) romantic
(d) possessive

9. Sternberg's triangular theory of love includes intimacy, passion, and:
   (a) Reciprocity.
   (b) Sexuality.
   (c) Commitment.
   (d) Delight.

10. In the early stages of a relationship, love and _____ may be difficult to distinguish.
    (a) infatuation
    (b) friendship
    (c) empty love
    (d) fatuous love

You'll find answers to the "Test Yourself" questions on page 489.

Questions for Critical Thinking

1. Have you ever been in love? How would you distinguish between love and infatuation?

2. What traits or characteristics are most important to you when you think about a potential date? A marriage partner? Are they the same or different? Why?

3. As Western society moves toward gender equality, will the emphasis on physical beauty for women and economic power for men as primary indicators of attractiveness be reduced? Or are these gender-based standards for attractiveness "hardwired" into us over millions of years of human evolution?

CHAPTER SEVEN

Relationships, Intimacy, and Communication

szefei/Shutterstock

In this chapter we'll define the stages that lead to intimacy in relationships. We'll see that not all relationships achieve this level of interrelatedness, even some supposedly deep and permanent relationships, such as marriage. Moreover, we don't all have partners to develop intimate relationships with; some of us remain alone and, perhaps, lonely. Finally, we'll discuss the ways communication contributes to relationships and sexual satisfaction, and outline ways to enhance communication skills.

The ABC(DE)s of Romantic Relationships

Romantic relationships, like people, undergo stages of development. According to **social-exchange theory**, this development reflects the unfolding of social exchanges, which involve the rewards and costs of maintaining a relationship, compared with the rewards and costs of dissolving it (Allen & de Tormes Eby, 2012). During each stage, positive factors sway the partners toward maintaining and enhancing their relationship. Negative factors incline them toward letting it deteriorate and end.

Numerous investigators have viewed the development of romantic relationships in terms of phases or stages (Allen & de Tormes Eby, 2012; Dindia & Timmerman, 2003; Hendrick & Hendrick, 2000). From their work, we can build a five-stage **ABCDE model** of romantic relationships, consisting of (A) attraction, (B) building, (C) continuation, (D) deterioration, and (E) ending, or termination. Before proceeding with a more in-depth discussion of relationships, intimacy, and communication, let's briefly define each of these five stages.

Social-exchange theory The view that a relationship's development reflects the unfolding of social exchanges—that is, the rewards and costs of maintaining the relationship, as opposed to those of ending it.

ABCDE model A model which conceptualizes romantic relationships in terms of five stages: attraction, building, continuation, deterioration, and ending.

ATTRACTION   Attraction occurs when two people become aware of and find one another appealing or enticing. We may find ourselves attracted to an enchanting person across a crowded room, in a nearby office, or in a new class. We may meet others through blind dates, introductions by mutual friends, computer match-ups, or by accident.

BUILDING   Building a relationship follows initial attraction. Factors that motivate us to build a relationship include similarity in level of physical attraction, similarity in attitudes and interests, and a generally positive evaluation of the partner. Factors that may deter us from trying to build a relationship include lack of physical appeal, dissimilarity in attitudes, and a mutually negative evaluation.

CONTINUATION   Once a basic level of attachment and intimacy has been established, a relationship typically enters a stage of continuation, during which established patterns of interaction remain relatively stable. While these patterns often continue, they don't remain entirely static. Within this stage, a relationship will mature and evolve as time passes and circumstances change. A relationship in the continuation stage that doesn't balance the stability of established patterns of intimacy and communication with the need for ongoing adaptation and development may enter a stage of deterioration.

DETERIORATION   A relationship begins to deteriorate when it becomes less rewarding than it was. A couple can respond to deterioration actively or passively. Active means of response include doing something that may enhance the relationship (e.g., working on improving communication skills, negotiating differences, or seeking professional help) or deciding to end the relationship. Passive methods of response include merely waiting for something to happen, doing little or nothing. The couple can sit back and wait for the relationship to improve on its own (occasionally, it does) or to deteriorate to the point where it ends. ("Hey, these things happen.")

It's irrational (and damaging to a relationship) to assume good relationships require no investment of time and effort. No two people are matched perfectly. When problems arise, it's better to work to resolve them than to act as though they don't exist and hope they'll just disappear.

ENDING   According to social-exchange theory, relationships draw to a close when the partners find little satisfaction in the affiliation, when the barriers to leaving the relationship are low (that is, the social, religious, and financial constraints are manageable), and especially when alternative partners are available. Problems with jealousy and communication are common reasons for ending a relationship.

Various factors can save a deteriorating relationship. For example, people who continue to find some source of satisfaction, are committed to maintaining the relationship, or believe they'll eventually be able to overcome their problems are more likely to invest what they must to prevent the collapse.

Breaking up is often associated with psychological distress and a decrease in life satisfaction, especially for the partner who wanted to maintain a deteriorating relationship (Rhoades et al., 2011). On the other hand, the swan song of a relationship—moving on—can be a sign of healthful decision-making, not a sign of failure. When people are highly incompatible and genuine attempts to preserve the relationship have failed, ending it can offer each partner a chance for happiness with someone else.

NOT-SO-SMALL TALK: AN AUDITION FOR A RELATIONSHIP   In the early stages of building a relationship, we typically look for common ground in the form of overlapping attitudes and interests, and we check out our feelings of

CRITICAL THINKING QUESTIONS

Would you be less likely to accept a date with someone who asked you out via a text message than over the phone? Why or why not?

A Closer Look

ONLINE DATING— A REVOLUTION IN MATCHMAKING?

Match.com? eHarmony? SpeedDate? Plenty of Fish? The use of online dating services has been mushrooming. Table 7.1 shows that the number of people who have met their partners through online dating has grown from essentially zero 20 years ago to 20% to 25% today.

TABLE 7.1

Percentage of Americans Who Have Met Their Partners Online

1970–1980	0–1%
1980–1990	1–3%
1990–2000	5–10%
2000–2010	20–25%

Data: Adapted from Finkel et al., 2012

Because online dating has become such an important way of finding prospective partners, Eli Finkel and his colleagues—Paul Eastwick, Benjamin Karney, Harry Reis, and Susan Sprecher (2012)—take an incisive look at online dating to answer two key questions: Is online dating different from offline (that is, traditional) dating? Are there better outcomes for online dating, as claimed by online dating services?

The investigators note that online dating sites offer users three things:

1. They provide access to other people who are also seeking potential dating partners—people they would be unlikely to meet in their everyday lives.

2. They facilitate communication between potential partners, enabling them to explore each other online before they have a face-to-face meeting.

3. They make some attempt to match potential partners according to demographic variables such as (desired) race, religion, and age and according to personality traits. Potential partners thereby obtain a great deal of factual information about potential partners before meeting them.

Yet the investigators note certain pitfalls related to these services. First, three-dimensional flesh-and-blood people tend to be reduced to a photograph and a pack of statistics, eliminating the subtle factors of interaction that often allow people to judge whether those they meet could be potential partners. Moreover, the sheer number of people displayed to the user of the service makes it necessary to eliminate people who might have worked out just fine if they had met offline.

Online meetings provide opportunities for extended communication before offline meetings. While such communication allows people to probe beneath the surface, it may also display too much too soon. Overly rapid self-disclosure can turn other people "off" (Park et al., 2011).

Concerning matching according to personality traits, the authors simply remark that they have not found any "compelling" evidence that such computer matching provides benefits that lead to greater satisfaction in relationships. Many dating sites say they use "scientific" matching techniques. One can question the variables the sites use. One can also question whether it is useful to seek complementarity in various traits— that is, a blending of opposites.

The authors conclude that "matching sites promise to identify potential mates who are uniquely compatible with their users, and this is a promise unlikely to have a great deal of empirical support. . . . Research on intimate relationships suggests that there are inherent limits to how well the success of a relationship between two individuals can be predicted in advance of their awareness of each other" (Finkel et al., 2012, p. 47).

Let us conclude that online dating has revolutionized the ways in which couples seek partners and start relationships. Using the power of the Internet has enabled many people who lack other significant means for finding potential partners to explore the universe of possibly compatible individuals who are also seeking partners. It even offers shy people a safer way to initiate a relationship; people who might be somewhat tongue-tied in person may find it easier to type messages at a keyboard. Knowing in advance that there are certain common backgrounds and common interests can give an individual a running start in developing a relationship if and when a couple does choose to meet in person. On the other hand, online dating sites remove the advantage of being able to "play it cool" because registering on the site means that one is looking for a partner. That disadvantage might be a small price to pay for those who desire relatively safe awareness of, and access to, the "universe" of potential partners.

Applied Knowledge

SEXTING AND CANADIAN YOUTH

Until a few years ago, the word "sexting" didn't exist. A combination of "sex" and "texting," the word refers to the sending of sexually explicit images from one mobile phone to another. In most instances, sexting includes nude or semi-nude photos of the senders.

The media in Canada have recently begun to pay attention to the topic of teen sexting. Headlines in Canadian newspapers and magazines include "Sexting Nude Photos a Teen Concern" (Baute, *The Toronto Star*, January 7, 2010) and "The Sexting Scare" (Kingston, *Maclean's*, March 12, 2009).

To date, no published studies have examined how many Canadian youth have used their cell phones to send or receive nude photos. An Associated Press and MTV (2009) survey of 1247 14- to 24-year-old respondents in the United States found that 13% of females and 9% of males had sent naked photos or videos of themselves.

A Pew Research Center (2009) study held focus groups asking young people to describe the situations in which teens are likely to sext. They found that most cases of sexting fall into three categories:

■ Exchange of photos solely between romantic partners in a relationship.

■ Exchange of photos between two people who aren't in a relationship, but one of the individuals sends a sext in the hope that it will help start a romantic relationship between the two.

■ Exchange of photos between romantic partners, or from an individual who hopes to start a relationship with the recipient and then sends the photos to additional people (Pew Research Centre, 2009).

For adults, exchanging nude photos electronically is legal under most circumstances. However, creating and sending nude photos of people who are under 18 does, technically, break Canada's child-pornography laws. Specifically, creating and distributing images depicting sexual activity or depicting the sexual organ of a person under the age of 18 is a criminal offense under Canada's *Criminal Code*.

In general, the intended purpose of the child pornography law does not include the prosecution of teens for taking and sharing nude photos, as long as the photos are kept private (Slane, 2009). Nevertheless, sending nude photos of teens under age 18 is, technically, a criminal offense.

In 2007, an 18-year-old male in Alberta was charged with distribution and possession of child pornography after he showed other people nude pictures of a 15-year-old female that she'd e-mailed him. He was allowed to plead guilty to the less severe charge of corrupting morals (Baute, 2010). In similar scenarios in the United States, the teens involved have been charged and convicted of distributing child pornography.

In the Associated Press and MTV (2009) survey, 17% of those who'd received sexts reported that they'd passed them along to others. In most cases, when people send nude photos of themselves to others, we can

safely assume they want those photos kept private. As this study shows, that doesn't always happen.

What's the take-home message? You may feel comfortable that your privacy will be protected, because you're sending a picture of yourself to a relationship partner you trust. But most relationships don't last forever. Will you feel the same level of trust and comfort with an ex-partner who still has the nude photos you sent months or years ago? In many cases where nude photos have been sent to large numbers of people, they've been sent by ex-partners of the individuals in the photos.

As the authors of a study conducted for the National Campaign to Prevent Teen and Unplanned Pregnancy and CosmoGirl.com (2008) note, "There is no changing your mind in cyberspace—anything you send or post will never truly go away" (p. 2).

Whether it's the result of a current or ex-partner's breaking your trust or simply the result of an accident (e.g., a lost or stolen cell phone with your image in it, an intercepted e-mail), sexting images that are eventually seen by family members, friends, people who don't like you, and even future employers can have lasting consequences.

And remember, if it involves nude images of people under the age of 18, sexting may violate Canadian child pornography laws.

Source: Adapted from SIECCAN. (2011). *Check the research: Sexting considerations for Canadian youth.* SexualityAndU.ca. Ottawa: The Society of Obstetricians and Gynaecologists of Canada. Retrieved from http://sexualityandu.ca/uploads/files /CTRsextingEnglishApril2011.pdf

Small talk A superficial kind of conversation that allows exchange of information but stresses breadth of topic coverage rather than in-depth discussion.

attraction. At this point, we often use **small talk** to help determine whether to develop the relationship. Small talk allows an exchange of information, stressing breadth of topic coverage rather than in-depth discussion. Engaging in small talk may seem "phony," but premature self-disclosure of intimate information may repel the other person, as we'll see.

Small talk is a trial balloon for friendship. Successful small talk encourages a couple to venture beneath the surface. At a cocktail party, people may flit about from person to person, exchanging small talk, but now and then a couple finds common ground and pairs off.

THE OPENING LINE   One kind of small talk is the greeting, or opening line. We usually precede verbal greetings with eye contact and decide to begin talking if this eye contact is reciprocated. Avoidance of eye contact may mean the person is shy, but it could also signify lack of interest. If you'd like to progress from initial attraction to surface contact, try a smile and direct eye contact. If the eye contact is reciprocated, choose a greeting. Because your opening line can be important, you may prefer to say something more meaningful than "one, two, one, two."

Here are some types of opening lines:

- Verbal salutes, such as "Good morning."
- Personal inquiries, such as "How are you doing?"
- Compliments, such as "I like your outfit."
- References to your mutual surroundings, such as "What do you think of that painting?" or "This is a nice apartment, isn't it?"
- References to people or events outside the immediate setting, such as "How do you like this weather we've been having?" (An opening gambit about the weather may work best when accompanied by a self-deprecating grin, to acknowledge how corny the remark might seem.)
- References to the other person's behaviour, such as "I couldn't help noticing you were sitting alone," or "I see you out on this track every Saturday morning."
- References to your own behaviour, or to yourself, such as "Hi, my name is Allan Felix." (Feel free to use your own name, if you prefer.)

Opening Lines.
What do you say when you meet someone new? Do you make small talk? About what? Do you use an opening line? Which one? Are you genuine? Are you phony? Are you tense? At ease? Small talk actually isn't so small at all. People use it to search for common ground and test possible feelings of attraction.

The simple "hi" or "hello" is very useful. A friendly glance followed by a cheerful hello ought to give you some idea of whether the attraction is reciprocated. If the hello is returned with a friendly smile and inviting eye contact, follow it up with another greeting, such as a reference to your surroundings, the other person's behaviour, or your name.

EXCHANGING NAME, RANK, AND SERIAL NUMBER   Early exchanges are likely to include name, occupation, marital status, and hometown. This has been likened to exchanging "name, rank, and serial number" with the other person. Each person seeks a sociological profile of the other, to discover common ground that may provide a basis for pursuing the conversation (Cunningham & Barbee, 2008). An unspoken rule seems to be at work: "If I provide you with some information about myself, you will reciprocate by giving me an equal amount of information about yourself. Or … I'll tell you my hometown if you'll tell me yours" (Knapp & Vangelista, 2000). If the other person is unresponsive, she or he may not be attracted to you. But you may also be awkward in your approach or perhaps turn the other person off if you disclose too much about yourself at the outset.

A generation or two ago, women rarely approached men to signal romantic interest or initiate relationships. Today, however, many women in developed nations do precisely that (Wade et al., 2009). Moreover, both women and men rate direct opening lines—lines that signal interest—as most effective in launching relationships (Wade et al., 2009).

DATING IN THE ERA OF NEW COMMUNICATION TECHNOLOGIES   Has the increasing utilization of communication technologies such as e-mail, texting, and Facebook transformed dating practices? Jocelyn Wentland at the University of Ottawa and her colleagues Amy Muise and Serge Desmarais (2010) at the University of Guelph surveyed 296 undergraduate university students to investigate the extent to which young people endorse the use of newer communication technologies as part of the contemporary dating script. As you can see in Table 7.2, while most men and women found it acceptable to communicate with a potential date online or via texting, the preferred way of asking someone out was over the phone or in person. This suggests that the newer communication technologies are accepted ways for potential dating partners to get to know one another in advance of a date, but that they're less accepted for actually asking a person for a date.

Wentland, Muise, and Desmarais (2010) were also interested in whether the newer communication technologies have affected traditional gender roles related to dating. The researchers found that in many respects, traditional gender roles were still in place. For example, 71% of the students in the survey agreed that it was part of the dating script for men to pay the bill, but only 4.1% said it was part of the script for women; 71.3% agreed that wearing sexy underwear was part of the dating script for women, but only 1.4% said it was part of the script for men.

Newer communication technologies, however, were viewed as part of the dating scripts for both men and women. For example, most students (89.2%) indicated that getting to know a potential dating partner via e-mail or texting was part of the dating script for both men and women, rather than for one gender in particular. The endorsement of newer communication technologies as part of the dating script for both men and women was also evident in the responses about getting to know a potential dating partner via Facebook (83.1%) and planning a date via e-mail or texting (70.3%). The authors conclude that " . . . the use of technology for dat-

TABLE 7.2

Acceptability of Different Technologies for Dating

It's acceptable to ...	Men's Responses	Women's Responses
Communicate with a potential date via the phone.	87.7%	88.0%
Communicate with a potential date online.	78.6%	88.0%
Communicate with a potential date via a text message.	78.8%	90.0%
Ask someone on date via a text message.	26.7%	35.5%
Ask someone on a date via MSN.	28.3%	30.9%
Ask someone on a date via Facebook.	21.2%	28.2%
Ask someone on a date via the phone.	73.8%	78.8%
Ask someone on a date in person.	95.9%	98.6%

Source: Wentland, J., Muise, A., & Desmarais, S. (2010). *Out with the old, in with the new: The new technologized dating script.* Poster presented at the 53rd Annual Meeting of the Society for the Scientific Study of Sexuality, Las Vegas NV.

ing appeared to allow women more freedom in terms of initiation and planning dates with a new partner, which have traditionally been primarily male dating activities."

SELF-DISCLOSURE: YOU TELL ME AND I'LL TELL YOU . . . CAREFULLY   Opening up, or **self-disclosure**, is central to building an intimate relationship (Uysal, et al., 2012). But just what sort of information is it safe to disclose upon first meeting someone? If you refuse to go beyond name, rank, and serial number, you may look uninterested or like you're trying to keep things under wraps. If, on the other hand, you blurt out the fact that you have a terrible rash on your thigh, it's likely that you've disclosed too much too soon.

Research suggests that we should refrain from disclosing certain types of information too rapidly if we want to make a good impression (Anderson et al., 2011). We may say we value openness and honesty in our relationships, but it may be a social mistake to open up too soon.

SELF-DISCLOSURE, SOCIAL NETWORKING, AND PRIVACY SETTINGS ONLINE   On the other hand, rapid self-disclosure seems to be more common when people meet online (Park et al., 2011; Special & Li-Barber, 2012). Depending on the nature of the site, cyberspace may allow for relative anonymity and enables people to control what they want to reveal—to safeguard their privacy even as they increase their emotional closeness and openness.

Research suggests that people who disclose more information on social networking sites, such as Facebook, are not necessarily more satisfied with their networking experience (Special & Li-Barber, 2012). Moreover, despite the generalization that females are more likely than males to engage in self-disclosure, the same "rule" does not hold for social networking sites. Because of concern with their safety, females are likely to use higher privacy settings on these sites than males are (Special & Li-Barber, 2012).

If the surface contact provided by small talk and initial self-disclosure has been mutually rewarding, partners in a relationship tend to develop deeper feelings of liking for each other (Abell et al., 2006). Self-disclosure may continue to build gradually through the course of a relationship as the partners come to trust each other enough to share confidences and more intimate feelings.

The Internet, because of its anonymity, facilitates self-disclosure. Frank sexual self-disclosure is seen on many sex blog sites. Amy Muise (2006), then at the University of Guelph, conducted a qualitative analysis of female sex blog sites. She gives examples of how the women describe their sexual fantasies and sexual behaviours in lustful detail. Most of the women also provided insight into their feelings and reactions regarding the development of their sexuality. In general, the women stated that they're much more revealing about their sex lives on the web than in real life.

SEX DIFFERENCES IN SELF-DISCLOSURE   A woman complains to a friend, "He never opens up to me. It's like living with a stone wall." Women commonly say men are loath to express their feelings. Researchers find that

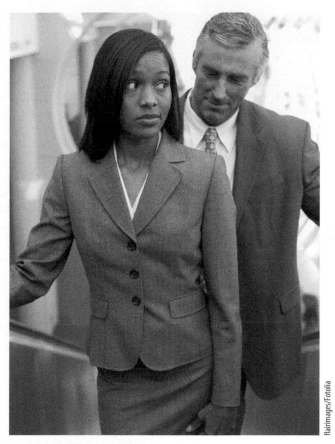

flairimages/Fotolia

Not Interested.
How will she get rid of him? Perhaps she'll give him a phony e-mail address. Some women now use e-mail as a method of avoiding seeing people they don't want to go out with. They may give out their actual e-mail addresses but never respond, or they may give out seldom-used or erroneous e-mail addresses.

Self-disclosure The revelation of personal—perhaps intimate—information.

CRITICAL THINKING QUESTIONS

Can you think of why couples—even those in long-term relationships—might not disclose their sexual likes and dislikes to each other?

masculine-typed (i.e., aggressive, assertive) individuals, whether male or female, tend to be less willing to disclose their feelings, perhaps in adherence to the traditional "strong and silent" masculine stereotype. A study by Susan Basow and Kimberly Rubenfeld (2003) found that feminine-typed (i.e., expressive, nurturing) individuals are more likely to be empathetic and to listen to other people's troubles than masculine-typed individuals, regardless of their anatomic sex.

A New Brunswick study of students in dating relationships found that women disclosed slightly more information about both sexual and nonsexual issues than men did (Byers & Demmons, 1999). However, a more recent study at Trent University (Humphreys & Newby, 2007), indicated that there were no gender differences in sexual self-disclosure.

In the New Brunswick study, the students disclosed to their dating partners more about nonsexual than sexual issues, and more about their sexual likes than their sexual dislikes. Those who disclosed more about nonsexual issues also disclosed more about sexual issues (although most didn't fully reveal all of their true sexual feelings). A key factor in the amount of disclosure was whether the partner also disclosed. Those who were more open were more satisfied with their level of sexual communication and ultimately with their sexual relationships.

SEXUAL SELF-DISCLOSURE   University of New Brunswick psychology professor E. Sandra Byers (2011) has been conducting research on the sexual communication of Canadians for three decades. In collaboration with Sheila MacNeil at Dalhousie University, she's focused much of her work on sexual self-disclosure within couple relationships. They've found that individuals who disclose more about their sexual likes and dislikes report higher sexual satisfaction (MacNeil & Byers, 2005, 2009). In a study of 104 couples in long-term relationships, averaging 14 years in duration, men and women indicated how much they disclosed to their partners about their sexual likes and dislikes, using a 7-point scale that ranged from telling their partners nothing at all to telling their partners everything. On average, both men (mean = 4.1) and women (mean = 4.6) scored in the middle of the scale. Thus, even after being in relationships for an average of 14 years, many of the people in this study kept information about their sexual likes and dislikes from their partners (MacNeil & Byers, 2009).

In another New Brunswick study, the process by which sexual self-disclosure related to sexual satisfaction seemed to differ for men and women (MacNeil, 2004). For men, there was a direct relationship between sexual disclosure and sexual satisfaction. For women, disclosing about nonsexual issues seemed to be more important—women who could freely disclose about other aspects of their relationships were more satisfied with their relationships in general, and this accounted for their greater sexual satisfaction. In other words, it seems that for women, relationship satisfaction is a key factor in sexual satisfaction.

It's likely that a person's cultural background affects his or her patterns of sexual self-disclosure in a relationship. In a culture where explicit discussion of sexual topics is less socially acceptable, verbal sexual disclosure to a partner may also be less accepted or less common. This doesn't necessarily mean couples with cultural backgrounds that are less accepting of "sex talk" are less satisfied with their relationships. Rather, it may be that they place less emphasis on the importance of sexual satisfaction as it's defined in Western culture, and/or they typically use different or less direct methods of communication about sexuality.

SEXUAL INITIATION   Sarah Vannier and Lucia O'Sullivan (2010) at the University of New Brunswick asked 63 18- to 24-year-old men and women in heterosexual relationships to keep diaries for three weeks, recording which partner initiated sex in each instance, whether the initiation was indirect or direct, and whether it was verbal or nonverbal. Examples of indirect verbal initiation were saying something like "I love you" or "I missed you," and examples of direct verbal initiation were "You make me so hot" or "I want you right now." Examples of indirect nonverbal initiation were smiling at the partner or lying on a bed, and examples of direct nonverbal initiation were fondling a partner's breasts or removing clothing.

Vannier and O'Sullivan (2010) found that almost half (49%) of the instances of sexual activity recorded in the diaries were initiated by the male partners, 32% were initiated by the female partners, and 19% were initiated equally by the male and female partners. Almost two-thirds (65%) of the instances involved some form of verbal initiation, with indirect verbal initiation more common than direct verbal initiation. Almost all (91%) of the instances of sexual activity involved some form of nonverbal initiation, with indirect nonverbal strategies more common than direct nonverbal strategies. When it came to initiating sex with their partners, the young adult Canadians in this study were more likely to rely on indirect verbal and nonverbal initiation strategies than on direct strategies.

Commitment

Numerous studies find that men tend to be more reluctant than women to make commitments. David Popenoe, co-director of the National Marriage Project at Rutgers University in New Jersey, conducted a study with 60 unmarried heterosexual men and found that the commonness of cohabitation was one reason they were reluctant to make commitments. In cohabitation, sex—traditionally a key reason for men to marry—is readily available. Popenoe (cited in Hussain, 2002) notes that "In a sense, with cohabitation, he gets a quasi-wife without having to commit."

In a committed relationship, a delicate balance exists between individuality and mutuality. In a healthy union, a strong sense of togetherness does not eradicate individuality. Partners in such a relationship remain free to be themselves. Neither seeks to dominate the other or to submerge him or herself into the personality of the other. Each partner maintains individual interests, likes and dislikes, needs, and goals.

Factors that can throw continuing relationships into a downward spiral include boredom, such as the feeling of falling into a rut in leisure activities or sexual practices. Yet boredom doesn't always end relationships. Consider a study of 12 men who admitted to experiencing sexual boredom in long-term heterosexual relationships (Tunariu & Reavey, 2003). The men weren't happy with sexual boredom, particularly in a culture in which men are viewed as highly sexual and romantic love is supposed to remain passionate. On the other hand, they viewed their boredom as a normal trade-off for so-called true love and long-term companionship.

Other factors that contribute to discontinuation of a relationship include evidence of negative evaluation (e.g., bickering, forgetting anniversaries and other important dates, or pretending they don't exist), lack of fairness in the relationship (e.g., one partner always deciding how the couple will spend their free time), jealousy, and general dissatisfaction.

Jealousy

Anthropologists find evidence of jealousy in all cultures, although it may vary in amount and intensity across and within cultures. It appears to be more common and intense among cultures with stronger machismo traditions, in which men are expected to display their virility. It's also powerful in cultures where men view women's infidelities as threats to their honour. Jealousy is found among gay males and lesbians as well as among heterosexuals (Peluso, 2008).

Sexual jealousy is aroused when we suspect that our intimate relationships are threatened by rivals (Buss, 2009). We can become jealous when others show sexual interest in our partners or when our partners show interest (even casual or nonsexual interest) in others. Jealousy can lead to loss of affection, feelings of

---

CRITICAL THINKING QUESTIONS

To what extent do you agree with the idea that one major reason cohabitation is more common today than in the past is that it provides access to regular sex without the formal commitment of marriage?

Innovative Canadian Research

OBTAINING SEXUAL CONSENT

A great deal has been written about the necessity of obtaining sexual consent before initiating sexual relations with a partner. There's been limited research on this topic, however (Beres, 2007).

University of Guelph students were asked how they asked for and gave sexual consent (Humphreys, 2004). Only about one-third said they explicitly asked for sex. The three most common nonverbal behaviours used by both genders were kissing their partners, moving closer, and touching their partners sexually. The most common ways two-thirds of both males and females indicated consent for sex were by not stopping their partners from kissing and sexually touching them, kissing their partners, moving closer, and touching their partners sexually. About half said they gave consent by *not* saying no. About half of the men and one-third of the women indicated consent by saying yes. The study clearly indicated that young people find directly asking for sex to be problematic. Two-thirds agreed that verbally asking for sexual consent was awkward.

When asked how consent should be obtained, more than half (65% of the females and 53% of the males) preferred that someone ask first, before engaging in any sexual activity. But a large minority (35% of the females, 47% of the males) preferred to assume consent and continue with the sexual behaviour until their partners indicated otherwise. Interestingly, although sexual consent has been stressed in many campus educational programs, only about half of the students had discussed the topic with their friends.

This research made a major contribution to the development of scales that measure sexual consent attitudes and sexual consent behaviours. These scales have solid reliability and validity (Humphreys & Herold, 2007).

In a follow-up study, Humphreys (2007a) found that students believed it was not as necessary to obtain sexual consent in a longer-term relationship as it was at the beginning of a relationship. This was true for sexual behaviours ranging from hugging to sexual intercourse. The one exception was anal intercourse, where students felt that explicit consent was required regardless of the status of the relationship. Humphreys speculates that students felt this way because most had not engaged in anal intercourse.

A controversial policy developed by Antioch College in Ohio requires that verbal consent be obtained at every step of a sexual encounter. For example, if a woman wants to kiss her partner, according to the policy, she needs to directly ask whether she can. Later, if he wishes to touch her breasts, he needs to ask directly whether he can do so, and she has to say yes, verbally, before he can proceed. When asked their opinions of this policy, students at the University of Guelph felt this type of consent procedure wasn't practical and wouldn't be followed by the great majority of young people (Humphreys & Herold, 2003).

In Banff, Alberta, Melanie Beres (2010) interviewed young men and women about how they communicated sexual consent with casual sex partners. When Beres analyzed the interviews, three main themes emerged:

First, the respondents said they simply knew whether their partners were interested in having casual sex and therefore felt it was unnecessary to make formal requests to initiate sexual activity.

Second, there were variations on the idea that "no means no" when communicating about casual sex. Rather than directly saying no, women used a diversity of tactics, such as saying they had boyfriends. Women also showed their discomfort with proceeding by pulling away or letting their bodies become tense and stiff. In the absence of these kinds of signals, men assumed women were interested in having sex.

And third, "yes means yes" was communicated via subtle cues. For example, it was assumed that if someone was willing to leave a bar setting and go to a more private location, such as the other person's home, this indicated an interest in engaging in casual sex. Other indications included pulling the partner closer and listening to physical signs such as sighing, heavy breathing, and moaning. However, the respondents agreed that despite these signals, it was possible at any stage that the other person (usually the woman) might change his or her mind and decide not to have sex (Beres, 2010).

These studies demonstrate the complexity of the process of obtaining and granting sexual consent. For most people, the process is more subtle than blatant.

insecurity and rejection, anxiety, loss of self-esteem, and mistrust of our partners and potential rivals. Jealousy is a common reason for relationship failure.

Feelings of possessiveness, which is related to jealousy, can also subject relationships to stress. In extreme cases, jealousy can cause depression or give rise to spousal abuse, suicide, or murder (Harmon-Jones et al., 2009). But milder forms of jealousy are not necessarily destructive to relationships. They may even serve the positive function of revealing how much we care for our partners. For this reason, we can distinguish between normal jealousy, which reflects occasional self-doubts and the belief that our partners are attractive to others, and obsessive jealousy, in which we're consumed by our fears of interference in our relationships.

Jealousy.
How do we explain feelings of jealousy? What does jealousy do to an intimate relationship?

STOCK4B/Getty Images

What causes jealousy? Experience and personality variables play roles. People may become mistrustful of their partners because former partners have cheated. People with low self-esteem may experience sexual jealousy because they've become overly dependent on their partners. They may fear that they won't be able to find new partners if their present partners leave.

JEALOUSY AND FACEBOOK   Facebook allows you access to information about your partner that you might not otherwise know. Three-quarters of the students in a University of Guelph study reported that they and their partners had former romantic or sexual partners as Facebook friends (Muise et al., 2008), and 92% said their partners had Facebook friends they didn't know. Correspondence with or seeing photos of these individuals triggered feelings of jealousy, especially among partners who already felt jealous. Those who spent the most time on Facebook were likely to be the most jealous (Muise et al., 2008).

JEALOUSY AND EVOLUTIONARY THEORY   Sex differences in jealousy appear to support evolutionary theory. Males seem to be more upset by sexual infidelity, females by emotional infidelity (Buss, 2009; Sagarin et al., 2012; Shackelford et al., 2005). That is, males become more insecure and angry when their partners have sexual relations with others. Females become more insecure and angry when their partners become emotionally attached to others. Why? Evolutionary theory hypothesizes that sexual jealousy has been shaped by natural selection as a method of assuring males that their female partners' offspring are their own, and of assuring females that their male partners will continue to provide resources to facilitate child-rearing (Buss, 2009).

SAME-SEX AFFAIRS   Interestingly, the hypothesized gender difference in reactions to infidelity disappears when our partners have affairs with others of their own sex (Sagarin et al., 2003). Is it because the affairs carry no threat of impregnation, a view that would be consistent with evolutionary theory?

Or is it because we console ourselves by thinking we really aren't competing in the same arenas with the intruders? Are both explanations and other explanations possible?

A COGNITIVE PERSPECTIVE   In recent years, cognitive theory has gained importance in many areas of the behavioural sciences, and sexual jealousy is no exception.

CRITICAL THINKING QUESTIONS

Evolutionary theory suggests that males are more upset by sexual infidelity, and females are more upset by emotional infidelity. To what extent do you think this statement is accurate?

MIXA/Getty Images

Stalking a Former Partner.
People who've been rejected sometimes stalk their former partners. Stalking includes such behaviours as breaking into their former partners' e-mail. (Hint: change your passwords from time to time.)

In two studies, Stacie Bauerle and her colleagues (2002) presented 156 college undergraduates and 128 members of the general population with various scenarios in which their partners were unfaithful. By and large, jealousy increased when the individuals attributed their partners' infidelity to internal causes, such as clear personal choice. When they attributed the infidelity to external causes, such as alcohol or social pressure, they reported feeling significantly less jealous. ("Don't blame me; it was the alcohol.")

Breaking Up

Breaking up, as the song goes, can be hard to do—both for the person terminating the relationship and for the person being let go. Some people obviously take breaking up better than others. A study of more than 5000 people who responded to an Internet survey found that anxious people were more likely to be highly preoccupied with their lost partners, suffer more physical and emotional distress, attempt to reestablish the relationships, and be angry and vengeful (Davis et al., 2003). Emotionally secure individuals were most likely to seek social support among their friends and families. Insecure individuals were most likely to turn to alcohol and drugs.

Breaking up is sometimes followed by **stalking**, or other unwanted pursuit behaviours, such as unwelcome phone calls or e-mails, asking third parties about the person who dissolved the relationship, and following, threatening, or attacking the person and/or his or her new partner (De Smet et al., 2012; Norris et al., 2011). Jealousy, abusiveness, and physical violence in relationships are key predictors of unwanted pursuit (Norris et al., 2011). Stalkers and violent individuals also tend to have strong needs to control others (Dye & Davis, 2003).

Intimacy

Intimacy is a feeling of emotional connectedness and the desire to share your innermost thoughts and feelings with another person (Burke & Young, 2012). Partners in the throes of romantic love usually want to disclose everything and know everything about one another (Kito, 2005; Vaculík & Hudecek, 2005).

Along with sex, intimacy is one of the key ingredients in passionate relationships (Burke & Young, 2012). Feelings of intimacy and affection tend to grow as romantic relationships develop (Perlman & Sprecher, 2012; Rubin & Campbell, 2012). Relationships also develop from casual and superficial to relatively committed. As couples age, intimacy becomes one of the most valued—if not *the* most valued—components of their relationships (Villar et al., 2005). Intimate relationships are also characterized by trust, caring, and acceptance.

Sternberg's (2007) triangular theory of love regards intimacy as a basic component of romantic love, but people can be intimate and not in love—at least, not in romantic love. Close friends and family members become emotionally intimate when they care deeply for one another and share their feelings and experiences.

People need not be sexually intimate to be emotionally intimate. Nor does sexual intimacy automatically create emotional intimacy. People who are

Stalking Following or observing a person persistently, especially because of obsession with the person. This can occur online as well as in person, such as when a person breaks into someone else's e-mail.

Intimacy Feelings of closeness and connectedness, marked by sharing of one's innermost thoughts and feelings.

sexually involved may not achieve emotional closeness. People can be more emotionally intimate with friends than with lovers.

Because intimacy involves sharing your innermost thoughts and feelings, honesty is a core feature of intimacy. You needn't be an open book to develop and maintain intimacy, however. Some aspects of experience are better kept even from your most intimate partner, especially when they're embarrassing or threatening (Anderson et al., 2011). For example, you wouldn't expect your partner to disclose every passing sexual fantasy. Nor would you expect your intimate partner to divulge details of past sexual experiences.

Intimacy is important not only to your interpersonal relationships but also to your health. Researchers have found that intimacy fosters well-being, and its absence can be psychologically and physically harmful (Rubin & Campbell, 2012; Perlman & Sprecher, 2012).

Commitment and trust within a relationship can be seen as developing according to a model of **mutual cyclical growth**, which includes five stages:

Working on the Relationship.
When one partner works on the relationship, the other partner is more motivated to reciprocate. Why did one partner give this gift? "Just because."

Mutual cyclical growth The view that your need for your partner promotes commitment, which promotes acts that enhance the relationship, and that these acts build trust, increasing your partner's commitment to the relationship.

- The feeling that you need your partner promotes your commitment to, and dependence on, the relationship.
- Your commitment to the relationship encourages you to do things that are good for the relationship.
- Your partner sees your pro-relationship acts.
- Your partner's perception of your pro-relationship acts enhances his or her trust in you and in the relationship.
- Your partner's feelings of trust increase his or her willingness to depend on the relationship.

Caring is an emotional bond that allows intimacy to develop. Caring means both partners try to satisfy each other's needs, gratify each other's interests, and make sacrifices, if necessary.

Heterosexual and LGB Relationships

Numerous researchers have studied the factors that predict satisfaction in a relationship or the deterioration and ending of a relationship (Holmberg et al., 2009). Much of this research has sought to determine whether there are differences in the factors that satisfy heterosexual and non-heterosexual (lesbian, gay, and bisexual) couples. The interesting finding is that we're hard pressed to find differences (Holmstrom, 2009).

One difference that does stand out favours gay and lesbian couples: they tend to distribute household chores evenly and not in terms of gender-role stereotypes (Kurdek, 2005, 2006; Wong, 2012).

Now for the similarities. Sexual satisfaction is tied to satisfaction with the relationship among both heterosexual and lesbian women (Wong, 2012). Gay, lesbian, and heterosexual couples are all more satisfied when they receive social support from their partners, they share power within their relationships, they fight fairly, and they perceive that their partners are committed to the relationships. But a couple of differences favour stability in the heterosexual relationships: they're more likely to have the support of their families, and they're less likely to be stigmatized by society at large.

Couples therapists who work with lesbian, gay, and bisexual individuals and couples find problems akin to those experienced by heterosexual couples, such as infidelity. They also find issues that require special sensitivity toward these commonly stigmatized subpopulations (Schwartz & Young, 2009):

- Lesbian/gay/bisexual (LGB) identity development, and its effect on the couple's functioning.
- Parenting, and its impact on the couple.
- LGB individuals as members of families.
- The kinds of stressors that affect individuals who are underrepresented in the LGB literature, including older LGB people, LGB members of ethnic minority groups, and LGB members of religious groups.
- Legal issues and their impact on the couple.
- Workplace issues, and their impact on the couple.

Communication Skills

Relationship counsellors and sex therapists might be less busy if more couples communicated with one another about their sexual feelings. Unfortunately, when it comes to sex, the most overlooked four-letter word may be "talk."

Many couples suffer for years because at least one partner is unwilling to speak up. Or problems arise when one partner misinterprets the other. One partner might interpret the other's groans or grimaces of pleasure as signs of pain, and pull back during sex, leaving the other frustrated. Improved communication may not be a panacea, but it helps. Clear communication can take the guesswork out of a relationship, averting misunderstanding, relieving resentment and frustration, and increasing both sexual and general satisfaction with the relationship.

In a University of Guelph study of communication about sexual health issues such as HIV and pregnancy prevention (Cleary et al., 2002), female students typically reported that they didn't discuss these issues prior to engaging in sexual activity for the first time with new partners. Generally, the women reported feeling uncomfortable about initiating discussions about sexual health topics and sensed that their partners were uncomfortable, as well. They feared offending their partners and risking negative reactions from them.

There's considerable variation in how comfortable people are with talking to their partners about sexual matters. Carleton University researchers Melanie Kristel Oates and Alia Offman (2007) found that individuals with higher sexual self-esteem were better able to communicate their sexual desires to their partners. Sexual self-esteem was measured by such statements as "I feel self-assured about my sexual abilities." Sexual self-esteem was a stronger predictor of sexual communication than general self-esteem was. Researchers at Trent University (Humphreys & Newby, 2007) found that students who felt more positive about their sexuality were more likely to use diverse verbal and nonverbal tactics to ask their partners to try something new sexually. Those who'd had more previous partners were more willing to make verbal requests to try new sexual activities.

Obstacles to Sexual Communication

Why is it so difficult for couples to communicate about sex? Following are some possibilities.

SEX TALK   Is sex talk vulgar? Vulgarity, like beauty, is to some degree in the eye of the beholder. One couple's vulgarity may be another couple's pillow talk. Some people may maintain a Victorian belief that no talk about sex is fit for mixed company, even between intimate partners. Sex is something you may do but not something you talk about. Other couples may be willing in principle to talk about sex but find the reality difficult because they lack an agreeable, common language.

How, for example, are they to refer to their genitals and to sexual activities? One partner may prefer to use coarse words to refer to them. (As forbidden fruit is often sweetest, some people feel sexually aroused when they or their partners "talk dirty.") The other might prefer more clinical terms. A partner who likes to use slang for the sex organs might be regarded by the other as vulgar or demeaning. One who uses clinical terms, such as "fellatio" and "intercourse," might be regarded as, well, clinical.

Some couples compromise and try to use terms that are neither vulgar nor clinical. They might speak, for example, of "doing it" rather than "screwing" (and the like) at one extreme or "engaging in sexual intercourse" at the other. Or they might speak of "going down on me" rather than "eating me" or "practising fellatio or cunnilingus."

IRRATIONAL BELIEFS Many couples also harbour irrational beliefs about relationships and sex, such as the notion that people should somehow *know* what their partners want without having to ask. Men, in particular, seem burdened with the stereotype that they should have a natural expertise at sex. Women may feel it's unladylike to talk openly about their sexual needs and feelings. Both partners may hold the idealized romantic notion that all you need to achieve sexual happiness is love. But such knowledge doesn't arise from instinct or from love. It's learned—or it remains unknown.

iofoto/Shutterstock

Communication.
Would it have been easier for him if he'd just listened to her? Listening can take skill, especially when a couple is in conflict.

A related irrational belief is that our partners will read our minds. We may erroneously assume that if our partners truly loved us, they'd somehow know what types of sexual stimulation we desire. Unfortunately—or fortunately—others can't read our minds. We must assume the responsibility for communicating our preferences.

Some people communicate more effectively than others, perhaps because they're more sensitive to others' needs or because their parents served as good models as communicators. But communication skills can be acquired at any time. Learning takes time and work, but the following guidelines should prove helpful if you want to enhance your communication skills. The skills can also improve communication in areas of intimacy other than the sexual.

Getting Started

How do you broach sexual topics? Here are some ideas:

You can admit that it's difficult to talk about sex. You can say your sexual relationship is important to you and that you want to do everything you can to enhance it. Gently probe your partner's willingness to set aside time to talk about sex, preferably when you can dim the lights and avoid interruptions.

The right time may be when you're both relaxed, rested, and not pressed for time. The right place can be anywhere you can enjoy privacy and talk

Innovative Canadian Research

KEEPING THE SPARK ALIVE IN ROMANTIC RELATIONSHIPS

Sexual desire tends to peak in the beginning stages of relationships as intimacy is rapidly increasing and then often declines over time (see review by Impett, Muise, & Peragine, 2013). How, then, can couples keep the sexual spark alive in their relationships? Amy Muise at the University of Toronto and colleagues found that people who are communal in the bedroom are more likely to maintain sexual desire. Communal motivation is the idea that romantic partners are responsive to each other's needs, when reasonable, without expecting direct reciprocation. People high in communal strength are motivated to meet their partner's needs and trust that their partner will be responsive to their own needs when they arise.

Muise, Impett, Kogan, and Desmarais (2013) studied long-term romantic couples (together on average for 11 years) using daily experience methods, meaning that they asked participants to report on their sexual desire and sexual experiences for 21 consecutive days. The researchers then followed up with the couples four months later and found that people who were low in sexual communal strength declined in desire over time, whereas people higher in sexual communal strength

began the study with slightly higher desire and were able to maintain desire over time. People high in sexual communal strength reported higher daily sexual desire and had more enjoyable sexual experiences. The authors suggest that communally motivated people reaped these benefits because of their focus on pursuing positive outcomes for their partners and their relationship as opposed to their own self-interested goals. In other words, being a giving, responsive partner was beneficial to the *self*, but it was not these self-focused benefits that motivated communal people to meet their partners' needs.

Partners of communally motivated people also reap important benefits. People who were high in sexual communal strength had partners who detected their responsiveness and who reported that they were, in fact, more attentive to their needs during sex. As a result, people with partners who were high in sexual communal strength felt more satisfied in their relationships and felt more committed to maintaining their relationships over time (Muise & Impett, in press). The findings of this research suggest that communal motivation in the domain of sexuality can help couples keep the spark alive in long-term relationships and maintain satisfaction and commitment over time.

David De Lossy/ThinkStock

Criticism Can Be Hard to Take.
How can you criticize a partner in a way that enhances the relationship?
How can you receive criticism in a helpful way?

undisturbed. Sex talk needn't be limited to the bedroom. You may feel more comfortable talking about sex over dinner, when cuddling on the sofa, or when just relaxing together.

Another possibility is asking permission to raise an issue. You can say something like this: "There's something on my mind. Do you have a few minutes? Is now a good time to tell you about it?" Or you can say, "There's something we need to talk about, but I'm not sure how to bring it up. Can you help me with it?"

You can tell your partner that it's okay to point out ways you can become a more effective lover. For example, you can say, "I know you don't want to hurt my feelings, but I wonder if I'm doing anything you'd rather I didn't do?"

Applied Knowledge

COMMUNICATING SEXUAL NEEDS

Listening is basic to learning about another person's needs, but sometimes it helps to go a few steps further.

Asking Questions to Draw the Other Person Out

You can ask open-ended questions that allow for a broader exploration of issues, such as these:

- "What do you like best about the way we make love?"
- "Do you think I do things to bug you?"
- "Does it bother you that I go to bed later than you do?"
- "Does anything disappoint you about our relationship?"
- "Do you think I do things that are inconsiderate when you're studying for a test?"

Closed-ended questions that call for a limited range of responses tend to be most useful when you're looking for a simple yes-or-no type of response. ("Would you rather make love with the TV off?")

Using Self-Disclosure

Self-disclosure is essential to developing intimacy. You can also use self-disclosure to learn more about your partner's needs, because communicating your own feelings and ideas invites reciprocation. For example, you might say, "There are times when I feel that I disappoint you when we make love. Should I be doing something differently?"

Granting Permission for the Other Person to Say Something That Might Upset You

You can ask your partner to level with you about an irksome issue. You can say you recognize that it may be awkward to discuss it, but you'll try your best to listen conscientiously and not get too disturbed. You can also limit communication to one difficult issue per conversation. If the entire emotional dam were to burst, the job of mopping up could be overwhelming.

Providing Information

There are many skillful ways of communicating information, including accentuating the positive and using verbal and nonverbal cues. When you want to get something across, remember that it's irrational to expect your partner to read your mind. He or she can tell when you're wearing a grumpy face, but your expression doesn't provide much information about your specific feelings. When your partner asks, "What would you like me to do?" responding with "Well, I think you can figure out what I want" or "Just do whatever you think is best" isn't very helpful. Only you know what pleases you. Your partner is not a mind reader.

Accentuating the Positive

Let your partner know when he or she does something right! Speak up or find another way to express your appreciation. Accentuating the positive is rewarding and informs your partner about what pleases you. In other words, don't just wait around until your partner does something wrong, then seize the opportunity to complain!

Using Verbal Cues

Sexual activity provides an excellent opportunity for direct communication. You can say something like "Oh, that's great" or "Don't stop." Or you can ask for feedback, as in "How does this feel?" Feedback provides direct guidance about what's pleasing. Partners can also make specific requests and suggestions.

Using Nonverbal Cues

Sexual communication also occurs without words. Couples learn to interpret one another's facial expressions as signs of pleasure, anxiety, boredom, even disgust. Body language also communicates likes and dislikes. If your partner leans toward or away from you when you touch him or her, or relaxes or tenses up, he or she speaks volumes in silence.

The following exercises may help you use nonverbal cues to communicate your sexual likes and dislikes. Similar exercises are used by sex therapists to help couples with sexual dysfunctions.

1. **Take turns petting.** This can help you and your partner learn what turns you both on. You take turns caressing each other, stopping frequently enough to receive feedback by asking questions like "How does that feel?" When you're receiving caresses, you're responsible for giving feedback, which can be expressed verbally (e.g., "Yes, that's it—yes, just like that" or "No, a little lighter than that") or nonverbally (e.g., making certain appreciative or disapproving sounds). Verbal feedback is usually more direct and less prone to misinterpretation. The knowledge you and your partner gain through this exercise can be incorporated into your regular pattern of lovemaking.

2. **Direct your partner's hand.** Gently guiding your partner's hand—to show your partner where and how you like to be touched—is a direct way of communicating your sexual preferences. While taking turns petting, and during other acts of lovemaking, one partner can gently guide the other's fingers and hands through the most satisfying strokes and caresses. You might show your partner how to caress your breasts or clitoral shaft in this manner, or you might cup your partner's hands to show how to stroke your penile shaft or caress your testes.

3. **Signal.** You can use agreed-upon nonverbal cues to signal sexual pleasure. For example, you might rub or tap your partner in a certain way to signal that he or she is doing something right. Your partner then makes a mental note and incorporates the pleasurable stimulation into your lovemaking. This is a sort of hit-or-miss technique, but even near misses can be rewarding.

Listening Effectively

Listening involves such skills as active listening, paraphrasing, using reinforcement, and valuing your partner even when the two of you disagree.

To listen actively rather than passively, first adopt the attitude that you may actually learn something—or perceive things from another vantage point—by listening. Second, recognize that even though the other person is doing the talking, you shouldn't just sit there. It's not helpful to stare off into space while your partner is talking. Instead, you can listen actively by maintaining eye contact and modifying your facial expression to show that you understand his or her feelings and ideas. For example, nod your head when appropriate.

Listening actively also involves asking helpful questions, such as "Would you please give me an example?"

Good listeners do not interrupt, change the topic, or walk away when their partners are speaking.

Paraphrasing shows that you understand what your partner is trying to say. In paraphrasing, you recast or restate the speaker's words to confirm that you've understood correctly. For example, suppose your partner says, "You hardly ever say anything when we're making love. I don't want you to scream or make obligatory grunts or do something silly, but sometimes I wonder if I'm trying to make love to a brick wall." You can paraphrase this comment by saying something like "So, it's sort of hard to know if I'm really enjoying it."

Even when you disagree with what your partner says, you can maintain good relations and keep channels of communication open by saying something like "I really appreciate your taking the time to try to work this out with me," or "I hope you'll think it's okay if I don't see things entirely the same way, but I'm glad we had a chance to talk about it."

When you disagree with your partner, do so in a way that shows you still value him or her as a person. In other words, say something like "I love you very much, but it annoys me when you . . . " rather than "You're really contemptible for. . . ." By so doing, you encourage your partner to disclose sensitive material without any risk of attack or of losing your love or support.

Summing Up

Many Canadians use the Internet to meet possible dating partners. However, one needs to be cautious of Internet-romance scams.

Levinger proposes an ABCDE model of romantic relationships. The letters refer to five stages: attraction, building, continuation, deterioration, and ending.

We're motivated to build relationships by similarity in physical attractiveness, similarity in attitudes, and liking.

Factors that encourage us to continue in relationships include variety, caring, positive evaluations, lack of jealousy, perceived fairness, and mutual satisfaction.

Factors that foster deterioration include failure to invest time and energy in the relationships, deciding to end the relationships, and simply permitting deterioration to proceed unchecked.

Relationships tend to end when the partners find little satisfaction in the affiliation, alternative partners are available, the partners aren't committed to preserving the relationships, and they expect the relationships to falter.

Intimacy involves feelings of emotional closeness with one another, and the desire to share your innermost thoughts and feelings.

Intimate relationships require trust, caring, and tenderness.

Honesty is a core feature of intimacy.

Communication is a two-way street. It embraces sending *and* receiving messages. We often express feelings through nonverbal channels, such as tone of voice, gestures, body posture, and facial expressions.

Couples may find it difficult to talk about sex because they lack an agreeable common language. Many couples also harbour irrational beliefs about relationships and sex.

Ways of getting started with communication include talking about talking, asking permission to raise an issue, and granting your partner permission to say things that might be upsetting.

Skilled listening involves such elements as active listening, paraphrasing, using of reinforcement, and valuing your partner even when you disagree.

Test Yourself

Multiple-Choice Questions

1. According to research by Wentland and Muise, which one of the following is an acceptable way to ask a person for a date?
   (a) A text message
   (b) MSM
   (c) A phone call
   (d) Facebook

2. Small talk:
   (a) Is a phony way to begin a relationship.
   (b) Stresses breadth of topic coverage.
   (c) Promotes premature self-disclosure.
   (d) Is an in-depth discussion of topics of mutual interest.

3. All of the following encourage the continuation of relationships except:
   (a) Maintaining interest.
   (b) Evidence of caring.
   (c) Mutual satisfaction.
   (d) Jealousy.

4. According to research by Finkel and colleagues, during the period 2000–2010 _____ of Americans met their relationship partners online.
   (a) 65–70%
   (b) 45–60%
   (c) 35–40%
   (d) 20–25%

5. Research shows that men are more upset by _____ infidelity and women are more upset by _____ infidelity.
   (a) sexual/emotional
   (b) emotional/sexual
   (c) sexual/sexual
   (d) emotional/emotional

6. A study of 5000 people who responded to an Internet survey found that after a relationship breakup, emotionally secure people were more likely to:
   (a) Seek support from friends and family.
   (b) Be preoccupied with their lost partners.
   (c) Attempt to re-establish the relationships.
   (d) Console themselves by drinking alcohol.

7. According to MacNeil and Byers, couples who disclose more about their sexual likes and dislikes report:
   (a) Lower levels of sexual satisfaction.
   (b) Higher levels of sexual satisfaction.
   (c) The same levels of sexual satisfaction as couples who disclose less.
   (d) Disclosing more about their sex lives to their friends.

8. Which of the following is NOT an irrational belief about communication?
   (a) Men should have a natural expertise at sex.
   (b) People should know what their partners want sexually without having to ask.
   (c) Good communication can enhance all aspects of a relationship.
   (d) It's unladylike for women to talk about their sexual needs and feelings.

9. Kurdek found that lesbian and gay couples tend to differ from heterosexual couples in that they
   (a) Distribute household chores more evenly.
   (b) Avoid conflict at all costs.
   (c) Do not consider sexual activity per se to be an important aspect of their relationship.
   (d) Believe that love conquers all and that it is not necessary to work on relationships.

10. Which of the following is accurate about self-disclosure?
    (a) Females tend to set higher privacy setting than males do on social networking sites.
    (b) Men are more likely to self-disclose than are women.
    (c) Couples should disclose their sexual histories to promote intimacy.
    (d) Self-disclosure is the same online and offline.

You'll find answers to the "Test Yourself" questions on page 489.

Questions for Critical Thinking

1. As long as it is kept private between the two individuals involved, is it appropriate for two teens to exchange nude photos of themselves? What if the two individuals are adults?

2. Do you think the availability of online dating sites makes it easier for people to successfully find compatible partners for long-term relationships?

3. In their study, MacNeil and Byers found that even after being in a relationship for an average of 14 years, many people kept information about their sexual likes and dislikes to themselves. Can you think of some reasons why some people find it difficult to communicate with their partners about what they want sexually?

4. Have you ever sat next to someone on a bus or a plane and disclosed details of your life that you wouldn't share with a friend? How did you feel about this afterwards? Why do many people find it easy to talk openly with total strangers?

5. Have you ever had communication problems in a relationship? How did they affect the relationship?

CHAPTER EIGHT

Sexual Behaviours and Fantasies

Dominique Douieb/PhotoAlto/Corbis

This chapter describes sexual behaviours and statistical breakdowns of who does what with whom. There's significant variation in human sexual expression. Some of us practise few, if any, of the behaviours described in this chapter. Some of us practise most or all of them. Some of us practise some of them, some of the time.

Readers are as varied as society in general when it comes to sexual values, preferences, and attitudes. Some of the behaviours we discuss may strike you as indecent. Our aim is to provide information about the diversity of sexual expression. We're not seeking consensus on what's acceptable, and we're not passing judgement or encouraging you to expand your sexual repertoire.

The human body is sensitive to many forms of sexual stimulation. Yet we reiterate the theme that biology is not destiny—a biological capacity does not impose a behavioural requirement. Cultural expectations, personal values, and individual experience—not just our biological capacities—determine our sexual behaviour. What's right for you is right for you, but not necessarily for your neighbour.

We'll begin by reviewing the techniques people practise by themselves to derive sexual pleasure—masturbation and sexual fantasy. We'll then consider techniques that involve a partner.

Solitary Sexual Behaviour

Various forms of sexual expression do not require a partner. Masturbation, which involves direct stimulation of the genitals, is one of the principal forms of one-person sexual expression. Other forms of individual sexual experience, such as thinking about sex and sexual fantasy, may or may not be accompanied by genital stimulation.

Sexual Fantasies

Sexual fantasy Mental imagery that's sexually arousing or erotic.

A **sexual fantasy** can be defined as "almost any mental imagery that is sexually arousing or erotic to the individual" (Leitenberg & Henning, 1995, p. 470). Sexual fantasies can occur because an individual wants them to (e.g., during masturbation), or they can happen spontaneously, without conscious effort. A sexual fantasy can range from a brief, erotic mental picture lasting a few seconds to a lengthy, highly explicit scenario. Nearly all of us have sexual fantasies of one kind or another.

People may use sexual fantasies either when they are alone or to heighten sexual excitement with a partner. Some couples find it sexually arousing to share fantasies or to enact them. Sexual fantasies may also be experienced without sexual behaviour, as in erotic dreams or daydreams. Masturbation often requires some form of cognitive stimulation, such as fantasy or viewing erotica, to reach orgasm.

There are many theories about sexual fantasies. One view that has little, if any, research evidence behind it is that people who fantasize about sex are less likely to have enjoyable sex lives. That is, the fantasy takes the place of life. In reality, fantasies can enhance sexual arousal, providing greater pleasure.

Research suggests that sexual fantasies are common. Most people have them—even during sex with another person. Canadian researchers have found that fantasies heighten sexual arousal during activity with partners (Dawson, Suschinsky, & Lalumiere, 2012). Males seem to engage in sexual fantasies more often than females, but most females do so, also. A survey of 349 university students and employees, aged 18 to 70, who were involved in heterosexual relationships found that the great majority—98% of the men and 80% of the women—reported sexual fantasies about someone *other* than their sex partner (Hicks & Leitenberg, 2001). These fantasies were more common among people who had been in their relationships longer, perhaps providing sexual novelty. Women were more likely than men to fantasize about prior sex partners, suggesting, perhaps, that they had less need to mentally stray from familiar relationships. According to a *New York Times* poll, men are somewhat more likely than women—52% versus 40%—to think it is acceptable to fantasize about sex with someone other than their partner (Eggers, 2000).

In keeping with gender role stereotypes, studies find that males are more likely to fantasize about forcing women into sexual activity. Women are more likely to fantasize about being victimized (Critelli & Bivona, 2008; Dawson et al., 2012).

Research also shows that women are more likely to report that they have more frequent and arousing sexual fantasies at time of ovulation (Dawson et al., 2012). In the by Dawson and colleagues, heterosexual women kept diaries in which they recorded their fantasies, and ovulation was assessed by means of self-administered urine tests. The number of males in their fantasies increases during ovulation, but not the number of females. Fantasies during ovulation are also more likely to emphasize sex within a relationship rather than explicit sexual content.

Researchers use the frequency and variety of sexual fantasies as one measure of the sex drive (Fisher et al., 2012). The sex drive—and the frequency of sexual fantasizing—is related to testosterone levels in both males and females. One study surveyed the frequency of sexual activity and sexual fantasies among women who had had their ovaries and uteruses surgically removed (Shifren et al., 2000). The women were then administered various doses of testosterone or a placebo via skin patches. Women given higher doses of testosterone doubled or tripled their reported incidence of sexual fantasies, masturbation, and sexual intercourse.

Studies suggest that most of us consider sexual fantasies acceptable. One study that surveyed 178 university students and staff found that 84% of them reported having sexual fantasies at least occasionally during sexual intercourse (Cado & Leitenberg, 1990). Most of these individuals said that they believed that such fantasies were common, normal, moral, socially acceptable, and more beneficial than harmful. Still, about one-quarter of the sample reported feeling guilty about the fantasies. Those who felt most guilty were also most likely to experience sexual dissatisfaction and problems in their actual lives.

There are also "deviant" sexual fantasies, such as sadistic rape fantasies. Research evidence with personality tests suggests that men with frequent deviant sexual fantasies are more likely to be socially isolated and emotionally unstable (Bartels & Gannon, 2011; Maniglio, 2011). Yet, the extent to which deviant sexual fantasies contribute to crimes involving sex and aggression remained clouded. Nevertheless, many helping professionals work with men who have deviant sexual fantasies in the hope that by changing their fantasies the men will be less likely to commit crimes of violence (Schmidt et al., 2012). And when it comes to fantasies about being victimized, Nancy Friday (2008) reports the following from a woman she interviewed:

> My fantasies are so personal, and the pleasure I get from them derives so much, I think, from the fact that they are private and locked away in my imagination, that I wouldn't dream of trying to make them come true…. But act my fantasies out? Make them come true? No, absolutely not. My real life's not what they're about; I don't want those things to really happen to me, I simply want to imagine what it would be like. So that's where they'll stay.

In other words, such fantasizing doesn't mean the fantasizers want these events to occur (Leitenberg & Henning, 1995). Women who imagine themselves being sexually coerced remain in control of their fantasies. Real assault victims are not in control. Needless to say, sexual fantasies that in any way involve sexual activity that's not consensual and legal should remain in the realm of fantasy and not become reality.

Researchers at the University of Guelph have found that mental excursions into fantasy during partnered sex may be used to enhance sexual arousal and response (Murray & Milhausen, 2012). Fantasies enable couples to inject sexual variety into their sexual activity without being unfaithful. Researchers find that most married people have fantasies during sex (Bader, 2003; Murray & Milhausen, 2012). There does not appear to be any connection between sexual dissatisfaction with one's relationship and having fantasies during partnered sexual activity (Davidson & Hoffman, 1986). Thus, fantasies during partnered sex are not a form of compensation for an unrewarding sexual relationship.

Fantasies during partnered sex, like masturbation fantasies, run a gamut of themes. They include making love to another partner, group sex, orgies, images of past lovers or special erotic experiences, and making love in fantastic and wonderful places, among others. Heterosexual men are likely to fantasize about women, and gay men are more likely to fantasize about men (Chivers et al., 2004). Researchers at Queens University have found that heterosexual women and lesbians are more flexible in their selection of the gender of the objects of their fantasies (Chivers et al., 2004; Chivers & Timmers, 2012).

LGB Fantasy

A survey of 129 women (85 lesbian, 44 bisexual) who'd been in same-sex relationships for five to ten years found connections between satisfaction in their relationships and the nature of their sexual fantasies (Robinson & Parks, 2003). By and large, the happier the women were with their relationships, the more likely they were to fantasize about common activities with their partners. If their relationships weren't going so well, they were more likely to fantasize about things they used to do with their partners, or things they'd done with former partners.

A study in India compared the sexual fantasies of 30 heterosexual males with those of 30 gay males (Bhugra et al., 2006). The heterosexual men's fantasy spheres appeared to be more limited, restricting these men to more standard sexual activities with females. The gay men were more open to fantasizing about a wider range of sexual behaviour.

Theoretical Perspectives on Sexual Fantasy

Evolutionary theorists conjecture that women are more likely than men to fantasize about familiar lovers, because female reproductive success in ancestral times was more likely to depend on emotionally close, protective relationships with reliable partners (Buss, 2009; Symons, 1995). Women can bear and rear relatively few offspring. They therefore have relatively greater genetic investments than men in each reproductive opportunity. Men, on the other hand, can enhance their reproductive success (i.e., improve their chances of passing on their genes to future generations) by having intercourse with high numbers of sexual partners. Men are therefore, according to evolutionary theory, more likely to have fantasies about casual sex with different partners.

Other researchers have noted that the tendency for women's sexual fantasies to be more romantic than men's, and the greater tendency for men's fantasies to involve new sexual partners, is a reflection of society's traditional sexual scripts—the double standard for male and female sexual behaviour (Renaud & Byers, 1999). That is, females in most cultures are raised to be more romance-oriented and more sexually passive than men, while males are raised to be sexually assertive and to desire a high number of sexual partners. According to this perspective, the content of our sexual fantasies is influenced primarily by the gender roles we learn as we grow up. As gender roles become more egalitarian in Western culture, it will be interesting to see whether men's and women's sexual fantasies become less reflective of society's traditional double standard. (See Chapter 5 for further discussion of gender roles related to sexuality.)

Sexual Dreams

There's been limited research on sexual dreams. Nevertheless, researchers at Trent University and University of British Columbia (Humphreys et al., 2007; King, DeCicco, & Humphreys, 2009) have found that sexual dreams are common among university students, and that most have sexual dreams at least once a week.

Almost all of the students in these studies rated their sexual dreams as pleasurable; many reported that their dreams were as pleasurable as having sexual intercourse. The most common activities in their dreams were kissing and sexual intercourse. Rarely did anyone dream about masturbation.

Students generally dreamed about behaviours they'd engaged in with partners, rather than untried behaviours. The females were more likely to dream about their current partners, whereas the males were more likely to dream about other people.

Masturbation in History

In solitude he pollutes himself, and with his own hand blights all his prospects for both this world and the next. Even after being solemnly warned, he will often continue this worse than beastly practice, deliberately forfeiting his right to health and happiness for a moment's mad sensuality.

—Kellogg, J. H. (1881). *Plain facts for old and young*. Burlington, IA: Segner and Condit.

Don't knock masturbation. It's sex with someone I love.

—Woody Allen as Alvy Singer. In Allen, W., & Brickman, M. *Annie Hall*. Hollywood: Metro-Goldwyn-Mayer, 1977.

Within the Judeo-Christian tradition, sexual self-stimulation, commonly known as masturbation, has been strongly condemned as sinful (Soble, 2009; Thomas & Murray, 2009). Early Judeo-Christian attitudes toward masturbation reflected the censure that was applied to non-procreative sexual acts. The Biblical story of Onan is often interpreted as a condemnation of masturbation. The influential philosopher and theologian St. Augustine (354–430 CE) associated sexual desire with original sin and argued that all non-procreative sex, including masturbation, was sinful (Bullough, 2002; Guttmann, 2006).

Figure 8.1   Devices to curb masturbation.
Because of the widespread belief that masturbation was harmful, various contraptions were introduced in the nineteenth century to prevent the practice in children. Some of the devices were barbarous.

St. Augustine's views were carried into medicine in the eighteenth century, and the medical profession translated sin into disease (Polansky, 2006). One of the more influential writers was the superintendent of the Battle Creek Sanitarium in Michigan, Dr. J. H. Kellogg (1852–1943). Kellogg believed sexual desires could be controlled by sticking to a diet of simple foods, especially grains, including the Corn Flakes he and his brother invented.

Many nineteenth-century physicians also advised parents to take measures to prevent their children from masturbating. Kellogg suggested that parents bandage or cage their children's genitals or tie their hands. Some of the contraptions devised to prevent masturbation were barbarous. (See Figure 8.1.)

Despite this history, there's no scientific evidence that masturbation is harmful, except for rare injuries to the genitals from rough stimulation. Sex therapists have even found that masturbation has therapeutic benefits. Indeed, most people, including doctors, view masturbation as a harmless pleasure. A more contemporary view is that masturbation can be an important part of healthy sexual development and a way for people to learn about their own sexual responses (Coleman, 2002).

Of course, people who consider masturbation wrong, harmful, or sinful may experience anxiety or guilt if they masturbate or wish to masturbate (Ortega et al., 2005). But these negative emotions are linked to their attitudes toward masturbation, not to masturbation itself.

Masturbation Today

Surveys indicate that most people—including many married people—masturbate at some time. The incidence of masturbation is generally greater among men than women. There are women who masturbate frequently, however, and men who rarely if ever do so (Michael et al., 1994).

CRITICAL THINKING QUESTIONS

If a younger brother or sister who was starting to go through puberty asked why people masturbate and whether it's an okay thing to do, how would you respond?

Innovative Canadian Research

ONLINE MASTURBATION

In a survey of 217 students with an average age of 19.5 years, University of New Brunswick and University of Windsor researchers Krystelle Shaughnessy, E. Sandra Byers, and Lindsay Walsh (2011) found that 83.3% of the men and 30.8% of the women had looked at sexually explicit online videos or photos during the previous month.

Almost three-quarters of the men (73.6%) and 17.8% of the women reported that they'd masturbated while watching sexually explicit online videos during the previous month. In addition, 11.1% of the men and 1.7% of the women reported that they'd masturbated while looking at strangers on webcams during that time.

According to the data in
Table 8.1, women in their
40s and 50s are more
likely than women in their
teens to report that they've
masturbated during the
previous month. Can you
think of reasons for this?

TABLE 8.1

Percentages of Males and Females, Aged 14 to 70+, Who Reported
Masturbating During the Past Month and the Past Year

Age	Past Month		Past Year	
	Male	**Female**	**Male**	**Female**
14–15	42.9	24.1	62.1	40.4
16–17	58.0	25.5	74.8	44.8
18–19	61.6	26.0	80.6	60.0
20–24	62.8	43.7	82.7	64.3
25–29	68.6	51.7	83.6	71.5
30–39	66.4	38.6	80.1	62.9
40–49	60.1	38.5	76.0	64.9
50–59	55.7	28.3	72.1	54.1
60–69	42.3	21.5	61.2	46.5
701	27.9	11.5	46.4	32.8

Source: Herbenick, D., et al. (2010). Sexual behavior in the United States: Results from a national probability sample of men and women ages 14–94. *Journal of Sexual Medicine, 7* (Supplement s5), 255–265.

Table 8.1 presents data on masturbation from a population-based sexual health survey of 5865 14- to 94-year-old men and women in the United States (Herbenick et al., 2010). A majority of respondents reported masturbating at least occasionally from ages 18 to 59. Among those aged 70 and up, almost one-third of the women and just under half of the men reported masturbating during the previous year. Men were more likely to masturbate than women, but just over half of the women in the 25–29 age group reported masturbating at least once during the previous month. Women in the 40–49 and 50–59 age groups were more likely than teenaged women to report masturbating during the previous month.

In a large national survey conducted in Britain (Gerressu et al., 2008), twice as many men (73%) as women (37%) reported that they'd masturbated during the previous four weeks. Men who reported more frequent partnered sexual activity (e.g., intercourse, oral sex) had lower masturbation rates. In contrast, women who had more partnered sexual activity had higher rates of masturbation. It seems that for men, masturbation is compensation for less partnered sex, whereas for women, more partnered sex increases the desire to masturbate. Both men and women with same-gender partners were more likely to masturbate than men and women with other-gender partners.

Despite the sexual revolution, some women may still find masturbation less acceptable than men do. Women may still be subject to traditional socialization pressures that teach that sexual activity for pleasure's sake is more taboo for women than for men. In the British study (Gerressu et al., 2008), women who were more religious were less likely to masturbate than women who were less religious. Education would appear to be a liberating influence on masturbation. For both genders, people with more education reported more frequent masturbation (Gerressu et al., 2008).

An American study found that 33.6% of men and 13.7% of women with advanced degrees masturbated at least once a week, compared to 20.0% of men and 5.6% of women with no college or university education (Laumann et al. 1994). Perhaps better-educated people are less likely to believe the old horror stories about masturbation or are less susceptible to traditional social restrictions.

Innovative Canadian Research

THE DEPICTION OF MASTURBATION IN NORTH AMERICAN MOVIES

Researchers from Simon Fraser University conducted a study of the portrayal of masturbation in popular, mainstream North American movies (Madanikia, Bartholomew, & Cytrynbaum, 2013). The study of 44 movies, produced between 2005 and 2010, was designed to identify some common social norms associated with masturbation. Each of the movies included a scene with either the intent to masturbate or the act of masturbation. The characters involved were primarily male (75%) and single (84%). Most (82%) were presented as being heterosexual, with only 18% of the characters portrayed as gay, lesbian, or bisexual. The researchers viewed the movies to determine how the characters were portrayed, the context of the masturbation experience, and the outcome. They also considered the nature of the experience—for example, whether it was fulfilling, frustrating, embarrassing, or traumatic. In over half of the masturbation scenes the character was interrupted, and most of the experiences depicted were neither pleasurable nor satisfying. Although research indicates that masturbation is common among individuals of all ages involved in satisfying relationships, most of the characters in the films were young, attractive, and single and were portrayed as being sexually frustrated and unfulfilled. However, masturbation by female characters was generally depicted in a more positive light as compared to male masturbation. The researchers suggest that this could reflect a societal view that female masturbation is an erotic and sexually liberating act, while male masturbation is associated with frustration and lack of a sexual partner. In general, the researchers found that masturbation was associated with negative outcomes and depicted in the context of troubled relationships and unfulfilled sexual desires.

At an Ontario university, more men (84%) than women (62%) had first masturbated before the age of 16 (Rye, 2001). More than 90% of the students had fantasized during masturbation, with 27% of the women and 7% of the men using mechanical aids such as vibrators. While 75% of the women and 92% of the men reported having had orgasms in more than half of their masturbation experiences, more women (17%) than men (6%) said they'd had more than one orgasm in more than half of these experiences (Rye, 2001).

In our efforts to correct misinformation about masturbation, we don't wish to leave the impression that there's anything wrong with people who choose *not* to masturbate. Rather, we believe it's up to individuals to decide for themselves.

MALE MASTURBATION TECHNIQUES

> Sex is like bridge—if you don't have a good partner, you'd better have a good hand.
> —Bathroom graffiti

Although masturbation techniques vary widely, most men report that they masturbate by manual manipulation of the penis. (See Figure 8.2.) Men tend to grip the penile shaft with one hand, jerking it up and down in a milking motion. Some men move the whole hand up and down the penis, while others use just two fingers, generally the thumb and index finger. Men usually shift from a gentler rubbing action during the flaccid or semi-erect state of arousal to a more vigorous milking motion once full erection takes place. Men are also likely to stroke the glans and frenulum lightly at the outset, tightening their grip and speeding up their motions as orgasm nears. At orgasm, they may grip the penile shaft tightly, but usually avoid touching the glans, which has become sensitive. (Likewise, because of increased sensitivity, women usually avoid directly stimulating the clitoris during orgasm.)

Figure 8.2 Male masturbation.
Masturbation techniques vary widely, but most men report that they masturbate by manual manipulation of the penis.

Some men prefer to masturbate by rubbing the penis and testicles against clothing or bedding. A few men rub their genitals against inflatable dolls sold in sex shops. These dolls may come with artificial mouths or vaginas that can be filled with warm water, to mimic the sensations of intercourse. Artificial vaginas are also for sale.

FEMALE MASTURBATION TECHNIQUES Masturbation techniques for women also vary widely. Masters and Johnson reported never seeing two women masturbate precisely the same way. Even when the general technique was similar, women varied in the tempo and style of their self-caresses. Some general trends have been noted, though. Most women masturbate by massaging the mons, labia minora, and clitoral region with circular or back-and-forth motions (Hite, 1976). They may also straddle the clitoris with their fingers, stroking the shaft rather than the glans. (See Figure 8.3.) In a study of university women, half (53%) preferred stimulation of the external part of the genitals when masturbating to orgasm, while 36% preferred using both external and internal stimulation (Maisel & Meggers, 2007). Only 11% preferred internal stimulation of the vagina.

Figure 8.3 Female masturbation.
Female masturbation techniques vary so widely that Masters and Johnson never observed two women masturbating in precisely the same way. Most women, however, masturbate by massaging the mons, labia minora, and clitoral region, either with circular or back-and-forth motions.

A World of Diversity

GOOD VIBES

The use of vibrators during sexual activity is one of the more apparent examples of the old General Electric slogan, "Better living through electricity." Surveys with nationally representative samples reveal that half of U.S. residents use vibrators, slightly less than half of men (Reece et al., 2009) and more than half of women (Herbenick et al., 2009). Vibrators are incorporated into both solo and partnered sexual activities (Herbenick et al., 2011). These include—but are not limited to—clitoral stimulation, stimulation of the G-spot, securing of the base of a condom (to prevent leakage), anal stimulation (external and internal), the simulation of cunnilingus, and couples' sex play (Herbenick et al., 2011).

A survey of 1047 men aged 18–60 found that 45% had incorporated a vibrator into their sexual activities over the course of their lifetime, and 10% had done so in the past month (Reece et al., 2009). Responses of 2056 women aged 18–60 to a survey found that 52.5% had incorporated vibrators into their sexual activities over their lifetime (Herbenick et al., 2009).

What do we know about the men and women who used vibrators? Responses to other survey questions showed that men who used vibrators were more likely to pay attention to their sexual health, such as being more likely to engage in testicular self-exams. Men who had used vibrators also reported more positively on their erectile functioning, their satisfaction with intercourse, their ability to reach orgasm, and their sexual desire. As with the men, use of a vibrator among women was connected with more healthful behaviors such as obtaining gynecological exams and doing self-genital exams. And as with the men, vibrator use was positively correlated with sexual desire, arousal, and orgasm and negatively correlated with sexual pain. More than 70% of the women reported that they had never had negative side effects from vibrator use.

Women may lightly touch the glans during early arousal, but because of its exquisite sensitivity, they rarely stroke it for any length of time. Women typically achieve clitoral stimulation by rubbing or stroking the clitoral shaft or pulling or tugging on the vaginal lips. Some women also massage other sensitive areas, such as their breasts or nipples, with their free hand. Many women, like men, fantasize during masturbation.

Sexual Behaviour with Others

Partners' feelings for one another, and the quality of their relationships, may be stronger determinants of sexual arousal and response than the techniques they employ. Partners are most likely to experience mutually enjoyable sexual interactions when they're sensitive to each other's sexual needs and incorporate techniques they're both comfortable with. As with other aspects of sharing relationships, communication is the most important sexual technique.

Foreplay

Foreplay consists of various forms of sexual activity that occur prior to penetrative sex (e.g., vaginal or anal intercourse), such as cuddling, kissing, petting, and oral–genital contact. The pattern and duration of foreplay vary widely within and across cultures. Foreplay is important because most couples aren't ready for penetrative sex without first building arousal and sexual response.

The sexual activities we commonly think of as foreplay are pleasurable in and of themselves—perhaps even more so than penetration, in some cases. Some sex therapists advise their clients to make sexual activity less goal-oriented and to enjoy activities such as mutual masturbation and oral sex for their own sake, rather than as activities that must inevitably lead to penetration.

Foreplay Physical interactions that are sexually stimulating and set the stage for penetrative sex.

Felix Mizioznikov/Shutterstock

Kissing.
It's almost universal in our culture, but kissing is practised less often in some societies, and not at all in others.

TANTRIC SEX Tantric sex is a type of lovemaking that emphasizes prolonged foreplay. It's based on Eastern spiritual philosophies that promote the integration of the mind and the body.

Tantric sex focuses on sexual union as a spiritual connection that leads to heightened sexual pleasure and ecstasy. The techniques include deep breathing, slowed sexual interactions, and delayed ejaculation. Some tantric sex instructors teach men how to have orgasms without ejaculating. There are numerous variations of tantric sex.

Kissing

Kissing is almost universal in our culture, but it's unknown in some societies, such as those of the Thonga in Africa and the Sirionó in Bolivia. Kissing is now practiced in Japan, because of the influence of Western culture, but it was previously unknown there.

There are cross-cultural variations in kissing style (Ford & Beach, 1951). Instead of kissing, the Balinese of Indonesia used to bring their faces close enough to smell each other's perfume and feel the warmth of each other's skin. This practice has been dubbed "rubbing noses" by Europeans. Among some preliterate societies, kissing consists of sucking the partner's lips and tongue, and allowing saliva to pass from one mouth to the other.

In simple kissing, the partners keep their mouths closed. Simple kissing may develop into caresses of the lips with the tongue, or nibbling of the lower lip. In what Kinsey called deep kissing, which we also call French kissing or soul kissing, the partners part their lips and insert their tongues into each other's mouths. Some prefer parting their lips slightly, while others open their mouths widely.

Kissing may be an affectionate gesture without erotic significance, as when you kiss someone good night. Some people kiss relatives and close friends affectionately on the lips. Others kiss relatives only on the cheeks. Sustained kissing on the lips and deep kissing are almost always erotic gestures.

Touching

Touching or caressing the erogenous zones with the hands or other parts of the body can be highly arousing. Even simple hand-holding can be sexually stimulating for couples who are sexually attracted to one another. The hands are rich in nerve endings.

Innovative Canadian Research

DESIRED DURATION OF FOREPLAY

In a study of heterosexual couples, Andrea Miller and E. Sandra Byers (2004) at the University of New Brunswick found that men and women were similar in terms of how long they wanted foreplay to last.

The women, however, underestimated how long their partners—and the average male—wanted foreplay to continue. Perhaps women are influenced by the stereotype that men are mainly interested in intercourse.

The men were accurate in estimating how much time their partners—and the average woman—wanted to spend on foreplay. Like the women, though, the men underestimated how much time the average man likes to spend on foreplay.

Touching is a common form of foreplay. Both men and women generally prefer manual or oral stimulation of the genitals as a prelude to penetrative sex. Women generally prefer that direct caressing of the genitals be focused around the clitoris, but not directly on the extremely sensitive clitoral glans. Men sometimes assume (often mistakenly) that their partners want them to insert their finger or fingers into the vagina as a form of foreplay, but not all women enjoy this form of stimulation.

Some women go along with it because it's what their partners want, or something they *think* their partners want. Ironically, men may do it because they assume *their* partners want it. When in doubt, it doesn't hurt to ask. If you're not sure what to say, you can always blame us: "Listen, I read this thing in my human sexuality textbook, and I was wondering. . . ." In a survey of students at an Ontario university, more than 90% reported that they'd experienced manual stimulation of their genitals by their partners (Rye, 2001).

Men typically like their partners to directly stroke their genitals early in sexual interaction. Women, however, tend to prefer that their partners caress their genitals after a period of general body contact that includes holding, hugging, and non-genital massage. This isn't a hard and fast (or slow) rule, but it concurs with other observations that men tend to be more genitally oriented than women.

How Touching.
Touching is a common form of foreplay. Most people like manual or oral stimulation of the genital organs as a prelude to sexual intercourse.

Breast Stimulation

Men are more likely to stimulate women's breasts than to enjoy having their own breasts fondled, even though the breasts (and especially the nipples) are erotically sensitive in both sexes. Most (but not all) women enjoy having their breasts stimulated, and some women are capable of achieving orgasm from breast stimulation alone.

The hands and the mouth can be used to stimulate the breasts and nipples. The desired type and intensity of breast stimulation varies from person to person, so partners need to communicate their preferences.

In general, women usually prefer several minutes of body contact and gentle caresses before they want their partners to kiss their breasts or suck or lick their nipples. Many women also usually don't prefer a hard sucking action unless they're highly aroused. Often, women are reluctant to tell their partners when sucking hurts, because they don't want to interfere with their partners' pleasure.

BREAST STIMULATION IN GAY MALES   Gay men apparently stimulate their partner's nipples more than heterosexual women do. Masters and Johnson's (1979) laboratory observations of sexual relations between gay males showed that they spent a good deal of time caressing their partners' bodies before approaching the genitals. After hugging and kissing, 31 of the 42 gay male couples observed by Masters and Johnson used oral or manual nipple stimulation.

Although some heterosexual men enjoy having their breasts and nipples stimulated, many do not. Many men are unaware that their breasts are erotically sensitive.

Fisting

Fisting refers to the insertion of all or most of a hand into the vagina or anus. There is little research documenting the prevalence of fisting. In a study of men who had sex with men in the previous six months, 8% reported fisting (Crawford et al., cited

Fisting Insertion of a hand into the vagina or anus.

in Richters et al., 2003). Vaginal and anal fisting appears to be less common among lesbian and bisexual women (Bailey et al., 2003) and heterosexual men and women (Richters et al., 2006). Typically, fisting does not involve the insertion of a clenched fist into the vagina or anus. Rather, the fingers are kept straight and held together in a beak-like shape and then inserted into a well-lubricated vagina or anus. The fingers are then clenched into a fist or remain straight. There is a risk of injury or infection from fisting.

Oral–Genital Sex

Fellatio Oral stimulation of the male genitals.

Cunnilingus Oral stimulation of the female genitals.

Oral stimulation of the male genitals is called **fellatio**. It's often referred to by slang terms such as "blow job," "sucking," "sucking off," and "giving head." Oral stimulation of the female genitals is called **cunnilingus**, which is referred to by slang expressions such as "eating" or "going down on" her.

The popularity of oral–genital sex has increased dramatically since Kinsey's research in the 1940s and '50s. In analyzing marriage and sex-advice manuals published over the course of the twentieth century, Carleton University researchers Alan Hunt and Bruce Curtis (2006) found a number of changes in advice about oral sex. Beginning as a taboo subject, oral sex became viewed as a normal activity over time, as first cunnilingus and then fellatio were accepted. Initially, oral sex was seen as a way of arousing the couple, especially the woman, in preparation for intercourse, and later it became accepted as a means of sexual pleasure in its own right. Of course, gays and lesbians have always used oral sex as a source of pleasure for its own sake.

CRITICAL THINKING QUESTIONS

Some people don't consider oral–genital contact to be "having sex." For them, only penile–vaginal intercourse counts as sex. What's your opinion?

SURVEY DATA Large-sample surveys of the Canadian and American populations reveal that oral sex is common. A recent large-sample survey of people in the United States who were 14 and older asked whether they'd given or received oral sex within the previous month or year (Herbenick et al., 2010). Several findings from this survey are noteworthy.

First, there's a common assumption that women in general, and young women in particular, are more likely to give their male partners oral sex than to receive it. Yet the survey indicates that, for most age groups, women are only slightly less likely to report receiving than giving oral sex.

Second, it's also commonly assumed that oral sex is predominantly practised by younger people, who are presumably more sexually adventurous than their elders. While previous research has shown that people who grew up before the sexual revolution of the 1960s and 1970s were less likely to engage in oral sex, a sizable percentage of people in their forties, fifties, and sixties report that they also engage in oral sex. (See Table 8.2.)

TABLE 8.2

Percentages of Males and Females, Aged 14 to 70+, Who Reported Giving and Receiving Heterosexual Oral Sex During the Past Year

	14–15	16–17	18–19	20–24	25–29	30–39	40–49	50–59	60–69	70+
Male received	11.9	30.9	53.6	62.8	77.2	77.6	62.1	48.5	37.5	19.2
Male gave	7.8	18.3	50.7	54.9	73.5	68.7	57.4	44.1	34.3	24.3
Female received	10.0	23.5	58.0	70.4	71.8	58.7	52.3	34.2	24.8	7.8
Female gave	11.8	22.4	58.5	74.3	75.9	59.2	52.7	36.2	23.4	6.8

Source: Herbenick, D., et al. (2010). Sexual behavior in the United States: Results from a national probability sample of men and women ages 14–94. *The Journal of Sexual Medicine, 7* (Supplement s5), 255–265.

The 1998 Compas poll is the only national survey to have asked Canadians about oral sex. The majority of both men (89%) and women (78%) reported giving and/or receiving oral sex (Fischtein & Herold, 2002). Canadians who hadn't completed high school were least likely to report experiencing oral sex. This was especially true for women—half of those who hadn't completed high school said they hadn't experienced oral sex (Fischtein & Herold, 2002). The data on oral sex and other sexual practices suggests that those with less education are less experimental and perhaps more concerned about whether these practices are "normal."

Tanya Hill at the University of Guelph (2005) found that 89% of female students had engaged in oral sex with their most recent partners. About half reported that they engaged in oral sex most of the time when having sexual relations with their partners. In a study of 181 women in Alberta aged 18 to 25, Malacad and Hess (2010) 74% had given fellatio at least once and 72.9% had received cunnilingus at least once. Sarah Vannier and Lucia O'Sullivan (2012) at the University of New Brunswick conducted an online survey assessing the sexual histories of heterosexual young adults and found that the majority of oral sex encounters occurred within committed relationships and during an encounter that also included intercourse. Both women and men reported that they were motivated to have oral sex by desire and attraction to their partner or to enhance emotional connection.

A study of gay and bisexual men in Ontario found that almost all of the men surveyed had engaged in oral sex during the previous three months (Myers et al., 2004). Similarly, in a study of lesbian and bisexual women, 72% reported that they "often" engaged in oral sex with their partners (Bailey et al., 2003).

NOT EVERYONE LIKES ORAL SEX   Despite oral sex's popularity today, some people choose to abstain from it. Some simply don't enjoy giving or receiving oral sex. Others object on grounds of cleanliness. They view the genitals as dirty, because of their proximity to the urinary and anal openings. Some abstain because they're concerned or embarrassed about providing (or receiving) direct views of parts of the body we've been reared to keep private. Some prefer not to taste or swallow semen, because they consider it dirty, sinful, or repulsive. Others are put off by the taste or texture; semen has a salty taste and a texture similar to egg white. Some people worry whether oral sex is morally accepted by their religion or culture.

If a couple wishes to engage in oral sex, open discussion of their feelings can enhance their pleasure and diminish anxiety. The man can be encouraged to tell his partner or remove his penis from her or his mouth as he nears ejaculation. And they can alleviate any concerns about offensive odours and cleanliness by thoroughly washing their genitals beforehand.

Oral Sex Techniques

FELLATIO   Although the word "fellatio" is derived from a Latin root that means "to suck," a sucking action is generally not highly arousing. The up-and-down movements of the penis in the partner's mouth and the licking of the penis are generally the most stimulating. (See Figure 8.4.) Gentle licking of the scrotum may also be highly arousing.

The mouth is stimulating to the penis because, like the vagina, it contains warm, moist mucous membranes. Muscles of the mouth and jaw can create varied pressure and movements. Erection may be stimulated by gently pulling the penis with the mouth (being careful never to touch the penis with the teeth) and simultaneously providing manual stimulation, as described earlier.

Higher levels of sexual arousal or orgasm can be promoted by moving the penis in and out of the mouth. The motions can be varied in speed and combined with manual stimulation.

Figure 8.4 Fellatio.
Fellatio involves stimulation of the penis and surrounding genital area with the mouth, lips, and tongue.

Some people may gag during fellatio, a reflex triggered by pressure of the penis against the back of the tongue or against the throat. Gagging may be avoided by grasping the shaft of the penis with one hand and controlling the depth of penetration.

Gagging is less likely to occur if the partner giving fellatio is on top, rather than below, and if there's verbal communication about how deep the man should penetrate. Gagging may also be overcome by allowing gradually deeper penetration over successive occasions, while keeping the throat muscles relaxed.

CUNNILINGUS   A woman can be highly aroused by her partner's tongue, because it's soft, warm, and well lubricated. (See Figure 8.5.) In giving cunnilingus, the partner may begin by kissing and licking the woman's abdomen and inner thighs, gradually nearing the vulva. Gentle tugging or sucking of the labia minora can be stimulating, but the partner should take care not to bite. Many women enjoy

Figure 8.5 Cunnilingus.
Cunnilingus involves stimulation of the vulva with the mouth, lips, and tongue.

licking of the clitoral region, and others desire sucking of the clitoris itself. The tongue may also be inserted into the vagina. A woman may be most receptive to direct clitoral contact by the tongue or circling of the clitoris with the tongue.

Cunnilingus provides such intense stimulation that many women find it the best means for achieving orgasm.

"69" The term "69" describes mutual, simultaneous oral–genital stimulation. The numerals "6" and "9" are used because they resemble two partners who are upside down and facing each other. The "69" technique may be practised side by side or with one partner on top of the other. Again, there are no strict rules, and couples often alternate positions.

The "69" position has the psychologically positive feature of allowing two people to experience simultaneous stimulation, but it can be awkward if the two are dissimilar in size. Some couples avoid "69" because it deprives each partner of the opportunity to fully focus on receiving or providing sexual pleasure.

Intercourse Techniques

In sexual intercourse, or coitus, the penis is inserted into the vagina. Intercourse can take place in many different positions, as long as the genitals are aligned so the vagina contains the penis. In addition to varying positions, couples vary the depth and rate of thrusting (in-and-out motions) and the sources of additional sexual stimulation.

Though the number of intercourse positions is virtually endless, we'll focus on four of the most common: male superior (man on top), female superior (woman on top), lateral entry (side entry), and rear entry. We'll also discuss anal intercourse, a sexual technique used by both male–female and male–male couples.

THE MALE-SUPERIOR (MAN-ON-TOP) POSITION The male-superior position (this "superiority" simply reflects the couple's body positions, but it has sometimes been taken as a symbol of male domination) has also been called the **missionary position**. In this position, the partners face each other. The man lies above the woman, perhaps supporting himself on his hands and knees rather than resting his full weight on her. (See Figure 8.6.) Even so, moving is easier for the man than for the woman, which suggests that he's responsible for directing their activity.

Missionary position The intercourse position in which the man is on top. It's also called the male-superior position.

Figure 8.6 The male–superior (man-on-top) intercourse position. The man-on-top position requires somewhat more physical effort on the part of the male. This is the most common sexual intercourse position in Western cultures.

Many sex therapists suggest that it's preferable for the woman to guide the penis into the vagina, rather than having the man do so. The woman can feel the location of the vaginal opening and determine the proper angle of entry. To accomplish this, the woman must feel comfortable taking charge of the couple's lovemaking. With the breaking down of the traditional passive-female stereotype, women are feeling more comfortable taking this role.

The male-superior position has the advantage of permitting the couple to face one another, so kissing is easier. The woman may run her hands along her partner's body, stroking his buttocks and perhaps cupping a hand beneath his scrotum to increase stimulation as he reaches orgasm.

But the male-superior position makes it difficult for the man to caress his partner while simultaneously supporting himself with his hands. The position may not be favoured by women who enjoy having their partners provide manual clitoral stimulation during intercourse.

THE FEMALE-SUPERIOR (WOMAN-ON-TOP) POSITION   In the female-superior position, the partners face each other, with the woman on top. The woman straddles the man from above, controlling the angle of penile entry and the depth of thrusting. (See Figure 8.7.) Some women maintain a sitting position; others lie on top of their partners. Many women vary their positions.

In the female-superior position, the woman may feel psychologically and physically in charge. She can move as rapidly or as slowly as she wishes, with little effort, adjusting her body to vary the angle and depth of penetration. She can, in effect, guarantee that she receives adequate clitoral stimulation, either from the penis or from his or her own hand. This position thus facilitates orgasm in the woman.

THE LATERAL-ENTRY (SIDE-ENTRY) POSITION   In the lateral-entry position, the man and woman lie side by side, facing each other. (See Figure 8.8.) This position has the advantages of allowing each partner relatively free movement and easy access to the other. The man and woman can kiss freely and stroke each other's bodies with a free arm.

The position isn't physically taxing, because both partners rest easily on the bedding. It's therefore an excellent position for prolonged coitus, older couples,

Figure 8.7   The female-superior (woman-on-top) intercourse position.
The female-superior position allows the woman more control over the angle and depth of penetration, and greater control over the orgasm.

Figure 8.8 The lateral-entry (side-by-side) intercourse position.
The side-by-side position requires less physical effort for both partners, and allows more freedom of movement for mutual caressing during intercourse.

and couples who are somewhat fatigued. The lateral position is also useful during pregnancy, at least until the final stages, when distension of the woman's abdomen may make lateral entry difficult.

THE REAR-ENTRY POSITION In the rear-entry position, the man faces the woman's back. In one variation (see Figure 8.9), she supports herself on her hands and knees while he supports himself on his knees, entering her from behind. In another, the two lie alongside each other and the woman lifts one leg, draping it backward over her partner's thigh. The second position is particularly useful during the later stages of pregnancy.

The rear-entry position may be highly stimulating for both partners. The man may enjoy viewing and pressing his abdomen against his partner's buttocks. He can reach around or underneath to provide additional stimulation of the clitoris and breasts, and she can reach behind (if she's on her hands and knees) to stroke or grasp his testicles.

Some couples feel uncomfortable about the position, however, because of its association with animal mating patterns. The position is also impersonal, in that the partners don't face each other, which may create a sense of emotional distance. Moreover, some couples dislike the feeling that the man is psychologically in charge, since he can see his partner, but she can't readily see him.

ANAL SEX The rectum is richly endowed with nerve endings and thus highly sensitive to sexual stimulation. Some people want their partner's fingers in the anus at the height of passion or at the moment of orgasm. A finger in the rectum during orgasm can heighten sexual sensation because the anal sphincters contract during orgasm. In a national survey of sexual practices among Australians, 17.3% of men and 14.3% of women reported digital (i.e., finger) anal stimulation during their most recent heterosexual encounter (Richters et al., 2006). In a study of bisexual and lesbian women, 14% reported occasional anal penetration with fingers (Bailey et al., 2003), and digital anal stimulation is a more common practice among gay men (Butler et al., 2009).

Anal intercourse can be practised by male–female couples and male–male couples. It involves

Figure 8.9 The rear-entry intercourse position.
The rear-entry position can be highly stimulating for both partners. It's particularly useful during the later stages of pregnancy.

insertion of the penis into the rectum. Anal intercourse is also referred to as "Greek culture," or lovemaking in the "Greek style," because of male bisexuality in ancient Greece. Both women and men may reach orgasm through receiving the penis in the rectum.

In anal intercourse, the penetrating male usually situates himself behind his partner. (He can also lie above or below his partner, in a face-to-face position.) The receiving partner can supplement anal stimulation with manual stimulation of the clitoral region or penis to reach orgasm. Because the rectum produces no natural lubrication, people engaging in anal intercourse are advised to use plenty of lubricant (note that water-based lubricants should be used with latex condoms).

Many couples are repulsed by the idea of anal intercourse. They view it as unnatural, immoral, or risky. Yet others find anal sex to be an enjoyable sexual variation, though perhaps not a regular feature of their sexual diet.

The National Health and Social Life Survey (NHSLS) of Americans found that one man in four (26%) and one woman in five (20%) had engaged in anal sex at some time during their lives (Laumann et al., 1994). Yet only about one person in 10 (10% of the men and 9% of the women) had engaged in anal sex during the previous year. Like oral sex, anal sex was more common among more highly educated respondents. Among men, about 30% of the college graduates had engaged in anal sex, compared to 23% of the high school graduates. Among women, about 29% of those with college degrees had engaged in anal sex, compared to about 17% of those who had graduated only from high school (Laumann et al., 1994). In a more recent national study of 18- to 26-year-old Americans in long-term relationships, 22% reported engaging in anal sex (Kaestle, 2007).

In a study of university students in British Columbia, 19% of the non-Asian females reported that they had engaged in anal intercourse, compared with 3% of the Asian females; 5% of the non-Asian men and 6% of the Asian men reported that they engaged in anal intercourse (Meston et al., 1996). More of the respondents had engaged in caressing of the anal area. About half (45%) of the non-Asian women and 28% of the non-Asian men reported having their anal areas caressed. About one-fifth of the Asian men and women had experienced caressing of the anal area.

In a University of Waterloo study (Rye, 2001), more students reported that they'd engaged in anal intercourse without a condom (15%) than with a condom (9%). In a University of Guelph study, 13% of the female respondents reported that they'd engaged in anal intercourse with their most recent partners, though most of those who'd engaged in anal sex said they rarely did so (Hill, 2005).

Anal intercourse is more common among gay males than heterosexual couples. In a study of almost 5000 gay males across Canada, 62% reported engaging in anal intercourse during the previous three months (Myers et al., 1996). In a more recent survey of 1139 men visiting gay venues in Vancouver, about 70% reported having anal sex during the previous six months (Trussler et al., 2010).

Not all gay males enjoy or practise anal intercourse. Of those who do, most alternate between being the inserter and being the recipient of the penis. Interviews with 51 gay men suggest that playing the inserter role in anal intercourse is sometimes associated with fantasies of domination, and the recipient role with fantasies of submission (Kippax & Smith, 2001). But some gays who practise anal intercourse deny that sex has anything to do with power or activity versus passivity; they feel that sex is about sharing.

Some couples kiss or lick the anus during foreplay. This practice is called **anilingus**. Oral–anal sex carries a serious health risk, however, because microorganisms that cause intestinal diseases and various sexually transmitted infections can be spread through oral–anal contact.

Many couples today hesitate to engage in anal intercourse for fear of HIV (the virus that causes AIDS) and other sexually transmitted infections (STIs). HIV and other micro-organisms that cause STIs, such as gonorrhea, syphilis, and hepatitis,

Anilingus Oral stimulation of the anus.

can be spread by anal intercourse, because small tears in the rectal tissues allow the microbes to enter the recipient's blood system. Women run a greater risk of contracting HIV from anal intercourse than from vaginal intercourse, just as gay men carry a high risk of infection from receptive anal intercourse (Voeller, 1991). It's important for couples engaging in anal intercourse to use condoms.

Gay and Lesbian Sexual Behaviour

In an Ontario survey of Canadian gay and bisexual men, more than half reported that they'd had sex with at least one regular partner (i.e., someone they'd had sex with more than once) in the three months prior to the survey. More than half had engaged in sex with at least one casual partner (i.e., someone they'd had sex with only once) during this time (Myers et al., 2004). The most common sexual activities they reported were deep-tongue kissing, oral sex without condoms, and mutual masturbation. (See Table 8.3.) The types of sexual behaviour they experienced were fairly similar for both regular and casual partners, with the exception of anal sex without condoms, which was experienced twice as often with regular as with casual partners. Forty-four percent said they'd never engaged in receptive anal intercourse without condoms.

Most research on the sexual behaviour of gay men, including that cited here, has been conducted with the express purpose of determining the risk of contracting HIV and other STIs. In other words, research on gay male sexuality has overwhelmingly focused on reducing risk, as opposed to increasing pleasure. While research on STI-related risk behaviours among heterosexuals, gay men, and lesbians are all important, perhaps the tendency to focus gay male research specifically on infection risk, rather than on capacity to give and receive pleasure, has caused many of us to view gay sex as inherently more dangerous than lesbian or heterosexual sex.

A Woman's Perspective.
Like heterosexual women, many lesbians are less genitally oriented and less fixated on orgasm than men are.

TABLE 8.3

Sexual Behaviours of Gay and Bisexual Men in Ontario over a Period of Three Months

	With Regular Male Partner	With Casual Male Partner
Mutual masturbation	81%	78%
Oral sex—no condom (I)	86	80
Deep tongue kissing	86	78
Oral sex—no condom (R)	80	73
Anal sex with condom (I)	44	47
Oral–anal sex	53	40
Anal sex—no condom (I)	41	21
Anal sex with condom (R)	36	35
Anal sex—no condom (R)	34	6

Note: I = Insertive, R = Receptive

Source: Myers, T., Allman, D., Calzavara, L., et al. (2004). *Ontario men's survey.* Toronto: HIV Social, Behavioural, and Epidemiological Studies Unit, Faculty of Medicine, University of Toronto.

A World of Diversity

SEXUAL BEHAVIOUR IN AUSTRALIA

In a national Australian survey involving 19 307 respondents between the ages of 16 and 59, researchers (Richters et al., 2006) asked heterosexuals which sexual behaviours they'd engaged in the last time they'd had sex with partners. The study made an important contribution by analyzing combinations of behaviours, rather than behaviours in isolation.

The researchers found than almost all of the encounters (95%) included vaginal intercourse, but only 12% of the encounters consisted of vaginal intercourse alone.

The most common combinations were intercourse and manual stimulation of the genitals (49%) and intercourse and manual and oral stimulation of the genitals (32%). Only 1% had anal intercourse, and 17% of the men and 14% of the women reported digital anal stimulation.

Men had orgasms in 95% of the encounters, while women had orgasms in 69%. Women were more likely to reach orgasm when the encounters included more sexual practices, especially cunnilingus.

Sexual techniques practised by lesbians vary. Lesbian couples report kissing, manual and oral stimulation of the breasts, and manual and oral stimulation of the genitals. Manual genital stimulation is a common and frequent sexual activity among lesbian couples. Many lesbian couples also engage in genital apposition. That is, they position themselves so as to rub their genitals together rhythmically.

Innovative Canadian Research

HOW TO HAVE GREAT SEX: ADVICE IN POPULAR MAGAZINES

University of Ottawa researchers Dana Menard and Peggy Kleinplatz (Kleinplatz et al., 2009) analyzed the advice for achieving "great sex" given by popular men's and women's magazines. The advice fell into five categories:

- Technical, mechanical, and physical factors—Recommendations included improving or learning new sexual techniques and positions, having sex for appropriate lengths of time, and improving physical health through diet and exercise.
- Variety—Readers were encouraged to experiment sexually, try "mild kink," watch steamy movies or porn, and engage in "rough" female-initiated sex.
- Relationship factors—Suggestions included improving communication about sexual desires and becoming more emotionally intimate.
- Personal and psychological improvements—Readers were encouraged to relax during sex, focus on sexuality

both during and outside of sex, improve their body image (for females), and increase their self-knowledge (usually through masturbation).

- Preparation for sex—Readers were encouraged to make themselves more physically attractive and to make the sexual settings more seductive.

Most of the advice centred on the first two categories—improving sexual techniques and increasing the variety of sexual experiences.

The magazines relied on a number of gender stereotypes, such as the belief that men preferred "quickies" and women preferred long, drawn-out sex. The magazines also relied on traditional scripts—that is, recommending regular partners, but not casual partners. Sometimes messages were contradictory; one magazine might suggest that couples view pornography, while another magazine discouraged this activity.

With the exception of *Men's Health*, sexual advice was more common in women's magazines than in men's magazines.

TABLE 8.4

Sexual Behaviours with Another Woman Reported by Women in Contact with the Gay and Lesbian Community in Sydney, Australia

Behaviours Experienced	Percent
Fingers on external genitals	96
Fingers inside vagina	94
Oral sex giving	85
Oral sex receiving	81
Sex toy used on external genitals	56
Sex toy used in vagina	57
Fingers inside anus	31
Rimming (her mouth, your anus)	15
Rimming (your mouth, her anus)	16
Sex toy inside anus	14

Source: Richters, J. (2007). Researching sex between women. Paper presented at the 1st World Congress for Sexual Health, Sydney, Australia.

Like gay males, lesbians spend a good deal of time holding, kissing, and caressing each other's bodies before they approach the breasts and genitals.

There's been far less research into lesbian sexual behaviour than into gay male and heterosexual sexual behaviour. One recent, detailed survey was conducted in Australia (Richters, 2007). It found that almost all of the women had engaged in manual and oral sex. (See Table 8.4.) The survey also asked about the use of dental dams as a means of preventing sexually transmitted infection during oral sex. Only 7% of the women reported that they'd used a dental dam during oral sex with other women. Of those who had used dental dams, three-quarters had used them only once (Richters, 2007).

CRITICAL THINKING QUESTIONS

In your experience, does the advice on how to have "great sex" provided in popular magazines sometimes reflect stereotypes about male and female sexuality?

Summing Up

Sexual fantasies are often incorporated into masturbation or into sex with another person, to heighten sexual response.

Masturbation can be practised by means of manual stimulation of the genitals, perhaps with the aid of a vibrator or an object that provides tactile stimulation. Surveys indicate that most people have masturbated at some point in their lives.

The pattern and duration of foreplay varies widely within and across cultures. Couples in many cultures kiss for its own enjoyment or as a prelude to intercourse.

Touching or caressing erogenous zones with the hands or other parts of the body can be highly arousing. Men typically prefer direct stroking of their genitals by their partners early in lovemaking.

Women, however, tend to prefer that their partners caress their genitals after a period of general body contact.

Most, but not all, women enjoy stimulation of the breasts.

Oral–genital sex is a common sexual practice.

Four of the most commonly used sexual intercourse positions are the male-superior position, the female-superior position, the lateral-entry position, and the rear-entry position.

Most gay males and a significant minority of heterosexuals engage in anal sex. There's been limited research on the sexual behaviours of lesbians.

Test Yourself

Multiple-Choice Questions

1. Which of the following statements about sexual fantasies is false?
   (a) A fantasy is a mental image that's sexually arousing or erotic.
   (b) Nearly all of us have sexual fantasies of one kind or another.
   (c) Fantasizing about being forced to have sex means you want to experience this in real life.
   (d) Research suggests that heterosexual women and lesbians are more flexible than heterosexual and gay men in their selection of the gender of the objects of their fantasies.

2. In Herbenick et al.'s study, what percentage of women reported that they had used a vibrator at some point in their lives?
   (a) 32.5%
   (b) 52.5%
   (c) 72.5%
   (d) 82.5%

3. In a survey of 14- to 94-year-old males and females, the group most likely to report masturbating during the previous month was aged:
   (a) 16 to 17.
   (b) 18 to 19.
   (c) 20 to 24.
   (d) 25 to 29.

4. What connection does the research show between masturbation and education?
   (a) Less educated men and women are more likely to masturbate.
   (b) Less educated women, but not men, are more likely to masturbate.
   (c) Less educated men, but not women, are more likely to masturbate.
   (d) More educated men and women are more likely to masturbate.

5. According to a survey of 14- to 94-year-old males and females, at what age is a male most likely to report that he's given oral sex to a female partner during the past year?
   (a) 20 to 24
   (b) 25 to 29
   (c) 30 to 39
   (d) 40 to 49

6. In a survey of 14- to 94-year-old males and females, what percentage of the 60- to 69-year-old women reported that they'd received oral sex from male partners during the previous year?
   (a) 24.8
   (b) 15.8
   (c) 5.8
   (d) 0.8

7. The varieties of physical contact that occur before penetrative sex are collectively called:
   (a) Prologue.
   (b) Foreplay.
   (c) Othercourse.
   (d) Afterplay.

8. Tantric sex includes:
   (a) A slowing of the sexual interaction process.
   (b) A speeding-up of the sexual interaction process.
   (c) Techniques that enable both partners to have as many orgasms as possible.
   (d) Techniques for attracting new sex partners.

9. Which of the following statements about the woman-on-top position is least accurate?
   (a) It allows either partner access to the woman's clitoris.
   (b) It allows a woman to move as rapidly or as slowly as she wishes.
   (c) It allows a woman to bring her partner to orgasm quickly.
   (d) It allows a woman to feel psychologically in charge.

2. According to the textbook, the tendency for research on the sexual behaviour of gay men to focus on HIV and STI risk may:
   (a) Increase compassion for men with HIV/AIDS.
   (b) Raise awareness of the risk of HIV infection from anal intercourse.
   (c) Call attention to the need for more research on HIV risk for heterosexuals.
   (d) Have biased us to view gay sex as inherently dangerous.

You'll find answers to the "Test Yourself" questions on page 489.

Questions for Critical Thinking

1. Have you ever wondered whether your sexual fantasies are normal?

2. Have your ideas about sexual fantasies, masturbation, oral sex, and anal sex changed as a result of reading this chapter ? If so, how? If not, why not?

3. How do you feel about masturbating to online sexual images? If you did so, would you tell your best friend? Your girlfriend or boyfriend? Why or why not?

4. Were you ever discouraged from masturbating as a child? Do you think this has affected your behaviour as an adult? Explain.

CHAPTER NINE

Sexual Orientation

BananaStock/Thinkstock

Getting Oriented to Sexual Orientation

Sexual orientation refers to a person's erotic attraction to—and interest in developing romantic relationships with—members of the same gender, the other gender, or both.

A **heterosexual orientation** is an erotic attraction to members of the other gender. Many people refer to heterosexuals as "straight."

A **homosexual orientation** is an erotic attraction to and preference for developing romantic relationships with members of the same gender. (From the Greek *homos*, meaning "same," not the Latin *homo*, which means "man").

A person with a **bisexual orientation** is sexually attracted to—and interested in forming romantic relationships with—both men and women.

Coming to Terms with Terms

The term "homosexuality" is somewhat controversial. Some gay and lesbian people object to it because they feel it draws attention to sexual behaviour. The term bears a social stigma, having historically been associated with deviance and mental illness. Moreover, the term is often used only in reference to men, rendering lesbians invisible. Many people therefore prefer such terms as "gay male" and "lesbian sexual orientation." We use the word "homosexuality" in this book because it provides a broad but useful way to differentiate same-gender attraction from opposite-gender attraction. We intend our use of the word to be respectful and nonjudgemental.

Sexual orientation The directionality of one's erotic attraction—that is, to members of the same gender, the other gender, or both.

Heterosexual orientation Erotic attraction to—and preference for romantic relationships with—members of the other gender.

Homosexual orientation Erotic attraction to—and preference for romantic relationships with—members of your own gender.

Bisexual orientation Erotic attraction to—and interest in romantic relationships with—both men and women.

The word "homosexual" is ambiguous (Savin-Williams, 2006). Does it refer to sexual behaviour or sexual orientation? When we speak of gay, lesbian, and bisexual orientations, we're referring to sexual attraction to the same gender. In other words, sexual orientation is defined not by sexual activity but by the direction of romantic interest and erotic attraction (Mosher et al., 2005). This distinction is useful because many heterosexual people have same-gender experiences, and many gay and lesbian people have opposite-gender experiences.

Sexual Orientation and Gender Identity

Since gay and lesbian people are attracted to members of their own gender, some people assume they'd prefer to be members of the other gender. Like most heterosexuals, however, most gays and lesbians have gender identities consistent with their anatomic sex. A small percentage of gays and lesbians are transgender—that is, they have gender identities that are different from their anatomic sex.

When heterosexuals think about gays and lesbians, they tend to focus almost exclusively on the sexual aspects of male–male and female–female relationships. But the relationships of gays and lesbians, like those of heterosexuals, involve more than sex. In a study of Ontario men, Barry Adam (2000b) at the University of Windsor found that for gay men, the concept of being gay centred on the possibility for emotional involvement and relationships with other people who felt the same way, rather than only on sexual behaviour. Gays and lesbians, like heterosexuals, spend only a small amount of time in sexual activity. More basic to a gay male or a lesbian sexual orientation is the formation of romantic attachments with members of one's own sex. These attachments, like male–female attachments, provide a framework for love and intimacy.

Kevin Alderson at the University of Calgary has been researching the concept of sexual orientation for several years. His findings have resulted in a new scale called the sexuality questionnaire. Alderson (2007) has concluded that sexual orientation should be conceptualized and measured as a combination of several factors: sexual attraction, sexual fantasies, sexual preference, sexual partners, tendency to fall in love romantically, and experience of falling in love romantically. The scale also measures a person's self-identified sexual identity.

Classifying Sexual Orientation

Determining a person's sexual orientation might seem clear-cut. Some people are exclusively gay and limit their sexual activities to partners of their own gender. Others are exclusively heterosexual and limit their sexual activities to partners of the other gender. However, a significant percentage of people are neither exclusively heterosexual nor exclusively gay or lesbian, falling somewhere in between.

It's not unusual for heterosexuals to have sexual experiences with people of their own gender (Mosher et al., 2005; Savin-Williams et al., 2012). In the absence of heterosexual outlets, adolescents and people in isolated populations (e.g., prison inmates) may have sexual experiences with members of their own gender while maintaining heterosexual identities. A number of studies have found

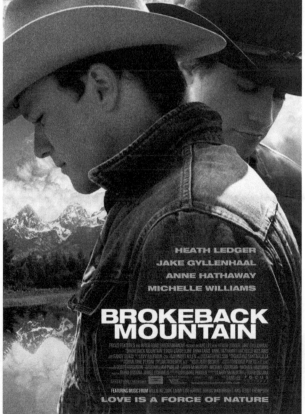

Brokeback Mountain.
In the film Brokeback Mountain, *Jake Gyllenhaal and Heath Ledger portray two cowboys who begin a love affair in 1963 Wyoming. Neither understands what it means to have a gay orientation.*

that Asians, Blacks, and Latinos may be less likely than whites to identify themselves as gay, lesbian, or bisexual even when they engage in sexual activity with people of their own gender (Chae & Ayala, 2010; Reback & Larkins, 2010).

Gay males and lesbians, too, may engage in male–female sexual activity while maintaining gay and lesbian sexual orientations. In the Ontario Men's Survey of gay and bisexual men, 83% of respondents identified themselves as gay, yet 61% reported having had sex with women (Myers et al., 2004). In the past, when homosexuality was more stigmatized in Western society than it is now, it wasn't uncommon for some gay and lesbian people to marry in order to fulfill social expectations, yet still have unfulfilled desire for members of their own gender. And some people are bisexual but may not act on their attraction to members of their own gender (Edser & Shea, 2002).

Sexual orientation isn't necessarily expressed in sexual behaviour. Many people see themselves as gay or heterosexual long before they ever have sex with members of their own gender (Thompson & Morgan, 2008; Savin-Williams & Diamond, 2000). And some people, gay, lesbian or heterosexual, adopt celibate lifestyles for religious or ascetic reasons.

People's erotic interests and fantasies may also shift over time. Gay males and lesbians may experience sporadic **heteroerotic** interests. Heterosexual people may have occasional **homoerotic** interests. Women's sexual orientations are apparently somewhat more flexible, or plastic, than men's, and women are somewhat more dependent on social experience (Diamond, 2003a; Savin-Williams et al., 2012; Thompson & Morgan, 2008). Lisa M. Diamond (2003b) conducted a survey of lesbian and bisexual women that involved three interviews over a five-year period. She found that more than 25% of the women relinquished their lesbian or bisexual orientations as time went on. Half of these relabelled themselves as heterosexual, and the other half renounced any effort at self-labelling.

Chivers and Bailey (2005) exposed men and women to visual male and female sexual stimuli and measured both their genital responses and their self-reports of sexual arousal. Male heterosexuals responded genitally only to the female stimuli, and gay males showed the reverse pattern. Their genital responses bore out their verbal reports. The women, both heterosexual and lesbian, were more likely to be aroused by both male and female sexual stimuli. Chivers and Bailey's findings are consistent with research showing that women's sexual orientations are more flexible than men's and apparently more intertwined with their social experience (Bailey, 2003a; Diamond, 2003b).

Attraction to people of the other gender and attraction to people of the same gender may thus not always be mutually exclusive. People may have various degrees of sexual interest in, and sexual experience with, people of either gender (Vrangalova & Savin-Williams, 2012). Kinsey and his colleagues recognized that the boundaries between homosexual and heterosexual orientations are sometimes blurry.

THE KINSEY CONTINUUM Kinsey and his colleagues (1948, 1953) found evidence of a continuum of sexual orientation among the people they surveyed, with bisexuality representing a midpoint between exclusively heterosexual and exclusively homosexual orientations. (See Figure 9.1.) People are located on the continuum according to their patterns of sexual attraction and behaviour. People in category 0 are considered exclusively heterosexual, while those in category 6 are considered exclusively gay or lesbian.

Kinsey and his colleagues reported that about 4% of the men and 1% to 3% of the women in their samples were exclusively gay (scoring six points on their scale). A larger percentage

Heteroerotic Of an erotic nature and involving members of the other gender.

Homoerotic Of an erotic nature and involving members of one's own gender.

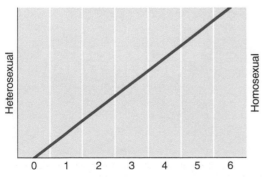

Figure 9.1 The Kinsey continuum.
Kinsey and his colleagues conceived of a seven-point heterosexual–homosexual continuum that classifies people according to their sexual behaviour and the magnitude of their attraction to members of their own gender.

were considered predominantly gay (scoring four or five points) or predominantly heterosexual (scoring one or two points). All in all, Kinsey's data suggested that close to 10% of the United States population was gay or predominantly gay—a number that dramatically exceeded today's estimates. Some people were classified as equally gay and heterosexual in orientation and could be labelled bisexual (scoring three points). Most people were classified as exclusively heterosexual (scoring zero points).

Statistics concerning past sexual activity with a member of one's own gender can be misleading. They may represent a single episode or a brief period of adolescent experimentation. Half of the men who reported male–male sexual activity in Kinsey's sample limited it to the ages of 12 to 14. Another third had male–male sexual experiences by age 18, but not again.

Kinsey's research also showed that sexual behaviour patterns can change, sometimes dramatically. Sexual experiences or feelings involving people of the same gender are common, especially in adolescence, and don't necessarily mean these individuals will engage in sexual activity exclusively with people of their own gender in adulthood (Diamond, 2003a; Savin-Williams et al., 2012).

CHALLENGES TO THE KINSEY CONTINUUM Alfred Kinsey believed that exclusive heterosexual and homosexual orientations lay at opposite poles on a single continuum. The more heterosexual a person was, the less gay s/he was, and vice versa.

However, it may be that these sexual orientations are in fact separate dimensions, rather than polar opposites (Vrangalova & Savin-Williams, 2012). Using self-reported content of erotic fantasies as an indication of sexual orientation, Storms (1980) found evidence that there are separate dimensions of responsiveness to male–female sexual stimulation (heteroeroticism) and same-gender sexual stimulation (homoeroticism). (See Figure 9.2.) According to this model, bisexuals are high in both dimensions, whereas people who are low in both are asexual (Bogaert, 2006).

Kinsey would see bisexuals as less responsive than heterosexuals to stimulation by the other gender, and more responsive to stimulation by the same gender. But Storms's two-dimensional model allows someone to be as responsive as a heterosexual to stimulation by the other gender, and as responsive as a gay person to stimulation by the same gender.

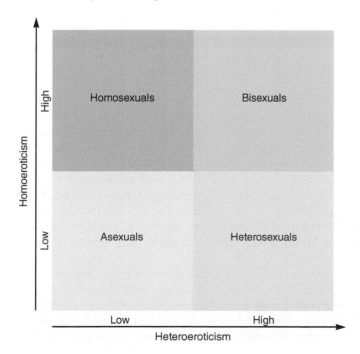

Figure 9.2 Heterosexuality and homosexuality as separate dimensions. According to this model, homosexuality and heterosexuality are independent dimensions. A person can therefore be high or low on both dimensions at the same time. Most people are high on one dimension. Bisexuals are high on both dimensions. People who are low on both are considered asexual.

ESTIMATES OF SEXUAL ORIENTATION   The controversy about how many people aren't heterosexual continues. About 7% of women and men in the United States define themselves as being "other than heterosexual," but the behaviour of the other 93% doesn't exactly match up with the way in which people label themselves. For example, nearly twice as many people—about 14%—say they have had oral sex with a person of the same gender (Herbenick et al., 2010a, 2010b, 2010c; Reece et al., 2010).

In 2003, for the first time, Statistics Canada included a question on sexual orientation as part of its Canadian Community Health Survey. Of the 135 000 respondents who were 18 to 59 years old, 1.0% reported that they were gay or lesbian, and 0.7% said they were bisexual. Twice as many men (1.3%) as women (0.7%) said they were gay or lesbian. However, more women (0.9%) than men (0.6%) said they were bisexual (Statistics Canada, 2004b). It is important to note that these figures very likely represent underreporting of gay, lesbian, and bisexual orientations because some non-heterosexual people may be reluctant to disclose their sexual orientation to a government agency.

Kris Wells at the University of Alberta conducted a survey of 13- to 29-year-old Canadians, in which 3.5% of the respondents identified themselves as gay, lesbian, bisexual, or transgender (GLBT) (Youthography Ping Survey, 2004). Slightly more males than females identified themselves as GLBT (Wells, 2008).

A more recent 2012 Forum research poll (cited in Blaze Carlson, 2012) used random telephone dialing in which a respondent interacted with a computer program rather than a live person to ask 2694 Canadians aged 18 and older if they identified as lesbian, gay, bisexual, or transgender. Five percent of men and 5% of women answered "Yes." Younger people were far more likely to identify as non-heterosexual with 10% of 18- to 34-year-olds identifying as lesbian, gay, bisexual, or transgender.

We should note that there is a clear trend for more recent surveys to find higher percentages of people reporting a non-heterosexual orientation than surveys conducted in the past. The most plausible explanation for this is that as Western societies have become increasingly accepting of diverse sexual orientations, more people feel comfortable identifying publically, or in anonymous surveys, as gay, lesbian, bisexual, or another non-heterosexual orientation. Non-heterosexual younger people, in particular, may feel emboldened by the increasing social acceptability and destigmatization of diverse sexual orientations to more freely disclose their sexual orientation to pollsters.

Bisexuality

Bisexual people are sexually attracted to both males and females. Many have somewhat stronger attractions to one gender than the other. Weinrich and Klein (2002) speak of bisexuals as being bi-gay, bi-straight, or bi-bi, meaning some have stronger leanings toward people of their own gender (bi-gays), some toward people of the other gender (bi-straights), and some to people of both genders equally (bi-bis).

About 1% of the people (0.8% of the men and 0.9% of the women) surveyed in the American National Health and Social Life Survey (Laumann et al., 1994) reported having a bisexual identity. These percentages are very similar to the percentages of people who reported that they were bisexual in Statistics Canada's 2003 Canadian Community Health Survey (discussed above in "Estimates of Sexual Orientation").

Some people believe claims to bisexuality are a cop-out used by some people to deny that they're gay or lesbian. Perhaps they fear leaving their spouses or coming out (i.e., publicly declaring their gay or lesbian orientations). Others view bisexuality as a form of sexual experimentation by people who are mostly heterosexual. Surveys of more than 600 college undergraduates confirm that **biphobia**, or hatred

Biphobia Negative attitudes and feelings toward bisexual people, including intolerance, hatred, and fear.

of bisexuals, can be found in both heterosexual and gay/lesbian populations (Mulick & Wright, 2002). To help bisexuals deal with these issues, groups such as Bisexual Women of Toronto (BiWoT) provide counselling and support. One of BiWoT's objectives is to educate community service groups about the effects of prejudice and discrimination against bisexuals.

Many avowed bisexuals and researchers assert that bisexuals can maintain erotic interests in—and romantic relationships with—members of both genders. They insist that bisexuality is an authentic sexual orientation with its own developmental patterns and not just a cover for a gay or lesbian orientation (Savin-Williams et al., 2012).

Some bisexual people follow lifestyles that permit them to satisfy their dual inclinations. Others feel pressured by heterosexual and gay people alike to commit themselves one way or the other (Savin-Williams et al., 2012). Some gays and lesbians also mask their sexual orientations by adopting bisexual lifestyles; that is, they get married and also have sexual liaisons with members of their own gender.

Asexuality

Anthony Bogaert (2012; 2006a) at Brock University in Ontario argues that asexuality should be considered a sexual orientation. He defines asexuals as people who have a lack of sexual attraction to anyone or anything—that is, they're low on both heteroeroticism and homoeroticism. However, they might be romantically attracted to others. Most have low interest in any kind of sexual stimulation. In a population-based survey in the United Kingdom, 1% of respondents agreed with the statement

Innovative Canadian Research

BISEXUALITY AND INTIMATE RELATIONSHIPS

McMaster University researcher Tina Li and colleagues used focus groups to conduct semi-structured interviews with 55 bisexual people from across Ontario in an effort to understand the challenges encountered in their intimate relationships (Li, Dobinson, Scheim, & Ross, 2013). Focus group discussions were based on two areas: the ways in which bisexuality had been a positive or negative force in the participant's lives, and the extent to which participants experienced relationship concerns or issues related to being a bisexual person.

Many participants revealed that they had experienced rejection by potential relationship partners because of their bisexuality (Li et al., 2013). This type of rejection came from both gay/lesbian and heterosexual partners. For example, some male participants reported that gay men saw bisexual men as being in the process of coming out as gay. Others reported that heterosexual partners viewed bisexuals as promiscuous and unable to commit to monogamous relationships.

Participants in the Li et al. (2013) study identified a number of unique concerns that bisexuals faced in their relationships. They noted that bisexuals often struggle with the decision of whether to disclose their sexual orientation. Potential partners may worry about rivals of both genders, and some female participants reported that male partners encouraged their bisexual female partners to engage in same-gender behaviour for voyeuristic reasons. Some bisexual people expressed a conflict between a need for sexual and emotional connections with both men and women, and a desire for committed intimate relationships.

However, participants also noted that bisexuality offered them more freedom and options for forming intimate relationships. As one participant put it, "It's the person inside, it's not their body parts, it's the soul of the person and their essence that I find attractive" (Li et al., 2013, p. 26).

"I have never felt sexually attracted to anyone at all" (Bogaert, 2004). One-third of these people said they were in long-term marital or cohabiting relationships, and another 11% had been in such relationships in the past. Some of the asexual people still engaged in sexual activity with partners, but the frequency was very low.

Researchers at the University of British Columbia studied 54 men and 133 women recruited from the Asexuality Visibility and Education Network (Brotto et al., 2010). According to their questionnaire responses, their sexual response levels were low, but the respondents didn't experience this lack of response as distressing. Participants who were in romantic relationships reported that they had to "negotiate" sexual activity with their partners.

Bogaert (2006a) notes that his definition of asexuality is narrow in scope, since it doesn't take into account whether someone is romantically attracted to another person or is engaging in sexual activity. C. J. DeLuzio Chasin (2011) at the University of Windsor notes that there is considerable diversity within the asexual community, and that future research needs to account for varying levels of romantic and sexual attraction and sexual desire among people who identify themselves as asexual.

Researchers have only recently begun to explore asexuality. So far, research suggests that asexuality isn't pathological and shouldn't be seen as a sexual dysfunction, and that asexual people can live happy lives (Bogaert, 2006a; Brotto et al., 2010; Brotto & Yule, 2011).

QUEER, PANSEXUAL, QUESTIONING, TRANSGENDER, AND TWO-SPIRITED   Most surveys about sexual orientation ask whether people are heterosexual, homosexual, or bisexual. This classification system doesn't necessarily correspond to the way people see or identify themselves. Some people self-identify as queer, pansexual, questioning, transgendered, or two-spirited.

Most organizations that represent gays and lesbians today also include transgender people, although this wasn't true in the past. As a sign of inclusivity, many organizations have adopted the label *LGBTQ* (lesbian, gay, bisexual, transgender, and queer). Some people who previously classified themselves as gay, lesbian, or bisexual now prefer to identify themselves as "queer." In general, queer people reject the labels "gay," "straight," and "bisexual" as too limiting, viewing them as designations that reflect the oppression so often faced by non-heterosexual people. "Queer," from their perspective, is a positive, self-affirming term for people who don't see themselves as fitting into standard classifications of sexual orientation.

Some lesbians are uncomfortable with the term "queer" and worry that general use of the term may hide some of the issues they face. For example, Alberta therapists Bonita Decaire and Deborah Foster (2010) believe lesbians, because of sexism, have more in common with other women than with gay men when it comes to power inequity and discrimination.

Some people who reject traditional classifications of sexual orientation and gender identify as "pansexual." Pansexuality is sexual or emotional attraction to people regardless of their gender identity or sexual orientation. While the term "bisexuality" challenges the heterosexual/homosexual dichotomy, it leaves the male–female gender dichotomy unchallenged (Elizabeth, 2013). In contrast, a pansexual person can be attracted to people of diverse sexual orientations and diverse gender identities (e.g., male, female, transgender, gender fluid).

Other people, especially youth, may describe themselves as "questioning." They're unsure which of the currently available labels best describes their sexual orientations. They may consider themselves to be in the process of discovering their sexual identities, or in some cases, coming to terms with the possibility that they're not heterosexual. In a survey of high school students in California, 28.8% of those who identified themselves as non-heterosexual said they were questioning or queer or used terms other than gay, lesbian, and bisexual to describe themselves (Russell, Clarke, & Clary, 2009).

A World of Diversity

YOUTH CHALLENGING TRADITIONAL CONCEPTS OF SEXUAL ORIENTATION AND GENDER

Ritch C. Savin-Williams (2005) of Cornell University, in his book *The New Gay Teenager*, argues that today's urban teenagers no longer accept traditional gender and sexual orientations. In his interviews with urban American teenagers, Savin-Williams discovered that many no longer consider gender categories important. Rather, they view themselves as "pansexuals," or bisexuals who reject gender labels. Savin-Williams believes the media have played a key role in changing the gender perspectives of young people by normalizing same-sex attraction in television and films.

Savin-Williams (2005) is highly critical of social scientists who force their research participants to label themselves as either gay or straight. Bisexuals are typically ignored or forced into one of these categories. The researchers don't allow for broader choices, such as polysexual, or for multiple identities, such as bi-lesbian.

Savin-Williams (2005) argues that the standard image of gay youth as depressed, isolated, drug-dependent, and suicidal is exaggerated. He believes many of the studies have been flawed, purposely oversampling troubled teens. From his own research, he concludes that most gay males and lesbians are psychologically healthy, and in this regard no different from heterosexual youth.

Kristopher Wells (2008) of the University of Alberta reports on a Canadian study that found similar trends among gay youth. According to Wells, Canadian youth are challenging the traditional stereotypes of sexuality and gender and are reluctant to have their sexual identities forced into narrow categories.

Holly Devor (2002)—now Aaron Devor—argues that transgender people (discussed in Chapter 5) should be included in discussions of sexual orientation. Devor reasons that, since transgender people are the most visible minority among people engaged in same-sex practices, they face many of the same issues and concerns as gays, lesbians, and bisexual people. Yet transgender people lack the legal protections granted to gays and lesbians. Unlike Devor, some within the transgender community identify themselves as "trans" and view the term as being related to gender, not to sexual orientation.

Within aboriginal North American communities, there are people who identify themselves as "two-spirited." Aboriginal communities are less likely to incorporate simple divisions of gay/lesbian and straight (Tafoya, 1997). "Two-spirited" refers to gender or social identity, and in many cases also includes same-gender behaviour. Many two-spirited people would not easily identify as gay, lesbian, or bisexual.

The queer, pansexual, questioning, transgender, and two-spirited examples show that while the gay, lesbian, and bisexual classifications have been useful basic categories, they need to be expanded to reflect more accurately the diversity of ways people conceptualize and identify their sexual orientations. Increasingly, researchers are incorporating identities such as queer, pansexual, questioning, transgender, and two-spirited into research that asks people to identify their sexual orientations.

Perspectives on Gay and Lesbian Sexual Orientations

Gay and lesbian sexual orientations have existed throughout history. Attitudes toward them have varied widely. They've been tolerated in some societies, openly encouraged in others, and condemned in most.

Historical and Religious Perspectives

Some ancient societies, such as that of the Greeks, as we discussed in Chapter 1, openly accepted male–male sexual behaviour. Many famous people throughout history have been gay; Alexander the Great is just one example. Yet most cultures have held negative attitudes toward homosexuality.

Jews and Christians have traditionally referred to male–male sexual activity as the sin of Sodom. This has given us the term "sodomy," which generally denotes anal intercourse (and sometimes oral–genital contact). According to the Book of Genesis, the city of Sodom was destroyed by God, though it's unclear what behaviour incurred God's wrath. Pope Gregory III wasn't ambiguous in his eighth-century account of the city's obliteration, however, calling it a punishment for sexual activity between members of the same gender.

Despite the history of opposition to gay and lesbian orientations, some churches today perform marriages for gay couples—or at least "bless" their relationships. The Universal Fellowship of Metropolitan Community Churches has many gay male and lesbian parishioners in Canada. The first Canadian church to perform formal marriage ceremonies for same-sex couples was the Metropolitan Community Church of Toronto. Since then an increasing number of churches have performed same-sex marriages.

Many Canadian churches allow ordination of gay and lesbian clergy, as long as they remain celibate. Some, however, such as the Unitarian Church and the United Church of Canada, do accept clergy who are involved in same-gender relationships. The more conservative churches continue to oppose equal rights, including same-sex marriage, for anyone whose sexual orientation is not heterosexual.

A major international legal and political struggle over gay rights is taking place today, based on the opposing values of gay equality and religious freedom. At the United Nations (UN), a coalition of mainly Islamic countries has been leading a campaign to develop international laws to prohibit "defamation of religions" (Savage, 2008). One intent of this movement is to deter the United Nations and other international organizations from discussing issues such as gay rights, which are viewed by Islamic countries as an affront to their religious beliefs and therefore an act of religious discrimination (Savage, 2008). Nevertheless, in 2011 the UN Human Rights Council passed a non-legally-binding resolution by a vote of 23 to 19 asserting that people should not be subject to discrimination or violence based on their sexual orientation or gender identity (*The Globe and Mail*, 2011). Notable in their opposition to the resolution were Russia, Pakistan, Saudi Arabia, and a number of African countries, while China abstained from voting.

Some countries still harshly punish people convicted of engaging in homosexual acts. In 2008, five men in Egypt were sentenced to three years in prison for "debauchery," the term used in Egypt for homosexual acts (Associated Press, 2008). In 2014, the African country of Uganda passed laws criminalizing homosexual behaviour.

Cross-Cultural Perspectives

Male–male sexual behaviour has been practised in many preliterate societies. In their review of the literature, Ford and Beach (1951) found that male–male sexual interactions were viewed as normal and deemed socially acceptable for some members in 49 (64%) of 76 preliterate societies. Although the other 27 societies (36%) had sanctions against male–male sexual behaviour, it persisted there.

Sexual activity between males is sometimes limited to rites that mark boys' initiation into manhood. In some preliterate societies, semen is believed to boost strength and virility. Older males thus transmit semen to younger males through oral or anal sexual activities. Among the Sambia of New Guinea, a society of warlike headhunters, 9- to 12-year-old males leave their parents' households and live in "clubhouses" with other prepubertal and adolescent males. There they undergo sexual rites of passage. To acquire the fierce manhood of the headhunter, they perform fellatio on older males and drink "men's milk" (semen) (Bailey, 2003b). By age 19, however, young men are expected to take brides and enter exclusively male-female sexual relationships.

These Sambian practices might seem to suggest that male sexual orientation is fluid and malleable. The practices involve behaviour, however, not sexual orientation. Male–male sexual behaviour among Sambians takes place within a cultural context that bears little resemblance to consensual male–male sexual activity in Western society. The prepubertal Sambian male doesn't seek sexual liaisons with other males; he's removed from his home and thrust into male–male sexual encounters by older males (Baldwin & Baldwin, 1989).

Sambian culture has a different perspective on gay identity than we find in Western societies. So does Turkish culture—according to Tarik Bereket of the University of Toronto and Barry D. Adam of the University of Windsor (2006), Turkish men also have same-sex relations without sharing the Western concept of gay identity. For example, Turkish men who assume the inserter role in anal intercourse don't consider themselves gay.

Little is known about female–female sexual activity in non-Western cultures. Evidence of female–female sexual behaviour was found by Ford and Beach in only 17 of the 76 societies they studied. Perhaps female sexual behaviour in general, not just sexual activity with other females, was more likely to be repressed.

Cross-Species Perspectives

Biologists have observed male–male and female–female sexual behaviour in at least 450 animal species, in every part of the world (Hird, 2006).

A male baboon may present his rear and allow himself to be mounted by another male. But is the behaviour sexually motivated? Mounting behaviour among male baboons may represent a type of dominance ritual, in which lower-ranking males adopt a submissive (feminine) posture to ward off attack by dominant males.

Paul Vasey of the University of Lethbridge has done considerable research on sexual preference and orientation in female Japanese macaques. Vasey (2002) has found that the females routinely engage in sexual behaviour with both males and females. Female Japanese macaques often have sex with other females even when willing male partners are available. Vasey and his colleagues (2006) have also found that female macaques mount other females differently than the males do. The female mounting styles are more varied and done in a way that provides greater genital pleasure. This physical drive for sexual pleasure with other females supports the assumption that this behaviour is sexual and indicates a bisexual orientation (Vasey et al., 2006).

Biological Perspectives

Biological perspectives focus on the possible roles of evolution, genetics, and hormonal influences in shaping sexual orientation.

THE EVOLUTIONARY PERSPECTIVE   It might seem odd that evolutionary theorists have endeavoured to explain gay and lesbian sexual orientations. After all, gays and lesbians aren't motivated to engage in sexual activity with the other sex, so how can their sexual orientations confer any evolutionary advantage?

To answer this question, we must look to the group or the species, rather than the individual. Kirkpatrick (2000) suggests that male–male and female–female sexual behaviours derive from individual selection for reciprocal altruism. That is, strong male–male and female–female alliances have advantages for group survival,

CRITICAL THINKING QUESTIONS

To what extent has your own cultural or religious background influenced your attitude toward sexual orientation?

in that they bind group members together emotionally. This hypothesis remains speculative.

Researchers have also compared the family trees of heterosexuals with those of gays and lesbians and found a significant increase in fecundity among women related to gays and lesbians in the maternal line, but not among women related to gays and lesbians in the paternal line (Iemmola & Ciani, 2009). These findings suggest that genetic factors linked to the X sex chromosome that might influence a gay orientation in males aren't eliminated by natural selection, because they also increase fecundity in female carriers. That is, women related to gay males apparently bear more children, compensating for the lesser likelihood that gay men will reproduce.

GENETICS AND SEXUAL ORIENTATION There's considerable evidence that gay and lesbian sexual orientations run in families (Jannini et al., 2010). In one study, 22% of the brothers of 51 predominantly gay men were either gay or bisexual—nearly four times as many as you'd expect in the general population (Pillard & Weinrich, 1986). Although such evidence is consistent with a genetic explanation, families also share common environments.

Twin studies also shed light on the possible role of heredity (Bailey, 2003b). **Monozygotic (MZ) twins,** or identical twins, develop from a single fertilized ovum and share 100% of their heredity. **Dizygotic (DZ) twins,** or fraternal twins, develop from two fertilized ova. Like other brothers and sisters, DZ twins share only 50% of their heredity. Thus, if a gay or lesbian sexual orientation were transmitted genetically, it would be found about twice as often among identical twins as among fraternal twins born to gay and lesbian people. Because MZ and DZ twins who are reared together share similar environmental influences, differences in the degree of concordance for a given trait between MZ and DZ twin pairs are further indication of genetic origins.

In one of the most carefully conducted twin studies, about 52% of identical (MZ) twin pairs were found to be concordant (in agreement) for a gay male sexual orientation, compared with 22% of fraternal (DZ) twins and only 11% of adoptive brothers (Bailey, 2003a). Bear in mind that MZ twins are more likely than DZ twins to be dressed alike and treated alike. Their greater concordance for a gay sexual orientation may therefore reflect environmental factors, at least in part (Hines, 2011; Jannini et al., 2010).

Researchers have found evidence linking a region on the X sex chromosome to a gay male sexual orientation (Bailey et al., 1999). Dean Hamer and his colleagues (1993) found that gay males were more likely than the general population to have gay male relatives on their mothers' sides of their families, yet they didn't have a greater than expected number of gay male relatives on their fathers' sides. This pattern of inheritance is consistent with genetic traits, such as hemophilia, that are linked to the X chromosome, which men receive from their mothers.

The researchers then examined the X chromosomes of 40 pairs of gay brothers who were not twins. In 33 of the pairs, the brothers had identical DNA markers on the ends of their X chromosomes. For pairs of brothers in the general population, about half would be expected to have inherited this chromosomal structure. This chromosomal region may therefore hold a gene that predisposes men to a gay sexual orientation.

HORMONAL INFLUENCES AND SEXUAL ORIENTATION Sex hormones strongly influence the mating behaviours of other species (Crews, 1994). Researchers have therefore looked into the role hormonal factors may play in determining sexual orientation in humans.

Testosterone is essential to male sexual differentiation. Thus, levels of testosterone and its by-products in the blood and urine have been studied as possible influences on sexual orientation. Research has failed to connect sexual

---

Monozygotic (MZ) twins Siblings who develop from the same fertilized ovum. They're also called identical twins.

Dizygotic (DZ) twins Siblings who develop from different fertilized ova. They're also called fraternal twins.

orientation in either sex with differences in male or female sex hormone levels in adulthood (Friedman & Downey, 2001, 2008). Testosterone appears to have **activating effects** in adulthood. That is, it affects the intensity of sexual desire but not the preference for partners of one sex or the other (Aarts & van Honk, 2009; Yeh et al., 2009).

BRAIN STRUCTURE AND SEXUAL ORIENTATION Researchers at the Stockholm Brain Institute (Savic & Lindstrom, 2008) have found structural differences between the brains of heterosexuals and the brains of gays and lesbians. In a study of 40 heterosexuals and 50 non-heterosexuals, they used MRIs and PET scans to examine the functioning of the amygdala, a part of the brain that's less likely than other parts to be affected by social conditioning. They also considered brain size, because both sides of a woman's brain are usually similar, while the right side of a man's brain is usually larger than the left side.

The researchers found similarities between the brains of gay men and heterosexual women, and similarities between the brains of lesbians and heterosexual men. In the lesbians and heterosexual men, the right hemisphere of the brain was larger than the left. In the gay men and heterosexual women, both sides of the brain were about the same size. The amygdala's functioning was similar for lesbians and heterosexual men, and it was similar for gay men and heterosexual women. These findings suggest that brain organization differs by sexual orientation as well as by gender, which further suggests that biology predisposes a person to be gay, lesbian, or heterosexual. Additional research is needed to confirm these findings.

Simon LeVay (1991), a neurobiologist at the Salk Institute in La Jolla, California, carried out autopsies on the brains of 35 AIDS victims—19 gay men and 16 (presumably) heterosexual men. He found that a segment of the hypothalamus (specifically, the third interstitial nucleus of the anterior hypothalamus) in the gay men was less than half the size of the same segment in the heterosexual men. This brain segment was larger in the heterosexual men than in a comparison group of 6 presumably heterosexual women. LeVay found no significant size differences between the gay men and the women.

LeVay's findings are intriguing but preliminary. We don't know, for example, whether the structural differences are innate or the result of something in the study subjects' environments.

BIOLOGY AND SEXUAL ORIENTATION Researchers in the United States and Canada (Mustanski, Chivers, & Bailey, 2003) have conducted a comprehensive review of the research relating to the role of biology in determining sexual orientation. They've concluded that, to some degree, sexual orientation is influenced by biological factors. These factors seem to play a stronger role for men than for women.

Biological factors likely play a key role prior to birth, as indicated by the handedness research and the older brothers research we've discussed. Genetic factors may be another important influence. Brain differences between gay and heterosexual men, and between lesbian and heterosexual women, suggest that biological influences are at play.

Psychological Perspectives

Psychoanalytic theory and learning theory are two major social-psychological approaches to understanding the origins of sexual orientation.

PSYCHOANALYTIC VIEWS Sigmund Freud, the originator of psychoanalytic theory, believed children enter the world open to all forms of sexual stimulation. Through proper resolution of the Oedipus complex, a boy will forsake his incestuous desires for his mother and come to identify with his father. As a result, he'll eventually

Activating effects Those effects of sex hormones that influence sex drive levels, but not sexual orientation.

CRITICAL THINKING QUESTIONS

There's considerable evidence that sexual orientation is at least partly determined by biological factors. In your view, is it relevant to consider such evidence when discussing gay and lesbian rights?

Innovative Canadian Research

BIRTH ORDER AND SEXUAL ORIENTATION

Ray Blanchard and his colleagues at the Centre for Addiction and Mental Health in Toronto have conducted several studies analyzing the relationship of birth order to sexual orientation. Blanchard et al. (2002) have built upon their previous findings that the odds of a man's being gay increase in proportion to the number of his older brothers. They concluded that a gay male with three or more older brothers can attribute most of the origin of his sexual orientation to this effect.

They also concluded that femininity in male children tends to be predictive of a gay sexual orientation (although not all gay men were feminine as boys). In their 2002 study, they analyzed a sample of feminine boys whom they assumed (on the basis of previous research) were likely to be gay. They confirmed that those with two or more older brothers weighed less at birth than heterosexual males with older brothers and concluded that prenatal factors increase the odds of being gay in later-born males.

In explaining this finding, the researchers hypothesized that the process is immunological—that anti-male antibodies are produced by the mothers in response to immunization by male fetuses—and that this could decrease the birth weights of later male fetuses, as well as increase the odds of their becoming gay. In effect, this process influences aspects of sexual differentiation in the fetal brain.

In 2004, Blanchard analyzed data from 10 143 respondents and again found that a gay sexual orientation in males was predicted by a higher number of older brothers but not by numbers of older or younger sisters or younger brothers. This relationship between older brothers and sexual orientation has not been found among females.

Anthony Bogaert (2005b) at Brock University has reported that fraternal birth order is more influential than sibling sex ratio in affecting men's sexual orientation. Blanchard and Bogaert (2004) estimate that about one in four gay men can attribute his sexual orientation to this fraternal birth order effect. In a more recent study, Bogaert (2006b) has found that the effect of having older brothers only applies to genetically related brothers and not to those with stepbrothers or adopted brothers. These findings strongly support a prenatal biological basis for sexual orientation.

Further evidence for prenatal influences is seen in a literature review by Lalumière et al. (2000) regarding handedness and sexual orientation. The reviewers concluded that "non-right-handedness" is related to homosexual orientation. More recently, Blanchard and Lippa (2007) have extended this line of research by analyzing the relationships among fraternal birth order, hand preference, and sexual orientation in a large British Internet sample. They've found that having older brothers increased the odds of being gay for right-handed males but not for non-right-handed males. These findings have been replicated in another study (Blanchard et al., 2006), which also found that, among men with no older brothers, gay men were more likely than heterosexuals to be non-right-handed, and among men with one or more older brothers, gay men were less likely than heterosexuals to be non-right-handed.

transfer his erotic attraction from his mother to more appropriate female partners. A girl, through proper resolution of her Electra complex, will identify with her mother and seek erotic stimulation from men when she becomes sexually mature.

In Freud's view, a gay or lesbian sexual orientation results from failure to successfully resolve the Oedipus complex by identifying with the parent of the same sex. In a man, faulty resolution of the Oedipus complex is most likely to result from the so-called classic pattern of an emotionally "close-binding" mother and a "detached-hostile" father. A boy reared in such a family may come to identify with his mother, and even to "transform himself into her" (Freud, 1922/1959, p. 40). He may thus become effeminate and develop a sexual interest in men.

Freud believed the mechanism of unresolved **castration anxiety** plays a role in a gay male orientation. During the throes of the Oedipus complex, the boy unconsciously comes to fear that his father, his rival for his mother's love, will retaliate by removing the organ the boy has come to associate with sexual pleasure. His fear causes him to repress his sexual desire for his mother and to identify with the potential aggressor—his father. The boy thus overcomes his castration anxiety and is headed along the path of adult heterosexuality. If he doesn't successfully resolve his Oedipus complex, his castration anxiety may persist. When he's sexually mature, he won't be able to tolerate sex with women—their lack of penises will arouse unconscious castration anxiety within him.

The supposed Electra complex in little girls follows a somewhat different course. Freud believed little girls become envious of boys' penises because they lack their own. This concept of **penis envy** was one of Freud's most controversial beliefs. In Freud's view, jealousy leads the little girl to resent her mother, whom she blame for her anatomic "deficiency," and to turn from her mother to her father as a sexual object. She now desires to possess her father, because his penis provides what she lacks. But incestuous desires bring the girl into competition with her mother. Motivated by fear that her mother will withdraw her love if these desires persist, the girl normally represses them and comes to identify with her mother. She develops traditional feminine interests and eventually seeks erotic stimulation from men. She supplants her childhood desire for a penis with a desire to marry a man and bear children. The baby, emitted from between her legs, serves as the ultimate penis substitute.

A nagging problem in assessing the validity of Freudian theory is that many of its concepts, such as castration anxiety and penis envy, are believed to operate at an unconscious level. As such, they lie beyond the scope of scientific observation and measurement.

Castration anxiety In psychoanalytic theory, a man's fear that his genitals will be removed. An element of the Oedipus complex, castration anxiety is implicated in the directionality of erotic interest.

Penis envy In psychoanalytic theory, a girl's wish to have a penis.

LEARNING THEORY   Learning theorists agree with Freud that early experiences play important roles in the development of sexual orientation. They focus, however, on the role of reinforcement of early patterns of sexual behaviour, rather than on the resolution of unconscious conflicts. We generally repeat pleasurable activities and discontinue painful ones. By connecting sexual pleasure with childhood sexual experimentation with same-gender friends, we may learn to engage in sexual activity with members of our own gender.

Although learning may play a role in the development of a gay or lesbian orientation, learning theorists have not identified specific learning experiences that would lead to these orientations. Moreover, most adolescent encounters with members of the same gender, even if they're pleasurable, don't lead to adult gay or lesbian sexual orientations. Many heterosexual people have had adolescent encounters with members of their own gender, without affecting their adult orientations. This is true even of people whose early sexual interactions with the other gender were fumbling and frustrating. The overwhelming majority of gay males and lesbians were aware of sexual interest in people of their own gender before they had sexual encounters with them, pleasurable or otherwise (Savin-Williams & Diamond, 2000).

GENDER NONCONFORMITY   Gender nonconformity means not behaving in a way that's consistent with the gender-role stereotype associated with one's anatomic sex in a given culture. On average, gay males tend to be somewhat feminine, and lesbians to be somewhat masculine, but there's a good deal of variation within each group (Dawood et al., 2009; Rieger et al., 2008). It seems that stereotypes of the effeminate gay male and the masculine lesbian are exaggerated.

Gender nonconformity begins in childhood. Gay men and lesbians are more likely than heterosexuals to report childhood behaviours stereotypical of the other gender (Green, 2008; Lippa, 2008). Many gays and lesbians recall acting and feeling different from their childhood peers. Gay males are more likely to recall feeling more sensitive than their peers during childhood (Green, 2008; Lippa, 2008). They had more artistic interests and were more likely than their heterosexual counterparts to prefer "girls' toys" (Dawood et al., 2000).

According to researchers at the University of British Columbia, this childhood gender nonconformity found in many gay males often leads to social rejection by parents and peers (Landolt et al., 2004). This rejection is a major factor in the difficulty many gay males have in accepting their sexual orientation.

There's also evidence of masculine-typed behaviour among lesbians in childhood (Lippa, 2008). Lesbians are more likely than heterosexual women to say they were tomboys. They were more likely to prefer rough-and-tumble games to playing with dolls, and enjoyed wearing boys' clothing, rather than dresses.

An important study by Devendra Singh and his colleagues (1999) relates gender nonconformity in lesbians to the butch–femme dimension and biological factors. The investigators compared self-identified **butch** (traditionally masculine) and **femme** (traditionally feminine) lesbians on various personality, behavioural, and biological measures. They found that butch lesbians were significantly more likely than femme lesbians to recall gender-atypical behavioural preferences in childhood. Butch lesbians also had higher waist-to-hip ratios and higher testosterone levels in their saliva, both of which are more typical of males. The Singh group suggests that their findings support the validity of the butch–femme distinction, and that the distinction may be caused by differences in exposure to prenatal androgens.

How might extreme childhood effeminacy lead to a gay male sexual orientation? Those who support an environmental perspective speculate that the social detachment of these boys from male peers and role models (especially fathers) creates strong, unfulfilled cravings for male affection. This craving then leads them to seek males as partners in sex and love relationships in adolescence and adulthood (Green, 2008).

Of course, there's another possibility (Green, 2008; Dawood et al., 2009): gender nonconformity appears to be somewhat heritable. If a tendency towards being gay or lesbian is inherited, gender nonconformity could also be an expression of that tendency.

Butch A lesbian who assumes a traditional masculine gender role.

Femme A lesbian who assumes a traditional feminine gender role.

Current Attitudes

Historically, negative attitudes toward gay and lesbian people have pervaded our society. Today, however, there's far greater acceptance of non-heterosexual orientations in Canadian society. Surveys that have asked Canadians about their attitudes towards homosexuality indicate a clear trend over time towards greater acceptance. For example, according to surveys conducted by Reginald Bibby (2002), the percentage of Canadians who indicated that they believed that homosexuality is "always wrong" was 63% in 1975, 62% in 1980, 62% in 1985, 59% in 1990, 44% in 1995, and 32% in 2000. A more recent Pew Research (2014) survey conducted in 2013 asked Canadians if they believed that homosexuality is morally unacceptable, morally acceptable, or that it is not a moral issue. Only 15% said that it is unacceptable while 30% said it is acceptable, 50% said it's not a moral issue, and 5% did not answer. It is notable that the same Pew Research survey found Americans were less accepting, with 37% indicating that they believed that homosexuality is morally unacceptable.

Although the data from these surveys indicate that Canadians are becoming more accepting of non-heterosexual orientations over time, the Canadian population remains segmented in its attitudes towards the moral acceptability of homosexuality. Langstaff (2011) reviewed the evolution of Canadians' attitudes towards homosexuality and found that although Canadian attitudes have become more accepting overall, much of the shift is the result of people who were more or less neutral shifting their views towards greater acceptance. From her analysis of the survey data, Langstaff concludes that people who have opposed homosexuality in the past have not changed their minds. Indeed, many of these people have become more firm in their disapproval of homosexuality. According to Langstaff, although the percentage of Canadians who are accepting has increased, ". . . a fairly stable minority of about one-third of Canadians are profoundly dismayed by growing societal acceptance of homosexuality" (p. 59). In Bibby's (2002) 2000 survey, women, younger people, and people who reported that they were not religious were more likely to approve of homosexuality while, with respect to religious affiliation, conservative Protestants were most likely to disapprove.

Despite opposition by a vociferous minority, most Canadians accept same-sex marriage. In a 2010 public opinion survey conducted by Angus Reid, 61% of Canadian adults approved of same-sex couples' continuing to have the right to marry, and another 23% approved of same-sex couples' forming civil unions. Younger Canadians are more likely to approve of same-sex marriage than older Canadians. In the Angus Reid (2010) survey, 81% of people born between 1980 and 1995 said same-sex couples should continue to be allowed to marry, compared to only 43% of people born before 1946 and 53% of people born between 1946 and 1964.

HOMOPHOBIA   **Homophobia** takes many forms, including the following:

- Using derogatory names (e.g., queer, faggot, dyke).
- Telling disparaging "queer jokes."
- Barring gay people from housing, employment, and social opportunities.
- Taunting (e.g., verbal abuse).
- **Gay bashing** (e.g., physical abuse, which is sometimes lethal).

Homophobia derives from root words that mean "fear of homosexuals." Although some psychologists link homophobia to fear of a gay or lesbian orientation within oneself, homophobic attitudes may also be embedded within a cluster of stereotypical gender-role attitudes (Lewis & White, 2009; Rosky, 2009). People who have strong stakes in maintaining stereotypical gender roles may feel more

Homophobia A cluster of negative attitudes and feelings toward gay, lesbian, and bisexual people, including intolerance, hatred, and fear.

Gay bashing Violence against gay, lesbian, or bisexual people.

Innovative Canadian Research

MEASURES OF HOMONEGATIVITY

Waterloo, Ontario, researchers (Rye et al., 2008) analyzed three measures of homonegativity to determine which instrument best measured negative attitudes toward homosexuals:

- Herek's attitudes toward lesbians and gay men scale (ATLGS).
- Morrison and Morrison's modern homonegativity scale (MHS).
- Hudson and Ricketts's index of homophobia (IH).

All three scales were found to be good measures of homonegativity.

For a sample of university students, each scale determined that attitudes toward homosexuals were more positive than negative. The ATLGS and the MHS did the best job of assessing both cognitive and emotional reactions, whereas the IH focused mainly on emotional reactions.

The MHS had a slight edge over the two other scales, with stronger psychometrics.

High school students in Ottawa protest the bullying of Jamie Hubley, who committed suicide after being relentlessly bullied because he was gay.

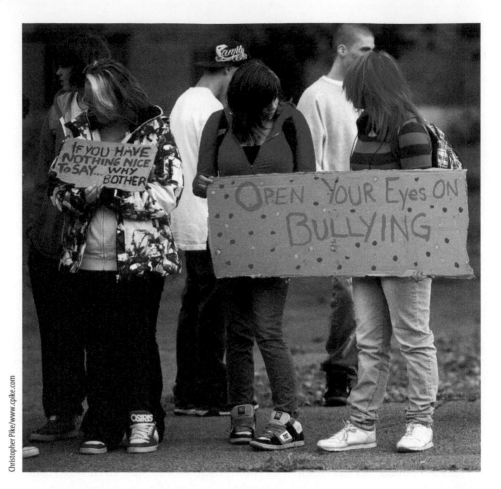

Christopher Pike/www.cpike.com

threatened by non-heterosexual people, since gays and lesbians appear to confuse and reverse these roles. Men have more at stake in maintaining the tradition of male dominance, so perhaps it's not surprising that college men are more intolerant of gay males than college women are (Lewis & White, 2009; Rosky, 2009).

Homophobic attitudes are more common among males who identify with traditional male gender roles and conservative political orientations (Lewis & White, 2009; Rosky, 2009), and among people who hold fundamentalist religious views (Davies, 2004) and those who identify with Nazi beliefs (Zezima, 2006). But those who actually engage in violence against gay people, especially those who kill, tend to be criminal psychopaths (Parrot et al., 2006). That is, they're in frequent conflict with the law, and they don't feel guilt or shame when they inflict pain.

Some homophobic men may have homoerotic impulses they're unaware of. Denial of these impulses may be connected with their fear and disapproval of gay men. Henry Adams and his colleagues (1996) showed men sexually explicit videotapes of male–female, female–female, and male–male sexual activity and measured their sexual responses by means of a penile plethysmograph (which measures the size of an erection). Subjects were also asked to report how sexually aroused they felt in response to the videos. The men were evaluated for their attitudes toward gay males as well.

Heterosexual men who were not homophobic were sexually aroused (according to penile circumference) only by videos of male–female and female–female sexual activity. The homophobic viewers were also physiologically aroused (again according to penile circumference) by the video of male–male sexual activity but reported that they didn't feel aroused by it. Were they out of touch with their biological responses, or were their biological responses misleading?

HARASSMENT OF LGBTQ YOUTH IN CANADA   Although Canadian society has made significant strides toward sexual-orientation equality, in many respects Canada remains a hostile and damaging environment for LGBTQ youth.

In a national survey of Canadian youth conducted by the marketing organization Ping, 28% of those between the ages of 15 and 19 reported witnessing acts of violence or verbal abuse directed toward LGBTQ youth (Wells, 2008).

Egale Canada's national survey of more than 3700 students on homophobia, biphobia, and trans-phobia in Canadian schools revealed that 64% of LGBTQ students felt unsafe at school, and 21% reported that they'd been physically harassed or assaulted due to their sexual orientations (Taylor et al., 2011). LGBTQ students attending schools with anti-homophobia policies were less likely than students attending schools without anti-homophobia policies (20% versus 33%) to report that they'd been physically harassed at school.

Canadian and American studies have also found that LGBTQ youth are more likely than heterosexual youth to have been physically and sexually abused, both by family members and by people from outside their families (Saewyc et al., 2006b).

HETEROSEXISM   Heterosexism, also known as heterosexual bias, is the tendency of society to view the world in heterosexual terms—that is, to assume that heterosexual relationships are "normal." This perspective devalues other kinds of relationships, such as same-sex relationships, and tends to make them invisible.

Lesbians and gay males are often just as concerned about heterosexism as they are about homophobia, because it's so pervasive in society.

SEXUAL ORIENTATION AND CANADIAN LAW   The fight for legal equality for gays and lesbians has progressed considerably. The first major breakthrough came in 1969, when Parliament passed an amendment to Canada's Criminal Code that decriminalized same-sex behaviour between consenting adults. Since then, other major pieces of legislation have benefited gay men and lesbians:

- In 1996, Parliament added the words "sexual orientation" as a prohibited ground of discrimination in the Canadian Human Rights Act.
- In 1996, Parliament amended the Criminal Code to increase sentences when criminal offenses are motivated by bias, prejudice, or hate based on sexual orientation (and other characteristics such as race and religion).
- In 2003, the House of Commons extended hate-propaganda protection to gay males and lesbians.
- In 2005, the House of Commons and the Senate passed legislation to extend civil marriage rights to same-sex couples. In 2006, Stephen Harper's Conservatives reopened the issue of same-sex marriage, but the majority of the members in the House of Commons voted against changing the 2005 law.

The national lobby group Equality for Gays and Lesbians Everywhere (EGALE) is at the forefront in fighting for equality through the legal system. Other significant advances for gay rights have come from court rulings under the Canadian Charter of Rights and Freedoms and the Canadian Human Rights Act:

- In 1992, the Supreme Court of Canada ruled that the Canadian Forces cannot discriminate against gays and lesbians, and must allow them the right to join the military.
- In 1998, the Supreme Court of Canada ordered the Alberta government to include protection for gays and lesbians under Alberta human rights legislation.
- In 1999, the Supreme Court of Canada ruled that the province of Ontario's definition of spouse violated the Charter of Rights and Freedoms because it applied only to heterosexuals and not to gay males and lesbians.
- In 2002, when the Durham Catholic District School Board in Oshawa refused to allow Marc Hall to take his same-sex partner to his high school prom, Hall

> **CRITICAL THINKING QUESTIONS**
>
> Generally, would you describe your high school as homophobic, positive toward gays and lesbians, or something in between?

went to court to appeal the board's decision. The Ontario Supreme Court judge ruled that Hall and his date could go to the prom because the school board had violated his constitutional right to equality.

- In 2002, the Ontario Superior Court ruled that because the legal definition of marriage is discriminatory, it should be changed to include same-sex couples. (We'll discuss this in Chapter 12.)
- In 2004, the Supreme Court of Canada ruled that Parliament has the authority to redefine marriage to include same-sex couples.
- Many provinces have allowed only a mother and a father to be registered on a birth certificate. In 2007, an Ontario court ruled that two women can be registered, and in another case, the Ontario Court of Appeal held that two women and a man can be registered.
- In 2010, the Saskatchewan Court of Appeal ruled that a proposed provincial law allowing marriage commissioners to refuse on religious grounds to marry same-sex couples would be unconstitutional.
- In 2013, an amendment to the Newfoundland and Labrador Human Rights Act specified gender identity and gender expression as prohibited grounds for discrimination. The inclusion of gender identity as prohibited grounds for discrimination has also been adopted by Ontario (2012), Nova Scotia (2012), Manitoba (2012), and the Northwest Territories (2004).

CRITICAL THINKING QUESTIONS

What myths and stereotypes about sexual orientation have you encountered within your family, at school, or among your friends?

GAY ACTIVISM In recent decades, gay and lesbian people have organized effective political action to fight discrimination. In a comprehensive analysis of the history of same-sex relationships and the gay rights movement in Canada, Gary Kinsman (1996) of Laurentian University argues that, by challenging heterosexuality as the societal norm and affirming their right to sexual self-determination, gays and lesbians are also helping other groups achieve greater sexual freedom.

STEREOTYPES AND SEXUAL BEHAVIOUR Among heterosexual people, sexual aggressiveness is linked to the stereotypically masculine gender role, and sexual passivity to the feminine role. Some heterosexual people assume that in a gay or lesbian relationship, one partner consistently assumes the masculine role and the other the feminine role in sexual relations.

This assumption is often mistaken. Many gay couples vary the active and passive roles. Gay male couples, for example, often alternate their roles in anal intercourse (i.e., insertive versus receptive) and fellatio. And contrary to popular assumptions, sexual behaviour between lesbians seldom reflects distinct butch–femme gender roles. Most lesbians report both providing and receiving oral–genital stimulation. Typically, partners alternate roles or simultaneously perform and receive oral stimulation.

Many gay and lesbian people claim that the labels "masculine" and "feminine" represent nothing more than the straight community's efforts to pigeonhole them in terms straights can understand.

The Coming-Out Process

Because of the backdrop of social condemnation and discrimination, gays and lesbians in our culture often struggle to come to terms with their sexual orientations (Legate et al., 2012). Gay, lesbian, and bisexual people usually speak of the process of accepting and then disclosing their sexual orientations to others as "coming out" or "coming out of the closet." This is a two-pronged process: coming out to themselves (recognizing and accepting their sexual orientations) and then coming out to others (declaring their orientations to the world). Coming out can create a sense of pride in their sexual orientations and foster their ability to form emotionally and sexually satisfying relationships (Grov et al., 2006).

Self-Acceptance and Coming Out

Given the stigma historically associated with homosexuality, it's not surprising that some gay, lesbian, and bisexual people have a difficult time recognizing—let alone accepting—their sexual orientations.

Youths with emerging gay, lesbian, and bisexual identities often live in generally hostile climates. They're well aware that in many high schools, the words "fag" and "dyke" are denigrating labels, and that anyone who's openly gay, lesbian, or bisexual is open to social exclusion and psychological and physical violence. Some of their families also express negative feelings about people who are gay, lesbian, or bisexual. Young people in such families may be victimized if they disclose the fact that they're not heterosexual (Bagley & D'Augelli, 2000; Katz-Wise & Hyde, 2012).

Self-acceptance of being gay, lesbian, or bisexual becomes part of a person's self-definition. The terms "gay identity" refers to the subjective sense of being gay. According to Ritch Savin-Williams and Lisa Diamond (2000), the development of sexual identity in gay males and lesbians involves four steps or features:

- Attraction to members of the same gender.
- Self-labelling as gay or lesbian.
- Sexual contact with members of the same gender.
- Disclosure of their sexual orientation to other people.

The researchers have found, by and large, a ten-year gap between initial attraction to members of one's own sex, which tends to occur at about the age of eight or nine, and disclosure of one's orientation to other people, which usually occurs around age 18. In keeping with the gender differences we discussed in Chapter 5, females are more likely to focus on the emotional or romantic aspects of their budding feelings, and males are more likely to focus on the sexual aspects. Males—who are generally more open than females to sexual experimentation— are likely to become involved in sexual activity with other males before they label themselves as gay. Females, on the other hand, are more likely to label themselves as lesbians before pursuing relationships with other females. Males also tend to form sexual identities and come out about two years earlier than females (Grov et al., 2006).

Younger cohorts (people who are 18 to 24 years old) tend to come out earlier than older cohorts (Grov et al., 2006). Factors such as the growing acceptance of diverse sexual orientations and the more common positive portrayals of gays and lesbians in the media have contributed to more younger people feeling comfortable enough to come out.

Alderson (2003) criticizes fixed-stage models of gay identity development, such as those proposed by Savin-Williams and Diamond (2000), which assume that everyone who comes out goes through a series of well-defined stages. Alderson believes identity development is an individualized process, affected by environmental influences. In other words, not everyone goes through the same stages in the same order.

Alderson (2003) has developed an ecological model of gay male identity that incorporates the external (social and environmental) and the internal (psychological) influences that lead to a gay self-definition. In his model, cognitive dissonance about being gay plays a key role in the movement toward identity development. Alderson believes his ecological model provides clinicians with a useful framework for counselling gay males, and in particular for helping those who are questioning their sexual identities.

Coming Out to Others

There are different patterns of coming out to others. Coming out occasionally means making an open declaration to the world. Some individuals inform only one or a few select people. Others may tell friends but not family members.

CRITICAL THINKING QUESTIONS

How do you account for differences between males and females in the coming-out process?

Applied Knowledge

COUNSELLING GAYS AND LESBIANS

Karine Blais and her colleagues (2004) at the Université de Montréal have outlined some key issues pertaining to sexual orientation that therapists need to be knowledgeable about.

They include homophobia, HIV, the lack of conjugal role models, and the coming-out process.

It's also important for therapists to recognize that gay and lesbian couples face many of the same issues as heterosexual couples.

Toronto's Centre for Addiction and Mental Health has prepared a handbook to guide therapists who counsel gay and lesbian clients. It's called *Asking the Right Questions 2: Talking with Clients About Sexual Orientation and Gender Identity in Mental Health, Counselling and Addiction Settings.*

In Ontario, Brock University researchers Anthony Bogaert and Luanne Jamieson (2008) have analyzed several factors to determine which ones might predict the age of coming out among gay and bisexual men. They've found that men who are attractive and men who believe in a just world are more likely to come out at a younger age. Those with more feminine behavioural traits in childhood tend to delay coming out.

Many gays and lesbians remain reluctant to declare their sexual orientations, even to friends and family. Disclosure is fraught with the risk of losing jobs, friendships, and social standing (Legate et al., 2012; Rosario et al., 2009). On the other hand, if a person's place of work is generally supportive, coming out can be related to greater job satisfaction and less anxiety (Griffith & Hebl, 2002).

Gays and lesbians often anticipate negative reactions from family members, including denial, anger, and rejection (Legate et al., 2012). Barrett (1990) has found that parents, children, neighbours, and friends of lesbians may deny,

Coming Out to Parents. Coming out to their parents can be scary, and many lesbians and gays avoid it for years—even lifetimes.

Comstock/ThinkStock

compartmentalize, or struggle with their knowledge the same way the women do themselves.

> My parents know I've lived with my partner for six years. She goes home with me. We sleep in the same bed there. The word "lesbian" has never been mentioned. I told my mother, and she said, "Well, now that's over with. We don't need to mention it again." She never has, and that was 10 years ago. I don't know if she ever told my father. (Barrett, 1990, p. 52)

Some families are more accepting. They may have wondered whether their children were gay or lesbian, and prepared themselves for such news. Many families are initially rejecting but eventually come to at least grudging acceptance that family members are gay or lesbian.

Dave Vervoort (1999), a University of Guelph graduate student, conducted an online survey of gay fathers, almost all of whom lived in Canada or the United States. Most had full or joint custody of their children. In coming out to their children, the fathers reported that their children's responses were generally more positive than they'd anticipated. Only about 10% of the children were clearly upset about the disclosure. Older children were more negative. Over time, however, many of these children became more positive about accepting their fathers' gay status.

As Canadian society becomes more accepting of diverse sexual orientations, and as positive gay and lesbian role models such as politicians, Olympic athletes, and media celebrities become more visible, it's likely that more and more people will be better able to adjust to the reality that their children, siblings, or parents are gay or lesbian.

Gay and Lesbian Adjustment

King and his colleagues (2008) identified 13 706 research articles about the mental health of gay men, lesbians, and bisexuals. They selected 476 of these for analysis, ultimately comparing the mental health of 214 344 heterosexuals and 11 971 non-heterosexuals. A sophisticated statistical averaging technique revealed that lesbian, gay, and bisexual people were more than twice as likely as heterosexuals to attempt suicide. They were also one and a half times as likely to be diagnosed with depression, anxiety, and dependence on alcohol and other substances. It's clear, however, that societal oppression is responsible for the greater incidence of such mental disorders among gays, lesbians, and bisexuals. "Surely," writes psychologist J. Michael Bailey (1999), "it must be difficult for young people to come to grips with their homosexuality in a world where homosexual people are often scorned, mocked, mourned, and feared" (p. 884).

In a large-scale British Columbia study of students in grades 7 to 12, gays, lesbians, and bisexuals had much higher rates of psychological and social difficulties than heterosexual females and males did (McCreary Centre Society, 2007). For example, compared to heterosexual youth, LGB youth:

- Were more likely to have experienced physical and sexual abuse, harassment in school, and discrimination in the community.
- Were more likely to have run away from home at least once during the previous year.
- Were more likely to be sexually experienced.
- Were more likely to have been pregnant or gotten someone pregnant.
- Were more likely to have reported emotional stress, suicidal thoughts, and suicide attempts.
- Were less likely to participate in sports and physical activities.
- Were more likely to spend time on the computer.
- Felt less cared about by parents and less connected to their families.
- Felt less connected to school (lesbian and bisexual females).

The study also found that LGB youth who felt highly connected to their families and schools were far less likely to attempt suicide than bisexual teens who felt less connected. This was true even for LGB youth who were strongly at risk for suicide because of histories of sexual abuse and symptoms of emotional distress, for example.

Lesbian, gay, and bisexual youth are less likely than heterosexual youth to have supportive family and school environments (Saewyc, 2006a). For some, adjustment is related to conflict over their sexual orientations (Simonsen et al., 2000). Yet most gay males and lesbians are well adjusted. Those who accept their sexual orientations and, in particular, those who are openly gay or lesbian are more likely to be well adjusted.

An international study of lesbian, gay, and bisexual youth in Canada, New Zealand, and the United States found that those who had experienced stigma because of sexual orientation were more likely to engage in high HIV-risk sexual behaviours (Meininger et al., 2007). These findings suggest that helping sexual-minority youth deal with stigmatization could help reduce their sexual risk-taking.

The British Columbia study found that gay, lesbian, and bisexual youth were also more likely than heterosexuals to engage in high HIV-risk behaviour (Saewyc et al., 2006b). In each sexual-orientation group, those who had experienced sexual abuse had higher risk scores. The findings indicate that because sexual-minority youth experience greater sexual abuse than heterosexual youth, they're more likely to engage in risky sexual behaviours.

In their classic research, Bell and Weinberg (1978) found variations in adjustment in the gay community that seem to mirror the variations in the heterosexual community. Gay people who lived with partners in stable, intimate relationships—so-called close couples—were about as well adjusted as married heterosexual couples. Older gay people who lived alone and had few sexual contacts were less well adjusted. So are many heterosexual people with solitary lifestyles. All in all, Bell and Weinberg found that differences in adjustment were more likely to reflect individuals' lifestyles than their sexual orientations.

Most gays and lesbians who share close relationships with their partners are satisfied with the overall quality of their relationships. Researchers find that heterosexuals, gay, and lesbian couples report similar levels of relationship satisfaction (Henderson et al., 2009; Kurdek, 2005). Gay men and lesbians in enduring relationships generally report high levels of love, attachment, closeness, caring, and intimacy.

Applied Knowledge

INCREASING RESILIENCE AMONG LGBTQ YOUTH

In reviewing studies of the social adjustment of LGBTQ youth, Kristopher Wells (2008) concluded that the following protective factors are crucial in providing a social environment that results in greater resiliency and fewer adjustment problems:

- Positive representations of LGBTQ people in classrooms and the media.
- Family acceptance and support.
- School support programs, including gay–straight alliances.
- School policies that explicitly prohibit discrimination on the grounds of sexual orientation.
- Support networks that include other LGBTQ youth.
- Inclusive, nonjudgmental sexual health education that challenges negative stereotypes about specific sexual identities.

Innovative Canadian Research

INNOVATION IN GAY MALE RELATIONSHIPS

Barry Adam (2006) of the University of Windsor interviewed 70 gay men in couple relationships in Toronto about how they managed sexual inclusivity.

He found that monogamy was most common among younger men and among men involved in new relationships. Monogamy was more accepted among men from cultural settings where they weren't exposed to—or had limited exposure to—autonomous gay scenes such as gay bars.

Most of the couples, however, were involved in sexually open relationships that allowed sexual experiences with other men. They wanted both the emotional security of committed love relationships and the experience of sexual pleasure with other men.

To achieve this, they agreed that their couple relationships were their primary or most important ones, and they negotiated rules for having sex with others. They typically practiced sexual exclusivity during the first two years of their relationships. This allowed mutual trust to develop. Some couples were monogamous for longer periods, but for most, monogamy was a passing phase.

Adam notes that his sample consisted of men who were in successful relationships, but that many other gay men who engage in casual sex wish they could develop deeply emotional relationships with someone.

Like those of heterosexuals, not all gay people's relationships are satisfying. Among both groups, satisfaction is higher when both partners feel that the benefits outweigh the costs of the relationship (Henderson et al., 2009). Like heterosexual people, gay men and lesbians are happier in relationships where they share power and make joint decisions.

Gay and Lesbian Lifestyles

One of the mistakes lay people (and some researchers) make is treating gay people as though they're all the same. Variations in sexual expression exist within and across sexual orientations. Descriptions of gay, lesbian, and heterosexual lifestyles must consider individual differences.

University of Lethbridge researchers Doug VanderLaan and Paul Vasey (2008) compared gay, lesbian, and heterosexual couples with respect to the strategies they used to "retain their mates." They found that, in a number of aspects, gay and heterosexual males were typical of their gender, whereas lesbians were less so. For example, lesbian women and both gay and heterosexual men were less concerned than heterosexual women about their partners' economic status. Heterosexual women were more concerned than the other groups about their physical appearance. Heterosexual women were also more likely to be concerned about their partners' spending time away, and more likely to threaten to end their relationships if their partners were to have sex with others. Heterosexual men were more likely than gays and lesbians to threaten to end their relationships over infidelity. Gay men, however, were more likely than straight women to denigrate potential competitors.

Gays and lesbians in larger urban centres can usually look for services and supports from gay communal structures. These include gay rights organizations and gay-oriented newspapers, magazines, bookstores, housing cooperatives, and

Many lesbian couples have children. Sometimes the children derive from earlier marriages, and sometimes they're adopted. Some lesbians are artificially inseminated or engage in sexual intercourse with men for the purpose of becoming pregnant.

Anton Gvozdikov/Shutterstock

medical services. The gay community provides a sense of acceptance and belonging that gays and lesbians don't typically find in society at large.

Not all gays and lesbians feel a part of the gay community, however, or participate in gay rights organizations. For many, their sexual orientations are part of their identities but not dominant themes governing their social and political activities. Gays and lesbians, like heterosexuals, have many different styles of life. Things are no simpler in the gay world than in the straight world.

In closing this chapter, we wish to acknowledge a study of human sexuality textbooks, including this one, that contained a chapter devoted to sexual orientation. Researchers Glenn Meaney of Wilfrid Laurier University and B. J. Rye of the University of Waterloo (2008) concluded that each of the textbooks they examined provided adequate, accurate information about sexual orientation and promoted more positive attitudes toward gay, lesbian, and bisexual people.

GAY AND LESBIAN PARENTING   Deborah Foster (2005a), a therapist in Alberta, has provided a comprehensive analysis of the research on lesbian families. She notes that most lesbian families have formed as a result of the birth mothers' having children in heterosexual relationships, leaving those relationships, and then living in lesbian relationships.

Foster has summarized her key findings from comparisons of children raised in lesbian families with those raised in heterosexual families. She's found that children raised in lesbian families:

- Develop typical gender identities and gender roles.
- Develop typical peer relationships.
- Exhibit normal emotional and behavioural development.
- Have fewer issues regarding their sexual identity than children raised in heterosexual families.
- Are no more likely to grow up gay or lesbian than children raised in heterosexual families. (Foster, 2005a, pp. 291–292)

According to Foster, a key factor in the tendency for children in lesbian families to develop normally is the fact that lesbian families tend to be equalitarian, nurturing, and empathic (Foster, 2005b). Foster concludes that children raised in lesbian families are at least as well adjusted as those raised in heterosexual families.

Based on a consistent body of research on lesbian and gay parents and their children, the American Psychological Association (2012) concluded that there is no scientific evidence that parenting effectiveness is related to parental sexual orientation. In other words, lesbian and gay parents are as likely as heterosexual parents to provide supportive and healthy environments for their children.

Summing Up

Sexual orientation describes the directionality of one's sexual and romantic interests—toward members of one's own gender, members of another gender, or both. A gay male or a lesbian orientation involves sexual and romantic interest in members of one's own gender.

Kinsey and his colleagues found evidence of degrees of homosexuality and heterosexuality, with bisexuality representing a midpoint between the two.

Bisexual people are attracted to both males and females.

Traditional classifications of sexual orientation based on the heterosexual-homosexual dichotomy are increasingly being abandoned in favour of identities such as queer, pansexual, questioning, transgendered, and two-spirited that more accurately reflect the diversity of ways people conceptualize their sexual orientations.

Throughout much of Western history, gay and lesbian people have been deemed sinful and criminal.

Male–male sexual behaviour is practised by at least some members of many preliterate societies.

Many animals engage in behaviours that resemble male–male and female–female contacts among humans, but we must be cautious in ascribing motives to animals.

Attitudes toward gay and lesbian people have shifted, though homophobia persists. The majority of Canadians now approve of gay and lesbian relationships.

Evidence of a genetic contribution to sexual orientation is accumulating. Prenatal sex hormones may also play a role in determining sexual orientation in humans.

Psychoanalytic theory connects sexual orientation with unconscious castration anxiety and incomplete resolution of the Oedipus complex.

Violence and harassment directed towards LGBTQ people remains a serious problem in Canada. Many LGBTQ youth feel unsafe at school.

Coming out is a two-pronged process: coming out to one's self and coming out to others.

Some gay males and lesbians fear rejection if they disclose their sexual orientations. Some families struggle with the knowledge, while others are more accepting.

Gay and lesbian people do not adopt a single, stereotypical lifestyle.

Lesbian and gay parents are as likely as heterosexual parents to provide supportive and healthy environments for their children.

Test Yourself

Multiple-Choice Questions

1. Sexual orientation is:
(a) The gender identity of a person who feels trapped in the body of the other sex.
(b) The constellation of biological and environmental factors that contribute to the development of a gay, lesbian, or bisexual identity.
(c) Sexual behaviour with people of the same gender.
(d) Erotic attraction toward members of the same gender, another gender, or both.

2. According to studies conducted by Reginald Bibby, the percentage of Canadians who believed that homosexuality is "always wrong" was ___ in 1975 and ___ in 2000:
(a) 78%, 53%
(b) 63%, 32%
(c) 35%, 23%
(d) 51%, 47%

3. According to an Egale Canada survey, what percentage of LGBTQ youth reported that they felt unsafe at school?
(a) 34%
(b) 44%
(c) 54%
(d) 64%

4. Psychologist Michael Storms suggests that:
(a) Heterosexuality and homosexuality are at opposite ends of a continuum of sexual orientation.
(b) Asexuality and bisexuality are both low in heteroeroticism.
(c) Homosexuality and heterosexuality are separate and independent dimensions.
(d) Bisexual individuals are at the midpoint of a continuum between heterosexuality and homosexuality.

5. Bell and Weinberg found that gay couples' adjustment was related to:
(a) The level of stability and intimacy in their relationships.
(b) The ability of one partner to take on decision-making authority.
(c) Their frequency of sexual activity.
(d) Their acceptance of multiple sexual partnerships.

6. A 2010 poll of Canadians found that _____ approved of same-sex couples retaining the right to marry.
(a) 21%
(b) 41%
(c) 61%
(d) 81%

7. According to Savin-Williams and Diamond, the first step in the development of sexual identity among gay and lesbian people is
(a) Sexual contact with members of the same gender.
(b) Attraction to members of the same gender.
(c) Self-labelling as gay or lesbian.
(d) Disclosure to other people.

8. The cluster of negative attitudes toward gay, lesbian, and bisexual people that includes intolerance, hatred, and fear is referred to as:
(a) Heterophobia.
(b) Homophobia.
(c) Heteroeroticism.
(d) Homoeroticism.

9. _____ are most likely to share a gay sexual orientation.
(a) Monozygotic twins
(b) Dizygotic twins
(c) Parents and their biological children
(d) Adoptive parents and their adopted children

10. In comparing homosexual and heterosexual couples, Doug VanderLaan and Paul Vasey found that _____ were most likely to be concerned about their partners' economic status.
(a) heterosexual women
(b) gay men
(c) lesbians
(d) heterosexual men

You'll find answers to the "Test Yourself" questions on page 489.

Questions for Critical Thinking

1. What messages about sexual orientation did you receive from your parents as you were growing up? Did you receive different messages from your friends?

2. Why do you think men tend to be more homophobic than women?

3. Over time, Canadians have become more accepting of diversity related to sexual orientation. What factors do you think explain this change in attitudes?

CHAPTER TEN

Conception, Pregnancy, and Childbirth

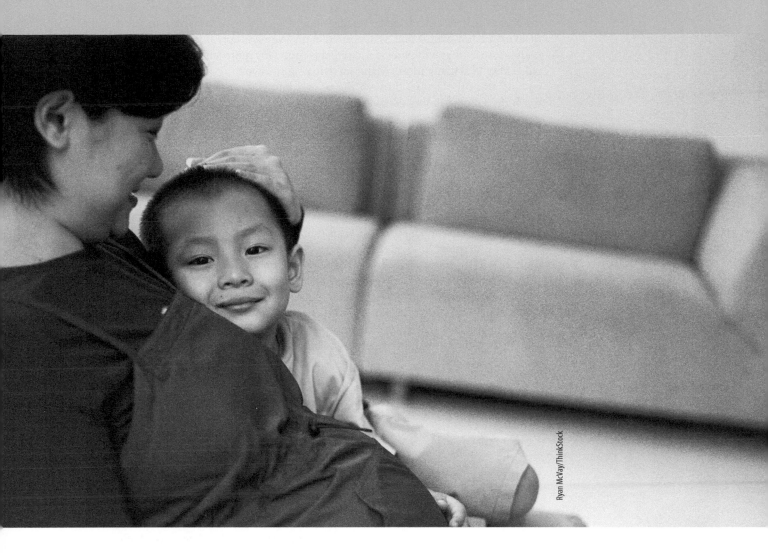

Ryan McVay/ThinkStock

Conception

Conception is the union of a sperm cell and an ovum. On one hand, conception is the beginning of a new human life. On the other hand, conception is the end of a fantastic voyage, in which a viable ovum—one of only several hundred that will mature and ripen during a woman's lifetime—unites with one of several hundred million sperm produced by a man in the average ejaculate.

Ova carry X sex chromosomes. Sperm carry either X or Y sex chromosomes. Girls are conceived from the union of an ovum and an X-bearing sperm, boys from the union of an ovum and a Y-bearing sperm. Sperm that bear Y chromosomes appear to be faster swimmers than those bearing X chromosomes. This is one of the reasons 120 to 150 boys are conceived for every 100 girls. What seem to be natural balancing factors favour the survival of female fetuses, however. Male fetuses are more likely to be lost in spontaneous abortions, which often occur during the first month of pregnancy. In many cases of early spontaneous abortion, the women never realize they've been pregnant. Despite spontaneous abortions, however, boys still outnumber girls at birth, but boys suffer a higher incidence of infant mortality.

The 200 to 400 million sperm in an average ejaculation may seem excessive, given that only one can fertilize an egg. Only 1 in 1000 will ever arrive in the vicinity of an ovum, however. Millions deposited in the vagina simply flow out of the woman's body because of gravity, unless she remains prone for quite some time. Normal vaginal acidity kills many more. Many surviving sperm swim (against the current of fluid coming from the cervix) through the os and into the uterus. Surviving sperm may reach the fallopian tubes 60 to 90 minutes after ejaculation. About half of the sperm end up in the wrong tube—that is, the one that doesn't contain the egg. Perhaps some 2000 sperm find their way into the right tube. Fewer still manage to swim the final 5 centimetres against the currents generated by the cilia that line the tube.

The journey of sperm may be blind, but it's not random. Ova secrete a chemical that attracts sperm. Because sperm cells have odour receptors, it's conceivable (pardon the pun) that sperm are attracted to ova through a variation of the sense of smell.

Fertilization normally occurs in a fallopian tube. (Figure 10.1 shows sperm swarming around an egg in a fallopian tube.) Ova contain chromosomes, proteins, fats, and nutritious fluid, and are surrounded by a gelatinous layer called the **zona pellucida**. This layer must be penetrated if fertilization is to occur. Sperm that have completed their journey secrete the enzyme **hyaluronidase**, which briefly thins the zona pellucida, enabling one sperm to penetrate. Once a sperm has entered, the zona pellucida thickens, locking other sperm out. The corresponding chromosomes in the sperm and the ovum line up opposite one another. Conception occurs as the chromosomes from the sperm and the ovum combine to form 23 new pairs of chromosomes, which carry a unique set of genetic instructions.

Infertility and Assisted Reproductive Technologies

For couples who want children, few problems are more frustrating than the inability to conceive. Physicians often recommend that couples try to conceive on their own for six months before seeking medical assistance. The term **infertility** isn't usually applied until a couple has failed to conceive for more than a year.

Infertility can have significant psychological and emotional effects on individuals and couples. Some psychologists have found that dealing with infertility can be likened to dealing with the death of a child. Couples often go through a grief process that involves acceptance of the diagnosis of infertility before proceeding to treatment to help them conceive.

Because the likelihood of infertility increases with age, the current somewhat elevated incidence of infertility is partly the result of a rise in the number of couples who've postponed childbearing until their 30s and 40s. All in all, about 15% of couples in Canada and the United States have fertility problems (American Fertility Association, 2012a; Bushnik et al., 2012). About half of them eventually succeed in conceiving, however. Many treatment options are available, ranging from drugs that stimulate ovulation to newer reproductive technologies such as in vitro fertilization (IVF).

Infertility treatments can be costly. In vitro fertilization can cost up to $15,000. There's debate in Canada about whether government medical insurance should cover the cost of IVF (Alcoba, 2009). Much of this debate

CRITICAL THINKING QUESTIONS

Should the government cover the cost of in vitro fertilization?

Zona pellucida A gelatinous layer that surrounds an ovum.

Hyaluronidase An enzyme that briefly thins the zona pellucida, enabling one sperm to penetrate.

Infertility Inability to conceive a child.

Francis Leroy/Science Source

Figure 10.1   Human sperm swarming around an ovum in a fallopian tube.
Fertilization normally occurs in a fallopian tube, not in the uterus.

Applied Knowledge

OPTIMIZING THE CHANCES OF CONCEPTION

Some couples wish to optimize their chances of conceiving during a particular month so birth occurs at a desired time. Others may have difficulty conceiving, and wish to maximize their chances for a few months, before consulting a fertility specialist. Some fairly simple procedures can dramatically increase the chances of conceiving for couples without serious fertility problems.

The ovum can be fertilized for about 4 to 20 hours after ovulation. Sperm are most active within 48 hours after ejaculation. One way of optimizing the chances of conception is to engage in coitus within a few hours of ovulation. There are a number of ways to predict ovulation.

Using the Basal Body Temperature Chart
Few women have perfectly regular cycles, so they can only guess when they're ovulating. A basal body temperature (BBT) chart (see Figure 10.2) may help provide a more reliable estimate.

As Figure 10.2 shows, body temperature is fairly even before ovulation. Early-morning body temperature is generally below 37°C. Just before ovulation, basal temperature dips slightly. On the day after ovulation, temperature tends to rise by about 0.2°C to 0.4°C, and it remains higher until menstruation. Thermometers that provide finely graded readings, such as electronic digital thermometers, are best suited for determining these minor changes.

In using the BBT method, a woman attempts to detect these temperature changes by tracking her temperature just after she awakens each morning, before she rises from her bed. She records her temperature, the day of her cycle, and the day of the month, and indicates whether she and her partner have engaged in sexual

intercourse. With regular charting for six months—assuming her cycles are fairly regular—she may learn to more accurately predict the day of ovulation.

Opinion is divided about whether it's better to have intercourse every 24 hours or every 36 to 48 hours for the several days when ovulation is expected. More frequent intercourse around the time of ovulation gives more chances for conception. Less frequent intercourse—that is, every 36 to 48 hours—results in a higher sperm count during each ejaculation. Most fertility specialists recommend that a couple seeking to conceive have intercourse once every day or two during the week in which the woman expects to ovulate. They may advise a man with a lower-than-normal sperm count to wait for 48 hours between ejaculations.

Analyzing Urine or Saliva for Luteinizing Hormone
Over-the-counter kits are more accurate than the BBT method for predicting ovulation. These kits analyze a woman's urine or saliva for the surge in luteinizing hormone (LH) that occurs about 12 to 24 hours before ovulation.

Tracking Vaginal Mucus
A woman can track the thickness of her vaginal mucus during the phases of the menstrual cycle by rolling it between her fingers and noting changes in texture. The mucus is thick, white, and cloudy during most phases of the cycle. It becomes thin, slippery, and clear

for a few days before ovulation. A day or so after ovulation, the mucus again thickens and becomes opaque.

Additional Considerations
A woman may improve her chances of conceiving by lying on her back and drawing her knees close to her breasts after ejaculation. This position, perhaps aided by the use of a pillow beneath the buttocks, may elevate the pool of semen in relation to the cervix and prevent sperm from dripping out quickly. It thus makes gravity work for rather than against conception. She may also lie as still as possible for about 30 to 60 minutes after ejaculation, to help sperm move toward the cervical opening.

A woman with a severely retroverted (tipped) uterus may profit by supporting herself on her elbows and knees and having her partner enter her from behind. This position helps prevent semen from dripping out of the vagina.

The man should penetrate the woman as deeply as possible just before ejaculation, hold still during ejaculation, and then withdraw slowly, in a straight line, to avoid dispersing the pool of semen.

Figure 10.2   A basal body temperature (BBT) chart.
Because most women have somewhat irregular menstrual cycles, they may not be able to predict ovulation perfectly. The basal body temperature (BBT) chart helps them to do so.

Body temperature is fairly even before ovulation but dips slightly just before ovulation. On the day after ovulation, a woman's body temperature increases about 0.4 to 0.8°F above the level before ovulation.

Source: *Adapted from Kolodny, R.C., Masters, W.H., & Johnson, V.E. (1979).* Textbook of Sexual Medicine. *New York: Little Brown and Company.*

centres around the question of whether infertility should be considered a medical condition requiring publicly funded medical treatment. Quebec was the first province or territory to cover the cost of IVF when it began doing so in 2010, and Ontario became the second when it announced in 2014 that it would begin covering the cost.

Male Fertility Issues

Although most concerns about fertility have traditionally centred on women, in about 40% of cases, the difficulty lies with men. In about 20% of cases, problems are found in both partners.

The following fertility problems are found in men (American Fertility Association, 2012a):

Motility Self-propulsion. Motility is a measure of the viability of sperm cells.

- Low sperm counts.
- Irregularly shaped sperm (e.g., malformed heads or tails).
- Low sperm **motility**.
- Chronic diseases such as diabetes.
- Infections such as sexually transmitted infections.
- Injuries to the testes.
- **Autoimmune responses**, in which the man produces antibodies that deactivate his sperm.
- A pituitary imbalance and/or thyroid disease.

Autoimmune response The production of antibodies that attack naturally occurring substances that are (incorrectly) recognized as foreign or harmful.

Problems in producing normal, abundant sperm may be caused by genetic factors, advanced age, hormonal problems, diabetes, injuries to the testes, varicose veins in the scrotum, drugs (alcohol, narcotics, marijuana, and/or tobacco), antihypertensive medications, environmental toxins, excess heat, and emotional stress. Sperm production gradually declines with age, but normal aging does not necessarily produce infertility. Men in late adulthood can often father children.

Low sperm count (or the absence of sperm) is the most common problem. Sperm counts of 40 million to 150 million sperm per millilitre of semen are considered normal. A count of less than 20 million is generally regarded as low. Sperm production may be low among men with undescended testes that weren't surgically corrected before puberty. Frequent ejaculation can reduce sperm counts. Sperm production may also be impaired in men whose testicles are consistently one or two degrees above the typical scrotal temperature of 34°C to 35°C. Frequent hot baths and tightly fitting underwear may also be responsible for low sperm production, at least temporarily. Some men may encounter fertility problems from prolonged athletic activity, electric blankets, or even long, hot baths. In such cases, the problems can be easily corrected. Male runners with fertility problems are often advised to take time off to increase their sperm counts.

Sometimes the sperm count is adequate, but prostate, hormonal, or other factors reduce motility or deform the sperm. Motility can also be hampered by scar tissue from infections, which may prevent sperm from passing through the vas deferens or other parts of the male reproductive system. To be considered normal, sperm must be able to swim for at least two hours after intercourse, and most (60% or more) must be normal in shape.

Sperm counts have been increased by surgical repair of varicose veins in the scrotum. Microsurgery can also open blocked passageways that prevent the outflow of sperm. Researchers are investigating the effects of special cooling undergarments. Most men whose infertility is the result of higher-than-normal scrotal temperatures show increased sperm counts and sperm quality when they wear such undergarments.

Artificial insemination The introduction of sperm into the reproductive tract through means other than sexual intercourse.

ARTIFICIAL INSEMINATION   The sperm of men with low sperm counts can be collected and quick-frozen. The sperm from multiple ejaculations can then be injected into a woman's uterus at the time of ovulation. This is one kind of **artificial insemination**. The sperm of a man with low sperm motility can also be injected into his partner's uterus, so the sperm begin their journey closer to the fallopian tubes. Sperm from a donor can be used to artificially inseminate a woman whose partner is completely infertile or has an extremely low sperm count. The child then bears the genes of just one of the natural parents—the mother. A donor can be chosen who resembles the father in physical traits and ethnic background.

A variation of artificial insemination has been used with some men with very low (or zero) sperm counts, immature sperm, or immotile sperm. Immature sperm is removed from a testicle via a thin needle, and directly injected into an egg in a laboratory dish.

Female Fertility Issues

Women encounter the following major fertility problems (American Fertility Association, 2012a):

- Irregular ovulation, including failure to ovulate.
- Obstructions or malfunctions of the reproductive tract, often caused by infections or diseases involving the reproductive tract.
- Endometriosis.
- Declining hormone levels of estrogen and progesterone that occur with aging and may prevent the ovum from becoming fertilized or remaining implanted in the uterus.

Between 10% and 15% of female infertility problems stem from failure to ovulate. Many factors can play roles, including hormonal irregularities, malnutrition, genetic factors, stress, and chronic disease. Failure to ovulate may occur in response to low levels of body fat, as we see in athletes and women with eating disorders (Frisch, 2002).

Ovulation can often be induced by fertility drugs such as clomiphene (sold as Clomid), which stimulates the pituitary gland to secrete FSH and LH, which in turn stimulate the maturation of ova. Clomiphene leads to conception in most cases of infertility that are due solely to irregular or absent ovulation. But because infertility can have multiple causes, only about half of the women who use clomiphene become pregnant.

Another infertility drug, Pergonal, contains a high concentration of FSH, which directly stimulates maturation of ovarian follicles. Like clomiphene, Pergonal has a high success rate with women whose infertility is due to lack of ovulation. These drugs may cause multiple births by stimulating more than one ovum to ripen during a month (McClamrock, 2012).

Local infections that scar the fallopian tubes and other organs impede the passage of sperm or ova. Such infections include pelvic inflammatory disease, which is an inflammation of the woman's internal reproductive tract that can be caused by various infectious agents, such as the bacteria responsible for chlamydia and gonorrhea (see Chapter 14) Sexually transmitted infections are therefore a major cause of infertility.

In **endometriosis**, endometrial tissues, which are normally found in the lining of the uterus, implant and grow elsewhere. When they develop on the surface of the ovaries or fallopian tubes, they may block the passage of ova or impair conception. About one in six cases of female sterility is believed to be due to endometriosis. Hormone treatments and surgery sometimes reduce the blockage to the point where the woman can conceive. A physician may suspect endometriosis during a pelvic exam, but it's diagnosed with certainty by **laparoscopy**. A long, narrow tube is inserted through an incision in the navel, permitting the physician to visually inspect the organs in the pelvic cavity. The incision is practically undetectable.

Several methods help many women with problems such as blocked fallopian tubes bear children, as we'll see next.

IN VITRO FERTILIZATION When Louise Brown was born in England in 1978, after being conceived by **in vitro fertilization (IVF)**, she made headlines around the world. Louise was dubbed the world's first "test-tube baby." Conception actually took place in a laboratory dish (not a test tube), and the embryo was implanted in her mother's uterus, where it developed to term.

Endometriosis An abnormal condition in which endometrial tissue is sloughed off into the abdominal cavity, rather than out of the body during menstruation. The condition is characterized by abdominal pain, and may cause infertility.

Laparoscopy A medical procedure in which a long, narrow tube (a laparoscope) is inserted through an incision in the navel, permitting visual inspection of organs in the pelvic cavity.

In vitro fertilization A method of conception in which mature ova are surgically removed from an ovary, and placed in a laboratory dish with sperm.

Gamete intrafallopian transfer (GIFT) A method of conception in which sperm and ova are inserted into a fallopian tube, to encourage conception.

Zygote intrafallopian transfer A method of conception in which an ovum is fertilized in a laboratory dish, then placed in a fallopian tube.

Donor IVF A variation of in vitro fertilization in which an ovum is taken from one woman, fertilized, and injected into the uterus or fallopian tube of another woman.

Embryonic transfer A method of conception in which a female volunteer is artificially inseminated by the male partner of the intended mother, then the embryo is removed from the volunteer and inserted into the uterus of the intended mother.

Intracytoplasmic sperm injection A method of conception in which a single sperm is injected directly into an ovum.

Surrogate mother A woman who is impregnated with the sperm of a prospective father via artificial insemination, carries the embryo and fetus to term, and then gives the child to the prospective parents.

Before a woman undergoes in vitro fertilization, she's given fertility drugs to stimulate her ova to ripen. The ripe ova are then surgically removed from one of her ovaries, and placed in a laboratory dish with the man's sperm. Fertilized ova are then injected into the woman's uterus, where they become implanted in the uterine wall.

A variation of IVF is vitrification, which involves rapid freezing of a woman's ova. Rapid freezing prevents ice crystals from forming, which ensures that a high proportion of the ova will survive. This procedure appeals to women who want to delay becoming mothers until they're older, but want to preserve their young ova, to improve their fertility chances. The McGill Reproductive Centre in Montreal has pioneered research on this procedure (Ogilvie, 2008).

GIFT   In **gamete intrafallopian transfer (GIFT)**, sperm and ova are inserted together into a fallopian tube for fertilization. Conception occurs in a fallopian tube, rather than in a laboratory dish.

ZIFT   **Zygote intrafallopian transfer (ZIFT)** involves a combination of IVF and GIFT. Sperm and ova are combined in a laboratory dish. After fertilization, the zygote is placed in the mother's fallopian tube, to begin its journey to the uterus for implantation.

ZIFT's advantage over GIFT is that the fertility specialists can ascertain that fertilization has occurred before insertion is performed.

DONOR IV   **Donor IVF** is a variation of the IVF procedure. The ovum is taken from another woman, fertilized, and then injected into the uterus or fallopian tube of the intended mother. The procedure is used when the intended mother doesn't produce ova.

EMBRYONIC TRANSFER   **Embryonic transfer** can be used with women who don't produce ova of their own. A female volunteer is artificially inseminated by the male partner of the infertile woman. Five days later, the embryo is removed from the volunteer and inserted into the uterus of the mother-to-be, where it becomes implanted.

INTRACYTOPLASMIC SPERM INJECTION   **Intracytoplasmic sperm injection (ICSI)** can be used when a man has too few sperm for IVF, or when IVF fails. A sperm cell is injected directly into an ovum.

This method may be associated with an increase in birth defects, including heart, stomach, kidney, and bladder problems, cleft palates, hernias, and malformation of the penis (Shevell et al., 2005).

Intracytoplasmic Sperm Injection.
ICSI is sometimes used when the man has too few sperm for IVF, or when IVF fails. As you can see in the photograph, a very thin needle injects a single sperm directly into an ovum.

SURROGATE MOTHERHOOD   A **surrogate mother** is artificially inseminated by the partner of an infertile woman or by one of two men who are a couple. She carries the baby to term and then turns the baby over to the father and his partner. Surrogacy is legal in Canada, but there can be no contract and it is illegal to pay a woman to be a surrogate.

ADOPTION   Adoption is another way for people to have children. Despite the occasional conflicts between adoptive parents and biological parents who change their minds about giving up their children, most adoptions create loving new families.

Adopted children may, in some cases, feel less secure than biological children with their caregivers (Gilmore, 2008). Everything else being equal, however, the younger a child is at the time of adoption, the more smoothly the adoption seems to go

A World of Diversity

LGBT FAMILY BUILDING

Not only heterosexual couples want children. So do heterosexual and gay and lesbian singles. And so do couples who belong to the gay, lesbian, bisexual, transgender community. Many gays and lesbians use reproductive technologies to become parents. At some fertility clinics in Toronto, about one-third of the clients are gay men or lesbians (Epstein, 2008).

Some gay and lesbian couples, of course, bring children from previous marriages or other kinds of relationships. But if they want children, they have to make decisions about how to make it happen. Increasingly, transgender people who incorporate hormonal or surgical procedures into the transitioning process are consulting with their health care providers regarding options for fertility preservation.

Lesbians, of course, can conceive through sexual intercourse with a friend or confidant, but many prefer not to do so. The American Fertility Association (2012b) notes that they can also conceive through assisted productive technologies such as at-home insemination, intrauterine insemination (IUI), in vitro fertilization (IVF), and reciprocal in vitro fertilization (RIVF). All these methods require obtaining donor sperm, from either a known or anonymous source. IUI, known better perhaps as artificial insemination, is a low-technology method in which washed sperm are inserted directly into the uterus through a catheter. If IUI does not work, a woman may consider IVF. When both members of a lesbian couple are fertile, they sometimes choose to harvest the eggs from one partner, have them fertilized with donor sperm, and then insert the resulting embryos in the other partner, who may become pregnant through this process. The other partner may do the same. That's why this method is called *reciprocal* IVF. It permits both partners to play a role in bearing the child.

Gay males will need a surrogate mother to become impregnated by their sperm and carry the embryo and fetus to term. The two potential fathers' sperm is analyzed, and either the sperm with the strongest likelihood to impregnate the surrogate are selected, or the sperm may be mixed so that the fathers do not know which partner actually fathered the child. On the other hand, actual fatherhood usually becomes clear enough in terms of the child's appearance and behavior as time goes on. DNA testing can also be used to make the determination. But both men played a role in the process and as long as their relationship remains stable, they usually make no effort to precisely determine paternity.

(Klahr et al., 2011). Despite potential challenges, most adopted children and adoptive parents fare well.

In 1996, British Columbia became the first province to pass legislation granting same-sex couples the same adoption rights as heterosexual couples. Since then, most provinces have passed similar legislation. Canada has become a world leader in facilitating adoptions for gays and lesbians. This doesn't mean same-sex couples don't still face prejudice by adoption agencies, however. Rye and Meaney (2008) looked at university students' attitudes toward gay and lesbian adoption. While the students were generally positive about gay and lesbian adoption, they were more positive about heterosexual adoption. Women were more accepting than men of adoption by gay and lesbian parents.

Canadian Legislation and Reproductive Technologies

In 2004, Parliament passed legislation to regulate reproductive technologies. This legislation came 12 years after the first commission on reproductive technologies was established, a fact that highlights just how contentious the issues are.

The main provisions of the *Assisted Human Reproduction Act* include:

- A ban on human cloning.
- A ban on selection of a baby's sex for non-medical purposes.
- A ban on payment to a surrogate mother.
- A ban on payment to a sperm donor.

After the act was passed, there were fewer sperm donations in Canada, and fertility clinics had to import sperm from the United States. The United States allows payment to sperm donors and surrogate mothers.

One of the most controversial provisions was the permitting of research using stem cells from embryos left over from infertility treatments. Activists calling themselves "pro-life" are critical of the legislation, arguing that the use of embryos in this way diminishes the value of human life. Proponents of the research argue that stem cells can play vital roles in finding cures for such diseases as cancer, diabetes, and Parkinson's.

In December 2010, the Supreme Court of Canada ruled that those aspects of the 2004 legislation pertaining to fertility clinic licensing and monitoring should be provincial rather than federal responsibilities (Fitzpatrick, 2010).

Pregnancy

Women react to becoming pregnant in different ways. For those who are psychologically and economically prepared, pregnancy may be greeted with joyous celebration. On the other hand, an unwanted or unexpected pregnancy may evoke feelings of distress or uncertainty. Planned or not, a pregnancy, especially for women experiencing it for the first time, is likely to cause some level of anxiety.

In this section we examine biological and psychological aspects of pregnancy: signs of pregnancy, prenatal development, complications, influences on prenatal development, sexual activity during pregnancy, and the psychological experiences of pregnant women and fathers.

Early Signs of Pregnancy

For many women, the first sign of pregnancy is a missed period. But some women have irregular menstrual cycles or miss periods because of stress. Missing a period is therefore not a fully reliable indicator.

Some women also experience cyclic bleeding or spotting during pregnancy, although the blood flow is usually lighter than normal. If a woman's basal body temperature remains high for about three weeks after ovulation, there's reason to suspect pregnancy, even if she spot-bleeds two weeks after ovulation.

Human chorionic gonadotropin (hCG) A hormone produced by a woman shortly after conception. hCG stimulates the corpus luteum to continue producing progesterone. The presence of hCG in a woman's urine indicates that she's pregnant.

Pregnancy Tests

You may have heard your grandparents say they learned your grandmother was pregnant by means of a "rabbit test." Once commonly used to confirm pregnancy, this procedure involved injection of a sample of a mother's urine into a laboratory animal. The procedure relied on the fact that women produce **human chorionic gonadotropin** (hCG) shortly after conception, and hCG causes rabbits, mice, and rats to ovulate.

Today, pregnancy can be confirmed within minutes—and without animals—by tests that directly detect hCG in the urine as early as the third week of pregnancy. A blood test (the radioimmunoassay [RIA] of beta subunit hCG) can detect hCG in the woman's blood as early as the eighth day of pregnancy, about five days before her expected period.

Over-the-counter home pregnancy tests are available. Intended to be used as early as one day after a missed period, they test the urine for hCG. Laboratory-based tests are considered 98% or 99% accurate; home-based tests performed by lay people are somewhat less accurate. Women are advised to consult their physicians if they suspect that they're pregnant or wish to confirm home pregnancy test results.

Early Effects of Pregnancy

Just a few days after conception, a woman may note tenderness in her breasts. Hormonal stimulation of the mammary glands may make her breasts more sensitive and cause sensations of tingling and fullness.

The term **morning sickness** refers to the nausea, food aversions, and vomiting a woman may experience during pregnancy. It's actually not a sickness at all, but a perfectly normal part of pregnancy (Flaxman & Sherman, 2000). Morning sickness can be so severe that a woman can't eat regularly and must be hospitalized to ensure that she and her fetus receive adequate nutrition. In milder cases, it can be helpful to eat small amounts of food throughout the day. Many women find that eating a few crackers at bedtime and before getting up in the morning are effective. Other women benefit from medication. Morning sickness usually—but not always—subsides by about the twelfth week of pregnancy.

Morning sickness Symptoms of pregnancy, including nausea, aversions to specific foods, and vomiting.

Pregnant women may experience greater-than-normal fatigue during the early weeks, sleeping longer and falling asleep more readily than usual. They may also experience frequent urination.

Miscarriage

In most cases of **miscarriage**, a specific cause is not identified. Known causes include chromosomal defects in the fetus and abnormalities of the placenta and uterus. Miscarriage is more prevalent among older mothers (Stein & Susser, 2000). About three in four miscarriages occur in the first 16 weeks of pregnancy, and the great majority of these occur in the first seven weeks. Some miscarriages occur so early that the women don't know they're pregnant.

Miscarriage A spontaneous abortion.

After a miscarriage, a couple may feel a deep sense of loss and undergo a period of mourning. Emotional support from friends and family often helps the couple cope with the loss. Most women who miscarry are able to carry subsequent pregnancies to term.

Sexual Activity During Pregnancy

Most health professionals concur that intercourse is safe throughout the pregnancy, until the start of labour, as long as the pregnancy develops normally and the woman has no history of miscarriage. Women who experience bleeding or cramps during pregnancy may be advised by their obstetricians not to engage in intercourse.

A study of 188 women showed a decline in sexual activity as pregnancy progressed (Pauleta et al., 2010). The frequency of sexual intercourse was greatest during the first trimester, followed by the second and then the third trimester. Nearly one in four of the women (23.4%) reported having fear of sexual intercourse during the pregnancy. About 10% said they feared intercourse could harm the baby. A few were concerned that sex would be painful.

In another study, pregnant women often experienced an initial decline in sexual interest during the first trimester, followed by increased interest during the second trimester, and another decline during the third (Fox et al., 2008). The declines in sexual interest and activity during the first trimester result from hormonal changes and, in many cases, fatigue and nausea. Vasocongestion may cause tenderness of the breasts at this time, discouraging the desire for fondling and sucking.

During the third trimester, some women want to continue with sexual activity, and some don't. In one study, three women in five (61%) reported having intercourse at least once a month during the third trimester, and 24% reported having intercourse at least once a week (Fox et al., 2008). During the two weeks prior to delivery, 40% reported having intercourse, and almost one woman in five (17%) reported having intercourse during the two days prior to delivery.

As a woman's abdominal region swells, the male-superior position becomes uncomfortable. For heterosexual couples, the female-superior, lateral-entry, and rear-entry positions are common alternatives. Masturbation and oral sex can continue.

Some women are concerned that the uterine contractions of orgasm may dislodge an embryo, but such concerns are usually unfounded. Still, women and their partners are advised to consult their obstetricians about sex during pregnancy.

Psychological Changes During Pregnancy

A woman's psychological response to pregnancy reflects her desire to be pregnant, her physical changes, and her attitudes toward these changes. Women with the financial, social, and psychological resources to meet the needs of pregnancy and child-rearing may welcome pregnancy. Other women may question their ability to handle pregnancy and childbirth. Or they may fear that pregnancy will interfere with their careers or their mates' feelings about them.

The first trimester may be difficult for women who are ambivalent about pregnancy. At that stage, symptoms like morning sickness are most pronounced, and women must come to terms with being pregnant. The second trimester is generally smoother. Morning sickness and other symptoms largely vanish. It's not yet difficult to move about, and the woman needn't face delivery just yet. Women first note fetal movement during the second trimester, and for many the experience is stirring:

> I was lying on my stomach and felt—something, like someone lightly touching my deep insides. Then I just sat very still and . . . felt the hugeness of having something living growing in me. Then I said, no, it's not possible, it's too early yet, and then I started to cry. . . . That one moment was my first body awareness of another living thing inside me. (Boston Women's Health Book Collective, 2005)

In general, men respond to pregnancy according to the degree to which they want to become fathers. Many men are proud and look forward with great anticipation to having babies. In such cases, pregnancy may bring parents closer together. But male partners who are financially or emotionally unprepared or who don't want to become fathers may consider the pregnancies unwanted.

Prenatal Development

We can date pregnancy from the onset of the last menstrual cycle before conception, which makes the normal gestation period 280 days. We can also date pregnancy from the date at which fertilization is assumed to have taken place, which normally corresponds to two weeks after the beginning of the woman's last menstrual cycle. In this case, the normal gestation period is 266 days. A pregnancy can also be dated through an ultrasound scan during the first trimester.

Once pregnancy is confirmed, we can use Naegele's rule to calculate the delivery date:

1. Write down the date of the first day of the last menstrual period.
2. Add seven days.
3. Subtract three months.
4. Add one year.

Few babies are born exactly when they're due, but the great majority are delivered during 10-day periods that span their due dates.

The Germinal Stage

Within 36 hours of conception, the zygote divides into two cells. It then divides repeatedly, becoming 32 cells within another 36 hours as it continues its journey to the uterus. It takes the zygote three or four days to reach the uterus. This mass of dividing cells then wanders about the uterus for another three or four days before it begins to implant itself in the uterine wall. Implantation takes about another week. This period from conception to implantation is termed the **germinal stage** or the **period of the ovum.** (See Figure 10.3.)

Several days into the germinal stage, the cell mass takes the form of a fluid-filled ball of cells, which is called a **blastocyst.** Already some cell differentiation has begun. Cells begin to separate into groups that will eventually become different structures.

Implantation may be accompanied by some bleeding, which results from the usual rupturing of some small blood vessels that line the uterus. Bleeding can also be a sign of miscarriage—although most women who experience implantation bleeding don't miscarry, but go on to have normal pregnancies and deliver healthy babies.

The Embryonic Stage

The period from implantation to about the eighth week of development is called the **embryonic stage.** The major organ systems of the body begin to differentiate during this stage.

Germinal stage The period of prenatal development before implantation in the uterus.

Period of the ovum Germinal stage.

Blastocyst An embryo that consists of a sphere of cells surrounding a cavity of fluid. This occurs at the germinal stage of embryonic development.

Embryonic stage The stage of prenatal development that lasts from implantation through the eighth week. It's characterized by differentiation of the major organ systems.

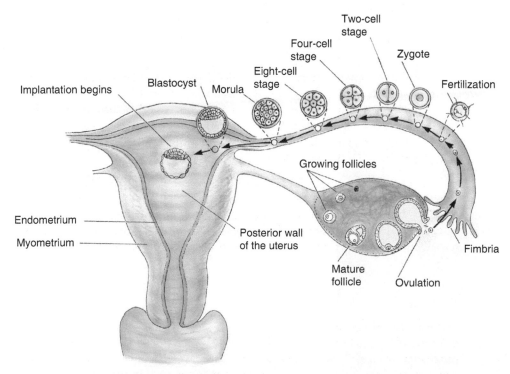

Figure 10.3 The ovarian cycle, conception, and the early germinal stage.
The zygote first divides about 36 hours after conception. Continuing division creates the hollow sphere of cells termed the blastocyst, which normally becomes implanted in the wall of the uterus.

Development of the embryo follows two trends: cephalocaudal growth and proximodistal growth. Growth of the head (the cephalic region) takes precedence over growth of the lower parts of the body. You can also think of the body as containing a central axis that coincides with the spinal cord. The growth of the organ systems that lie close to this axis (that is, proximal to the axis) takes precedence over the growth of those that lie farther away, toward the extremities (that is, distal to the axis). Relatively early maturation of the brain and organ systems that lie near the central axis allows these organs to facilitate further development of the embryo and fetus. The embryo—and later the fetus—develops within a protective environment in the mother's uterus called the **amniotic sac**, which is surrounded by a clear membrane. The embryo or fetus is suspended within the sac in **amniotic fluid**. The amniotic fluid acts like a shock absorber, cushioning the embryo.

Nutrients and waste products are exchanged between mother and embryo (or between mother and fetus) through a mass of tissue called the **placenta**. Unique in origin, the placenta develops from material supplied by both the mother and the embryo. The fetus is connected to the placenta by the **umbilical cord**.

Ultimately, the placenta passes from the woman's body after delivery. For this reason, it's also called the afterbirth.

The Fetal Stage

The fetal stage begins by the ninth week and continues until birth. By about the ninth or tenth week, the fetus begins to respond to the outside world by turning in the direction of external stimulation. By the end of the first trimester, the major organ systems, fingers, toes, and external genitals are formed, the gender can be visually determined, and the eyes are clearly distinguishable.

Amniotic sac The sac containing the fetus.

Amniotic fluid Fluid within the amniotic sac. It suspends and protects the fetus.

Placenta An organ connected to the fetus by the umbilical cord. The placenta serves as a relay station between the mother and the fetus, allowing the exchange of nutrients and wastes.

Umbilical cord A tube that connects the fetus to the placenta.

Prenatal Development.
Developmental changes are most rapid and dramatic during prenatal development. Within a few months, a human embryo becomes a fetus and advances from a gram to several kilograms in weight, and from one cell to billions of cells.

Near the end of the second trimester, the fetus approaches the **age of viability**. Still, only a minority of babies born at the end of the second trimester who weigh under a kilogram will survive—even with intense medical efforts.

During the final months of pregnancy, the mother may become concerned that the fetus seems less active. Most of the time, the change in activity level is normal. The fetus has merely grown so large that it's cramped, and its movements are restricted.

Environmental Influences

MATERNAL DIET   Malnutrition in the mother can adversely affect fetal development and result in a low birth weight. Pregnant women who are adequately nourished are more likely to deliver babies of average or above-average size. Their infants are also less likely to develop colds and serious respiratory disorders. Maternal obesity, however, is linked with a higher risk of stillbirth (Cnattingius et al., 1998).

MATERNAL DISEASES AND DISORDERS   Pre-existing conditions in the mother, such as diabetes, can have significant impacts on prenatal grow and development. Environmental influences and agents that cause permanent, harmful structural alterations of the embryo or fetus are called **teratogens**. They include alcohol, the metals lead and mercury, radiation, and disease-causing organisms such as viruses and bacteria. Although many disease-causing organisms cannot pass through the placenta to infect the embryo or fetus, some extremely small organisms, such as those that cause syphilis, measles, mumps, and chicken pox, can. Substances produced by the mother's body, including Rh-positive antibodies, can also affect the fetus.

Teratogens Environmental influences or agents that can damage an embryo or fetus.

CRITICAL PERIODS OF VULNERABILITY   The times at which exposure to particular teratogens can cause the greatest harm are termed **critical periods of vulnerability**. Critical periods correspond to the times when the structures most affected by the teratogens are developing. The heart, for example, develops rapidly from the third to the fifth week after conception. It may be most vulnerable to certain teratogens at this time.

Critical period of vulnerability A period when an embryo or fetus is vulnerable to the effects of a teratogen.

RUBELLA (GERMAN MEASLES)   **Rubella** is a viral infection. Women who contract rubella during the first month or two of pregnancy, when rapid differentiation of major organ systems take place, may bear children who are deaf or who develop mental retardation, heart disease, or cataracts.

Most Canadian women have either had rubella as children or been vaccinated against it. Women who don't know whether they're immune to rubella may be tested. If they're not immune, they can be vaccinated *before pregnancy*.

Rubella A viral infection that can cause mental retardation and heart disease in an embryo. It's also called German measles.

SYPHILIS   Maternal **syphilis** can cause miscarriage or **stillbirth**, or it can be passed along to the child in the form of congenital syphilis. Congenital syphilis can impair the vision and hearing, damage the liver, and deform the bones and teeth.

Routine blood tests early in pregnancy can diagnose syphilis. The fetus will probably not contract syphilis if the infected mother is successfully treated with antibiotics before the fourth month of pregnancy.

Syphilis A sexually transmitted disease caused by a bacterial infection.

Stillbirth Birth of a dead fetus.

HIV/AIDS   **Acquired immunodeficiency syndrome (AIDS)** is caused by the human immunodeficiency virus (HIV). Because it's blood-borne, HIV is sometimes transmitted through the placenta to infect the fetus. Rupturing blood vessels in the mother and baby during childbirth provide more opportunities for HIV transmission.

The majority of babies born to mothers who are infected with HIV do not become infected themselves. Using antiviral medication can minimize the probability of transmission.

HIV can also be transmitted to children by breastfeeding.

Acquired immunodeficiency syndrome (AIDS) A sexually transmitted infection that destroys white blood cells in the immune system, leaving the body vulnerable to various opportunistic infections.

Pregnancy-induced hypertension A life-threatening condition characterized by high blood pressure.

Ectopic pregnancy A pregnancy in which the fertilized ovum becomes implanted somewhere other than the uterus.

Rh incompatibility A condition in which antibodies produced by a pregnant woman are transmitted to the fetus, where they may cause brain damage or death.

PREGNANCY-INDUCED HYPERTENSION **Pregnancy-induced hypertension**, also known as pre-eclampsia, is a life-threatening condition characterized by high blood pressure. It may afflict women late in the second or in the third trimester of pregnancy. If left untreated, it can lead to maternal and/or fetal death. Babies born to women with pregnancy-induced hypertension are often undersized or premature.

ECTOPIC PREGNANCY In an **ectopic pregnancy**, the fertilized ovum implants itself somewhere other than the uterus. Most ectopic pregnancies occur in fallopian tubes ("tubal pregnancies"). If ectopic pregnancies don't abort spontaneously, they must be removed by surgery or via medicines.

RH INCOMPATIBILITY Rh is a blood protein found in some people's red blood cells. **Rh incompatibility** occurs when an Rh-negative woman (who doesn't have the Rh blood protein) carries an Rh-positive fetus (who does have the Rh factor). This can happen if the father is Rh-positive. In Rh incompatibility, antibodies produced by the mother are transmitted to a fetus or newborn infant, potentially causing brain damage or death. This becomes a problem, however, only in a minority of the resulting pregnancies.

MATERNAL (AND PATERNAL) DRUG USE Although most of the attention on drug use during pregnancy is focused on the mother, a father's use of certain drugs may also negatively impact on the fetus. One question is whether drug use alters the genetic material in a man's sperm. A father-to-be who smokes tobacco or marijuana in the presence of the mother is exposing her and the fetus to secondhand smoke.

Several antibiotics can harm a fetus, especially if they're taken during certain periods of fetal development. Tetracycline may yellow the child's teeth and deform his or her bones (Koren et al., 1998). Other antibiotics have been implicated in deafness and jaundice. Acne drugs such as Accutane can cause physical and mental handicaps in the children of women who use them during pregnancy. Antihistamines, commonly used for allergies, may deform the fetus.

Women who are (or suspect they might be) pregnant should review the drugs they're taking with their obstetricians, and consult with them again before taking any new drugs, including non-prescription drugs.

VITAMINS Many pregnant women are prescribed daily doses of multivitamins to maintain their own health and promote healthy pregnancies. Too much of a good thing, however, can be hazardous. While normal doses can be beneficial, high doses of vitamins such as A, B6, D, and K have been linked to birth defects.

NARCOTICS Narcotics such as heroin and methadone can readily pass from mother to fetus through the placental membrane. Narcotics are addictive. Fetuses of mothers who use them regularly during pregnancy can become addicted in utero. At birth, such babies may experience withdrawal. Women who use narcotics should tell their obstetricians, so measures can be taken to aid their infants before and after delivery.

MARIJUANA The active ingredient in marijuana, THC, readily crosses the placenta. Research into the cognitive effects of maternal marijuana use suggests that there may be no impairment in the child's global intellectual functioning per se (Fried & Smith, 2001). However, there may be increased hyperactivity and impulsivity. Researchers also find a connection between prenatal exposure to marijuana and anxiety and depression later on (LaGasse et al., 2012).

Fetal alcohol syndrome (FAS) A cluster of symptoms in the infant caused by maternal alcohol consumption during pregnancy. These symptoms are typified by developmental lags, characteristic facial features, and a smaller-than-average body and brain.

ALCOHOL A mother who drinks during pregnancy increases the risk of birth defects, infant mortality, sensory and motor problems, and mental retardation in her child (Paintner et al., 2012). Nearly 40% of children whose mothers drink during pregnancy develop **fetal alcohol syndrome (FAS)**. FAS is a cluster of symptoms typified by developmental lags and characteristic facial features, such as underdeveloped upper jaws, flattened noses, and widely spaced eyes. Infants with FAS are often smaller than average and have smaller-than-average brains. They're also more susceptible to developing conduct disorders in middle childhood (Disney et al., 2008).

Although research suggests that light drinking is unlikely to harm the fetus, FAS has been found among the children of mothers who drank only 60 millilitres of alcohol a day during the first trimester (Astley & Clarren, 2001).

A high proportion of children in Canadian foster homes waiting for adoption have FAS. It's estimated that about half of the permanent wards of Winnipeg Child and Family Services, for example, have FAS (Gower & Philp, 2002b). Yet not all adoptive parents are aware of FAS or realize that their adopted children are likely to have been damaged by alcohol in the womb.

CIGARETTE SMOKING   Cigarette smoke contains chemicals such as carbon monoxide and the stimulant nicotine, which are transmitted to the fetus. It also lessens the amount of oxygen received by the fetus. Maternal smoking increases the risks of spontaneous abortion, premature rupturing of the amniotic sac, stillbirth, premature birth, low birth weight, and early infant mortality (Beyerlyn et al., 2011). These risks increase with the amount smoked (Bernstein et al., 2005). Low birth weight is a common risk factor for infant disease, mortality, and learning problems (O'Keeffe et al., 2003).

The combination of smoking and drinking alcohol places the child at greater risk for low birth weight than either practice alone (Spencer, 2006). Maternal smoking affects fetal heart rate and increases the risk of sudden infant death syndrome (SIDS) (Gordon et al., 2002; Pollack, 2001). Maternal smoking has been linked to reduced lung function in newborns (Sasaki et al., 2008) and asthma in children (Goodwin et al., 2009). Evidence also points to reduced attention spans, hyperactivity, and lower IQs and achievement test scores in children exposed to maternal smoking during and after pregnancy.

Smoking by the father (or another household member) may be dangerous to a fetus, because secondary smoke (exhaled by the smoker or emitted from the tip of a lit cigarette) may be absorbed by the mother and passed to the fetus. Passive exposure to secondhand smoke during infancy is linked to increased risk of SIDS (Gordon et al., 2002).

Many women don't stop using alcohol or cigarettes until they learn that they're pregnant, which may not occur until weeks into their pregnancies (Cnattingius, 2004). It may be easier for a woman to quit if she thinks of it as quitting for the duration of her pregnancy, rather than forever. If she remains abstinent after delivery, perhaps she won't be disappointed.

Chromosomal and Genetic Abnormalities

Not all of us have the normal complement of chromosomes. Some of us have genes that threaten our health.

On the basis of a couple's medical background and family histories, a genetic counsellor can help assess the risks of passing genetic defects to a child. Some couples who face high risks decide to adopt. Others decide to abort fetuses that are determined to have certain abnormalities.

Various medical procedures are used to detect fetal disorders. Parental blood tests can suggest the presence of sickle-cell anemia, Tay-Sachs disease, and neural tube defects. Tests of fetal DNA can indicate the presence of Huntington's disease, cystic fibrosis, and other disorders.

The risk of giving birth to a child with Down's syndrome increases with the mother's age. Amniocentesis can detect Down's syndrome before birth.

Childbirth

Early in the ninth month of pregnancy, the fetus's head settles in the pelvis. This shift is called "dropping" or "lightening." The woman may actually feel lighter, because there's less pressure on her diaphragm.

About a day or so before labour begins, the woman may notice blood in her vaginal secretions, because fetal pressure on the pelvis has ruptured superficial blood vessels in the birth canal. Tissue that has plugged the cervix, possibly preventing the entry of infectious agents from the vagina, has become dislodged, with a resultant discharge of bloody mucus. At about this time, one woman in 10 also has a rush of warm "water" from the vagina. This is amniotic fluid, and its presence means the amniotic sac has burst.

Labour usually begins within a day of rupture of the amniotic sac. For most women, the amniotic sac doesn't burst until the end of the first stage of childbirth. Labour begins with the onset of regular uterine contractions.

The first uterine contractions are relatively painless and are called **Braxton Hicks contractions**, or false labour contractions. They're considered false because they don't widen the cervix or advance the baby through the birth canal. They tend to increase in frequency, but are less regular than labour contractions. Real labour contractions, by contrast, become more intense when the woman moves around or walks.

Braxton Hicks contractions So-called false labour contractions, which are relatively painless.

Stages of Childbirth

Childbirth begins with the onset of labour, and has three stages.

In the first stage, uterine contractions **efface** and **dilate** the cervix to about 10 centimetres in diameter, so the baby can pass. Stretching of the cervix causes most of the pain of childbirth. A woman may experience little or no pain if her cervix dilates easily and quickly. The first stage may last from a couple of hours to more than a day. Twelve to 24 hours of labour is considered about average for a first pregnancy. In later pregnancies, labour takes about half this time.

The initial contractions are usually mild and widely spaced, at intervals of 10 to 20 minutes. They may last 20 to 40 seconds. As time passes, contractions become more frequent and regular, longer, and stronger.

Transition is the process that occurs when the cervix becomes almost fully dilated and the baby's head begins to move into the vagina, or birth canal. Contractions usually come quickly now. Transition usually lasts for up to 30 minutes and is often accompanied by nausea, chills, and intense pain.

The second stage of childbirth begins after transition, when the cervix is fully dilated and the baby begins to move into the birth canal (vagina). Each contraction propels the baby farther along the birth canal. When the baby's head becomes visible at the vaginal opening, it's said to have crowned. Typically, the baby fully emerges a few minutes after crowning. Full emergence ends the second stage of childbirth, which lasts from a few minutes to a few hours and is shorter than the first stage.

Sometimes an **episiotomy** is performed on the mother when the baby's head has crowned. This prevents random tearing of the **perineum**, which can occur if it becomes extremely effaced. Episiotomies are controversial. The incision can cause infection and pain, creating discomfort and itching as it heals. In some cases, the discomfort interferes with intercourse for months. Physicians generally agree that an episiotomy should be performed if the baby's shoulders are too wide to emerge without causing tearing, or if the baby's heartbeat drops for an extended period of time.

In Canada, the number of episiotomies is decreasing. In 1991, episiotomies were performed in almost half of all vaginal births. By 2004, they occurred in only about one-fifth of vaginal births (Public Health Agency of Canada, 2008) and more recent surveys suggest that the percentage of women having episiotomies during childbirth continues to decline (Public Health Agency of Canada, 2012).

The third, or placental, stage of childbirth can last from a few minutes to an hour or more. During this stage, the placenta is expelled and the uterus begins the process of contracting. Detachment of the placenta from the uterine wall may cause some bleeding.

The attending physician now sews up the episiotomy or any tears in the perineum.

Efface Cause to become thin.

Dilate Open or widen.

Transition The process during which the cervix becomes almost fully dilated and the infant's head begins to move into the birth canal.

Episiotomy A surgical incision in the perineum that widens the birth canal, preventing random tearing during childbirth.

Perineum The area between the vulva and the anus.

INTO THE WORLD   As the baby's head emerges, the doctor may use suction aspiration to clear away mucus from its mouth and prevent obstruction of the breathing passageway. Once the baby is breathing adequately, the doctor clamps and severs the umbilical cord about 7.5 centimetres from the baby's body. The stump of the umbilical cord dries and falls off in its own time, usually within 7 to 10 days.

While the mother is in the third stage of labour, the caregiver may perform procedures on the baby, such as placing drops of silver nitrate or an antibiotic ointment into the eyes. This procedure prevents bacterial infections in the newborn's eyes.

Methods of Childbirth

Until the twentieth century, childbirth usually happened at home and involved the mother, a midwife, family, and friends. Today, women in Canada typically give birth in hospitals, attended by physicians who use surgical instruments and anaesthetics to protect them and their babies from infection, complications, and pain.

Medical procedures save lives but make childbearing more impersonal. Social critics argue that these procedures have medicalized a natural process, usurping control over women's bodies and, through the use of drugs, denying many women the experience of giving birth.

MEDICATED CHILDBIRTH   During the past two centuries, science and medicine have led to the expectation that women should experience minimal discomfort during childbirth. Today, some anesthesia is used to minimize or eliminate pain in most Canadian deliveries.

Anaesthetic drugs, as well as tranquillizers and narcotics, decrease the strength of uterine contractions during delivery. They may thus delay the process of cervical dilation and prolong labour. They also reduce a woman's ability to push the baby through the birth canal. Because they cross the placental membrane, they also lower the newborn's overall responsiveness. There's little evidence, however, that medicated childbirth has serious, long-term consequences for children.

PREPARED CHILDBIRTH (THE LAMAZE METHOD)   When the French obstetrician Fernand Lamaze visited the Soviet Union in 1951, he found that many Russian women bore babies without anaesthetic and without reporting a great deal of pain. Lamaze returned to Western Europe with some of the techniques the women used. These are now termed the **Lamaze method**, or prepared childbirth.

Lamaze (1981) argued that women could learn to conserve energy during childbirth and reduce the pain of uterine contractions by associating the contractions with other responses, such as thinking of pleasant mental images (e.g., beach scenes) and engaging in breathing and relaxation exercises.

A pregnant woman typically attends Lamaze classes with a coach—usually the father or a partner—who will aid her in the delivery room by timing contractions, offering emotional support, and coaching her in the breathing and relaxation exercises. The partner is integrated into the process. Many couples report that their relationships are strengthened as a result.

The Lamaze method is flexible about the use of anaesthetics. Many women report some pain during delivery and are given anaesthetics. However, the Lamaze method appears to help women to gain a greater sense of control over the delivery process.

CAESAREAN SECTION   In a **Caesarean section**, the baby is delivered via surgery, rather than naturally, through the vagina. In a Caesarean section (or C-section, for short) the woman is anaesthetized, and incisions are made in the abdomen and uterus, so the surgeon can remove the baby. The incisions are then sewn up and the mother can begin walking, often on the same day, although generally with some discomfort for a while.

Lamaze method A childbirth method during which a woman learns how to relax and breathe in patterns that conserve energy and lessen pain, with the help of a coach (usually the father) who's present during the birth. The Lamaze method is also called prepared childbirth.

Caesarean section A method of childbirth in which the fetus is delivered through a surgical incision in the abdomen.

Transverse position A cross-wise birth position.

C-section is most likely to be advised when normal delivery is difficult or threatens the health of the mother or the child. Vaginal delivery can be difficult if the baby is large, the mother's pelvis is small or misshapen, or the mother is tired, weak, or aging. C-section is used to bypass herpes and HIV infections in the birth canal. C-section is also likely to be performed if the baby presents for delivery in the breech position (feet downward) or in the **transverse position** (lying crosswise), or if the baby is in distress.

Use of the C-section has mushroomed. In 2006, C-section rates in Canada reached an all-time high of 26.3% of all in-hospital deliveries, compared with 17% in 1993 (Canadian Institute for Health Information, 2007). In 2011, the C-section rate was slightly higher, at 27.1% (Canadian Institute for Health Information, 2011).

The Society of Obstetricians and Gynaecologists of Canada (SOGC) is concerned by the rising use of C-sections. The Society urges women to opt for C-sections only when medically necessary (Society of Obstetricians and Gynaecologists of Canada, 2008). According to the SOGC, women considering C-sections should be informed that a C-section is potentially more dangerous than a vaginal delivery for a healthy mother. Women who have C-sections take substantially longer to recover. C-sections present greater risks for complications such as infection, bleeding, scarring, chronic pelvic pain, and damage to the intestines or the bladder. C-sections also increase the risks during subsequent pregnancies, making repeat C-sections more likely (Society of Obstetricians and Gynaecologists of Canada, 2008).

Sometimes, however, there are excellent reasons for having a C-section. It makes no sense to avoid a C-section if vaginal delivery might put the mother or the baby at risk.

Birth Difficulties

Most deliveries are uncomplicated, or "unremarkable" in the medical sense—although childbirth is the most remarkable experience of many parents' lives. Difficulties with birth can and do occur, however.

Preterm Born before 37 weeks of gestation.

PRETERM AND LOW-BIRTH-WEIGHT CHILDREN A neonate is considered premature, or **preterm**, if it's born before 37 weeks of gestation. The normal period of gestation is 40 weeks. Prematurity is generally linked with low birth weight, because the fetus normally makes dramatic gains in weight during the last weeks of pregnancy.

Regardless of the length of its gestation, a newborn baby is considered to have a low birth weight if it weighs less than about 2500 grams. Preterm and low-birth-weight babies face heightened risks of infant mortality from causes that range from asphyxia and infections to sudden infant death syndrome (SIDS) (Berger, 2000; Kramer et al., 2000). Neurological and developmental problems are also common among preterm infants, especially those born at or before 25 weeks of gestation (Saigal et al., 2006; Wood et al., 2000).

Preterm infants usually remain in the hospital for a time. They're monitored and placed in incubators that provide temperature-controlled environments and offer some protection from infection. If necessary, they may also receive oxygen. Although

Too Early.
A baby is considered premature if it's born before 37 weeks of gestation. Premature babies are vulnerable to various developmental problems.

remarkable advances are being made in the ability to help preterm babies survive, the likelihood of developmental disabilities continues to dramatically increase for babies who are born at 25 weeks of gestation or earlier (Cole, 2000).

STILLBIRTH   Stillbirth, in which the baby is born dead, is the gravest of birth problems. Stillbirth is connected with fetal abnormalities, infection, the mother's medical condition, and pregnancy complications such as pre-eclampsia and problems with the placenta (Pasupathy & Smith, 2005). Yet the majority of cases have no clear cause and are considered unexplainable. In Canada there are about 2200 stillbirths each year, or 6.4 stillbirths for every 1000 total births (Statistics Canada, 2007b).

Stillbirth has a deep psychological impact on parents, leading in many cases to post-traumatic stress disorder (PTSD), which is characterized by ruminations

A World of Diversity

MATERNAL AND INFANT MORTALITY AROUND THE WORLD

Modern medicine has made vast strides in decreasing the rates of maternal and infant mortality, but the advances are not equally spread throughout the world. Save the Children (2011), a nonprofit relief and development organization, tracks the likelihood that a woman will die in childbirth and that an infant will die during its first year. The likelihood of maternal and infant mortality is connected with factors such as the percentage of births that are attended by trained people, the literacy rate of adult women (which is one measure of the level of education of women), and the participation of women in national government (which is one measure of the extent to which a society empowers women).

The safest place for a woman to deliver and for her baby to survive is Greece, where the chances of the woman dying are about 1 in 31 800, and where only 3 infants in 1000 die during the first five years after birth.

Female life expectancy at birth in Greece is 82, and the average number of years of schooling is 17. Afghanistan may have the world's most frightening statistics. One woman in 11 will die as a result of pregnancy, and 199 children of 1000 will die during their first five years. In Afghan society, only 14% of births are attended by trained personnel, and female life expectancy at birth is 45. European countries in general are safest. One out of 2100 women die in pregnancy or childbirth in the United States, and in Canada the figure is 1 out 5600.

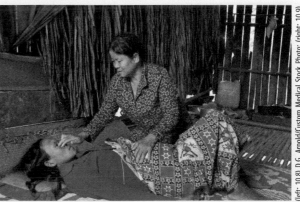

(left: 10.8) D.G. Arnold/Custom Medical Stock Photo; (right: 10.9) © Sean Sprague/The Image Works

Special Delivery?
A mother's safety depends on where she gives birth. It's not just about the medical care—it's about the wider issue of whether the culture empowers women.

Source: *Data from Save the Children (2011).* State of the World's Mothers 2008: Closing the Survival Gap for Children Under 5. Westport, CT: Save the Children. *Retrieved from http://www.savethechildren.org/publications/mothers/2008/SOWM-2008-full-report.pdf*

about the loss, intrusive thoughts, and nightmares (Born et al., 2006). When a baby is declared dead while still within the mother, she may need a few hours to adjust to the fact before labour is induced (Trulsson & Rådestad, 2004).

The Postpartum Period

Postpartum Following birth.

The weeks after delivery are called the **postpartum** period. The first few postpartum days are frequently happy ones. The long wait is over, and so are the discomforts of childbirth. However, about 70% of new mothers have periods of tearfulness, sadness, and irritability that the American Psychiatric Association (2000) refers to as "baby blues." Baby blues and other postpartum mood problems are so common that they're statistically normal (Gavin et al., 2005).

Baby blues affect most women in the weeks after delivery. Researchers believe they're common because they're caused by the hormonal changes that accompany and follow delivery (Bloch et al., 2006; Morris, 2000). They last for about 10 days and aren't severe enough to impair the mother's functioning.

One in five or ten women encounters a more serious mood disorder called postpartum depression (PPD). PPD begins within four weeks after delivery and may linger for weeks or months. PPD is symptomized by serious sadness, feelings of hopelessness and helplessness, feelings of worthlessness, difficulty concentrating, and major changes in appetite (usually loss of appetite) and sleep patterns (often insomnia). There can also be severe fluctuations in mood, from depression to elation and then back to depression. Some women show obsessive concern over the well-being of their babies at this time.

Some researchers suggest that PPD is caused by the interactions of biological (mainly hormonal) factors, including that precipitous drop-off in estrogen (Johnstone et al., 2001). Psychological factors may also be involved, such as concerns about the life changes wrought by motherhood, concerns about whether she'll be a good mother, marital problems, and a baby who is sick or unwanted.

The research focus, however, is on biological factors, because the body undergoes major chemical changes during and after pregnancy, and because women around the world seem to experience similar disturbances in mood, even when their life experiences and support systems are very different from those we find in Canada and the United States (Cohen et al., 2006).

Women who experience PPD may benefit from psychotherapy or drugs. Medications that increase estrogen levels or antidepressants may help. Most women recover from PPD on their own. At the very least, women need to know the problem isn't unusual, and doesn't necessarily mean something is seriously wrong with them, or that they're not living up to their obligations.

LESBIAN MOTHERS   Lesbian mothers are also at risk for maternal depression. In reviewing the research literature, University of Toronto researcher Lori Ross (2005) has concluded that lesbian mothers may experience more stress than heterosexual mothers, because they receive less support from their own parents, and because of societal prejudices. On the other hand, there are factors that reduce stress and the likelihood of postpartum depression in lesbians. Their pregnancies are more likely to be planned, and the division of childcare labour is more equal for lesbian couples than for heterosexual couples.

Breastfeeding

Health Canada and the Canadian Paediatric Society recommend breastfeeding as the preferred method for feeding infants because it provides optimal nutritional, immunological, and emotional benefits for the child's growth and development.

The percentage of Canadian women who breastfed their last babies increased from 81.5% in 2001 to 89.0% in 2011/2012 (Gionet, 2013).

The most common reasons mothers give for not breastfeeding are medical factors, such as premature or multiple births or the medical condition of the mother or the infant. Many also find breastfeeding unappealing or bottle-feeding easier.

One drawback of breastfeeding is that HIV can be transmitted to infants via breast milk. According to United Nations estimates, one-third of the infants around the world with HIV have been infected via breast milk (UNICEF, 2012). Another drawback is that when undernourished mothers in developing countries breastfeed, their babies can also become malnourished.

The hormones prolactin and oxytocin are involved in breastfeeding. **Prolactin** stimulates milk production, or **lactation**, two to three days after childbirth. Oxytocin, which is secreted in response to suckling, causes the breasts to eject milk. When an infant is weaned, prolactin and oxytocin secretion are discontinued, and lactation comes to an end.

Uterine contractions that occur during breastfeeding help return the uterus to its typical size, flattening the belly. Because of the expenditure of energy, breastfeeding may also help women lose the extra weight of pregnancy.

Although breastfeeding delays resumption of normal menstrual cycles, it's not a reliable birth-control method.

DOES BREASTFEEDING AFFECT SEXUAL BEHAVIOUR? In analyzing the literature, researchers at the University of British Columbia found that women who breastfeed are more likely than those who bottle-feed to experience decreased sexual desire, decreased frequency of sexual intercourse, and painful intercourse due to lack of vaginal lubrication (LaMarre et al., 2003).

LaMarre and her colleagues (2003) concluded that breastfeeding decreases both androgen levels, leading to decreased sexual desire, and estrogen levels, leading to vaginal dryness. Breastfeeding mothers are also more fatigued, from having to get up at night to feed their infants. Sexuality differences between breastfeeders and bottle-feeders diminish considerably after 12 months.

Should a woman breastfeed her baby? The issue has become highly politicized (Knaak, 2005). Much of the vast literature on breastfeeding has little to do with the relative advantages of breast milk or formula, but with occupational and domestic arrangements, daycare, maternal bonding, and the politics of domestic decision-making. Although breastfeeding has benefits for both mother and infant, each woman must weigh these benefits against the difficulties breastfeeding may pose for her.

Resumption of Ovulation and Menstruation

For close to a month after childbirth, women experience a reddish vaginal discharge called **lochia**. A non-nursing mother doesn't resume actual menstrual periods until two to three months postpartum. The first few cycles are likely to be irregular.

Many women incorrectly assume that they'll resume menstruating after childbirth by having a menstrual period and then ovulating two weeks later. In most cases, the

Prolactin A pituitary hormone that stimulates milk production. It comes from root words that mean "for milk."

Lactation Production of milk by the mammary glands.

CRITICAL THINKING QUESTIONS

Some people are offended by the sight a woman breastfeeding in public. Is this reaction reasonable?

Lochia A reddish vaginal discharge that may persist for a month after childbirth.

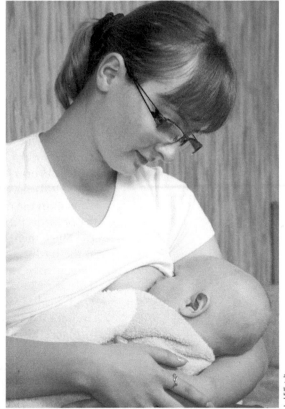

JackF/Fotolia

Breast Is Best?
Breastfeeding seems to be the gold standard for mothers in Canada today. Why? Is it always possible? Under what circumstances should women not breastfeed their children?

opposite is true. Ovulation precedes the first menstrual period after childbirth. A woman can therefore become pregnant before the menstrual phase of her first postpartum cycle.

Some (but not all) women who suffer premenstrual syndrome before pregnancy find that their periods give them less discomfort after they give birth.

Resumption of Sexual Activity

The resumption of intercourse depends on a couple's level of sexual interest, the healing of episiotomies or other injuries, fatigue, the recommendations of physicians, and, of course, tradition. Obstetricians usually advise a six-week waiting period, for safety and comfort. One study of 570 women found that they actually resumed sexual intercourse an average of seven weeks after childbirth (Byrd et al., 1998).

Women typically prefer to delay intercourse until it becomes physically comfortable—generally, when episiotomies and other lacerations have healed and the lochia has ended. This may take several weeks. Women who breastfeed may find that they have less vaginal lubrication, resulting in discomfort during intercourse. K-Y Jelly and other lubricants can help. Couples may enjoy other forms of sexual activity earlier, as soon as both partners are comfortable and interested.

The return of sexual interest and the resumption of sexual activity may take longer for some couples than for others. Sexual interest depends more on psychological than on physical factors. Many couples encounter declining sexual interest and activity in the first year after childbirth, generally because childcare can sap energy and limit free time. Generally, couples whose sexual relationships were satisfying before parenthood tend to show greater sexual interest and to resume sexual activity earlier than those who had less satisfying relationships beforehand.

Canadian Birth Rates and Teen Pregnancy

Birth Rates

Birth rates in Canada have varied considerably over time. Immediately after the Second World War, the Canadian birth rate dramatically rose to its highest level since 1921, the previous high. In 1947, Canada's fertility rate was 3.6 children per woman. In the mid-1960s, with the introduction of the birth-control pill, the number of births dropped sharply, reaching an all-time low in 2000.

Since then, the number of births has increased, mainly because of the increase in the birth rate among women who are 30 and older. The average age at which women have their first babies has climbed from 25.9 in 1980 to 28.5 in 2011. Thirty- to 34-year-old women have the highest proportion of births (Milan, 2013).

Canadian women today have an average of 1.61 children each. This is below the level needed to replace the population, which is 2.1 children per Canadian woman. As Figure 10.4 shows, the lowest birth rates are in Newfoundland and Labrador, and the highest are in Nunavut and the Northwest Territories (Statistics Canada, 2013).

The provinces and territories with the highest birth rates also have the largest proportions of aboriginal people. Birth rates among aboriginal populations are much higher than among the general population.

Why is the birth rate among Canadian women lower now than in past generations? Why are women giving birth later in life? There are a number of reasons:

- Improved access to safe, effective contraception allows women to choose whether and when they'll have children, how many they'll have, and how far apart they'll space them.

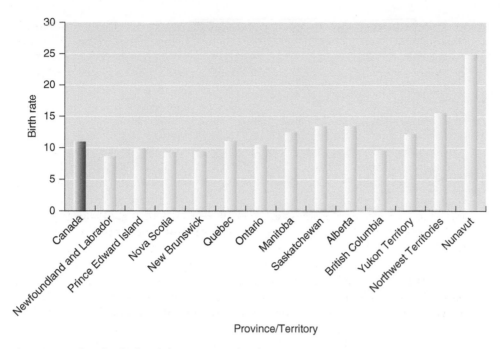

Figure 10.4   Canadian birth rates by province and territory, 2011.

Source: Statistics Canada. (2013). CANSIM Table 102-4505—Crude birth rate, age-specific and total fertility rates (live births), Canada, provinces and territories, annual (rate).

- More women are completing post-secondary education during their child-bearing years and are therefore delaying motherhood.
- Increasing numbers of women choose to limit the number of children they have, so they can continue working full time.
- Financial constraints lead some women to limit the number of children they decide to have.
- It's becoming more and more socially acceptable in Western society to choose not to have children.

TEEN PREGNANCY   The percentage of Canadian teens who become pregnant each year has declined sharply since the mid-1970s (McKay, 2012; McKay & Barrett, 2010). Looking at the most recent period for which Canadian statistics are available, the combined birth/abortion rate fell from 44.9 per 1000 15- to 19-year-old women in 1990 to 28.2 in 2010 (McKay, 2012). When looked at separately, the birth rate among teens fell from 25.5 per 1000 in 1990 to 13.5 in 2010, and the abortion rate fell from 19.4 to 14.7 during the same period (see Figure 10.5).

Teen pregnancy rates have also been falling in other Western countries, such as the United States, England, and Wales (McKay & Barrett, 2010). The decline has been greater in Canada than in the United States, England, and Wales. Sweden has typically had a low teen pregnancy rate, but it has increased in recent years, until Canada's teen pregnancy rate is now lower than Sweden's.

A number of factors influence teen pregnancy rates. Anderson Moore (2008) categorizes these factors as compositional (e.g., demographic aspects of the population), distal (e.g., economic inequality), and proximal (e.g., contraceptive use).

COMPOSITIONAL FACTORS   One compositional factor affecting teen pregnancy rates in Canada is the province or territory in which the young women live.

In 2010, the teen birth/abortion rates were higher than the national average of 28.2 per 1000 in Nunavut (115.2), Yukon (59.5), Manitoba (48.7), Saskatchewan

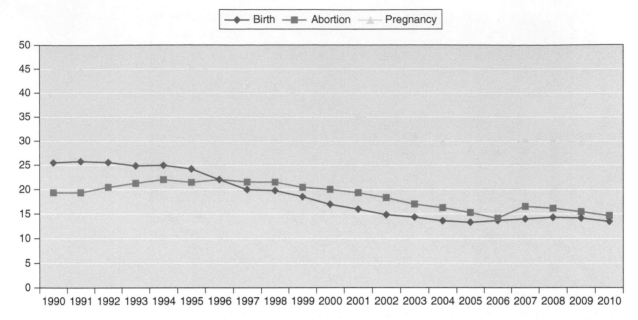

Figure 10.5 Birth/Abortion/Pregnancy Rates per 1000, Canada, Ages 15–19, 1990–2010

Source: McKay, A. (2012). Trends in Canadian national/territorial teen pregnancy rates: 2001–2010. Canadian Journal of Human Sexuality, 21(3–4), 161–176.

CRITICAL THINKING QUESTIONS

Can you think of reasons the teen pregnancy rate is higher in some parts of Canada than in others?

(44.1), Northwest Territories (40.4), Alberta (34.8), New Brunswick (34.8), Newfoundland (32.7), Nova Scotia (31.8), British Columbia (29.5), and Quebec (28.5), and lower than the national average in Ontario (21.2), and Prince Edward Island (14.9) (McKay, 2012).

DISTAL FACTORS   It's been shown that teen pregnancy rates are higher among economically disadvantaged populations (Best Start, 2007).

The rates for under-18 children in households whose incomes are lower than the national medians are higher in the United States and England than in Canada and Sweden (UNICEF, 2007). And as we have seen, the United States and England have higher teen pregnancy rates than Canada and Sweden.

It's likely that teenaged women who feel optimistic about their futures with respect to education and employment opportunities are more likely to delay childbearing until they're older (Best Start, 2008).

PROXIMAL FACTORS   It's obviously no coincidence that as the teen pregnancy rate in Canada has fallen, the percentage of sexually active teenagers who use contraception has increased.

A study of British Columbia youth found that the percentage who'd used an effective birth-control method (e.g., the pill, condom) at last intercourse increased from 77.4% in 1998 to 86.9% in 2003 (Saewyc, Taylor, Homma, & Ogilvie, 2008). A Statistics Canada study found that from 2003 to 2009/2010, condom use at last intercourse increased from 81.3% to 82.9% among 15- to 17-year-olds and from 70.4% to 76.7% among 18- to 19-year-olds (Rotermann, 2012).

Why are more sexually active teens using contraception now than in the past? It's likely that a range of factors are involved. Perhaps it's because today's teens have an easier time finding information about contraception and sexual health, using sources such as the Internet, and this has made them more knowledgeable about the issues. Perhaps it's because teens feel more comfortable buying condoms or asking their doctors for prescriptions for birth-control pills. Perhaps it's because more teens are getting high quality sexual-health education in schools.

TABLE 10.1

Sexual Orientation and Pregnancy Rates Among Sexually Active Teenagers in British Columbia

Sexual Orientation	Males*	Females
Gay	17%	
Lesbian		13%
Bisexual	17%	9%
Heterosexual	5%	5%

*Note: Male percentages refer to teenage males who had a heterosexual partner who became pregnant.

Source: Saewyc, E. M., Poon, C., Wang, N., Homma, Y., Smith, A., & McCreary Centre Society. (2007). Not yet equal: The health of lesbian, gay & bisexual youth in BC. *Vancouver: McCreary Centre Society.*

SEXUAL ORIENTATION AND TEEN PREGNANCY A study of 74 000 teenagers in British Columbia led by the University of British Columbia's Elizabeth Saewyc (2007) found that pregnancy rates are higher among sexually active gay, lesbian, and bisexual teenagers than among heterosexual teenagers. (See Table 10.1.) Data from the Toronto Teen Survey indicated that lesbian, gay, bisexual, and questioning youth youths were 3.2 times more likely than their heterosexual counterparts to be involved in a pregnancy (Flicker et al., 2009).

Based on qualitative interviews and focus groups with 71 sexually diverse youth and 23 service providers, Travers, Newton, and Munro (2011) concluded that pregnancy involvement among sexual minority youth can be understood as a response to heterosexism, where the "dominance of heterosexuality" in youths' lives produces extreme pressures to conform to heterosexist expectations of relationships and a desire to prove one's heterosexuality through heterosexual sex. Sexual assault can also lead to pregnancy among lesbian youth (Saewyc et al., 2007).

LIFE AFTER TEENAGE MOTHERHOOD Teen motherhood has generally been associated with long-term, negative socioeconomic consequences, but it doesn't necessarily condemn women to low incomes for a lifetime, according to a Statistics Canada (2008) study.

The study, "Life after teenage motherhood," published in *Perspectives on Labour and Income*, used the Survey of Labour and Income Dynamics to examine the personal and long-term socioeconomic characteristics of 30- to 39-year-old women who'd given birth as teenagers. Specifically, it compared women who'd been teen mothers with those who'd been adult mothers on the basis of educational outcome, long-term labour force participation, and income status.

Overall, teen mothers in Canada had a lower probability than their adult counterparts of completing high school and post-secondary education, even after controlling

Wavebreakmedia Ltd/123RF

Teen Motherhood.
Giving birth to a child during the teenage years can present significant challenges to a young woman. Teen mothers who receive adequate support from their families and communities and who are able to continue with their education are more likely to do well in the future.

for family background and other characteristics. But the study found that education may help counter the negative impact of teen motherhood on labour-force participation and income status. Overall, women with similar education levels, regardless of when they'd first had children, had a similar likelihood of full-year, full-time employment. Teen and adult mothers with less than high school education were both less likely to be working in full-time jobs for the full year. On the other hand, teen mothers who completed post-secondary studies were actually more likely than their adult counterparts to work full time.

Summing Up

Conception is the union of a sperm cell and an ovum. Fertilization normally occurs in a fallopian tube.

Optimizing the chances of conception means engaging in intercourse at the time of ovulation. Ovulation can be predicted by calculating the woman's basal body temperature, analyzing the woman's urine for luteinizing hormone, or tracking the thickness of vaginal mucus.

Fertility problems in the male include low sperm counts, irregularly shaped sperm, low sperm motility, certain chronic or infectious diseases, trauma to the testes, autoimmune responses to sperm, and pituitary imbalances and/or thyroid disease.

The major causes of infertility in women include irregular ovulation, obstructions or malfunctions of the reproductive tract, endometriosis, and the decline of hormone levels with age. Failure to ovulate can often be overcome by fertility drugs. Methods for overcoming other female fertility problems include in vitro fertilization, GIFT, ZIFT, donor IVF, embryonic transfer, and surrogate motherhood.

In Canada, the federal government act respecting assisted human reproduction and related research, whose short title is the Assisted Human Reproduction Act, includes a controversial provision that allows researchers to use stem cells from embryos left over from infertility treatments.

Early signs of pregnancy include a missed period and the presence of human chorionic gonadotropin (hCG) in the blood or urine.

Pregnancy tests detect hCG in the woman's urine or blood.

Miscarriages have many causes, including chromosomal defects in the fetus and abnormalities of the placenta and uterus.

Most health professionals concur that, in most cases, intercourse is safe until the start of labour.

A woman's psychological response to pregnancy reflects her desire to be pregnant, her physical changes, and her attitudes toward these changes.

The germinal stage is the period from conception to implantation.

The embryonic stage begins with implantation, extends to about the eighth week of development, and is characterized by differentiation of the major organ systems.

The fetal stage begins by the ninth week, continues until the birth of the baby, and is characterized by continuing maturation of the fetus's organ systems and dramatic increases in size.

Environmental factors that affect prenatal development include maternal diet, maternal diseases and disorders, and maternal drug use. Maternal malnutrition has been linked to low birth weight and infant mortality. Exposure to particular teratogens causes the greatest harm during critical periods of vulnerability.

Chromosomal and genetic abnormalities can lead to birth defects.

In the first stage of childbirth, uterine contractions efface and dilate the cervix, so the baby can pass through. The second stage begins when the cervix is fully dilated, and ends with the birth of the baby. During the third stage, the placenta is expelled.

Contemporary methods for facilitating childbirth include anaesthetized childbirth, natural childbirth, the Lamaze method, and Caesarean section.

Prenatal anoxia can cause brain damage and mental retardation in the child. Preterm and low-birth-weight babies have heightened risks of infant mortality.

Many new mothers experience transient mood changes after childbirth. Women with postpartum depression experience lingering depression after childbirth.

Breastfeeding is associated with fewer infections and allergic reactions in the baby than bottle-feeding.

Obstetricians usually advise waiting about six weeks after childbirth before resuming intercourse. Couples needn't wait this long to enjoy other forms of sexual activity.

In recent years, the teen pregnancy rate has fallen substantially in Canada. Teen mothers are more likely to fare well if they are able to continue with their education.

Test Yourself

Multiple-Choice Questions

1. In 2011, the average age of Canadian women having their first babies was:
   - (a) 24.5
   - (b) 26.5
   - (c) 28.5
   - (d) 30.5

2. _____ may carry either X or Y chromosomes.
   - (a) Sperm
   - (b) Ova
   - (c) Gametes
   - (d) Blastocysts

3. The most common cause of fertility problems in males is
   - (a) Sexually transmitted infections.
   - (b) Injury to the testes.
   - (c) Low sperm counts.
   - (d) High scrotal temperature.

4. All of the following can lead to infertility in women except:
   - (a) Failure to ovulate.
   - (b) Sexually transmitted infections.
   - (c) Declining levels of estrogen.
   - (d) Laparoscopy.

5. As of 2014, the only provinces or territories to cover the cost of in vitro fertilization were:
   - (a) Saskatchewan and Nova Scotia.
   - (b) Quebec and Ontario.
   - (c) New Brunswick and Manitoba.
   - (d) Ontario and Alberta.

6. The first stage of prenatal development is the _____ stage.
   - (a) embryonic
   - (b) placental
   - (c) fetal
   - (d) germinal

7. Most ectopic pregnancies occur in the:
   - (a) Ovaries.
   - (b) Cervix.
   - (c) Fallopian tubes.
   - (d) Uterus.

8. In 2010, which of the following provinces or territories had a teen birth/abortion rate lower than the national average?
   - (a) Manitoba.
   - (b) Ontario.
   - (c) New Brunswick.
   - (d) Yukon.

9. Approximately _____ of women experience some sadness, irritability, or low mood following the birth of a baby.
   - (a) 25%
   - (b) 40%
   - (c) 50%
   - (d) 70%

10. Which statement about postpartum depression (PPD) is false?
    - (a) Women who lack social support are more likely to suffer from PPD.
    - (b) PPD can involve feelings of extreme sadness and apathy.
    - (c) PPD may be caused by a combination of physiological and psychological factors.
    - (d) Women with PPD are always a danger to their babies.

You'll find answers to the "Test Yourself" questions on page 489.

Questions for Critical Thinking

1. In vitro fertilization can cost up to $15 000. Do you believe that government medical insurance should cover the cost? Explain your answer.

2. A good friend of yours is pregnant. You notice that she's still drinking alcohol and smoking cigarettes. Do you talk to her about how these behaviours could harm her fetus? Why or why not?

3. In your opinion, what are the most important factors that explain the decline in teen pregnancy rates in Canada?

4. Should it be legal in Canada for an infertile couple to pay a woman to be a surrogate mother? Where do you stand on this issue?

CHAPTER ELEVEN

Contraception and Abortion

Niixx Photography/Shutterstock

People have been devising means of contraception since they became aware of the relationship between penile–vaginal intercourse and conception. Greek and Roman women placed absorbent materials within their vaginas to absorb semen.

The use of sheaths or coverings for the penis has a long history. Sheaths worn over the penis as decorative covers can be traced to ancient Egypt (1350 BCE). Sheaths of linen were first described in European writings in 1564 by the Italian anatomist Fallopius (after whom the fallopian tube is named). The term **condom** wasn't used to describe the penile sheath until the 18th century. At that time, sheaths made of animal intestines became popular as a means of preventing sexually transmitted infections and unwanted pregnancies.

Condoms made of rubber (hence the slang term "rubbers") were introduced shortly after Charles Goodyear invented vulcanization of rubber in 1843. Many other forms of contraception were also widely used in the nineteenth century, including withdrawal, vaginal sponges, and douching.

Condom A sheath made of latex, polyurethane/poliso-phene or animal membrane (lambskin) that covers the penis and serves as a barrier to sperm following ejaculation.

Contraception in Canada

Contraceptive Use among Canadian Women

The most recent national survey of contraceptive use in Canada conducted by Amanda Black and her colleagues (2009) asked 2751 Canadian women of reproductive age who'd had penile–vaginal intercourse within the previous six months about their contraceptive practices. Although none of the women were trying to get pregnant, 410 (14.9%) used no contraception. The methods used by the women who did use contraception are shown in Table 11.1.

It's immediately apparent from these findings that the vast majority of Canadian women rely on male condoms and oral contraceptives for birth control. When all age groups were combined, 54.3% used condoms and 43.7% used oral contraceptives. Withdrawal was the third most popular method, used by 11.6% of the women.

Contraceptive Use among Canadian Teens and University Students

A large-scale study of female and male teenagers in British Columbia by the McCreary Centre Society measured contraceptive use at last intercourse with 66% reporting they used a condom, 41% the birth control pill, and 23% withdrawal (Smith et al, 2009).

More recently, Milhausen et al. (2013), as part of the *Trojan/SIECCAN Sexual Health Study*, presented findings on contraceptive methods used at last intercourse among 653 university students aged 18 to 24 from across Canada who reported having penile–vaginal intercourse in the previous three months. Among women, 63.0% reported using oral contraception, 42.3% a condom, 17.7% another method, and 7.8% no method. Among men, 55.4% reported using a condom, 40.0% oral contraception, 15.1% another method, and 11.7% no method (respondents could indicate that more than one method was used). When asked what their most preferred

TABLE 11.1

Contraceptive Methods Used by Canadian Women for Penile–Vaginal Intercourse within the Previous Six Months (%)

Contraceptive Method	Ages 15–19	Ages 20–29	Ages 30–39	Ages 40+
Male condom	74.6	55.5	48.8	42.5
Oral contraceptive	66.6	58.3	31.5	17.1
Withdrawal	17.3	12.0	10.3	8.1
Male sterilization	0.2	1.4	9.6	19.6
Female sterilization	0.0	0.7	8.1	16.4
Rhythm method	1.5	2.8	3.0	6.6
Natural family planning	1.5	1.3	5.2	2.4
Injection	1.8	3.4	2.6	1.0
IUD	0.5	1.8	5.8	0.8
Morning-after pill	4.4	1.7	1.5	0.0
Contraceptive patch	1.6	2.3	0.7	0.0
Contraceptive sponge	0.2	1.0	0.7	1.0
Female condom	0.4	0.2	0.0	0.8
Diaphragm	0.3	0.5	0.0	0.0
Cervical cap	0.2	0.0	0.0	0.0

Note: Column totals may exceed 100%, as women were allowed to choose more than one method.

Source: Adapted from Black, A., Yang, Q., Wen, S. W., Lalonde, A. B., Guilbert, E., & Fisher, W. (2009). Contraceptive use among Canadian women of reproductive age: Results of a national survey. Journal of Obstetrics and Gynaecology Canada, 31(7), 627–640.

A World of Diversity

A HISTORY OF BIRTH CONTROL IN CANADA

Birth control was legal in Canada until the nineteenth century, when laws were introduced forbidding both birth control and abortion. It was even illegal to provide information about birth control. Because contraceptives were associated with loose morals and prostitution, it was considered unacceptable for doctors to discuss birth control with their patients.

The movement to legalize contraception in Canada began in the 1920s, when female activists in Vancouver formed the Canadian Birth Control League. In the following years, several women's groups across Canada began to lobby politicians to change the law that prohibited the use of birth control. A few men also joined the cause.

Despite protests by some physicians, Mary Hawkins established the first Canadian birth control clinic in Hamilton, Ontario, in the early 1930s. In 1937, clinics were also set up in Windsor and Kitchener. A prominent supporter of birth control education

at that time was A. R. Kaufman, a wealthy Kitchener businessman who hired women to deliver birth control information door to door.

The first major legal challenge to the law forbidding the dissemination of birth control information came with the arrest of Dorothea Palmer (an employee of Kaufman) for promoting birth control in the poorer districts of the Ottawa region. Her arrest sparked protests and support by birth-control activists, including Kaufman, who helped win her acquittal in court. This victory helped legitimize birth-control education and spurred the birth-control movement to make greater efforts in the struggle to legalize all birth-control activities.

By the 1960s, the use of contraceptives (particularly the birth-control pill) had become so widespread that most Canadians didn't realize contraceptives were still illegal. The 1960 arrest of Toronto pharmacist Harold Fine for selling condoms enraged many Canadians. As a result, Barbara Cadbury and her husband George Cadbury established the Planned Parenthood Association of Toronto in

1961, with the objective of amending the *Criminal Code.*

In 1965, another leader in the birth-control movement, Dr. Marion Powell, opened the first city-funded public health clinic (focused on family planning) in Scarborough, Ontario. It wasn't until 1969, under the leadership of Prime Minister Pierre Trudeau, that contraception became legal and abortion was allowed under restricted conditions.

Today, contraceptives are widely advertised in popular magazines and openly displayed on pharmacy shelves.

The use of **artificial contraception** continues to be opposed by some groups, including the Roman Catholic Church. Yet many individual Catholics, including many priests, hold liberal attitudes toward contraception.

Sources: Planned Parenthood Federation of Canada. (1999). A history of birth control in Canada. Brochure. Ottawa: Planned Parenthood Federation of Canada; Liu, K. E., & Fisher, W. A. (2002). Canadian physicians' role in contraception from the 19th century to now. Journal of Obstetrics and Gynaecology Canada, 24(3), 239–244.

CRITICAL THINKING QUESTIONS

What might explain differences between female and male university students' preferred methods of contraception?

Artificial contraception A method of contraception that applies a human-made device.

Oral contraceptive A contraceptive that consists of sex hormones and is swallowed.

Combination pill A birth-control pill that contains synthetic estrogen and progesterone.

contraceptive method was, more women chose oral contraception than condoms (60.7% vs. 21.8%) whereas more men chose condoms than oral contraception (49.7% vs. 33.7%).

Methods of Contraception

Oral Contraceptives (The Pill)

An **oral contraceptive** is commonly referred to as a birth-control pill, or simply "the pill." There are many kinds of birth-control pills, varying in hormone types and dosages. Birth-control pills fall into two major categories: combination pills and minipills.

Combination pills contain a combination of synthetic forms of the hormones estrogen and progesterone. (The synthetic form of progesterone is called progestin.) Most combination pills provide a steady dose of synthetic estrogen and progesterone.

Other combination pills, called multiphasic pills, vary the dosages of these hormones across the menstrual cycle, reducing the overall dosages and possible side effects women are exposed to. The **minipill** contains only synthetic progesterone (progestin).

HOW IT WORKS   Women can't conceive when they're already pregnant, because their bodies suppress maturation of egg follicles and ovulation. The combination pill fools the brain into thinking the woman is already pregnant, so no additional ova mature or are released. If ovulation doesn't take place, a woman can't become pregnant.

In a normal menstrual cycle, low estrogen levels during and just after the menstrual phase stimulate the pituitary gland to secrete the follicle-stimulating hormone (FSH), which in turn stimulates maturation of the ovarian follicles. The estrogen in the combination pill inhibits FSH production, so follicles don't mature. The progestin inhibits the pituitary's secretion of luteinizing hormone (LH), which would otherwise lead to ovulation. The woman continues to have menstrual periods, but there are no unfertilized ova to be sloughed off in the menstrual flow.

The combination pill is taken for 21 days of the typical 28-day cycle. Then, for seven days, the woman takes no pill, or she takes an inert placebo pill, to maintain the habit of taking a pill a day. The sudden drop in hormone levels causes the endometrium to disintegrate and menstruation to follow three or four days after the last pill is taken. The cycle is then repeated.

The progestin in the combination pill also increases the thickness and acidity of the cervical mucus. The mucus thus becomes a more resistant barrier to sperm, and inhibits development of the endometrium. Therefore, even if an egg were somehow to mature and be released, sperm wouldn't be likely to survive the passage through the cervix. Even if sperm were somehow to succeed in fertilizing an egg, the failure of the endometrium to develop would mean the fertilized ovum couldn't become implanted in the uterus. Progestin may also impede the progress of ova through the fallopian tubes and make it more difficult for sperm to penetrate the ova.

The minipill contains progestin, but no estrogen. Minipills are taken daily through the menstrual cycle, even during menstruation. They act in two ways: they thicken the cervical mucus, to impede the passage of sperm through the cervix, and they render the inner lining of the uterus less receptive to a fertilized egg. Thus, even if the woman does conceive, the fertilized egg will pass from her body, rather than becoming implanted in her uterine wall.

EFFECTIVENESS   When it's used consistently and correctly, the failure rate of the birth-control pill is very low—0.5% or less, depending on the type of pill. (See Table 11.2.) Under typical use, the failure rate increases to 3%. Failures can occur when women forget to take the pill for two days or more, don't use backup methods when they first go on the pill, or switch from one brand to another. But forgetting to take the pill for a day or two might allow ovulation—and fertilization.

REVERSIBILITY   A woman may temporarily experience reduced fertility after discontinuing oral contraceptives, but their use is not associated with permanent infertility. Nearly all women begin ovulating regularly within three months of suspending use (Hatcher et al., 2011). When a woman appears not to be ovulating after going off the pill, a drug like clomiphene is often used to induce ovulation.

ADVANTAGES AND DISADVANTAGES   The great advantage of oral contraception is that it's nearly 100% effective when it's used properly. Unlike many other forms of contraception, such as the condom and the diaphragm, its use doesn't interfere with sexual spontaneity or diminish sexual sensation.

The birth-control pill may also have some healthful side effects. It appears to reduce the risk of pelvic inflammatory disease (PID), benign ovarian cysts,

TABLE 11.2

Failure Rates, Reversibility, and Protection against Sexually Transmitted Infections by Various Methods of Birth Control (in Percentage of Women Who Become Pregnant within the First Year of Use)

Method	Percent (%) of Women Who Have an Unplanned Pregnancy within the First Year of Use		Is It Reversible?	Does It Protect against Sexually Transmitted Infections (STIs)?
	Typical Use[1]	Consistent, Correct Use		
None	85	85	yes	no
Spermicides	29	18	yes	no
Rhythm Methods	20		yes	no
Calendar		9		
Ovulation Method		3		
Basal Body Temperature		2		
Post-Ovulation		3		
Withdrawal	27	4	yes	no
Cervical Cap[2]	20–40	10–30	yes	some
Diaphragm[2]	16	6	yes	some
Condom alone				
Female condom	21	5	yes	(scarce information)
Male condom	15	2	yes	yes
The Pill	8	0.3	yes	no, but may *reduce* the risk of pelvic inflammatory disease
Progestin Only		0.5		
Combined		0.1		
IUD	0.2–0.8	0.2–0.6	yes, except if fertility is impaired	no
Depo-Provera	3	0.3	yes	no
Injectable Contraceptives	0.5	0.5	yes	no
Female Sterilization	0.5	0.5	questionable	no
Male Sterilization	0.15	0.10	questionable	no

[1]*Accidental pregnancies among typical couples.* [2]*With spermicide.*

Sources: American Academy of Family Physicians. (2012, June 13). Family planning and contraception. Retrieved from http://www.aafp.org/afp/topicModules/viewTopic-Module.htm?topicModuleId=71; Cleland, K., Zhu, H., Goldstuck, N., Cheng, L., & Trussell, J. (2012). The efficacy of intrauterine devices for emergency contraception: A systematic review of 35 years of experience. Human Reproduction, 27(7), 1994–2000; Hatcher, R. A., Trussell, J., Nelson, A. L., Cates, W., Kowal, D., & Policar, M. (Eds). (2011). Contraceptive Technology: Twentieth Revised Edition. *New York, NY: Ardent Media.*

and fibrocystic (benign) breast growths. The pill regularizes menstrual cycles and reduces menstrual cramping and premenstrual discomfort. The pill may be helpful in treating iron-deficiency anemia and facial acne. The combination pill reduces the risks of ovarian and endometrial cancer, even for a number of years after the woman stops taking it (Hatcher et al., 2011; Phipps et al., 2011).

The pill does have some disadvantages. It confers no protection against STIs. Moreover, it may reduce the effectiveness of antibiotics used to treat STIs. Going on the pill requires medical consultation, so a woman must plan to begin using the pill at least several weeks before becoming sexually active or before discontinuing the use of other contraceptives.

There has been concern about a potential link between oral contraceptive use and breast cancer. However, results from several large-scale studies show no overall increase in the rates of breast cancer among pill users (Hatcher et al., 2008). Marchbanks and her colleagues (2002) compared 4575 women who had breast cancer with 4682 controls, for example, and found no increased risk for breast cancer among women who were using or had used oral contraceptives. The pill didn't increase the risk of breast cancer in women with family histories of the disease, either.

Among the main drawbacks of birth-control pills are potential side effects and health risks. Although a good deal of research suggests that the pill is safe for healthy women, many researchers (e.g., the American College of Obstetricians and Gynecologists, 2006; Sun & Ren, 2012) suggest caution for women with various pre-existing medical conditions. These include hypertension, diabetes, migraine headaches, fibrocystic breast tissue, uterine fibroids, and elevated cholesterol levels.

The estrogen in combination pills may produce side effects such as nausea and vomiting, fluid retention (which leaves a woman feeling bloated), weight gain, increased vaginal discharge, headaches, tenderness in the breasts, and dizziness. Many of these are temporary. When they persist, women may be switched from one pill to another, perhaps to one with lower doses of hormones. Pregnant women produce high estrogen levels in the corpus luteum and placenta. The combination pill artificially raises levels of estrogen, so it's not surprising that some women who use it have side effects that mimic the early signs of pregnancy, such as weight gain and nausea ("morning sickness"). Weight gain can result from estrogen (through fluid retention) or progestin (through increased appetite and muscle development) (Hatcher et al., 2011). Women who experience high blood pressure from taking the pill are usually advised to switch to another form of contraception.

Many women experience hormone withdrawal symptoms during the week they don't take the active pill (Spencer & Bonnema, 2011). These include headaches, pelvic pain, bloating, and breast tenderness.

Many women have avoided the pill because of the risk of blood clots. Most birth-control pills today have lower dosages of estrogen than pills in the 1960s and 1970s, and therefore much lower risks for blood clotting (Hatcher et al., 2011). Still, women who are at increased risk for blood clotting, such as those with histories of circulatory problems or stroke, are typically advised not to use the pill.

Women who are considering the pill need to discuss the benefits and risks with their physicians. For the great majority of young, healthy women in their twenties and early thirties, the pill is unlikely to cause blood clots or other cardiovascular problems (Hatcher et al., 2011). Although research has found the pill safe for most women under age 35 who don't smoke, pill users may have a slightly higher chance than nonusers of experiencing blood clots in the veins and lungs, strokes, and heart attacks.

Some women shouldn't be on the pill at all. Woman should avoid the pill if they've had circulatory problems, blood clots, coronary disease, heart attacks, strokes, breast or uterine cancers, undiagnosed genital bleeding, liver tumours, or sickle-cell anemia (because of associated blood-clotting problems). Because of the increased risk for cardiovascular problems, women over 35 who smoke should exercise caution with the combination pill (Hatcher et al., 2011). Nursing mothers should also avoid the pill, to prevent passing the hormones to their babies through their milk.

The pill may also have psychological effects. Some users report depression and irritability. Switching brands or altering the dosage may help. There's insufficient evidence about the effects of lower-estrogen pills on sexual desire.

Because they can produce vaginal dryness, minipills can hinder vaginal lubrication during intercourse, decreasing sexual sensation and making sex painful. Irregular bleeding between menstrual periods, or so-called breakthrough bleeding, is another common side effect of the minipill. Irregular bleeding should be brought to a doctor's attention.

Evidence linking the pill to increased risk of cervical cancer is mixed. Some studies show a link, and others don't (Hatcher et al., 2011).

Women considering the pill are advised to have thorough medical evaluations, to rule out pre-existing conditions that might make its use unsafe. Women who begin to use the pill, regardless of their age or risk status, should pay attention to changes in their physical condition, have regular checkups, and promptly report any physical complaints or unusual symptoms to their physicians.

EMERGENCY CONTRACEPTION (EC)   Emergency contraception—the so-called morning-after pill—is taken after unprotected sexual intercourse or when contraception fails, such as when a condom breaks.

Two forms of EC pills are available in Canada (Katzman & Taddeo, 2010). The most popular is two 0.75-milligram tablets of levonorgestrel (progestin-only), known as Plan B. The other, known as the Yuzpe regimen (combined estrogen and progestin) combines multiple birth-control pills. According to Katzman and Taddeo (2010), Plan B has fewer side effects and is more effective than the Yuzpe regimen. Plan B isn't generally considered an abortion pill, because it can't end an established pregnancy. It prevents pregnancy by preventing the joining of sperm and egg and preventing a fertilized egg from attaching to the uterine wall.

Innovative Canadian Research

EMERGENCY CONTRACEPTION

In British Columbia, Soon and her colleagues (2005) studied EC use both before and after it became available without a prescription. They made several key findings:

- EC use was highest among women who were 20 to 24 years old, and second highest among women who were 15 to 19 years old.
- More than half of the users (56%) obtained EC within 24 hours of having unprotected intercourse, and almost all (98%) within 72 hours.
- Very few women used EC on a regular basis. Only 2.5% received EC three or more times a year, and just 1.1% obtained EC for future use.
- More than half of the women receiving EC (56%) reported that they'd used birth control methods that had failed.
- The availability of EC without a prescription significantly increased its use.

Anne Marie Whalen, Donald Langille, and Eileen Hurst (2013) from Dalhousie University in Halifax surveyed pharmacists in Nova Scotia to explore their knowledge of and attitudes towards non-prescription Plan B, the only available form of emergency contraception in Canada at the time of the study. The experiences of pharmacists in the provision of information and advice to consumers were also studied.

Questionnaires were completed by 451 community pharmacists across Nova Scotia. Even though Plan B was allowed to be sold in the public areas of pharmacies, most pharmacists (83.6%) reported that they still kept the drug behind the counter. Over 90% of respondents indicated that they continued to offer consumers consultation and counseling about emergency contraception. A very small percentage (1.6%) of respondents cited moral, religious, or ethical objections to the provision of Plan B. Most pharmacists were generally knowledgeable about emergency contraception; however, only 39.2% were aware that it can be effective when taken up to five days after unprotected sex, and 30% were unaware that vomiting was an adverse side effect for less than 50% of women. Lack of privacy and lack of backup staff to allow for interaction with the public were cited as the main barriers to the provision of effective consultation.

EC should be taken as soon as possible after unprotected intercourse. It's most effective when taken within 72 hours, though recent research suggests it may be effective even when taken within 120 hours. Overall, EC is relatively effective in reducing the probability of pregnancy after unprotected intercourse. Studies have shown pregnancy rates of 1% to 3% among women using Plan B (Katzman & Taddeo, 2010). In 2014, Health Canada stipulated that emergency contraceptive pills carry a warning that they are less effective for women weighing 75–80 kg and not effective for women who weigh over 80 kg.

In 2005, Health Canada allowed pharmacists to provide Plan B without a prescription. Pharmacies were required to keep supplies of Plan B behind the counter, which meant women who wanted Plan B had to first consult with the pharmacists. In 2008, Health Canada permitted Plan B to be available on customer-accessible pharmacy shelves, rather than behind the counter. Along with this change, it was expected that women would no longer need to consult pharmacists about its use. Some pharmacists have resisted this change, however, and kept Plan B behind the counter, believing their customers should be counselled on the proper use of this medication.

EC pills have a higher hormone content than most birth-control pills. For this reason, nausea is a common side effect. Nausea is usually mild and passes within a day or two after treatment, but it can be treated with anti-nausea medications.

The Contraceptive Patch

The contraceptive patch is another method of delivering estrogen and progestin, to prevent ovulation and implantation. A patch named Ortho Evra has been available in Canada since 2004. The patch is thin and measures about 5 centimetres. It's worn on the abdomen, buttocks, upper arm, or upper torso, but not on the breasts. The patch contains a week's worth of hormones, which it gradually releases into the bloodstream. The patch is worn weekly for three weeks, then the fourth week is patch-free, to allow menstrual bleeding. It can be worn in water.

Like the birth-control pill, when used correctly, the patch is more than 99% effective. Women who use the patch needn't think about contraception daily. Also like the pill, the patch doesn't interrupt sex. Its side effects and potential hazards are similar to those of the pill.

The Vaginal Ring

A relatively new contraceptive in Canada is a vaginal ring, called the NuvaRing. The vaginal ring delivers hormones through the skin. Shaped like a diaphragm, the ring contains a combination of estrogen and progestin. A doctor's prescription is needed to obtain the ring from a pharmacy.

The ring is inserted into the vagina and worn for three consecutive weeks, followed by a ring-free week, to allow menstruation. At the end of the ring-free week, the woman inserts another ring, beginning a new cycle.

The ring is left in place during sex. If it slips out of the vagina, it can be reinserted. Most men and women don't notice it during intercourse, although some women may experience vaginal discomfort. The ring is as effective as the birth control pill, and may be more effective if a woman has trouble remembering to take her pill every day.

More research is needed on both the ring and the patch, to determine whether they have long-term side effects.

Plan B.
The morning-after pill is now available in Canada without a prescription.

Injectable Contraception

Depo-Provera is an injectable hormone solution that's available by prescription. Containing just progestin, it prevents ovulation and is 99.7% effective in preventing pregnancy. It's administered by a needle in the muscle of the arm or buttocks every 12 weeks, preventing pregnancy for three months.

Injectable contraception has the advantage of being highly effective, permitting spontaneous sex, and remaining effective without having to be taken every day. It has side effects similar to those of other types of hormonal contraceptives, including oral contraceptives. These include vaginal bleeding, headaches, tenderness in the breasts, irregular menstrual cycles, weight gain, bloating, nausea, and vomiting. Prolonged use—two years or more—has been associated with bone loss. Depo-Provera's effects on fertility are reversible, but ovulation may take a few months to return.

Injectable contraceptives are usually not recommended for women who smoke or have elevated blood pressure, breast or uterine cancers, histories of blood clotting, histories of heart attack or stroke, diabetes, liver disease, or hormone allergies.

Intrauterine Devices (IUDs)

Intrauterine device (IUD) A small object that is inserted into the uterus and left in place to prevent conception.

Intrauterine devices (IUDs) are used by more than 100 million women around the world (Hatcher, 2011). Most of them live in China, where nearly one in three married women uses an IUD during her childbearing years. By contrast, IUDs are used by less than 5% of sexually active women of reproductive age in Canada (Black et al., 2009).

An IUD is a small object that comes in a variety of shapes and is inserted into the uterus by a physician or a nurse practitioner. A fine plastic thread or string hangs down from the IUD into the vagina, so the woman can check to be sure it's still in place.

Two main intrauterine devices and systems are currently available in Canada: copper IUDs (Flexi-T and Nova-T) and a levonorgestrel-releasing IUD system (Mirena). These devices are about 99% effective for up to five years. The IUD prevents sperm from fertilizing an egg. If sperm does fertilize the egg, the IUD prevents the fertilized egg from implanting in the uterus. Women who use IUDs are advised to check the strings several times a month, to ensure that the IUDs are in place.

IUDs can be readily removed by professionals. About nine out of ten former IUD users who wish to become pregnant do so within a year.

IUDs are highly effective and relatively maintenance-free. So, why aren't they more popular? One reason is side effects. The most common are excessive menstrual cramping, irregular bleeding (spotting) between periods, and heavier-than-usual menstrual bleeding (Hatcher et al., 2011). A more serious concern is the risk of pelvic inflammatory disease, which is serious and can become life-threatening if left untreated. PID can produce scar tissue that blocks the fallopian tubes, causing infertility. Another risk is that the IUD may perforate (tear) the uterine or cervical walls.

Women with pelvic infections shouldn't use IUDs. Women with risk factors for PID—including recent episodes of gonorrhea or chlamydia—may also wish to consider the advisability of using IUDs. IUD users are also at greater risk for ectopic pregnancies.

The Diaphragm

Diaphragm A shallow rubber cup or dome that's fitted to the contours of a woman's vagina. It's coated with a spermicide and inserted before intercourse, to prevent conception.

The **diaphragm** is a shallow cup or dome made of thin latex rubber (see Figure 11.1.) The rim is a flexible metal ring covered with rubber. Diaphragms come in different sizes to allow a precise fit.

A diaphragm is available by prescription, and must be fitted to the contours of the vagina by a health-care professional. Several sizes and types may be tried during a fitting.

HOW IT WORKS   The diaphragm is inserted and removed by the woman, much like a tampon. It's akin to a condom in that it forms a barrier against sperm when placed snugly over the cervical opening. Yet it's unreliable when used alone. It should be used in conjunction with a spermicidal cream or jelly.

HOW IT'S USED   The woman (or her partner) places a tablespoon of spermicidal cream or jelly on the inside of the cup and spreads it inside the rim. The woman opens the inner lips of her vagina with one hand, and squeezes the ring to fold the diaphragm with the other. She inserts the diaphragm against the cervix, with the inner side facing upward (see Figure 11.2).

The diaphragm should be left in place *at least six hours* after intercourse, to allow the spermicide to kill all remaining sperm in the vagina (Hatcher et al., 2011).

EFFECTIVENESS   As Table 11.2 indicates, if the diaphragm is used consistently and correctly, its failure rate is estimated to be 6% during the first year of use. In typical use, however, the failure rate is believed to be three times as high—18%. Some women become pregnant because they don't use their diaphragms during every intercourse experience. Effectiveness is also seriously compromised when the diaphragm is used without a spermicide.

ADVANTAGES AND DISADVANTAGES   The major advantage of the diaphragm is that it's a fairly effective means of birth control when it's used correctly. It can be used as needed, whereas the pill must be used every day.

The major disadvantage of the diaphragm is the high pregnancy rate associated with typical use. Nearly one in five typical users (18%) of the diaphragm combined with spermicidal cream or jelly become pregnant during the first year of use (Hatcher et al., 2011). Another disadvantage is the need to insert the diaphragm before intercourse, which the couple may find disruptive.

The Cervical Cap

The cervical cap is a dome-shaped rubber cup. It comes in different sizes and must be fitted by a health-care professional. It's smaller than the diaphragm—about the size of a thimble—and is meant to fit snugly over the cervical opening.

Like the diaphragm, the cap is intended to be used with a spermicide applied inside it. When inserting it, the woman (or her partner) fills the cap about a third full of spermicide. Then, squeezing the edges together, the woman inserts the cap high into her vagina, so it presses firmly against her cervix. It should be left in place for at least eight hours after intercourse. The cap provides continuous protection for upwards of 48 hours without the need for additional spermicide.

The major disadvantage is the high failure rate of typical users. Nearly one in five typical users

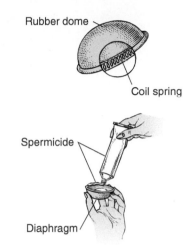

Figure 11.1   A diaphragm. The diaphragm is a shallow cup or dome made of latex. It must be fitted to the contours of the vagina by a health professional. The diaphragm forms a barrier to sperm, but should be used in conjunction with a spermicidal cream or jelly.

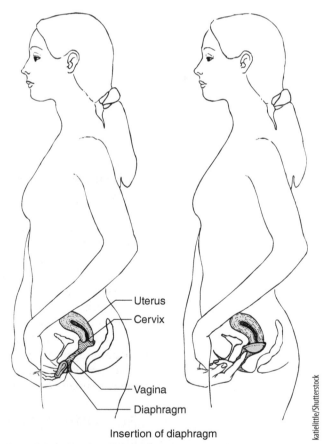

Insertion of diaphragm

Figure 11.2   Inserting and checking the diaphragm. Women are instructed in how to insert of the diaphragm by health-care professionals.

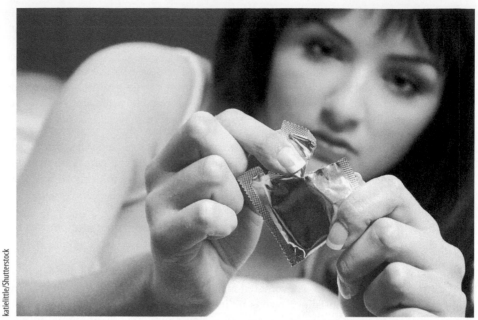

The Condom.
Condoms were once considered a man's domain. Today, many Canadian women insist on their use, and it's often the woman who buys and carries them.

(18%), who also use a spermicide, becomes pregnant during a year of use (Hatcher et al., 2011). Some women find the cap uncomfortable. Side effects include urinary tract infections and allergic reactions or sensitivities to the rubber or spermicide.

Spermicides

Spermicides coat the cervical opening, blocking the passage of sperm and killing sperm by chemical action. They come in different forms, including jellies, creams, suppositories, and aerosol foams.

Spermicides should be left in place in the vagina (no douching) for several hours after intercourse (Hatcher et al., 2011). Unlike spermicidal jellies, creams, and foams, which become effective as soon as they're applied, suppositories must be inserted at least 10 to 15 minutes before intercourse, so they have sufficient time to dissolve (Hatcher et al., 2011).

In typical use, the first-year failure rate for spermicides used alone is 21% (Hatcher et al., 2011). When used correctly and consistently, the failure rate is estimated to drop to about 6%. All forms of spermicide are more effective when combined with other forms of contraception, such as the condom.

Spermicides occasionally cause vaginal or penile irritation, and some partners find the taste unpleasant. Couples can engage in oral sex before applying spermicides.

It was once thought that spermicides containing nonoxynol-9 might provide protection against STIs such as chlamydia and HIV. Research has found that it doesn't provide protection against STIs (Zalenskaya et al., 2011), and that it actually increases susceptibility to HIV infection (Stephenson, 2000).

The Contraceptive Sponge

The contraceptive sponge is a soft, disposable device. Like the diaphragm, it provides a barrier that holds a spermicide, but the spermicide is built in. Unlike the diaphragm, the sponge doesn't need to be fitted.

The sponge can be inserted into the vagina several hours before intercourse, and has the advantage of absorbing sperm. On the negative side, about one user in 20 (male and female) is mildly irritated by the spermicide.

The sponge is currently unavailable in Canadian pharmacies.

The Male Condom

The majority of condoms used in Canada are made from latex rubber. Latex condoms are effective in preventing pregnancy and reducing the risk of STIs, especially HIV.

Condoms made from polyurethane are also now available in Canada. Although they can be effective in preventing pregnancy and STIs, they have higher rates of breakage and slippage than latex condoms (Gallo, Grimes, Lopez, & Schulz, 2006). Polyurethane condoms provide an alternative for people who are allergic to latex.

There are also condoms made from the intestinal membranes of lambs. These are often referred to as lambskin or natural condoms. Although they can reduce the risk of pregnancy, condoms made of animal intestines have pores large enough to permit HIV and other viruses, such as the one that causes hepatitis B, to slip through (Hatcher et al., 2011).

Many condoms have nipples or reservoirs to catch semen. (See Figure 11.3.) These reservoirs may help prevent the condoms from bursting during ejaculation.

Condoms come in different sizes. Men with larger penises should use larger condoms, to lessen the chances of condom breakage. Tight, uncomfortable condoms may discourage men from using them.

HOW IT WORKS   A condom is a cylindrical sheath that serves as a barrier, preventing the passage of sperm and disease-carrying micro-organisms from the man to his partner. It also helps prevent infected vaginal fluids (and micro-organisms) from entering the man's urethral opening or penetrating through small cracks in the skin of the penis.

HOW IT'S USED   The condom is rolled onto the penis once erection is achieved, but before contact between the penis and the vagina (see Figure 11.4). If the condom isn't used until moments before the point of ejaculation, sperm-carrying fluid from pre-orgasmic spasms may already have passed into the vagina. Nor does the condom afford protection against STIs if it's fitted after penetration.

EFFECTIVENESS   In typical use, the male condom's failure rate is estimated at 15%. This rate drops dramatically if the condom is used correctly and in combination with a spermicide (Hatcher et al., 2011).

ADVANTAGES AND DISADVANTAGES   Condoms offer a protection against STIs that's unparalleled among contraceptive devices. Research has definitively demonstrated that condoms provide impermeable barriers to STI/HIV pathogens, and that the proper, consistent use of latex condoms substantially reduces the risk of such infections (McKay, 2007).

Both partners can share in putting on the condom, making it an erotic part of lovemaking, rather than an intrusion. The use of textured or ultra-thin condoms may increase sensitivity, especially for the male. It's tempting to claim that the

Figure 11.3   Condoms.
Some condoms are plain-tipped, whereas others have nipples or reservoirs that catch semen and may help prevent the condoms from bursting during ejaculation.

Keith Brofsky/ThinkStock

Figure 11.4 Applying a condom.
The rolled-up condom is placed on the head of the penis, then rolled down the shaft of the penis. If a condom without a reservoir tip is used, a one-centimetre space should be left at the tip, where the ejaculate can accumulate.

condom has a perfect safety record and no side effects, but let's settle for calling it close to perfect.

Some people have allergic reactions to the spermicides some lubricated condoms are coated with or that women may apply. In such cases, a couple may need to use a condom without a spermicidal lubricant or stop using supplemental spermicides. Some people are allergic to latex. Condoms also sometimes slip off, break, or tear, allowing sperm to leak through.

One disadvantage of the condom is that it may make sex less spontaneous. The couple must interrupt lovemaking to put the condom on. Condoms may also lessen sensation.

Some men experience erectile difficulties when using condoms. In a study of heterosexual university males, one-fifth lost their erections before the condoms were put on, and one-fifth lost their erections after the condoms were on and intercourse had begun (Crosby et al., 2002). Men who reported erection loss were less likely to use condoms. Unfortunately, the problem of erection loss with condoms often isn't given serious consideration by some sex educators. The issue should be discussed in educational and counselling situations. Some educators recommend putting the condom on while the man is standing up rather when he is on his back to minimize the possibility of erection loss.

Although health educators emphasize the importance of using condoms to prevent transmission of STI/HIV, many people use them primarily to prevent pregnancy. Only 7% of the women in the 2002 Canadian Contraception Study said they chose to use condoms primarily to protect against STIs or HIV (Fisher & Black, 2007). In Milhausen et al.'s (2013) study of Canadian university students, among those who reported using a condom at last intercourse, 62.0% of men and 56.4% of women said their main reason for using one was birth control, while 29.2% of men and 40.0% of women said birth control and STI prevention equally, and only 8.8% of men and 3.6% of women said their main reason for using a condom was STI prevention.

The Canadian Contraception Study also found that many women used condoms when first beginning sexual relationships with new partners, then switched to oral contraceptives (Fisher et al., 2003). The most common reasons they gave for discontinuing condom use were having only one partner (47%) and knowing and trusting their partners (46%). Other reasons were decreased sexual sensation for themselves (14%) and for their partners (19%). Fisher and his colleagues noted that, in switching from condoms to oral contraceptives, many women are putting themselves at increased risk for STIs.

The Female Condom

The female condom consists of a polyurethane (plastic) sheath that's used to line the vagina during intercourse. It's held in place at each end by a flexible plastic ring. The female condom provides a secure but flexible shield that barricades against sperm but allows the penis to move freely within the vagina during intercourse. It can be inserted as much as eight hours before intercourse but should be removed immediately afterwards (Hatcher et al., 2011). A new one must be used for each act of intercourse.

The female condom (sold under the brand name Reality) carries a warning label that it appears to be less effective than the male latex condom in preventing pregnancies and transmission of STIs. During test trials, the pregnancy rate was estimated to range between 21% and 26%, though it's estimated to be as low as 5% among cautious users (Hatcher et al., 2011).

Douching

Douche Rinse or wash the vaginal canal by inserting a liquid and allowing it to drain out.

Many couples believe that if a woman douches shortly after intercourse, she won't become pregnant. Women who **douche** for contraceptive purposes often use syringes to flush their vaginas with water or spermicidal agents. Douching is

Applied Knowledge

ERRORS IN USING CONDOMS

Condoms are highly effective—when used properly. However, the authors of a review of the literature (Sanders et al., 2012) found that many couples experience problems such as the following in using condoms:

- Breakage: From 1% to 41% of condom users report discovering that the condom they were using was broken. In fact, 2% to 11% of users say they have used sharp objects to open the condom package, clearly exposing the condom to cutting.
- Slippage: From 13% to 19% of users reported that a condom had slipped, allowing semen to leak.
- Leakage: Condoms can also leak when they do not slip, with 8% of men and 13% of women reporting at least one such experience.
- Late application: In perhaps the most common error, 17% to 51% of users report putting on the condom after they have begun sexual intercourse. Better late than never? Perhaps, but …
- Early removal: At least as problematic as late application is removing a condom before the couple has finished having sexual intercourse—an error that is

nevertheless reported by 14% to 45% of users.
- Unrolling a condom before putting it on: Manufacturers intend for condoms to be unrolled onto the penis, yet 2% to 25% of users unroll them first and then struggle to put them on—increasing the chances of breakage and leakage.
- No space at the tip: Space should be left at the tip of the condom to collect semen without placing undue pressure on the condom, yet from 24% to 46% of users fail to leave such a reservoir for semen.
- Failing to remove air: Users should squeeze out air from the tip of the condom to help make room for semen, but 48% of women and 42% of men admit to failing to do so.
- Inside-out condoms: No, condoms are not manufactured inside out, but 4% to 30% of users report rolling condoms on inside out, and then removing them and applying them the correct way, but exposing the woman to semen during the process.
- Failing to unroll all the way: Condoms should be completely unrolled, but 11% of women and 28% of men have begun

intercourse before the condom was completely unrolled.
- Assuming the condom is not damaged: 83% of women and 75% of men admit to having sex without checking whether or not the condom is damaged.
- Lack of lubrication: From 16% to 26% of users use condoms with no lubrication, increasing friction and the risk of breakage. Meanwhile, from 3% to 5% of users use the wrong lubrication with latex condoms, such as an oil-based lubrication that can degrade the rubber, increasing the risk of breakage.
- Incorrect withdrawal: Then there are users—perhaps as many as half!—who do not withdraw the penis promptly and carefully after ejaculating, increasing the possibility of leakage.
- Condom reuse: Condoms are meant to be used once, but a few people admit to re-using the same condom during a given sexual encounter—increasing the probabilities of leakage and breakage.
- Incorrect storage: Finally, from 3% to 19% of users store condoms in ways that will promote degradation, such as exposing them to high temperatures, bending, and so on.

ineffective, however, because large numbers of sperm move beyond the range of the douche seconds after ejaculation. Regular douching can also alter the natural chemistry of the vagina, increasing the risk of vaginal infection. Douching, in short, is a "non-method" of contraception.

Withdrawal

In using withdrawal, the man removes his penis from the vagina before ejaculating.

Withdrawal has a first-year failure rate among typical users of about 27% but with consistent and correct use the failure rate is 4% (Hatcher et al., 2011). There are several reasons for failure. The man may not withdraw in time. Even if he withdraws his penis just before ejaculation, some ejaculate may still fall onto the vaginal lips, and sperm may find its way to the fallopian tubes. A man may not be aware that he has begun to ejaculate seminal fluid, especially if he's trying to delay his orgasm. It's also possible that active sperm is present in the pre-ejaculatory secretions of fluid from the Cowper's glands, a discharge the man is usually unaware of and cannot control. Despite the risks of using withdrawal as a method of birth control, 11.2% of Canadian women report using this method (Black et al., 2009).

Fertility-Awareness Methods

Fertility-awareness methods, or rhythm methods, rely on awareness of the fertile segments of a woman's menstrual cycle. Terms such as "natural birth control" and "natural family planning" also refer to these methods. The essence of such methods is that intercourse is avoided on days when conception is most likely.

Because the rhythm method doesn't employ artificial devices, it's acceptable to the Roman Catholic Church. However, as Table 11.1 shows, few Canadian women rely on this method of birth control.

HOW THEY WORK   A number of rhythm methods are used to predict the likelihood of conception. They're mirror images of the methods couples use to increase their chances of conceiving (see Chapter 10). Methods for enhancing the chances of conception seek to predict the time of ovulation, so the couple can arrange to have sperm present in the woman's reproductive tract at about that time. As methods of birth control, however, rhythm methods seek to predict ovulation so the couple can abstain from intercourse when the woman is fertile.

Calendar method A fertility-awareness (rhythm) method of contraception that relies on predicting ovulation by tracking menstrual cycles, typically for 10 to 12 months, and assuming that ovulation occurs 14 days before menstruation.

THE CALENDAR METHOD   The **calendar method** assumes that ovulation occurs 14 days before menstruation. The couple abstains from intercourse during the period that begins three days before day 13 (because sperm are unlikely to survive for more than 72 hours in the female reproductive tract) and ends two days after day 15 (because an unfertilized ovum is unlikely to remain receptive to fertilization for longer than 48 hours). The period of abstention thus covers days 10 to 17 of the woman's cycle.

When a woman has regular 28-day cycles, predicting the period of abstinence is relatively straightforward. Women with irregular cycles are generally advised to chart their cycles for 10 to 12 months, to determine their shortest and longest cycles. The first day of menstruation counts as day one of the cycle. The last day of the cycle is the day preceding the onset of menstruation.

Most women who follow the calendar method need to abstain from intercourse for at least 10 days during the middle of each cycle. The calendar method cannot ensure that the woman's longest or shortest menstrual cycles will occur during the 10- to 12-month period of baseline tracking. Some women have such irregular cycles that the range of unsafe days cannot be predicted reliably, even if baseline tracking is extended.

Basal-body-temperature (BBT) method A fertility-awareness method of contraception that relies on predicting ovulation by tracking the woman's temperature during the course of the menstrual cycle.

THE BASAL-BODY-TEMPERATURE (BBT) METHOD   In the **basal-body-temperature (BBT) method**, the woman tracks her body temperature upon awakening each morning, to detect the small changes that occur directly before and after ovulation. A woman's basal body temperature sometimes dips slightly just before ovulation, then tends to rise between 0.2°C and 0.4°C just before, during, and after ovulation. It remains elevated until the onset of menstruation. Thermometers that provide finely graded readings, such as electronic thermometers, are best suited for determining minor changes.

A major problem with the BBT method is that it doesn't indicate the several unsafe pre-ovulatory days when sperm deposited in the vagina may remain viable. Rather, the BBT method indicates when a woman *has* ovulated. Many women therefore use the calendar method to predict the number of safe days prior to ovulation, and the BBT method to determine the number of unsafe days after. They avoid intercourse during the unsafe pre-ovulatory period (as determined by the calendar method), and continue to avoid it for three days when their temperatures rise and remain elevated.

Another drawback of the BBT method is that changes in body temperature may result from factors unrelated to ovulation, such as infections, sleeplessness, and stress. This is why some women triple-check by also tracking their cervical mucus.

THE CERVICAL-MUCUS (OVULATION) METHOD   The **ovulation method** tracks changes in the **viscosity** of the cervical mucus.

Following menstruation, the vagina feels rather dry. There's also little or no discharge from the cervix. These dry days are relatively safe. Then a mucus discharge appears in the vagina that's thick, sticky, and white or cloudy in colour. Unprotected intercourse should be avoided at the first sign of any mucus.

As the cycle progresses, the mucus discharge thins and clears, becoming slippery or stringy, like raw egg white. These are the **peak days**. This mucus discharge, called the ovulatory mucus, may be accompanied by a feeling of vaginal lubrication or wetness. Ovulation takes place about a day after the last peak day (about four days after this ovulatory mucus first appears). Then the mucus becomes cloudy and tacky once more. Intercourse may resume four days following the last peak day.

One problem with the mucus method is that some women have difficulty detecting changes in the mucus discharge. Such changes may also result from infections, certain medications, and contraceptive creams, jellies, and foams. Sexual arousal may also induce changes in viscosity.

OVULATION-PREDICTION KITS   Predicting ovulation is more accurate with ovulation-prediction kits. These kits enable women to test their urine every day for the presence of luteinizing hormone. LH levels surge about 12 to 24 hours before ovulation.

Some couples use the kits to enhance their chances of conceiving, by engaging in intercourse when ovulation appears imminent. Others use them as a means of birth control, to find out when to avoid intercourse.

EFFECTIVENESS   The estimated first-year failure rate for typical use of fertility-awareness methods is 20%. Fewer failures occur when these methods are applied conscientiously, a combination of rhythm methods are used, and women's cycles are quite regular.

ADVANTAGES AND DISADVANTAGES   Because they're natural forms of birth control, rhythm methods appeal to many people who, for religious or other reasons, prefer not to use artificial means. No devices or chemicals are used, so there are no side effects. Rhythm methods are inexpensive, except for ovulation-prediction kits.

One disadvantage of the rhythm methods is low reliability. They may be unsuitable for women with irregular cycles. Those who ovulate as early as a week after their menstrual flows can become pregnant even if they engage in unprotected intercourse only when they're menstruating, because some sperm can survive in the female reproductive tract for up to eight days, fertilizing ova that are released then. Moreover, the rhythm methods require abstaining from intercourse for several days, or perhaps weeks, each month.

Sterilization

Many people decide to be sterilized when they plan to have no children or no more children. As Table 11.1 shows, male and female sterilization are most popular among people who are 40 and older.

Sterilization is the most effective form of contraception. Yet the prospect of **sterilization** arouses strong feelings, because a person is transformed all at once,

Ovulation method A fertility-awareness method of contraception that relies on predicting ovulation by tracking the viscosity of cervical mucus.

Viscosity Stickiness, consistency.

Peak days The days during the menstrual cycle when a woman is most likely to be fertile.

Sterilization Surgical procedures that render people incapable of reproduction, without affecting sexual activity.

and presumably permanently, from someone who might be capable of bearing children to someone who isn't. This transformation often involves a profound change in self-concept. These feelings are especially strong in men and women who link fertility to their senses of masculinity and femininity.

MALE STERILIZATION   The male sterilization procedure used today is the **vasectomy**. It's usually carried out in a doctor's office, under local anaesthesia, in 15 to 20 minutes.

Small incisions are made in the scrotum. Each vas is cut, a small segment is removed, and the ends are tied off or cauterized (to prevent them from growing back together). (See Figure 11.5.) Now sperm can no longer reach the urethra. Instead, they're harmlessly reabsorbed by the body.

The man can usually resume sexual relations within a few days. However, health-care providers recommend follow-ups to check for the presence of sperm in the ejaculate, since sperm can be found for many weeks and sometimes months even when operations have been successful. And rarely—in about 1 case in 500—the vas "recanalizes," meaning that the severed ends rejoin spontaneously (Jayaraman & Mann, 2012).

Vasectomy does not diminish the sex drive or result in any change in sexual arousal, erectile or ejaculatory ability, or sensations of ejaculation. Male sex hormones and sperm are still produced by the testes. Without a passageway to the urethra, however, sperm are no longer expelled with the ejaculate. Sperm account for only about 1% of the ejaculate, so the volume of the ejaculate is not noticeably different.

Vasectomy The surgical method of male sterilization in which each vas deferens is cut and tied back or cauterized, to prevent sperm from reaching the urethra.

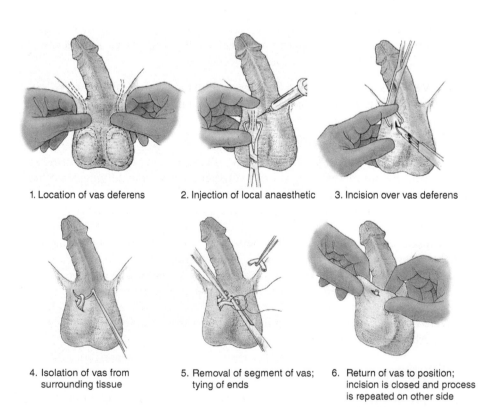

1. Location of vas deferens

2. Injection of local anaesthetic

3. Incision over vas deferens

4. Isolation of vas from surrounding tissue

5. Removal of segment of vas; tying of ends

6. Return of vas to position; incision is closed and process is repeated on other side

Figure 11.5   Vasectomy.
Small incisions are made in the scrotum. Each vas deferens is cut, and the ends are tied off or cauterized, to prevent sperm from reaching the urethra. The vasectomy is nearly 100% effective. The few failures occur when sperm remains in the male's genital tract shortly after the operation, or when the segments of a vas deferens grow back together.

Few serious complications from vasectomies have been reported, but minor complications are not uncommon. They typically involve temporary local inflammation or swelling after the operation. Ice packs and anti-inflammatory drugs such as Aspirin can help reduce swelling and discomfort. More serious but rarer medical complications include infection of the epididymis.

Reversibility is simple in concept, but not in practise. Vasectomies should therefore be considered permanent. In an operation to reverse a vasectomy, called a **vasovasotomy**, the ends of the vas deferens are sewn together, and in a few days they grow together. Estimates of success at reversal, as measured by subsequent pregnancies, range from 16% to 79% (Hatcher et al., 2011).

FEMALE STERILIZATION   **Tubal sterilization**, also called tubal ligation, is the most common method of female sterilization. Tubal sterilization prevents ova and sperm from passing through the fallopian tubes.

The two main surgical procedures for tubal sterilization are minilaparotomy and laparoscopy. In a **minilaparotomy**, a small incision is made in the abdomen, just above the pubic hairline, to provide access to the fallopian tubes. Each tube is cut and either tied back or clamped with a clip. In a **laparoscopy** (see Figure 11.6), sometimes called belly-button surgery, the fallopian tubes are approached through a small incision in the abdomen, just below the navel. The surgeon uses a narrow, lighted viewing instrument called a laparoscope to locate the tubes, then cauterizes, cuts, or clamps a small section of each tube. The woman usually returns to her daily routine in a few days and can resume intercourse when it becomes comfortable. In an alternative sterilization procedure, a **culpotomy**, the fallopian tubes are approached through an incision in the back wall of the vagina.

None of these methods disrupts sex drive or sexual response. The menstrual cycle is undisturbed. The unfertilized egg is simply reabsorbed by the body rather than sloughed off in the menstrual flow.

A **hysterectomy** also results in sterility. A hysterectomy is a major operation that's commonly performed because of cancer and other diseases of the reproductive tract. It's inappropriate as a method of sterilization. Hysterectomy carries the risks of major surgery, and when the ovaries are removed along with the uterus, it induces a "surgical menopause," because the woman no longer produces female sex hormones.

Vasovasotomy The surgical method of reversing a vasectomy. The cut or cauterized ends of the vas deferentia are sewn back together.

Tubal sterilization The most common method of female sterilization, in which the fallopian tubes are surgically blocked, to prevent the meeting of sperm and ova. It's also called tubal ligation.

Minilaparotomy A kind of tubal sterilization in which a small incision is made in the abdomen to provide access to the fallopian tubes.

Laparoscopy A procedure used for tubal sterilization. A laparoscope is inserted through a small incision just below the navel, and used to cauterize, cut, or clamp the fallopian tubes. This is sometimes called belly-button surgery.

Culpotomy A kind of tubal sterilization in which the fallopian tubes are approached through an incision in the back wall of the vagina.

Hysterectomy Surgical removal of the uterus. This procedure is not appropriate as a method of sterilization.

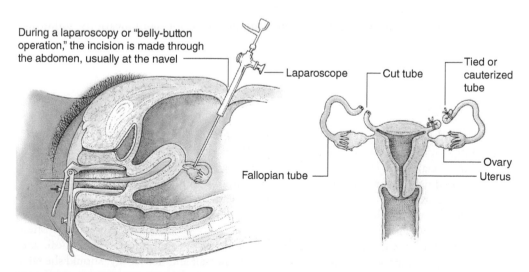

Figure 11.6   Tubal ligation via laparoscopy.
In this method of female sterilization, the surgeon approaches the fallopian tubes through a small incision in the abdomen, just below the navel. S/he inserts a narrow instrument called a laparoscope through the incision, and cauterizes, cuts, or clamps a small section of each fallopian tube, to prevent ova from joining with sperm.

Selecting a Contraceptive. Should you and your partner use contraception? If so, how can you determine which method is right for you?

Philippe Garo/Science Source

Female sterilization is highly effective in preventing pregnancy, although slightly less effective than male sterilization. Overall, about one woman in 200 (0.4%) is likely to become pregnant in the first year after a tubal sterilization (Hatcher et al., 2011). This is most likely to result from a failed surgical procedure, or the pregnancy may have been undetected at the time of the procedure.

Like vasectomy, tubal ligation should be considered irreversible. Although reversals are successful, as measured by subsequent pregnancies, in 43% to 88% of cases (Hatcher et al., 2011), reversal is difficult and costly.

ADVANTAGES AND DISADVANTAGES The major advantages of sterilization are effectiveness and permanence. Sterilization is nearly 100% effective. Following surgery, the couple needn't do anything more to prevent conception. The permanence is also its major drawback, however. People sometimes change their minds about wanting to have children.

Sterilization procedures create varying risks for complications following surgery, and women generally incur greater risks than men.

Sterilization gives no protection against STIs.

Abortion

Induced abortion The purposeful termination of a pregnancy before the embryo or fetus is capable of sustaining independent life.

An **induced abortion** (in contrast to a spontaneous abortion, or miscarriage) is the purposeful termination of a pregnancy. Perhaps more than any other contemporary social issue, induced abortion—hereafter referred to simply as abortion—has divided neighbours and family members into opposing camps.

Abortion is rarely used as a primary means of birth control. It usually comes into play when other methods have failed. The many reasons women have abortions include psychological factors, as well as external circumstances. Abortion is often motivated by a desire to reduce the risk of physical, economic, psychological, and social disadvantages the woman perceives for herself and her family, should she take the pregnancy to term.

Moral concerns about abortion often turn on the question of when human life begins. The question of when *human* life begins is a matter of definition that's apparently unanswerable by science.

Applied Knowledge

SELECTING A METHOD OF CONTRACEPTION

If you don't want to risk pregnancy, you're well advised to practise contraception when engaging in penile–vaginal intercourse—whether you're male or female. How can you determine which method is right for you?

There's no simple answer. What's right for your friends may be wrong for you. You and your partner must make your own selections. You may want to consider the following issues when deciding:

- *Convenience*—A method's convenience depends on a number of factors. Does it require a device that must be purchased in advance? If so, can it be purchased over the counter as needed, or are a consultation with a doctor and a prescription required? Will the method work at a moment's notice, or, like the birth-control pill, will it require time to reach maximum effectiveness?
- *Moral acceptability*—A method that's morally acceptable to one person may be objectionable to another. For example, those who strictly follow the teachings of the Roman Catholic Church may find any artificial means of contraception objectionable.
- *Cost*—Methods vary in cost.
- *Sharing responsibility*—Most forms of birth control place the burden of responsibility largely (if not entirely) on the woman. Some couples prefer methods that allow for greater sharing of responsibility, such as alternating the use of condoms and diaphragms. A man can also share the responsibility for the birth-control pill by accompanying his partner on her medical visits, sharing the expense, and helping her remember to take her pill.
- *Safety*—How safe is the method? What are its side effects?
- *Reversibility*—In most cases, the effects of birth control methods can be fully reversed by discontinuing their use. Sterilization should be considered irreversible, although many attempts at reversal have been successful.
- *Protection against STIs*—Birth-control methods vary in the degree of protection they afford against sexually transmitted infections. Condoms provide greater protection against STIs than any other form of birth control.
- *Effectiveness*—Techniques and devices vary widely in their effectiveness in actual use. The failure rate for a particular method refers to the percentage of women who become pregnant when using the method for a given period, such as during the first year of use. Most contraceptive methods are not used correctly all or even much of the time. It's instructive to compare the failure rate among people who use a particular method or device consistently and correctly with the failure rate among typical users of that method of device. Failure rates among typical users are often considerably higher, because of incorrect, unreliable, or inconsistent use.

Table 11.2 shows the failure rates, reversibility, and degrees of STI protection associated with various contraceptive methods.

Historical and Legal Perspectives

Attitudes toward abortion have varied across cultures and eras. Abortion was permitted in ancient Greece and Rome. The Bible doesn't specifically prohibit abortion (Sagan & Dryan, 1990). For much of its history, the Roman Catholic Church held to Thomas Aquinas's belief that ensoulment of the fetus didn't occur for at least 40 days after conception. In 1869, Pope Pius IX declared that human life began at conception, and abortion at any stage of pregnancy became murder in the eyes of the Church and grounds for excommunication.

The right-to-life or pro-life movement asserts that human life begins at conception, and views abortion as the murder of an unborn child. Some in the pro-life movement brook no exception to their opposition to abortion. Others would permit abortion to save the mother's life or when a pregnancy results from rape or incest. The pro-choice movement contends that abortion is a matter of personal choice, and that the government has no right to interfere with a woman's right to terminate a pregnancy. Pro-choice advocates argue that women are free to control what happens within their bodies, including pregnancies.

Many people in the pro-choice movement argue that if abortions were to be made illegal again, thousands of women, especially poor women, would suffer serious physical consequences or die from unsterile or botched abortions. People in the pro-life movement counter that alternatives to abortion, such as adoption, are available to pregnant women. Pro-choice advocates argue that the debate about abortion should be framed not only by notions of the mother's right to privacy, but also by the issue of quality of life for an unwanted child. They argue that minority and physically or mentally disabled children are often hard to place for adoption. These children often spend their childhoods being shuffled from one foster home to another. Pro-life advocates counter that killing a fetus eliminates any potential that it might have, despite hardships, of living a fruitful, meaningful life.

At Canadian universities, there have been clashes between student unions and anti-abortion groups over whether the latter should be allowed to operate on campus as official student organizations. The anti-abortion groups have argued that the student unions violate their constitutional human rights to free speech and discriminate against religious beliefs. The student unions have countered that these groups threaten women's right to abortions.

Although Canadians are divided in their opinions, most accept abortion under certain circumstances. In a 2010 poll (EKOS Research Associates, 2010), 52% of Canadians described themselves as pro-choice, 27% said they were pro-life, 10% were neither pro-choice nor pro-life, and 11% didn't know or didn't respond. In terms of the regulation of abortion, an Angus Reid Global (2013) poll found that 35% of Canadians believed that a woman should be able to have an abortion at any point during her pregnancy without any restrictions, and 34% felt that abortion should be available during the first three months of a pregnancy without any restrictions; only 5% said that abortion should not be available under any circumstances.

CRITICAL THINKING QUESTIONS

What factors have influenced your opinion about abortion?

Abortion in Canada

Abortion was illegal in Canada until 1969, when Parliament amended the *Criminal Code* to allow abortion under limited circumstances. Abortions could be performed only in accredited hospitals, with the approval of Therapeutic Abortion Committees. It had to be shown that the abortions were justified, in that continuation of the pregnancies would endanger the women's health or lives.

The struggle has continued between pro-life groups, which seek greater restrictions on abortion, and the pro-choice movement, which seeks to make abortion available to any Canadian woman who wants one. Both sides have heavily lobbied politicians to support their causes.

Some pro-life groups use such tactics as picketing hospitals and clinics where abortions are performed, as well as the homes of physicians who perform abortions. Three Canadian physicians have been shot in their homes by anti-abortion extremists. The harassing tactics used by some of these groups have led provinces such as Ontario and British Columbia to restrict picketing outside abortion clinics.

THE CANADIAN PRESS/Sean Kilpatrick

Pro-life groups marched in Ottawa in support of Prime Minister Harper's decision not to fund international aid organizations that provide abortions.

Dr. Henry Morgentaler, the leader of the pro-choice movement in Canada, challenged the law by establishing private abortion clinics beginning in 1969. He won several legal challenges against provincial governments that wanted to close his clinics, although in 1974 he was imprisoned for ten months after the Quebec Court of Appeal overturned a jury's acquittal. Juries refused to convict Morgentaler because they believed he provided an important medical service for women. Morgentaler was awarded the Order of Canada in 2008 for his commitment to increased health-care opportunities for women and his efforts to influence public policy. This award was strongly opposed by pro-life groups and caused considerable controversy. Nevertheless, according to a national Ipsos-Reid poll taken in July of 2008, 65% of Canadians supported the awarding of Canada's highest civilian honour to Dr. Morgentaler.

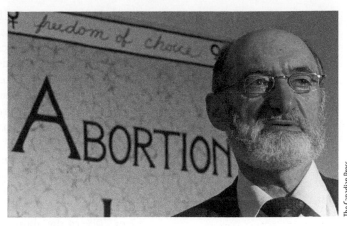

Dr. Henry Morgentaler.
Dr. Henry Morgentaler fought numerous court battles to secure Canadian women greater access to abortion.

The Supreme Court of Canada overturned the abortion law in 1988, stating that it violated the Charter of Rights and Freedoms, and there has been no federal law restricting abortion since.

Despite these legal decisions, only a minority of hospitals perform abortions today, and these are only in urban areas. In 2007, just 16% of the general hospitals in Canada provided abortion services (Shaw, 2007). Prince Edward Island offers no abortion services, while some provinces, such as New Brunswick, restrict women's access to abortions at public hospitals and refuse to pay for abortions performed at private abortion clinics. New Brunswick's only abortion clinic was slated to close in July, 2014, due to a lack of funding. Women who live in rural or northern areas of Canada often have to travel long distances to obtain abortion services (Shaw, 2007). In sum, although there are no federal legal restrictions on abortion, for many women, access to abortion services is difficult to obtain.

In the federal election campaign of 2011, Prime Minister Stephen Harper pledged that his government would not seek to pass new legislation restricting access to abortion in Canada. As of 2014, Harper has reaffirmed that his government will not introduce legislation to regulate abortion in Canada. Liberal Party leader Justin Trudeau announced in 2014 that all new Liberal candidates running in the 2015 federal election will need to be pro-choice (existing Liberal MPs are not required to state that they are pro-choice).

In 2010, the Conservative government announced Canada's participation in a maternal health initiative to benefit women in developing countries. Considerable controversy occurred when it was revealed that no Canadian funds for the program would be made available for abortion services. Polls taken at the time showed that almost 60% of Canadians opposed the exclusion of funding for abortion services (Canadian Press, May 17, 2010). In 2014, Prime Minister Harper announced a renewed Canadian funding commitment to the initiative but again stipulated that none of the Canadian funds would be directed to the provision of abortion services.

Canadian Abortion Statistics

It is estimated that about 30% of Canadian women have at least one abortion in their lifetime (Norman, 2012). However, current, reliable abortion statistics for Canada as a whole are not available. The majority of abortions conducted in Canada are performed in clinics, which are not legally required to report the number of abortions they perform, and in many provinces don't do so. The Canadian Institute for Health Information (CIHI) currently collects abortion data from hospitals and clinic data from the provinces from which it is available. The lack of complete reporting from abortion clinics makes the drawing of accurate conclusions on abortion rates in Canada very difficult.

Keeping in mind that the data is incomplete, it does appear that the number of abortions conducted in Canada has been declining. According to CIHI (2014), there were 83 708 abortions reported by hospitals and clinics in 2012. In comparison, 96 815 induced abortions were reported in 2005, and 105 154 were reported in 2002.

In a study of teen pregnancy rates, McKay (2012) calculated abortion rates for young women aged 15 to 19 and found that from 2001 to 2010, the abortion rate among Canadian teens declined 24% from 19.4 per 1000 to 14.7 per 1000. In 2010, just over half (52.1%) of teen pregnancies ended in abortion.

Over 70% of the abortions reported to CIHI (2014) in 2012 occurred within the first 12 weeks of pregnancy.

Methods of Abortion

The two methods of abortion most often used in Canada are vacuum aspiration and dilation and evacuation.

Vacuum aspiration Removal of the uterine contents via an aspirator (suction machine).

VACUUM ASPIRATION **Vacuum aspiration**, or suction curettage, is the safest, most common method of abortion used in Canada. Relatively painless and inexpensive, it can be done with little or no anaesthesia in a medical office or clinic.

The cervix is dilated either via insertion of progressively larger curved metal rods, or dilators, or by insertion hours earlier of a stick of seaweed called *Laminaria digitata*, which expands as it absorbs moisture, providing a gentler means of opening the os. An angled tube connected to an aspirator (suction machine) is then inserted through the cervix into the uterus and used to evacuate (empty) the uterine contents by suction.

Vacuum aspiration is used only during the first trimester. Later, thinning of the uterine walls increases the risks of perforation and bleeding.

Dilation and evacuation (D&E) Removal of the uterine contents via a suction tube and forceps. The uterine wall may be scraped, to ensure that the lining has been fully removed.

DILATION AND EVACUATION (D&E) The **dilation and evacuation (D&E)** method is used most often during the second trimester, when vacuum aspiration alone is too risky. The D&E is usually performed under general anesthesia in a hospital.

The cervix must be dilated more fully than with vacuum aspiration, to allow for passage of the larger fetus. A suction tube is then inserted and used to remove some of the uterine contents. Suction alone cannot safely remove everything from the uterus, so forceps are used to remove whatever remains. A blunt scraper may also be used to scrape the uterine walls, to be sure the lining has been fully removed.

ABORTION DRUGS RU-486, or mifepristone, was developed and approved in France in the late 1980s. Mifepristone induces early abortion by blocking the effects of progesterone, the hormone that stimulates proliferation of the endometrium and allows implantation of the fertilized ovum. It hasn't yet been approved for use in Canada although it is available in several European countries and the United States. It has been under consideration by Health Canada since December, 2012. It usually takes nine months for drugs to work their way through the approval process, making RU-486 overdue for a decision. Some people believe that RU-486's introduction in Canada is being delayed largely because of opposition by pro-life groups. Supporters of RU-486 argue that it offers a safe, non-invasive substitute for the more costly and unpleasant abortion procedures.

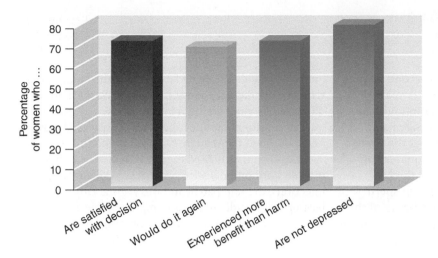

Figure 11.7 Women's psychological adjustment two years after abortion.
Of several hundred respondents in an *Archives of General Psychiatry* survey, 72% of those who'd had abortions reported satisfaction with their decisions two years later. How do you interpret this finding? Do you focus on the fact that the great majority of women are satisfied with their choices, or on the fact that significant numbers of women (28%) are not satisfied with their choices?

Psychological Consequences of Abortion

The woman who faces an unwanted pregnancy may experience a range of negative emotions, including fear, anger that she directs inward ("How could I let this happen?"), guilt ("What would my parents think, if they knew I was having an abortion?"), and ambivalence ("Will I regret it, if I have an abortion? Will I regret it more if I don't?").

Women's reactions depend on various factors, including the support they receive (or don't receive) from others and the strength of their relationships with their partners. Women with greater support from their male partners or parents tend to show more positive emotional reactions following abortion (Williams, 2001).

Consider one survey of 882 women who showed up at three sites for first-trimester abortions, as reported in *Archives of General Psychiatry* (Major et al., 2000). The researchers followed 442 of these women for two years. As Figure 11.7 shows, the majority (72%) said they were satisfied with their decisions to have the abortions. A majority said they'd make the same decision if they had to do it over (69%), and that they'd experienced more benefit than harm from having the abortions (72%). Moreover, 80% were *not* depressed.

Innovative Canadian Research

WOMEN WHO HAVE REPEAT ABORTIONS

In Canada, about one-third of induced abortions are for women who've had previous abortions.

A group of University of Western Ontario researchers led by William Fisher (2005) conducted a study to determine the characteristics of women who have repeat abortions. Contrary to the stereotype, most of these women were not using abortion as a method of birth control. About one-half of those undergoing repeat abortions reported that they or their partners had been using some method of birth control at the time of conception.

They were, in fact, more likely to be using birth control than a comparison group of women who were having their first abortions.

The key finding of the study was that women who had repeat abortions were significantly more likely to have experienced physical abuse by their male partners, sexual abuse, or coercion. Women seeking abortions should therefore be screened for their experience with physical or sexual abuse. This could result in counselling that might help avert subsequent abuse, and possibly help prevent future abortions (Fisher et al., 2005).

Summing Up

The provision of contraceptive information and services was illegal in Canada until 1969.

Birth-control pills include combination pills and minipills. Combination pills contain estrogen and progestin, and fool the brain into thinking the woman is already pregnant, so no additional ova mature or are released. Minipills contain progestin, thicken the cervical mucus to impede the passage of sperm through the cervix, and render the inner lining of the uterus less receptive to a fertilized egg. Morning-after pills prevent implantation of a fertilized ovum in the uterus.

The intrauterine device (IUD) is highly effective, but there are possible troublesome side effects and the potential for serious health complications.

The diaphragm covers the cervix, and should be used with a spermicidal cream or jelly.

Spermicides block the passage of sperm and kill sperm. Their failure rate is high.

Latex condoms afford protection against STIs, as well as against pregnancy.

Withdrawal requires no special equipment but has a high failure rate.

Rhythm methods rely on awareness of the fertile segments of the woman's menstrual cycle. Rhythm methods include the calendar method, the basal-body-temperature method, and the cervical-mucus method. Their failure rates are high in typical use.

Sterilization methods should be considered permanent, although they can be reversed in many cases.

Less commonly used methods of contraception include hormone-delivery systems (e.g., Depo-Provera injections, the skin patch, and the vaginal ring) and barrier/spermicide methods (e.g., the cervical cap, the female condom, and the contraceptive sponge).

Moral concerns about abortion often turn on the question of when human life begins. It's a question of definition.

Societal attitudes toward abortion have varied across cultures and history. In 1988, the Supreme Court of Canada ruled that the abortion law restricting the rights of women was unconstitutional, and that women should therefore have an unrestricted right to abortion. In reality, however, abortion services are limited in many parts of Canada.

The two most common methods of abortion used in Canada are vacuum aspiration and dilation and evacuation.

Women may experience distress after an abortion, but most are satisfied with their decision to have one.

Test Yourself

Multiple-Choice Questions

1. According to a 2009 study of Canadian women of reproductive age (15 to 40+) the most commonly used method of contraception was the:
(a) IUD.
(b) Rhythm method.
(c) Oral contraceptive pill.
(d) Male condom.

2. Which of the following is the most effective method of birth control?
(a) Withdrawal.
(b) Oral contraceptives.
(c) The rhythm method.
(d) The cervical cap.

3. Which of the following methods of birth control has the most side effects?
(a) The IUD.
(b) The male condom.
(c) The diaphragm.
(d) The minilaparotomy.

4. All of the following are potential side effects of birth-control pills except:
(a) Nausea and vomiting.
(b) Low blood pressure.
(c) Fluid retention.
(d) Weight gain.

5. In Canada, emergency contraception (the morning-after pill):
(a) Is illegal.
(b) Is available without a prescription.
(c) Contains higher levels of testosterone than the pills available in Europe.
(d) Is available only to victims of sexual assault.

6. Research has found that nonoxynol-9 _____ a woman's susceptibility to HIV infection.
(a) has no measurable effect on
(b) has mixed effects on
(c) increases
(d) decreases

7. Rhythm methods rely on:
(a) Fertility awareness.
(b) Hormonal preparations.
(c) Barriers.
(d) Spermicides.

8. It is estimated that about ___ of Canadian women have at least one abortion in their lifetimes.
(a) 10%
(b) 20%
(c) 30%
(d) 40%

9. There has been no federal law restricting abortion in Canada since the Supreme Court ruling of:
(a) 1965.
(b) 1977.
(c) 1988.
(d) 2004.

10. The safest, most common method of abortion is
(a) Dilation and evacuation (D&E).
(b) Intra-amniotic infusion.
(c) Dilation and curettage (D&C).
(d) Vacuum aspiration.

You'll find answers to the "Test Yourself" questions on page 489.

Questions for Critical Thinking

1. Have you ever discussed the use of birth control with a partner or potential partner? If not, why not? If you have, did you find it difficult to talk about? Why or why not?

2. If you're female, have you ever been faced with an unintended pregnancy? If so, what did you do about it? What factors influenced your decision? Were your friends supportive of your choice? Your partner? Your family?

3. If you're male, has a sexual partner of yours ever been faced with an unintended pregnancy? If so, what was done about it? Were you part of the decision-making process? Why or why not?

4. A friend of yours, whom you know doesn't want a child, tells you she's sexually active but not using birth control. Do you discuss this behaviour with her? Why or why not?

Sexuality Across the Life Span

Childhood Sexuality

We don't often think of children as sexual beings. Many people assume the development of sexuality begins at puberty, when we become biologically capable of reproduction. Although young children typically don't have conscious sexual desires the same way teens and adults do, in many respects, sexuality begins to develop in the womb and continues throughout childhood. The seeds of adult sexuality are planted during childhood, and this early development partially shapes the extent to which adult sexuality is characterized by self-confidence and satisfaction or by doubt and shame.

We know far less about the development of sexuality in childhood than we do about sexuality in adolescence and adulthood. Few empirical studies on the sexual behaviour of children are available (Thigpen, 2009). One reason is the cultural belief that children are sexually innocent, and that this innocence should be protected. Researchers have been reluctant to ask children about their sexual behaviour or their understanding of sexuality. We tend to rely either on adults' often unreliable retrospective reports of their experiences during childhood or on the observations of caregivers (Thigpen, 2009). In Canada, as in other countries, far more attention has been paid to the impact of child sexual abuse than to the course of typical child sexual development.

Table 12.1 provides an overview of the how sexuality develops in childhood. In addition to common characteristics and behaviours that may be evident in each age category, the table lists the appropriate learning domains and corresponding developmental outcomes for children at these ages. You'll notice that the age categories overlap

TABLE 12.1

Development of Childhood Sexuality, 0 to 12 Years of Age

Age (Years)	Common Characteristics and Behaviours	Learning Domains	Developmental Outcomes
0–2	■ Explores own body, including genitals ■ Displays spontaneous, reflexive sexual response (erection, lubrication) ■ Enjoys touch from caregivers ■ Enjoys nudity	■ Learns correct names for body parts, including genitals ■ Learns to differentiate between male and female ■ Learns to experience pleasure from touch (cuddling, nonsexual touching)	■ Develops capacity to trust caregivers ■ Develops capacity to experience sensory (touch) pleasure ■ Begins to distinguish between males and females ■ Begins to develop sense of autonomy ■ Begins first social/play interactions with peers
2–5	■ Engages in occasional masturbation (focused on soothing, not arousal) ■ Engages in consensual exploration of same-aged playmates' bodies in curiosity-focused manner ■ Enjoys nudity ■ Uses slang terms for bodily functions	■ Learns basics of reproduction ■ Learns basic rules of privacy ■ Learns "your body belongs to you" ■ Learns difference between appropriate and inappropriate touching (good touch versus bad touch)	■ Develops ability to identify self as male or female ■ Begins to understand basics of human reproduction ■ Understands concept of privacy related to nudity and sexuality
5–8	■ Engages in curiosity-based body exploration with same-sex and opposite-sex playmates ■ Engages in occasional masturbation (may begin to focus on pleasure) ■ Uses slang words to describe body parts and sexual behaviours ■ May have crushes	■ Acquires basic understanding of human reproduction ■ Acquires preparatory understanding of basic physical changes associated with puberty ■ Acquires understanding of basic distinction between heterosexuality and homosexuality	■ Has well-established sense of gender identity (male or female) ■ May show early signs of puberty (breast development) ■ Understands terminology for body parts (penis, vagina) ■ Develops basic understanding of sexual orientation (heterosexuality, homosexuality, bisexuality)
9–12	■ May masturbate more regularly, with a sexual focus ■ Experiences more frequent crushes, which can develop into relationships ■ May begin partnered sexual activity (though it's rare in this age group) ■ Becomes more curious about sexuality ■ Becomes interested in sexually oriented media	■ Acquires reasonably complete knowledge of physical and psychological aspects of puberty ■ Acquires basic knowledge of concepts of delaying first intercourse and contraception/safer sex ■ Learns social skills related to rights and responsibilities in relationships ■ Learns media literacy skills, to understand and evaluate sexual imagery and messages	■ Exhibits physical and psychological changes associated with puberty ■ Understands basic rights and responsibilities related to sexuality and relationships

Source: Adapted from Society of Obstetricians and Gynaecologists of Canada. (2006). Sexuality and child development. SexualityAndU.ca. Ottawa: Society of Obstetricians and Gynaecologists of Canada. Retrieved from http://www.sexualityandu.ca/health-care-professionals/sexuality-and-child-development

somewhat (e.g., 0–2 and 2–4). This is because not all children develop at the same pace. There's considerable variability in the precise ages at which children exhibit different sexuality-related behaviours and the rates at which their bodies develop.

The table reflects a primarily Western and secular conceptualization of both child development and sexuality. In other words, it reflects the assumption that, beginning in early childhood, the sequential acquisition of increasingly sophisticated knowledge and skills related to sexuality is beneficial. This assumption may conflict with religious and cultural traditions. Within some traditions, for example, sexuality-related exploratory play and masturbatory behaviour may be viewed as unhealthy or inappropriate for children.

Infancy (Birth to Two Years)

Infants (and fetuses!) engage in a variety of "sexual" behaviours, although the meanings of these behaviours—if there are any—are a matter for speculation. Imaging techniques such as ultrasound have shown, for example, that male fetuses have erections. Most boys have erections during the first few weeks of life. Signs of sexual arousal in infant girls, such as vaginal lubrication, are less readily detected, though evidence of lubrication and genital swelling has been reported (Mazur, 2006). Table 12.1 shows the initial aspects of child sexual development.

Stimulation of the genitals in infancy can produce pleasure. Parents who touch their infants' genitals while changing or washing them may find the infants smiling or becoming excited. Infants discover the pleasure of self-stimulation (masturbation) for themselves when they gain the ability to manipulate their genitals with their hands.

Be careful not to interpret children's reflexes according to adult concepts of sexuality. The reflexes of lubrication and erection don't necessarily signify interest in sex. We can't say what, if anything, infants' sexual reflexes mean to them. Masturbation is typical for infants and young children, and may start as early as five months of age (Narchi, 2003; Zhu et al., 2011), but masturbation to orgasm is rare until the second year (Reinisch, 1990). Some children begin masturbating to orgasm later. Most people do not purposely masturbate to orgasm as a means of sexual gratification until adolescence.

It's important for young children to begin to learn about their bodies, including their genitals. Parents can teach them the proper names for their genitals, just as they do for their other body parts.

Early Childhood (Two to Five Years)

As Table 12.1 shows, the major developmental tasks related to sexuality during early childhood include the ability to identify oneself as a boy or a girl. (This is a more complex process for the small number of children whose genitalia are neither

Dawning Curiosity. Children are naturally inquisitive about sexual anatomy and sexual behaviour. Much curiosity is triggered when they become aware that males and females differ in anatomy.

Pearson

clearly male nor clearly female or who are gender independent: see Chapter 5) Children at this age may play doctor and show their curiosity about sexual anatomy in other ways, such as wanting to watch parents take showers and baths (de Graaf & Rademakers, 2011; Pike, 2005).

Children in Canada typically don't engage in genital play with others until they're about two or older. To satisfy curiosity about their surroundings and other people, they may investigate other children's genitals or hug, cuddle, kiss, or climb on top of them. None of this need cause concern. There's no reason to infer that children are seeking sexual gratification. Rough-and-tumble play, including touching the genitals, is common among children. Three- and four-year-olds commonly express affection through kissing.

At this phase in their development, children should begin to learn the basic rules of privacy, that they have basic autonomy over their own bodies, and that there's a distinction between good touch (e.g., nonsexual touch by a trusted adult) and bad touch (e.g., non-consensual touch by a peer or sexual touch by an older person).

Middle Childhood (Five to Eight Years)

Many adults still recall their first attractions (sometimes called crushes), which often involved classmates. Childhood attractions, while typically not overtly sexual in nature, represent our first conscious romantic attachments. Some children at this age have relationships with special friends that resemble an early form of dating. Two children may hold hands and share a strong attachment, but this relationship doesn't usually involve explicitly sexual feelings.

Curiosity about the genitals increases at this stage. Sex games like show and playing doctor may begin earlier, but they become common between the ages of six and ten (Pike, 2005). Much of this sexual activity takes place in same-gender groups, although mixed-gender games are not uncommon. Children may show their genitals to one another, touch one another's genitals, and, in rare cases, masturbate together. Because of difficulties in conducting research on childhood sexuality, statistics on masturbation and other sexual activities are largely speculative (de Graaf & Rademakers, 2011).

Exploratory same-gender play may be more common at this age than play with another gender. It typically involves handling the other child's genitals, although it may include oral or anal contact. It may also include an outdoor variation of the game of show, in which boys urinate together and see who can reach farthest or highest. Same-gender sexual play in childhood does not foreshadow adult sexual orientation (Reinisch, 1990). In the mind of the child, these experiences aren't interpreted as overtly sexual in terms of desire or sexual gratification. Rather, they function as opportunities to satisfy their curiosity.

It's common for children in middle childhood to be very curious about human reproduction, asking the quintessential question "Where do babies come from?" Very basic factual explanations usually satisfy children, although they may outwardly express revulsion ("Yuck! Gross!") when first learning that reproduction involves the insertion of a penis into a vagina.

Children at this age may also have some degree of awareness that not all people are heterosexual. They may ask what slang terms for homosexuality mean, or they may hear about a family that has two mommies or two daddies. Again, basic, factual explanations will likely satisfy them. In same-sex families, parents are likely to proactively discuss these differences in family structures.

Preadolescence (Nine to Twelve Years)

Some preadolescent behaviours are sexually related, rather than sexual per se. Preadolescents typically form relationships with best friends of the same gender, enabling them to share secrets and confidences. Preadolescents also tend to socialize with larger networks of friends in gender-segregated groups. At this stage, boys

CRITICAL THINKING QUESTIONS

How should a parent who sees a seven-year-old son or daughter playing doctor with a friend of the same age handle the situation? How should a babysitter who sees this situation react?

are likely to think girls are dorks. To girls at this stage, "dork" is too nice an epithet to apply to most boys.

Preadolescents grow increasingly preoccupied with—and self-conscious about—their bodies. They feel pressure from their peers to conform to dress codes, the proper slang, and group norms concerning sex and drugs. Peer disapproval can be an intense punishment. Sexual urges are experienced by many preadolescents, but may not emerge until adolescence (O'Sullivan, 2003).

As Table 12.1 indicates, one of most important developmental tasks of the preadolescent period is preparation for puberty. Some girls and a few boys begin the physical changes associated with puberty before age 13. Most of their peers follow soon afterwards. It's therefore critical for children in this age group to be properly educated about the physical and emotional changes they'll experience. The onset of puberty can be a source of stress and anxiety. The better informed a child is about the changes s/he can expect, the more likely s/he is to accept these changes in a positive way when they begin.

Kinsey and his colleagues (1948, 1953) reported that masturbation is the primary means of achieving orgasm for both boys and girls during preadolescence. They found that 45% of males and 15% of females had masturbated by age 13. Although these frequencies are suspect, other studies agree that adolescent males are more likely to masturbate than adolescent females (Petersen & Hyde, 2011; Robbins et al., 2011). As Pinkerton et al. (2002) have noted, frequency of masturbation is likely influenced by social norms that appear to hold masturbation as more acceptable or normal for males than for females.

Preadolescent sex play often involves mutual display of the genitals, with or without touching. Such sexual experiences are quite common and don't appear to affect future sexual adjustment (Martinez et al., 2011).

Although preadolescents tend to socialize in same-gender groups, interest in other-gender individuals among heterosexual youth tends to increase gradually as they approach puberty. Sexual intercourse in this age group is uncommon. Data from the Canadian Community Health Survey (Rotermann, 2012) indicated that 9.7% of males and 8.2% of females had intercourse before age 15, and a study of British Columbia youth found that 6.2% of males and 4.5% of females had experienced intercourse before age 14 (Saewyc, Taylor, Homma, & Ogilvie, 2008).

Adolescent Sexuality

In reflecting on how contemporary Canadian society views adolescence, Maticka-Tyndale (2001) notes that although teens, fuelled by surging sex hormones, are biologically ready for sexual activity, parents and adults in general often see them as too cognitively, emotionally, and socially immature to be sexually active. Combine this with a culture saturated with sexual imagery—on television, on the Internet, in music, and in advertising—and it's not surprising that adolescence can be a turbulent time.

There are four major developmental tasks of adolescent sexuality:

- Adapt to the physical and emotional changes of puberty.
- Accept yourself as a sexual being.
- Explore romantic and sexual relationships.
- Learn to protect your sexual health.

Each task can play an important role in determining the extent to which a young person successfully navigates this sensitive, important period of sexual development. What takes place now will impact what happens later in life. Just as child sexual development sets the stage for adolescent sexuality, adolescent sexual development influences adult sexuality.

Adapting to the physical and emotional changes of puberty is a task for early adolescence. Self-acceptance as a sexual being is an ongoing process that begins in and likely extends beyond the adolescent years. Exploring romantic and sexual relationships and learning to protect sexual health also begin in early adolescence, or soon after, and are continually addressed throughout life.

When adolescence begins and ends is open to interpretation. In many respects, adolescence formally begins with the onset of puberty, and ends at some point in the late teen years. The psychological and social tasks of adolescent sexual development unfold throughout the teen years.

Puberty

Puberty begins with the appearance of **secondary sex characteristics** and ends when the long bones make no further gains in length. The appearance of strands of pubic hair is often the first visible sign of puberty. Puberty also involves changes in **primary sex characteristics**. Once puberty begins, most major changes occur within three years in girls and within four years in boys.

Toward the end of puberty, reproduction becomes possible. The two principal markers of reproductive potential are menarche in girls and first ejaculations in boys, though these events may not signify immediate fertility.

FEMALE CHANGES   Several changes set the stage for menarche. Between eight and 14 years of age, FSH released by the pituitary gland causes the ovaries to begin to secrete estrogen. Estrogen has several major effects on pubertal development. For one thing, it stimulates the growth of breast tissue ("breast buds"), perhaps as early as age eight or nine. The breasts usually begin to enlarge during the tenth year.

Menarche (first menstruation) commonly occurs between the ages of 11 and 14. But it is quite normal for menarche to occur as early as age 9 or as late as age 16 (Natsuaki et al., 2011). In the middle 1800s, European girls first menstruated at about the age of 16. During the past century and a half, however, puberty has been occurring at earlier ages in Western nations, most likely because of improved nutrition and health care. By the 1960s, the average age of menarche in the United States had plummeted to its current figure of 12½. No single theory of the onset of puberty has found wide acceptance. In any event, the average age of the advent of puberty for girls and boys appears to have leveled off in recent years.

Estrogen also promotes growth of the uterus, thickening of the vaginal lining, and growth of fatty and supporting tissue in the hips and buttocks. This tissue and the widening of the pelvis causes the hips to become rounded, to permit childbearing. But growth of fatty deposits and connective tissue varies considerably. Some women may have pronounced breasts; others may have relatively large hips.

Small amounts of androgens produced by the female's adrenal glands, along with estrogen, stimulate development of pubic and underarm hair, beginning at about age 11. Excessive androgen production can darken or thicken facial hair.

Estrogen stimulates growth of the vagina, uterus, and labia during puberty, while androgens cause the clitoris to develop. Estrogen also typically slows the female growth spurt (some years before the male's growth spurt begins to slow down). As it becomes cyclical, estrogen production regulates the menstrual cycle.

Following menarche, a girl's early menstrual cycles are typically **anovulatory**— without ovulation. Girls cannot become pregnant until ovulation occurs, and ovulation may lag behind menarche by as much as two years. Ovulation may be unreliable at first, so a girl may be relatively infertile. Some teenagers, however, are highly fertile soon after menarche.

MALE CHANGES   At puberty, the hypothalamus signals the pituitary to increase production of FSH and LH. These hormones stimulate the testes to increase their output of testosterone, which in turn prompts growth of the testes, scrotum, and

Puberty The stage of development when reproduction first becomes possible. Puberty begins with the appearance of secondary sex characteristics and ends when the long bones make no further gains in length.

Secondary sex characteristics Physical characteristics that differentiate males and females, usually appearing at puberty but not directly involved in reproduction. Examples include bodily distribution of hair and fat, development of muscle mass, and deepening of the voice.

Primary sex characteristics Physical characteristics that differentiate males and females and are directly involved in reproduction. These are the sex organs.

Menarche The onset of menstruation; first menstruation.

Anovulatory Without ovulation.

A World of Diversity

THE MANY MEANINGS OF MENARCHE

In different times, in different places, menarche has had different meanings. The Manus of New Guinea greet menarche with elaborate ceremony (Lohmann, 2004). The other girls of the village sleep in the menstruating girl's hut. They feast and have parties. In the West, menstruation has historically received a mixed response. The menstrual flow itself has generally been seen, erroneously, as polluting, and the frequent discomforts of menstruation have led menstruating women to be stereotyped as irrational (Hubbard, 2009). Menarche itself has generally been perceived as the event in which a girl suddenly develops into a woman, but because of taboos and prejudice against menstruating women, girls historically matured in ignorance of menarche.

Girls' attitudes toward menarche reflect their level of education as well as certain physical realities. A Hong Kong study of 1573 Chinese high school students found a mixed response to the onset of menstruation (Tang et al., 2003). The average age of menarche was 11.67 years. Although most of the girls reported that menstruation was annoying (it involved some discomfort for them, along with the need to dispose of the menstrual flow), two in three reported feeling more "grown up," and four in ten felt that they had become more feminine. Girls who felt positive about menarche were more likely to be educationally prepared to welcome it as a natural event, have a positive body image, and reject traditional negative attitudes. On the other hand, the circulating hormones connected with menarche may make the girl more vulnerable to stress (Allison & Hyde, 2011).

Most Canadian girls currently receive advance information about menstruation, not only from family and girlfriends, but also from school health classes. The old horror stories are pretty much gone, at least in societies in developed countries. However, most girls experience at least some menstrual discomfort and need to discreetly dispose of the menstrual flow (Harel, 2008). Most girls can separate pride in "becoming women" from the realities of some discomfort and the fact that menarche usually means that the girl will not be growing much taller because of the braking effects of estrogen.

---

penis. Testosterone also fosters differentiation of secondary male characteristics— growth of facial, body, and pubic hair, and deepening of the voice. Testicle growth, in turn, accelerates testosterone production and pubertal changes. The testes continue to grow, and the scrotal sac becomes larger and hangs loosely from the body. The penis widens and lengthens, and pubic hair appears.

By age 13 or 14, erections become frequent. Many middle-school boys dread being caught with erections between classes, or being asked to stand before their classes.

Under the influence of testosterone, the prostate and seminal vesicles—the organs that produce semen—increase in size, and semen production begins. Boys typically experience their first ejaculations by age 13 or 14, most often through masturbation. About a year after their first ejaculations, boys may begin to experience **nocturnal emissions**, which are also called "wet dreams" because they usually accompany erotic dreams.

Nocturnal emission
Involuntary ejaculation of seminal fluid while asleep.

Underarm hair appears at about age 15. Facial hair is at first a fuzz on the upper lip; a beard doesn't appear for another two or three years. Only half of all boys have to shave by age 17. Beard and chest hair continue to develop past age 20.

At age 14 or 15, the voice deepens as the **larynx** grows and the vocal cords lengthen.

Larynx A structure of muscle and cartilage that lies at the upper end of the trachea and contains the vocal cords. It's also called the voice box.

Boys and girls undergo general growth spurts during puberty. Although girls usually shoot up before boys, individuals differ, and some boys spurt sooner than some girls.

Increases in muscle mass produce increases in weight. The shoulders and the circumference of the chest widen. Males stop growing taller at age 18 or so, because estrogen prevents their long bones from getting longer. Males normally produce some estrogen in the adrenal glands and testes. Estrogen also causes nearly one in two boys to experience temporary enlargement of the breasts during puberty.

SEXUAL SELF-ACCEPTANCE   As Moore and Rosenthal note, "It is especially important that the adolescent be able to integrate his or her sexual feelings, needs, and desires into a coherent and positive self-identity, which contains, as one aspect, a sexual self" (Moore & Rosenthal, 1993, p. x). In other words, young women and men are getting to know themselves as sexual beings. They're becoming more familiar with what their sexual desires are (their likes and dislikes), whether they're more assertive or more passive, and what types of people they're attracted to (in terms of personality, physical attributes, and gender).

Adolescence is a time of rapid physical change and intense pressure to meet physical and social expectations (such as being "cool"). Body image can be a huge concern, with a significant impact on sexual well-being. Western culture—indeed, every culture—places considerable pressure on young people to conform to stereotypes of sexual desire and attraction. For example, young men are supposed to be attracted to and aggressively pursue young women, who are supposed to take passive roles in relationship development and conform to cultural ideals of feminine attractiveness. Many (if not most) adolescents realize that they don't exactly fit these stereotypes, which can be a source of considerable anxiety.

Lesbian, gay, bisexual, transgender, and queer (LGBTQ) youth are obvious examples of adolescents who don't fit the traditional, stereotypical molds of what it means to be sexual beings. Girls who are assertive about their sexual feelings and desires and boys who aren't aggressive about asserting traditional expressions of masculinity are more examples of adolescents who don't conform to cultural stereotypes of "normal." There's an endless array of less obvious examples, too. The point is that these stereotypes can make it difficult for adolescents to fully accept themselves for who they are. Being able to move beyond these stereotypes, not using them to judge ourselves, is an important factor in fully accepting ourselves as sexual beings.

Developing self-acceptance as sexual beings can be especially challenging for LGBTQ youth, who face the additional burden of integrating their sexual orientations into their self-concepts while growing up in a heterosexist society. The process of sexual identity integration among LGBTQ youth is linked to overall psychological development and well-being. Social context issues such as the degree of support LGBTQ youth receive from their friends and families can affect this integration process (Rosario, Schrimshaw, & Hunter, 2011).

Researchers at the University of Guelph (Muise, Preyde, Maitland, & Milhausen, 2010) explored the relationship between sexual well-being and sexual identity—the definition of oneself as a sexual being—among female university students. They found that young women who devoted more attention to exploring their sexual identities scored higher on measures of sexual well-being (e.g., satisfaction with their sex lives).

ROMANTIC AND SEXUAL RELATIONSHIPS   It's during the teenage years that most adolescents have their first romantic and sexual relationships. (See Table 12.3 for statistics on Canadian teen sexual behaviour.) Many young people fall in love for the first time, experiencing the emotional turmoil that comes along with that. Adolescents face the developmental task of learning to integrate romantic relationships, with or without sexual components, into their lives in the absence of any prior experience. Learning to develop satisfying, mutually beneficial relationships is often a process of trial and error, and few emerge from this learning process without at least one experience of heartbreak.

At any age, communication is a key component of a mutually satisfying romantic or sexual relationship. However, relatively little research has explored sexual communication among adolescents. In one of the few studies of its kind, Laura Widman and her colleagues (2006) found that open communication about sex was associated with greater relationship satisfaction for dating couples who were 14 to 21 years of age.

Lily Tsui and Elena Nicoladis (2004) surveyed students at the University of Alberta on their first intercourse experiences. On average, the students who were sexually active reported an average age of 17 for first intercourse. Most (84%) said they were in romantic relationships when they had their first intercourse experiences. Fewer—63% of females and 43% of males—said they were in love with their partners at the time. Of the males, 62% reported that their first sexual intercourses were physically satisfying, and 42% said they were emotionally satisfying. Among females, less than half (35%) said it was physically satisfying, and 54% found it emotionally satisfying. Far more males (76%) than females (12%) reported that they'd had orgasms.

Trent University researcher Terry Humphreys (2007b) found that twice as many university females (40%) as males (21%) viewed their first intercourse experiences as giving their partners the gift of their virginity. On the other hand, about three times as many men (22%) as women (6%) viewed their virginal status as a stigma or an embarrassment that they were glad to get rid of when they had intercourse for the first time. Students who perceived virginity as a stigma were more likely to lose their virginity with a stranger or a friend, rather than with a love partner. More than half of both genders viewed first intercourse as a naturally occurring process that was a desirable and inevitable transition to adulthood.

Lucia O'Sullivan and Joann Majerovich (2008) at the University of New Brunswick examined sexual satisfaction and sexual functioning among 17- to 21-year-old students. They found that, overall, this group of young people reported fairly high levels of sexual desire, pleasure, and satisfaction. Nevertheless, a sizable percentage reported sexuality-related problems. For example, 81.4% of the males and 75% of the females reported that they'd felt anxious about "performing sexually" at some point. And 60.5% of the males and 66.9% of the females reported that they hadn't found sex pleasurable on at least one occasion.

Perhaps not surprisingly, research has found that adolescents tend to overestimate how much sex their peers are having, especially in comparison with themselves. ("Everybody's doing it, except me.") A study of university students with an average age of 18.5 found that about 90% of both males and females thought they'd had fewer sex partners than their classmates (Stephenson & Sullivan, 2009). Sexual behaviour data from the sample indicated that they'd significantly overestimated the number of sex partners their peers had had in their lifetimes. What's particularly interesting about this study is the finding that the more students overestimated their peers' sexual experience, the more likely they were to report that they were unsatisfied with their own sex lives. In other words, our often inaccurate assumptions about what our peers are doing sexually can negatively affect how we assess our own sex lives.

These findings suggest that, contrary to media portrayals and the boasting of peers about their sexual exploits, adolescent sexual experiences and relationships are not uniformly blissful. Learning from the trials and errors of early relationships and developing patterns of open communication with partners about all aspects of a relationship, including the sexual component, sets the stage for a satisfying sex life in adulthood.

Adolescent Sexual Behaviour

MASTURBATION Masturbation is a major sexual outlet during adolescence. In an American study, 80% of male and 58% of female 17-year-olds reported that they had masturbated (Fortenberry et al., 2010). Surveys consistently show that boys are more likely than girls to masturbate (Kaestle & Allan, 2011; Schmitt et al.,

2012). Boys who masturbate may do so frequently—several times a week. Girls who masturbate are likely to do it less frequently. It's unclear whether this sex difference reflects a stronger sex drive in boys, greater social constraints on girls, or both. Cultural and religious norms surrounding masturbation can affect the likelihood and frequency of masturbation among both male and female adolescents. Researchers find no links between adolescent masturbation and sexual adjustment in adulthood (Leitenberg et al., 1993).

SEXUAL TOUCHING (PETTING)   Most adolescents experiment with various forms of sexual touching (sometimes known as petting). For some adolescents who choose to be sexually active but don't feel ready for oral sex or intercourse, or who want to avoid sexually transmitted infections or pregnancy, mutual masturbation (i.e., partners masturbating one another) is the primary form of partnered sexual expression.

ORAL SEX   In the popular media, anecdotal stories about young teenagers engaging in frequent and indiscriminate oral sex have led to an unsubstantiated assumption that oral sex is increasingly common among young people. Although oral sex is practised by some adolescents, it's about as common as intercourse and often occurs at about the same age (Lindberg, Jones, & Santelli, 2008).

Table 12.2 provides data on the percentage of U.S. teens who report giving and receiving oral sex in the previous year. It is notable that these data suggest, perhaps contrary to common perceptions, that less than a third of adolescents under age 18 regularly engage in oral sex.

INTERCOURSE   Data from the Canadian Community Health Survey indicates that about a third of youth experience sexual intercourse before age 17 and that the proportion of younger adolescents who have had intercourse has remained stable in recent years (Rotermann, 2012). (See Table 12.3.)

Data on older adolescents from the Canadian Community Health Survey shows that from 1996–97 to 2005, the percentage of 18- to 19-year-olds who'd experienced intercourse declined from 70% to 65%, suggesting that about two-thirds of Canadians have sexual intercourse before they reach age 20 (Rotermann, 2008).

Canadian street youth have more sexual experience than those in high school. A British Columbia study has found that 82% of street youth have had sexual intercourse—two-thirds by age 14 or younger (Smith et al., 2007).

The 2009/2010 Canadian Community Health Survey asked sexually active young people how many sexual partners they'd had in the previous 12 months (Rotermann, 2012). Thirty-five percent of those aged 15 to 17 and 39% of those aged 18 to 19 reported more than one sexual partner in the previous 12 months. This suggests that most sexually active youth have only one intercourse partner at a time.

CRITICAL THINKING QUESTIONS

There are significant differences of opinion about the age and circumstances in which it's appropriate to become sexually active. In your opinion, what are the most important factors to consider?

TABLE 12.2

Percentages of Males and Females Reporting Giving and Receiving Heterosexual Oral Sex in the Past Year

Oral Sex Behaviours	Age 14–15	Age 16–17	Age 18–19
Male Received	11.9%	30.9%	53.6%
Male Gave	7.8%	18.3%	50.7%
Female Received	10.0%	23.5%	58.0%
Female Gave	11.8%	22.4%	58.5%

Source: Herbenick, D., Reece, M., Schick, V., Sanders, S.A., Dodge, B., & Fortenberry, J.D. (2010). Sexual behavior in the United States: results from a national probability sample of men and women ages 14–94. Journal of Sexual Medicine, 7 (suppl 5), 255–265.

TABLE 12.3

Percentage of 15- to 24-Year-Olds Who Had First Sexual Intercourse before Age 17, Canada, 2003 and 2009/2010

	2003	**2009/2010**
Male	35%	36%
Female	34%	33%

Source: Rotermann, M. (2012). Sexual behaviour and condom use of 15- to 24-year-olds in 2003 and 2009/2010. Health Reports, 23(1), 1–6.

EARLY AGE AT FIRST INTERCOURSE   Various social factors are predictive of intercourse at a young age. The 2002 Canadian Youth, Sexual Health, and HIV/AIDS Study indicated that poor school attachment and poor relationships with parents are also predictive of early sexual intercourse (Boyce et al., 2003). And among both male and female students in Regina, having male and female peers who are having sex is strongly predictive of intercourse experience (Hampton et al., 2005). In British Columbia, sexual intercourse at a young age for both boys and girls was linked with low connectedness to family, low connectedness to school, and sexually permissive peers (Saewyc et al., 2008).

CASUAL SEX   Most adolescent sexual behaviour, especially intercourse, takes place within ongoing romantic relationships that are monogamous. Some sexual behaviour, however, is more casual.

Some evidence suggests that a double standard continues to exist with regard to casual sex among adolescents. A study of high school students in Vancouver, British Columbia, and Amherst, Nova Scotia, found that girls were judged more negatively than boys for engaging in casual sex. Girls who displayed greater self-confidence and whose parents were from higher social classes were less likely to be judged negatively (Shoveller et al., 2004).

In recent years, a newer set of terms for various forms of casual sex among young people have appeared. Using focus groups of university students and sex educators, Jocelyn Wentland and Elke Reissing (2011) at the University of Ottawa identified and examined four types of casual sexual relationships: one-night stands, booty calls, fuck buddies, and friends with benefits. One-night stands were considered the least intimate because they most often involved strangers, whereas booty calls and fuck buddies involve repeated sexual activity with an acquaintance. Friends with benefits, on the other hand, tend to occur between individuals who have an existing friendship prior to having sex. Wentland and Reissing found that friends with benefits relationships often include formal discussions of the initiation of the sexual relationship, monogamy, and the termination of the sexual component of the relationship.

One small study of students on an American college campus found that 60% of students had engaged in some form of friends with benefits relationship (Bisson & Levine, 2009). In 18.7% of the cases, the friends had sex just once, while 52.1% had sex occasionally, and 29.3% had sex frequently. When asked how their friends with benefits relationships had turned out, 28% reported that they were still friends with benefits, 35.8% said they'd stopped having sex but were still friends, 9.8% said they'd become romantic partners, and 25.9% said they'd ended their relationships. In other words, a friendship was more than twice as likely to end as to become a committed romantic relationship.

Among the potential problems of a friends with benefits relationships is that one partner may begin to want a more committed relationship, while the other doesn't. In some cases, the friendship ends over conflict about the sexual aspect of the relationship, or when one partner wants to stop having sex.

A World of Diversity

DO SEXY TV SHOWS ENCOURAGE TEEN SEX AND PREGNANCY?

What happens when teenagers watch *Sex in the City* and other shows with sexual content? Does what they see roll off their backs or encourage them to go for a roll in the hay?

A study reported in *Pediatrics* (Collins et al., 2004) found an association between watching sexual content on television and initiation into sexual intercourse. The study included more than 1700 12- to 17-year-olds.

The researchers followed up with the same cohort of adolescents after three years, to determine whether watching sex on television led to a higher incidence of pregnancy (Chandra et al., 2008).

The 718 adolescents (57% male, 43% female) who reported having engaged in sexual intercourse and who provided information about pregnancy were included in the analysis. The researchers controlled for other variables connected with teenage pregnancy, such as school grades and conduct problems.

They found that teenage pregnancy, like initiation into sexual intercourse, was significantly correlated with exposure to sexual content on television. Teenagers categorized as having high levels of exposure (that is, those in the 90th percentile on the variable) were two to three times more likely to have been pregnant or responsible for a pregnancy than teenagers in the 10th percentile. Total hours of television watching was not significantly correlated with pregnancy.

Conclusions

It might seem that we can conclude that watching sexual content on television is a cause of sexual initiation and teenage pregnancy.

However, the study showed a correlation between what teenagers watched and sexual outcomes. As we noted Chapter 2, correlational studies may show relationships, but they don't show cause and effect. Because the researchers didn't run an experiment in which some teens watched shows with sexual content while others did not, there may be alternate explanations for the correlation researchers found.

The research findings could be due to a selection factor. For example, it's possible that teenagers who had more interest in sex, who came from more permissive homes, or who had friends who touted sexy shows were more likely to watch sexy television shows, and also more likely to have sex and get pregnant. In this case, sexual interest, home atmosphere, and peer relationships would be more likely to be causal than sexy television content.

Critical Thinking

Consider why researchers can't run experiments in which watching sexy shows is the treatment or independent variable. What ethical issues would be involved in showing racy TV to teens? Moreover, could the researchers prevent teens assigned to non-sexy shows from watching racy TV on their own?

Obstacles Faced by Sexual-Minority Youth

It's important to examine some of the obstacles faced by lesbian, gay, bisexual, transgendered, and queer (LGBTQ) youth in the developmental tasks of adolescent sexuality. Canadian society has become more accepting of diverse sexual orientations in recent years, but LGBTQ youth continue to face discrimination, prejudice, and violence because of their sexual orientations. Self-acceptance as sexual beings is therefore more challenging for sexual-minority youth, because they have to grow up in a society that doesn't fully accept their sexual orientations. The vast majority of research on the sexual behaviour of Canadian adolescents groups all teens together, or looks at behaviours such as heterosexual intercourse. We know comparatively little about the timing and context of sexual behaviour among sexual-minority youth.

University of Alberta researcher Christopher Wells (2009) reviewed research on sexual-minority youth and found that, in addition to experiencing higher rates of sexual violence, lesbian, gay, and bisexual youth were more likely than their heterosexual counterparts to feel emotionally distressed and to report low self-esteem. A Canadian study found that school could be a very unwelcoming place for sexual-minority youth. Among the findings: 76% heard expressions like "that's so gay" on a daily basis, 60% had been verbally harassed, and 25% had been physically harassed because of their sexual orientations (Egale Canada, 2009). A welcoming, nonthreatening school environment can reduce the negative health and social outcomes for sexual-minority youth (Saewyc et al., 2009).

School-based sexual-health education in Canada tends to be predominantly—if not exclusively—heterosexual in focus. This can make it difficult for LGBTQ youth to acquire accurate sexual-health information that's specific to their needs. To fill this gap, many LGBTQ youth are able to find information from alternate sources, such as LGBTQ-friendly community organizations and the Internet. As Canadian society becomes more accepting of sexual diversity, more and more LGBTQ youth will successfully complete the developmental tasks of adolescent sexuality.

Protecting Sexual Health in Adolescence

As we've seen, most Canadian young people become sexually active to some extent during their teen years. Protecting their sexual health is therefore an important developmental task. Preventing unintended pregnancy and STIs are priorities. STIs are common among Canadian youth, presenting significant threats to their health and well-being.

Canadian teen pregnancy rates have fallen significantly over the last several decades. From 1990 to 2010, the pregnancy rate among 15- to 19-year-old females declined 37.2% (McKay, 2012).

Adolescents can use a number of strategies to protect their sexual health. Obviously, abstaining from partnered sexual activity protects them from pregnancy and STIs. Some adolescents choose to engage only in sexual activities with lower risks for these outcomes, such as petting and oral sex. (For a full discussion of lower-risk sexual behaviours, Chapter 17.)

For Canadian youth, using condoms is by far the most popular choice for protecting sexual health. Condoms are relatively easy to get; unlike the birth-control pill, they don't require a prescription. Condoms also provide protection against both unwanted pregnancy and STIs. Most Canadian teens who have intercourse use condoms. The Canadian Community Health Survey found that from 2003 to 2009/2010 condom use at last intercourse increased from 78.5% to 79.9% among 15- to 17- year-olds and from 67.6% to 73.7% among 18- to 19-year-olds (Rotermann, 2012). It appears, then, that younger teens are more responsible than older teens when it comes to condom use. Some of these older teens may have switched to other forms of birth control, in the belief that they were at low risk for STIs. This belief is often mistaken, as rates of common STIs such as chlamydia are high among older teens and young adults.

Taking decreasing teen pregnancy rates and higher levels of condom use into account, we can conclude that the sexual health of Canadian youth is improving in many respects. Challenges remain, however. STI rates remain high among Canadian young people, and sexual-health educational needs are less well addressed for lesbian, gay, bisexual, transgender, and queer youth than for heterosexual youth.

Adult Sexuality

So far in this chapter we've looked at sexuality in childhood and adolescence from a developmental perspective. Does our development as sexual beings finish once we complete the transition from adolescence to adulthood? Do growth and development of sexuality stop as we begin to settle into adult roles?

A World of Diversity

A GAY PROM DATE

They danced the night away.

Marc Hall, the shy, blue-coiffed 17-year-old Oshawa student who wouldn't take no for an answer when told he couldn't take his boyfriend to his high-school prom, won a major court victory for Catholic students in 2002.

In a comprehensive and clear decision granting Hall's request for an injunction, Mr. Justice Robert MacKinnon of the Superior Court of Justice said a ban on same-sex dates at the prom was a clear violation of Hall's constitutional rights and ordered the Durham Catholic School Board to allow Hall and Jean-Paul Dumond, 21, to attend the dance.

School board chair Mary Ann Martin said the board was extremely disappointed with the ruling but that Hall and his date would be allowed to attend the prom.

Hall, in a white tuxedo and blue tie, said he "was very happy and so excited that we won." When he first heard the news from his lawyer at his home in Oshawa, he said, "I was jumping up and down, and everybody was shouting."

"I feel at ease now, knowing that we are free of discrimination," said the grade 12 student at Monsignor John Pereyma Catholic High School.

Source: Josey, S. (2002, May 11). "Gay Prom Battle Ends with a Waltz." The Toronto Star. Reprinted with permission–Torstar Syndication Services.

The Canadian Press/Aaron Harris

A Gay Prom Date.
Marc Hall, 17, heads to his Toronto school prom with Jean-Paul Dumond, 21. Coming to terms with adolescence can frequently be a difficult struggle, but it's often more intense for gay people.

We can answer these questions with a definitive "no." With respect to sexuality, each phase of life brings new challenges and new opportunities for growth. Adulthood has its own set of developmental tasks. We'll now discuss four of the most important ones.

Developmental Tasks

While adolescent romantic relationships tend to be inherently unstable, with little sense of permanence or longevity, adults (some of them, anyway) tend to seek more stable, more long-term, complete relationships, including permanent romantic relationships. Marriage has traditionally been the primary relationship form for adult Canadians, and it continues to be, though less so than in the past.

The successful integration of sexuality into longer-term relationships implies a number of developmental tasks.

PASSION   In Western culture, romantic relationships usually begin with some element of physical and emotional attraction. The first episodes of sexual interaction tend to be fuelled by passion and spontaneous sexual arousal. Physical attraction ("chemistry") is often the spark that initially brings a couple together. At first, the degree to which a couple is compatible in other ways, such as mutual interests or perspectives, may take a back seat to sexual passion as the determinant of each partner's satisfaction with the relationship.

As the relationship progresses, the initial passionate infatuation inevitably wanes, and broader aspects of compatibility become more important. If, once the novelty of the new sexual partnership subsides, the partners discover that they're not so compatible in other important dimensions, it's not uncommon to hear them say, "I was blinded by passion."

Understanding that other factors beyond passion will determine the sustainability of sexual or romantic relationships is therefore a necessary developmental task of adult sexuality.

FRIENDSHIP   By early adulthood, most individuals have some level of experience with sexual and romantic relationships. This experience usually teaches us that sexual passion alone is not enough to sustain a relationship, especially if the couple hopes to maintain the relationship over time.

There are many dimensions to a strong, mutually satisfying relationship, and a sense of friendship is one of the most important. The qualities that contribute to a mutually beneficial friendship—such as shared interests and goals—also contribute to the intimacy of a romantic relationship. Over time, sexual satisfaction becomes a function of the couple's sense of shared intimacy along a range of dimensions, including both physical pleasure and friendship.

Learning to approach sexual and romantic relationships in a broader way that includes a range of aspects of intimacy is an important developmental task for adults hoping to maintain relationships beyond the short term.

COMMUNICATION   For many couples, openly discussing specific sexual likes and dislikes doesn't come naturally. Many people rely on nonverbal cues ("body language") to make assumptions about their partner's sexual preferences. This isn't always the most effective form of communication. More direct communication about sexuality may be an important contributor to a mutually satisfying longer-term relationship. In a study of men and women in long-term relationships, University of New Brunswick researchers MacNeil and Byers (1997) found that better communication, particularly about specific sexual likes and dislikes, was associated with overall sexual satisfaction. In another study , Byers (2005) found that individuals who were good communicators within their relationships experienced greater sexual and relationship satisfaction.

For many adults, learning to communicate directly and effectively with partners about sexuality is an important developmental task.

SEXUAL HEALTH   As we have seen, protecting their sexual health is a major developmental task for adolescents. It's no less so for adults. Taking measures to prevent STIs and HIV infection and unwanted pregnancy are still important, particularly since more and more adults are remaining single, or becoming single after separation or divorce.

A national study of sexually active Canadian women of reproductive age who were not trying to conceive found that, while most used some form of contraception, a sizable number were putting themselves at risk for unintended pregnancy (Black et al., 2009). Condoms and oral contraceptives were the most popular methods of contraception. Almost 15% of the women said that they "never" used birth control, and only 65.2% said they "always" did.

It appears that as adolescents make the transition to adulthood, their commitment to using condoms often decreases, even though their risks for STIs and HIV remain high. Rotermann and McKay (2009) looked at trends in condom use at last intercourse among unmarried, non-cohabitating 20- to 34-year-old Canadians, and found that condom use decreased as people got older. For example, 63.7% of males and 53.8% of females in the 20 to 24 age group used condoms at last intercourse,

CRITICAL THINKING QUESTIONS

How would you explain the finding that condom use among sexually active, unmarried, non-cohabitating 20- to 34-year-old Canadians declines as they get older?

compared to 56.0% of males and 47.1% of females in the 25 to 29 age range, and 54.7% of males and 42.2% of females in the 30 to 34 age group. In the total sample, 35.8% of those with more than one partner during the previous year and 30% of males and nearly 40% of females with three or more partners didn't use condoms at last intercourse. These statistics clearly suggest that many young Canadian adults are placing themselves at high risk for STIs and HIV.

Being Single

Recent years have seen a sharp increase in the number of single young people in our society. "Singlehood," not marriage, is now the most common lifestyle among people in their twenties. (See Table 12.4.)

Several factors contribute to the increased proportion of singles. More people are postponing marriage to pursue educational and career goals. Many young people are deciding to "live together" (also referred to as cohabiting and living common-law), at least for a while, rather than get married.

As Figure 12.1 shows, people are getting married later than they used to. In 2004, the typical man in Canada got married for the first time at 30.5 years of age, compared with 25 in 1960. The typical woman got married at 28.5, compared with 22 in 1960 (Statistics Canada, 2007). The average age at marriage is highest in Quebec and lowest in Saskatchewan. Statistics Canada no longer measures average age of first marriage among Canadians, but it appears likely that the current average age is similar to or slightly higher than in 2004.

Some single people don't choose to be single. Some remain single because they haven't found Mr. or Ms. Right. Many, however, see singlehood as an alternative, open-ended way of life, not just a temporary stage that precedes marriage. Now that career options for women have expanded, they're not as financially dependent on men as their mothers and grandmothers were. A number of career-oriented women, like young career-oriented men, choose to remain single (at least for a time) so they can focus on their careers.

Being single is not without its problems. Many single people are lonely. Some singles express concern about their lack of steady, meaningful social relationships. Some, usually women, worry about their physical safety. Some people who live alone find it difficult to satisfy their needs for intimacy, companionship, sex, and emotional support. Despite these concerns, however, most singles are well adjusted

CRITICAL THINKING QUESTIONS

Agree or disagree with the following statement, and support your answer: Marriage is an old-fashioned, outdated lifestyle that has become irrelevant for today's young people.

TABLE 12.4

Percentage of Canadians Who Were Single, Cohabiting, and Married in 1986, 1996, 2006, and 2011

Ages 20–24	Single (%)	Cohabiting (%)	Married (%)
1986	71.6	9.3	19.1
1996	79.2	12.0	8.8
2006	82.2	12.6	5.2
2011	85.6	11.6	4.8
Ages 25–29			
1986	37.7	10.2	52.1
1996	47.6	12.5	34.9
2006	51.5	22.6	25.9
2011	53.2	22.4	24.4

Source: Statistics Canada. (1986, 1996, 2006, 2011). Census Data Products. Ottawa: Government of Canada.

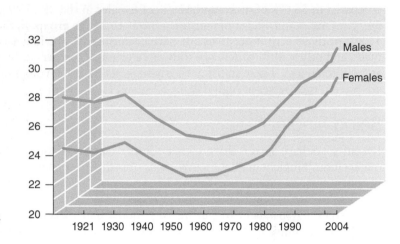

Figure 12.1 Average age at first marriage in Canada. The age at first marriage has substantially increased in Canada, partly because many adults now live together before getting married.

Source: Statistics Canada. (2010). CANSIM Table 101-1002: Mean age of males and females, by type of marriage and marital status, Canada, provinces and territories, annual. Ottawa: Government of Canada.

and content. Singles with more friends and supportive social networks tend to be more satisfied with their lifestyles.

There's no one "singles scene." Single people differ in their sexual interests and lifestyles. Many achieve emotional and psychological security through a network of intimate relationships with friends. Most are sexually active and practise **serial monogamy**.

Modern technology, especially the Internet, has transformed the singles scene. While the proverbial "singles bar" was the predominant setting for singles to meet before the new millennium, online dating sites such as Lavalife and eHarmony have since gained widespread acceptance. Social networking sites such as MySpace and Facebook are another form of Internet-based communication that allows singles to become familiar with potential sexual and romantic partners.

The Canadian-based online dating site Lavalife boasts 1.7 million members (Lavalife.com, 2011). On Lavalife, singles can choose from a variety of relationship types: dates, relationships, and intimate encounters. This allows potential partners to make clear what types of relationship they're interested in before meeting potential partners, removing a layer of ambiguity about their intentions. While some might feel that this level of up-front disclosure removes some of the mystery, intrigue, and romance of dating, others think the direct matching of compatible partners provided by Internet dating sites increases the likelihood that mutually satisfactory relationships will form. Research indicates that an increasing number of marriages and long-term relationships begin through some form of Internet communication (Sprecher, 2009).

Some singles remain celibate, either by choice or for lack of opportunity. People choose **celibacy** for a number of reasons. Nuns and priests do so for religious reasons. Others believe celibacy allows them to focus their energies and attentions on work or important causes. They see celibacy as a temporary accommodation to other pursuits. Still others remain celibate because they view sex outside of marriage as immoral. And some remain celibate because they find the prospect of sexual activity uninteresting, or because they're afraid of STIs.

Cohabitation

Mainstream societal attitudes towards unmarried partners living together as a couples changed dramatically during the last half of the twentieth century. **Cohabitation** has become acceptable within the social mainstream. We seldom hear cohabitation referred to as "living in sin" or "shacking up" anymore. People today are more likely to refer to cohabitation with value-free expressions such as "living together."

Serial monogamy A pattern of becoming involved in one exclusive relationship after another, as opposed to engaging in multiple sexual relationships at the same time.

Celibacy Complete sexual abstinence. The term is sometimes used to describe the state of being unmarried, especially for people who take vows to remain single.

Cohabitation The state whereby two people live together as a couple but are not legally married.

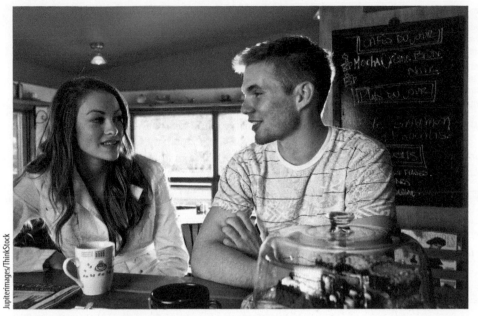

Meeting Other Singles. There's no one "singles scene." Although some people meet in singles bars, many meet in more casual settings, such as neighbourhood laundromats. Some singles advertise online and in newspapers and magazines.

Statistics Canada defines a relationship as a **common-law relationship** if it consists of two people of the opposite or the same sex who live together as a couple but are not legally married. Canadians of various ethnic backgrounds differ considerably in their acceptance of cohabitation. Acceptance is higher among those of British origin than among Southern Europeans. The Chinese are less accepting, and the Indo-Canadian community is the least accepting (Michell, 2001).

As Table 12.4 shows, common-law relationships are becoming increasingly prevalent in Canadian society. Clearly, more and more people in their 20s are opting for common-law relationships as an alternative to marriage.

COHABITATION BEFORE MARRIAGE Cohabiting couples may believe cohabitation will strengthen their eventual marriages by helping them iron out the kinks in their relationships. Yet cohabiters who later marry run a serious risk of divorce. Canadian couples who live together before marriage are twice as likely to separate as those who don't (Statistics Canada, 2002c). Sixty-three percent of those in their 30s who live together before marriage separate, compared with 30% of those who don't live together before marriage.

Why might couples who cohabit before marriage run a greater risk of divorce than couples who don't? Cohabiters tend to be more committed to personal independence than non-cohabiters (Bumpass, 1995). They also tend to be less traditional and less religious (Menard, 2011). All in all, people who cohabit before marriage tend to be less committed to the values and interests traditionally associated with the institution of marriage. Their attitudes, and not cohabitation itself, may thus account for their higher rates of marital dissolution (see Figure 12.2).

Marriage

Marriage is found in all human societies. Most people in every known society—sometimes nearly all—get married at least once. Marriage is our most common lifestyle. Statistics Canada (2005e) estimates that three-quarters of Canadians who are in their 30s will marry at some point in their lives. Most people see marriage as something they hope will be permanent.

SAME-SEX MARRIAGE Traditionally, societies have defined marriage as applying only to heterosexual couples. This definition was challenged by same-sex

Common-law relationship
A relationship in which two people live together as a couple but are not legally married. The term can refer to both opposite- and same-sex couples. Some jurisdictions recognize a common-law relationship as marriage.

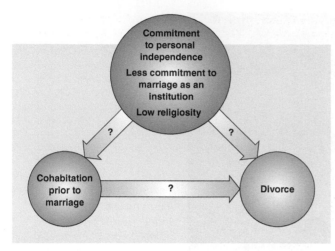

Figure 12.2 Does cohabitation prior to marriage increase the risk of divorce?
There's a correlation between premarital cohabitation and divorce. Does cohabitation increase the risk of divorce, or do other factors—such as a commitment to personal independence—contribute to the likelihood of both cohabitation and eventual divorce?

CRITICAL THINKING QUESTIONS

More and more Canadians in their 20s are living in common-law relationships, rather than getting married. In your opinion, what are the advantages and disadvantages of each lifestyle?

couples in Canada, who argued that not allowing same-sex marriage restricted their freedom. In July 2002, ruling that the traditional definition of marriage was discriminatory to lesbians and gays, the Ontario Superior Court of Justice ordered governments to redefine the term "marriage" to include same-sex couples. In this landmark decision, the judges argued that prohibiting same-sex couples from marrying was a violation of the Canadian Charter of Rights and Freedoms. In 2005, Canadian Parliament passed legislation allowing same-sex couples to marry. (We also discussed same-sex marriage in Chapters 1 and 9.)

The Canadian census obtained data about same-sex couples for the first time in 2001, recording 34 200 same-sex common law couples in Canada. By the 2011 census, that number had almost doubled to 64 575 (Statistics Canada, 2012). In 2011, about a third of same-sex couples were married, and two-thirds were living common-law. After same-sex marriage became legal in 2005, the number of same-sex married couples in Canada jumped from 7500 in 2006 to 21 000 in 2011, an increase of 181%. In 2011, 54.5% of same-sex couples were male, and 45.5% were female.

Two Canadian studies have analyzed married lesbian and gay couples (Alderson, 2004; MacIntosh, Reissing, & Andruff, 2010), and found the following benefits of marriage:

- Greater acceptance of their relationships by friends and family members.
- Equality with heterosexuals in terms of making decisions for ill partners, caring for children, and receiving inheritance and insurance benefits.
- Greater relationship satisfaction, including feeling closer to their partners and more secure about their relationships.
- Decreased feelings of internalized homophobia.
- More openness to the idea of having children.

Not everyone in the gay community supports same-sex marriage. Opponents tend to criticize marriage as a patriarchal, heterosexual institution. Married same-sex couples don't share this view; they argue that legalization of same-sex marriage offers freedom of choice.

WHY DO PEOPLE MARRY?   In this era of serial monogamy and cohabitation, people still get married. Why?

Because marriage meets personal and cultural needs and provides a legal sanction for deeply committed relationships. For many people, it permits maintenance of a home life and provides an institution in which children can be supported and socialized into adopting the norms of the family and the culture at large. In theory, marriage restricts sexual relations, so a man can be assured—or at least can assume—that children born to his wife are his. Marriage also permits the orderly transmission of wealth from one family to another and from one generation to another.

Notions such as romantic love, equality, and the radical concept that men as well as women would do well to aspire to the ideal of faithfulness are recent additions to the structure of marriage in Western society. Not until the nineteenth century did the notion of love as a basis for marriage become widespread in Western culture. When Canadians were asked in 1998 why people should get married, almost all (95%) said for love (Compas, 1998). The next common reasons were

Aaron Vincent Elkaim/*The Toronto Star*

Married at Last.
Douglas Elliott, second from left, and Greg Lawrence, centre, are congratulated after their wedding in Toronto. Elliott was one of the leading lawyers in the fight to make gay marriage legal in Canada. He and Lawrence had been a couple for 32 years before they married.

for companionship (83%) and to have children (82%). Two-thirds cited having a regular and safe sex partner as a reason to get married.

In another national survey almost 10 years later, Canadians were asked about the importance of marriage (Canadian Press, 2007). There was a major discrepancy between the importance of marriage in the respondents' own lives and their perception of its importance in society. When asked about their personal attitudes, 42% said marriage had become more important in their own lives, 17% said it had become less important, and 39% said its importance hadn't changed. Only 13% believed marriage had become more important in society, while 53% felt it had become less important. Three-quarters said making a marriage work was harder today than in the past.

Nevertheless, an Abacus Data survey for the Huffington Post Canada (Grenier, 2012) found that among those aged 18 to 30 (millennials), 63% said they wanted to get married at some point in their lives, 24% were unsure, and only 13% said they did not want to get married. Only 47% of respondents living in Quebec said they wanted to get married, while in other regions of the country, the number was 65% or higher. Of those who attended religious services once a week or more, 95% said they wanted to get married.

TYPES OF MARRIAGE   There are two major types of marriage—monogamy and polygamy. In **monogamy**, a husband and wife are wed only to each other. But let's not confuse monogamy, which is a form of matrimony, with sexual exclusivity. People may have extramarital affairs, but they're considered to be married to just one person at a time. In **polygamy**, a person has more than one spouse and is permitted sexual access to all of them.

In Bountiful, British Columbia, a breakaway sect of the Mormon Church has been openly practising polygamy since the 1950s. Teenage girls are often forced to marry much older men who already have wives. The British Columbia government has been reluctant to charge community members with violating Canada's anti-polygamy law, because the Canadian Charter of Rights and Freedoms protects religious freedom (Canadian Press, 2005b). Yet in 2009, after 20 years of investigations, the British Columbia government brought charges of polygamy against two leaders of the community, Winston Blackmore and James Oler.

Monogamy Marriage to one person.

Polygamy Simultaneous marriage to more than one person.

Polygyny A form of marriage in which a man is married to more than one woman at the same time.

Polyandry A form of marriage in which a woman is married to more than one man at the same time.

Some Muslims in Canada also have plural wives, although the great majority do not (Javed, 2008). Aly Hindy, imam at an Islamic centre in Scarborough, claims to have officiated at more than 30 polygamous marriages over a five-year period (Javed, 2008). Islam allows men to marry up to four wives, while the Mormon sect in British Columbia allows an unlimited number of wives. Whereas the Bountiful sect requires polygamous marriage in order to reach heaven, Islam accepts but does not require polygamy.

Polygyny is by far the most prevalent form of polygamy among the world's preliterate societies (Frayser, 1985). **Polyandry** is practised only rarely. In polygynous societies, men are permitted multiple wives if they can support them; less often, a man will have one wife and one or more concubines. Economic factors and the availability of prospective mates, however, usually limit the opportunities for men to wed more than one woman at a time. In many cases, only wealthy men can afford to support multiple wives and their children. Few societies have enough women to allow most men to have two or more wives (Harris & Johnson, 2000; Whitten, 2001). For these reasons, even in societies that prefer polygyny, fewer than half of the men at any given time actually have multiple mates (Ford & Beach, 1951).

ARRANGED MARRIAGE In Western cultures, mate selection is presumably unrestricted. Parents today seldom arrange marriages, although they may still encourage their children to date those wonderful sons and daughters of the solid, churchgoing couples who live down the street. Among recent immigrants to Canada from the Middle East and East Asia, however, arranged marriage is relatively common.

WHO WE MARRY The universal incest taboo proscribes mating between close relatives. Other societal rules and customs also determine which people are desirable mates, and which are not.

Homogamy The practise of marrying someone who's similar to yourself in social background and standing.

Because we make choices, we tend to marry people who attract us. These people are usually similar to us in physical attractiveness and attitudes, and even in minute details. We're more often than not similar to our mates in characteristics such as height, weight, personality traits, and intelligence (Buss, 1994). The people we marry also seem likely to meet our material, sexual, and psychological needs. The concept of "like marrying like" is termed **homogamy**. We usually marry people of the same racial or ethnic background, educational level, and religion. With Canada's increased cultural diversity, however, the number of people who choose partners outside of their racial or ethnic groups is increasing. According to Statistics Canada, in 2006 there were 286 400 mixed union couples in Canada—a 33.1% increase from 2001 (Milan, Maheux & Chui, 2010). Mixed unions represented 3.9% of all couples in Canada. People of Japanese origin had the highest proportion marrying or forming unions outside their visible minority group followed by Latin Americans and black people. Mixed race couples were more common in urban compared to rural areas. In Vancouver, 8.5% of couples were in mixed unions, the highest proportion among Canadian cities.

Marital Sexuality

Patterns of marital sexuality vary across cultures, yet anthropologists have noted some common threads (Harris & Johnson, 2000; Whitten, 2001). Privacy for sexual relations is valued in nearly all cultures. Most cultures also place restrictions on intercourse during menstruation, during at least some stages of pregnancy, and for a time after childbirth.

The sexual revolution, however, ushered in profound changes in marital sexuality. In particular, it helped dislodge the view that sexual pleasure is meant only for men and that it's women's duty to satisfy their husbands' sexual needs.

How frequently do married couples have sex? According to an Environics Research Group (2013) survey of 1003 sexually active Canadians aged 18 to 49, among people who were married, 2% reported having sex every day, 34% a few times a week, 46% a few times a month, and 16% said once a month or less. In comparison, people in unmarried relationships, were more likely to report having sex every day (20%) and a few times a week (43%).

MARITAL SATISFACTION   Marital satisfaction is a complex phenomenon that includes the following (Wilcox & Marquardt, 2011):

- Commitment
- An adequate income (yes, money matters)
- Sharing in housework
- Generosity toward one's spouse (Dew & Wilcox, 2011)
- The support of one's family and friends (yes, in-laws can make a difference one way or the other)
- Agreement on attitudes toward having and raising children
- Sexual satisfaction (see Figure 12.3)
- For many couples, a belief in the religious or spiritual value of marriage

Attracted to Similarity.
We tend to marry people who are similar to us in physical appeal and attitudes. We also tend to be similar in height and weight, intelligence, and use of alcohol and other drugs.

There are many ways to view the link between sexual satisfaction and marital satisfaction. Does marital satisfaction lead to feelings of attraction and sexual desire for one's spouse? Does "good sex" contribute to happiness with a marriage? It's likely that the answer to both questions is "yes." When it comes to understanding human behavior and mental processes, it is often useful to look for an interaction between variables—in this case, marital satisfaction and sexual satisfaction—rather than to think that one must directly cause the other. Then, too, in a cultural setting in which marriage partners (usually) choose one another, sexual attraction and sharing of important attitudes are likely to play key roles both in the selection process and the outcome.

Figure 12.3   Marital Satisfaction 18- to 46-Year-Old Married Mothers and Fathers, by Sexual Satisfaction

Source: W. Bradford Wilcox & Elizabeth Marquardt (Eds.). (2011). The State of Our Unions: Marriage In America 2011. Reprinted by permission of the National Marriage Project at the University of Virginia and the Institute for American Values. marriage@virginia.edu, Figure 15, p. 37.

Researchers at the University of New Brunswick have found that perception of rewards and costs is related to feelings of sexual satisfaction (Lawrence & Byers, 1995). Rewards include the amount of fun people experience during sex, pleasurable physical sensations from touching and caressing, and feeling comfortable with their partners. Costs include too-infrequent sexual activity and poor sexual communication with their partners.

People who believe they're getting many sexual rewards and low sexual costs are likely to have higher levels of sexual satisfaction. This is especially true when the rewards turn out to be greater and the costs lower than they expect.

Other researchers have found that wives who talk openly to their husbands about their sexual feelings and needs report higher levels of sexual satisfaction than wives who don't. Among both men and women in New Brunswick who are in long-term relationships, sexual satisfaction is higher for those who can tell their partners about their sexual likes and dislikes (MacNeil & Byers, 1997). Satisfaction is also higher for those who can openly communicate about nonsexual topics.

Couples who are in more-committed relationships report higher levels of sexual satisfaction than those who are in uncommitted relationships. When asked how satisfied they are with their sex lives, two-thirds of Canadians who are married or in common-law relationships say they're very satisfied, compared with 44% of those who are single (Compas, 1998) (see Figure 12.4).

SEXUAL CONFLICT Couples can experience conflict over any number of sexual issues. In a study of couples in New Brunswick, one-quarter of the men agreed with the comment "I like to do things my partner does not," and one-third of the women agreed with the comment "My partner chooses inconvenient times for sex" (MacNeil & Byers, 1997). More than one-third of Canadians have conflicts over sex at least once a month. Those in common-law relationships have conflicts more often than married couples (Compas, 1998). (See Table 12.5.)

B. J. Rye (2001) at the University of Waterloo found that 21% of students often had serious disagreements about the occurrence of sex. Almost three times as many males (45%) as females (15%) were concerned that their partner's sexual desires were lower than what they would have liked.

Sexual Orientation and Relationship Satisfaction

Numerous researchers have studied the factors that predict relationship satisfaction and deterioration. Much of the research has asked whether there are differences in the factors that satisfy heterosexual versus homosexual couples, and few have emerged. One difference is that gay and lesbian couples tend to distribute household chores evenly, whereas in heterosexual couples, women tend to do more of the chores than their male partners (Kurdek, 2005, 2006).

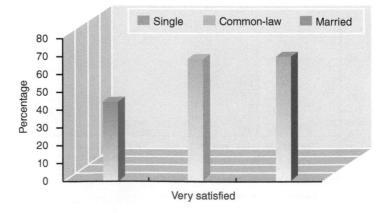

Figure 12.4 Relationship status and sexual satisfaction. According to the 1998 Compas study, married Canadians report greater sexual satisfaction than Canadians who are single (including those who are divorced and widowed) or live common-law. Do these results mean married people are more satisfied, or are they just more likely to say they're satisfied?

Source: Compas Inc. (1998). Modern life survey of the Canadian adult population. Unpublished raw data. Toronto: Compas Inc.

TABLE 12.5

Frequency of Conflicts Canadians Experience with Their Partners over Sex

	Males		Females	
	Common-Law	**Married**	**Common-Law**	**Married**
Often	1.4%	1.4%	3.6%	2.5%
Several times a month	4.2	3.5	8.9	7.8
Once or twice a month	39.4	30.1	35.7	28.6
Never	54.9	65.1	51.8	61.2

Source: Data from Compas. (1998). Modern life survey of the Canadian population.

For both heterosexual and lesbian women, sexual satisfaction is tied to relationship satisfaction (Mathews et al., 2006; Twist, 2005). Gay, lesbian, and male–female couples are all more satisfied when they receive social support from their partners, share power within their relationships, fight fairly, and perceive that their partners are committed to their relationships. But there are a couple of differences that favour stability in the relationships of male–female couples: they're more likely to have the support of their families, and less likely to be stigmatized by society at large.

Extramarital Sex

Why do people engage in extramarital sex? Some do it for variety (Peluso, 2008). Some have affairs to break the routine of confining marriages (Allen & Atkins, 2005; Markman, 2005). Others enter affairs to express hostility toward their spouses or to retaliate for injustice. Husbands and wives who engage in affairs often report that they're not satisfied with or fulfilled by their marital relationships. Curiosity and desire for personal growth are often more prominent motives than marital dissatisfaction. Middle-aged people may have affairs to boost their self-esteem, or to prove that they're still attractive.

The sexual motive is often less pressing than the desire for emotional closeness. Some women say they're seeking someone they can talk to or communicate with (Lamanna & Riedmann, 2005). There's a notable gender difference here (Petersen & Hyde, 2011). According to Janis Abrahms Spring, author of *After the Affair: Healing the Pain and Rebuilding Trust When a Partner Has Been Unfaithful*, women are usually seeking "soulmates," whereas men are seeking "playmates." Women tend to justify affairs when they're based on love, but men tend to do so when they're not based on love (Smart, 2006).

Women are less accepting of sex without emotional involvement (Petersen & Hyde, 2011). Men are more likely than women to distinguish between sex and love, whereas women see love and sex as going together so that falling in love justifies sex (Petersen & Hyde, 2011). But these are *group* differences. Many individual men are interested primarily in the extramarital relationship rather than the sex per se. Similarly, some women are out for the sex and not the relationship.

PATTERNS OF EXTRAMARITAL SEX   Let's begin with a few definitions. **Extramarital sex** (an "affair") is usually conducted without the spouse's knowledge or approval. A secret affair is referred to as **conventional adultery**, infidelity, or "cheating." Conventional adultery runs the gamut from the one-night stand to the affair that persists for years. In **consensual adultery**, an extramarital relationship is

Extramarital sex Sexual relations between a married person and someone other than his or her spouse.

Conventional adultery Extramarital sex that's kept hidden from one's spouse.

Consensual adultery Extramarital sex that's engaged in openly, with the knowledge and consent of one's spouse.

A World of Diversity

MATING IN CAPTIVITY

Do love and intimacy lead to hot sex?

In her best-selling book *Mating in Captivity: Reconciling the Erotic and the Domestic*, New York therapist Esther Perel (2006) offers a provocative analysis that challenges commonly held views of the relationship between intimacy and sex.

The book stems from Perel's counselling of heterosexual and gay couples who have secure, caring relationships but dull, unsatisfactory sex lives. Using case studies, she illustrates how the desire for intimacy and security can stifle marital lust.

Perel argues that the human desire for safety and closeness in a long-term relationship conflicts with the desire for novelty, excitement, and risk-taking. In particular, she believes that too much closeness can feel like imprisonment. Desire needs freedom to thrive. People are most sexually attracted to partners they see as separate individuals. This requires that they not totally rely on their partners to satisfy all of their emotional needs.

The women and men discussed in Perel's book long for more vibrant, exciting sex lives with their partners. She asserts that couples need to unlock their erotic intelligence, by removing the restraints they have placed on their lustful imaginations. This requires moving away from the security of dull but comfortable ways of having sex, and accepting the risk-taking involved in adventurous sex. Sexual desire, response, and pleasure are heightened by the erotic elements of anticipation, surprise, and mystery.

One of Perel's (2006) most controversial conclusions is that hot sex requires not only that we feel a sense of independence from our partners, but also that we're more sexually aroused and alive when we're free to objectify our partners.

Swinging A form of consensual adultery in which both spouses share extramarital sexual experiences. This is also referred to as mate swapping.

Comarital sex Swinging, or mate swapping.

conducted openly—that is, with the knowledge and consent of the partner. And in what's called **swinging**, **comarital sex**, or mate swapping, the partner participates.

How many people "cheat" on their spouses? With respect to Canadians, in a 2005 Compas poll, 10% of married people said extramarital affairs had occurred in their marriages. However, in a more recent poll by *The Globe and Mail* (2013) of their readers, with 8 429 respondents, 44% of men and 39% of women reported that they had "cheated" on a partner. It should be noted that people choosing to respond to a newspaper survey are unlikely to be representative of the Canadian population as a whole, and these results included both married and unmarried people. In the 2005 Compas survey, Canadians were asked whether acts of unfaithfulness by their partners would mean the end of their relationship. Fewer than half (41%) said it definitely would, and 27% said it probably would.

Research suggests that the prevalence of infidelity may be increasing. Results from surveys in the United States have found that the lifetime rate of infidelity for men aged 60 and above increased to 28% in 2006, up from 20% in 1991 (Parker-Pope, 2008). For older women, the lifetime incidence rose to 15%, up from 5% in 1991. The researchers also found changes in newer marriages. About 20% of the men and 15% of the women under age 35 say they were unfaithful at some time, up from about 15% for men and 12% for women in 1991. A *USA Today*/Gallup Poll found that 54% of respondents said they personally knew someone who had been unfaithful (Blow, 2009).

Having presented the percentages of reported extramarital sex, we point out that these reports cannot be verified. People may be reluctant to reveal they have "cheated" even when they are assured of anonymity (Parker-Pope, 2008; Peluso, 2008). One study surveyed 4 884 married women, used both face-to-face interviews and anonymous computer questionnaires (Whisman & Snyder, 2007). Only 1% of women said they had been unfaithful during the previous year in the face-to-face interviews. However, 6% of the same sample admitted to infidelity on the computer questionnaire.

Some people who suspect that their spouses are having affairs collect DNA samples from bed sheets, underwear, cigarette butts, and other places, and send them for DNA testing. Paragon Genetics in Toronto receives such samples from across North America and Europe. Forty percent of the samples test positive, indicating that the DNA is from people other than the spouses (White, 2008).

EFFECTS OF EXTRAMARITAL SEX   The discovery of infidelity can evoke a range of emotional responses. The spouse may be filled with anger, jealousy, or even shame. Feelings of inadequacy and doubts about one's attractiveness and desirability may surface. Infidelity may be seen by the betrayed spouse as a serious breach of trust and intimacy. A marriage that's not terminated in the wake of such a disclosure may survive in a damaged condition.

The harm an affair does to a marriage depends on the meaning the affair has for each marriage partner (Peluso, 2008). There appear to be some gender differences in how men and women react to learning that their spouse has had an affair. A wife's affair, especially if the husband perceives that it was motivated primarily by sexual desire and attraction, may be an often unforgivable blow to his ego or pride (Rasmussen & Kilborne, 2008). A woman may be more likely to see her husband's affair as an emotional betrayal and as a threat to the structure of her life (Allen & Atkins, 2005; Peluso, 2008).

If a person has an affair because the marriage is deeply troubled, the affair may be one more factor that speeds its dissolution. The effects on the marriage may depend on the nature of the affair. It may be easier to understand that a spouse has fallen prey to an isolated, unplanned encounter than to accept an extended affair (Rasmussen & Kilborne, 2008). In some cases, the discovery of infidelity stimulates the couple to work to improve their relationship.

SWINGING   Swinging—also called mate swapping, or comarital sex—is a form of consensual adultery in which both partners openly share sexual experiences with other people. Most swingers seek to avoid emotional entanglements with their swinging partners, but they may fail to separate their emotions from their sexual activities. Emotional intimacy between swinging partners can be even more threatening to the swingers' primary relationships than sexual intimacy.

Until recently, Canadians who engaged in swinging or ran swingers' clubs could be charged with various offences under the *Criminal Code*, usually with having sex in a public place (public indecency) or with running a common bawdy house (a place used for prostitution or for acts of indecency). In 2005, the Supreme Court of Canada ruled that swinging was not illegal. The case, which involved the owners of two Montreal swingers' clubs, turned on the concept of indecency. The Court declared that the sexual activity of consensual swingers wasn't harmful to Canadian society, and therefore wasn't indecent. The Supreme Court's verdict is highly significant, because it used the criteria of harm to society, rather than community standards of morality, as a test for indecent behaviour.

Polyamory

A term commonly used today to refer to extramarital relationships in various forms is **polyamory**. Based on the view that people's needs for intimacy are unlikely to be gratified through one relationship, polyamory refers to open relationships that allow for consensual sexual and/or emotional interactions with more than one partner. Proponents argue that the core marriages can be enhanced if the partners have opportunities to develop emotionally intimate relationships with others.

Polyamory Any form of open relationship that allows for consensual sexual and/or emotional interactions with more than one partner.

Ashleymadison.com

A Website for Flings.
Ashley Madison, the online site that helps people have affairs,
deliberately targets young women with ads like this one.

Divorce

My wife and I were considering a divorce,
but after pricing lawyers we decided to buy
a new car instead.
　　—Henny Youngman (American Comic)

According to Statistics Canada projections, 37.9% of marriages that took place in 2004 will end in divorce, and the average age at divorce will be 44 years for men and 41.2 years for women (Vanier Institute of the Family, 2010). More recent projections indicate that 40.7% of marriages that took place in 2008 will end in divorce (Kelly, 2012). The divorce rate in 2003 was about three times as high as in 1968. The peak was reached in 1987, in response to 1985 changes in the Divorce Act in 1985 that made it easier to obtain a divorce.

There's also been a significant increase in the number of people experiencing second divorces. In 2003, 16.2% of divorces involved men who had been previously divorced, compared with just 5.4% in 1973 (Statistics Canada, 2005). Divorces are most likely to occur after three to four years of marriage. The Yukon and Quebec have the highest rates of divorce, while Newfoundland and Labrador and New Brunswick have the lowest (Kelly, 2012).

With the increasing acceptance of cohabitation, more and more divorced people choose to live common-law instead of remarrying (Statistics Canada, 2005). The rate of breakups in common-law relationships, however, is much greater than for married couples.

Canada's no-fault divorce laws allow divorces without findings of marital misconduct. Women's increased economic independence has also contributed to the rising divorce rate, enabling them to break away from troubled marriages. And more people today consider marriage an alterable condition than prior generations did.

Today, Canadians have higher expectations for marriage than their parents and grandparents did. They expect marriage to be personally fulfilling, as well an institution for rearing children. Many demand the right to be happy. The most common reasons for divorce today are problems in communication and lack of understanding. When women seek to end their marriages, their reasons often include husbands' criticism, defensiveness, contempt, and stonewalling, not lack of financial support (Carrère et al., 2000; Mahoney & Knudson-Martin, 2009).

THE COSTS OF DIVORCE　Divorce often causes financial and emotional problems. When a household splits, the resources often can't maintain the earlier standard of living for both partners. Financially, divorce hits women harder than men. Divorced mothers often face the combined stresses of being solely responsible for rearing their children and needing to increase their incomes to make ends meet. Divorced fathers may find it difficult to pay alimony and child support while attempting to establish new lifestyles.

Divorce can prompt feelings of failure as a spouse and parent, loneliness, uncertainty about the future, and depression. Married people appear better able to cope with the stresses and strains of life, perhaps because they can rely on one another for emotional support. Divorced and separated people have the highest rates of physical and mental illness in the population, and divorced people have higher rates

Pixland/ThinkStock

For the Sake of the Children?
Research suggests that children may fare better when parents who are in regular conflict separate than when they stay together.

of suicide than married people (Carrère et al., 2000). On the other hand, divorce can be a catalyst for personal growth and renewal. It can provide an opportunity for people to take stock of themselves and establish new, more rewarding lives.

Senior Sexuality

According to Statistics Canada (2013), in the 10-year period from 2004 to 2013, the number of people in Canada aged 65 or older grew from 4 127 579 to 5 379 622, an increase of 30%. They are the fastest growing segment of the Canadian population. People are also living longer. The average age at death is

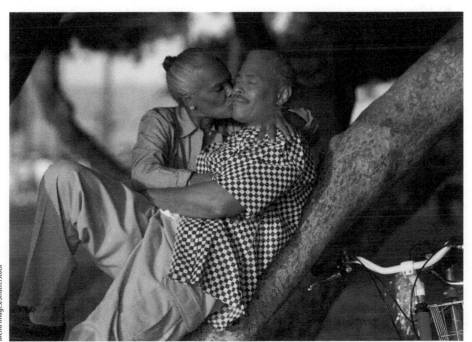

Blend Images/Shutterstock

Sexuality in Late Adulthood.
Are older people sexually active? If they are, are they abnormal or deviant? Young people often find it difficult to imagine older people engaging in sexual activity, but it's normal to retain sexual interest and activity for a lifetime.

now 79 years for men and 83 years for women (Statistics Canada, 2012). This "greying" of the population may have a profound effect on our views of older people, especially concerning sexuality. Many people in our culture see sexual activity as appropriate only for the young. This belief falls within a constellation of unfounded cultural myths about older people, including the notions that older people are sexless, older people with sexual urges are abnormal, and older males with sexual interests are "dirty old men."

Research doesn't support the belief that people inevitably lose their sexuality as they age. Yes, the physical ability to function sexually diminishes somewhat. However, a number of studies have shown that psychological and social factors may be at least as important as physical factors in determining sexual behaviour and satisfaction among older people (Delamater & Karraker, 2009; Loe, 2012).

Using data from a study of 1384 people who were 45 and older, Delamater and Moorman (2007) explored associations between age, biological and social factors, and sexual behaviours. The average age of the participants was 60 for men and 61 for women. Although the researchers found that sexual behaviour decreased as people got older, they also found that positive attitudes toward sexuality and satisfaction with relationships were important factors in determining the frequency of sexual activity with partners. Not surprisingly, they also found that social-context factors such as whether participants had partners affected sexual frequency. The researchers concluded that "individuals who are healthy and satisfied with their relationships remain sexually active into their 70s and 80s. The nature of sexual expression in later life reflects the interplay of body, mind, and social context" (Delamater & Moorman, 2007, p. 944).

We've discussed the sexuality-related developmental tasks of children, adolescents, and adults. With the increasing recognition that sexuality can play a vital role in the lives of older people, it's appropriate to consider the sexuality-related developmental tasks of later life. These include:

- Maintaining self-perception as a sexual being while living in a culture that tends to equate sexuality with youth
- Adapting to reduced frequency of sexual desire
- Adapting to reduced intensity of genital sexual response
- Adapting to the death of a partner
- Adapting to entry into a long-term-care facility such as a nursing home
- Using protection against STIs and HIV

Physical Changes

Although many older people retain the capacity to respond sexually, physical changes do occur as the years pass. (See Table 12.6.) If we're aware of these changes, we won't view them as abnormal or find ourselves unprepared to cope with them. We can avert many potential problems by adjusting our expectations and making changes to accommodate the aging process. By fine-tuning our expectations, we may find ourselves leading some of the most sexually fulfilling years of our lives when we reach our senior years. Indeed, a survey of Canadians over the age of 40 has found that 61% agree with the statement "Sex gets better with age" (Leger Marketing, 2010).

CHANGES IN THE FEMALE   Many of the physical changes in women stem from the decline in estrogen production around menopause.

The uterus decreases in size, no longer becoming so congested during sexual arousal. The vaginal walls lose a great deal of elasticity, as well as the thick, corrugated texture that's typical of the childbearing years. As the walls grow paler and thinner, intercourse may become irritating. Thinning walls may also lead to greater

TABLE 12.6

Changes in Sexual Arousal Often Associated with Aging

Changes in the Female	Changes in the Male
Reduced myotonia (muscle tension)	Longer time to erection and orgasm
Reduced vaginal lubrication	Need for more direct stimulation for erection and orgasm
Reduced elasticity of the vaginal walls	Less semen emitted during ejaculation
Smaller increases in breast size during sexual arousal	Erections may be less firm
Reduced intensity of muscle spasms at orgasm	Testicles may not elevate as high into the scrotum
	Less intense orgasmic contractions
	Lessened feeling of a need to ejaculate during sex
	Longer refractory period

Source: Data from The Kinsey Institute for Research in Sex, Gender, and Reproduction. From The Kinsey Institute New Report on Sex. *1990. New York: St. Martin's Press.*

pressure on the bladder and urethra during intercourse, leading in some cases to urinary urgency and burning urination that can persist for days.

Women produce less vaginal lubrication after menopause, and the lubrication they do produce may take minutes, rather than seconds, to appear. Lack of adequate lubrication is another major reason for painful intercourse.

The vagina shrinks in size, while the labia majora lose a great deal of their fatty deposits and become thin. The introitus becomes relatively constricted, sometimes making penile entry difficult. This "problem," however, has a positive aspect: increased friction between the penis and the vaginal walls may heighten sexual sensations.

Many of these changes can be slowed or reversed through estrogen-replacement therapy (see Chapter 3) or topical application of estrogen cream. Natural lubrication may also be increased through more elaborate foreplay. The need for more foreplay may encourage men to become more considerate lovers. (Older men are also likely to need more time to become aroused.) An artificial lubricant can ease problems posed by difficult entry or painful thrusting.

Women's breasts show smaller increases in size with sexual arousal as they age, but the nipples still become erect. Because the muscle tone of the urethra and the anal sphincters decreases, the spasms of orgasm become less powerful and fewer in number, making orgasm feel less intense. The uterine contractions that occur during orgasm become discouragingly painful for some postmenopausal women. Despite these changes, women can retain their ability to achieve orgasm well into their advanced years.

CHANGES IN THE MALE   Age-related changes tend to occur more gradually in men, and are not clearly connected with any single biological event. Male adolescents may achieve erection in a matter of seconds through sexual fantasy alone. After about age 50, men take progressively longer to achieve erections. Their erections become less firm, perhaps because of lowered testosterone production, and may require minutes of direct penile stimulation to achieve. Couples can adjust to these changes by extending the length and variety of foreplay.

Most men remain capable of erection throughout their lives. Erectile dysfunction is not inevitable with aging. Men generally require more time to reach orgasm as they age, however, which may also reflect lowered testosterone production. In the eyes of their sex partners, however, delayed ejaculation may make them better lovers.

Testosterone production gradually declines from about age 40 to age 60, then begins to level off. The decline is not inevitable, however, and may be related to the man's general health. Sperm production tends to decline as the seminiferous tubules degenerate, but viable sperm may be produced late in life. Men in their seventies, eighties, and even nineties have fathered children.

Nocturnal erections tend to diminish in intensity, duration, and frequency as men age, but they don't normally disappear in healthy men. The refractory period tends to lengthen with age. An adolescent may require only a few minutes to regain erection and ejaculate again after a first orgasm, whereas a man in his thirties may require half an hour. After age 50, the refractory period may increase to several hours.

Older men produce less ejaculate, and it may seep, rather than shoot, out. The contractions of orgasm become weaker and fewer. Still, older men may enjoy orgasm as thoroughly as they did when they were younger. Attitudes and expectations can be as important as the contractions themselves.

Most physical changes don't bring men's and women's sex lives to a grinding halt. People's attitudes, sexual histories, and partners are usually more important factors in sexual behaviour and enjoyment.

Patterns of Sexual Activity

Despite the decline in certain physical functions, older people can continue to lead vibrant, fulfilling sex lives. In fact, years of sexual experience may more than compensate for any diminution of physical responsiveness (Laumann et al., 2006; Loe, 2012).

Unfortunately, people who overreact to expected changes in sexual response may conclude that their sex lives are over, and give up on sexual activity, or even on expressing any physical affection (Dunn, 1998). However, despite general trends, sexuality among older people is variable (Loe, 2012). Many older people engage in intercourse, oral sex, and masturbation at least as often as they did when they were younger.

One of the most recent comprehensive studies of sex and aging was conducted by researchers at the University of Chicago, who sampled more than 3000 American adults between the ages of 57 and 85 (Tessler Lindau et al., 2007). They found that:

- Sexual relations declined with age.
- 73% of those aged 57 to 64, 53% of those aged 65 to 74, and 26% of those aged 75 to 85 reported having sex with partners during the previous year.
- The average frequency of sex for those who were sexually active was two to three times a month.
- Women were less likely than men to have sexual relations, because more women than men were widowed.
- People in good health were twice as likely as those in poor health to be sexually active.
- Half of those who were sexually active had one or more sexual problems, yet most hadn't discussed these problems with doctors after turning 50.
- 14% of the men used Viagra or other supplements to improve their sexual functioning.
- Only a minority (13% of men and 35% of women) felt that sex was "not all that important." (Tessler Lindau et al., 2007)

In a study of 35- to 55-year-old women, researchers found that body image is a more important influence than menopause on sexual functioning and satisfaction

(Koch et al., 2005). One-fifth of the respondents were unable to name even one attractive feature about themselves and reported overall dissatisfaction with their bodies. The features women considered least attractive were their stomachs and abdomens, hips, and thighs and legs. The less attractive a woman thought she was, the less likely she was to experience sexual desire and activity during the previous ten years. Two-thirds of the women reported one or more changes in their sexual response, such as desiring sex less and engaging in sex less often. Some women, however, had improved sexual response, and when these women did have sex, they experienced high levels of enjoyment (Koch et al., 2005).

Taking an innovative, more positive approach, University of Ottawa researcher Peggy Kleinplatz and her team focused on couples who experienced optimal sexuality, rather than sexual problems (Kleinplatz et al., 2010). They found that for some couples, "great sex" didn't occur until midlife, and that great sex was possible well into the later years. The couples talked about such factors as erotic intimacy, interpersonal exploration, authenticity and the freedom to be themselves, and communication as the ingredients for great sex. For them, having young, toned bodies and quickly responding genitalia had little to do with satisfying sexual relationships.

Couples may accommodate the physical changes of aging by broadening their sexual repertoires to include more diverse forms of stimulation, including oral–genital sex, sexual fantasy, sexually explicit materials, anal stimulation, vibrators, and other techniques. They may derive sexual satisfaction from manual and oral stimulation, cuddling, caressing, and tenderness, as well as from intercourse to orgasm.

LOSING A PARTNER   As people enter the later stages of life, the death of a partner becomes a reality for many. The surviving partner faces a loss of companionship and physical intimacy, including sexual expression. In many cases, reduced sexual activity among older people is due more to the loss of partners than to reduced physical capacity.

Since women tend to live longer than men, partner loss and its impact on sexuality affects them disproportionately. One study found that 42% of married 60- to 69-year-old women had been sexually active during the previous three months, compared to just 7% of unmarried 60- to 69-year-old women, and that 22% of married 70- to 79-year-old women were sexually active, compared to a mere 3% of unmarried 70- to 79-year-old women (Patel, Gillespie, & Foxman, 2003).

It's important to recognize that the need for and the benefits of physical intimacy don't decline with age.

Aging and Gay and Lesbian Sexuality

Limited research has been carried out on the effects of aging on gay men. James Murray of the AIDS Committee of Toronto and Barry Adam of the University of Windsor (2001) conducted interviews in Toronto with gay and bisexual men who were 40 and over, to determine some of their concerns about aging in the context of HIV. They found that, because the gay community values youth and attractiveness, many older men felt at a disadvantage in finding sexual partners, and saw themselves as "invisible" to younger men. Several of the men clearly believed they were no longer desirable and felt unwelcome in gay social gatherings. Feelings of isolation and loneliness were common, especially among those who had lost partners and close friends to AIDS.

They also expressed positive feelings about aging. For some, attaining intimate relationships outweighed diminished sexual prowess. And because their sex drives were now less urgent, some men felt they could be in greater control of their sexuality. Those who were most involved in gay community organizations felt that the social connections they established there would be sources of support as they aged (Murray & Adam, 2001).

Montreal researchers have found that older gays and lesbians feel excluded by gay and lesbian organizations because of age discrimination (Brotman et al., 2003). The older groups feel doubly discriminated against in their interactions with health agencies in the broader society, because of both sexual orientation and age. Many among the older generation have not been open about their sexual orientations and experience considerable fear when dealing with health and social agencies. Not surprisingly, most agencies don't know how to respond to the unique needs of older lesbians and gay men, especially in settings such as nursing homes, where workers may be homophobic (Brotman et al., 2003).

In the United States, the National Resource Center on LGBT Aging (*www. lgbtagingcenter.org*) seeks to improve the quality of services and supports offered to lesbian, gay, bisexual, and transgendered older adults. Established in 2010 through a grant from the United States Department of Health and Human Services, the organization provides training, technical assistance, and educational resources for aging-related service providers, LGBT organizations, and LGBT older adults.

PROTECTING SEXUAL HEALTH IN LATER LIFE   A number of factors have led to increased risks for STIs among older Canadians. Changes in attitudes toward sexuality in later life have made it more socially acceptable for older people to pursue active sex lives. Medical advances have increased the likelihood that older people are healthy enough for sexual activity. As divorce rates have increased, more older Canadians have again become part of the singles scene. Together, these factors add up to higher percentages of older people with new or multiple sex partners. However, many older singles may not be getting the message about the need to practise safer sex. A study of 46- to 64-year-old Canadians commissioned by the Canadian Liver Foundation in 2010 found that while 82% said it was important to have an active sex life at any age, and 65% of those who were single had dated, some were at high risk for STIs and HIV. Almost one-quarter of the men (22%) and 12% of the women had engaged in unprotected sex with new partners after age 40. As we'll see Chapter 14, rates of common STIs such as chlamydia are increasing among older Canadians (Fang, Oliver, Jayaraman, & Wong, 2010). Clearly, just as there are developmental tasks related to sexuality at all phases of the life cycle, there is also a need for sexual-health education at every stage of life.

Summing Up

Developmental tasks pertaining to sexuality can be identified for each phase of the life cycle.

The developmental tasks of childhood sexuality include learning the correct names for genitals, differentiating between males and females, developing a sense of gender identity, distinguishing between good touch and bad touch, understanding the basics of human reproduction, and acquiring a basic knowledge of the physiological and psychological aspects of puberty.

The developmental tasks of adolescent sexuality include adapting to the physical and emotional changes of puberty, learning self-acceptance as a sexual being, exploring romantic and sexual relationships, and learning to protect sexual health.

The developmental tasks of adult sexuality include understanding the role of passion in romantic and sexual relationships, understanding the role of friendship in romantic and sexual relationships, learning to communicate effectively with partners about sexuality, and protecting sexual health.

The developmental tasks of sexuality in later life include maintaining self-perception as a sexual being while living in a culture that equates sexuality with youth, adapting to a reduced frequency of desire for sex and to a reduced intensity of sexual response, and using protection against STIs and HIV. The extent and quality of sexual health education in schools varies across Canada.

Test Yourself

Multiple-Choice Questions

1. Masturbation in childhood:
(a) Almost always indicates that the child has been sexually abused.
(b) Can be observed in children of all ages.
(c) Rarely occurs among girls.
(d) Reflects a premature interest in sex.

2. Same-sex sexual play in childhood:
(a) Is a sign that the children will grow up gay or lesbian.
(b) Is much more common among boys than girls.
(c) Is much more common among girls than boys.
(d) Does not predict adult sexual orientation.

3. In Stephen and Sullivan's study, the more university students _____ the number of lifetime sex partners their peers had, the more likely they were to be _____ with their own sex lives.
(a) Overestimated, unsatisfied.
(b) Underestimated, unsatisfied.
(c) Accurately estimated, satisfied.
(d) Overestimated, satisfied.

4. From 1990 to 2010, the pregnancy rate among 15- to 19-year-old females in Canada:
(a) Increased 17%.   (c) Declined 37%.
(b) Increased 27%.   (d) Declined 47%.

5. The practice of marrying someone who's similar to yourself in social background and standing is called:
(a) Polygyny.   (c) Monogamy.
(b) Polyandry.   (d) Homogamy.

6. In a study of about 3 000 American adults, _____ of 65- to 74-year-olds said they'd had sex with partners during the previous year.
(a) 13%   (c) 53%
(b) 25%   (d) 70%

7. In a 2005 Compas poll of Canadians _____ of married people said extramarital affairs had occurred in their marriages.
(a) 5%   (c) 15%
(b) 10%   (d) 20%

8. A survey of Canadians over the age of 40 has found that _____ agree with the statement "Sex gets better with age":
(a) 21%   (c) 51%
(b) 31%   (d) 61%

9. According to an Environics Research Group (2013) survey of 1003 sexually active Canadians aged 18 to 49, among people who were married _____ reported having sex every day.
(a) 2%   (c) 8%
(b) 4%   (d) 16%

6. In 1986, the percentage of Canadians aged 25 to 29 who were married was ____. In 2011, it was ____.
(a) 62%, 34%
(b) 52%, 24%
(c) 52%, 14%
(d) 34%, 24%

You'll find answers to the "Test Yourself" questions on page 489.

Questions for Critical Thinking

1. There's a growing perception that sexual imagery in the media damages child and adolescent sexual development. To what extent do you think this is the case?

2. The average age of marriage has been increasing. What impact do you think this has had on our sex lives? Because of this change, are people today happier with their sex lives than previous generations were?

3. The idea that sexuality gets better with age is heard more and more these days. Is this just hype from an aging Baby Boomer generation, or is there something to it? In your opinion, at what point in life are we likely to have the highest levels of sexual satisfaction?

CHAPTER THIRTEEN

Sexual Dysfunction

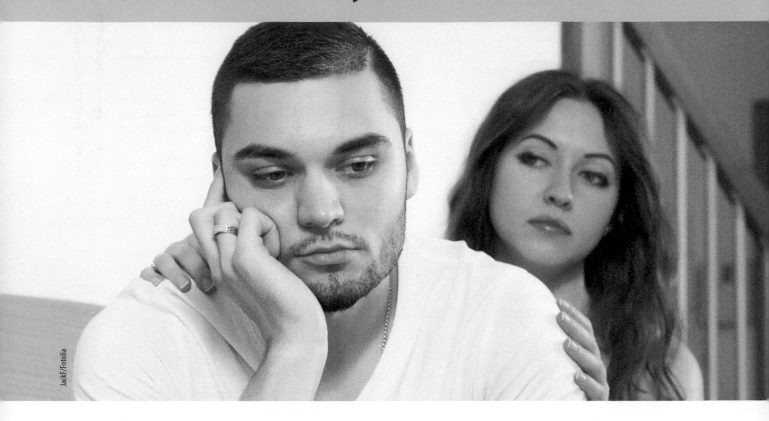

JackF/Fotolia

Sexual dysfunction is a persistent or recurring lack of sexual desire or difficulty becoming sexually aroused or reaching orgasm. Many (if not most) people experience some type of sexual problem from time to time. Many men occasionally have difficulty getting and keeping erections, or ejaculate more quickly than they or their partners would like. Some women notice that their desire for sexual activity is sometimes lower than they'd like it to be, or that they occasionally have difficulty becoming sexually aroused or reaching orgasm. Temporary or occasional problems with sexual response, such as those experienced by nearly everyone at some point, do not qualify as sexual dysfunctions. A person is not considered to have a sexual dysfunction unless the problem persists over time and causes distress.

People who do have sexual dysfunctions may avoid opportunities for sexual interaction with partners. They may anticipate that sex will result in frustration or physical pain, rather than pleasure and gratification. Because of the emphasis our culture places on sexual competence, people with sexual dysfunctions may feel inadequate or incompetent, which diminishes their self-esteem. They may experience guilt, shame, frustration, depression, and anxiety.

Many people with sexual problems or dysfunctions find them difficult to talk about with their partners and health care professionals. A woman who can't have an orgasm may be reluctant to mention it to her doctor, and a man who can't get an erection may never bring up the topic during his annual physical. Patient embarrassment about bringing up sexual concerns is often compounded by physicians who may never ask about them.

Sexual dysfunction
A persistent or recurrent difficulty with a lack of sexual desire or arousal, or difficulty reaching orgasm.

Prevalence of Sexual Problems and Dysfunctions

Because many people are reluctant to reveal their problems with sexual functioning to researchers, we don't have precise figures on their prevalence. Furthermore, studies measuring their prevalence have yielded different results. A general estimate of the prevalence of sexual dysfunction, based on a review of surveys from around the world, found that about two women in five and about one in four men report experiencing at least one sexual dysfunction (Lewis et al., 2010).

One of the best sources of information we have about sexual problems among women in Canada is the Canadian Contraception Study (Fisher, Boroditsky, & Morris, 2004b). The survey asked women if they had experienced three types of sexual difficulty: low sexual desire, painful intercourse, and lack of orgasm during intercourse. About half of the women had experienced at least one of these problems. More married women reported sexual difficulties than single women did. The most common problem was diminished sexual desire (43%). Married women (57%) were twice as likely to report low desire as unmarried women (26%). The second most common problem was difficulty with orgasm; 24% of the women said they didn't usually have orgasms during intercourse. Painful intercourse was reported by 15% of the women. The percentages of Canadian women reporting these sexual problems was similar to the percentages of American women reporting the same problems (Laumann et al., 1994).

In a survey of 40- to 80-year-old Canadian men and women, Brock, Moreira, Glasser, and Gingell (2006) found that 23% of the men experienced rapid ejaculation, and 16% had problems with erection. Thirty percent of the women reported lack of interest in sex, and 24% reported difficulties with vaginal lubrication. Another survey looked at 40- to 88-year-old Canadian men, and found that 49% experienced some degree of erectile dysfunction (Grover et al., 2006).

The rates of sexual dysfunction reported in these and other studies depend on the measures used and the populations studied. The higher the average age of the participants, for example, the higher the percentage who will report erectile dysfunction. Nevertheless, it's clear from the available studies that sexual problems are common within the adult Canadian population. A national survey of people between the ages of 40 and 64 found that more than half were often too tired to have sex, 42% were too stressed, and 40% didn't have time (Reuters, 2006).

Unfortunately, many Canadians who experience difficulty with sexual functioning don't seek help. In the study by Brock and his colleagues (2006), 75% of those with sexual-function problems hadn't sought help from health professionals.

To what extent are people frustrated by their sexual problems? Traditionally, our society believed women didn't get sexually frustrated, because of the stereotype that sexual pleasure wasn't important to women. However, when Tanya Hill (2005) conducted an online survey of 236 17- to 24-year-old women at the University of Guelph, she found that three-quarters felt sexually frustrated at least some of the time, and 9% felt frustrated often. The most frustrating situations they reported were

- Lack of orgasm during intercourse.
- Unaffectionate partners.
- Unavailability of partners.
- Refusal of partners to have sex.

CRITICAL THINKING QUESTIONS

Are you surprised at how high the rates of sexual dysfunction are in the Canadian population?

Types of Sexual Dysfunction

The most widely used system of classification for sexual dysfunction is based on the American Psychiatric Association's *Diagnostic and Statistical Manual of Mental Disorders* (DSM). In 2013, a new edition of the DSM, referred to as the *DSM-5*, was released (American Psychiatric Association, 2013b). Compared to the previous edition, which was published in 2000, the new *DSM-5* made several important changes in the way sexual dysfunctions are classified (IsHak & Tobia, 2013). Among the most important changes were that what was previously called "female hypoactive desire disorder" and "female arousal disorder" were merged into a single disorder called "female sexual interest/arousal disorder." This change was made because, for many women, the desire and arousal phases of sexual response often overlap (Brotto, 2010; Graham, 2010). Another significant change that was made in the *DSM-5* was that the female sexual pain dysfunctions, "dyspareunia" and "vaginismus," which also often overlap, were merged into a single category called "genito-pelvic pain/penetration disorder." Although the *DSM-5* merges some previous DSM sexual disorders, it is still useful to conceptualize problems with sexual function in terms of four basic categories:

1. *Sexual-desire*—Two *DSM-5*-listed sexual dysfunctions (*female sexual interest/ arousal disorder; male hypoactive sexual desire disorder*) involve lack of interest in sex or aversion to sexual contact.
2. *Sexual-arousal*—Two *DSM-5* sexual dysfunctions involve problems with sexual arousal. In men, *erectile disorder* refers to a persistent difficulty in obtaining or sustaining erections sufficient to engage in satisfactory sexual activity. In women, the arousal component of *female sexual interest/arousal disorder* typically involves insufficient lubrication.
3. *Orgasm*—Three *DSM-5* sexual dysfunctions involve problems related to orgasm. *Female orgasmic disorder* refers to persistent problems having an orgasm among women. In men, *delayed ejaculation* involves the inability to ejaculate and *premature (early) ejaculation* involves reaching orgasm too quickly.
4. *Sexual-pain*—One *DSM-5* sexual dysfunction involves pain during sexual activity. *Genito-pelvic pain/penetration disorder* refers to women who experience pain in the vaginal area (often called **dyspareunia**) and/or involuntary contraction of the muscles that surround the vaginal barrel, preventing or making penetration painful (often called **vaginismus**).

Dyspareunia Persistent or recurrent pain during sexual activity.

Vaginismus Involuntary contraction of the muscles surrounding the vaginal barrel, preventing or making penetration painful.

The *DSM-5* specifies that in order for a sexual problem or difficulty to be diagnosed as a sexual dysfunction it must have occurred for a period of about six months or more, happen 75–100% of the time, and cause the person significant distress (American Psychiatric Association, 2013b). An exception are sexual problems that are caused by medications or substances which do not require a minimum six-month duration to be labelled as a sexual dysfunction. Sexual dysfunctions are classified as lifelong or acquired (acquired dysfunctions follow periods of unproblematic functioning), and as *generalized* or *situational*. Generalized dysfunctions occur in all situations. Situational dysfunctions affect sexual functioning only in some situations, such as during partnered sexual activity but not with solo masturbation, or with one partner but not another. Thus, if a man has never been able to obtain an erection during sexual activity with a partner but can do so during masturbation, his dysfunction is lifelong and situational.

Sexual Desire-Related Disorders

Sexual dysfunctions that involve a lack of sexual desire affect both men (*male hypoactive sexual desire disorder*) and women (*female sexual interest/arousal disorder*). People with these conditions often report an absence of sexual thoughts or fantasies. A survey of 2000 American women (West et al., 2008) found that the incidence of low sexual desire was 26.7% for premenopausal women and 52.4% for postmenopausal women. The problem is more common among women than men. Nevertheless, the belief that men are always eager for sex is a myth (Hackett, 2008).

Lack of sexual desire doesn't imply that a person is unable to get an erection, lubricate adequately, or reach orgasm. Some people with low sexual desire can become sexually aroused and reach orgasm when adequately stimulated. Many enjoy sexual activity, even if they're unlikely to initiate it. Many appreciate the affection and closeness of physical intimacy but have no interest in genital stimulation.

A lack of sexual interest or desire is one of the most common complaints related to sexual functioning. Yet there's no clear consensus among clinicians and researchers about how to define "low sexual desire" (Heiman, 2008). How much sexual interest or desire is "normal"? There's no standard level of sexual desire, and instances of low desire often become apparent only when there's a discrepancy between levels of desire experienced by a couple.

Although many women have strong levels of sexual desire, the literature on gender differences suggests that men are generally more interested in sex than women are (Petersen & Hyde, 2011). As a result, when discrepancies in desire arise for heterosexual couples, the men are more likely than the women to have higher levels of desire. To the extent that gender differences in sexual interest levels exist, it's been speculated that gay and lesbian couples may have fewer discrepancy troubles than heterosexual couples. When one member of a couple is more interested in sex than the other, sex therapists often recommend that the couple try to compromise. They also attempt to uncover and resolve problems in the relationship that may be dampening sexual ardour (Aubin et al., 2009).

When is lack of sexual desire a dysfunction? Not everyone has the same level of sexual desire as other men and women in the same age group. A person with a lower level of desire doesn't necessarily have a sexual dysfunction. Remember, lack of desire should be classified as a dysfunction only when the person finds his or her level of sexual desire personally distressing. Basson (2010) suggests that many women can lead active, satisfying sex lives without ongoing or frequent feelings of desire between sexual engagements with their partners.

People with low sexual desire may have little or no interest in sex, but they are not repelled by genital contact. Some people, however, find sex disgusting or aversive and avoid such contact. A history of sexual trauma, such as sexual assault or childhood sexual abuse or incest, often figures prominently in cases of sexual aversion, especially in women (Colangelo & Keefe-Cooperman, 2012).

Sexual Arousal-Related Disorders

When we're sexually stimulated, our bodies normally respond with **vasocongestion**, which produces erection in the male and vaginal lubrication in the female. People with sexual arousal related disorders, however, fail to achieve or sustain the erections or lubrication necessary to facilitate sexual activity (Rowland & Incrocci, 2008). Or they lack the subjective feelings of sexual pleasure or excitement that normally accompany sexual arousal.

In the past, problems with arousal were referred to as impotence in men and frigidity in women. These terms have come to be seen as unnecessarily negative, belittling, and unhelpful. Today health professionals use the less pejorative terms *erectile dysfunction* in men and *female sexual interest/arousal disorder* in women.

MALE ERECTILE DISORDER   Sexual-arousal disorder in the male is called **male erectile disorder** or *erectile dysfunction*. It's characterized by persistent difficulty in achieving or maintaining an erection sufficient to allow completion of sexual activity. In most cases, the problem is limited to sexual activity with partners,

CRITICAL THINKING QUESTIONS

To what extent do you think it's important for partners in a long-term relationship to have roughly equal levels of sexual desire?

CRITICAL THINKING QUESTIONS

What myths or misinformation about sexuality have you heard that might contribute to the development of sexual problems?

Vasocongestion Engorgement of blood vessels with blood, which swells the genitals and breasts during sexual arousal.

Male erectile disorder Persistent difficulty getting or maintaining an erection sufficient to allow the man to engage in or complete sexual activity. Also termed *erectile dysfunction*.

or with some partners and not others. It can thus be classified as *situational*. In some cases, the dysfunction is found during any sexual activity, including masturbation. In such cases, it's classified as *generalized*. Some men with erectile dysfunction are unable to attain erections, while others can achieve but not sustain erections.

The incidence of erectile dysfunction increases with age. The Grover et al. (2006) survey found that about 30% of men in their 40s, a little over 40% in their 50s, and about 65% in their 60s have some degree of erectile dysfunction. Occasional problems in achieving or maintaining erection are quite common, happening to nearly all men. Fatigue, too much alcohol, anxiety over impressing a new partner, and other factors may cause occasional erectile difficulties. Even an isolated occurrence, however, can lead to a persistent problem if the man fears it will happen again. The more anxious and concerned he becomes about his ability to have an erection, the more likely he is to suffer with **performance anxiety**. This anxiety can contribute to repeated difficulty in gaining and maintaining an erection, resulting in a vicious circle of anxiety and erection problems.

A man with erectile problems may try to achieve an erection by force of will, which can compound the problem. Each time it happens, it's more demoralizing. He may ruminate about his sexual problem, setting the stage for yet more anxiety. His partner may try to comfort and support him by saying things like "It can happen to anyone," "Don't worry about it," or "It will get better in time." But attempts at reassurance may be to no avail.

The vicious circle of anxiety and erectile failure may be interrupted if the man recognizes that occasional problems are normal and doesn't overreact. However, the emphasis on sexual prowess in our culture may spur him to view occasional erectile problems as catastrophes, rather than transient disappointments. Viewing occasional problems as inconveniences, rather than tragedies, may help avert the development of persistent erectile difficulty.

Performance anxiety is a prominent cause of erectile disorder. So are other psychological factors, including depression, lack of self-esteem, and problems with the relationship. Biological factors such as diabetes and heart disease can also play causal roles. In fact, medical conditions are frequently associated with erectile dysfunction (especially among middle-aged and older men (Grover et al., 2006).

It's a common belief that sexual arousal is much simpler for men than for women. However, a focus group study (Jansen et al., 2008) suggests that men's sexual arousal is also complex, and that there's considerable variation in what men find arousing. The older men in the study reported that emotional connections with their partners were now more important than physical attractiveness when it came to sexual arousal. Some men reported that they were less likely to be aroused by women with low self-esteem, even if they were physically attractive.

FEMALE SEXUAL INTEREST/AROUSAL DISORDER   As noted above, the *DSM-5* replaced what was formerly known as *female arousal disorder* with the new classification of *female sexual interest/arousal disorder* because problems in the desire and arousal phases of female sexual response often overlap. For instance, women who experience a generalized lack of sexual desire are quite likely not to become sexually aroused easily. In other words, the desire and arousal phases of sexual response are closely intertwined for many women. As we discussed Chapter 4, Basson's (2008) intimacy-based model of sexual response suggests that some women, particularly those in longer-term relationships, may begin to experience sexual arousal that is sparked by feelings of intimacy with their partners rather than by a pre-existing sense of sexual desire. Thus, female sexual desire and arousal may not occur in a linear, step-by-step process. For many women, they may occur simultaneously, and it, therefore, makes more sense to conceptualize problems in these areas of sexual function together rather than as separate and distinct sexual dysfunctions.

Performance anxiety Anxiety concerning one's ability to perform behaviours, especially behaviours that may be evaluated by other people.

Some women may encounter persistent difficulties in becoming sexually excited or sufficiently lubricated in response to sexual stimulation. In some cases, these difficulties are lifelong. In others, they develop after periods of normal functioning. In some cases, difficulties are pervasive and occur during both masturbation and sex with partners. More often, they occur in specific situations. For example, they may occur with some partners and not with others, or during vaginal penetration but not during oral–genital sex or masturbation.

According to Basson (2004), most women with arousal-related sexual dysfunctions experience little or no subjective arousal or sexual excitement. These women can be categorized into two groups. Those with combined-arousal problems experience no subjective arousal and feel no genital response. Women with subjective arousal problems are aware that their genitals physically respond to stimulation but feel no subjective arousal.

A minority of women can become aroused by many different kinds of stimuli but don't find stimulation of their genitals arousing. They can still be highly interested in sex and become subjectively aroused as long as they experience non-genital stimulation (Basson, 2004).

Arousal-related disorders may have physical causes. A thorough evaluation by a medical specialist is recommended. Any neurological, vascular, or hormonal problem that interferes with the lubrication or swelling response of the vagina to sexual stimulation may contribute to a sexual arousal related disorder. For example, diabetes mellitus may lead to diminished sexual excitement, because the nerves that service the clitoris degenerate and the blood vessels become damaged. Reduced estrogen production can also result in vaginal dryness.

Another interesting line of research suggests that the skin of some women with sexual-arousal problems is less sensitive to touch than the skin of women who don't have such problems (Frohlich & Meston, 2005). Such women might seek to increase their sexual stimulation by psychological as well as physical means.

Female sexual arousal-related disorders more often have psychological causes. In some cases, women may harbour deep-seated anger and resentment toward their partners (McCabe et al., 2010). Or they may fail to become aroused during sexual activity simply because they're no longer sexually attracted to their partners, or because they're experiencing nonsexual conflicts in their relationships. It would be incorrect to say these women have arousal disorders; rather than problems with sexual functioning, they have relationship difficulties.

Childhood sexual abuse is especially prevalent among women with sexual arousal-related disorders (Colangelo & Keefe-Cooperman, 2012). Survivors of sexual abuse often find it difficult to respond sexually to their partners. Feelings of helplessness, anger, or guilt—or even flashbacks of the abuse—may surface when these women begin sexual activity, undermining their ability to become aroused. Other psychosocial causes include anxiety and guilt about sex, and ineffective stimulation by the women's partners (McCabe et al., 2010).

Orgasmic Disorders

Orgasmic disorders include female orgasmic disorder, delayed ejaculation, and premature (early) ejaculation. In female orgasmic disorder and delayed ejaculation, the individual is persistently delayed in reaching orgasm, or doesn't reach orgasm at all, despite achieving sexual stimulation that would normally be of sufficient intensity to result in orgasm. The problem is more common among women than men. In some cases, a person can reach orgasm without difficulty while engaging in sexual relations with one partner, but not with another.

FEMALE ORGASMIC DISORDER   Women with female orgasmic disorder are unable to reach orgasm or have difficulty reaching orgasm after what would usually

Anorgasmic Unable to reach orgasm, through any means.

be adequate sexual stimulation. Women who have never reached orgasm through any means are sometimes labelled **anorgasmic** or pre-orgasmic.

A woman who reaches orgasm through masturbation or oral sex might not reach orgasm during intercourse with a male partner. Penile thrusting may not provide sufficient clitoral stimulation to facilitate orgasm. In other words, a woman who doesn't reach orgasm during intercourse but can reach orgasm through other types of sexual stimulation doesn't have an orgasmic disorder. University of Waterloo researcher B. J. Rye (2001) found that 93% of university women sometimes or usually needed direct clitoral stimulation during intercourse to reach orgasm. Only 46% of the women surveyed had orgasms during at least half of their intercourse experiences, and 49% said it often took them a long time to have orgasms.

DELAYED EJACULATION   The *DSM-5* sexual dysfunction *delayed ejaculation* has also been called male orgasmic disorder, retarded ejaculation, and ejaculatory incompetence. The problem may be lifelong or acquired, generalized or situational.

Very few men have never ejaculated. In most cases, the disorder is limited to intercourse. The men may be capable of ejaculating during masturbation or oral sex but find it difficult or impossible to ejaculate during intercourse, despite high levels of sexual excitement. There's a myth that men with delayed ejaculation and their partners enjoy this condition, because it enables them to "go on forever." Actually, the experience is frustrating for both partners (Althof, 2012).

Delayed ejaculation may be caused by physical problems, such as multiple sclerosis or neurological damage that interferes with neural control of ejaculation. It may also be a side effect of certain drugs. Various psychological factors may also play a role, including performance anxiety, sexual guilt, and hostility toward a partner.

Premature ejaculation (PE) A sexual dysfunction in which ejaculation occurs with minimal sexual stimulation, and before the man desires it. It's also called "rapid" ejaculation.

PREMATURE EJACULATION   Men with **premature ejaculation (PE)**, also referred to as early ejaculation, or rapid ejaculation ejaculate too quickly to permit their partners or themselves to fully enjoy sexual relations (Graziottin & Althof, 2011). Excluding erectile dysfunction in elderly men, premature ejaculation is the most common male sexual dysfunction (Lewis et al., 2010). The degree of rapidity varies. Some men ejaculate almost immediately after any form of sexual stimulation, even at the sight of their partners disrobing. But most men with this condition ejaculate either just before or immediately after penetration, or after a few penile thrusts. The *DSM-5* stipulates that in order for a clinical diagnosis of PE to be made, ejaculation must occur within one minute of penetration (American Psychiatric Association, 2013b).

Guy Grenier and Sandra Byers (2001) at the University of New Brunswick studied the ejaculatory behaviour of a community sample of men. The men reported that intercourse typically lasted for about eight minutes before they ejaculated. They also reported that ejaculation happened more quickly than they wished in about one-third of their acts of sexual intercourse. They attempted to delay the timing of their ejaculations during about half of their intercourse experiences. In another study, involving 52 New Brunswick couples, Byers and Grenier (2003) compared the men's and women's reports of the men's ejaculatory behaviour. There was only moderate agreement. The women tended to underestimate how seriously their male partners viewed PE. However, both the men and the women reported lower sexual satisfaction as a result of the men's PE problems.

The percentage of men experiencing PE varies, depending on the criteria the researchers use. Twenty-three percent of the men in Grenier and Byers's (2001) study said they had problems with premature ejaculation. They ejaculated sooner than other men, perceived that they had less control over the timing of ejaculation, and were concerned about ejaculating earlier than they wished. Another Canadian study found a prevalence of PE ranging from 16% to 24%, depending on how PE was defined (Brock et al., 2009). The authors noted that 90% of the men with PE in their study had not discussed the problem with their doctors.

Just what constitutes "rapid"? There's no clear cutoff. Some scholars argue that the focus should be on whether the couple is satisfied with the duration of sexual activity, rather than on a specific time period.

Helen Singer Kaplan (1974) suggested that the label "premature" be applied to cases in which men persistently or recurrently lack voluntary control over their ejaculations. This may sound like a contradiction in terms, given that ejaculation is a reflex, and reflexes needn't involve thought or conscious control. Kaplan meant men might control their ejaculations by learning to regulate the amount of sexual stimulation they experienced, keeping it below the threshold at which the ejaculation reflex was triggered.

Sexual Pain-Related Disorders

For most of us, sexual activity is a source of pleasure. For some of us, however, it causes pain and discomfort. With respect to sexual pain among women, the *DSM-5* combines dyspareunia and vaginismus into the single diagnostic entity of *genital-pelvic pain penetration disorder* (American Psychiatric Association, 2013b). Although there is clearly overlap between the two conditions, they each have some distinct features.

DYSPAREUNIA   Traditionally, dyspareunia has been defined as painful intercourse. However, it also includes persistent pain associated with any stimulation of the vaginal area (Basson, 2004). Most of the discussion and research on dyspareunia, and on sexual dysfunction in general, has focused on problems related to heterosexual intercourse. Obviously, women with female partners can also experience genital pain during sexual activities, especially during the insertion of fingers or a dildo into the vagina. Painful intercourse is less common in men, and then it's generally associated with genital infections that cause burning or painful ejaculation.

Dyspareunia is one of the most common sexual dysfunctions and a common complaint of women seeking gynecological services. The location of the pain can vary. It can be at the entrance to the vagina, for example, in the vagina, or in the pelvic region (Pukall et al., 2003). Unfortunately, many women are too embarrassed to talk about genital pain, and they don't seek treatment. Few doctors and therapists are properly trained in the diagnosis of dyspareunia, so many women with this condition don't receive adequate care (Pukall et al., 2005). Researchers at Queen's University have developed a vulvalgesiometer, which can measure the severity of pain experienced by women (Pukall et al., 2007).

Pain is a sign that something is wrong—physically or psychologically. Dyspareunia may result from physical causes, emotional factors, or an interaction of the two (Binik, 2005). The most common cause of pain during intercourse is inadequate lubrication. In this case, additional foreplay or artificial lubrication may help. Vaginal infections and sexually transmitted infections (STIs) may also produce genital pain. Allergic reactions to spermicides, even the latex material in condoms, can give rise to genital irritation. Pain during deep penetration may be caused by endometriosis, pelvic inflammatory disease (PID), other diseases, or structural disorders of the reproductive organs.

Psychological factors such as unresolved guilt or anxiety about sex or the lingering effects of sexual trauma may also be involved. They may inhibit lubrication and cause involuntary contractions of the vaginal musculature, making penetration painful or uncomfortable.

Researchers in Montreal (Binik et al., 2002) have extensively studied dyspareunia in women and evaluated various treatment strategies. They've found that women with dyspareunia tend to have a lower tolerance for pain, not only in the vaginal area, but also on the upper arms, suggesting that a generalized hypersensitivity may contribute to this problem in some women (Pukall et al., 2002).

Binik (2005) believes every case of dyspareunia has both physiological and psychological components. Researchers have found that women who believe their pain is due to psychosocial factors report higher levels of pain and more sexual problems than women who believe their pain is due to physical causes. For many women, the pain of dyspareunia cannot be totally eliminated, but they can often be taught coping strategies for managing the pain.

VULVODYNIA

The pain has lasted for months. You're so uncomfortable you can hardly sit. Having sex is unthinkable. Nothing alleviates the pain, burning, and irritation, at least not for long. (Mayo Clinic Staff, 2006)

This is a description of vulvodynia posted online by the Mayo Clinic (2006). Vulvodynia is a gynecological condition, affecting up to 16% of women, characterized by vulval pain, particularly a chronic burning sensation, irritation, itching, and/or rawness (Sadownik, 2014). In some cases, these symptoms involve the whole vulva or are specific to the clitoris or vestibule of the vagina.

VAGINISMUS

Vaginismus involves an involuntary contraction of the pelvic muscles that surround the outer one-third of the vaginal barrel, resulting in pain. Avoidance of penetration seems to be the key factor differentiating vaginismus from dyspareunia (Bergeron & Lord, 2003). Vaginismus occurs reflexively during attempts at vaginal penetration, making entry by a penis, fingers, or a dildo painful or impossible. Some women with vaginismus are unable to tolerate penetration by any object, including a tampon or a physician's speculum.

Some experts believe vaginismus is usually caused by a fear of penetration, rather than by physical injury or defect (Brauer et al., 2009; ter Kuile et al., 2009). Women with vaginismus often have histories of sexual trauma, sexual assault, or botched abortions that have resulted in vaginal injury. They may desire sexual relations, and may be capable of becoming sexually aroused and achieving orgasm, but their fear of penetration triggers an involuntary spasm of the vaginal musculature at the point of insertion of an object into their vaginas. Vaginismus can also be a cause or an effect of dyspareunia. Women who experience painful penetration may develop a fear of it, which leads to involuntary vaginal contractions. Vaginismus and dyspareunia may also give rise to, or result from, erectile disorder in men, as feelings of failure and anxiety overwhelm both partners.

Some Canadian researchers (Reissing et al., 2004) disagree that vaginismus is easily diagnosed and easily treated. Instead, they propose that vaginismus be reconceptualized as either an aversion to vaginal penetration or a genital pain disorder. These distinctions are important in suggesting different courses of treatment.

Origins of Sexual Dysfunction

Human beings are complex, with complex bodies and complex mental processes. We're reared in families, within cultural settings. For these reasons, we need to consider possible biological, psychological, and social factors in sexual dysfunction, which can interact in a number of ways (Brown & Haaser, 2005). For example, biological and psychosocial factors—hormonal deficiencies, depression, dissatisfaction with a relationship, and so on—can contribute to lack of desire. Researchers refer to an approach that considers the interactions of biological, psychological, and sociocultural factors as a **biopsychosocial model**.

Biological Causes

Among the medical conditions that diminish sexual desire are testosterone deficiencies, thyroid overactivity, thyroid underactivity, and temporal lobe epilepsy.

Biopsychosocial model An approach to explaining dysfunction that looks at the interactions of biological, psychological, and sociocultural factors.

Sexual desire is stoked by testosterone, which is produced by men in the testes and by both men and women in the adrenal glands (Buvat et al., 2010). Women may experience lower sexual desire when their adrenal glands are surgically removed. Low sexual interest, along with erectile difficulty, is also common among men with **hypogonadism**, which is treated with testosterone (Buvat et al., 2010).

The reduction in testosterone levels that occurs in middle and later life may in part explain the gradual decline in male sexual desire (Hackett, 2008). Female sexual desire may also decline with age, however, because of physical and psychological changes (Wierman et al., 2010). Some medications, especially those used to control anxiety or hypertension, may reduce desire. Changing medications or doses may increase a person's level of desire.

People with sexual dysfunctions are generally advised to undergo physical examinations, to determine whether their problems are biologically based. For example, men with erectile disorder may be evaluated in sleep centres, to determine whether they attain erections while they're asleep. The technique is termed nocturnal penile **tumescence** (NPT). Healthy men usually have erections during REM sleep, which occurs every 90 to 100 minutes. Men with biologically based erectile disorder often don't have nocturnal erections.

A physical examination, particularly in the pelvic area, and assessment of hormone levels can uncover the root causes of some cases of sexual dysfunction among women. Medical investigation of a sexual dysfunction can lead to the discovery of an underlying medical condition that might otherwise remain unknown to the patient and his or her doctor.

Fatigue may lead to erectile disorder and orgasmic disorder in men, and to inadequate lubrication and orgasmic disorder in women, but these remain isolated incidents unless the person attaches too much meaning to them and becomes concerned about future sexual activity.

HEALTH PROBLEMS Researchers find that health problems—especially cardiovascular disorders, hypertension, and obesity—contribute to several kinds of sexual dysfunction in men (Tan et al., 2012), and particularly to sexual pain in women (van Lankveld et al., 2010). Painful sex often reflects an underlying infection. Medical conditions that affect sexual response include heart disease (Lane & Thayer, 2008), diabetes mellitus, multiple sclerosis, spinal-cord injury, complications from surgery (such as removal of the prostate in men), hormonal problems, and the use of some medicines, such as those that treat hypertension and psychiatric disorders (Byerly et al., 2006; Olfson et al., 2005; Wooten, 2008). Even when biological factors are involved in sexual dysfunctions, psychological factors such as anger and depression can prolong or worsen them (Tan et al., 2012).

Cardiovascular problems can lead to erectile disorder by affecting the flow of blood to and through the penis, a problem that becomes more common as men age. Damage to the nerves involved in erection can also play a role (Eardley et al., 2010). Erectile problems can arise when clogged or narrow arteries leading to the penis deprive it of oxygen (Miner et al., 2011). For example, erectile disorder is common among men with diabetes mellitus, a disease that can damage blood vessels and nerves.

Hypogonadism An endocrine disorder that reduces the output of testosterone.

Tumescence Swelling; erection.

Chad Baker/Jason Reed/Ryan McVay/Thinkstock

Too Tired for Sex.
They were tired, and it didn't happen. Should they keep trying, or wait until they've had a good night's sleep?

Rimm (2000) studied 2000 men and found that erectile dysfunction was connected with a large waist, physical inactivity, and too much alcohol consumption (or no alcohol consumption!). The common condition among these men may have been high cholesterol levels. Cholesterol can impede the flow of blood to the penis, just as it impedes the flow of blood to the heart. Another study connects erectile dysfunction with heart disease and hypertension (Johannes et al., 2000).

Sexual functioning in women seems to be less affected by cardiovascular disease. For both men and women, however, hypertension (high blood pressure) and the drugs used to treat it can negatively affect sexual functioning (Perez, Gadgil, & Dizon, 2009). Also, medications used to lower cholesterol, such as statins (e.g., Zocor, Lipitor), can contribute to erectile dysfunction (Trivedi et al., 2012).

AGING Perimenopausal and post-menopausal women usually produce less vaginal lubrication than younger women, and their vaginal walls become thin—changes that can render sex painful (van Lankveld et al., 2010). These physical changes, along with negative stereotypes about older women and men, can create performance anxiety and discourage both partners from initiating sexual activity (Brotto et al., 2010; McCabe et al., 2010). In such cases, artificial lubrication can supplement the woman's own production, and estrogen replacement may halt or reverse some of the sexual changes of aging (Wierman et al., 2010). However, the partners also need to have realistic expectations and consider enjoyable sexual activities they can engage in without discomfort or high demands (Althof, 2010).

The findings of the Massachusetts Male Aging Study suggest that men who exercise regularly seem to ward off erectile dysfunction (Derby, 2000). Men who burned 200 calories or more a day in physical activity—an amount that can be achieved by walking briskly for three kilometres—cut their risk of erectile dysfunction almost in half. Exercise seems to prevent clogging of the arteries, keeping them clear for the flow of blood into the penis.

Nerve damage resulting from prostate surgery may impair erectile response (Koehler et al., 2012). Erectile disorder may also result from multiple sclerosis (MS), a disease in which nerve cells lose the protective coatings that facilitate transmission of neural messages (Keller et al., 2012). MS has also been implicated in male orgasmic disorder.

Medical conditions associated with advancing age, such as chronic kidney disease, hypertension, cancer, emphysema, and heart disease, can all impair erectile response. So can endocrine disorders that impair testosterone production (Ralph & McNicholas, 2000). Women can also develop vascular and nervous disorders that impair genital blood flow, reducing lubrication and sexual excitement, rendering intercourse painful, and reducing their ability to reach orgasm. All of these problems become more likely as people age.

DRUGS Use of certain prescription and illicit drugs can contribute to sexual dysfunction in both women and men. Antidepressant medications and antipsychotic drugs can impair erectile functioning and cause orgasmic disorders (Olfson et al., 2005; Taylor et al., 2005). Tranquilizers such as Valium and Xanax may cause orgasmic disorder in either sex. Some drugs used to treat high blood pressure can impair erectile response. Switching to other blood-pressure drugs or adjusting dosages may help. Other drugs that can lead to erectile disorder include adrenergic blockers, diuretics, cholesterol-lowering drugs (statins), anticonvulsants, anti-Parkinson drugs, and dyspepsia- and ulcer-healing drugs (Do et al., 2009).

Central nervous system depressants such as alcohol, heroin, and methadone can reduce sexual desire and impair sexual arousal (Brown et al., 2005). Narcotics also depress testosterone production, thereby reducing sexual desire and leading to erectile dysfunction. Regular use of cocaine can cause erectile disorder or male orgasmic disorder and may reduce sexual desire in both men and women (Rawson et al.,

2002). While moderate alcohol consumption (one or two drinks per day) is unlikely to affect sexual functioning, long-term heavy drinking is clearly associated with sexual dysfunction among both women and men (McKay, 2005). (See Chapter 4 for further discussion of the effects of drugs on sexual response.)

SSRIS AND SEXUAL RESPONSE   People—especially physicians—need to be aware of the sexual side effects of some drugs used to treat depression. Selective serotonin reuptake inhibitors (SSRIs) are widely prescribed not only for depression, but also for panic disorder, obsessive-compulsive disorder, anorexia nervosa, and other conditions. Most physicians are aware that these drugs have some sexual side effects in some patients. However, they almost completely impair sexual arousal in many patients, especially older patients (Burri et al., 2012; Fabre et al., 2012). Moreover, even when patients discontinue the drugs, sexual functioning doesn't necessarily bounce back (Bolton et al., 2006; Csoka & Shipko, 2006).

Some drugs that are helpful with depression may not impair sexual functioning—at least in the short run. Wellbutrin, for example, can improve sexual functioning and is sometimes prescribed along with an SSRI to help prevent sexual side effects.

Psychosocial Causes

Abrupt changes in sexual desire are often explained by psychological and interpersonal factors such as depression, stress, and problems in the relationship (Aubin et al., 2009; McCabe et al., 2010). Anxiety is the most commonly reported factor. Sexual desire can be dampened by performance anxiety (anxiety over being evaluated negatively), anxiety involving fears of pleasure or loss of control, and deeper sources of anxiety relating to fear of injury (Janssen & Bancroft, 2006). Depression is also a common cause (Laurent & Simons, 2009), and a history of childhood sexual abuse or sexual assault has been linked to low sexual desire (Colangelo & Keefe-Cooperman, 2012).

Psychosocial factors connected with sexual dysfunction include cultural influences, economic problems, psychosexual traumas, dissatisfaction with relationships, lack of sexual skills, irrational beliefs, and performance anxiety (McCabe et al., 2010).

CULTURAL INFLUENCES   Children reared in sexually repressive cultural or home environments may learn to respond to sex with feelings of anxiety and shame, rather than anticipation and pleasure (Woo et al., 2011). People whose parents instilled in them a sense of guilt over touching their genitals may find it difficult to accept their sex organs as sources of pleasure (McCarthy et al., 2006).

In most cultures, sexual pleasure has traditionally been a male preserve. Young women may be reared to believe sex is a duty they're to perform for their husbands, not a source of personal pleasure. Although the traditional double standard has diminished in developed countries (Fugl-Meyer et al., 2006), some girls are still exposed to repressive attitudes. Women are more likely than men to be taught to suppress sexual desires (Nobre & Pinto-Gouveia, 2006). Self-control and vigilance—not sexual awareness and acceptance—become identified as feminine virtues. Women reared with such attitudes may not learn about their sexual potential or express their erotic desires to their partners.

Many women who were exposed to negative attitudes about sex during childhood and adolescence find it difficult to suddenly view sex as a source of pleasure and satisfaction as adults. A lifetime of learning to turn themselves off sexually may impair sexual arousal and enjoyment when acceptable opportunities arise (Woo et al., 2011).

PSYCHOSEXUAL TRAUMA   Women and men who were sexually victimized in childhood are more likely to have trouble becoming sexually aroused (Colangelo & Keefe-Cooperman, 2012; McCabe et al., 2010). Some learning theorists contend that conditioned anxiety explains many cases of sexual dysfunction. Sexual stimuli come to elicit anxiety when they've been paired with traumatic experiences, such as rape, incest, or sexual molestation. Unresolved anger, misplaced guilt, and feelings of disgust also make it difficult for victims of sexual trauma to respond sexually, even years later and with loving partners.

EMOTIONAL FACTORS   Pleasurable, fulfilling sexual activity with a partner typically involves allowing oneself to let go emotionally, at least to some extent. Fear of losing control or of letting go may make it more difficult for a person to let down his or her guard enough to become sexually aroused. Other emotional factors, especially depression, are often implicated in sexual dysfunction (Laurent & Simons, 2009). Prolonged and high levels of stress can also interfere with sexual interest and response.

MYTHS AND MISINFORMATION   Although Western culture often seems to be saturated in superficial sexual imagery, many people grow up badly misinformed about sexuality. Sex-education programs in schools focus mainly on pregnancy and STI prevention and rarely teach about sexual response. Some non-Western cultural traditions restrict and discourage learning about sexual pleasure, particularly for women. Since many, if not most, people have few credible and easily accessible sources of information about sexual functioning, it's not surprising that myths and misinformation about sexuality often prevail. In many cases, these are contributing factors in the development of sexual dysfunction. Providing corrective information is a key factor in overcoming them.

INEFFECTIVE SEXUAL TECHNIQUES   People who lack information about sexuality, and particularly about sexual response, are more likely to be unaware of what techniques are sexually pleasurable for themselves and their partners. For example, a woman who remains ignorant about the erotic importance of her clitoris may be unlikely to seek direct clitoral stimulation. People often make assumptions about what's pleasurable for their partners on the basis of their own preferences and past experiences with previous partners. Based on his own preferences, for example, a man may assume he knows which techniques are pleasurable for his male partner, simply because they're both men. As we'll see, effective sexual communication is an important factor in the prevention and resolution of sexual dysfunction.

BOREDOM AND ROUTINE   It's common for couples to fall into narrow sexual routines, in which the timing and sequence of sexual activity follow constant, familiar patterns. A couple may have sex only once they've gone to bed for the night, for example, and may always use the same one or two favoured positions or techniques.

While some people remain sexually satisfied with standard routines, others find that, over time, their sexual relationships become monotonous. Once boredom and complacency about the sexual component of a relationship sets in, arousal often diminishes.

LACK OF SEXUAL COMMUNICATION   Partners who don't communicate their sexual preferences or experiment with new techniques may find themselves losing interest.

Canadian researchers MacNeil and Byers (2009) have examined how communicating sexual likes and dislikes can affect sexual satisfaction within relationships. Their research indicates that, for both women and men, communicating sexual likes and dislikes contributes to greater sexual satisfaction within long-term relationships.

Holmberg and Blair (2009) compared heterosexual, gay, and lesbian couples' responses on a sexual communication scale (e.g., "My partner often complains that I am not very clear about what I want sexually"). They found that levels of sexual communication generally don't differ among lesbian, gay, and heterosexual couples.

In all of these relationship types, clear communication about sexual likes and dislikes may improve sexual satisfaction, while lack of such communication may lead to, or compound, existing sexual problems.

RELATIONSHIP ISSUES   Problems in a relationship are not easily left at the bedroom door (McCarthy et al., 2006; Moore & Heiman, 2006). Heterosexual and gay and lesbian couples alike usually find that sex is no better than other facets of their relationships (Matthews et al., 2006). Partners who have trouble communicating in general may also be unable to communicate their sexual desires. Couples who harbour resentments may make sex one of their conflict areas. They may not allow themselves to become aroused by their partners, or they may withhold orgasm to express their resentment (Firestone et al., 2006b).

The following hypothetical cases highlight how sexual problems or dysfunctions can develop against the backdrops of troubled relationships.

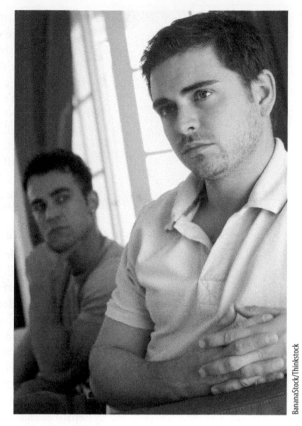

A Vicious Cycle.
Conflict in a relationship may dampen sexual interest, and lack of sexual interest may further strain the relationship.

Alia and Fernando met in university, when they were both in their early twenties. After graduation, they moved into an apartment together. At first, the sexual component of their relationship was characterized by passion and discovery. After a few years, however, tensions began to build in their relationship, as conflicts around finances, when and whether they'd have children, and other domestic issues began to emerge. For Fernando, having sex with Alia was a way to restore intimacy between them, and he frequently tried to initiate sex after they argued. Alia, on the other hand, was reluctant to have sex when she and Fernando had been arguing. Even when their relationship was going well, Alia was slower to respond to sexual stimulation than Fernando. Now, as conflict in their relationship has grown, Alia finds that she has difficulty becoming aroused when they do have sex, which Fernando finds both frustrating and hurtful. Alia feels under increasing pressure to respond sexually to Fernando, as she senses that her lack of arousal is making their relationship problems worse. Both Alia and Fernando are committed to making their relationship work. What began as a series of problems in other aspects of their relationship, however, has now spread to their sexual relationship.

Kim and Lisa have been in a relationship for several years. Kim grew up in a family with a cultural tradition that didn't accept homosexuality. She only fully accepted that she was a lesbian in her mid-thirties. Lisa, on the other hand, readily embraced her lesbian identity, and proudly came out to her friends and family when she was 16. From the beginning, Lisa took a more assertive role in most aspects of the relationship. She feels very much in touch with her sexuality, and has a clear sense of what her turn-ons are. Although Kim has always been happy that Lisa seems to be so enthusiastic about their sex life, she's been less certain about her own likes and dislikes in the bedroom, and it seems to her that she may not enjoy exactly the same sexual activities as Lisa. Over time, Kim has begun to resent Lisa, complaining that their relationship is increasingly one-sided. Kim's growing sense of resentment has spilled over into their sex life, as she's increasingly unable to have an orgasm when they have sex.

Huang and Mila are a middle-income couple in their forties with three children. Like many couples, they struggle with the financial obligations of maintaining their household. Mila has enjoyed some degree of career success, and her income has gradually increased. Huang, on the other hand, has seen his career stall, and his income has failed to grow at the same pace as Mila's. Mila and Huang frequently argue about family finances. Huang's self-esteem has declined, and he feels that Mila's putting pressure on him to pull his weight financially. Mila and Huang's sexual relationship has been reasonably satisfying for both of them, though Huang has had occasional difficulties getting and maintaining an erection when he's having sex with Mila. Lately, however, as their arguments about money have become more intense, Huang finds that he's unable to achieve an erection with Mila.

PERFORMANCE ANXIETY   Anxiety—especially performance anxiety—plays an important role in sexual dysfunction (Althof & Needle, 2011; Althof, 2010). Performance anxiety occurs when a person becomes overly concerned with how well he or she performs a certain act or task. Performance anxiety may place a dysfunctional individual in a spectator role, rather than a performer role. Rather than focusing on erotic sensations and allowing reflexes such as erection, lubrication, and orgasm to occur naturally, the person focuses on self-doubts and thinks, "Will I be able to do it this time? Will this be another failure?"

In men, performance anxiety can either inhibit erection or trigger rapid ejaculation (Althof & Needle, 2011). Erection is mediated by the parasympathetic nervous system and can be blocked when anxiety activates the sympathetic nervous system. Because ejaculation, like anxiety, is mediated by the sympathetic nervous system, arousal of this system can increase the level of stimulation and heighten the potential for rapid ejaculation.

Performance anxiety can reduce vaginal lubrication and contribute to female orgasmic disorder (Goldstein et al., 2006). Women with performance anxieties may try to force orgasm, only to find that the harder they try, the more elusive it becomes.

As its name suggests, performance anxiety often involves the thought that sexual activity with a partner is a "performance," similar to what an actor does on stage or screen. When we think of sex as a performance, we're more likely to judge ourselves as performing well or inadequately. When we're able to conceptualize sex as an undemanding exchange of pleasure, rather than as a performance, we may feel less anxiety.

OTHER FACTORS   Using data from the Canadian Contraception Study, researchers at the University of Western Ontario found a number of factors related to common sexual concerns in women (Gruszecki et al., 2005). Higher body weight was associated with low sexual desire and infrequent orgasm during intercourse. These sexual issues could be due to health issues, as well as to self-esteem issues connected with body weight. Married women, older women, and those with higher levels of education were also more likely to report low desire.

Treatments for Sexual Dysfunction

Sex therapy A collective term for behavioural models for treating sexual dysfunctions.

The most common models in **sex therapy** are cognitive and behavioural. Sex therapy aims to modify dysfunctional cognitions (beliefs and attitudes) and behaviours as directly and as quickly as possible. Sex therapists also recognize the roles of childhood conflicts and the quality of current relationships, so they draw on various forms of therapy, as needed (Adams, 2006; Althof, 2010; Annon, 1976; Kleinplatz, 2003). Sex therapy usually involves both partners, although individual therapy is preferred in some cases. Although the particular approaches vary, sex therapy generally aims to change self-defeating beliefs and attitudes, enhance sexual knowledge, improve sexual communication, teach sexual skills, and reduce performance anxiety.

Biological treatments are now emerging for various sexual dysfunctions. Most public attention has been focused on Viagra and similar drugs, which are helpful in most cases of erectile dysfunction. Biological treatments are also being developed for rapid ejaculation, female orgasmic dysfunction, and lack of sexual desire. Research findings indicate that psychotherapy combined with medical treatments such as drugs for erectile dysfunction can be more effective than medicine alone (Aubin et al., 2009).

The PLISSIT Model

Developed by Annon (1976), the PLISSIT model is used by many therapists to address the sexual concerns of their clients (Ohl, 2007; Timm, 2009). This model allows health professionals and their clients to differentiate between sexual problems that can be resolved through basic education and counselling and problems that require intensive or specialized sex therapy.

Feeling Good Naked.
Among women, higher body weight is associated with low sexual desire. The goal of the television show How to Look Good Naked *is to teach women to love their bodies, no matter what imperfections they believe they have. The show features overweight women who appear in bras and panties.*

The PLISSIT model consists of four escalating levels:

- *Permission* (P)—At the first level, the therapist gives the client permission to talk about sexuality and personal concerns. The therapist often asks exploratory questions, to bring out the relevant issues and put the client at ease.
- *Limited information* (LI)—Some sexual problems may be rooted in myths and misinformation about sexuality. Providing a limited amount of correct information about sexual functioning is often a key step in resolving a problem.
- *Specific suggestions* (SS)—Once the basic nature of a sexual problem is identified, the therapist provides suggestions to help resolve it. The client may be encouraged to read books about sexual enhancement, for example, such as sex manuals, or to watch instructional sex videos. With a basic understanding of the client's sexual issues, the therapist may also make specific suggestions for incorporating specific sexual techniques, or suggest ways the couple can refocus their sexual interaction.
- *Intensive therapy* (IT)—If the first three levels of therapy are unsuccessful in solving the problem, a more intensive form of sex therapy may be required. At this point, a therapist who doesn't specialize in sex therapy will refer the client to someone with advanced training in treating sexual dysfunction.

The Masters and Johnson Approach

Masters and Johnson pioneered the use of direct behavioural approaches to treating sexual dysfunction (Masters & Johnson, 1970). A female-and-male therapy team focuses on the couple as the unit of treatment during a two-week residential program. Masters and Johnson considered the couple dysfunctional, not the individual. A couple may describe the male partner's erectile disorder as the problem, but it's likely to have led to other problems by the time the couple seeks therapy. Similarly, a man whose female partner has an orgasmic disorder is likely to be anxious about his ability to provide effective sexual stimulation.

Masters and Johnson developed their approach with heterosexual couples, so it's uncertain how well it applies to same-sex couples. There's no reason, however, to believe a focus on couple dynamics would be less effective with lesbian and gay couples than with heterosexuals.

In this approach, anxieties and resentments are aired, but the focus of treatment is behavioural change. A couple performs daily sexual homework assignments, such as **sensate-focus exercises**, in the privacy of their own room.

Sensate-focus exercises
Exercises in which sexual partners take turns giving and receiving pleasurable stimulation in non-genital areas.

Sensate-focus sessions are carried out in the nude. Partners take turns giving and receiving stimulation in non-genital areas. Without touching the breasts or genitals, the giver massages or fondles the receiving partner, to provide pleasure under relaxing, undemanding conditions. Because genital activity is restricted, there's no pressure to "perform." The giving partner is free to engage in trial-and-error learning about the receiving partner's sensate preferences. The receiving partner is free to enjoy the experience, without feeling rushed to reciprocate or obliged to respond by becoming sexually aroused. The receiving partner's only responsibility is to direct the giving partner, as needed.

In addition to these general sensate-focus exercises, Masters and Johnson used specific assignments to help couples overcome particular sexual dysfunctions.

Integrating Sex Therapy and Psychotherapy

Sex therapy has cognitive components, such as the need to address self-defeating attitudes and expectations and to provide sex education. Because sexual activity is so often embedded in relationships, many therapists (e.g., Althof, 2010; Coyle, 2006; McCarthy et al., 2004, 2006) use psychotherapy and couples therapy to help couples learn how to share power, improve sexual communication, and negotiate differences. The combination of sex therapy and couples therapy appears to be a powerful tool for enhancing relationships as well as sex lives.

Helen Singer Kaplan (1974) combined sex therapy with psychoanalytic methods. She saw sexual dysfunctions as having immediate causes and remote causes (i.e., conflicts that dated to childhood). As a sex therapist, Kaplan focused on improving a couple's sexual communication, eliminating performance anxiety, and fostering sexual skills and knowledge. As a psychoanalyst, she used insight-oriented therapy when it appeared that remote issues impaired a client's response to sex therapy. By so doing, she aimed to bring to awareness unconscious conflicts that might have stifled the person's sexual desire or response.

Treatments for Sexual-Desire Related Disorders

Some sex therapists help kindle sexual appetites in people with hypoactive sexual desire by prescribing self-stimulation exercises combined with erotic fantasies. Sex therapists also assist dysfunctional couples by prescribing sensate-focus exercises, enhancing communication, and expanding the couples' repertoires of sexual skills. Sex therapists recognize that low sexual desire is often a complex problem that requires more intensive treatment than problems of the arousal or orgasm phases. Counselling or psychotherapy may be helpful in treating low sexual desire and sexual aversion, by uncovering and resolving psychological conflicts (Carvalho & Nobre, 2010).

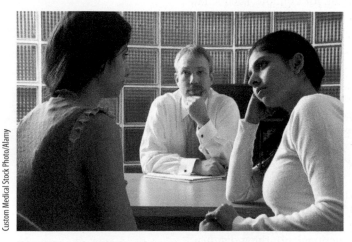

Working with LGB Couples.
Therapists who work with LGB couples find many problems akin to those of heterosexual couples, but some problems reflect the couple's sexual orientation. Examples include LGB identity development and gay/lesbian parenthood.

Custom Medical Stock Photo/Alamy

Applied Knowledge

HOW DO YOU FIND A QUALIFIED SEX THERAPIST?

How do you locate a sex therapist, if you think you have a sexual dysfunction?

Since the provinces don't regulate use of the term "sex therapist," it's essential to determine that a sex therapist is a member of a recognized profession—such as psychology, social work, medicine, or marriage and family counselling—and has had training and supervision in sex therapy.

Professionals are usually licensed or certified by their provinces. All provinces require licensing of psychologists and physicians, but some don't license social workers or marriage counsellors. Only physicians are permitted to bill their provincial health plans for providing sex therapy.

If you're uncertain how to locate a qualified sex therapist in your area, contact your university or college psychology department, health department, or counselling centre, a medical or psychological association, a marriage and family therapy association, or a family physician.

Relatively few people in Canada have been trained as specialists in sex therapy. The only Canadian organization that certifies sex therapists is the Board of Examiners in Sex Therapy and Counselling in Ontario (BESTCO), which includes professionals from diverse backgrounds with clinical expertise in human sexual concerns.

Some Canadian therapists are also certified by American-based organizations such as the American Association of Sex Educators, Counselors, and Therapists (AASECT) and the Society for Sex Therapy and Research (SSTAR).

It's a good idea to ask a therapist the following:

- What discipline(s) has s/he been educated in?
- Where did s/he earn degrees, and what are those degrees?
- Is s/he licensed or certified?
- What fees does s/he charge?
- What treatment plans does s/he use?
- What training has s/he received in human sexuality and sex therapy?

These questions are important because there's such a wide diversity in professional backgrounds and training for sex therapists. Accordingly, the types of treatments and services they offer vary enormously. If the therapist becomes uncomfortable, asks why you're asking such questions, or fails to provide a direct answer, beware.

Remember, under no circumstances is it ethical for a professional therapist to engage in any form of sexual activity with a client.

Some cases of low sexual desire in men involve hormonal deficiencies, especially deficiencies in testosterone. But testosterone replacement therapy works with only about half of men who have low testosterone levels (Buvat et al., 2010). Among women, as among men, lack of sexual desire can be connected with low levels of androgens. One study of post-menopausal women found that after using testosterone patches of various doses for 24 weeks, women taking 150 micrograms of testosterone had a mean increase of 1.2 satisfying sexual episodes per four-week period, whereas women taking 300 micrograms testosterone had a mean increase of 2.1 episodes over the same period (Davis et al., 2008). Those using the patch also experienced heightened sexual desire.

When lack of desire is connected with depression, sexual interest may rebound when the depression lifts. Treatment in such cases may involve psychotherapy, rather than sex therapy. When problems in the relationship are involved, couples therapy may be required, to improve the relationship. Once interpersonal problems are ironed out, sexual interest may return.

Treatment of sexual-aversion may involve a multi-faceted approach, including biological treatment, such as a medication to reduce anxiety, and psychological treatment designed to help the individual overcome the underlying sexual phobia. Couples therapy may be used in cases where sexual aversions arise from relationship problems. Sensate-focus exercises may be used to lessen generalized anxiety about sexual contact. But fears of specific aspects of the sexual act may need to be overcome through behavioural exercises in which the clients learn to manage the stimuli that evoke fears of sexual contact.

Treatments for Sexual Arousal-Related Disorders

Men with chronic erectile disorder may believe they've "forgotten" how to have erections. Erection is an involuntary reflex, however, not a skill.

In sex therapy, women who have trouble becoming lubricated and men who have erectile problems learn that they needn't do anything to become sexually aroused. As long as their problems are psychologically and not organically based, they need only receive sexual stimulation under relaxed circumstances, so anxiety doesn't inhibit their natural reflexes.

To reduce performance anxiety, the partners engage in undemanding sexual contacts that don't demand lubrication or erection. They may start with non-genital sensate-focus exercises, in the style of Masters and Johnson. After a couple of sessions, sensate focus extends to the genitals. The position shown in Figure 13.1 allows the woman easy access to her partner's genitals. She repeatedly teases him to erection and allows the erection to subside. She thereby avoids creating performance anxiety that could lead to erection loss. By repeatedly regaining his erection, the man loses his fear that losing an erection means it won't return. He also learns to focus on erotic sensations for their own sake. He experiences no demand to perform, because the couple is instructed to refrain from intercourse.

Even when the dysfunctional partner can reliably become sexually excited (denoted by erection in the male and lubrication in the female), the couple doesn't immediately attempt intercourse; this might rekindle performance anxiety. Rather, they engage in a series of undemanding, pleasurable sexual activities, which eventually culminates in intercourse if that's what they desire.

With Masters and Johnson's approach, the couple begin intercourse after about 10 days of treatment. The woman teases the man to erection while she sits above him, straddling his thighs. When he's erect, she inserts the penis (to avoid fumbling attempts at entry) and moves slowly back and forth in an undemanding way. Neither attempts to reach orgasm. If the man loses his erection, the two repeat the teasing and intercourse. Once the partners become confident that the man can retain his erection—or reinstate it, if he loses it—they may gradually increase coital thrusting, to reach orgasm.

ERECTILE DISORDER The world's attention has recently been focused on biological approaches to treating erectile disorder. Biological or biomedical approaches can be helpful, especially when organic factors are involved.

Oral medications are by far the most popular biological treatment for erectile problems. Oral forms of several compounds—sildenafil (Viagra), vardenafil (Levitra), and tadalafil (Cialis)—relax the muscles that surround the small blood vessels in the

Figure 13.1 A behavioural approach to treating erectile disorder.
In one part of a program designed to overcome erectile disorder, a man's partner repeatedly teases him to erection and allows the erection to subside. This avoids the creation of performance anxiety that could lead to his losing the erection. Through repeatedly regaining his erection, the man loses his fear that losing an erection means it won't return.

penis, allowing them to dilate so blood can flow into them more freely. After taking the drug, a man must still be aroused through manual, oral, or other stimulation for an erection to occur. The amount of time it takes to become effective varies with the drug. Viagra can become effective within half an hour, and is effective for up to four hours. The oral form of tadalafil (Cialis) becomes effective in about half an hour and lasts for up to 36 hours. Users in France have dubbed it "the weekender."

The most common side effects of these drugs are facial flushing, stuffy nose, and headache, sometimes including migraine. These drugs shouldn't be used by individuals taking any type of nitrate drug, such as nitroglycerine, due to the risk of developing potentially life-threatening low blood pressure.

Viagra was hailed as an important new treatment for erectile dysfunction when it hit the market in early 1998. A study published in the *New England Journal of Medicine* tested the effects of Viagra on more than 800 men with erectile dysfunction

Applied Knowledge

THINKING CRITICALLY ABOUT BUYING DRUGS ONLINE

Viagra, Levitra, and Cialis are prescription drugs. Many men who might otherwise use them are reluctant to discuss erectile dysfunction with their physicians. The anonymity of doing things on the Internet is therefore a lure—you don't have to admit your personal worries to your doctor face to face, or feel embarrassment about asking for an erectile dysfunction drug. Some men don't even have regular physicians. What to do?

Many have discovered that by searching for Viagra on the Internet, they can find many websites where they can "consult" with online physicians, obtain a prescription, and order the drug for home delivery. Easy! A few questions and a fee, and they've got it.

But is it wise?

Prescriptions are needed for various drugs because physicians are better equipped than lay people to diagnose individuals' health problems, understand the chemical natures and side effects of the drugs available for treatment, and predict how the drugs will affect individual patients. Physicians are also usually prepared to deal with the unexpected effects of the drugs—and there can be many.

Ask yourself what kind of physician will prescribe drugs online, without personally examining the patient to determine his health status and the appropriateness and safety of specific treatments for him. If you have a question about the drug once you use it, or if you experience side effects, will you be able to get back to the prescriber easily for an answer, or will you wind up making an embarrassed call to your own physician—or a trip to the emergency room?

There's also the possibility that when you buy prescription drugs online, you'll become the victim of a scam in which an unscrupulous website sells fake pills that may contain harmful substances.

While surfing the net, you may also come across sites that claim to have "natural" preparations (including a variety of herbs) that are as effective as Viagra, but without the

Hemera/Thinkstock

The Lure of Online Drugs.
You might like the idea of not having to talk to a physician face to face, but how trustworthy is an online source? Does the "expert" behind the website understand how it will affect you in light of your particular medical history? Is the drug even real? Is it safe?

side effects and without the need for a prescription. Use some critical thinking: are you convinced of the effectiveness and safety of these preparations? Many of them escape the scrutiny of government regulators—the government isn't watching over them. Be warned.

Even if it's convenient to buy a drug online, you're well advised to get your prescription face to face from a doctor who knows your specific medical history.

Figure 13.2 A penile implant.
A penile implant provides erection when a man's cardiovascular system doesn't do the job. Cylinders are implanted in the penis and a fluid reservoir (shown at top left) is placed near the bladder. A pump (shown in lower middle) is typically inserted in the scrotum. Squeezing the pump forces fluid into the cylinders, inflating the penis. Tripping a release valve later returns the fluid to the reservoir, deflating the penis.

Figure 13.3 A clitoral device for stimulating vasocongestion.
This device works by creating gentle suction over the clitoris, stimulating blood flow into the woman's genitals. This allows vaginal lubrication, which in turn facilitates sexual activity.

caused by both psychological and organic factors (Goldstein et al., 1998). In one phase of the study, 69% of attempts to engage in intercourse were successful for men taking Viagra, compared to 22% for men taking a placebo. A Canadian study (Carrier et al., 2005) found that Viagra was still effective for men who had been taking it for three years. There's ample evidence that these oral medications are effective for most men (Hatzichristou et al., 2000, 2005).

In a study by the University of Western Ontario's Bill Fisher and his colleagues (2005), many women whose partners had erectile dysfunction reported that they experienced lower levels of sexual desire, arousal, orgasm, and sexual satisfaction. A significant proportion of the women whose partners used an erection drug experienced increased sexual desire, arousal, and orgasm.

Hormone treatments can also be effective in some cases. Testosterone helps restore the sex drive and erectile ability in many men who have abnormally low levels of testosterone (Granata et al., 2011). There's no evidence that hormone therapy helps men who already have normal hormone levels.

Various other treatments are available, such as vascular surgery on the penis, penile implants (Figure 13.2), penile injections, penile suppositories, and a vacuum pump held over the penis to increase blood flow. Relatively few men use these techniques, however, because they're not very practical or comfortable to use.

FEMALE SEXUAL INTEREST/AROUSAL DISORDER   As noted above, the *DSM-5* (American Psychiatric Association, 2013) has combined the former categories of *female arousal disorder* and *female hypoactive desire disorder* because problems in these areas of female sexual function tend to overlap. With respect to problems related to desire, treatment often begins with sexuality education (identifying the parts of the body involved in sexual response, discussing their functions, and explaining how to arouse them), searching out and coping with possible cognitive interference (such as negative sexual attitudes), creating undemanding situations in which sexual arousal may occur, and—when appropriate—working on problems in the relationship.

Yet many cases of female sexual-arousal problems involve impaired blood flow to the genitals, just as erectile disorder does. Female sexual arousal involves vaginal lubrication, which permits sexual activity without a great deal of painful friction. Lubrication is made possible by vasocongestion—the flow of blood into the genitals. Lack of lubrication can reflect the physical effects of aging, menopause, or surgically induced menopause.

Sometimes all that's necessary to deal with lack of lubrication is an artificial lubricant such as K-Y Jelly or other commercially available lubricants designed to enhance sexual activity. But lessened blood flow to the genitals can also sap sexual pleasure, and thereby lessen a woman's desire for sex.

The development of effective biological treatments for female sexual dysfunction has lagged behind the development of treatments for men. Some have speculated that this is because female sexual response tends to be tied more directly to psychosocial influences, such as relationship factors. Nevertheless, researchers continue to search for medical treatments to enhance female arousal. For example, researchers are investigating the use of alprostadil (a vasodilator) for use with women, in the form of a cream that's inserted into the vagina to enhance the flow of blood and hence lubrication. Other biological treatments for women include testosterone skin patches. There's even a device called Eros that creates gentle suction over the clitoris, increasing vasocongestion and sexual sensations. (See Figure 13.3.)

After Viagra was shown to be highly effective in treating erectile dysfunction in men, researchers began investigating the potential benefits of Viagra for women. Reviews of the research have not shown a consistent positive effect of Viagra in

Applied Knowledge

PROMOTING EROTICISM IN SEX THERAPY

Ottawa sex therapist Peggy Kleinplatz (2003) has developed an innovative approach to sex therapy. She argues that most sex therapy is too focused on treating symptoms and solving problems, and should focus instead on personal growth, which includes enhancing sexual relationships and erotic potential.

Kleinplatz is especially concerned about the focus on pills and devices. She argues that the medical model emphasizes performance measures such as frequency and firmness of erections, and ignores the quality of interactions (e.g., satisfaction, intimacy).

Kleinplatz presents a thorough critique of the field of sex therapy in her 2012 book *New Directions in Sex Therapy: Innovations and Alternatives*. She believes many therapists are personally uncomfortable with promoting eroticism and attempt only to enable couples to engage in the mechanics of sexual intercourse, rather than helping them maximize sexual pleasure (Kleinplatz, 2012). This mechanical approach results in sexual boredom for many couples, who come to rely on specific routines for achieving orgasm and are then afraid to risk trying new, possibly more fulfilling approaches.

According to Kleinplatz (2003), many people want to excite their partners and establish deep, sensual connections that will bring more intense sexual ecstasy. Eroticism, in her view, is the key to maintaining sexual desire. The erotic encounter should focus on pleasure for its own sake, rather than on the tension release of orgasm (Kleinplatz, 2003).

women with arousal disorders (Chivers & Rosen, 2010). However, the research does indicate that Viagra may be useful for women who experience arousal difficulties caused by antidepressant medications (Nurnberg et al., 2008).

Canadian sex therapists Peggy Kleinplatz (2003) and Rosemary Basson (2000) have been vocal in their opposition to what they view as the medicalization of female sexuality. Indeed, other factors are often involved in sexual dysfunction, including intimacy and relationship issues, and if these aren't addressed, the sexual problems will likely persist.

Orgasmic Disorders

FEMALE ORGASMIC DISORDER Women who have never experienced orgasm often harbour negative attitudes about sex that cause anxiety and inhibit sexual response. Treatment in such cases may first address these attitudes.

The Masters and Johnson method is a couples-oriented approach to treating anorgasmic women. It begins with sensate-focus exercises. Then, during genital massage and later during intercourse, the woman guides her partner in the caresses and movements she finds sexually exciting. Taking charge helps free the woman from the traditional stereotype of the passive, subordinate female role.

The Masters and Johnson approach recommends a training position (see Figure 13.4) that gives the man access to his partner's breasts and genitals. She can guide his hands, to show him the types of stimulation she enjoys. The genital play is *undemanding*. The goal is to learn to provide and enjoy effective sexual stimulation, not to reach orgasm. The clitoris is not stimulated early, because doing so may produce a high level of stimulation before the woman is prepared.

After a number of occasions of genital play, the couple has intercourse in the female-superior position. (See Figure 13.5.) This position allows the woman

Figure 13.4 The training position for undemanding stimulation of the female genitals.
This position gives the woman's partner access to her breasts and genitals. She can guide her partner's hands, to show him what types of stimulation she enjoys.

freedom of movement and control over her genital sensations. She is told to regard the penis as her toy. She and her partner engage in several sessions of deliberately slow thrusting, to sensitize her to sensations produced by the penis and to break the common, counterproductive pattern of desperate, rapid thrusting.

Orgasm cannot be willed or forced. When a woman receives effective stimulation, feels free to focus on erotic sensations, and feels that nothing is being demanded of her, she will generally reach orgasm. Once she's able to attain orgasm in the female-superior position, she and her partner may extend their sexual repertoire to other positions.

Masters and Johnson preferred working with the couple in cases of anorgasmia. Other sex therapists prefer to begin working with the woman individually, and suggest masturbation as therapy. Masters and Johnson worked with heterosexual couples, but placing the focus on undemanding genital play may be equally

Figure 13.5 The female-superior position.
In treatment for female orgasmic disorder, the couple has intercourse in the female-superior position after a number of occasions of genital play. This position allows the woman freedom of movement and control over her genital sensations. She's told to regard the penis as her toy. She and her partner engage in several sessions of deliberately slow thrusting, to sensitize the woman to sensations produced by the penis and to break the common, counterproductive pattern of desperate, rapid thrusting.

applicable to lesbian couples in which one of the partners has difficulty reaching orgasm.

Masturbation allows individuals to get in touch with their sexual responses at their own pace. Many sex therapists recommend that women having difficulty with orgasm focus on masturbation. It frees them of the need to rely on, or please, a partner. The sexual pleasure they experience helps counter lingering sexual anxieties. Although there is some variation, the following elements are commonly found in directed masturbation programs for women:

- *Education*—The woman and her partner (if she has one) are educated about female sexuality.
- *Self-exploration*—Self-exploration is encouraged as a way of increasing the woman's sense of body awareness. She may hold a mirror between her legs to locate her sexual anatomic features.
- *Self-massage*—The woman creates a private, relaxing setting for self-massage. She begins to explore the sensitivity of her body to touch, discovering and repeating the caresses she finds pleasurable. She may use non-alcohol-based oils and lotions to enhance the sensuous quality of the massage and provide lubrication for the external genitalia. To prevent performance anxiety, the woman doesn't attempt to reach orgasm during the first few occasions.
- *Self-permission*—The woman may be advised to challenge lingering guilt and anxiety about sex in general and self-pleasuring in particular. For example, she might reassure herself that experiencing sexual pleasure is a natural and positive part of life, giving herself permission to enjoy it.
- *Fantasy*—Arousal is heightened through the use of sexual images, fantasies, and fantasy aids, such as erotic books or videos.
- *A vibrator*—Millions of women use vibrators, either during solo masturbation or with their partners. Because vibrators may provide more intense stimulation, they can be useful for women seeking to have orgasms more easily.
- *Partner involvement*—After the woman is capable of regularly achieving orgasm through masturbation, the focus may shift to her sexual relationship with her partner. She can teach her partner how to stimulate her in ways that enable her to reach orgasm.

Our focus has been on sexual techniques, but a combination of approaches that focus on sexual techniques and underlying interpersonal problems may be more effective than focusing on sexual techniques alone, at least for couples whose relationships are troubled.

DELAYED EJACULATION   Treatment for delayed ejaculation generally focuses on increasing sexual stimulation and reducing performance anxiety (Althof, 2012). The Masters and Johnson approach has the couple practise sensate-focus exercises for several days, during which the man makes no attempt to ejaculate. The couple is then instructed to bring him to orgasm any way they can, usually by having the partner stroke the man's penis. Once he can ejaculate in his partner's presence, the partner brings him to the point at which he's about to ejaculate. Then, if the couple is heterosexual, they use the female-superior position, with the woman thrusting vigorously to bring him to orgasm.

PREMATURE (EARLY) EJACULATION   In the Masters and Johnson approach, sensate-focus exercises are followed by practise in the training position shown in Figure 13.1. The partner teases the man to erection, and uses the **squeeze technique** when he indicates that he's about to ejaculate. The partner holds the penis between the thumb and the first two fingers of one hand. The thumb presses against the frenulum. The fingers straddle the coronal ridge on the other side of the penis. Squeezing the thumb and forefingers

Squeeze technique
A method for treating premature ejaculation. The tip of the penis is squeezed to temporarily prevent ejaculation.

together fairly hard for about 20 seconds (or until the man's urge to ejaculate passes) prevents ejaculation. The erect penis can withstand fairly strong pressure without discomfort, but erection may be partially lost. The couple repeats this process three or four times in a 15- to 20-minute session before the man purposely ejaculates.

For heterosexual couples, after two or three days of these sessions, the couple is instructed to begin intercourse in the female-superior position, because it creates less pressure to ejaculate. The woman inserts the penis. At first she contains it without thrusting, allowing the man to get used to intravaginal sensations. If he signals that he's about to ejaculate, she lifts off and squeezes his penis. After some repetitions, she begins slowly to move backward and forward, lifting off and squeezing as needed. The man gradually learns to tolerate higher levels of sexual stimulation without ejaculating.

The alternating stop-start method for treating premature ejaculation was introduced by urologist James Semans (1956). The method can be applied to manual stimulation or intercourse. For example, the partner can manually stimulate the penis until the man is about to ejaculate. He then signals his partner to suspend sexual stimulation, and allows his arousal to subside before stimulation is resumed. This process enables him to recognize the cues that precede his point of ejaculatory inevitability, or point of no return, and to tolerate longer periods of sexual stimulation.

When the stop-start technique is applied to intercourse, the partners begin with simple vaginal containment, with no pelvic thrusting, preferably in the female-superior position. The man withdraws if he feels he's about to ejaculate. As the man's sense of control increases, thrusting can begin, along with variations in intercourse positions. They again stop when the man signals that he's approaching ejaculatory inevitability.

Gay men sometimes face problems with premature ejaculation when engaging in anal sex. Their partners can also try either the squeeze technique or the stop-start method.

Although the squeeze and stop-start techniques have been widely recommended as methods to alleviate rapid ejaculation, there's little research showing that they're effective, particularly for men with severe or persistent cases (Sharlip, 2005). While these techniques may be more useful for men with mild cases of premature ejaculation, emphasis is increasingly being placed on biological treatments.

BIOLOGICAL TREATMENTS FOR PREMATURE (EARLY) EJACULATION

Some drugs that are usually used to treat psychological problems can be effective in treating premature ejaculation (McMahon, 2011). Clomipramine, which is used to treat obsessive-compulsive disorder and schizophrenia, can impair erectile response at high doses. But in a study with 15 couples, low doses helped men engage in intercourse five times longer than usual without ejaculating (Althof, 1994). Antidepressant drugs have also been helpful in the treatment of premature ejaculation, but are associated with erectile dysfunction (Waldinger, 2011).

Why do drugs used to treat psychological problems help with premature ejaculation? The psychological problems are frequently connected with imbalances in body chemicals, such as neurotransmitters—the chemical messengers of the brain. Neurotransmitters are also involved in other bodily functions, including ejaculation. Anti-depressant drugs all work by increasing the action of the neurotransmitter serotonin. Serotonin, in turn, may inhibit the ejaculatory reflex (Waldinger, 2011). But note the cautions about using SSRIs we discussed earlier in the chapter.

Innovative Canadian Research

TREATMENT FOR DYSPAREUNIA

A team of Canadian and American researchers led by Sophie Bergeron and Yitzchak Binik of McGill University (Bergeron et al., 2001) has conducted controlled studies of the effectiveness of three types of treatment programs for dyspareunia resulting from provoked vestibulodynia (a sharp, burning pain experienced when direct pressure is applied just inside the vaginal opening). The three approaches were cognitive-behavioural therapy, biofeedback, and surgery involving the excision of the vestibular area.

While each treatment resulted in pain reduction, the surgery had the highest success rate. The three treatment approaches were equally successful in improving psychological adjustment and sexual functioning. The researchers noted, however, that some of the women who were assigned to the surgical treatment refused to go ahead with that intervention.

The findings indicate that both psychological and surgical interventions can be useful in the treatment of dyspareunia.

Sophie Bergeron and others from the University of Quebec (Bergeron et al., 2008) did a follow-up study with participants from the original sample. Treatment gains were still maintained for each intervention. Over this longer period, however, cognitive-behavioural therapy was found to be as effective as surgery in reducing levels of reported pain during intercourse. Women who held negative attitudes toward sex and sexual pleasure responded less favourably to the surgery.

In a subsequent study, surgical treatment combined with cognitive-behavioural–based sex therapy was effective in reducing pain and increasing sexual satisfaction among many, but not all, women with provoked vestibulodynia (Lambert, Bergeron, Desrosiers, & Lepage, 2012).

Treatments for Sexual-Pain Related Disorders

DYSPAREUNIA   Dyspareunia, or painful intercourse, generally calls for medical intervention, to identify and treat any underlying physical problems that might cause pain, such as urinary-tract infections (van Lankveld et al., 2010). When dyspareunia is caused by vaginismus, treatment through the behavioural approach we'll describe next may reduce pain.

VAGINISMUS   Vaginismus is generally treated with behavioural exercises in which fingers or plastic vaginal dilators of increasing size are inserted to help relax the vaginal musculature (Reissing, 2012). A gynecologist may first demonstrate insertion of the narrowest dilator. Later, the woman practises inserting wider dilators at home. She increases the size of the dilator as she becomes capable of tolerating insertion and containment for 10 or 15 minutes without discomfort or pain.

The woman herself—not her partner or her therapist—controls the pace of treatment. The woman's or her partner's fingers (first the littlest finger, then two fingers, and so on) may be used in place of the plastic dilators, with the woman controlling the speed and depth of penetration. When the woman is able to tolerate dilators (or fingers) equivalent in thickness to a penis or dildo, the couple may attempt penetration. Still, the woman should control insertion. Circumstances should be relaxed and undemanding. The idea is to avoid re-sensitizing her to fears of penetration.

Because vaginismus often occurs among women with histories of sexual trauma, such as rape or incest, treatment may also be in order for the psychological effects of these experiences (Crowley et al., 2006).

Innovative Canadian Research

A PORTRAIT OF GREAT SEX

Most research on human sexuality focuses on sexual problems, rather than sexual pleasure. In contrast, Ottawa researcher Peggy Kleinplatz and her colleagues (2009) interviewed people who reported experiencing "great sex" with the objective of building a conceptual model that would outline the key characteristics of optimal sexuality.

Many of the people participating in the study were over the age of 60, and some had been in relationships for 25 years or longer. In describing great sex, many of them were drawing on several decades of experience with sex and relationships. Perhaps younger people have something to learn from the wisdom of those with more experience.

Eight major components of great sex emerged from the interviews:

- *Being present, focused, and embodied*—The most basic characteristic of great sex was being totally immersed in and intensely focused on the experience. This led to total surrender of the body to the experience, without any other distracting thoughts.
- *Connection, or being in sync*—A strong sense of connection and a feeling of synchronicity was an important component of great sex for many of the participants. As one woman said, it's a feeling of "two people being in the right head space at the right time together, being able to share that" (Kleinplatz et al., 2009, p. 6).
- *Deep sexual and erotic intimacy*—Regardless of whether the sexual encounters occurred in long-term or other kinds of relationships, there was a powerful sense of intimate engagement and trust in the relationships. As one participant suggested, "It's part of the way you act with each other long before you're actually engaged in any kind of, you know, technical sex" (Kleinplatz et al., 2009, p. 6).
- *Extraordinary communication and heightened empathy*—Being able to communicate, both

verbally and nonverbally, and being tuned in to their partners' responses were seen by some as crucial to great sex.
- *Authenticity*—Participants felt they could be free to be themselves and open about their own desires. They spoke of feeling totally uninhibited and transparent.
- *Transcendence and transformation*—Some participants indicated that great sex was a "high" similar to what can be experienced through meditation. Others noted that great sex with a partner could be transformative, carrying over in a positive way to other aspects of life.
- *Exploration and interpersonal risk-taking*—Great sex was seen as on ongoing process of discovery, with the partners continuing to explore their sexuality over time. This required taking some personal risks in exploring new things. Many participants stressed that sexual exploration was done with a sense of fun and humour.
- *Vulnerability*—Freely allowing themselves to be vulnerable was, for some participants, an important aspect of great sex. An older male participant believed vulnerability was what distinguished good from great sex:

> In normal good sex or good relationships, I think there's always some maybe small but detectable barriers, some things held back. In great sex, I think those for me disappear, and so that one is quite transparent to the other person, and therefore quite vulnerable, but it feels, it goes with an intensely erotic and good feeling, rather than a scary feeling (Kleinplatz et al., 2009, p. 9).

The participants emphasized that they had developed their ability to experience great sex over time, in some cases many years. For many, their perceptions of great sex changed with their life experiences and personal growth.

A World of Diversity

AN ALTERNATIVE APPROACH TO ENHANCING FEMALE SEXUALITY

by Lori A. Brotto, PhD, Department of Obstetrics and Gynaecology, University of British Columbia

Treatment approaches designed to help women with sexual problems have generally focused on improving sexual response.

A healthy sexual response, however, doesn't necessarily signify overall sexual satisfaction or lack of sexual distress. Specifically, 5.5% of American women aged 30 to 79 reported that sexual activity is unsatisfying (Lutfey et al., 2008), despite the fact that they experienced no difficulties with desire, arousal, or orgasm.

In the Global Study of Sexual Attitudes and Behaviors (Laumann et al., 2005), 8% to 18% of the 40- to 80-year-old women reported not finding sex pleasurable. Some women therefore weren't sexually satisfied, even though the mechanics of sexual response were operating, and the women didn't meet the criteria for a sexual dysfunction.

These women (Ogden et al., 2007) described their sexual experiences as boring, dry, and unemotional. In response to this situation, Ogden and colleagues (2007) have called for a non-goal-oriented, spiritual element to sexuality.

Eastern techniques, with their origins in the *Kama Sutra* of the fourth to sixth centuries, might provide some of the spiritual dimensions the traditional Western approaches lack. One Eastern technique that might improve women's sexuality is mindfulness.

Mindful Meditation

Mindfulness involves nonjudgmental, present-moment awareness. It has roots in Buddhist meditation. Although it's a non-religious practise, transcending all organized religions, it does have a spiritual component (Carmody et al., 2008).

Recently, mindfulness has been incorporated into a brief, psycho-educational treatment program for women with disorders of sexual desire and arousal, and found to be effective as part of a larger treatment program that includes education, cognitive and behavioural skills, and couples-therapy exercises. In the study, women who used a combination of in-session and at-home exercises evaluated the mindfulness component as the most valuable aspect of treatment (Brotto & Heiman, 2007).

Specifically, mindfulness was introduced to women by giving them instructions about how to be mindful in their nonsexual lives. They were introduced to the topic with the following:

Many of us go through life not living in the present moment. We fluctuate between thinking in the future (worrying, planning, thinking), and living in the past (reviewing past events, conversations, plans). We miss out on valuable and meaningful experiences in the present. We have evolved to multi-task, and this reinforces mindlessness. However, in instances when we wish to be present, such as the sexual scenario, it's difficult if not impossible for us to turn off the cerebral chatter. The net effect is a reduction in arousal, thereby making the sexual experience less rewarding and pleasurable.

The heart of mindfulness is practising the body scan exercise, which involves attending to the sensations in specific parts of the body. Women can practise the body scan a few times a week, in addition to practising mindfulness every day, usually for 10 minutes, during other activities (e.g., eating, driving, having a conversation, playing a sport or instrument).

They're also given a set of body-focused mindfulness exercises to practise at home.

The first is a focusing exercise. The women are asked to visually attend to their bodies during and after their baths or showers. They're encouraged to describe what they see in nonjudgmental ways, and are given a list of possible statements to repeat during the exercise, such as "My body is my own," "My body is alive," and "I appreciate the following aspects of my body."

The self-observation exercise asks women to use hand-held mirrors to observe their genitals. They're reminded that this is a nonsexual exercise, with the goal of allowing them to remain in the present while letting any judgments about themselves, their bodies, or how they're struggling with the exercise to float away.

The self-observation and touch exercise asks women to gently touch their own genitals while repeating the self-observation exercise.

After some weeks of practise, a sexual goal is added. The woman is encouraged to repeat the self-observation-and-touch exercise while imagining herself as a competent sexual, feminine, sensual woman. There's then a discussion about incorporating mindfulness while being sexual, either alone or with a partner.

Three studies have tested the efficacy of a mindfulness-based sex therapy intervention for women with low desire and arousal. These studies found a significant improvement in sexual response and a decrease in sexual distress (see Brotto, 2013).

Mindfulness techniques therefore show great promise in treating women's sexual concerns, and may fill the spiritual gap for some women who have unsatisfying sexual experiences.

Summing Up

A sexual dysfunction is a difficulty with sexual desire, arousal, or orgasm.

Sexual-desire related disorders involve dysfunctions in sexual desire, interest, or drive. The individuals experience a lack of sexual desire or an aversion to genital sexual contact.

In men, sexual-arousal disorders involve recurrent difficulty in getting or sustaining erections sufficient to successfully engage in sexual intercourse. In women, they typically involve failure to become sufficiently lubricated.

Women are more likely to encounter difficulties reaching orgasm, and men are more likely to have trouble with premature ejaculation.

Sexual pain disorders include dyspareunia, vaginismus, and vulvodynia.

Many sexual dysfunctions involve the interaction of organic and psychological factors.

Fatigue may lead to erectile disorder in men, and to orgasmic disorder and dyspareunia in women. Dyspareunia often reflects vaginal infections and STIs. Organic factors are believed to be involved in the majority of cases of erectile disorder. Medications and other drugs may also impair sexual functioning.

Psychosocial factors connected with sexual dysfunction include cultural influences, psychosexual traumas, marital dissatisfaction, psychological conflicts, lack of sexual skills, irrational beliefs, and performance anxiety. Performance anxiety may place a dysfunctional individual into a spectator role, rather than a performer role.

Sex therapy aims to modify behaviours directly by changing self-defeating beliefs and attitudes, fostering sexual skills and knowledge, enhancing sexual communication, and providing behavioural exercises to enhance sexual stimulation while reducing performance anxiety.

Masters and Johnson pioneered the direct, behavioural approach to treating sexual dysfunction.

Some sex therapists help kindle sexual appetites in people with inhibited sexual desire by prescribing self-stimulation exercises combined with erotic fantasies.

Men and women with impaired sexual arousal receive sexual stimulation from their partners under relaxed circumstances, so anxiety doesn't inhibit their natural reflexes. Biological treatments such as the drug Viagra are also used for male erectile disorder.

Masters and Johnson used a couples-oriented approach in treating anorgasmic women. Other sex therapists prefer a program of directed masturbation, to enable women to learn about their own bodies at their own pace and free them of the need to rely on partners or on pleasing partners.

Premature (early) ejaculation is usually treated with the squeeze technique, the stop-start method, or medical treatments.

Dyspareunia, or painful intercourse, is generally treated with medical interventions. Vaginismus is generally treated with plastic vaginal dilators of increasing size.

Test Yourself

Multiple-Choice Questions

1. The sexual problem most commonly reported by women in the 2002 Canadian Contraception Study was
   (a) Rapid ejaculation.
   (b) Painful intercourse.
   (c) Low sexual desire.
   (d) Lack of orgasm.

2. According to the study of Canadian adults by Brock et al., what percentage of people with sexual-function problems sought help from health professionals?
   (a) 0
   (b) 25
   (c) 50
   (d) 75

3. Permission and specific suggestions are components of:
   (a) An insight-oriented approach to treating low desire.
   (b) The Masters and Johnson approach to sex therapy.
   (c) The biological treatment of sexual dysfunction.
   (d) The PLISSIT model.

4. According to the study by Kleinplatz, which of the following was not found to be a key component of great sex?
   (a) Expertise in performing oral sex
   (b) Erotic intimacy
   (c) Communication
   (d) Exploration and interpersonal risk-taking

5. _____ is a common cause of erectile difficulties.
   (a) Orgasm anxiety
   (b) Ejaculatory incompetence
   (c) Performance anxiety
   (d) Hyposensitivity of the penis

6. An involuntary contraction of the muscles that makes penetration painful or impossible is known as:
   (a) Dyspareunia.   (c) Phimosis.
   (b) Vaginismus.   (d) Anorgasmia.

7. A low level of _____ can lessen sexual desire.
   (a) testosterone   (c) Depo-Provera
   (b) sildenafil   (d) alprostadil

8. Which of the following is not one of the psychosocial factors associated with sexual dysfunction?
   (a) Dissatisfaction with the relationship.
   (b) Lack of sexual skills.
   (c) Anxiety due to a previous negative experience.
   (d) Side effects of prescription drugs.

9. A behavioural approach to treating sexual disorders might include all of the following except:
   (a) Adjusting hormone balance to improve sexual functioning.
   (b) Changing self-defeating beliefs and attitudes.
   (c) Enhancing sexual knowledge.
   (d) Improving communication skills.

10. Sex therapists are most likely to recommend masturbation as a treatment for:
    (a) Rapid ejaculation.
    (b) Female orgasmic disorder.
    (c) Vaginismus.
    (d) Retarded ejaculation.

You'll find answers to the "Test Yourself" questions on page 489.

Questions for Critical Thinking

1. It's been argued that the increasing emphasis on biological treatments for sexual dysfunction has resulted in over-medicalization of human sexuality. What's your opinion?

2. Why do you think so many people find it difficult to ask health care providers such as doctors about sexual problems? Do you think men or women find it more difficult to talk about their sexual problems? Why?

3. Would you buy a drug such as Viagra over the Internet? Why or why not?

CHAPTER FOURTEEN

Sexually Transmitted Infections

Traudl/Shutterstock

Harold and Carin, both 20, have been seeing each other for about a month. They feel strong sexual attraction toward each other, but haven't become sexually intimate, in part because of fears about sexually transmitted infections. Harold believes using condoms is no guarantee against infection, and wants the two of them to be tested for HIV and other **sexually transmitted infections**. Carin has resisted undergoing these tests, partly because she feels insulted that Harold fears that she may be infected, and frankly, partly in fear of the test results. She's heard that symptoms of many STIs may not be visible, or may not develop for years after infection. She wonders whether she might have been infected by one of the men she's had sex with in the past.

Keisha has genital herpes. A 19-year-old pre-law student, she's had no recurrences since her initial outbreak, two years ago. She knows, however, that herpes is a lifelong infection that may recur from time to time. She also knows she may inadvertently pass the herpes virus along to her sex partners. She's begun thinking seriously about Steve, a man

Sexually transmitted infection (STI) An infection that's passed from one person to another through sexual contact. (Some STIs, such as HIV, can also be transmitted in other ways.)

she's been dating for the past month. She'd like to tell him she has herpes before they become sexually intimate, yet she fears that telling him might scare him off.

José, 21, is a math and computer science major. He lives off campus with several buddies, in a run-down house they've dubbed "the Nuclear Dumpsite." He's been seeing Bill, a history major, for several months. They've begun having sexual relations, and have practised safer sex—at least, most of the time. During the past week José has noticed some odd-looking bumps around his penis that didn't seem to be there before. For now, he's adopting a wait-and-see attitude, hoping they'll go away, but in the back of his mind he wonders whether he should see a doctor.

Scenarios like these play out thousands of times each year on college and university campuses across Canada. If you have an STI, think you might have one, or are worried that you're at risk for infection, you're not alone. STIs are more common than most of us think. The World Health Organization estimates that more than 365 million people around the world are infected with STIs each year (World Health Organization, 2013). STIs are something many of us prefer not to think or talk about with friends and intimate partners, mainly because it would involve frank discussions about sexual behaviour, which Western culture has often discouraged. Many people—if not most—lack even a basic knowledge of STIs and their own personal risks for infection.

Although discussions about STIs often focus on their medical implications, when someone learns s/he has an STI, the emotional impact can be as great as—if not greater than—the medical consequences. There remains a stigma associated with STIs, rooted in the false belief that they only happen to certain types of people, especially those who some might call promiscuous. Many people with STIs worry about the implications of their infections for current and future relationships. The reality is that STIs can happen to anyone who's sexually active, and they're very common among Canadians. Becoming knowledgeable about STIs enables us to reduce our risk of infection and deal with any infections that may occur.

STIs in Canada

Canadian rates vary by STI type. Human papillomavirus (HPV) and genital herpes (herpes simplex virus, or HSV) are the most common. Unfortunately, we don't have comprehensive national statistics on them, as physicians aren't required to report cases of these STIs. We'll discuss the prevalence of HSV and HPV as well as HIV/AIDS later in the chapter. For now, let's look at some statistics on nationally notifiable (often referred to as "reportable") bacterial STIs in Canada.

Of the STIs for which cases are reported to public health authorities, chlamydia is the most common. There were 94 690 reported cases of chlamydia in 2010 (Public Health Agency of Canada, 2012e). Keep in mind that these numbers reflect only those cases of chlamydia that were diagnosed through testing. Many more cases went undetected. Teens and young adults have the highest rates of chlamydia (see Figure 14.1). Chlamydia rates declined between 1992 and 1997, but have since increased. For example, from 1997 to 2010, the reported rate of chlamydia among females aged 20 to 24 years rose 117%. McKay and Barrett (2008) suggest that large reported rate increases in chlamydia in Canada are likely attributable, in large part, to more sensitive testing methods and increases in the number of people tested, as has happened in the United States. That is, if more people are being tested for chlamydia over time, and the tests used to detect the infection are more effective, the number of confirmed cases that are reported to public health authorities will increase. Nevertheless, the reported rates of chlamydia indicate that chlamydia is a common infection among Canadian young people. With respect to the age distribution of chlamydia within the population, studies conducted in Western countries

CRITICAL THINKING QUESTIONS

How knowledgeable are you about STIs? What questions do you have?

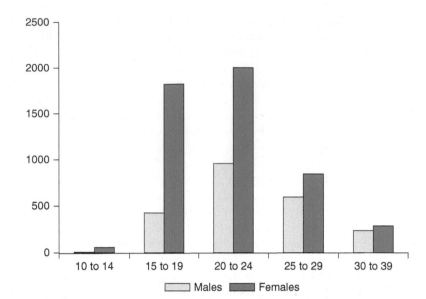

Figure 14.1   Reported rates per 100,000 of chlamydia among males and females aged 10–14, 15–19, 20–24, 25–29, 30–39, 2010, Canada

Source: Public Health Agency of Canada. (2012) Report on Sexually Transmitted Infections in Canada: 2010. *Centre for Communicable Diseases and Infection Control.*

consistently find that chlamydia is most common among people under age 25 (Dielissen, Teunissen, & Largo-Janssen, 2013).

As shown in Figure 14.1, reported rates of chlamydia are much higher among females, compared to males. However, lower reported rates among males are most likely due to lower rates of testing of males compared to rates of testing among females (Satterwhite & Douglas, 2013).

Rates of chlamydia and other STIs vary across Canada. The highest STI rates occur in Canada's North, and the next highest in the western provinces, especially Saskatchewan. This trend is attributed to the higher rates among Canada's First Nations people. We'll discuss these differences in the section on social factors and STIs, near the end of the chapter.

Gonorrhea is less common than chlamydia. From 2001 to 2010, the reported gonorrhea rate increased by 53.7% and in 2010, there were 11 397 reported cases (Public Health Agency of Canada, 2012e). Like chlamydia, however, only a small proportion of actual cases are diagnosed and reported. Similar to chlamydia, people under 30 years of age accounted for the majority (70.5%) of reported gonorrhea cases in 2010.

Compared with gonorrhea and chlamydia, the number of syphilis cases is relatively small. Syphilis infection rates decreased in Canada with the introduction of penicillin in the 1940s. In recent years it's been increasing, however, especially among men who have sex with men. In 2010, 1757 cases of syphilis were diagnosed in Canada, and 90.5% of those were in men (Public Health Agency of Canada, 2012e). Most of the increase has been due to localized outbreaks in Vancouver, Yukon, Calgary, Edmonton, the Northwest Territories, Winnipeg, Toronto, Ottawa, Montreal, and Halifax.

Researchers at the Public Health Agency of Canada compared STI rates in different age groups between 1997 and 2007. They found that although rates were still highest among younger people, rates of chlamydia, gonorrhea, and syphilis were increasing faster among 40- to 59-year-olds (Fang, Oliver, Jayaraman, & Fong, 2010). The researchers suggested that "There is a need for sexual-health information targeting Canada's middle-aged adults and their health care providers" (Fang, Oliver, Jayaraman, & Fong, 2010, p. 18).

Again, we want to emphasize that the actual prevalence of these STIs (in terms of percentage of the population) is much higher than the numbers that make up the reported rates. The reported rates represent only the cases that are officially diagnosed.

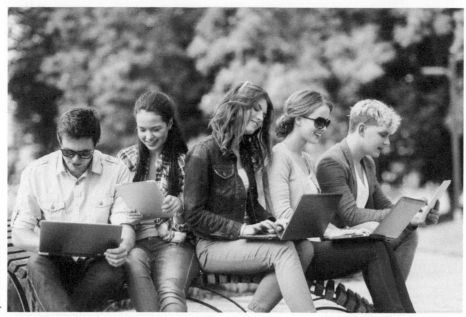

Syda Productions/Fotolia

Who's at Risk?
Adolescents and young adults tend to have shorter relationships than older adults, and therefore more sexual partners. This helps explain why STI rates are highest among young people.

Bacterial Infections

Bacteria cause a range of diseases, such as pneumonia, tuberculosis, meningitis, and the STIs chlamydia, gonorrhea, and syphilis.

Chlamydia

Although some viral STIs are more common, chlamydia is the most common bacterial STI in Canada. Chlamydia infection is caused by the *Chlamydia trachomatis* bacterium, a parasitic organism that can survive only within cells. This bacterium can cause several types of infection, including non-gonococcal urethritis in men and women, epididymitis (infection of the epididymis) in men, and cervicitis (infection of the cervix), endometritis (infection of the endometrium), and pelvic inflammatory disease in women (Public Health Agency of Canada, 2010d).

TRANSMISSION   Chlamydia is usually transmitted through sexual intercourse—vaginal or anal. Chlamydia may also cause an eye infection if a person touches his or her eyes after handling the genitals of an infected partner. Oral sex with an infected partner can infect the throat.

SYMPTOMS   Chlamydia usually produces symptoms similar to those of gonorrhea, but milder.

In men, chlamydia can lead to non-gonococcal urethritis (NGU), an inflammation of the urethra that's not caused by the gonococcus bacterium. NGU used to be called non-specific urethritis, or NSU. Many organisms can cause NGU, but chlamydia accounts for about half of the cases among men. It causes a thin, whitish discharge from the penis, burning or other pain during urination, soreness in the scrotum, and feelings of heaviness in the testes. These symptoms contrast with the yellow-green discharge and more intense pain produced by gonorrhea. NGU is two to three times as prevalent among American men as gonorrhea (Hatcher et al., 2011).

Bacteria A class of single-celled micro-organisms that have no chlorophyll and can give rise to many illnesses. The singular is "bacterium."

In women, a chlamydia infection usually occurs in the urethra or cervix. Women may experience burning when they urinate, genital irritation, and a mild vaginal discharge. If the infection progresses, women are likely to have pelvic pain and irregular menstrual cycles. The cervix may look swollen and inflamed.

Up to 90% of men and 70% of women infected with chlamydia show no symptoms (Centers for Disease Control and Prevention, 2014). People without symptoms may go untreated, and unknowingly pass their infections to their partners. In women, an untreated chlamydial infection can spread throughout the reproductive system, leading to **pelvic inflammatory disease (PID)** and scarring of the fallopian tubes, resulting in infertility (Public Health Agency of Canada, 2010d). Untreated chlamydial infections can also damage the internal reproductive organs of men.

Chlamydial infections frequently occur together with other STIs, most often gonorrhea. Nearly half of all cases of gonorrhea involve coexisting chlamydial infections (Hatcher et al., 2011).

Pelvic inflammatory disease (PID) Inflammation of the pelvic region in women, possibly including the cervix, uterus, fallopian tubes, abdominal cavity, and ovaries. Its symptoms are abdominal pain, tenderness, nausea, fever, and irregular menstrual cycles. The condition may lead to infertility.

DIAGNOSIS AND TREATMENT   Various tests can verify a diagnosis of chlamydia in women. Some tests analyze cervical or urethral smears, while others use self-obtained urine samples and vaginal swabs, which are also highly reliable and preferred by most women because they're less invasive (Public Health Agency of Canada, 2010d). To test men, swabs are inserted through the penile openings, and fluid is extracted for analysis.

Antibiotics other than penicillin are highly effective in eradicating chlamydia infections. Penicillin, which is effective in treating gonorrhea, is ineffective against chlamydia. Treatment of sex partners is critical to preventing the infection from bouncing back and forth (Public Health Agency of Canada, 2010d).

Gonorrhea

Gonorrhea is the second most commonly reported bacterial STI in Canada. Caused by the *Neisseria gonorrhoeae* bacterium, it's characterized by a discharge and burning urination. Left untreated, gonorrhea can cause pelvic inflammatory disease and infertility.

TRANSMISSION   The gonococcus bacterium requires a warm, moist environment like that found along the mucous membranes of the urinary tract in both genders and the cervix in women. Outside the body, they die in about a minute. There's no evidence that gonorrhea can be picked up from public toilet seats or by touching dry objects. In rare cases, gonorrhea can be contracted by contact with a moist, warm towel or sheet immediately after it's been used by an infected person. Gonorrhea is nearly always transmitted by unprotected vaginal, oral, or anal sexual activity, or from mother to newborn during delivery.

Pharyngeal gonorrhea A gonorrheal infection of the pharynx, which is the cavity leading from the mouth and nasal passages to the larynx and esophagus. It's characterized by a sore throat.

A person who performs fellatio on an infected partner may develop **pharyngeal gonorrhea**, which produces a throat infection. Mouth-to-mouth kissing and cunnilingus are less likely to spread gonorrhea.

A gonorrheal infection may also be spread from the penis to the partner's rectum during anal intercourse. Likewise, a cervical gonorrheal infection can be spread to the rectum if an infected woman and her partner follow vaginal intercourse with anal intercourse. Gonorrhea is less likely to be spread by vaginal discharge than by penile discharge.

Gonorrhea is highly contagious. Women stand nearly a 50% chance of contracting gonorrhea after one exposure. Men have a 25% risk of infection (Hatcher et al., 2011). The risks to women are apparently greater because women retain infected semen in the vagina. The risk of infection increases with repeated exposure.

SYMPTOMS   Some men experience symptoms within two to five days of infection. Symptoms include a penile discharge that's clear at first (see Figure 14.2) and turns yellow to yellow-green, thickens, and becomes pus-like within a day or two. The urethra becomes inflamed, and urination is accompanied by a burning sensation. About 30% to 40% of males have swelling and tenderness in the lymph glands of the groin.

The initial symptoms usually abate within a few weeks without treatment, leading people to think gonorrhea is no worse than a bad cold. However, the gonococcus bacterium usually continues to damage the body even if the early symptoms fade. If left untreated, inflammation and other symptoms may become chronic.

The primary site of infection in women is the cervix, where gonorrhea causes **cervicitis**. This results in a yellowish to yellow-green, pus-like discharge that irritates the vulva. If the infection spreads to the urethra, women may also note burning urination. About 80% of women who contract gonorrhea have no symptoms during the early stages of the infection. Because many don't seek treatment until symptoms develop, they may unknowingly infect other sex partners.

When gonorrhea isn't treated early, it may spread through the urogenital systems in both men and women, striking the internal reproductive organs. In men, it can lead to **epididymitis**, which can cause fertility problems. Swelling and tenderness or pain in the scrotum are the principal symptoms of epididymitis. Fever may also be present. Occasionally the kidneys are affected.

In women, the bacterium can spread through the cervix to the uterus, fallopian tubes, ovaries, and other parts of the abdominal cavity, causing PID. PID symptoms include cramps, abdominal pain and tenderness, cervical tenderness and discharge, irregular menstrual cycles, pain during intercourse, fever, nausea, and vomiting. PID may also occur without symptoms. Whether or not there are symptoms, it can cause scarring that blocks the fallopian tubes, leading to infertility. PID is a serious illness that requires aggressive treatment with antibiotics. Surgery may be needed, to remove infected tissue. Unfortunately, many women become aware of gonococcal infections only when they develop PID.

These consequences are all the more unfortunate because gonorrhea, when diagnosed and treated early, clears up rapidly more than 90% of the time.

DIAGNOSIS AND TREATMENT   Diagnosis of gonorrhea involves clinical inspection of the genitals by a physician, and culturing and examination of a sample of genital discharge.

Antibiotics are the standard treatment. Penicillin was once the favoured antibiotic, but the rise of penicillin-resistant strains of *Neisseria gonorrhoeae* has required the use of alternate antibiotics (Hatcher et al., 2011). An injection of the antibiotic ceftriaxone is often recommended. Other antibiotics used for treating gonorrhea include ciprofloxacin and ofloxacin.

Because gonorrhea and chlamydia often occur together, people who are infected with gonorrhea are usually also treated for chlamydia with another antibiotic (Hatcher et al., 2011). Sex partners of people with gonorrhea should be examined.

Syphilis

In 1905, the German scientists Fritz Schaudinn and Erich Hoffmann isolated *Treponema pallidum* (*T. pallidum*), the bacterium that causes **syphilis**. Although syphilis isn't as widespread as it used to be, its effects can be extremely harmful, including heart disease, blindness, gross confusion, and death.

TRANSMISSION   Syphilis is most often transmitted by vaginal or anal intercourse or by oral–genital or oral–anal contact with an infected person. The spirochete (bacterium) is usually transmitted when an infected person's open lesions

Figure 14.2   A gonorrheal discharge.
Gonorrhea in the male often causes a thick, yellowish, pus-like discharge from the penis.

Cervicitis Inflammation of the cervix.

Epididymitis Inflammation of the epididymis.

Syphilis An STI caused by the *Treponema pallidum* bacterium. It may progress through several stages of development, often from a chancre to a skin rash to damage to the cardiovascular or central nervous system.

Chancre A sore or ulcer.

Congenital syphilis A syphilis infection that's present at birth.

come into contact with the mucous membranes or skin abrasions of the partner's body during sexual activity. The chance of contracting syphilis from one sexual contact is estimated at one in three. Syphilis can also be contracted by touching an infectious **chancre**, but not by using the same toilet seat as an infected person.

Pregnant women can transmit syphilis to their fetuses, because the spirochete crosses the placental membrane. Miscarriage, stillbirth, or **congenital syphilis** may result. Congenital syphilis can impair vision and hearing and deform bones and teeth. Blood tests are administered routinely during pregnancy to diagnose syphilis in the mother, so congenital problems can be prevented in the baby.

SYMPTOMS   Syphilis develops through several stages. In the first stage, or primary stage, two to four weeks after contact, a painless chancre—a hard, round, ulcer-like lesion with raised edges—appears at the infection site. When a woman is infected, the chancre usually forms on the vaginal walls or the cervix. It may also form on the external genitalia, most often on the labia. When a man is infected, the chancre usually forms on the penile glans. It may also form on the scrotum or the penile shaft. If the mode of transmission is oral sex, the chancre may appear on the lips or tongue (see Figure 14.3). If the infection is spread by anal sex, the chancre may appear in the rectum. The chancre disappears within a few weeks, but if the infection remains untreated, syphilis will continue to work within the body.

The secondary stage begins a few weeks to a few months later. A skin rash develops, consisting of painless, reddish, raised bumps that eventually darken and burst, oozing a discharge. Other symptoms include sores in the mouth, painful swelling in the joints, a sore throat, headaches, and fever. A person with syphilis may thus wrongly assume that s/he has the flu.

These symptoms also disappear. Syphilis then enters the latent stage, in which it may lie dormant for one to 40 years. But spirochetes continue to multiply and burrow into the circulatory system, central nervous system (brain and spinal cord), and bones. The person may no longer be contagious to sex partners after several years, but a pregnant woman can still transmit the infection to her newborn during delivery.

In many cases, the disease eventually progresses to the late stage, or tertiary stage. A large ulcer may form on the skin, muscle tissue, digestive organs, lungs, liver, and other organs. This destructive ulcer can often be successfully treated, but still more serious damage can occur as the infection attacks the central nervous system or the cardiovascular system (the heart and the major blood vessels). Either outcome can be fatal.

The primary and secondary symptoms of syphilis inevitably disappear. Infected people may therefore be tempted to believe they're no longer at risk, and fail to see their doctors. This is unfortunate, because failure to eradicate the infection through proper treatment can eventually lead to dire consequences.

DIAGNOSIS AND TREATMENT   Primary-stage syphilis is diagnosed by clinical examination. If a chancre is found, fluid drawn from it can be examined under a microscope. The spirochetes are usually quite visible. Blood tests are not definitive until the secondary stage begins.

Penicillin is the treatment of choice for syphilis, although people allergic to

Figure 14.3   A syphilitic chancre.
The primary stage of a syphilis infection is marked by the appearance of a painless sore, or chancre, at the infection site.

penicillin can use doxycycline and some other antibiotics (Hatcher et al., 2011). Sex partners of individuals infected with syphilis should be evaluated by physicians.

Vaginal Infections

Vaginitis is any kind of vaginal infection or inflammation. Women with vaginitis may encounter genital irritation or itching and burning during urination, but the most common symptom is an odorous discharge.

Most cases of vaginitis are caused by organisms that reside in the vagina or by sexually transmitted organisms. Organisms that reside in the vagina may overgrow and cause symptoms when the environmental balance of the vagina is upset by such factors as birth control pills, antibiotics, dietary changes, excessive douching, nylon underwear, or pantyhose. (See Chapter 3 for suggestions about reducing the risk of vaginitis.) Other cases are caused by sensitivities or allergic reactions to various chemicals.

The great majority of vaginal infections involve bacterial vaginosis, candidiasis (commonly called a yeast infection), or trichomoniasis. The microbes that cause vaginal infections in women can also infect men's urethral tracts. A "vaginal infection" can therefore be passed back and forth between sex partners.

Bacterial Vaginosis

Bacterial vaginosis (BV) is most often caused by overgrowth of the bacterium *Gardnerella vaginalis*. The bacterium is transmitted primarily through sexual contact. The most characteristic symptom is a thin, foul-smelling vaginal discharge, but infected women often have no symptoms. Diagnosis requires culturing the bacterium in the laboratory.

Besides causing troublesome symptoms in some cases, BV may increase the risk of various gynecological problems, including infections of the reproductive tract. Oral treatments are recommended and effective in most cases. Topical treatments are also effective. Recurrences are common, however.

Questions remain about whether the male partner should also be treated. The bacterium can usually be found in the urethras of symptom-free males.

Candidiasis

Also known as moniliasis, thrush, or (most often) a yeast infection, **candidiasis** is caused by a yeast-like fungus called *Candida albicans*. Candidiasis commonly produces soreness, inflammation, and intense (sometimes maddening!) itching around the vulva, accompanied by a thick, white, curd-like vaginal discharge (see Figure 14.4). Yeast infections can also occur in the mouth in both men and women, and in the penis in men.

Yeast generally produces no symptoms when the vaginal environment is normal. Infections most often arise from changes in the vaginal environment that allow the fungus to overgrow. Antibiotics, birth-control pills, intrauterine devices, pregnancy, and diabetes may alter the vaginal balance, allowing the fungus that causes yeast infections to grow to infectious levels. Nylon underwear and tight, restrictive, poorly ventilated clothing may also set the stage for a yeast infection.

Although most cases aren't the result of sexual transmission, candidiasis can be passed back and forth between sex partners

Vaginitis Any type of vaginal infection or inflammation.

Bacterial vaginosis (BV) A form of vaginitis usually caused by the *Gardnerella vaginalis* bacterium.

Candidiasis A form of vaginitis caused by a yeast-like fungus called *Candida albicans*.

Figure 14.4 Candidiasis.
A yeast infection causes soreness, inflammation, and itching around the vulva that's accompanied by a thick, white vaginal discharge.

through vaginal intercourse. It can also be passed back and forth between the mouth and the genitals through oral–genital contact, and can infect the anus through anal intercourse. Most infections in women are believed to be caused by an overgrowth of the yeast normally found in the vagina. Still, it's advisable to evaluate both partners simultaneously. Whereas most men with *Candida* have no symptoms, some may develop NGU or a genital thrush accompanied by itching and burning during urination, or reddening of the penis. Candidiasis can also be transmitted by nonsexual means, such as between women who share a washcloth.

At least half of adult women will experience at least one episode of candidiasis in their lifetimes, and about 25% of women have recurrent infections. Recommended treatments include vaginal suppositories or creams (Hatcher et al., 2011), many of which are sold over the counter. Women with vaginal complaints should consult their physicians before taking any of these medications, to ensure that they receive the proper diagnosis and treatment.

Trichomoniasis

Trichomoniasis A form of vaginitis caused by the protozoan *Trichomonas vaginalis*.

Trichomoniasis ("trich") is caused by *Trichomonas vaginalis*, a single-celled parasite. It's the most common parasitic STI. Symptoms in women include burning or itching in the vulva, mild pain during urination or intercourse, and an odorous, foamy, whitish to yellowish-green discharge. Many women notice that symptoms appear or worsen during, or just after, their menstrual periods. Trichomoniasis facilitates the transmission of HIV and is linked to the development of tubal adhesions that can result in infertility. Women can be infected with trichomoniasis and have no symptoms.

Unlike candidiasis, trichomoniasis is nearly always sexually transmitted. Because the parasite can survive for several hours on moist surfaces outside the body, trich can be communicated via contact with infected semen or vaginal discharge on towels, washcloths, and bedclothes. This parasite is one of the few disease agents that can be picked up from a toilet seat, but the penis or vulva has to directly touch the seat.

Trichomonas vaginalis can cause NGU in men, and can cause a slight penile discharge that's usually noticeable before first urination in the morning. There may be tingling, itching, and other irritating sensations in the urethral tract. Yet most infected men are symptom-free. They can therefore unwittingly transfer the organism to their sex partners.

Diagnosis is frequently made by microscopic examination of a smear of vaginal fluid in a physician's office. Diagnosis based on examination of cultures grown from the vaginal smear is considered more reliable, however. When both partners are treated simultaneously, the success rate approaches 100% (Hatcher, 2011).

Viral Infections

Viruses are tiny particles of DNA surrounded by protein coatings. They're incapable of reproducing on their own. When they invade a body cell, however, they can direct the cell's own reproductive machinery to spin off new viral particles that spread to other cells, causing infection. In this section we'll discuss several viral STIs: HIV and AIDS, herpes (HSV), viral hepatitis, and human papillomavirus (HPV).

HIV and AIDS

Human immunodeficiency virus (HIV) A sexually transmitted virus that destroys white blood cells in the immune system, leaving the body vulnerable to life-threatening diseases.

Acquired immunodeficiency syndrome (AIDS) A condition caused by the human immunodeficiency virus (HIV) and characterized by destruction of the immune system, stripping the body of its ability to fend off life-threatening diseases.

Human immunodeficiency virus (HIV) is the virus that causes **acquired immunodeficiency syndrome (AIDS)**. HIV attacks and disables the immune system, the body's natural line of defence, stripping it of its ability to fend off disease-causing organisms. AIDS is considered fatal, although many people now live with

HIV/AIDS for many years, thanks to the development of powerful antiviral medications. For people in industrialized nations like Canada, HIV/AIDS may become a chronic but manageable condition, like diabetes. But for many millions in developing nations, where medications are expensive or difficult to deliver, HIV/AIDS may remain a death sentence.

Globally, about 35.3 million people were living with HIV in 2012, 2.3 million new infections occurred, and 1.6 million people died from AIDS-related causes (UNAIDS, 2013). More than 90% of those with HIV live in low- or middle-income countries, particularly in sub-Saharan Africa. In many parts of the world (e.g., Africa), most new HIV infections are transmitted through heterosexual sex, but in some countries, men having sex with men, injection drug use, and sex work are major risk factors.

Figure 14.5 Percentage Distribution of Positive HIV Test Reports Among Males Age 15 and Older by Exposure Category, 2012, Canada

Source: Public Health Agency of Canada. (2013). HIV and AIDS in Canada: Surveillance Report to December 31, 2012. Surveillance and Epidemiology Division, Centre for Communicable Diseases and Infection Control, Public Health Agency of Canada.

CANADIAN HIV TRENDS According to the Public Health Agency of Canada (2013), from 1985 (when HIV testing began) through December 2012, 76 275 people in Canada were diagnosed with HIV (including those with AIDS). The reported number of positive HIV tests remained relatively stable between 2002 and 2008 when there were 2619 cases. However, since 2008, there has been a steady decrease. In 2012, there were 2062 newly diagnosed and reported cases. The number of people in Canada living with HIV (including AIDS) grew from an estimated 57 000 in 2005, to 65 000 in 2008, to 71 300 in 2011. Of these 71 300, it's estimated that 17 825 (25%) were unaware that they were infected (Public Health Agency of Canada, 2013).

As shown in Figure 14.5, the proportion of positive HIV test reports among males age 15 or over in Canada in 2012 was highest for the category "men who have sex with men" (MSM) which accounted for almost two out of every three cases (65%). Heterosexual contact and injection drug use (IDU) accounted for most of the remaining third. The exposure category profile of women testing positive for HIV in Canada looks quite different than it does for men. As indicated in Figure 14.6, nearly three out of every four (73%) HIV test reports for women in Canada in 2012 were categorized as "heterosexual contact," and IDU accounted for about a quarter of cases.

The proportion of new HIV test reports that were among women remained stable at 26% from 2005 to 2008 and decreased slightly to 23% in 2012 (Public Health Agency of Canada, 2013). The number of aboriginal people living with HIV has increased in recent years. The HIV infection rate for aboriginal people is 3.5 times higher than for non-aboriginal populations. A significant proportion of the heterosexual HIV infections originate in countries with high HIV prevalence rates, such as those in Africa. The estimated infection rate for individuals who have immigrated from countries where HIV is endemic is nine times higher than for other Canadians (Public Health Agency of Canada, 2012d).

CANADIAN AIDS TRENDS Between 1979 until the end of 2012, a total of 22 702 cases of AIDS were reported in Canada (Public Health Agency of Canada, 2013). The annual number of new AIDS cases reported peaked in 1993, and has declined steadily since then. A primary reason for this decline was the introduction of highly active

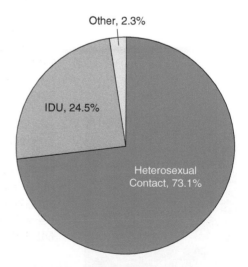

Figure 14.6 Percentage Distribution of Positive HIV Test Reports Among Females Age 15 and Older by Exposure Category, 2012, Canada

Source: Public Health Agency of Canada. (2013). HIV and AIDS in Canada: Surveillance Report to December 31, 2012. Surveillance and Epidemiology Division, Centre for Communicable Diseases and Infection Control, Public Health Agency of Canada.

antiretroviral therapy (HAART) in 1996. In 2012, 172 AIDS cases were reported, representing an 18.1% decrease from 2011 and a 90.6% decrease since 1993, when 1833 AIDS cases were reported (the highest number ever in Canada in a single year).

Immune system The complex of mechanisms the body uses to protect itself from disease-causing agents such as pathogens.

Pathogen An agent, especially a micro-organism, that can cause disease.

Leukocytes White blood cells that are essential to the body's defences against infection.

Antigen A protein, toxin, or other substance to which the body reacts by producing antibodies. The word is formed from "antibody generator."

Antibody A specialized protein that attaches itself to a foreign body, inactivates it, and marks it for destruction.

THE IMMUNE SYSTEM The **immune system** is the body's natural line of defense against disease-causing organisms. The immune system combats disease in a number of ways. It produces white blood cells that envelop and kill **pathogens** such as bacteria, viruses, and fungi, as well as worn-out body cells and cancer cells.

White blood cells are referred to as **leukocytes**. They engage in microscopic warfare, undertaking search-and-destroy missions to identify and eradicate foreign agents and debilitated cells. Leukocytes recognize foreign agents by their surface fragments, which are called **antigens** because the body reacts to their presence by developing specialized proteins, or **antibodies**. Antibodies attach themselves to the foreign agents, inactivate them, and mark them for destruction. HIV infection can therefore be determined by examining blood or saliva for the presence of antibodies to the virus.

Rather than destroying or marking pathogens for destruction, special memory lymphocytes are held in reserve. Memory lymphocytes can remain in the bloodstream for years, forming the basis for a quick immune response if an invader appears a second time.

HIV INFECTION Spikes (technically known as gpl20 spikes) on the surface of HIV allow it to bind to sites on cells in the immune system. Like other viruses, HIV uses the cells it invades to spin off copies of itself. HIV uses an enzyme called reverse transcriptase to cause genes in the attacked cells to make proteins the virus needs for reproduction.

HIV directly attacks the immune system by invading and destroying a type of lymphocyte called the CD4 cell, or helper T cell (see Figure 14.7). The CD4 cell is the quarterback of the immune system. CD4 cells recognize invading pathogens and signal B lymphocytes, or B cells (another kind of white blood cell), to produce antibodies that inactivate and mark the pathogens for annihilation. CD4 cells also signal another class of T cells, called killer T cells, to destroy infected cells. By attacking and destroying helper T cells, HIV disables the very cells which the body relies on for fighting off HIV and other diseases. As HIV cripples the body's defences, the individual is exposed to infections that wouldn't otherwise take hold. Cancer cells might also proliferate. Although the CD4 cells appear to be its main target, HIV also attacks other types of white blood cell.

The blood normally contains about 1000 CD4 cells per cubic millimetre. The number of CD4 cells may remain at about this level for years following HIV infection. Many people show no symptoms, appearing healthy, while CD4 cells remain at this level. Then, for reasons that aren't clearly understood, the CD4 cell level begins to drop off, although symptoms may not appear for a decade or more. As the number of CD4 cells declines, symptoms generally increase, leaving the individual vulnerable to diseases the weakened immune system can't fight off. A person becomes most vulnerable to opportunistic infections when the level of CD4 cells falls below 200 per cubic millimetre.

Bill Longcore/Science Source

Figure 14.7 HIV (the AIDS virus) attacks a white blood cell. HIV progressively weakens the immune system, leaving the body vulnerable to infections and diseases that would otherwise be fended off.

HIV/AIDS PROGRESSION HIV follows a complex course once it enters the body. Shortly after infection, the person may experience mild, flu-like symptoms—fatigue, fever, headaches, muscle pain, lack of appetite, nausea, swollen glands, and possibly a rash. These symptoms usually disappear within a few weeks, and the person may dismiss them as a passing case of flu. Once people enter this symptom-free or carrier state, they generally look and act well, and don't realize they're infectious, so they may unwittingly pass the virus to others.

Most people who are infected with HIV remain symptom-free for years. Some enter a symptomatic state that's typically marked by chronically swollen lymph nodes and intermittent weight loss, fever, fatigue, and diarrhea. This symptomatic state doesn't constitute full-blown AIDS, but it shows that HIV is undermining the integrity of the immune system.

The beginnings of full-blown AIDS are often marked by such symptoms as swollen lymph nodes, fatigue, fever, night sweats, diarrhea, and weight loss that can't be attributed to dieting or exercise.

AIDS is connected with the appearance of diseases such as pneumonia, Kaposi's sarcoma (a form of cancer), toxoplasmosis of the brain (an infection by parasites), and herpes simplex with chronic ulcers. These diseases are termed **opportunistic diseases**, because they're unlikely to emerge unless a disabled immune system provides the opportunity.

Opportunistic diseases Diseases that take hold only when the immune system is weakened and unable to fend them off.

About 10% of people with AIDS have a wasting syndrome. Wasting, the unintentional loss of more than 10% of a person's body weight, is connected with AIDS, some other infections, and cancer. As AIDS progresses, the individual grows thinner and more fatigued. S/he becomes unable to perform ordinary life functions, and falls prey to opportunistic infections.

If left untreated, AIDS nearly always results in death within a few years.

TRANSMISSION   HIV can be transmitted by certain infected bodily fluids—blood, semen, vaginal secretions, and breast milk. The first three of these may enter the body through vaginal, anal, or oral–genital intercourse with an infected partner. HIV can enter the body through tiny cuts or sores in the mucosal lining of the vagina, the rectum, and even the mouth. These cuts or sores can be so tiny that you're unaware of them. Transmission of HIV through kissing—even prolonged or French kissing—is unlikely.

Another avenue of infection is by sharing a hypodermic needle with an infected person. When someone injects drugs, a small amount of his or her blood remains inside the needle and syringe. If s/he's infected with HIV, the virus may be in the blood that remains in the needle and syringe. Others who use the needle inject the infected blood into their bloodstreams. HIV can also be spread by sharing needles used for other purposes, such as injecting steroids, piercing ears, or tattooing.

HIV can be transmitted from mother to fetus during pregnancy, or from mother to child through childbirth or breastfeeding. Transmission is most likely during childbirth. Because of HAART therapy provided to HIV-positive mothers, the number of babies born HIV infected has been dramatically reduced in Canada (Public Health Agency of Canada, 2013).

Male-to-female transmission through vaginal intercourse is about twice as likely as female-to-male transmission, partly because more of the virus is found in ejaculate than in vaginal secretions. A man's ejaculate may also remain for many days in the vagina, providing greater opportunity for infection. Worldwide, male–female sexual intercourse accounts for most HIV/AIDS cases (UNAIDS, 2006).

Male–female and male–male anal intercourse are especially risky, particularly to the recipient, because the

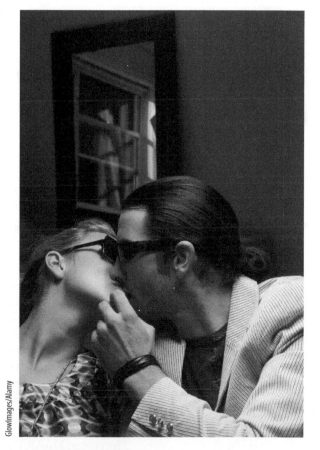

Glowimages/Alamy

Can Kissing Transmit HIV?
HIV is a blood-borne virus that's transmitted via various bodily fluids, including blood, semen, and vaginal fluids. The Centers for Disease Control and Prevention (CDC) has found that HIV does not occur in infectious quantities in saliva.

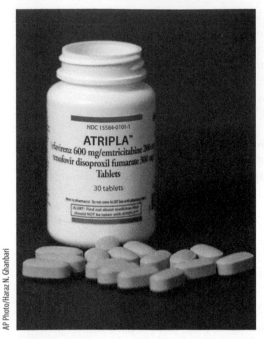

Atripla.
This new three-in-one pill makes it easy to manage the regimen of highly active antiretroviral therapy (HAART). Atripla contains a cocktail of antiviral drugs that have become the standard treatment for HIV/AIDS in developed countries.

Seropositive Having a pathogen or antibodies to that pathogen in the bloodstream.

Seronegative Lacking a pathogen or antibodies to that pathogen in the bloodstream.

Highly active antiretroviral therapy (HAART) A combination of drugs used to treat HIV and AIDS. It's a protease inhibitor combined with a couple of other antiretroviral agents.

rectal tissue often tears or abrades, facilitating the virus's entry into the bloodstream (Chandra et al., 2012).

DIAGNOSIS   The most widely used test for HIV infection is the enzyme-linked immunosorbent assay (ELISA or just EIA for short), which may take up to three weeks to yield results. ELISA doesn't directly detect HIV in the blood. Instead, it reveals HIV antibodies. People may show an antibody response to HIV long before they develop symptoms of infection. A positive (**seropositive**) test result means antibodies have been found, and usually indicates that the person is infected with HIV. A negative (**seronegative**) outcome means antibodies to HIV have not been detected. EIA can be performed on a sample of blood, saliva, or urine.

HIV tests are not considered fully accurate until three months have passed since the person's last exposure to the virus. This is how long the body generally takes to produce antibodies. Some newer EIA tests are able to detect exposure to HIV in 15 to 20 days in most people.

The most significant change in testing procedure has been the development of rapid testing technologies, which allow test results to be provided much sooner after testing than they used to be (within 60 seconds). The tests are administered at the point of care (e.g., a clinic or doctor's office) and must be used under professional supervision with pre- and post-test counselling provided (Public Health Agency of Canada, 2012e).

In a 2011 survey, 49% of Canadians aged 16 and older reported that they had been tested for HIV at least once (Calzavara et al., 2012). In 2014, the government of British Columbia announced it would introduce guidelines for health care providers to encourage all adults in the province to get tested for HIV.

TREATMENT   For many years, researchers were frustrated by their failure to develop effective vaccines and treatments for HIV and AIDS. Work continues on development of a vaccine for HIV, but to date there's still no safe, effective vaccine.

A combination, or "cocktail," of antiviral drugs has become the standard treatment for HIV/AIDS. This combination, referred to as **highly active antiretroviral therapy (HAART)**, decreases the likelihood that HIV will develop resistance to treatment. Research has shown that after a year of HAART treatment, over 80% of people with HIV have no detectable virus in their bloodstreams (DeJesus, 2012). HAART has created hope that AIDS will become increasingly manageable—a chronic health problem, as opposed to a terminal illness. However, the side effects of these medications can be unpleasant, including nausea and, in the case of protease inhibitors, unusual accumulations of fat.

HAART has worked wonders in reducing the death rate from AIDS. For example, HAART has cut the U.S. death rate from HIV/AIDS related causes by about 75% since the mid- to late 1990s (Sherer, 2012). Yet even when HIV has been reduced to levels that are undetectable by ordinary means, scientists have been able to use methods of close scrutiny to locate it in resting (non-replicating) CD4 cells (Lederman & Valdez, 2000). HAART therefore doesn't appear to be a cure. The cost of HAART treatment is high, about $10,000 a year in Canada. The cost is subsidized through Medicare but the extent of the subsidy varies across the country (Hogg, et al., 2012).

PREVENTION   What can we do to curb the spread of HIV and AIDS? Given that we lack both a vaccine and a cure, prevention is our best hope. Our discussion of prevention will focus on sexual transmission, but other efforts have been made to prevent transmission via pregnancy, childbirth, and breastfeeding, shared needles, and blood transfusions. For example, HIV-infected women are advised to avoid breastfeeding. The drug zidovudine, Caesarean section, and other measures decrease the probability of transmission through childbirth (Ricci et al., 2000). And screening of potential blood donors has rendered the probability of transmission via blood transfusion almost negligible.

Canadian researchers have found evidence that HAART is effective in reducing HIV transmission (Hogg et al., 2012; Montaner et al., 2010). Examining data from British Columbia, researchers have found that as the number of HIV-positive individuals taking HAART therapy increases, the number of new HIV infections decreases. This is because HAART reduces levels of HIV in the body, and as a result decreases the likelihood of virus transmission. The findings suggest that making HAART therapy easily accessible and affordable to HIV-positive people can be an important tool in HIV prevention.

Research has shown that taking a daily pill that has one or two antiviral HIV/AIDS drugs prevents many people from becoming infected with HIV (Grady, 2012; McNeil, 2011). The pill called Truvada contains a mix of tenofovir and emtricitabine and was shown in African studies to decrease the likelihood of infection by 63% to 73%. Another pill, Viread, contains tenofovir only, and lowered the probability of infection somewhat less, by 62%. Studies show, however, that only 10% of users take the drug as directed—daily (Grady, 2012).

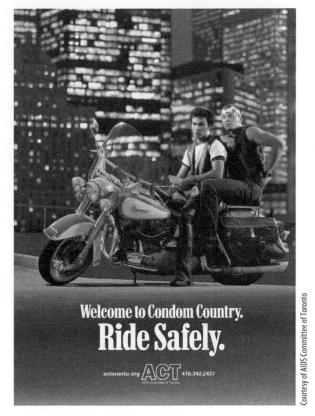

Welcome to Condom Country.
Condom ads based on the ruggedly masculine Marlboro tobacco ads have been used by the AIDS Committee of Toronto during Pride Week to encourage gay men to use condoms.

There's evidence from Africa that male circumcision reduces the risk of HIV acquisition for men. Studies conducted in South Africa, Uganda, and Kenya have found that circumcision reduces HIV infection among heterosexual men by 38% to 66% (Siegfried, Muller, Deeks, & Volmink, 2009).

Most prevention efforts focus on education. According to the World Association for Sexual Health (2008), the success of HIV/AIDS-prevention education in the developing world depends on access to effective education interventions, access to condoms, and adequate funding for prevention programming. To some extent, these same factors apply to the developed world, including Canada. In Canada, HIV/AIDS prevention is often integrated into broader sexual-health education in the schools. (See Chapter 15) Public-health units or agencies and community groups also conduct HIV/AIDS-prevention interventions aimed at higher-risk groups, including men who have sex with men and injection-drug users.

Herpes (HSV)

Genital herpes is an STI caused by the *Herpes simplex* virus. Different types of herpes are caused by variants of the herpes simplex virus. The most common type, **herpes simplex virus, type 1 (HSV-1)**, causes oral herpes, which is characterized by cold sores (fever blisters) on the lips and in the mouth and throat. It can be transmitted to the genitals by the hands or by oral–genital contact. **Genital herpes** is usually caused by a related but distinct virus, the **herpes simplex virus, type 2 (HSV-2)**, which produces painful, shallow sores and blisters on the genitals. HSV-2 can be transferred to the mouth through oral–genital contact. Both types of herpes

Herpes simplex virus, type 1 (HSV-1) The virus that causes oral herpes, which is characterized by cold sores (fever blisters) on the lips and in the mouth and throat.

Genital herpes An STI usually caused by the herpes simplex virus, type 2. It's characterized by painful, shallow sores and blisters on the genitals.

Herpes simplex virus, type 2 (HSV-2) The virus that causes most cases of genital herpes.

can be transmitted sexually. Herpes is a chronic infection, which means the virus remains in the body for life.

Genital herpes is a very common STI—likely much more common than most people assume. Data from the *Canadian Health Measures Survey* indicates that 13.6% of Canadians aged 14 to 59 have HSV-2 (Rotermann et al., 2013). The prevalence of HSV-2 was higher among women than men (16.1% versus 11%) and lower among Canadians aged 14 to 34 (6.1%) compared to those aged 35 to 49 (19.1%).

Approximately 60% of genital herpes infections are asymptomatic—that is, they have no observable signs or symptoms (Public Health Agency of Canada, 2008). In the *Canadian Health Measures Survey*, the vast majority of people with HSV-2 were unaware that they had the virus (Rotermann et al., 2013). People with asymptomatic infections can transmit the virus to others.

People with symptoms experience recurrent outbreaks that often happen at the worst times, such as around final exams. This isn't just bad luck—stress can depress the immune system and heighten the likelihood of an outbreak. Outbreaks can continue to recur, sometimes with annoying frequency. On the other hand, some people have no recurrences. Still others have mild, brief recurrences that become less frequent over time.

TRANSMISSION Herpes can be transmitted through oral, anal, or vaginal sexual activity with an infected person. The herpes viruses can also survive for several hours on toilet seats and other objects, where they can be picked up by direct contact. Oral herpes is easily contracted by drinking from the same cup as an infected person, by kissing, and even by sharing towels. But genital herpes is generally spread by vaginal intercourse or by oral or anal sex.

Many people don't realize they're infected, so they unknowingly transmit the virus through sexual contact. Many of those who know they're infected don't realize they can pass the virus along even when they don't have noticeable outbreaks (Wald et al., 1995). Although genital herpes is most contagious during active flare-ups, it can also be transmitted when an infected partner has no symptoms (genital sores or feelings of burning or itching in the genitals). Any intimate contact with an infected person carries some risk of transmission, even if the infected person never has another outbreak. People may also be infected with the virus and have no outbreaks, yet pass the virus along to others.

Herpes can be spread from one part of the body to another by touching. One potentially serious result is a herpes infection of the eye, called **ocular herpes**. Thorough washing with soap and water after touching an infected area may reduce the risk of spreading the infection to other parts of the body.

Research has shown that consistent condom use reduces the risk of transmission of HSV-2 (Martin et al., 2009). However, herpes lesions can occur on skin that's not covered by condoms, so condom effectiveness is limited.

Women with genital herpes are more likely to have miscarriages than women in the general population. Passage through the birth canals of infected mothers can infect babies with genital herpes, damaging or killing them. Obstetricians thus often perform Caesarean sections if mothers have active lesions or **prodromal symptoms** at the time of delivery.

SYMPTOMS Genital lesions or sores appear about six to eight days after infection with genital herpes. At first they appear as reddish, painful bumps, or papules, along the penis or vulva. (See Figure 14.8.) They may also appear on the thighs or buttocks, in the vagina, or on the cervix.

These papules turn into groups of small blisters that are filled with fluid containing infectious viral particles. The blisters are attacked by the body's immune system (white blood cells). They fill with pus, burst, and become extremely painful, shallow sores (ulcers) surrounded by red rings. People are especially infectious during such

Ocular herpes A herpes infection of the eye, usually caused by touching an infected area of the body and then touching the eye.

Prodromal symptoms Warning symptoms that signal the onset or flare-up of a disease.

outbreaks, because the ulcers shed millions of viral particles. Other symptoms may include headaches and muscle aches, swollen lymph glands, fever, burning urination, and vaginal discharge.

The blisters crust over and heal in one to three weeks. Internal sores in the vagina or on the cervix may take 10 days longer than external (labial) sores to heal. Physicians therefore advise infected women to avoid unprotected intercourse for at least 10 days after the external sores heal.

Although the symptoms disappear, the disease doesn't. The virus remains in the body permanently, burrowing into nerve cells in the base of the spine, where it may lie dormant for years or for a lifetime. The infected person is least contagious during this dormant stage. For reasons that remain unclear, in most cases the virus becomes reactivated and gives rise to recurrences.

Recurrences may be related to infections (such as a cold), stress, fatigue, depression, exposure to the sun, and hormonal changes such as those that occur during pregnancy or menstruation. Recurrences tend to occur within three to 12 months of the initial episode, and affect the same parts of the body.

The symptoms of oral herpes include sores and blisters on the lips, inside the mouth, on the tongue, and in the throat. The person may experience fever and feelings of illness, as well as swollen, reddened gums. The sores heal over in about two weeks, and the virus retreats into nerve cells at the base of the neck, where it lies dormant between flare-ups.

John F. Wilson, MD./Science Source

Figure 14.8 **A herpes lesion on the male genitals.** Herpes lesions or sores can appear on the genitals in both men and women. In contrast to the syphilis chancre, they can be quite painful. Herpes is most likely to be transmitted during outbreaks of the disease (when the sores are present, that is), but it can also be transmitted at other times.

DIAGNOSIS AND TREATMENT Genital herpes is first diagnosed by clinical inspection of herpetic sores or ulcers in the mouth or on the genitals. A sample of fluid may be taken from the base of a genital sore, and cultured in the laboratory, to detect the growth of the virus.

Viruses, unlike the bacteria that cause gonorrhea or syphilis, do not respond to antibiotics. Antiviral drugs such as acyclovir (brand name Zovirax), famciclovir, and valacyclovir can relieve pain, speed healing, and reduce the duration of viral shedding (Hatcher et al., 2011). Acyclovir can be applied directly to the sores in ointment form but must be taken orally, in pill form, to help combat internal lesions in the vagina or on the cervix. Oral administration of antiviral drugs may reduce the severity of the initial episode and, if taken regularly, the frequency and duration of recurrent outbreaks (Hatcher et al., 2011). Warm baths, loosely fitting clothing, aspirin, and cold, wet compresses may relieve pain during flare-ups. People with herpes are advised to maintain regular sleeping habits and learn to manage stress.

There's no safe, effective vaccine for genital herpes, but clinical trials of experimental vaccines are underway (National Institute of Allergy and Infectious Diseases, 2009).

COPING WITH GENITAL HERPES The psychological impact of herpes can be more distressing than its physical effects. The prospect of a lifetime of recurrences and concern about infecting sex partners exacerbate the emotional impact of herpes. However, most people with herpes learn to cope with the infection, and with adjustments, are able to establish and maintain satisfying intimate relationships. Some are helped by support groups that share ways to live with the infection. A caring, trusting partner is important.

The attitudes of people with herpes affect their success in adjusting to it. People who view herpes as a manageable condition, not as a medical disaster or a character deficit, find it easier to adjust.

Viral Hepatitis

Hepatitis An inflammation of the liver.

Hepatitis is an inflammation of the liver that may be caused by such factors as chronic alcoholism and exposure to toxic substances. Viral hepatitis includes several types of hepatitis caused by related but distinct viruses. The major types are hepatitis A, hepatitis B, hepatitis C, and hepatitis D.

Jaundice A yellowish discoloration of the skin and the whites of the eyes.

Most people with acute hepatitis have no symptoms. When symptoms do appear, they often include **jaundice**, feelings of weakness and nausea, loss of appetite, abdominal discomfort, whitish bowel movements, and brownish or tea-coloured urine. The symptoms of hepatitis B tend to be more severe and long-lasting than those of hepatitis A or C. In about 10% of cases, hepatitis B leads to chronic liver disease. Hepatitis C tends to have milder symptoms, but often leads to chronic liver diseases such as cirrhosis and cancer of the liver. Hepatitis D occurs only in the presence of hepatitis B. It has symptoms similar to those of hepatitis B, can produce severe liver damage, and often leads to death.

The hepatitis A virus is transmitted through contact with infected fecal matter in contaminated food or water, and by oral contact with fecal matter, such as through oral–anal sexual activity (licking or mouthing the partner's anus). It's largely because of the risk of hepatitis A that restaurant employees are required to wash their hands after using the toilet. Ingesting uncooked infested shellfish is also a frequent means of transmission for hepatitis A.

Hepatitis B can be transmitted through anal, vaginal, or oral intercourse with an infected partner; transfusion with contaminated blood supplies; sharing of contaminated needles or syringes; and contact with contaminated saliva, menstrual blood, nasal mucus, or semen. Sharing razors, toothbrushes, and other personal articles with an infected person can also transmit hepatitis B.

Hepatitis C and hepatitis D can be transmitted sexually or through contact with contaminated blood. Hepatitis D can occur only if hepatitis B is present (Hatcher et al., 2011). People can transmit the viruses that cause hepatitis even if they're unaware that they have the disease.

In Canada, infection rates for hepatitis A and B declined significantly during the 1990s. Today the incidence of hepatitis B is about 2.3 per 100 000, and twice as high in men as in women (Public Health Agency of Canada, 2008). The rate for hepatitis C has been increasing.

Hepatitis is usually diagnosed by testing blood samples for the presence of hepatitis antigens and antibodies. There's no cure for viral hepatitis. Bed rest and fluids are usually recommended until the acute stage of the infection subsides, generally in a few weeks. Full recovery may take months. A vaccine provides protection against hepatitis B and D (Hatcher et al, 2011).

Human Papillomavirus (HPV)

The human papillomavirus (HPV) is the most common STI. It's estimated that about 70% of adult Canadians will have at least one HPV infection in their lifetimes (Public Health Agency of Canada, 2008). Studies of university students in Canada has reported HPV rates of 29% to 50% (Burchell et al., 2010; Richardson et al., 2003).

Most HPV infections are asymptomatic and harmless. In up to 90% of cases, the body's immune system clears up the infection within two years (Centers for Disease Control and Prevention, 2007).

Genital warts An STI caused by the human papillomavirus. It takes the form of warts around the genitals and anus.

There are many different subtypes of HPV. Some, such as types 6 and 11, cause genital warts. Others, such as types 16 and 18, which don't cause **genital warts**, can eventually lead to cervical cancer if they persist undetected for a number of years. The Pap test is designed to detect abnormal changes in the cervix caused by HPV infection, so Pap tests can reduce women's chances of developing cervical cancer

(Public Health Agency of Canada, 2008). HPV is also associated with penile cancer in men, as well as some cases of oral cancer.

It bears repeating that HPV infection is extremely common, usually resolves on its own, and only in rare instances progresses to cancer. In most cases, the cancer can be effectively treated, especially if it's detected early (Barrett, 2006).

TRANSMISSION   Vaginal and anal intercourse are the most common means of HPV transmission. Oral sex can also transmit HPV (Wright, 2009), and other types of skin-to-skin contact with infected areas can transmit HPV.

Because HPV is so common, reducing the risk of infection is difficult, especially for people who are sexually active. Abstaining from sexual activity is clearly one way a person can avoid HPV infection. While condoms cannot protect against transmission of HPV to and from genital areas not covered by a condom, studies have indicated that that consistent condom use reduces the risk of HPV infection (Hariri & Warner, 2013; Winer et al., 2006).

Some types of HPV can result in genital warts, which vary in size and shape. Genital warts can be hard and yellow-grey when they form on dry skin, or they can take on a pink, soft, cauliflower appearance in moist areas such as the lower vagina. (See Figure 14.9.) In men, they appear on the penis, foreskin, and scrotum and in the urethra. In women, they appear on the vulva, along the vaginal wall, and on the cervix. They can also occur outside the genital area—for example, in the mouth; on the lips, eyelids, or nipples; around the anus; and in the rectum. The incubation period from time of infection to appearance of the warts can range from a few weeks to more than a year.

There are several treatments for genital warts. Cryotherapy, or freezing the warts with liquid nitrogen, is a preferred treatment. Another treatment involves painting or coating the warts over several days with an alcohol-based podophyllin solution, gel, or cream, which causes the warts to dry up and fall off (Hatcher et al., 2011). The warts can also be treated by a doctor, who may burn them off with electrodes or remove them by laser or conventional surgery. Unfortunately, removing the warts doesn't rid the body of the virus (Hatcher et al., 2011), and there may be recurrences. Eventually, the warts will clear up. People with active warts should probably avoid sexual contact until the warts are removed and the area heals completely.

VACCINE   The most recent advance in the fight against STIs has been the development of a vaccine that immunizes against HPV strains 6, 11, 16, and 18. These strains are responsible for 90% of genital warts and 70% of cases of cervical cancer. The vaccine Gardasil was approved in Canada for females between the ages of nine and 26 in 2006, and more recently for males of the same age (Public Health Agency of Canada, 2010). Another HPV vaccine called Cervarix has recently been approved for use in Canada. The main target for the vaccine are females who haven't yet been sexually active and thus have never had HPV infections. Three injections of the vaccine are required over a six-month period.

All provinces and territories in Canada have implemented publicly funded school vaccine programs to lower cervical risk for women, but acceptance of the HPV vaccine hasn't been universal. Some have questioned whether a large-scale HPV vaccination program is appropriate, given that cervical cancer is relatively rare in Canada and Pap tests are an effective method of screening (Lippman et al., 2007). Some parents and religious groups have opposed the vaccine, fearing that it might encourage promiscuity.

Figure 14.9   Genital warts. Genital warts are caused by the human papilloma virus (HPV) and may have a cauliflower-like appearance. Many cases occur where they remain visually undetected. HPV is implicated in cervical cancer.

Ectoparasitic Infestations

Ectoparasites live on the outer surfaces of animals. They're larger than the agents that cause other STIs. In this section, we'll consider two types of STIs caused by ectoparasites—pediculosis and scabies.

Ectoparasite A parasite that lives on the outer surface of an animal.

A World of Diversity

A SCHOOL-BASED HIV PREVENTION EDUCATION PROGRAM FOR YOUTH IN KENYA

Eleanor Maticka-Tyndale (2007) of the University of Windsor led an international group of researchers in developing and evaluating a primary-school-based HIV-prevention program in Kenya. They used a quasi-experimental research procedure, along with both quantitative and qualitative research methods. They compared the effects in 40 schools that received the educational HIV-prevention program with the effects in 40 schools that didn't receive the program.

The research showed that the educational program had a significant impact on 11- to 16-year-olds. These students learned about HIV prevention and how to communicate more openly about HIV. The effects on behaviour were gender-specific: the girls delayed engaging in sexual activities, and the boys used condoms more frequently. The educational program had its greatest impact on youth who weren't yet sexually active. The researchers therefore concluded that it should be implemented with the youngest age groups possible (Maticka-Tyndale et al., 2007).

In a follow-up study, the researchers found that the positive impact of the program delivered during primary school continued when the students had moved on to secondary school (Maticka-Tyndale, 2010). That is, students who had received the program in primary school were more likely than those who had not to practice safer sex and get tested for HIV when they attended secondary school.

Pediculosis

Pediculosis An infestation of pubic lice.

Pediculosis is the name given to an infestation of a parasite whose proper Latin name, *Phthirus pubis*, sounds rather too dignified for these bothersome creatures. Their common name is pubic lice, but they're commonly called crabs, because that's what they look like under the microscope. (See Figure 14.10.)

In the adult stage, pubic lice are large enough to be seen with the naked eye. They're spread sexually, and can also be transmitted via contact with infested towels, sheets, and—yes—toilet seats. They can survive for only about 24 hours without a human host, but they may deposit eggs that can take up to seven days to hatch in bedding and towels. All bedding, towels, and clothes that have been used by an infested person must be dry cleaned or washed in hot water and dried on the hot cycle, to ensure that they're safe.

Scabies A parasitic infestation by a tiny mite that may be transmitted through sexual contact or contact with infested fabrics.

Fingers may also transmit the lice from the genitals to other hair-covered parts of the body, including the scalp and armpits. Sexual contact should be avoided until the infestation is eradicated.

Itching that ranges from mildly irritating to intolerable is the most prominent symptom of an infestation of pubic lice. The itching is caused by the crabs' attaching themselves to the pubic hair and piercing the skin to feed on the blood of their hosts. An infestation can be effectively treated with medication.

E. Gray/Science Source

Figure 14.10 Pubic lice. Pediculosis is an infestation of pubic lice (*Phthirus pubis*). Pubic lice are commonly called crabs, because of their appearance under a microscope.

Scabies

Scabies (*Sarcoptes scabiei*) is a parasitic infestation by a tiny mite that may be transmitted through sexual contact or contact with infested clothing, bed linens, towels, and other fabrics. The mites attach themselves to the base of the pubic hair and burrow into the skin, where they lay eggs and subsist for the duration of their 30-day life spans.

Like pubic lice, scabies are often found in the genital region, where they cause itching and discomfort. They're responsible for reddish lines (created by burrowing), sores, welts, and blisters on the skin. Unlike lice, they're too tiny to be seen with the naked eye. Diagnosis is made by detecting the mite or its by-products via microscopic examination of scrapings from suspicious-looking areas of skin. Scabies are most often found on the hands and wrists, but they may also appear on the genitals, buttocks, armpits, and feet.

Scabies, like pubic lice, can be effectively treated with medication. To avoid reinfection, sex partners and others in close bodily contact with infected individuals should also be treated. Clothing and bed linens used by an infested person must be dry-cleaned or washed and dried on the hot cycle. Sexual contact should be avoided until the infestation is eliminated.

STI Epidemiology: Biological, Psychological, and Social Factors

Despite advances in medical knowledge about the biology of STIs and HIV/AIDS, and extensive research on how they spread through the population, these infections are still common in Canada and around the world. Why?

One obvious answer is that too many people are unaware of their own personal risks for STIs and HIV, and therefore engage in high-risk behaviours. At a basic level, this is undoubtedly true. Many people lack a basic knowledge of STIs and HIV, and are unaware that they're at risk. To fully understand why it's so difficult to eliminate these infections, however, we need to examine several important factors that drive the spread of STIs and HIV.

At the beginning of this book, we emphasized the importance of a multidisciplinary approach to understanding human sexuality. You may recall that we need to account for the biological, psychological, and social factors that shape our sexuality. This multidisciplinary approach helps us more fully understand how STIs and HIV spread within the population.

Biological Factors

MULTIPLE MEANS OF TRANSMISSION   STIs and HIV can be transmitted in multiple ways. These include high-risk sexual behaviours, such as unprotected penile–vaginal and penile–anal intercourse. Oral sex is another form of potential transmission. For STIs such as herpes and the human papillomavirus, transmission can occur through skin-to-skin contact with an infected area. STIs and HIV can also be spread in nonsexual ways. Sharing contaminated needles for injecting drugs is one of the most common ways of transmitting HIV. Using contaminated needles for tattooing can also transmit HIV and hepatitis. Some infections, such as HIV and HSV, can be transmitted from an infected mother to her infant, in the womb or during birth.

LIFELONG INFECTIONS   Among the most effective ways to reduce the spread of STIs and HIV are effective treatments and cures. Although medical science has made progress in developing treatments, some viral infections are lifelong. Once a person has been infected with HSV, for example, the virus will stay in the body for life.

There are now more effective treatments to manage the symptoms, and in some cases to reduce the chances of transmitting these infections. But because they can't be cured, it's more difficult to control the spread of these infections in the population.

ASYMPTOMATIC CASES   Many people who become infected with STIs have no observable symptoms. These cases are referred to as asymptomatic. The symptoms may never show up, or there may be time lags between the infections and the appearance of symptoms.

CRITICAL THINKING QUESTIONS

Are you surprised to learn that so many cases of STI are asymptomatic? Does this change the way you think about how STIs spread?

Because many are asymptomatic, people with HIV, HSV, HPV, chlamydia, and other STIs often don't know they're infected. These people are unlikely to get treatment or take preventive measures, such as using condoms. This is a key biological factor that facilitates the spread of these infections.

INCREASED VULNERABILITY   STIs that produce genital ulcers, such as syphilis and genital herpes, heighten vulnerability to HIV infection by allowing other viruses to enter the circulatory system through the ulcers. Some STIs, such as gonorrhea, trichomoniasis, and chlamydia, can inflame the genital region, which heightens the risk of sexual transmission of other STIs.

GENDER   Women are more susceptible to STI infection than men. The warm, moist environment of the vagina is more hospitable to bacteria, viruses, and fungi than is the exterior of the penis. The location of the urethra and bladder in women also makes them more susceptible to infection.

LACK OF VACCINES AND CURES   It has been very difficult to develop vaccines to prevent STIs. The HIV virus has been especially resistant to vaccines. Fortunately, an effective vaccine has recently been developed that prevents many strains of HPV. There's also a vaccine being developed that appears to be successful in preventing herpes infections.

Psychological Factors

A number of psychological factors predict sexual risk-taking. These include perceived low risks of infection, the myth of personal invulnerability, lack of awareness of a partner's infection, negative attitudes toward condoms, drug and alcohol abuse, and difficulty discussing sexual-health issues.

PERCEIVED LOW RISK   One of the major stumbling blocks in promoting safer-sex practices such as condom use is the fact that many people perceive themselves at low risk for contracting STIs and HIV. For example, Langille and Steenback (2013) at Dalhousie University conducted an online survey and found only 14% of Halifax university students with two to five sex partners in the previous year and who did not use a condom at last intercourse rated themselves as being at high risk. In a study of over 10 000 young adults in the United States, of those with a current or recent bacterial STI, 71% indicated that they were at low risk for STI (Kaestle & Walker, 2011). Research suggests that many youth and young adults significantly underestimate their risk for STI and, as a result, do not prioritize consistent condom use (Pollack, Boyer, & Weinstein, 2013).

Gay men may also operate under an "I'm not the type" fallacy, underestimating their personal risks. In a survey of men who have sex with men across Canada, although 75% of the men reported that they had been tested for HIV, 74% of the those who had never had an HIV test said it was because they believed they were at low risk of infection (Myers et al., 2013).

LACK OF COMMUNICATION   Many people are embarrassed about asking partners about their past risk behaviours and their STI or HIV status. And people who have engaged in high-risk behaviours or contracted STIs or HIV may be uncomfortable about revealing this information, because they fear their partners will refuse to have sex or end the relationships. In other cases, people may not feel empowered enough in their relationships to assertively communicate about the need to practice safer sex. Promoting and facilitating an increased level of sexual communication and condom use negotiation skills can be an important element of effective STI/HIV prevention programs (Sales et al., 2012).

In a University of Guelph study of communication about sexual-health issues such as HIV and pregnancy prevention, female students typically reported that they didn't discuss these issues prior to engaging in sexual intercourse for the first time with new partners (Cleary et al., 2002). Generally, the women reported feeling uncomfortable about initiating discussions about sexual-health topics and sensed that their partners were also uncomfortable.

An emerging issue is the question of whether people with HIV have a legal obligation to inform their sexual partners of their status before having sex. Currently, in Canada, HIV-positive individuals who are aware of their status and don't inform their partners or take measures to prevent infection are committing criminal acts. There have been more than 60 criminal convictions related to HIV transmission, including one for murder (Picard, 2010). There are different perspectives on this issue among HIV/AIDS specialists in Canada. Some argue that criminally prosecuting people who knowingly transmit HIV is a valid approach (Berger, 2009), while others argue that these types of laws discourage people from getting tested for HIV, because someone who doesn't know s/he's infected can't be prosecuted (Wainberg, 2009).

PSYCHOLOGICAL OBSTACLES TO CONDOM USE   Effectively promoting the consistent use of latex condoms may be the most important factor in reducing the burden of STIs and HIV in Canada. Yet many Canadians who are at risk don't use condoms.

A recent national survey found that condoms are the most popular method of contraception among Canadian women, especially younger women (Black et al., 2009). When the survey was taken, 74.3% of 15- to 19-year-olds, 55.5% of 20- to 29-year-olds, 48.8% of 30- to 39-year-olds, and 42.5% of women over 40 who'd had vaginal intercourse in the previous six months said they'd used condoms for contraception. Notice that the percentage of people who use condoms declines with age; sexually active teens are those most likely to use condoms.

Analyzing data from the Canadian Community Health Survey, Rotermann and McKay (2009) found that among unmarried, non-cohabiting 20- to 34-year-old Canadians, 35.8% had had more than one intercourse partner during the previous 12 months, while about 30% of the males and nearly 40% of the females who'd had three or four partners during the previous year hadn't used condoms at last intercourse.

There are a number of explanations for why Canadians at risk for STIs and HIV don't use condoms. Some we've already discussed, such as perceived low risk for infection. As adolescents get older and form longer-term relationships, some switch from condoms to the pill. Although birth-control pills are reliable methods of contraception, they don't prevent STIs. After examining data from the Canadian Contraception Study, Fisher et al. (2004) concluded that many young women were using the condom first and foremost as a method of birth control, not as a method of STI/HIV prevention, and were therefore unconcerned about switching to the pill. In many cases, this also speaks to their low perceived risk for infection. A more recent study of Canadian university students confirms that decision-making related to condom use or nonuse tends to be related to contraception rather than STIs (Milhausen et al., 2013).

Researchers at Okanagan University College in British Columbia have found that young people in monogamous relationships don't use condoms because they're in love and trust their partners to be faithful (Netting & Burnett, 2004). In the Canadian Contraception Study, 47% of the women who'd reduced or discontinued their condom use gave the reason "I have only one sexual partner," and 46% said "I know and trust my husband or partner" (Fisher et al., 2004). While many of these women may have been correct in their assessments, if their known, trusted partners had unknown asymptomatic STI or HIV infections from previous relationships, their discontinuation of condom use resulted in high risks for infection.

CRITICAL THINKING QUESTIONS

In your opinion, what's the most important obstacle to condom use among sexually active college and university students?

It has also been found that the more in love a woman is with her partner, the more strongly she believes she's not at risk for getting an STI from him (Knäuper et al., 2002). Rupert Klein and Bärbel Knäuper (2002) at McGill University have found that female university students believe condom use signifies lack of commitment and trust in their relationships. These studies, and many others, indicate that one of the most significant obstacles to condom use involves the dynamics of a couple relationship.

Other obstacles to condom use are more practical. Some people, including university students, feel embarrassed about buying them (Ronis & LeBouthillier, 2013). Some feel that interrupting the sexual act to apply a condom reduces spontaneity. Some men and women say condoms reduce sexual pleasure. In an Ontario study (Adam et al., 2005), gay and bisexual men gave the following reasons for not using condoms:

- Fear of erection loss.
- Urgency of passion overcoming fear of infection.
- Stress and depression overcoming rational prevention.
- Low self-esteem, leading to indifference about consequences.
- Reliance on intuition to determine whether a partner is HIV-negative.
- Development of a trusting relationship with a partner.

Unless such obstacles to using condoms are overcome, efforts to stem the tide of STI and HIV infection may be thwarted.

ALCOHOL AND DRUG USE   There is substantial evidence linking alcohol consumption and illicit drug use to elevated risk for STI. A number of studies have found an association between problematic levels of alcohol consumption (e.g., binge drinking) and STI (Cook & Clark, 2005). A study of women aged 18 to 29 found that alcohol consumption predicted the likelihood of STI diagnosis (Seth et al., 2011), and another study of STI clinic patients found that binge-drinking women were five times more likely to be diagnosed with gonorrhea than abstainers (Hutton et al., 2008).

The degree to which illicit drug use is associated with STI is dependent on a number of factors including the drug in question and the level of use. An analysis of data from the U.S. Youth Risk Behavior Survey found an association between unprotected sex and illicit drug use (Anderson & Mueller, 2008). Research with young aboriginal people in British Columbia who used drugs found high levels of unprotected sex (Chavoshi et al., 2012). A review of the literature by the Public Health Agency of Canada (2012d) concluded that drug use (e.g., amphetamines, ecstasy, poppers, cocaine, opiates) is linked to risk-taking during sexual encounters.

Many other psychological factors can account for sexual risk-taking. Barry Adam (2006) at the University of Windsor has taken a broader perspective by critiquing some health educators' contention that rational decision-making should result in avoidance of risky sexual behaviours. He argues that the drive to satisfy certain emotional needs can often override longer-range safety concerns. For example, someone who is less attractive, less secure, or more needy than his or her partner may not insist on condom use, for fear of losing the partner. And someone who believes true sexual intimacy involves ejaculation without a condom may feel emotionally and sexually unfulfilled if a condom is used.

Social Factors

STI rates are linked to a number of social factors such as socio-economic status, social capital, gender inequality, sexual orientation, ethnocultural factors, and negative societal attitudes toward STI-infected people.

SOCIO-ECONOMIC STATUS   Socio-economic status (SES) (e.g., level of income, education, employment) is one of the strongest predictors of health, including risk for STI (Public Health Agency of Canada, 2014a).

Some studies find a direct association between SES and STI prevalence. For example, a large-sample study in the United States found an association between both income and racial/ethnic identity and prevalence of bacterial STIs (Harling, 2013). Bush et al. (2008) found that lower SES (income, education) census tracts in the Calgary Health Region had a higher prevalence of chlamydia than higher SES tracts. In a similar study of census tracts in the city of Toronto, Hardwick and Patychuk (1999) found an association between low income and chlamydia among 15- to 24-year-olds. A high level of STI prevalence was also found among street youth in Ottawa (Shields, et al., 2004).

SOCIAL CAPITAL   University of Windsor researchers (Smylie et al., 2006) have found that Canadian youth with strong social ties to family, peers, and community organizations are less likely to engage in risky sexual behaviours than youth without these strong ties. Their social networks provide intangible resources that enable them to make healthier decisions, resulting in fewer social problems for themselves and for society. In a study of adolescents in Nova Scotia, Langille et al. (2014) found that lower levels of school connectedness, which can be a salient form of social capital for youth, were associated with having two or more sex partners in the previous year and not using a condom at last intercourse for boys but not girls. The results of both of these studies suggest that social capital factors may play a stronger role in shaping STI risk behaviour among male youth compared to female youth.

GENDER INEQUALITY   As we discussed in Chapter 5, stereotypical gender roles for men and women include sexual behaviour within relationships. The traditional sexual script, for example, provides men with relatively more control over sexual behaviour and, as a result, places women in a disadvantaged position in negotiating condom use. Thus, women who have low levels of power within their romantic/sexual relationships with men are more likely to be at high risk for STI than women in more egalitarian relationships.

A study of young women aged 15 to 21 found that those who perceived themselves to have less power in their relationship were almost four times as likely to have an STI than those who perceived themselves to have more relationship power (Raiford, Seth, & DiClemente, 2013). Research on youth in Canada found that girls—but not boys—who'd been pressured to have sex were less likely to use condoms than girls who'd had sex without being pressured (Gallupe, Boyce, & Fergus, 2009). A Toronto study found that young fathers with higher gender equitable attitudes were more likely to use condoms with their partners than those with lower scores on a gender equity scale (Nelson, Thach, & Zhang, 2014).

Experiencing intimate partner violence (i.e., physical, sexual, verbal/psychological harm) is associated with increased odds of contracting an STI. For example, results from a large sample U.S. study found that being involved in a verbally abusive relationship was associated with not using a condom at last intercourse among female teenagers (Roberts, Auinger, & Klein, 2005). A number of studies have shown that women who are victims of intimate partner violence have a higher prevalence of STI than women in nonviolent relationships (Coker, 2007; Hess et al., 2012).

SEXUAL ORIENTATION   An international study of adolescents in Canada, New Zealand, and the United States has revealed that lesbian, gay, and bisexual (LGB) youth are more likely than heterosexuals to engage in behaviours that pose high risk for HIV (Meininger et al., 2007). In all three countries, LGB youth experience more discrimination and stigmatization than heterosexual youth. In the

Applied Knowledge

REDUCING YOUR RISKS FOR STIS AND HIV

STIs are very common, especially among young adults, and HIV/AIDS presents a significant threat to the health and well-being of Canadians. You can do a number of things to lower your risk for STI and HIV infection.

Be Knowledgeable

The first step in protecting yourself is to get the facts. In this chapter we've provided extensive information about STIs and HIV. You can use this information to make well-informed choices that will lower your risk of infection or of transmitting an infection to a sexual partner.

Refrain from Partnered Sexual Activity (Abstinence)

The most effective way to avoid the sexual transmission of STIs and HIV is to refrain from engaging in sexual activity with a partner, commonly referred to as "abstinence."

For preventing infection, abstinence means not engaging in any sexual behaviours that carry a risk of transmission. This includes penile–vaginal and penile–anal intercourse, oral sex, skin-to-skin genital contact, and the exchange of body fluids such as semen, vaginal secretions, and blood.

Use Latex Condoms

Using latex condoms every time you have sex substantially reduces—but doesn't eliminate—the risk of contracting or transmitting STIs and HIV. Latex condoms have been shown to be highly effective in preventing HIV transmission, and studies indicate that they can significantly reduce the risk of common STIs such as chlamydia, HPV, and HSV.

Remember, to be effective as an STI-prevention tool, condoms must be used properly every time you have sex, not just sometimes. Carry condoms with you, so you'll be prepared, and be clear in your mind about how and when you'll bring up the topic of condom use with a partner.

Limit Your Number of Sexual Partners

The fewer sexual partners you have in your lifetime, the lower your chances of coming into contact with STIs and HIV. Practising monogamy (having only one sexual partner at a time) is one way to reduce your risk.

Most of us will be serially monogamous, however, having a series of monogamous relationships over our lifetimes. There's a tendency for some couples to use condoms at the beginnings of their relationships, but to stop using them as the relationships become serious. Heterosexual couples often stop using condoms when the female partners start using oral contraception, because their biggest concern is pregnancy, not STIs and HIV.

If you stop using condoms in each of a series of monogamous relationships over a number of years, you'll have unprotected sex with as many partners as you have relationships with, which will increase your chances of STI and HIV infection.

Get Tested for STIs and HIV

It's common for people to assume that if they and their partners have no STI symptoms and have been selective in their partner choices, there's little or no chance that they have STIs. But remember, most cases of STI and HIV are asymptomatic, and STIs and HIV can happen to anybody.

You can significantly reduce your risk of contracting or transmitting STIs and HIV by agreeing with a new partner that you'll both be tested before having sex. If you regularly have new sexual partners, having equally regular STI and HIV testing is a good idea.

Most doctors and clinics offer routine testing for HIV and common STIs such as chlamydia, but you may need to ask your doctor or clinic to specifically arrange tests for HPV and HSV.

If you think you may have been exposed to an STI or HIV, consult a doctor as soon as possible. Early detection and treatment can make a big difference in reducing or eliminating the infection.

Avoid Nonsexual Risk Behaviours

Avoid contact with bodily substances from other people that can transmit infections—blood, semen, vaginal secretions, fecal matter, and so on.

Don't share hypodermic needles, razors, cuticle scissors, or other instruments that may have another person's blood on them. Be careful when handling wet towels, bed linens, and other materials that may contain bodily substances.

Get Regular Medical Checkups

As part of a regular medical checkup, your doctor will examine your genitals to see if you have any visible

Canadian and American samples, this stigmatization has a significant influence on risk-taking, regardless of sexual orientation. The researchers have concluded that reducing discrimination against LGB youth may reduce sexual risk-taking among this age group.

symptoms of STI infection. More and more doctors are asking about their patients' sexual behaviours, to determine whether they're at high risk for STIs and HIV, and whether testing is needed.

If you're a woman, talk to your doctor about whether you should have a Pap test to check for abnormal changes to your cervix that may have resulted from HPV infection. A medical checkup is a great opportunity to ask any questions you may have about sexual health.

Engage in Lower-Risk Sexual Behaviours

Some sexual behaviours present higher risks for STIs and HIV than others. Unprotected penile–vaginal and penile–anal intercourse are high-risk behaviours. Although oral sex is less risky than intercourse for HIV and some STIs, it still carries some risk of transmission.

You can lower your risks when engaging in these behaviours by using condoms for vaginal and anal intercourse and fellatio. For cunnilingus, you can cover the genital area with a piece of latex.

Other risky behaviours include inserting a hand or fist into a person's rectum or vagina (fisting). Oral–anal sex (anilingus, or "rimming") is also risky, because of its potential for transmitting microbes between the mouth and the anus.

Mutual masturbation with your partner is a good way to exchange sexual pleasure and carries lower risks than intercourse and oral sex. Some couples find that watching each other masturbate can be a pleasurable

means of sexual intimacy, with no risk of STI or HIV transmission.

Using sex toys such as vibrators and dildos—as long as you wash them with soap and water before and after you use them—is another lower-risk way to enjoy sexual activity.

Rubbing your bodies together is also a lower-risk activity, as long there's no genital-to-genital contact, and semen and vaginal sections don't come into contact with the other person's genital area or with breaks in the skin.

Engage in **outercourse**, or forms of sexual expression that don't involve the exchange of body fluids. Examples include massage, hugging, caressing, mutual masturbation, and rubbing your bodies together.

Make Your Own Sexual-Health Plan

Many people make decisions about sexual behaviour spontaneously. These decisions are made in the heat of passion, sometimes under the influence of alcohol or drugs.

One way to avoid making snap sexual decisions that may put you at risk for STIs and HIV is to make your own sexual-health plan. In other words, make some of these decisions in advance.

Here are some questions you can ask yourself in making your sexual-health plan:

- At this point in my life, do I want to be sexually active?
- What types of sexual activities am I ready to engage in (e.g., intercourse, oral sex, genital touching)?
- Under what circumstances am I willing to have sex (e.g., hooking up,

friends with benefits, dating relationships, committed relationships)?
- What steps will I take to avoid STIs and HIV (e.g., always use condoms, get tested for STIs and HIV, engage in lower-risk behaviours)?

Talk to Your Partners about Sexual Health

If you're comfortable enough to have sex with a partner, you should also be comfortable enough to talk about the importance of protecting your sexual health.

For example you can mention that you've read about how common STIs are, and that most cases don't have visible or obvious symptoms. This can open the way for you to bring up the topic of condom use, choosing to engage in lower-risk sexual behaviours, and getting tested for STI/HIV.

Consult Your Physician if You Suspect You've Been Exposed

If you think you may have been exposed to an STI or HIV, see a doctor as soon as possible.

Many STIs are detectable in the early stages, and can be successfully treated. If you're infected with HIV, early treatment may keep the virus levels low and prevent you from developing AIDS.

Early intervention may also prevent the dangers of an STI spreading to your vital organs.

Be sensitive to any physical changes that may be symptomatic of STIs. Talk to a health professional if you're in doubt.

A study of adolescents in British Columbia and Seattle has found that LGB youth experience higher rates of sexual abuse and coercion than heterosexual youth (Saewyc, 2006). Those who have experienced sexual abuse are more likely to engage in behaviours that are high-risk for STI.

Outercourse Forms of sexual expression, such as massage, hugging, caressing, mutual masturbation, and rubbing bodies together, that don't involve the exchange of body fluids.

Innovative Canadian Research

THE MALE CALL CANADA SURVEY OF MEN WHO HAVE SEX WITH MEN

In 2011–2012, a research team led by Ted Myers at the University of Toronto conducted *Male Call Canada*, a national telephone survey of men who have sex with men (MSM) to gather information on attitudes, behaviours, and other relevant factors related to HIV and risk for HIV infection (Myers et al., 2013). All of the survey participants reported that they had engaged in sexual activity with a man at some point in their lives. Interviews were conducted with 1 235 MSM from all provinces and territories, ranging in age from 16 to 89 years. The findings included the following:

- Just over half (54.6%) of the men identified as gay, 35.6% as bisexual, 5.7% as other, and 4.1% as straight. Older men (60+) were more likely to identify as bisexual, and younger men were more likely to identify as gay. Men living in rural areas were more likely to identify as bisexual, and urban men were more likely to identify as gay.
- For number of male sex partners in the last six months, 16.8% reported none, 22.3% reported one, 36.8% reported two to five, and 24.0% reported six or more.

- With respect to condoms, 88.1% agreed that the benefits of using condoms outweigh the disadvantages, 67.8% agreed that it feels good to use a condom because it makes you feel safe, and less than half (48.6%) agreed that condoms make sex feel less pleasurable. When asked how often they used a condom for anal sex in the previous six months, 50.7% responded "not always."
- Three quarters (75%) of the men said they had been tested for HIV. Among those who had been tested, 52.2% had their most recent test within the previous year.
- Less than a tenth (6.6%) of the men reported that they were HIV-positive, 67.2% said they were HIV-negative, and 26.2% indicated that they did not know their HIV status.
- Of the men who were HIV-positive, most rated their mental health and physical health as good to excellent (88.9%, 87.3% respectively). However, 82.5% of the HIV-positive men reported that they were worried that they would be discriminated against or stigmatized because of HIV.

It is well known that men who have sex with men who practice unprotected anal intercourse without a condom are at high risk for HIV and other STIs. However, a common misperception is that STIs can't be transmitted between female sex partners. There's a high prevalence of bacterial vaginosis among lesbians. One study of lesbian and bisexual women found that even though one-half of those between the ages of 18 and 22 had histories of BV, they perceived little risk of STI infection from female partners (Marrazzo, 2005). The women took no precautions to prevent STIs. In particular, they didn't wash their hands before sexual activity, didn't use rubber gloves for vaginal or oral penetration, and shared sex toys without washing them or using them with condoms.

CRITICAL THINKING QUESTIONS

Has any of the information in this chapter changed your attitudes toward STIs? If so, how have your attitudes changed?

ETHNOCULTURAL FACTORS   Areas of Canada where Aboriginal people make up a large proportion of the population have higher than average STI rates (Public Health Agency of Canada, 2014b). For example, in 2010, chlamydia and gonorrhea rates in Nunavut and the Northwest Territories were more than seven times higher than the national average. Socioeconomic disadvantage, social exclusion and isolation, and inadequate access to quality health care and services have been identified as underlying determinants of high STI rates in First Nations communities (Wynne & Currie, 2011). First Nations women are especially at risk. They're more likely to be poor than other Canadian women, and more likely to live in environments where substance abuse and spousal violence are common (Prentice, 2005). Among aboriginal youth, STI infection is associated with sexual abuse and substance abuse (Devries, Free, Morison, & Saewyc, 2009).

Canada is home to recent immigrants from around the world. Their native ethnocultural traditions and customs related to sexuality are often quite different from those of "mainstream" Canadian society. In some cases, newcomers may come from countries where open discussion of sexuality, particularly with strangers is taboo. As a result, some immigrants may be uncomfortable seeking sexual health care (Shirpack, Maticka-Tyndale, & Chinichian, 2007). Research has found that newcomers and longer-term immigrants are less likely to access sexual health services compared to the Canadian-born population, and this can present an important obstacle to STI and HIV prevention, diagnosis, and treatment (Public Health Agency of Canada, 2014b).

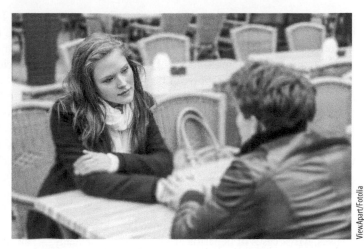

Talking about Prevention.
Most people don't find it easy to talk frankly about preventing STIs, including HIV—but what's the alternative?

Education and Prevention

A wide variety of groups in Canada provide STI- and HIV-prevention education and programming. These include the Public Health Agency of Canada, provincial ministries of health, universities, schools, and community groups. These programs are often integrated into broader sexual-health education programs.

The most effective programs go beyond simply providing information, and try to motivate people to reduce their risks and acquire specific behavioural skills (such as negotiating condom use) to enable them to put what they learn into practice.

In Chapter 15, we discuss the status of Canadian sexual-health education, including STI and HIV prevention, and the ingredients of effective sexual-risk-reduction programming.

Summing Up

Although public attention has been riveted on AIDS for more than two decades, other STIs such as chlamydia and HPV are more common.

Chlamydia, gonorrhea, and syphilis are STIs caused by bacteria.

Human papillomavirus (HPV) and herpes simplex virus, type 2 (HSV-2), are two common STIs caused by viruses.

The highest rates of common STIs in Canada are among adolescents and young adults.

A large proportion of cases of common STIs such as chlamydia and HPV are asymptomatic (i.e., have no symptoms).

Chlamydia is the most common bacterial STI. In Canada, rates are highest among young women. Many cases have no symptoms. If untreated, chlamydia can damage a woman's reproductive tract.

Gonorrhea is a less-common bacterial STI that can also damage the reproductive system.

Syphilis undergoes several stages of development. Although it can lie dormant for many years, it can be lethal.

Vaginitis is usually characterized by a foul-smelling discharge, genital irritation, and burning during urination. Most cases involve bacterial vaginosis, candidiasis, or trichomoniasis.

AIDS is caused by HIV, a virus that attacks the body's immune system. As HIV disables the body's natural defences, the person becomes vulnerable to opportunistic diseases—such as serious infections and cancers—that are normally held in check. HIV is a blood-borne virus that's also found in semen, vaginal secretions, and breast milk.

The most common avenues of HIV transmission are vaginal and anal intercourse and shared hypodermic needles. There's no cure for AIDS, and an effective, safe vaccine hasn't been developed. Condoms are highly effective in preventing the sexual transmission of HIV.

Oral herpes is caused by the Herpes simplex virus, type 1 (HSV-1). Genital herpes is caused by the Herpes simplex virus, type 2 (HSV-2), which produces painful, shallow sores and blisters on the genitals. HSV-1 can also infect the genitals.

Several types of hepatitis are caused by different viruses. Most cases of hepatitis are transmitted sexually or through contact with contaminated blood or fecal matter.

Human papillomavirus (HPV) is the most common STI. HPV types 6 and 11 can cause genital warts. Types 16 and 18 can, if undetected, lead to cervical cancer. A vaccine is available to protect against these four types of HPV.

The spread of STIs and HIV is driven by a combination of factors that are biological (e.g., multiple means of transmission, lack of vaccines for HIV and most STIs), psychological (e.g., perceived low risk of infection, lack of communication about risk), and social (e.g., socio-economic status, gender inequality).

Consistent condom use, limiting your number of sexual partners, and getting tested for STIs and HIV are three important steps you can take to reduce your risk of infection.

Test Yourself

Multiple-Choice Questions

1. Many Canadian university students are unaware of HPV, which causes:
(a) Genital herpes.
(b) Hepatitis B.
(c) Genital warts.
(d) Molluscum contagiosum.

2. As many as _____ of men and _____ of women with chlamydia have no symptoms.
(a) 90%; 70%   (c) 35%; 10%
(b) 75%; 50%   (d) 25%; 70%

3. Untreated chlamydia can lead to _____ in women.
(a) yeast infections
(b) wasting syndrome
(c) cervical cancer
(d) pelvic inflammatory disease

4. The vaccine Gardasil immunizes against:
(a) Herpes.   (c) HIV.
(b) Hepatitis B.   (d) HPV.

5. According to the *Canadian Health Measures Survey*, what percentage of Canadians aged 14 to 59 have HSV-2?
(a) 6.1%   (c) 21.3%
(b) 13.6%   (d) 31.1%

6. HIV directly attacks the immune system by destroying:
(a) Pathogenic cells.   (c) Red blood cells.
(b) CD4 cells.   (d) Platelets.

7. All of the following have been shown to transmit HIV infection except:
(a) Artificial insemination with infected semen.
(b) Kissing.
(c) Breastfeeding.
(d) Unprotected sexual intercourse.

8. The current standard of treatment for HIV/AIDS, known as _____, consists of a mixture of anti-retroviral drugs and protease inhibitors.
(a) ELISA   (c) HAART
(b) AIDSBS   (d) LSMFT

9. Which of the following is a social factor in the spread of STIs?
(a) Socio-economic status.
(b) Lack of vaccines.
(c) Perceived low risk of infection.
(d) The fact that many STIs are asymptomatic.

10. Which of the following is not considered an effective prevention strategy for reducing your risk of STIs and HIV?
(a) Going with your partner to a clinic so you can both be tested for STIs and HIV.
(b) Using birth-control pills.
(c) Engaging in mutual masturbation instead of vaginal or anal intercourse.
(d) Using latex condoms.

You'll find answers to the "Test Yourself" questions on page 489.

Questions for Critical Thinking

1. How would you bring up the topic of condom use with a new sexual partner? What might stop you from bringing it up?

2. What are some of the steps society can take to reduce the number of STI and HIV cases in Canada?

3. You and some friends are sitting around having a drink. One of your friends is certain s/he can tell what sort of person is likely to have an STI, and would never have sex with "someone like that." How do you respond?

CHAPTER FIFTEEN

Sexual Health Education

Hero Images/Fancy/Corbis

This chapter is about sexual health education. Notice that we are not using the term "sex education," which may be more familiar to you. The distinction between "sex education" and "sexual health education" is important for several reasons. First, as we shall see, school-based programs that provide information about sexuality tend to be controversial, with opponents of such programs sometimes claiming that "sex education" is inappropriately focused on teaching about, and inadvertently promoting, sexual behaviour among youth. Second, the term "sexual health education" implies a more specific focus on the health-related aspects of sexuality. Let's begin, then, our examination of this topic with clear definitions of both "sexual health" and "sexual health education." A World Health Organization (2006) working definition of sexual health is as follows:

> Sexual health is a state of physical, emotional, mental and social well-being in relation to sexuality; it is not merely the absence of disease, dysfunction or infirmity. Sexual health requires a positive and respectful approach to sexuality and sexual relationships, as well as the possibility of having pleasurable and safe sexual experiences, free of coercion, discrimination and violence. For sexual health to be attained and maintained, the sexual rights of all persons must be respected, protected and fulfilled (p. 5).

Typically, education related to sexuality has been thought of as a mechanism for preventing problems such as sexually transmitted infections (STIs) or unwanted pregnancies. But, as the World Health Organization definition shows, education aimed at helping

people achieve and maintain sexual health is not just an exercise in problem prevention. A broadly based conceptualization of sexual health education balances problem prevention with a recognition that sexual health is a positive aspect of personal
health and well-being. In stating the goals of sexual health education, the Public
Health Agency of Canada's (PHAC, 2008) *Canadian Guidelines for Sexual Health
Education* reflect this balanced approach. According to the *Guidelines*, the goals of
sexual health education are:

1. To help people achieve positive outcomes (e.g., self-esteem, respect for self
   and others, non-exploitive sexual relations, rewarding human relationships,
   informed reproductive choices.
2. To avoid negative outcomes (e.g., STI/HIV, sexual coercion, unintended pregnancy) (PHAC, 2008, p. 8).

We'll return to the *Canadian Guidelines for Sexual Health Education* later in this
chapter, but first, let's take a brief look at the history of sexual health education in
the schools in North America.

Sexual Health Education in the Schools: A Brief History

Christabelle Sethna (1994, 2010) at the University of Ottawa has done extensive
research on early twentieth-century forms of sex education for youth. At the time,
instruction related to sexuality often took the form of what was called "purity education" or "nature study." Sethna documents how such teaching arose primarily
out of concern about the spread of venereal disease (as STIs were called) which had
increased during the First World War. Nature study focused on biological reproduction with the objective of inducing children to adopt standards of abstinence,
chastity before marriage, and procreative marital sex. Nature study was a popular
form of sex education in Ontario up to the 1930s, and again after venereal disease
rates rose once again after the Second World War.

During the 1960s and 1970s, most students in Canadian schools received little,
if any, sexual health education. During this period, information about sexuality was
often provided in programs called "Family Life Education" (FLE), which focused
on human reproduction, puberty, and, in some cases, birth control. A survey done in
1975 found that about one-third of Canadian schools provided some form of FLE
(Barrett, 1990). In the 1970s, increasing concern about teen pregnancy combined
with increasing societal openness about sexuality led to the gradual implementation
of FLE programs in Canada.

In the 1980s and 1990s, alarm over HIV/AIDS, high rates of other sexually
transmitted infections (STI) in youth, as well as a growing recognition that many
Canadian youth were becoming sexually active in their teens, prompted most secondary schools in Canada to introduce some form of sexuality education. By the
mid-1990s, every province and territory in Canada either mandated or strongly recommended, through provincial departments of education or health, that some form
of sexuality education be taught in the schools (Barrett, 1994). More recently, the
province of Quebec removed sexual health education from its formal curriculum in
2005, although the Quebec Ministry of Education recommends that teachers find
ways to integrate sexual health issues into classroom teaching.

Because education in Canada is a provincial and territorial responsibility, the
extent and quality of sexual health education in the schools can vary from province
to province, from school board to school board, from school to school, and from
classroom to classroom. And rather than being taught as a separate subject, sexual
health education—which is only a small part of the overall school curriculum—is
usually part of a broader health curriculum that covers a wide range of topics.

Applied Knowledge

EDUCATING YOUR CHILDREN ABOUT SEX

"Daddy, where do babies come from?"

"What are you asking me for? Go ask your mother."

Most children don't find it easy to talk to their parents about sex. Yet most young children are curious about where babies come from, how girls and boys differ, and so on (Pike, 2005). Parents who avoid discussing these matters convey their own uneasiness about sex, and may teach children that sex is something to be ashamed of.

Parents needn't be sex experts to talk to their children about the subject. They can read books or surf the Internet to fill gaps in their knowledge, or consult books written for parents to read to children. They can admit they don't know all the answers. Children often respect such honesty.

In answering children's questions, parents need to think about what the children can understand. The four-year-old who wants to know where babies come from is probably not interested in sexual details. It may be enough to say, "From Mommy's uterus," and point to the abdominal region. Why say "tummy"? "Tummy" is wrong and confusing.

Sexual health educators offer the following pointers for discussing sexuality with children.

- Be approachable. Be willing to answer questions about sexuality.
- Use appropriate language. Children need to learn the correct names of their sex organs, and that the dirty words others use to refer to the sex organs are unacceptable in most social settings. Nor should parents use silly words like "pee-pee" or "privates" to describe sex organs.

- Give advice in the form of information the child can use to make sound decisions, not as an imperial edict. Parents who lay down the law may be less effective than parents who provide information and encourage discussion.
- Share information in small doses. Pick a time and a place that feels natural for these discussions, such as when the child is preparing for bed, or when you're in the car.
- Encourage the child to talk about sex. Children may feel embarrassed about talking about sex, especially with family members. You can leave a children's book about sex around, or give it to the child with a suggestion such as "I thought you might be interested in this book about sex. If you want to read it, we can talk about it."
- Respect the child's privacy rights. Most of us—parents and children alike— value privacy at times. A parent who feels uncomfortable sharing a bathroom with a child can say so. The parent might explain, "I like privacy when my door is closed. If you knock, I'll tell you whether you may come in. I'll knock when your door is closed, too." Fair is fair.
- By the time they are approaching puberty, most children will have seen various forms of sexual imagery, including explicit sexual activity, on the Internet. Some children will find such imagery repellent or confusing, while others will be fascinated by it. Talking with children about what they have seen on the Internet is one way for parents to initiate a discussion about sexuality and relationships. Parents can help to dispel myths about sexual behaviour that are propagated on the web and counter it with factual information and discussion of healthy relationships.

Golden Pixels LLC/Shutterstock

Educating Your Child about Sex.
Answer the questions truthfully. Use language the child will understand, but don't make it silly child language. In other words, don't talk about "pee-pees" and "wee-wees" and "Mommy's tummy." Use words like "penis," "vagina," and "uterus." Get a book with drawings or pictures.

Innovative Canadian Research

SEXUAL HEALTH EDUCATION IN SCHOOLS ACROSS CANADA

The *Canadian Guidelines for Sexual Health Education* (PHAC, 2008) suggests that

Sexual health education should include an understanding of developmental changes (e.g., puberty), rewarding interpersonal relationships, developing communication skills, setting of personal limits, developing media literacy, challenging of stereotypes, prevention of STI/HIV, effective contraceptive methods, information on sexual assault/coercion, sexual orientation and gender identity and a critical examination of evolving gender-roles and expectations (p. 22).

As part of an effort to advocate for a new sexual health curriculum for the province of Ontario, after a proposed 2010 revised curriculum was withdrawn by the provincial government in response to political and media controversy, the organization Ophea, Healthy Schools, Healthy Communities (2013) compared provincial sexual health curriculum documents from British Columbia, Alberta, Saskatchewan, Manitoba, and New Brunswick to the existing 1998 Ontario curriculum. (It is expected that the Ontario government will reintroduce a new curriculum in 2015):

- In all provinces included in the review, except Saskatchewan, it was recommended that children in Kindergarten or Grade 1 be taught the proper name for body parts, and in several provinces it specified that children identify terms such as "penis," "vagina," and "breasts." In Saskatchewan, the curriculum documents did not recommend teaching the correct terminology for body parts until Grade 5.
- In all six provinces, the curriculum documents recommended that children be taught about the physical changes of puberty in Grade 5, with several provinces

also including information about psychological, social, and interpersonal changes. Alberta and British Columbia began teaching about puberty in Grade 4.
- In all six provinces, curriculum documents recommend teaching about abstinence from sexual activity in Grades 7 and/or Grade 8. In most cases, abstinence was presented as a "healthy" choice or as "the best and healthiest decision for adolescents." Most of the curriculum documents provide opportunities for contraception and condoms for STI prevention to be discussed. For example, the Saskatchewan Grade 6 to 8 curriculum overview indicates that students who decide to become sexually active need information about effective methods to protect against pregnancy and STIs. In British Columbia, it was recommended that, as part of classroom activities, students in Grade 8 create a list of practices to reduce the risk of STIs.
- The provincial curriculum documents took very different approaches to teaching about gender identity, gender roles, and sexual orientation. In some provinces, these topics were not addressed at all, as was the case with the 1998 Ontario curriculum. In Manitoba, Grade 5 students were required to identify how social and cultural influences affect sexuality and gender roles, and these same topics were addressed in Grade 7 in Alberta. In New Brunswick, it was broadly recommended that Grade 8 students be required to discuss sexual orientation issues. In sum, specific information and discussion of gender identity and sexual orientation appeared to be lacking in the curriculum documents of all six provinces.

The findings of the Ophea review suggest that most schools in Canada do not provide sexual health education programs consistent with the breadth of content areas suggested by the *Canadian Guidelines for Sexual Health Education* (PHAC, 2008).

Sexual health education, therefore, often receives limited time and attention in the classroom.

In the elementary grades, instruction tends to focus on biological development and, as students approach their teen years, the changes associated with puberty. At the secondary school level, the most extensive coverage of sexual health topics

CRITICAL THINKING
QUESTIONS

On a scale of 1 to 10,
how would you rate the
sexual-health education you
received in high school?

often occurs as part of a Grade 9 health course. Information on STIs is typically a central focus, although discussion of methods of prevention, such as abstinence and condom use, can be highly variable, depending on the school. Because of this variability, it's nearly impossible to reach general conclusions about the quality of sexual health education in Canadian schools.

A number of factors can influence the quality of sexual health education. The importance school administrators place on sexual health education, and the degree to which they sense community support for it, can dramatically influence the quality of the sexual health education that's delivered in the classroom.

The Canadian Guidelines for Sexual Health Education

To facilitate the development of broadly based sexual-health education programs, the PHAC (2008) has produced the *Canadian Guidelines for Sexual Health Education*. The first edition, developed by experts from across Canada, was published in 1994; the third and most recent edition appeared in 2008. The guidelines are designed to guide and unify professionals who provide sexual health education in Canada.

The *Guidelines* document is designed to provide curriculum and program planners, educators, and education policy makers, with a basic guide for the initiation, development, implementation, and evaluation of sexual health education programs in schools and communities (PHAC, 2008).

The *Guidelines* suggest a basic three-step process for the development of sexual health education programs:

- **Assessment and Planning.** In the first step, educators assess a target group's sexual health education needs and plan the education program accordingly. For example, peer educators at a university might ask students to fill out anonymous questionnaires that assess student's knowledge, attitudes, and skills related to STIs affecting young adults. Based on the student's questionnaire responses, the peer educators can plan an educational program or intervention that will address, and be specifically relevant to, the STI education needs of the students on campus.
- **Intervention.** In the second step, educators implement an educational program or intervention specifically designed to address the educational needs of the group identified in the assessment step. If, for example, the university peer educators discovered from the student questionnaires that many students on campus were unaware that most cases of STI have no symptoms (see Chapter 14), they could include the relevant information to close the student's knowledge gap related to STI in a brochure designed for campus distribution.

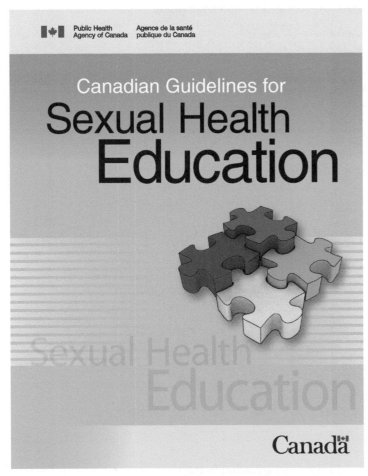

Figure 15.1   The *Canadian Guidelines for Sexual Health Education* were produced by the Public Health Agency of Canada to assist educators, program planners, and policy makers in the development, implementation, and evaluation of effective, broadly based sexual health programs in Canada.

Source: Public Health Agency of Canada. (2008). Canadian Guidelines for Sexual Health Education. *Catalogue No: HP40-25/2008E. Ottawa: Author. Retrieved from http://www.phac-aspc.gc.ca /publicat/cgshe-ldnemss/pdf/guidelines-eng.pdf*

■ **Evaluation.** In the third step, educators attempt to measure the extent to which the educational program or intervention has been effective in reaching its objectives. After the brochure had been circulated on campus, the peer educators in our example could then again use a student questionnaire to assess if student awareness about cases of STI often not having symptoms had increased. The evaluation step can be particularly helpful in identifying how sexual health education programs or interventions can be improved the next time they are implemented.

Using Theory and Research to Inform Sexual Health Education

Sexual health education can take many forms and range in scope and comprehensiveness, from Twitter text messages containing small bits of sexual health information, to multi-session, intensive interventions designed to modify participants' sexual health-related behaviour in specific ways. School-based sexual health education for youth typically falls somewhere in- between these two ends of the continuum.

Ideally, sexual health education programs in the schools will be sufficiently comprehensive that they enable young people to protect and enhance their sexual health. The *Canadian Guidelines for Sexual Health Education* (PHAC, 2008) note that in order for sexual health education programs to be effective in promoting sexual health, including behavioural change, it is necessary that they incorporate an appropriate theoretical model to guide the creation and implementation of the program.

There are a number of appropriate theoretical models for application to sexual health education interventions. These include Social Cognitive Theory (Bandura, 2004) which focuses on personal, behavioural, and environmental factors that can be used to predict and change sexual behaviour, and the Transtheoretical Model, which suggests a five-stage process for behavioural change related to sexual health (Albarracin et al., 2005).

The PHAC (2008) *Guidelines* are based on the Information–Motivation–Behavioural Skills (IMB) model, which provides a relatively straightforward theoretical basis for developing and teaching sexual health education. For example, as applied to sexual health education for youth, the IMB model specifies that in order for it to be effective, it must provide *information* that is directly relevant to sexual health (e.g., information on effective forms of birth control and where to access them), address *motivational factors* that influence sexual health behaviour (e.g., discussion of social pressures on youth to become sexually active and benefits of delaying first intercourse), and teach the specific *behavioural skills* that are needed to protect and enhance sexual health (e.g., learning to negotiate condom use and/or sexual limit-setting) (see Figure 15.2).

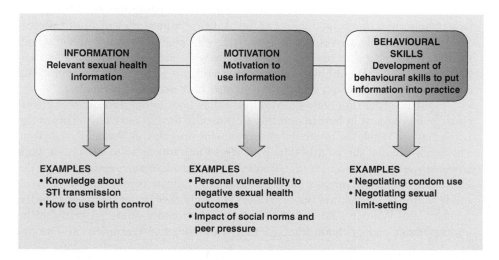

Figure 15.2 The IMB Model Applied to Sexual Health Education

Source: Based on Sex Information and Education Council of Canada. (2010). Sexual health education in the schools: Questions and answers (3rd Ed.). Toronto: SIECCAN.

Innovative Canadian Research

THE INFORMATION–MOTIVATION–BEHAVIOURAL SKILLS (IMB) MODEL

William Fisher of the Department of Psychology and the Department of Obstetrics and Gynaecology at the University of Western Ontario, and his brother Jeffrey Fisher at the University of Connecticut, developed the IMB model through extensive research into factors that shape and drive sexual and reproductive health behaviour (Fisher & Fisher, 1992; 1998). The IMB model has been applied to a wide range of groups, including high school and university students, inner-city minority youth, STI clinic patients, low-income women, and men who have sex with men.

For example, Fullerton, Rye, Meaney, and Loomis (2013) found support for the IMB model in predicting hormonal contraceptive use, condom use, and dual (i.e., condom and hormonal contraception) protection among a sample of 267 sexually active female Ontario university students.

Kiene et al. (2013) utilized the IMB model to understand the HIV transmission risk behaviour of a sample of 1388 HIV-infected male and female South Africans receiving antiretroviral therapy. The study indicated important directions for prevention efforts to curb HIV in South Africa.

The IMB model has also been successfully used as the theoretical basis for effective sexual health education interventions. For example, Fisher, Fisher, Bryan, and Misovich (2002) evaluated an IMB-based HIV risk behaviour change intervention provided to inner-city high school students in Connecticut. The evaluation found that sexually active students who completed the classroom IMB-based intervention were significantly more likely than a control group of students to be using condoms one year later.

Effective Sexual-Health Education

Incorporation of a theoretical model such as IMB is just one of the key ingredients in effective education about sexual health. There has been extensive research into what's required for such education to be effective (Albarracin et al., 2005; Kirby, Laris, & Rolleri, 2007; World Association for Sexual Health, 2008). The Sex Information and Education Council of Canada (SIECCAN, 2010) has summarized this research, outlining ten key ingredients for effective sexual-health education, as shown in Table 15.1.

Advanced Training in Sexuality for Professionals

A major limitation to the effectiveness of sexual health education programs is the lack of specific training in the area of sexuality for educators and health professionals. For example, two-thirds of New Brunswick elementary and middle school teachers report that they haven't received training to teach sexual health education (Cohen et al., 2004). Although many Canadian universities offer undergraduate courses in human sexuality, a surprising number have no sexuality courses.

The Université du Québec à Montréal offers both undergraduate and graduate degree programs in human sexuality (in French). St. Jerome's University at the University of Waterloo offers an undergraduate program in sexuality, marriage, and family studies, directed by Dr. B. J. Rye. Programs are also offered at York University and the University of Toronto. Other Canadian universities, such as the University of Guelph, provide undergraduate and graduate courses and/or research specialization opportunities in sexuality. Through the Department of Gender, Sexuality and Women's Studies, Simon Frasier University offers programs at the undergraduate and graduate level. McGill University and University of Toronto

TABLE 15.1

The Key Ingredients for Effective Sexual Health Education

1. Provide sufficient classroom time to achieve the program's objectives.

2. Give teachers the training and administrative support required for delivering the program effectively.

3. Use a theoretical model such as IMB to develop and deliver the curriculum materials.

4. Tailor the program to the students' characteristics, needs, learning styles, ethnocultural backgrounds, sexual orientations, and developmental stages.

5. Target behaviours (e.g., unprotected sex) that lead to negative sexual-health outcomes (e.g., STIs and HIV infection).

6. Deliver and reinforce prevention messages that target the setting of sexual limits (e.g., delaying first intercourse) and the use of condoms.

7. Include program activities that focus on students' social environments and social contexts (e.g., peer pressure).

8. Incorporate the information, motivation, and behavioural skills necessary for students to refuse sexual activity and practise safer sex.

9. Give the students opportunities to practise (e.g., role playing) the setting of sexual limits, negotiation of condom use, and other communication skills, so they're active participants in the program, rather than passive recipients of information.

10. Evaluate the program's strengths and weaknesses, to improve future delivery.

Source: Sex Information and Education Council of Canada. (2010). Sexual health education in the schools: Questions and answers *(3rd ed.). Toronto: SIECCAN.*

have programs in Sexual Diversity Studies. York University and Carlton University offer programs in Sexuality studies. Nearly every university in Canada now has one or more faculty members who have specialties in sexuality and/or sexual health. They can be found in a range of disciplines, including psychology, sociology, nursing, medicine, education, social work, and public health.

The Guelph Sexuality Conference, offered by the University of Guelph, is the largest annual conference on human sexuality in Canada, providing a range of training opportunities for teaching and promoting sexual health. The Western Canadian Sexual Health Conference is another major conference, offered every two years.

The Impact of Sexual Health Education: Abstinence-Only Versus Broadly Based Approaches

Traditionally, one of the most hotly debated topics related to sexual health education has been whether or not school-based programs should focus exclusively on encouraging teens to not be sexually active, or whether programs should take a more balanced approach that also includes information and skills related to contraception and STI prevention.

ABSTINENCE-ONLY PROGRAMS   Abstinence-only programs, as they are commonly called, seek to motivate teens to not become sexually active until they are older, and in the case of some programs, until they are married. Because they are focused on the goal of abstinence, these programs typically do not include information on birth control methods or safer sex practices, except to mention that they are not 100% effective in preventing pregnancy or STI. The underlying philosophy behind abstinence-only programs is that by not engaging in sexual activity, a teen cannot become pregnant or become infected with an STI. Being abstinent, according to the proponents of these programs, also allows teens to continue to grow up without the burden of the potential emotional turmoil that can be part of the territory with relationships that involve sex. For schools that are affiliated with religious institutions or are located in communities that are perceived to be socially conservative, school administrators may feel obligated to instruct their teachers to stress abstinence primarily or exclusively when teaching about sexual health.

Community and school-based abstinence-only programs receive large amounts of government funding in the United States and, as a result, they are widely used in that country. In order to receive the government funding, a program must have "as its exclusive purpose, teaching the social, psychological, and health gains to be realized by abstaining from sexual activity" and teach students "that sexual activity outside the context of marriage is likely to have harmful psychological and physical effects" (Social Security Administration USA, n.d.). Abstinence-only programs are not nearly as popular in Canada as they are in the United States, but they have been used in some parts of the country.

Two key questions arise when critically assessing abstinence-only education. Are abstinence-only programs effective in reaching their goal of persuading youth not to be sexually active? And do these programs infringe on young people's rights in regard to making autonomous and fully informed decisions about their sexual and reproductive health?

Let's begin with the first question. Many studies have been conducted to see whether abstinence-only education works. Most have found that it does not. An evaluation of abstinence-only programs conducted for the United States Congress indicated that students who had taken abstinence-only courses were no more likely to be sexually abstinent, to delay first intercourse, or to have fewer sexual partners than students who didn't receive such courses (Trenholm et al., 2007). Many other reviews of available studies have replicated the finding that abstinence-only programs are usually ineffective (e.g., Bennett & Assefi, 2005; Kohler, Manhart, & Lafferty, 2008; Protogerou & Johnson, 2014).

With respect to the second question, abstinence-only programs have been criticized as unethical, because they don't provide the information young people need to make their own choices about sexual behaviour. In this respect, abstinence-only programs appear to be in conflict with *Canadian Guidelines for Sexual Health Education* (PHAC, 2008), which stresses that sexual-health education should support "informed decision-making" (p. 25). Others have argued that abstinence-only programs violate young people's human rights by withholding potentially lifesaving information about the prevention of HIV and AIDS (Ott & Santelli, 2007).

BROADLY BASED PROGRAMS   Sexual health education can be *broadly based* in two distinct ways. A defining characteristic of broadly based sexual health education is that it incorporates a wide range of objectives and content areas. For example, broadly based sexual health education goes beyond the topics of the biology of human reproduction and pregnancy and STI prevention to address topics such as integration of sexuality into mutually satisfying relationships, sexual orientation, sexuality related gender-role stereotyping, gender identity and other topics that are relevant to the sexual health of students. In sum, it is the breadth of topic area coverage that partially defines broadly based sexual health education.

The second defining characteristic of broadly based sexual health education is that it allows space for students to use the information they have learned to make decisions for themselves. If we look at the example of education about STI prevention, we have seen that the abstinence-only approach communicates only one possible path for protecting oneself: abstinence. In contrast, a broadly based approach would provide education that equips students to delay involvement in sexual activity and develop personal limits for sexual behaviour, but it would also provide education to similarly equip students to, for example, negotiate condom use with partners if they are sexually active. In sum, broadly based sexual health education is structured so that students are able to exercise informed decision-making (PHAC, 2008).

The defining characteristics of broadly based sexual health education (e.g., breadth of topic coverage, emphasis on informed decision-making) as described in documents such as the *Canadian Guidelines for Sexual Health Education* (PHAC, 2008) are roughly synonymous with what, in the United States, is called *comprehensive sex education*. For example, the Sexuality Information and Education Council of the United States (SIECUS, 2014) defines key aspects of comprehensive sex education as being evidence-informed, medically accurate and complete, and responsive to the needs of all people.

What do we know about the potential behavioural impact of broadly based approaches to sexual health education? Opponents of school-based sexual-health education have often argued that teaching young people about sexuality, including birth control and the use of condoms to prevent STIs and HIV, gives them the green light to become sexually active. This has become a central question in debates about whether sexual-health education belongs in school.

A large number of studies have examined this question. A review of studies measuring the behavioural impact of sexual health education programs has found that "the evidence is strong that programs do not hasten or increase sexual behaviour" (Kirby, Laris, & Rolleri, 2007, p. 206). In other words, sexual health programs are unlikely to encourage young people to become sexually active at an earlier age.

According to the Sex Information and Education Council of Canada (SIECCAN, 2010), a large number of studies indicate that sexual-health education can have a significant, positive impact on behaviour. The Kirby, Laris, and Rolleri (2007) review of 83 sexual health and HIV program evaluations found that two-thirds of the programs had positive behavioural effects on youth. In particular, the review showed that sexual-health education can effectively equip youth to delay first intercourse and to use condoms if they're sexually active. Other, more recent, reviews of the literature have confirmed the potential for broadly based sexual health education to reduce sexual risk behaviour (e.g., Protogerou & Johnson, 2014).

Have sexual health education programs in Canadian schools been effective in this regard? While many have provided youth with basic information, it's unlikely that most programs have been extensive enough to have sustained effects on behaviour. While most sexual-health education programs in Canadian schools don't contain most of these key ingredients, documents such as *Canadian Guidelines for Sexual Health Education* (PHAC, 2008) point the way to a new generation of programs that will potentially make more meaningful contributions to the sexual health of Canadians.

Attitudes Toward Sexual Health Education

Media reports often suggest that sexual health education, particularly for youth in schools, is a highly controversial topic. But how controversial is it really? To be sure, sexual health education controversies do flare up from time to time. The 2010 media-driven controversy surrounding the sexual health education components of the Ontario Health Curriculum is one recent example.

Some have suggested that conflicts about sexual health education in the schools are often rooted in opposing ideological perspectives related to human sexuality. For example, McKay (1998) has suggested that those who argue strenuously that sexual health education does not belong in the schools or that programs should adopt an "abstinence-only" approach hold a restrictive sexual ideology that is based on traditional moral standards for sexual behaviour. Restrictive sexual ideology stipulates that sexual behaviour should be limited to procreative heterosexual intercourse within marriage. According to McKay's analysis, on the other side of sexual health education conflicts are those who hold a permissive sexual ideology, based on the premise that sexual behaviour should be guided by secular moral principles such as honesty, equality, responsibility, and informed consent. People with a permissive sexual ideology typically support broadly based sexual health education, in which young people are provided with a broad range of information that they can use to make decisions about their sexual health. Ideologically based conflicts about sexual health education tend to be relatively rare in Canada but they are quite common in the United States, where the content of school curricula is frequently the subject of ideologically charged debate.

Parental Attitudes

Although media reports sometimes give the impression that Canadian parents are divided in their opinions about sexual health education in the schools, a series of surveys of parents with school-aged children conducted in several parts of Canada, including New Brunswick (Weaver et al., 2002), Saskatchewan (Advisory Committee on Family Planning, 2008), and Ontario (McKay, Pietrusiak, & Holowaty, 1998; McKay et al., 2014) suggest that parents have favourable attitudes toward the provision of sexual health education in the schools. In all of these surveys, more than 85% of parents *strongly agreed* or *agreed* with the statement "Sexual health education should be provided in the schools." Furthermore, parents in these studies also approved of providing youth with information on a wide range of topics including puberty, reproduction, healthy relationships, STI/HIV prevention, birth control, abstinence, sexual orientation, and sexual abuse/coercion. Because these surveys were voluntary, it is possible that some parents who were opposed to sexual health education in the schools would have refused to participate. Despite this caveat, among parents who did participate in the surveys, support for sexual health education in the schools was strong and consistent.

Youth Attitudes

Several surveys have indicated that Canadian youth want sexual health education to be taught in school (Byers & Grenier, 2003; McKay & Holowaty, 1997). In a survey of New Brunswick high school students, 92% agreed that "sexual-health education should be provided by the schools." The students rated topics such as puberty, reproduction, personal safety, sexual coercion and assault, sexual decision-making in dating relationships, birth control and safer-sex practices, and STIs as "very important" or "extremely important" (Byers & Grenier, 2003).

Unfortunately, many students are disappointed with the quality of the sexual health education they received. In the New Brunswick survey, only 13% rated their sexual health education as very good or excellent (Byers & Grenier, 2003). In Newfoundland and Labrador, most adolescents felt they had only limited access to sex education and services (Johns & Lush, 2004).

A major criticism of school-based sex-education programs is that they focus on the negative. In an interview study, young adults in British Columbia and Nova Scotia expressed dissatisfaction because their sexual health education neglected the emotional and potentially positive aspects of sex. They felt these programs were concerned only with providing information about pregnancy and STI prevention (Shoveller et al., 2004).

The *Toronto Teen Survey* of 1216 ethnically and religiously diverse teens assessed their experiences with, and opinions about, sexual health education (Causarano et al., 2010; Salehi et al., 2010). Overall, 92% of the teens reported

CRITICAL THINKING QUESTIONS

In your opinion, should sexual health education in the schools provide students with the information, motivation, and behavioural skills to practice safer sex? If yes, at what grade level do you think education about safer sex should begin?

that they had received some form of sexual health education through classes or workshops. When asked about which topics they had learned about, the most common were HIV/AIDS (78%), STIs (71%), and pregnancy and birth control options (65%). Under two-thirds of the teens had learned about communication about sex (61%) and healthy relationships (61%). Fewer teens reported that they had learned about sexual abuse/assault (58%), sexual orientation (51%), or sexual pleasure (42%). Interestingly, when the teens were asked what topics they wanted to learn more about, the order was somewhat different with healthy relationships being the most common response, followed by HIV/AIDS, sexual pleasure, and communication about sex.

A study of first-year university students in Ontario who were asked to assess the sexual health education they'd received in school presents a somewhat more optimistic picture (Meaney, Rye, Wood, & Solovieva, 2009). Overall, the students reported that they were generally satisfied with their school-based sexual-health education and the teachers who had taught it.

Current Sources of Information About Sexuality

When a representative sample of Canadian 14- to 17-year-olds were asked to identify their sources of information about sexuality, they identified school as their number one choice (80%), followed by friends (76%), parents (63%), television (54%), books (52%), the Internet (44%), magazines (39%), doctors, (37%), chat lines (20%), and nurses (19%) (Frappier, et al., 2008). When asked which of these sources were most useful and valuable, they ranked school and parents highest.

Parents and guardians can play an important and constructive role in the sexual health education of young people. In the *Canada Youth and AIDS Survey*, about one-quarter of the boys said they could talk openly about sex with their fathers or mothers, while 37% of the girls said they could talk to their mothers, and far fewer (12%) said they could talk to their fathers (Boyce et al., 2003). About two-thirds of high school students in a New Brunswick survey rated the sex education they'd received from their parents as good to excellent, but about one-half didn't want to talk more with their parents about sexuality (Byers & Grenier, 2003).

In Regina, most high school students said they preferred learning about topics such as pregnancy and STI prevention at school. When the topics were dating and relationships, however, most preferred learning from personal experience, friends, and parents (Hampton et al., 2005).

In recent years, the Internet has become a key source of information about sexuality and sexual health. In a study of online sexual activity among Canadian university students, 17.6% of men and 31.2% of women reported that they had visited an educational website on sexuality in the previous month (Shaughnessy, Byers, & Walsh, 2011). A Swedish study found that adults of all ages sought information about sex online (Daneback et al., 2012). For example, 68% of women and 53% of men aged 25 to 34 reported that they had ever sought out sexuality information online, and 53% of women and 55% of men aged 50 to 65 also reported doing so.

There are many advantages to using the Internet as a platform for the delivery of sexual health information. For example, the information can be accessed anonymously, in private, and at any time a person chooses. The Internet can be useful as a sexual health education tool if a person feels embarrassed about seeking out information about a particular aspect of sexuality. For example, some people may feel embarrassed or ashamed to seek out information about sexually transmitted infections. The Internet can be an especially potent and accessible conduit for the provision of sexual health education to people who may feel isolated or stigmatized with respect to their sexuality. For example, for a young person who is queer or

CRITICAL THINKING QUESTIONS

Have you ever used the Internet as a personal source of sexual health education? If yes, did you feel confident that the information you found was accurate?

transgender and living in a rural community, the Internet may be the only source of sexual health education that is relevant or available.

On the other hand, it can sometimes be very difficult to verify if the information about sexuality being displayed on a website or app is accurate and credible. As more and more people search the Internet to learn about sexuality and attempt to find the specific pieces of information about sexual health, providing students with the media literacy skills to identify reputable sources of information will become an important objective of school-based sexual health education.

Although its producers usually intend it to be used for sexual gratification rather than as a credible source of sexual health education, more and more people are acquiring their assumptions and beliefs about sexuality from online pornography. We don't yet have comprehensive research on how viewing online pornography may affect sexuality. We do know that plenty of people, including youth, look at online porn. A study of Canadian university students found that 72% of the males and 24% of the females had used the Internet to access sexually explicit material in the previous 12 months (Boies, 2002). In a more recent study of Canadian university students, 83% of males and 31% of females indicated that they had looked at sexually explicit videos or photos online in the previous month (Shaughnessy et al., 2011).

There's considerable concern about how online porn may affect young people (Bryant, 2010). As anyone who has surfed the net looking for sexual titillation knows, online pornography often presents distorted pictures of sexual behaviour and relationships. The question is, are people able to separate the fantasy life of porn from the reality of real-life sexuality and relationships, and use the Internet as a safe way to explore and learn about sexuality? Or is Internet pornography an influential source of very inaccurate information and harmful attitudes about sexuality? We don't have enough research yet to help us understand the role, for better or worse, of online porn in teaching people about sexuality.

Innovative Canadian Curricula and Resources

There is a large and growing number of innovative Canadian curricula and resources, many of them available online, to guide and assist educators in providing sexual health education. In addition, there are a number of Canadian websites

Sexual Health Education. Despite the availability of sexual health education in most schools, many young people learn about sex from their peers. Survey data show that most parents want sexual health education to cover abstinence, pregnancy, sexually transmitted infections, abortion, and sexual orientation.

Jonathan Nourok/Photo Edit Inc.

designed to provide credible sexual health education to different audiences. Below is a sampling of some these materials.

An Ontario group led by University of Waterloo researcher B. J. Rye (2008) developed and tested *Girl Time: Grade 7/8 Healthy Sexuality Program*, based on the IMB model. The objectives were to encourage young girls to delay sexual intercourse until they were mature enough for it, and to practice safer sex when they were ready. Girls who participated in the program were more likely than nonparticipants to discuss sexual topics with their parents, feel confident about their ability to have safer sex (e.g., by obtaining condoms), and plan to engage in safer-sex practices such as abstinence (Rye et al., 2008).

Media Smarts, Canada's Centre for Digital and Media Literacy (2012) provides an extensive online lesson plan for grades 7 to 9 titled *I heard it 'round the Internet: Sexual health education and authenticating online information*. This lesson plan with student handouts is designed to help educators teach students how to find, access and evaluate information on sexual health on the Internet.

Based on consultation with 500 youth, parents, and experts in sexual health, the Nova Scotia Department of Health and Wellness (2014) produces a book called *Sex? A Healthy Sexuality Resource*. The book was first created in 2004 to be distributed to all Grade 7 students in the province. Designed to be colourful and practical in content, the book provides information on topics such as how to avoid STIs and how to talk to parents about sex.

Alberta educators and researchers have developed and evaluated a theatrical play for 14- to 16-year-olds (Esmail et al., 2007). *Are We There Yet?* is a theatre-based sexual education program based on learning theory. It uses a student-centred approach to present real-life situations that students can relate to. This encourages greater student participation in the play. Student evaluations indicate that the play is an effective means of providing sex education to youth (Esmail et al., 2007).

Developed by Alberta Health Services (2014), *Teachingsexualhealth.ca* provides an extensive range of lesson plans on sexual health topics, online workshops, information on instructional methods, and questions and answers often asked by students about sexuality in the classroom. The site also contains a parent portal that includes answers to common questions that children ask parents about sex and provides strategies for parents to talk to their children about sexuality.

The website *SexualityAndU.ca*, developed by the Society of Obstetricians and Gynaecologists of Canada, provides sexual health information for all age groups. This site contains a section for teachers that includes curriculum materials, as well as guidance for parents and health professionals about teaching sexuality. The website *WeKnowSex.ca*, developed by the Trojan Sexual Health Division of Church and Dwight Canada, in partnership with the Sex Information and Education Council of Canada, is designed to provide university student and young adult Canadian audiences with sexual health information specifically relevant to their needs.

Meeting the Sexual Health Education Needs of Diverse Groups

Sexual-Minority Youth

Many sex education programs don't address the needs of lesbian, gay, bisexual, transgender, and queer (LGBTQ) youth. University of Alberta researcher Kristopher Wells (2009) has analyzed many of the difficulties LGBTQ people face, including feelings of isolation, fear of humiliation, and lack of social support. Grace and Wells (2006) have developed a series of professional-development workshops for teachers, to help them address sexual-minority issues in schools.

The Public Health Agency of Canada (2010a) has published a booklet called *Questions & Answers: Sexual Orientation in Schools*, which provides teachers and other school personnel with guidance on supporting sexual-minority youth. The PHAC (2010b) has also produced a parallel document, *Questions & Answers: Gender Identity in Schools*, to help support gender-variant youth.

Sexual minority high school students play important activist roles in challenging heterosexism and homophobia in schools. They promote inclusivity through such strategies as creating gay–straight student alliances, initiating positive-space campaigns, and sharing LGBTQ resources (Grace & Wells, 2007).

Teachers' organizations across Canada have adopted policies that support LGBTQ youth. The Alberta Teachers' Association has been in the forefront in fighting discrimination based on sexual orientation. Kristopher Wells (2006) has written a *Gay–Straight Student Alliance Handbook*, published by the Canadian Teachers' Federation. Its primary objective is to help Canadian educators create safe, inclusive, welcoming spaces for LGBTQ youth. Gay–straight student alliances (both student-run and teacher-supported groups) are an important means of achieving this objective. The Canadian Teachers' Federation has also published *Challenging Silence, Challenging Censorship: Inclusive Resources and Policy Directives for Addressing Bisexual, Gay, Lesbian, Trans-Identified and Two-Spirited Realities in School and Public Libraries* (Schrader & Wells, 2007), which discusses practical resources to help educators and decision-makers challenge discrimination and promote positive change for sexual minorities.

The development of these resources indicates that many Canadian schools are recognizing the need to address the requirements of sexual-minority youth. Although most Canadian classrooms likely have at least one non-heterosexual or gender-variant student, the bottom line is that sexual-health education is often taught in a strictly heterosexual context. A British Columbia study has found that parents, students, educators, and public health personnel acknowledge that sexual education curricula often fail to address the needs of sexually diverse students (Options for Sexual Health, 2004).

Youth with Disabilities

As we discussed Chapter 4, physical and developmental disabilities can affect sexuality. Although young people with disabilities are as fully sexual as their peers, their specific sexual health education needs are often ignored. This may be the result of inaccurate negative stereotypes about the sexuality of disabled people. This lack of attention is especially problematic since studies indicate that young people with disabilities are more than twice as likely as young people without disabilities to be sexually abused (Murphy & Young, 2005).

In examining key issues related to sexuality and disability, Gina Di Giulio (2003) at the University of Ottawa has noted that the five principles of effective sexual health education outlined in *Canadian Guidelines for Sexual Health Education* can be applied to the development and delivery of education specific to the needs of people with physical and developmental disabilities.

Fortunately, as physically and developmentally disabled youth's right to broadly based sexual health education designed to meet their needs is increasingly being recognized, appropriate curricula are becoming available. The teachers' section of SexualityAndU.ca, for example, provides guides for teaching sexual health education to people with physical and developmental disabilities.

There is a growing awareness of the need for sexual health education programming specific to the needs of youth and young adults with autism spectrum disorders (ASD) (Tullis & Zangrillo, 2013). As is too often the case for adolescents with disabilities, teens with ASD may receive only broadly based sexual health education as a reaction to problematic behaviours they have exhibited. Tullis and Zangrillo

Innovative Canadian Research

SEXUAL HEALTH EDUCATION FOR YOUTH WITH PHYSICAL DISABILITIES

Lauri East and Treena Orchard at the University of Western Ontario interviewed youth with physical disabilities, as well as their parents and health providers, and explored attitudes and experiences related to sexuality and sexuality education (East & Orchard, 2013). The study included four youth (aged 15–20 years), four parents, and four health care providers, and used focus groups to explore the unique needs and challenges of youth with physical disabilities, as well as ways to improve the content and delivery of relevant sexuality education. Youth highlighted the need to discuss disability related issues in general sexual health education classes to counteract the myth that those with disabilities are asexual and to normalize the concept of sexuality and disability. As well, youth expressed a need for more sex positive discussions on topics such as masturbation, arousal, intimacy, and relationships and less emphasis on protection and prevention. Most parents acknowledged the importance of sexual health education; however, some felt that it was not necessarily a priority for socially isolated children with few peer interactions. Parents did not always feel competent to deliver sexual health education to their children and preferred to pass on this responsibility to schools and health providers. Health care providers noted that they sometimes lacked relevant sexuality information on specific conditions and were often unable to address sexual matters due to lack of time and privacy concerns during appointments. Some health care providers also sensed parental and societal disapproval related to the provision of sexual health education for children with disabilities. In general, the study highlighted the need to address sexuality and disability issues among youth, parents, and health providers and to encourage sex positive messages and images of individuals with disabilities within society as a whole.

recommend a more proactive approach, suggesting that in some instances standard sexual health curricula can be adapted to the specific needs of ASD youth. However, some young people with ASD may require sexual health education tailored to their specific needs. Sexual health education for children with ASD may emphasize social rules and privacy issues, while for teens and young adults with ASD, education may focus specifically on social skills related to dating and sexuality.

Adults

Sexual health education is usually associated with the need to provide children and adolescents with school-based programs. This is where the vast majority of research attention has been focused. In many respects, however, adults need sexual health education just as much. Many are at high risk for STIs and HIV. And as people grow older, they often have emerging concerns about sexual functioning and need related education and health services.

The most accessible and credible sources of sexual health education and services for many adults are their physicians. Research suggests that many patients are reluctant to ask their doctors about sexual concerns, and many doctors don't proactively bring up sexual health issues (Wittenberg & Gerber, 2009). A survey of Canadian women found that while 58% had one or more sexual concerns, only 34% had discussed a sexual issue with a doctor (Fisher, Boroditsky, & Morris, 2004).

A survey of North American medical schools also revealed that physicians in training often receive inadequate education in discussing sexuality with patients (Solursh et al., 2003). A study of sexual health curriculum and training in Canadian medical schools found that most programs placed considerable or heavy emphasis on topics such as contraception (98%), prevention of STIs (76%), and sexual violence/assault (73%), but far fewer medical school programs placed the same level of emphasis on topics such as social and cultural differences in sexual beliefs and customs (27%), sexuality and disability (22%), and childhood sexuality (17%) (Barrett et al., 2012).

Fortunately, this situation appears to be improving. Physicians are increasingly provided with guidance on screening patients for STI and HIV risk and on providing STI and HIV education (PHAC, 2010). As public awareness of sexual dysfunction increases, patients may feel more comfortable asking their doctors about sexual function concerns. Television advertisements for erectile dysfunction medications that encourage men to ask their doctors about sexual functioning may make people more comfortable about such discussions.

This greater awareness of sexual function issues combined with a greater emphasis on sexual issues within the medical community has resulted in a substantial growth in the literature advising physicians about interviewing techniques for assessing sexual functioning in male and female patients. Since the 1970s, there's been an exponential growth in the sexual medicine field, to the point where it's now an established academic and clinical discipline (Schultheiss & Glina, 2010). Although there's controversy about the extent to which the medicalization of sexuality is appropriate (e.g., Tiefer, 1996), it's likely that people will increasingly view doctors as important sources of sexual health information and services.

Accessing health care that's specifically relevant to their sexuality can still be a challenge for gay, lesbian, bisexual, and transgender people. Some doctors don't ask their patients about sexual orientation (Dahan, Feldman, & Hermoni, 2008).

Education and Services in a Multicultural Society

Canada is a diverse country with respect to religion, ethnicity, and culture. With each passing year, our society becomes more ethnoculturally diverse as newcomers from a wide range of different cultural traditions immigrate to Canada. This presents a challenge to sexual health educators and health care providers. It's clear that ethnic differences extend to the realm of sexuality (Ahrols & Meston, 2010). Cultural background can influence attitudes towards issues such as marriage, sexual orientation, gender identity and expression, sexual relationships, and sexual health education in the schools.

Canadian studies have found, for example, that East Asian men have more conservative sexual attitudes than do men of European descent (Brotto, Woo, & Ryder, 2007) and that recent Iranian immigrants to Canada tend to have more conservative sexual norms and values (Shirpak, Maticka-Tydale, & Chinichian, 2007). Iranian women often have difficulty communicating with health care providers about issues pertaining to sexuality and reproductive health (Shirpak, Maticka-Tydale, & Chinichian, 2007). And a survey of Toronto teens has found that the extent to which they access and benefit from sexual health services varies with cultural heritage and length of residence in Canada (Flicker at al., 2009).

To constructively engage with individuals, families, and communities with ethnocultural minority backgrounds, it is important for sexual health educators to adopt an inclusive practice approach that acknowledges differences within and between cultural groups. An inclusive practice approach to sexual health education emphasizes the importance of self-determination, cultural uniqueness, and building the capacity to advocate for and access sexual health services (PHAC, 2014b).

An inclusive practice approach to sexual health education includes not just immigrant cultures, but also First Nations, Inuit, and Métis cultures, which have distinct values and norms pertaining to sexuality. This requires consulting and establishing partnerships with diverse communities to create and implement inclusive sexual health education programs and to deliver sexual health services.

Summing Up

The purpose of sexual health education is to help people achieve positive outcomes (e.g., self-esteem, respect for self and others, non-exploitive sexual relations, rewarding human relationships, informed reproductive choices) and to avoid negative outcomes (e.g., STIs/HIV, sexual coercion, unintended pregnancy).

Early twentieth-century forms of sex education for youth often took the form of what was called "purity education" or "nature study." During the 1960s and 1970s, sex education in Canadian schools was typically provided in "Family Life Education" classes.

The Public Health Agency of Canada has published the *Canadian Guidelines for Sexual Health Education* to guide and unify professionals who provide sexual health education in Canada.

The *Canadian Guidelines for Sexual Health Education* are based on the information–motivation–behavioural skills (IMB) model.

The Sex Information and Education Council of Canada (SIECCAN) has identified ten key ingredients of sexual health education.

Broadly based sexual health education programs cover a wide range of topics and are structured so that students can exercise informed decision-making.

Abstinence-only programs focus exclusively on persuading students not to be sexually active.

Research has shown that broadly based programs are more effective than abstinence-only programs in reaching their stated objectives.

Surveys of parents in Canada indicate that the vast majority of them approve of sexual health education in the schools, and most parents also approve of providing youth with information on a wide range of topics including puberty, reproduction, healthy relationships, STI/HIV prevention, birth control, abstinence, sexual orientation, and sexual abuse/coercion.

In recent years, the Internet has become a key source of information about sexuality and sexual health. However, online porn may be teaching unhealthy messages about sexuality.

The sexual health education needs of sexual-minority youth and youth with disabilities are not being adequately met.

Among the challenges facing Canadian sexual health educators is the need to provide high-quality education in the context of a multicultural society.

Test Yourself

Multiple-Choice Questions

1. Which province removed sexual health education from its formal curriculum in 2005?
   (a) Quebec
   (b) British Columbia
   (c) Ontario
   (d) New Brunswick

2. Which of the following is not one of the ten key ingredients of effective sexual health education identified by the Sex Information and Education Council of Canada?
   (a) Giving teachers training and administrative support.
   (b) Including a focus on students' social environments.
   (c) Bringing in guest speakers.
   (d) Evaluating to identify program strengths and weaknesses

3. When surveyed, Canadian teens indicated that their most valuable sources of information about sexuality were
   (a) Schools and parents.
   (b) Parents and the Internet.
   (c) The Internet and friends.
   (d) Friends and television.

4. The Canadian Guidelines for Sexual Health Education are based on a theoretical model called the:
   (a) Social-cognitive model.
   (b) Trans-theoretical model.
   (c) IMB model.
   (d) Health-belief model.

5. Canadian studies have found that:
   (a) Youth want sexual-health education taught in school, but parents don't.
   (b) Parents want sexual-health education taught in school, but youth don't.
   (c) Both parents and youth want sexual-health education taught in school.
   (d) Neither parents nor youth want sexual-health education taught in school.

6. According to the text, the government of which country provides large amounts of funding for abstinence-only sex education?
    (a) Sweden   (c) Canada
    (b) United States   (d) China

7. According to the results of the *Toronto Teen Survey*, when teens were asked what topics they wanted to learn more about the most common response was
    (a) Healthy relationships.
    (b) STIs.
    (c) Sexual abuse/assault.
    (d) Communication about sex.

8. According to the available research, which of the following statements about sexual health education is false?
    (a) Most evaluated abstinence-only programs have resulted in delayed first intercourse.
    (b) Most evaluated sexual-health education programs don't result in earlier or more frequent sexual activity.

    (c) Sexual-health education can result in more frequent condom use among sexually active youth.
    (d) None of the above.

9. According to the Shaughnessy et al. (2011) study, what percentage of male and female university students had visited an educational website on sexuality in the previous month?
    (a) 56.3%, 47.1%
    (b) 38.9%, 22.6%
    (c) 17.6%, 31.2%
    (d) 8.7%, 19.4%

10. In a study of Canadian medical school training, the topic that programs were least likely to place emphasis on was
    (a) Childhood sexuality
    (b) Prevention of STIs
    (c) Sexuality and disability
    (d) Sexual violence/assault

You'll find answers to the "Test Yourself" questions on page 489.

Questions for Critical Thinking

1. Should sexual health education in the schools stick to providing basic information about reproduction and sexually transmitted infections? Or should programs include topics like healthy relationships and sexual response? Explain your answer.

2. Sexual health education in the schools can be a controversial topic. What are some of the reasons why it can be controversial?

3. If you agree that young people should be encouraged to use condoms if they are sexually active, at what age do you think education in this area should begin?

4. If you were given the task of designing a one-hour sexual health education session for the students at your college or university, what specific topics would you prioritize?

CHAPTER SIXTEEN

Sexual Variations

Sarah Ashun © Dorling Kindersley

In Western society, there's a tendency to classify behaviour as "normal" or "abnormal," and this is often the case with sexual behaviours. People often wonder, "Am I normal?" In this chapter, we'll examine a number of sexual behaviours that deviate from the norm. First, however, it's important to clarify what we mean when we say a sexual behaviour is abnormal, or deviant.

Normal Versus Deviant Sexual Behaviour

One approach to defining normality versus deviance is statistical (Laws & O'Donohue, 2012). That is, something that falls outside a statistical norm can be considered abnormal. Put another way, something can be considered deviant because it deviates from the norm. So, for example, only a small percentage of people have naturally red hair. In statistical terms, we can say that, with respect to hair colour, red-haired people are abnormal. A sexual behaviour that's unusual is, by statistical definition, abnormal and deviant. But this statistical abnormality doesn't necessarily make an unusual sexual behaviour problematic or harmful.

A second approach to assessing whether a behaviour is normal is to determine how closely it adheres to the accepted norms of a society. For example, in Western culture, oral sex used to be thought of as immoral and "dirty." It violated societal norms for acceptable behaviour. Oral sex was, in other words, considered abnormal and deviant. Today, oral sex is considered a typical sexual behaviour. This example is instructive, because it demonstrates that societal standards for abnormality and deviance can change over time. Societal standards for sexuality can also vary considerably among cultures.

A third approach to determining whether a sexual behaviour is normal focuses on harm—for the individual(s) involved, for others, and for society. In this approach, a sexual behaviour is considered abnormal if it causes stress, anxiety, or unhappiness for the individual who engages in it, or if it's non-consensual or it harms someone else. The discipline of abnormal psychology, for example, focuses less on how statistically rare a specific behaviour is and more on whether the behaviour causes problems in a person's life or harms or disrupts the lives of others.

These differences in how the terms "abnormal" and "deviant" are used are extremely important. Some of the behaviours we'll discuss in this chapter may be unusual in a statistical sense, and may be contrary to the accepted norms of mainstream society, but they may also be quite harmless for the individuals in question. Other sexual variations can be quite destructive, both for the individuals who practise them and for others.

The Paraphilias

Paraphilia Sexual interest and arousal in response to unusual stimuli such as children, other nonconsenting persons, nonhuman objects, or pain and humiliation. Mutually consenting and unharmful paraphilic behaviours are often referred to as *kinky sex*.

Because of the confusing array of meanings for "deviant" and "abnormal," we prefer to speak about unusual patterns of sexual arousal or behaviour as atypical variations in sexual behaviour, rather than as sexual deviations. The psychiatric community uses the term **paraphilia** which is defined in the American Psychiatric Association's (2013b) *Diagnostic and Statistical Manual of Mental Disorders*, 5th ed. (*DSM-5*) as "any intense and persistent sexual interest other than sexual interest in genital stimulation or preparatory fondling with phenotypically normal, physically mature, consenting human partners" (p. 685). In other words, paraphilias involve sexual arousal in response to unusual stimuli such as children or other nonconsenting persons (such as unsuspecting people who one watches or to whom one exposes one's genitals), nonhuman objects (such as shoes, leather, rubber, or undergarments), or pain and humiliation (Fisher et al., 2011). Paraphilic behaviours that involve mutually consenting adults or unharmful solitary sexual practices can be more simply described as *kinky sex*.

Paraphilic disorder A diagnostic designation for a paraphilia that causes the person distress and/or is harmful to the self or other people.

In an important change from previous editions of the DSM, the *DSM-5* makes a distinction between a paraphilia and a **paraphilic disorder**, which is defined as a paraphilia that causes distress or impairment to the individual or which causes harm to the individual or poses a risk of harm to others (American Psychiatric Association, 2013b). In other words, a paraphilic disorder involves atypical patterns of sexual arousal or behaviour that become problematic in the eyes of the individual and/or potentially cause harm to the self or other people. According to Ottawa psychiatrist Paul Fedoroff, a major factor in delineating paraphilic disorders is that they "involve sex without the possibility of a consensual, mutually reciprocal relationship" (Fedoroff, 2003, p. 336).

CRITICAL THINKING QUESTIONS

When you've heard someone call a sexual behaviour abnormal, what criteria for abnormality do you think s/he's used?

It's important to keep in mind that some paraphilias are generally harmless and victimless. Examples include fetishism and cross-dressing to achieve sexual arousal (transvestic fetishism). Indeed, because behaviours such as cross-dressing don't harm others, some experts, including San Francisco physician Charles Moser and Ottawa psychologist Peggy Kleinplatz, believe that atypical sexual inclinations shouldn't be used as the basis for a category of psychiatric disorders (Moser & Kleinplatz, 2005a).

From this perspective, people who have a mental illness that involves sexuality in some way should be classified according to more generic classifications of psychiatric disorders. Moser and Kleinplatz argue that because unusual sexual interests aren't, in and of themselves, signs of pathology, paraphilias should be removed from the DSM.

Moser and Kleinplatz (2005b) also argue that the section of the DSM on paraphilia is based not on current scientific findings but on political values about what's considered acceptable behaviour. A number of authors have pointed out that sexual preferences for particular types of people and activities are strongly influenced by cultural values (e.g., Seto & Barbaree, 2001). For example, until relatively recently in Western culture, oral sex, anal sex, masturbation, and homosexuality were considered to be symptoms and even causes of mental disorders, but now these behaviours and orientations are considered part of the spectrum of healthy sexual expression (Federoff, Di Gioacchino, & Murphy, 2013).

In their more extreme forms, people with paraphilias usually feel that their urges are insistent, demanding, or compulsive (Fedoroff, 2003; Lehne, 2009). They may describe themselves as overcome by them and tend to experience their urges as uncontrollable, just as drug addicts and compulsive gamblers feel helpless to avert their irresistible urges.

Paraphilias vary in severity. In some cases, people can function sexually in the absence of the unusual stimuli, seldom (if ever) acting on their unusual urges. In other cases, people resort to paraphilic behaviour only in times of stress. In more extreme forms, individuals repeatedly engage in paraphilic behaviour and may become preoccupied with thoughts and fantasies about these experiences. People in this last category may be unable to become sexually aroused without either fantasizing about, or being in the presence of, the paraphilic stimuli. For them, paraphilic behaviour may be the only means of attaining sexual gratification (Lehne, 2009).

CRITICAL THINKING QUESTIONS

Can you think of examples from other chapters in this book that illustrate how standards for what's normal sexual behaviour vary across cultures?

(left) Miranda Langguth/Reuters/Landow, (right) Reuters/Landow

From Paraphilic to Convicted Murderer.
The 2010 case of Colonel Russell Williams in Ontario illustrates an extreme form of paraphiliac behaviour in which the individual's urges become compulsive. Williams' behaviour escalated from stealing and wearing women's underwear to sexual assault and murder.

The person with a paraphilia typically replays the paraphilic act in sexual fantasies to stimulate arousal during masturbation or sexual relations. It's as though s/he mentally replays a videotape of the paraphilic scene. The scene grows stale after a while, and the individual feels the urge to perform another paraphilic act, to make a new "video."

Paraphilias are more common among men than women (Hucker, 2008; Logan, 2008). Because people are generally unwilling to talk about them, the prevalence of paraphilias in the general population remains unknown. Much of what we've learned about paraphilias derives from the reported experiences of people who've been apprehended for performing illegal acts (such as exposing themselves in public), and from the few who have voluntarily sought help or participated in studies. The characteristics of people who haven't been identified or studied remain virtually unknown.

In this chapter, we'll discuss all of the major types of paraphilia except pedophilia, which we'll discuss in Chapter 17. In pedophilia, children become the objects of sexual arousal. It often involves sexual coercion, including incest and sexual molestation (Lalumière, et al., 2005; Seto, 2008).

Fetishism

In **fetishism**, an inanimate object elicits sexual arousal. Articles of clothing (e.g., women's panties, bras, lingerie, stockings, gloves, shoes, or boots) and materials made of rubber, leather, silk, or fur are among the more common fetishistic objects (Kafka, 2010). Leather boots and high-heeled shoes are especially popular.

The fetishist may act on the urges to engage in fetishistic behaviour, such as masturbating while stroking or fantasizing about an object, or he or she may be distressed about such urges or fantasies, and not act on them (Kafka, 2010). In a related paraphilia, **partialism**, people are excessively aroused by a particular body part, such as the feet, breasts, or buttocks.

Most fetishes and partialisms are harmless. Fetishistic practises are nearly always private, involving masturbation, or are incorporated into sexual activity with willing partners (Darcangelo, 2008). Only rarely have fetishists coerced others into paraphilic activities. Yet some partialists have touched parts of women's bodies in public. And some fetishists have committed burglaries to acquire fetishistic objects.

Transvestism

Fetishism appears to include **transvestism**. Although other fetishists become sexually aroused by handling fetishistic objects while they masturbate, transvestites become excited by wearing articles of clothing—the fetishistic objects—of the other gender (Blanchard, 2010). A fetishist may find the object—or sex involving the object—erotically stimulating. The transvestite finds the object sexually alluring only by wearing it. Transvestites are mostly male (Långström & Zucker, 2005). Transvestism has been described among both heterosexual and gay males (Taylor & Rupp, 2004; Wheeler et al., 2008). Many are in committed male–female relationships and are otherwise stereotypically masculine in behaviour.

Fetishism A paraphilia in which an inanimate object, such as an article of clothing or items made of rubber, leather, or silk, elicits sexual arousal.

Partialism A fetishism-related paraphilia in which sexual arousal is exaggeratedly associated with a particular body part, such as feet, breasts, or buttocks.

Transvestism A paraphilia in which a person repeatedly cross-dresses to achieve sexual arousal or gratification, or is troubled by persistent, recurring urges to cross-dress.

Fuse/Getty Images

Fetishism.
In fetishism, inanimate objects such as leather shoes or boots, or parts of the body such as feet, elicit sexual arousal. Many fetishists cannot achieve sexual arousal without contact with the desired objects or without fantasizing about them.

Transvestism differs markedly from transgenderism. It's true that some transvestites and some trans people appear to be motived by autogynephilia, a condition in which an individual is sexually stimulated by fantasies that his own body is female (Bailey, 2003b; Lawrence, 2004), but transvestites are usually sexually gratified by cross-dressing and masturbating, or by cross-dressing and having sex with others. They may also find it gratifying to masturbate while fantasizing about cross-dressing.

Many transvestites have masculine gender identities and don't seek to change their anatomic sex. Transgender people, on the other hand, usually cross-dress because they're uncomfortable with the attire associated with their anatomic sex and truly wish to be members of the other gender. For this reason, some transgender people seek gender reassignment.

Like fetishism in general, the origins of transvestism remain obscure. Evidence of hormonal and neurological abnormalities in transvestism is mixed (Bailey, 2003b). Långström and Zucker (2005) surveyed 2 450 Swedes and found transvestism in about 2.8% of the men and 0.4% of the women. They found that transvestism was associated with separation from parents, same-sex sexual experiences, use of pornography, high rates of masturbation, and paraphilias—namely, sexual masochism, exhibitionism, and voyeurism.

Some men cross-dress for reasons other than sexual arousal, and so aren't true transvestites. Some make their livings by impersonating women such as

Transvestism.
Transvestites cross-dress for sexual arousal and gratification.

Marilyn Monroe and Madonna on stage and are not motivated by sexual arousal. Among some segments of the gay community, it's fashionable to masquerade as a woman. Gay men don't usually cross-dress to become sexually stimulated.

Transvestic behaviours can range from wearing a single female garment when alone, to sporting a dress, wig, makeup, and feminine mannerisms at a transvestite club. Some transvestites become sexually aroused by masquerading as women and attracting the interest of unsuspecting males. They sometimes entice these men, stringing them along until they find some excuse to back out before their anatomic sex is revealed. The great majority of transvestites don't engage in antisocial or illegal behaviour. Most practise their sexual predilections in private and would be horrified to be discovered by associates while dressed in female attire.

Kathleen Cairns, a Calgary therapist, has found that wives of cross-dressers required several sessions with therapists to deal with the fear, betrayal, and grief they experience upon learning of their husbands' behaviour (Cairns, 1997). Wives were far more concerned than their husbands about their children finding out about the cross-dressing.

Exhibitionism

Exhibitionists ("flashers") have persistent, powerful urges and sexual fantasies that involve exposing their genitals to unsuspecting strangers, to achieve sexual arousal or gratification (Langstrom, 2010). They either act on the urges or find them

Exhibitionism A paraphilia characterized by persistent, powerful urges and sexual fantasies that involve exposing one's genitals to unsuspecting strangers. The exhibitionist achieves sexual arousal or gratification from this behaviour.

disturbing. Exhibitionists are almost always male, although there are some female exhibitionists (Hugh-Jones et al., 2005).

What we know of exhibitionists, like most people with paraphilias, is almost entirely derived from studies of men who've been apprehended or treated by mental-health professionals (Langevin, 2006). Such knowledge may yield a biased picture because relatively few incidents result in apprehension and conviction. The characteristics of most perpetrators may thus differ from those of people who are available for study.

About 4% of the males in a national probability sample reported exposing their genitals to obtain sexual pleasure; the prevalence dropped to about 2% for women (Murphy & Page, 2008). A survey of women at U.S. universities found exposure to exhibitionism to be widespread. About 32% to 39% report running into a "flasher" (Murphy & Page, 2008). A majority of the women had been approached for the first time (some had been approached more than once) by 16 years of age. Few of the women had reported these incidents to the police. The clinical definition of exhibitionism involves exposure to a stranger, but about one-third (36%) of the incidents among the college women were committed by acquaintances, relatives, or "good friends."

Based on the available information, the typical exhibitionist is thought to be young, lonely, or in an unhappy male–female relationship, and sexually repressed. An exhibitionist may claim that sex with his regular partner is reasonably satisfactory, but that he also experiences the compulsion to expose himself to strangers. Many exhibitionists are single, however. They typically have difficulties relating to women and are unable to establish meaningful heterosexual relationships (Leue et al., 2004; Murphy & Page, 2008).

Exhibitionism usually begins before age 18 (American Psychiatric Association, 2012). The urge to "flash," if not the actual act, usually begins in early adolescence, generally between the ages of 13 and 16. The frequency of exhibitionism declines markedly after age 40 (American Psychiatric Association, 2012). The typical exhibitionist doesn't attempt further sexual contact with the victim.

The police may sometimes trivialize exhibitionism as a "nuisance crime," but the psychological consequences can be serious for victims, especially young children. Victims may feel violated and may be bothered by recurrent images or nightmares. They may also develop fears of venturing out on their own. Moreover, exhibitionists are highly likely to repeat their crimes, even if they spend time in prison for them (Langevin et al., 2004).

An Ontario study of exhibitionists who were repeat offenders found that 12% were also convicted of other sexual offences, and 17% were convicted of violent crimes (Rabinowitz et al., 2002). Another Ontario study (Firestone et al., 2006a) found that men who exhibit may be at high risk for engaging in more serious offences. About one-third of the sample in the second study went on to commit sexual or violent offences.

Some evidence suggests that exhibitionists may attempt to assert their masculinity by evoking

BlueSkyImages/Fotolia

An Exhibitionist?
How do the motives of an exotic dancer differ from that of a para-philic exhibitionist?

responses from their victims, or that they exhibit themselves to express hostility toward women (Murphy & Page, 2008). A number of exhibitionists have reported that they've hoped the women would enjoy the experiences and be impressed with the size of their penises (Langevin et al., 1979).

Other studies show exhibitionists to be shy, dependent, passive, lacking in sexual and social skills, and even inhibited (Leue et al., 2004). Exhibitionists who are socially shy or inadequate may be using exhibitionism as a substitute for the intimate relationships they can't develop.

Exhibitionists and some other people with paraphilias may find the risk of being caught to heighten their erotic response because it causes a rush of stress hormones that are chemically similar to testosterone (Haake et al., 2003). The exhibitionist may even purposefully increase the risk, as by exposing himself in the same location in his own, easily identifiable car.

The preferred victims are typically girls or young women. The typical exhibitionist drives up to or walks in front of a stranger and exposes his penis. In one sample of 130 exhibitionists, about 50% reported that they always or nearly always had erections when they exposed themselves (Langevin et al., 1979). After his victim registers fear, disgust, confusion, or surprise, an exhibitionist typically covers himself and flees. He usually masturbates, either while exposing himself or shortly afterward while thinking about the act and the victim's response (American Psychiatric Association, 2012).

Definitions of exhibitionism also bring into focus the boundaries between normal and abnormal behaviour (Hugh-Jones et al., 2005; Laws & O'Donohue, 2012). People in intimate relationships may enjoy and become sexually aroused by showing their bodies to their partners, especially if the displays also arouse the partners. The behaviour is exhibitionist in some respects—but is it appropriate to label it as abnormal? If we assume both partners are consenting and the behaviour isn't motivated by a person's overwhelming, uncontrollable urge to expose his genitals, then we're likely to see the behaviour as harmless fun, rather than abnormal.

And we might ask whether exotic dancers (strippers) are exhibitionists. After all, aren't they exposing themselves to strangers? Yes, they are, but they are not exhibitionist in the paraphilic sense. They're more successful at their work if they sexually excite their audiences, but their audiences are not unsuspecting victims. They pay for the privilege of watching. The main motivation of exotic dancers is earning a living rather than their own sexual gratification (Philaretou, 2006).

Obscene Phone Calling (Telephone Scatologia)

Like exhibitionists, obscene phone callers (almost all of whom are male) seek to become sexually aroused by shocking their victims (Briken et al., 2005; Pakhomou, 2006). Whereas an exhibitionist exposes his genitals to produce the desired response, the obscene phone caller "exposes" himself verbally by uttering obscenities and sexual provocations to a nonconsenting person. The *DSM* labels this type of paraphilia **telephone scatologia** (American Psychiatric Association, 2013b). People practising chat scatologia are sexually aroused by sending obscene e-mails, instant messages, and chat-room messages (Abal et al., 2003; Quayle, 2008). These behaviours are sometimes considered a form of exhibitionism.

Telephone scatologia A paraphilia characterized by the making of obscene telephone calls.

Relatively few obscene callers are women (Quayle, 2008). Women who are charged with such offences are generally motivated by rage for some actual or fantasized rejection rather than the desire for sexual arousal. They use the phone to hurl sexual invectives against men who they feel have wronged them. By contrast, male obscene phone callers are generally motivated by a desire for sexual excitement and usually choose their victims randomly from the phone book or by chance dialing. They typically masturbate during or shortly after the phone calls. Most

Applied Knowledge

RESPONDING TO EXHIBITIONISTS AND OBSCENE PHONE CALLERS

How to Respond to an Exhibitionist

It's understandable that if you're an unsuspecting woman who's confronted by an exhibitionist, you may react with shock, surprise, or fear. Unfortunately, your display of shock or fear may reinforce the flasher's tendency to expose himself.

You may fear that the flasher, who has already broken at least one social code, is likely to assault you physically, as well. Fortunately, most exhibitionists don't seek actual sexual contact with their victims and run away before they can be apprehended by police or passersby.

When possible, showing no reaction or simply continuing on your way may be the best response. If you do want to respond to the flasher, you might calmly say something like "You really need professional help. You should see a professional to help you with this problem." You should then promptly report the incident to police, so authorities can apprehend the offender.

How to Respond to an Obscene Phone Caller

What should you do if you receive an obscene phone call? Advice generally parallels that given to women who are victimized by exhibitionists. Above all, remain calm and don't reveal shock or fright, because such reactions tend to reinforce the caller's behaviour and increase the probability of repeat calls.

You may be best advised to say nothing at all and gently hang up the phone. Or you might offer a brief response that alludes to the caller's problems before hanging up. You might say in a calm but strong voice, "It's unfortunate that you have this problem. I think you should seek professional help."

If you receive repeated calls, you might request an unlisted number or contact the police about tracing the calls. Many women list themselves only by their initials in the phone directory, to disguise their gender. This practise is so widespread, however, that obscene callers may assume people listed by initials are women who live alone.

obscene telephone callers also engage in other paraphilic acts, especially voyeurism and exhibitionism (Heil & Simons, 2008).

There are many patterns of obscene phone calling. Some callers limit themselves to obscenities. Others make sexual overtures. Some just breathe heavily into the receiver. Others describe their masturbatory activities to their victims. Some profess to have previously met the victims at social gatherings or through mutual acquaintances. Some even present themselves as "taking a sex survey," and ask a series of personally revealing questions.

The typical obscene phone caller is a socially inadequate heterosexual male who has difficulty forming intimate relationships with women (Leue et al., 2004). The relative safety and anonymity of the telephone may shield him from the risk of rejection (Leue et al., 2004). Reactions of shock or fright from his victims may fill him with the feelings of power and control that are lacking in his life, especially in his relationships with women. The obscenities may vent rage that he holds against women who have rejected him.

Obscene phone calls are illegal, but it's been difficult for authorities to track down perpetrators. Call tracing can help police track offending phone callers. Call tracing works in different ways in different locales. Caller ID shows the caller's telephone number on a display panel on the receiving party's telephone. In some locales, people can program their telephone services, so callers from private or anonymous numbers (i.e., numbers that don't provide caller ID) receive messages stating that the recipients only accept calls from people who provide their phone numbers or names. These services may deter some obscene callers, but others may use public phones instead of their home phones.

Voyeurism

Voyeurism involves strong, repetitive urges to watch unsuspecting strangers who are naked, disrobing, or engaged in sexual activity (Lavin, 2008). The voyeur becomes sexually aroused by the act of watching and typically doesn't seek sexual relations with the person he observes. Like fetishism and exhibitionism, voyeurism is more common among males than females (Langstrom, 2010). It usually begins before age 15. In Toronto, Kurt Freund and his colleagues found that 12% of university males and 23% of a sample of community males had masturbated while watching females who were unaware of their presence (Freund et al., 1997).

The voyeur may masturbate while peeping, or afterward while replaying the incident in his imagination or engaging in voyeuristic fantasies. The voyeur may fantasize about making love to the observed person but have no intention of actually doing so.

Are people voyeurs if they become sexually aroused by the sight of their lovers undressing? What about people who enjoy watching pornographic films, or stripteases? No, no, and no. The people being observed are not unsuspecting strangers. The lover knows his or her partner is watching. Porn actors and strippers know others are viewing them. They wouldn't be performing if they didn't expect or have audiences.

It's perfectly normal for men and women to be sexually stimulated by the sight of other people who are nude, undressing, or engaged in sexual activity. Voyeurism is characterized by urges to spy on *unsuspecting* strangers.

Research with voyeurs and exhibitionists has usually been conducted with people who've been charged with crimes or seeing therapists. We lack research on general populations. A national survey conducted in Sweden did reveal, however, that 11.5% of men and 4% of women had been sexually aroused by spying on others having sex, and that 4% of men and 2% of women had been sexually aroused by exposing their genitals to strangers (Langstrom & Seto, 2006).

Although most voyeurs are nonviolent, some commit violent crimes such as assault and rape (Lalumière et al., 2005a; Langevin, 2003). Voyeurs who break into and enter homes or buildings, or who tap on windows to gain the attention of victims, are among the more dangerous.

Walter Lockwood/Crush/Corbis

Blurring Boundaries.
How would you describe this scene? Is it voyeurism? Exhibitionism? Or normal behaviour?

Voyeurism A paraphilia characterized by strong, repetitive urges and sexual fantasies related to observing unsuspecting strangers who are naked, disrobing, or engaged in sexual relations.

Innovative Canadian Research

NORMAL VOYEURISM

Waterloo researchers B. J. Rye and Glenn Meaney (2007) conducted a survey to determine whether university students would, hypothetically, watch an attractive person undressing or two attractive people having sex.

Most (84% the males and 74% of the females) said they'd watch an attractive person undressing if they wouldn't be caught doing so. However, far fewer females (40%) than males (70%) said they'd watch a couple having sex if they wouldn't be caught. For both situations, fewer said they'd watch if there was a chance of being caught.

The finding that fewer students would watch a couple having sex suggests that this voyeuristic behaviour is considered more invasive of people's privacy.

A World of Diversity

IT SEEMS LIKE VOYEURS ARE EVERYWHERE!

Traditionally, the voyeur has been categorized as a "peeping Tom" who looks through windows in the hopes of seeing a woman undressing. In recent years, voyeurs have been caught in many other kinds of situations.

The development of small video cameras and lenses has made voyeurism easier. Consider the following examples:

- In Toronto, a man secretly videotaped women using a washroom in a rooming house.
- In Winnipeg, a restaurant owner installed a camera just above the toilet in the women's washroom.
- In Edmonton, a landlord using a camera hooked up to his computer spied on a female tenant living in the basement apartment.
- In Toronto, a man attached the lens of a video camera to his shoe, and used this to film under women's skirts in public locations. He posted these video shots for

sale on the Internet at an "Up-Skirt" website.

- In Toronto, a medical technician used a video camera hidden in a medical laboratory's change room to film women undressing.
- In Peterborough, a man used a two-way mirror in a KFC outlet to spy on women who were changing into their uniforms.
- In Toronto, a man secretly videotaped his sexual behaviour with a teacher's aide, and blackmailed her into giving him money so he wouldn't show the tape to her parents and her employer.

In 2005, Parliament passed legislation that makes it a crime to secretly observe or record a person in situations where privacy is expected. This includes situations where someone is nude or engaged in sexual activity. It also includes situations where a person is fully clothed and someone observes or records him or her for sexual purposes.

In 2010, for example, an Ontario man was convicted of voyeurism for

recording his friends and employees with a hidden camera in the bathroom of his house.

Because of concerns over the misuse of camera phones, some fitness centres and other organizations have banned them, especially in change rooms.

K. P. Adler/Fotolia

Shooting Private Parts in Public Places.
Police are beginning to catch people trying to shoot private parts in public places. The offenders aim compact camcorders up women's skirts in crowded stores, shopping malls, parks, and fairs. They sometimes post the pictures on the Internet, where they often wind up for sale on sex sites.

Sexual Masochism

As long as it occurs with mutual consent, it's considered normal to enjoy some mild forms of pain during sexual activity. Love bites, hair pulls, and minor scratches are examples that fall within normal limits (Laws & O'Donohue, 2012).

But people who prefer or need to have pain or humiliation inflicted on them by their sex partners are **sexual masochists**. A sexual masochist may act on, or be distressed by, persistent urges and sexual fantasies involving the desire to be bound, flogged, humiliated, or made to suffer in some way in order to achieve sexual excitement. In some cases, the sexual masochist can't become aroused unless s/he is bound, flogged, or humiliated by a sex partner. **Sexual masochism** is the most common paraphilia among women (Hucker, 2008; Logan, 2008).

The word "masochism" derives from the name of Austrian storyteller Leopold von Sacher-Masoch (1836–1895). He wrote tales of men who derived sexual satisfaction from having female partners inflict pain on them, typically by flagellation (beating or whipping).

Sexual masochist A person who becomes sexually aroused by experiencing pain or humiliation inflicted by a sexual partner.

Sexual masochism A paraphilia characterized by the desire or need for pain or humiliation to enhance sexual arousal and attain gratification.

Sexual masochists may derive pleasure from various types of punishing experiences, including being restrained (a practise known as **bondage**), blindfolded (sensory bondage), spanked, whipped, or made to perform humiliating acts, such as walking around on all fours and licking the boots or shoes of the partner, or being subjected to vulgar insults. Some masochists have their partners urinate or defecate on them. Some masochists prefer particular sources of pain; others seek an assortment. But we shouldn't think sexual masochists enjoy types of pain that don't involve sex. Sexual masochists are no more likely than anyone else to derive pleasure from the pain they experience when they stub their toes or touch hot stoves. Pain must be part of an elaborate sexual ritual, to provide erotic gratification (Hucker, 2008).

Sexual masochists and **sexual sadists** often form sexual relationships to meet one another's needs (Yates et al., 2008). Sexual sadism is a paraphilia characterized by the desire to inflict pain or humiliation on someone else in order to enhance sexual arousal and achieve gratification. Some sexual masochists enlist the services of prostitutes or their regular sexual partners to help them enact their masochistic fantasies.

It may seem contradictory for pain to become connected with sexual pleasure. The association of sexual arousal with mildly painful stimuli, however, is actually quite common. Kinsey and his colleagues (1953) reported that perhaps one person in four has experienced erotic sensations from being bitten during lovemaking. The eroticization of mild forms of pain (love bites, hair pulls, minor scratches) may fall within the normal range of sexual variation. Pain from these sources increases overall bodily arousal, which may enhance sexual excitement. Some of us become sexually excited when our partners "talk dirty" to us or call us vulgar names. When the urge for pain for purposes of sexual arousal becomes so persistent or strong that it overshadows other sources of sexual stimulation, or when the masochistic experience causes physical or psychological harm, we may say the boundary between normality and abnormality has been breached.

Some theorists suggest that independent and responsible selfhood become burdensome or stressful at times (Knoll & Hazelwood, 2009). Sexual masochism provides a temporary reprieve from the responsibilities of independent selfhood. It is a blunting of one's ordinary level of self-awareness by focusing on immediate painful and pleasant sensations, and on the experience of being a sexual object.

Sexual masochism can range from relatively benign to potentially lethal practises such as **hypoxyphilia** (also known as auto-erotic asphyxia). Hypoxyphiliacs put plastic bags over their heads, nooses around their necks, or pressure on their chests to temporarily deprive themselves of oxygen while engaging in some form of sexual stimulation, usually masturbation. They often fantasize that they're being strangled by a lover. They try to discontinue oxygen deprivation before they lose consciousness, but miscalculations result in death by suffocation or strangulation (Behrendt et al., 2002; Santtila et al., 2002).

Sexual Sadism

Sexual sadism is named after the infamous Marquis de Sade (1740–1814), a Frenchman who wrote tales of becoming sexually aroused by inflicting pain or humiliation on others. The virtuous Justine, heroine of his novel of the same name, endures terrible suffering at the hands of fiendish men.

Sexual sadism is characterized by persistent, powerful urges and sexual fantasies involving the inflicting of pain and suffering on others in order to achieve sexual excitement or gratification (Yates et al., 2008). The sexual sadist acts on his or her urges or finds them distressing. Some sexual sadists cannot become sexually aroused unless they make their sex partners suffer. Others can become sexually excited without such acts.

Bondage Ritual restraint (e.g., by shackles) practised by many sexual masochists.

Sexual sadist A person who becomes sexually aroused by inflicting pain or humiliation on a sexual partner.

Hypoxyphilia A practice in which a person seeks to enhance sexual arousal, usually during masturbation, by depriving himself or herself of oxygen.

Sexual sadism A paraphilia characterized by the desire to inflict pain or humiliation on others in order to enhance sexual arousal and attain gratification.

PBNJ Productions/Blend Images/Alamy

S&M.
An S&M club patron pays money for the services of a dominatrix.

Sado-masochism (S&M)
A mutually gratifying sexual interaction between consenting partners, in which sexual arousal is associated with inflicting and receiving pain or humiliation. It's commonly known as S&M.

Some sadists hurt or humiliate willing partners, such as sexual masochists. Others—a small minority—stalk and attack nonconsenting victims (Yates et al., 2008).

SADO-MASOCHISM **Sado-masochism (S&M)** is a mutually gratifying sexual interaction involving power exchange between consenting partners. A variation is bondage and discipline (B&D), which involves restraining and punishing a submissive partner physically or verbally. Today the term "BDSM" is often used instead of "S&M."

Occasional S&M is quite common among the general population. Couples may incorporate light forms of S&M into their lovemaking now and then, in the form of mild dominance-and-submission games or gentle physical restraint. It's not uncommon for lovers to scratch or bite their partners, to heighten their mutual arousal during sex. They generally don't inflict severe pain or damage.

Most S&M encounters are time-limited. They're often built around particular themes involving role play, such as a schoolteacher and a naughty schoolboy. Both the dominant person and the submissive person agree ahead of time on the rules, and usually choose a safe word that the submissive person will say to stop a particular action if it exceeds his or her limits. Once the scene is over, the participants assume their regular relationship (Dancer et al., 2006).

In a small minority of relationships, referred to as "24/7 S&M slavery," the participants attempt to live full-time in owner–slave relationships. In one study, the participants were almost evenly divided between female and male, and ranged in age from 18 to 72. Of the 66 men, 51 were involved with other men, and 15 were involved with women. Of the 80 women, 74 were involved with men, and six were involved with other women. According to the study respondents, the majority of these relationships were long-lasting and satisfying. The individuals who adopted the slave roles did have the right to exercise their free will, and could therefore leave the relationships at any time (Dancer et al., 2006).

Although some forms of sado-masochism may fall within the boundaries of normal sexual variation, sado-masochism becomes pathological when the fantasies are acted on in ways that become destructive, dangerous, or distressing to either partner. How would you categorize the following example?

A 25-year-old female graduate student described a range of masochistic experiences. She reported feelings of sexual excitement during arguments with her husband, when he'd scream at her or hit her in a rage. She would sometimes taunt him to make love to her in a brutal fashion, as though she were being raped. She found the brutality and the sense of being punished sexually stimulating. She had also begun having sex with strange men, and enjoyed being physically punished by them during sex more than any other type of sexual stimulus. Being beaten or whipped produced the most intense sexual experiences she'd ever had. Although she recognized the dangers posed by her sexual behavior, and felt somewhat ashamed about it, she wasn't sure she wanted treatment for it, because of the pleasure it provided her. (Adapted from Spitzer et al., 1989, pp. 87–88)

There's a subculture in which sexual sadists and sexual masochists form liaisons to inflict and receive pain and humiliation during sexual activity. The S&M

Innovative Canadian Research

WOMEN'S SUBMISSIVE DESIRES

Numerous websites deal with S&M behaviours. Amy Muise (2008), a researcher at the University of Guelph, conducted a study of anonymous women's blogs that focused on sexual desire.

On many of these blogs, the women wrote about their thoughts, experiences, and feelings about their submissive sexual desires. Because of the anonymity of the Internet, they felt comfortable revealing personal aspects of their sexual desires that they usually kept hidden. One woman wrote:

> I want to beg to be fucked and flogged. I know I look more innocent than sultry, but my inner slut is inside, just waiting to be set loose. I have kept her hidden all my life, and now that I've opened the door, my slut wants to share everything.

In analyzing these blogs, Muise (2008) found two main themes. First, the women described in explicit detail the intense degrees of physical arousal they felt, especially in their genitals, in response to S&M fantasies and experiences. Describing these powerful physical reactions helped validate their submissive desires. Second, several of the women put their experiences into the context of trusting love relationships with their partners. For some, this helped legitimize their desires (Muise, 2008).

subculture is catered to by sex shops that sell S&M magazines and paraphernalia, including leather restraints and leather face masks that resemble the ancient masks of executioners. People in the subculture seek one another out through mutual contacts, S&M social organizations, and personal ads in S&M magazines.

Participants in sado-masochism often engage in highly elaborate rituals involving dominance and submission. They stage rituals as though they're scenes in a play (Gross, 2006). In the master-and-slave game, the sadist leads the masochist around by a leash, and the masochist performs degrading or menial acts. In bondage and discipline (B&D), the dominant partner restrains and flagellates (spanks or whips) or sexually stimulates the submissive partner. The erotic appeal of bondage seems to be connected with controlling or being controlled.

Various types of stimulation may be used to administer pain during S&M encounters, but pain isn't always used. When it is, it's usually mild or moderate. Psychological pain, or humiliation, is perhaps as common as physical pain. Pain may also be symbolic, such as when a sadist uses a harmless, soft rubber paddle to spank the masochist. The erotic appeal of pain for some S&M participants may therefore derive from the ritual of control, rather than from the pain itself (Gross, 2006).

Extreme forms of pain, involving torture and severe beatings, are rarely reported by sado-masochists. Masochists may seek pain, but they usually avoid serious injury and dangerous partners (Gross, 2006).

S&M participants may be heterosexual, gay lesbian, or bisexual (Heil & Simons, 2008). They may assume just the masochistic or just the sadistic role, or they may alternate roles, depending on the sexual script. People who seek sexual excitement by enacting both roles are known as sado-masochists. In heterosexual relationships, the partners may reverse traditional gender roles. The men may assume submissive or masochistic roles, and the women may take dominant or sadistic roles (Gross, 2006). The majority of S&M participants are male, but a sizable minority are female (American Psychiatric Association, 2012). Most are in committed relationships.

The causes of sexual masochism and sadism, like other paraphilias, are unclear. Pain may have direct biological links to pleasure. Natural chemicals

Innovative Canadian Research

THE PERSONALITY CHARACTERISTICS OF DOMINANT AND SUBMISSIVE BDSM PRACTITIONERS

Much of the existing research on BDSM lumps dominants (desire to take control) and submissives (desire to be controlled) together. Ali Hébert and Angela Weaver (2014) at St. Francis Xavier University in Nova Scotia used an online survey to compare 80 self-identified dominants and 190 self-identified submissives on a range of personality characteristics.

Dominants scored significantly higher than submissives on measures of desire for control, extraversion, self-esteem, and life satisfaction. Submissives scored significantly higher than dominants on a measure of emotionality. Dominants and submissives did not differ on empathy, honesty-humility, conscientiousness, openness to experience, altruism or agreeableness.

Hébert and Weaver (2014) note that both the dominants and submissives scored in the normal range for all the personality characteristics measured except for altruism. This suggests, based on the data from the wide range of personality measures used in the study, that BDSM practitioners are not very different from people who do not practice BDSM.

called endorphins, similar to opiates, are released in the brain in response to pain, producing feelings of euphoria and general well-being. Perhaps pleasure is derived from pain because of endorphin release or augmentation.

Whatever their causes, the roots of sexual masochism and sadism apparently date to childhood (Barbaree & Blanchard, 2008). Sadomasochistic behaviour commonly begins in early adulthood, but sadomasochistic fantasies are often present in childhood (American Psychiatric Association, 2012).

Despite the popularity of S&M-themed entertainment, such as the erotic novel *Fifty Shades of Grey*, in Canadian society, there's the negative stereotype that people who engage in S&M behaviours are mentally disturbed. Research doesn't support this view (Moser & Kleinplatz, 2005a). There's no evidence that people involved in S&M have greater difficulty than other people in establishing intimate relationships. There's also no evidence that engaging in S&M is distressing or dysfunctional. Kleinplatz and Moser therefore conclude that S&M is not pathological.

Frotteurism

Frotteurism A paraphilia characterized by recurrent, powerful sexual urges and fantasies that involve rubbing against or touching a nonconsenting person.

Toucherism A practise related to frotteurism, characterized by the persistent urge to fondle nonconsenting strangers.

Frotteurism, also known as mashing or groping, is a paraphilia characterized by the desire to rub against or touch a nonconsenting person in order to become sexually aroused. Like other paraphilias, a diagnosis of frotteurism requires that the person act on or be distressed by these urges. Mashing has been reported exclusively among males (American Psychiatric Association, 2012).

Most mashing takes place in crowded places, such as buses, subway cars, and elevators. The man is sexually stimulated by the rubbing or touching, not by the coercive nature of the act. While rubbing against a woman, he may fantasize a consensual, affectionate sexual relationship with her. Typically, he incorporates images of mashing within his masturbation fantasies (Lussier & Piche, 2008). Mashing also incorporates a related practise, **toucherism**, the fondling of nonconsenting strangers.

Mashing may be so fleeting and furtive that the woman may not realize what's happened. Mashers therefore stand little chance of being caught.

Many mashers have difficulty forming relationships with women and are handicapped by fears of rejection. Mashing provides sexual contact in a relatively nonthreatening context.

Other Paraphilias

Let's consider some less common paraphilias.

ZOOPHILIA One of the less common paraphilias, **zoophilia** is often associated with other disorders (Dittert et al., 2005). A person with zoophilia experiences repeated, intense urges and fantasies involving sexual contact with animals. Someone with zoophilia may act on or be distressed by these urges. Actual sexual contact with an animal is referred to as bestiality.

Although the prevalence of zoophilia in the general population is unknown, Kinsey and his colleagues (1948, 1953) found that about 8% of the men and 3% to 4% of the women they interviewed admitted to sexual contacts with animals. Men more often had sexual contact with farm animals, such as calves and sheep. Women more often reported sexual contacts with household pets. Men were more likely to masturbate or copulate with the animals. Women more often reported general body contact. People of both genders reported encouraging the animals to lick their genitals. A few women reported that they'd trained dogs to engage in intercourse with them.

Urban–rural differences also emerged. Kinsey found rates of bestiality higher among boys reared on farms. Compared with only a few city boys, 17% of farm boys had reached orgasm at some time through sexual contact with dogs, cows, and goats. These contacts were generally restricted to adolescence, when human outlets were unavailable. Still, adults sometimes engaged in sexual contact with animals. In Canada, it's a criminal offence to have sex with an animal.

NECROPHILIA In **necrophilia**, a rare paraphilia, a person desires sex with corpses.

Three types of necrophilia have been identified (Holmes & Holmes, 2002). In regular necrophilia, the person has sex with a deceased person. In necrophilic homicide, the person commits murder to obtain a corpse for sexual purposes. In necrophilic fantasy, the person fantasizes about sex with a corpse but doesn't actually carry out necrophilic acts.

Necrophiliacs often get jobs that provide access to corpses, working in cemeteries, morgues, or funeral homes. The primary motivation for necrophilia appears to be the desire to sexually possess a completely unresisting and nonrejecting partner (Holmes & Holmes, 2002).

Many necrophiliacs have other serious psychological disorders.

OTHER LESS COMMON PARAPHILIAS In **klismaphilia**, sexual arousal is derived from the use of enemas. Klismaphiliacs generally prefer the receiving role to the giving role. They may have derived sexual pleasure in childhood from the anal stimulation provided when their parents gave them enemas.

In **coprophilia**, sexual arousal is connected with feces. The person may feel an urge to be defecated on or to defecate on a sex partner. The association of feces with sexual arousal may also be a throwback to childhood.

Frotteurism.
Mashing or groping occurs most often in crowded places, such as subways. It's been reported exclusively among males.

Zoophilia A paraphilia involving persistent or repeated sexual urges and fantasies that involve sexual contact with animals.

Necrophilia A paraphilia characterized by a desire for sexual activity with corpses.

CRITICAL THINKING QUESTIONS

What are some examples of paraphilic behaviours that are harmless? What are some examples that are harmful?

Klismaphilia A paraphilia in which sexual arousal is derived from the use of enemas.

Coprophilia A paraphilia in which sexual arousal is attained in connection with feces.

Urophilia A paraphilia in which sexual arousal is associated with urine.

In **urophilia**, sexual arousal is associated with urine. Again, the person may feel an urge to be urinated on or to urinate on a sexual partner. Urophilia may also have childhood origins.

Theoretical Perspectives

The paraphilias are among the most fascinating and perplexing variations in sexual behaviour. People without paraphilic desires may find it difficult to understand why some people have sexual desires so different from their own. Let's consider explanations that have been advanced from the major theoretical perspectives.

Biological Perspectives

Researchers are investigating whether there are biological factors in the paraphilias. The biological perspective looks at the involvement of factors such as the endocrine (hormonal) and nervous systems in paraphilic behaviour. The tendency of paraphilias to cluster within some families also raises the question as to whether genetic factors may be involved (Labelle et al., 2012).

Studies appear to confirm that many paraphiliacs have higher-than-normal sex drives (Jordan et al., 2011). A German study, for example, found that men with paraphilias had shorter refractory periods after orgasm by masturbation than most men and experienced more frequent sexual fantasies and urges (Haake et al., 2003).

But these studies have addressed the strength of the sex drive, not the direction it takes. More recent studies have used the electroencephalograph (EEG) to investigate electrical responses in the brain among paraphiliacs and others who engage in impulsive behaviour (e.g., Fisher et al., 2011).

Researchers measured what's called evoked electrical potentials to erotic stimuli in a sample of 62 right-handed men, half of whom were considered normal in terms of sexual fantasies and behaviours (the control subjects), and half of whom had been diagnosed as paraphilic (fetishistic and sado-masochistic) (Waismann et al., 2003). The men were shown three sets of 57 slides in random order—57 paraphilic slides that portrayed fetishistic and sado-masochistic themes; 57 "normal" sexual slides that depicted nude women, intercourse, and oral sex; and 57 neutral slides of landscapes, street scenes, and the like. An electrical response labelled "P600" was determined as the best indicator of sexual arousal in men. The researchers found that the main site for evoking the P600 response to "normal" sexual stimuli was in the right side of the brain. The main site for paraphilic stimuli was in the left frontal part of the brain. The paraphilic men showed significantly greater P600 response in the left frontal part of the brain than the control subjects did. Moreover, control subjects were more likely to differentiate between paraphilic and normal stimuli in the right side of the brain.

Another neurological study may offer some insight into masochism. A research team at Massachusetts General Hospital found that the same neural circuits in the brain are often activated by painful and by pleasurable stimuli (Becerra et al., 2001). The researchers discovered that a painfully hot (46°C) stimulus to the hand activated areas of the brain believed to involve "reward" circuitry. The researchers had set out to find ways to help chronic pain patients, not to investigate sexual masochism, but their findings certainly have implications for masochism.

As time goes on, we may learn more about potential biological foundations of paraphilic behaviour. A better understanding of these atypical patterns of sexual behaviour may lead to development of more effective treatments for paraphilic disorders.

Psychoanalytic Perspectives

Psychoanalytic theory suggests that paraphilias are psychological defences, usually against unresolved castration anxieties dating to the Oedipus complex (Friedman & Downey, 2008).

Perhaps the sight of a woman's vagina threatens to arouse castration anxiety in the transvestite, reminding him that women don't have penises and that he might suffer the same fate. Sequestering his penis beneath women's clothing symbolically asserts that women do have penises, providing unconscious reassurance against his own fears of castration.

By exposing his genitals, perhaps the exhibitionist unconsciously seeks reassurance that his penis is secure. It's as if he's asserting, "Look! I have a penis!" Shock or surprise on the victim's face confirms that his penis exists, temporarily relieving castration anxiety.

Perhaps masturbation with an object such as a shoe allows the fetishist to gratify his sexual desires while keeping a safe distance from the dangers he unconsciously associates with female sexual contact. Or he may unconsciously see the fetishistic object as a symbol of his penis.

Is a sadist attempting to defend him or herself against unconscious feelings of impotence by inflicting pain on others?

One psychoanalyst associates a type of male sexual masochism with a history of repressed feelings of sexual guilt and shame (Schrut, 2005). As an adult, the man wants to be punished for feelings of wrongdoing at the same time as he experiences sexual arousal. The pain or humiliation makes the experience okay.

The paraphilias have provided a fertile ground for psychoanalytic theories. Whatever evidence there is, however, consists of case studies and anecdotes, which are open to interpretation.

Cognitive-Behavioural Perspectives

Cognitive-behavioural theorists generally believe fetishes and other paraphilias are learned. An object may acquire sexually arousing properties through association with sexual arousal or orgasm. Alfred Kinsey and his colleagues (1953) wrote:

> Even some of the most extremely variant types of human sexual behavior may need no more explanation than is provided by our understanding of the processes of learning and conditioning. Behavior which may appear bizarre, perverse, or unthinkably unacceptable to some persons, and even to most persons, may have significance for other individuals because of the way in which they have been conditioned. (pp. 645–646)

For example, a boy who glimpses his mother's stockings hanging on the towel rack while he's masturbating may develop a fetish for stockings. Orgasm in the presence of the object reinforces the erotic connection, especially if it's repeated.

Friedrich and Gerber (1994) studied five adolescent boys who engaged in

Psychoanalysts suggest that some cases of early punishment by the mother can lead to the development of aberrant sexual fantasies and deviant behaviour.

PhotoAlto/Alamy

hypoxyphilia and found extensive early histories of choking in combination with physical or sexual abuse. The combination seems to have encouraged each boy to associate choking with sexual arousal.

Cognitive-behavioural explanations of sexual masochism focus on the pairing of sexual excitement with punishment. A child may be punished when discovered masturbating, for example, or a boy may reflexively experience an erection if his penis accidentally rubs against his parent's body while he's being spanked. With repeated encounters like these, pain and pleasure may become linked.

Many exhibitionists, voyeurs, frotteurs, and other people with paraphilias have poor interpersonal skills when it comes to women, and fear of rejection may cause them to avoid normal social interactions with women (Leue et al., 2004). Their furtive, paraphilic behaviours may provide sexual release without the risk of rejection.

Observational learning may also play a role. A parent, for example, may inadvertently model exhibitionistic behaviour to a young son, leading the son to eroticize the act of exposing himself. A young person may also read books or magazines or view films or TV programs with paraphilic content. Media may give young people the idea of trying paraphilic behaviour, and they may find it exciting, especially if acts such as exhibitionism or voyeurism provide rushes of adrenaline.

Sociological Perspectives

Sociological perspectives focus on the effects of the group and of society on individual and group behaviour. Sexual masochists and sadists, for example, require partners. Most sado-masochists learn S&M rituals, make sexual contacts, acquire sexual paraphernalia, and confirm their sado-masochistic identities within an S&M subculture—a loosely connected network of S&M clubs, specialty shops, organizations, magazines, and so on. But the S&M subculture exists within the context of the larger society, and its rituals mirror widely based social and gender roles.

Martin Weinberg (1987) proposes a sociological model that focuses on the social context of sado-masochism. S&M rituals generally involve some form of dominance and submission. Weinberg (1987) attributes their erotic appeal to the opportunity to reverse the customary power relationships that exist between males and females and between social classes. Within the confines of the carefully scripted S&M encounter, the meek can be powerful, and the powerful can be meek. People from lower social classes or in menial jobs may be drawn to S&M so they can enact dominant roles. Dominance-and-submission games allow people to accentuate or reverse the gender stereotypes that identify masculinity with dominance and femininity with submissiveness. Interviews and observations involving sado-masochists suggest that most often, dominance-and-submission relationships tend to be consistent with traditional masculine and feminine gender roles in society (Damon, 2002; Santtila et al., 2002). Although there are many exceptions, in S&M rituals, men more often tend to be dominant, and women to be submissive.

An Integrated Perspective

Paraphilias may have complex biopsychosocial origins (Seligman & Hardenburg, 2000). Might our understanding of them therefore be best approached from a theoretical framework that incorporates multiple perspectives?

John Money (2003), for example, traces the origins of paraphilias to childhood. He believes every person has what he calls a lovemap, which forms in the brain during childhood. The lovemap contains the image of the person's ideal lover, and includes the types of stimuli and activities that become sexually arousing to the individual. In the case of paraphilias, lovemaps become distorted by early traumatic experiences such as incest, anti-sexual upbringings, and abuse or neglect.

Research suggests that voyeurs and exhibitionists have often been victims of childhood sexual abuse (Barbaree & Blanchard, 2008). Not all children exposed to such influences develop paraphilic compulsions, however. For reasons that remain unknown, some children exposed to these influences appear to be more likely to develop distorted lovemaps than others. Genetic predispositions, hormonal factors, brain abnormalities, or a combination of these and other factors may play a role in determining one's vulnerability to vandalized lovemaps (Lehne, 2009).

Treatment for Paraphilias

Treatment for the paraphilias raises a number of issues.

First, many people with paraphilias don't want or voluntarily seek treatment. Ontario criminologist Ron Langevin (2006) followed nearly 800 sex offenders from the 1960s through the first decade of the twenty-first century and found that only about half wanted and completed courses of treatment. Many offenders are seen by health care providers only when they come into conflict with the law, or at the urging of family members or partners.

Second, health care providers may encounter ethical problems when asked to contribute to the judicial process by trying to persuade sex offenders (who are virtually all male) to change their behaviour. Health care providers traditionally help clients clarify or meet their own goals; it's not their role to impose societal goals on individuals. Some health care providers believe the criminal justice system—not the health care system—ought to enforce social standards.

Third, health care providers realize that they're generally unsuccessful in treating resistant or recalcitrant clients. Unless the motivation to change is present, therapeutic efforts are often wasted.

And fourth, sex offenders typically claim that they can't control their impulses. Accepting personal responsibility for one's actions is a prelude to change. If therapy is to be constructive, then, it must break through the offender's personal mythology that s/he's powerless to control the criminal behaviour.

Despite these issues, many offenders are referred for treatment by the courts. Some seek therapy themselves, because they've come to see how their behaviour harms themselves and others (Langevin, 2006).

Psychotherapy

Psychoanalysis focuses on resolving unconscious conflicts that are believed to originate in childhood and to give rise to pathological problems such as paraphilias in adulthood. The aim of therapy is to help bring unconscious conflicts, principally Oedipal conflicts, into conscious awareness, so they can be worked through in light of the individual's adult personality (Laws & Marshall, 2003).

Psychoanalytic therapy for the paraphilias has not been subjected to experimental evaluation. We therefore don't know whether successes are due to the psychoanalytic treatment itself or to other factors, such as spontaneous improvement or a client's willingness to change.

Cognitive-Behaviour Therapy

Whereas psychoanalysis tends to entail a lengthy process of exploring the childhood origins of problem behaviours, **cognitive-behaviour therapy** is briefer and focuses on changing behaviour. Cognitive-behaviour therapy has spawned a number of techniques to help eliminate paraphilic behaviours and strengthen appropriate sexual behaviours. These techniques include systematic desensitization, aversion therapy, social skills training, covert sensitization, and orgasmic reconditioning.

CRITICAL THINKING QUESTIONS

In your opinion, is it ethical for a health care provider to work with clients with paraphilic disorders who don't want treatment?

Cognitive-behaviour therapy Systematic application of the principles of learning in order to modify a problem behaviour.

Systematic desensitization A method for terminating the connection between a stimulus (such as a fetishistic object) and an inappropriate response (such as sexual arousal to the paraphilic stimulus). The individual practises muscle relaxation in the presence of a series of increasingly arousing stimuli, until s/he learns to remain relaxed (and not sexually aroused) in their presence.

Aversion therapy A method for terminating an undesirable sexual behaviour. The behaviour is repeatedly paired with an aversive stimulus, such as electric shock, until the person develops a conditioned aversion to the stimulus.

Covert sensitization A form of aversion therapy in which thoughts about engaging in undesirable behaviours are repeatedly paired with imagined aversive stimuli.

Pedophile A person with pedophilia, a paraphilia that involves sexual interest in children.

Social-skills training A method of behaviour therapy that relies on coaching and practise to build social skills.

Orgasmic reconditioning A method for strengthening the connection between sexual arousal and an appropriate sexual stimulus (such as a fantasy about an adult of the other gender). It involves repeatedly pairing the desired stimulus with orgasm.

Systematic desensitization attempts to break the link between the sexual stimulus (such as a fetishistic stimulus) and the inappropriate response (sexual arousal). The client is first taught to relax selected muscle groups in his or her body. Muscle relaxation is then repeatedly paired with a series of progressively more arousing paraphilic images or fantasies. Relaxation comes to replace sexual arousal in response to each stimulus, including the most provocative.

In **aversion therapy**, the undesirable sexual behaviour (e.g., masturbation to fetishistic fantasies) is repeatedly paired with an aversive stimulus (e.g., a harmless but painful electric shock or a nausea-inducing chemical), in the hope that the client will develop a conditioned aversion to the paraphilic behaviour.

Covert sensitization is a variation of aversion therapy in which paraphilic fantasies are paired with an aversive stimulus in the client's imagination. In a broad-scale application, 38 **pedophiles** and 62 exhibitionists, more than half of whom were court-referred, were treated by pairing imagined aversive images or odours with fantasies of the problem behaviours (Maletzky, 1980). Clients were instructed to fantasize pedophiliac or exhibitionistic scenes. Then:

> At a point when sexual pleasure is aroused, aversive images are presented. Examples might include a pedophiliac fellating a child, but discovering a festering sore on the boy's penis, an exhibitionist exposing to a woman, but suddenly being discovered by his wife or the police, or a pedophiliac laying a young boy down in a field, only to lie next to him in a pile of dog feces. (Maletzky, 1980, p. 308)

Maletzky used this treatment weekly for six months, then followed it with booster sessions every three months for three years. The procedure resulted in at least a 75% reduction in the deviant activities and fantasies for more than 80% of the study participants, at follow-up periods of up to 36 months.

Social-skills training focuses on helping the individual improve his ability to relate to the other gender. The therapist might first model a desired behaviour, such as asking a woman out on a date or handling a rejection. The client might then role-play the behaviour, with the therapist playing the part of the woman. Following the role-play enactment, the therapist provides feedback and additional guidance and modeling, to help the client improve his skills. This process is repeated until the client masters the skill.

Orgasmic reconditioning aims to increase sexual arousal to socially appropriate sexual stimuli, by pairing culturally appropriate imagery with orgasmic pleasure. The person is instructed to become sexually aroused by masturbating to paraphilic images or fantasies. But as he approaches the point of orgasm, he switches to appropriate imagery and focuses on it during orgasm. These images and fantasies eventually acquire the capacity to elicit sexual arousal. Orgasmic reconditioning is often combined with other techniques, such as social-skills training, so desirable social behaviours can be strengthened.

Although behaviour-therapy techniques tend to have higher reported success rates than most other methods, our knowledge about their efficacy is limited by reliance on uncontrolled case studies. Without appropriate controls, we can't isolate the effective elements of therapy or determine whether the results are due merely to the passage of time or to other factors unrelated to treatment. It's possible that clients who are highly motivated to change may succeed in doing so with *any* systematic approach.

Medical Approaches

There may be no medical cures for the paraphilias. No drug or surgical technique eliminates paraphilic ideas while leaving other cognitive functions intact. But some progress has been reported in the use of selective serotonin reuptake inhibitors

(SSRIs), which are mainly used as antidepressants, to treat exhibitionism, voyeurism, and fetishism (Grubin, 2008).

Why antidepressants? In addition to treating depression, SSRIs are often used to treat obsessive-compulsive disorder, a psychological disorder involving recurrent obsessions (intrusive ideas) and/or compulsions (urges to repeat certain behaviours or thoughts). Paraphilic behaviour has an obsessive-compulsive quality. People with paraphilias often experience intrusive, repetitive fantasies and urges (Saleh, 2009).

People who experience such intense urges that they risk committing sexual offenses may also be helped by drugs that reduce testosterone levels

Appropriate Behaviour?
Research indicates that parental nudity that isn't sexually suggestive isn't harmful to a child.

in the bloodstream (Briken et al., 2011; Houts et al., 2011). Testosterone is closely linked to sex drive and interest. In men, antiandrogen drugs reduce sexual desire and frequency of erection and ejaculation. Medroxyprogesterone acetate (MPA, sold as Depo-Provera), which is administered by weekly injection, is the antiandrogen most extensively used to treat sex offenders. It suppresses the male sexual appetite, lowering the intensity of the sex drive and erotic fantasies and urges, so the man may feel less compelled to act on them (Briken et al., 2011; Houts et al., 2011). Antiandrogens do not, however, eliminate all paraphilic urges or completely change a person's sexual behaviour.

The use of antiandrogens is sometimes incorrectly referred to as chemical castration. Surgical castration, the surgical removal of the testes, has sometimes been performed on convicted rapists and violent sex offenders (del Busto & Harlow, 2011). Surgical castration eliminates testicular sources of testosterone. Antiandrogens suppress but do not eliminate testicular production of testosterone. Unlike surgical castration, antiandrogen effects can be reversed when the treatment is terminated.

Evidence suggests that antiandrogens in conjunction with psychological treatment can help some people (Roesler & Witztum, 2000). The value of antiandrogens has been limited by high refusal and dropout rates (Fedoroff, 1995; Roesler & Witztum, 2000). Questions about side effects also remain.

Ottawa psychiatrist John Bradford (2000) has suggested a six-level schema for treatment, based on the severity of the deviation. The first level for any type of paraphilia involves cognitive-behavioural treatment. The second level involves treatment for mild paraphilias, and begins with an SSRI such as Prozac. If the SSRI isn't effective within four to six weeks, a small dose of an antiandrogen is added as treatment moves to level three. For moderate and some severe cases, antiandrogen or hormonal treatment is given in level four. For more severe cases, at level five, this treatment is given by injection. For the most serious cases, especially those considered catastrophic, at level six, the therapist attempts to completely reduce androgens and the sex drive by administering high dosages of an antiandrogen or a luteinizing-hormone-releasing hormone (LHRH).

At all levels of treatment, the goal is to suppress deviant fantasies, urges, and behaviours. Treatment at levels four and five aims for a strong reduction in sex drive, and at level six for elimination or near-elimination of the sex drive (Bradford, 2000). The broader objective of these treatments is to reduce the possibility of recidivism and further victimization.

Sexual Addiction, Compulsive Sexual Behaviour, and Hypersexuality

Three terms have been used to describe a psychological disorder in which a person is unable to control an excessively frequent sexual behaviour: sexual addiction, sexually compulsive behaviour, and hypersexuality (cybersex addiction will be discussed Chapter 18).

The terminology we use is important. While all three terms apply to out-of-control sexual behaviours, they each imply somewhat different conceptualizations of the factors underlying those behaviours, and therefore the most effective ways of addressing them.

SEXUAL ADDICTION   Of these three terms, you're probably most familiar with "sexual addiction," which is frequently used in the media. The concept of sexual addiction as a clinically defined psychological disorder was articulated and popularized by the 1983 book *Out of the Shadows: Understanding Sexual Addiction*, by Patrick Carnes.

In this conceptualization, sexual addiction is similar to other addictions, such as alcohol, drug, and gambling addictions. A sex addict engages in sexual behaviour to relieve anxiety but typically doesn't achieve a high level of gratification. The addict feels bad about the behaviour but is unable to control or resist it. Attempts to stop lead to further anxiety (withdrawal symptoms), which fuels the person's preoccupation or craving to engage in this behaviour. The sex addict becomes caught in a spiral of anxiety and loss of control that often leads to risk-taking, inappropriate behaviours, and excessive levels of sexual activity that take over the addict's life.

Treatments are similar to the treatments for other addictions, including 12-step programs and group therapies such as Sexaholics Anonymous (Schneider & Irons, 2001).

COMPULSIVE SEXUAL BEHAVIOUR   Although the term "sex addiction" is popular, some experts argue that excessively frequent, out-of-control sexual behaviour is not an indication that a person is addicted to sex. They reject the belief that a person can be addicted to a basic human function such as sex the same way s/he can be addicted to a substance such as alcohol or a drug. Rather, they argue that a sexual behaviour that's frequent enough to interfere with a person's ability to carry on with his or her daily life is best seen as an obsessive-compulsive disorder (Coleman, 2003, 2011).

Compulsive sexual behaviour is characterized by recurrent, sexually arousing fantasies that the individual is unable to get out of his or her mind, and intense sexual urges that, when acted upon, temporarily relieve anxiety. Psychotherapy similar to that used for other obsessive-compulsive behaviours is used to treat compulsive sexual behaviour. Medications such as certain types of antidepressants can also be helpful for obsessive-compulsive disorders (Ravindran & Stein, 2010).

HYPERSEXUALITY   Neither sexual addiction nor compulsive sexual behaviour is listed as a specific diagnostic category in the new fifth edition of the American Psychiatric Association's *Diagnostic and Statistical Manual of Mental Disorders (DSM 5)* (APA, 2013b). Hypersexuality, however, was being considered for inclusion as a distinct clinical disorder in the *DSM-5* (Kafka, 2010; Marshall & Briken, 2010) but was, ultimately, not included.

The proposed diagnostic criteria for hypersexuality are similar to those commonly described for sexual addiction and compulsive sexual behaviour (Kafka, 2010):

- Time consumed by the sexual fantasies or behaviours interferes with other important activities and obligations.
- The person repetitively engages the in sexual fantasies or behaviours in response to mood states such as anxiety or depression.
- Frequency and intensity of the sexual fantasies or behaviours causes clinically significant personal distress.
- The sexual fantasies or behaviours are not due to medication or drug abuse.
- The person has been unable reduce the frequency of the sexual fantasies or behaviours.

Like sexual addiction and compulsive sexual behaviour, the concept of hypersexuality as a specific mental disorder is controversial (e.g., Fedoroff, 2011; Federoff, Di Gioacchino, & Murphy, 2013) and, as noted above, was not included as a diagnostic category in the *DSM-5*. Paul Fedoroff at the Royal Ottawa Hospital argues that acceptance of the concept of hypersexuality as a mental disorder would pathologize consensual sexual thoughts and behaviours by linking them with psychiatric problems such as addiction, anxiety, depression, and compulsions. He's concerned that people with mood disorders will instead be labelled hypersexual and as a result will not receive appropriate treatment.

Although we've amassed a great deal of research on the paraphilias and other atypical sexual behaviours, our scientific understanding of them remains in its infancy.

Summing Up

Patterns of sexual arousal in response to atypical stimuli are called paraphilias. In many cases, paraphilias are harmless (e.g., cross-dressing). However, according to the *Diagnostic and Statistical Manual of Mental Disorders (DSM-5)* (APA, 2013b), when a paraphilia causes an individual to be distressed or potentially causes harm to the individual or others, it can be considered to be a paraphilic disorder.

In fetishism, an inanimate object comes to elicit sexual arousal. A transvestite becomes excited by wearing articles of clothing—the fetishistic objects—of the other gender. An exhibitionist experiences the compulsion to expose himself to strangers. The obscene phone caller becomes sexually aroused by shocking his victim. A voyeur becomes sexually aroused by watching and doesn't seek sexual relations with the target.

A sexual masochist associates the receiving of pain or humiliation with sexual arousal. Sexual sadism is characterized by persistent, powerful urges and sexual fantasies that involve inflicting pain and suffering on others in order to achieve sexual excitement or gratification.

Most frotteuristic acts—rubbing against nonconsenting persons—take place in crowded places such as buses, subway cars, and elevators. Frotteurism is also known as mashing.

Zoophiliacs desire sexual contact with animals. Necrophiliacs desire sexual contact with dead people.

The links between paraphilias and biological factors have yet to be fully explored.

Classical psychoanalytic theory suggests that paraphilias in males are psychological defenses against castration anxiety.

Some learning theorists argue that unusual stimuli may acquire sexually arousing properties through association with sexual arousal or orgasm. According to Weinberg's sociological model, the erotic appeal of S&M rituals may result from the opportunity to reverse the customary power relationships that exist between the genders and between social classes in society at large.

Money suggests that childhood experiences etch a pattern in the brain—a lovemap—that determines which stimuli and activities become sexually arousing. In paraphilias, these lovemaps become distorted by early traumatic experiences.

Psychoanalysis aims to bring unconscious Oedipal conflicts that prompt paraphilic behaviour into awareness, so they can be worked through in adulthood.

Cognitive-behaviour therapy attempts to eliminate paraphilic behaviours through such techniques as systematic desensitization, aversion therapy, social-skills training, covert sensitization, and orgasmic reconditioning.

SSRIs, which are usually used as antidepressants, tend to curb compulsive behaviour and depress sexual response. They've been used with some paraphilic individuals.

"Sexual addiction," "compulsive sexual behaviour," and "hypersexuality" are terms used to describe excessively frequent, out-of-control sexual behaviours.

Test Yourself

Multiple-Choice Questions

1. Which of the following is not used to distinguish normal from abnormal sexual behaviour?
(a) Statistical norms.
(b) Pain thresholds.
(c) Social norms.
(d) Personal distress and anxiety.

2. Which of the following are most likely to need to risk capture, to heighten their sexual arousal?
(a) Sado-masochists.
(b) Coprophiliacs.
(c) Exhibitionists.
(d) Mashers.

3. People who become sexually aroused by experiencing pain inflicted by their sexual partners are
(a) Partialists.
(b) Sexual masochists.
(c) Sexual sadists.
(d) Toucherists.

4. A man who dresses in women's clothing for the purposes of sexual gratification is labelled as a:
(a) Transsexual.
(b) Partialist.
(c) Frotteur.
(d) Transvestite.

5. All paraphilias:
(a) Pose physical threats to the victims.
(b) Are evidence that the perpetrators are out of touch with reality.
(c) Are more common among males than females.
(d) Can be treated with psychoanalysis.

6. Hypoxyphilia is related to:
(a) Sexual sadism.
(b) Sexual masochism.
(c) Fetishism.
(d) Zoophilia.

7. People who are excessively aroused by particular body parts, such as the feet, breasts, or buttocks, are said to exhibit:
(a) Partialism.
(b) Frotteurism.
(c) Voyeurism.
(d) Transvestism.

8. Which of the following is included as a distinct paraphilic disorder in the *DSM-5*?
(a) Hypersexuality.
(b) Sexual addiction.
(c) Compulsive sexual behaviour.
(d) None of the above.

9. Which approach to the treatment of paraphilia uses social-skills training and systematic desensitization?
(a) Psychoanalysis.
(b) Antiandrogen therapy.
(c) Cognitive-behaviour therapy.
(d) Antidepressant therapy.

10. The image of an ideal lover and of the types of activities a person finds arousing that forms in the brain during childhood is known as a:
(a) Sexual script.
(b) Lovemap.
(c) Gender stereotype.
(d) Fantasy.

You'll find answers to the "Test Yourself" questions on page 489.

Questions for Critical Thinking

1. How do you decide whether a sexual behaviour is normal? Where do you draw the line for yourself? For others?

2. Can you think of an example of paraphilic behaviour that is harmless?

3. Criminal behaviours such as flashing are sometimes referred to as nuisance offences, which implies that they're harmless. Do you agree with this representation? If you've ever experienced one of these offences, do you think your experience has affected your answer?

CHAPTER SEVENTEEN

Sexual Coercion

Ron Chapple Studios/Thinkstock

This chapter is about sexual coercion. As well as actual force or threat, sexual coercion includes *any* sexual activity between an adult and a child. Even when they cooperate, sexual relations with children are considered coercive, because children are below the legal age of consent.

In this chapter, we'll look at diverse forms of sexual pressure and sexual harassment. As we'll see from the statistics, sexual coercion affects large numbers of Canadians.

Promoting sexual health and well-being in Canadian society requires that we not only emphasize and accentuate the positive, life-enhancing aspects of human sexuality but also fully recognize and address sexual behaviour that violates the basic human rights of others.

Sexual Assault

Sexual assault
Any form of sexual activity forced on another person, or non-consensual bodily contact for a sexual purpose.

Until 1983, the word "rape" was used in the Canadian *Criminal Code* to describe forced sexual intercourse. "**Sexual assault**" has replaced "rape" in the Canadian legal system. The American justice system still uses the term "rape," although its definition varies from state to state.

In Canada, there are three levels of sexual assault:

- **Level 1**—Any form of sexual activity forced on another person, or non-consensual bodily contact for a sexual purpose (e.g., kissing, touching, oral sex, vaginal or anal intercourse). Level 1 sexual assault involves minor physical injury or no injury to the victim. Conviction for a level 1 sexual assault is punishable by up to ten years in prison.
- **Level 2**—A sexual assault in which the perpetrator uses or threatens to use a weapon, threatens the victim's friends or family members, causes bodily harm to a third party, or commits the assault with another person (multiple assailants). Conviction for a level 2 sexual assault is punishable by up to 14 years in prison.
- **Level 3**—A sexual assault that wounds, maims, or disfigures the victim or endangers the victim's life. Conviction for a level 3 sexual assault is punishable by up to life in prison.

There's no statute of limitations for prosecution of sexual assault. This means a victim can go to police many years after a sexual assault has occurred, and criminal charges can still be laid.

A central issue in determining whether an assault has occurred, especially at level 1, is whether consent has been freely given. The person has to be capable of giving consent. Someone who's drunk, under the influence of drugs, unconscious, fearful, or under age is unable to give consent.

Underlying the 1983 changes to the *Criminal Code* was the perspective that sexual assault is an act of power and dominance, rather than an act of sex. The Canadian law regarding sexual assault is gender-neutral, recognizing that sexual assault can be committed by women against men, as well as by people against others of their own gender. The law also acknowledges that sexual assault can be committed by a victim's spouse.

It's important to understand that consent for one type of sexual behaviour doesn't mean consent for other behaviours. In one case, an Ontario man was convicted of sexual assault because he'd engaged in anal sex despite his partner's objections. After having sexual relations together for some months, the man had asked the woman about having anal sex, but she hadn't wanted to try it. A week later, during a sexual interaction that had included vaginal intercourse, he penetrated her anally, despite her resistance. The woman later went to the police, and the man was charged with sexual assault ("Sexual assault plea," 1994). In another case, a Toronto man received a jail sentence after he'd removed his condom during sexual intercourse. The victim had consented to having intercourse only if he'd wear a condom, but he continued having sex with her, nonetheless (Oakes, 1994).

In Canada, people who are infected with HIV can be charged with sexual assault if they don't disclose their HIV status to their partners before engaging in sexual behaviour. There have been several such convictions across Canada. (We discussed this topic in Chapter 14.)

Incidence in Canada

Statistics Canada relies on two data sources to track the incidence of sexual assault—the Uniform Crime Reporting Survey (UCR) and the General Social Survey (GSS), which includes data on victimization. The UCR tracks the number of substantiated sexual assaults reported to police, and the GSS asks Canadians whether they've been victims of sexual assault, including assaults they may not have reported to police.

These surveys use different methods to collect data. While the UCR is an important data source for tracking trends in sexual assaults, particularly those of a more violent nature, it doesn't capture the many sexual assaults that are never reported to police.

According to data from the UCR, there were 21 311 sexual assaults reported to police in Canada in 2013 (Boyce, Cotter, & Perreault, 2014). The majority (98%) of these sexual assaults were classified as level 1. The total number of sexual assaults reported to police peaked in 1993 and has been declining ever since, including a 4% decline from 2012 to 2013. This trend reflects a decline in the rate of all three levels of sexual assault reported to police since 1993. For level 3 sexual assaults that are reported to police, victimization rates are four times greater for women than for men (Brennan & Taylor-Butts, 2008).

UCR data from 2013 shows that the highest rates (per 100 000 people) for sexual assaults reported to police occurred in Nunavut (511), Northwest Territories (397), and Yukon (199). Among the provinces, Manitoba (109) and Saskatchewan (95) had the highest rates, while Ontario (57), British Columbia (56), and Quebec (49) had the lowest (Boyce, Cotter, & Perreault, 2014).

The GSS, which is conducted at five-year intervals, uses a different method of data collection. It calculates self-reported crime rates by asking a nationally representative sample of 15-and-older Canadians whether they've been victims of various types of crime during the previous 12 months. Overall, the GSS results for sexual assault were similar in 1999, 2004, and 2009.

In 2009, the GSS revealed 677 000 incidents of sexual assault in Canada, or 24 incidents per 1000 people who were 15 and older (Perreault & Brennan, 2010). Most (81%) involved unwanted sexual touching, grabbing, kissing, or fondling, while about one in five involved more serious sexual attacks. In more than half of all the 2009 incidents, the perpetrators were friends, acquaintances, or neighbours of the victims (Perreault & Brennan, 2010). Seventy percent of the 2009 incidents involved female victims, and 87% involved male perpetrators (Perreault & Brennan, 2010). Sexual assault rates for 2009 were almost twice as high for 15- to 24-year-olds as for 25- to 34-year-olds, and many times higher than for people who were 35 and older (Perreault & Brennan, 2010).

If the 2009 GSS data for women are looked at separately, there were 34 incidents of sexual assault per 1000 women in Canada in the previous 12 months (Sinha, 2013).

As the URC and GSS statistics show, there's a large difference between the number of sexual assaults reported to police and the number that actually take place. Although the two surveys define sexual assault in slightly different ways, making direct comparisons difficult, researchers estimate that only about one in ten sexual assaults in Canada is reported to the police (Brennan & Taylor-Butts, 2008).

In a survey at an Ontario university, 12% of female students reported that they'd been forced by physical threats to have sex, and 8% said they'd been forced by verbal threats to have sex (Rye, 2001). At another Ontario university, a study found that 48% of female students reported that they experienced some form of sexual coercion involving pressure or force (Hartwick et al., 2007). A study of street youth in Toronto found that young women who are homeless are at high risk of being sexually assaulted (Gaetz, 2004).

Occasionally, there have been documented cases of false reporting of sexual assaults. In Toronto, for example, a male elementary school teacher was found not guilty of sexually assaulting a 13-year-old student (Small, 2007). The student admitted that before making the allegations she'd had a crush on the teacher and had left a phone message saying she loved him. The student was embarrassed when the man's wife phoned and said the message was inappropriate. After seeing a television show detailing a sexual assault, the student used the program's storyline to fabricate sexual assault allegations against the teacher, in hopes that he'd be transferred to another school (Small, 2007).

It's important to put documented cases of false allegations of sexual assault into perspective. They're rare, and outnumbered by a wide margin by actual instances of assault that are never reported.

CRITICAL THINKING QUESTIONS

Sexual abuse of boys by women isn't always recognized as traumatizing, but sexual abuse of girls by men is almost universally condemned. Why does this double standard exist? How might it affect boys and their willingness to report abuse?

In Canada, there's a rising incidence of drug-facilitated sexual assault. A study in British Columbia concluded that in 2002, 27% of sexual assaults involved drugs such as GHB (gamma-hydroxybutyric acid) and Rohypnol (McGregor et al., 2004). A survey of 977 sexual assault victims in Ontario found that 20.9% of the assaults were drug-facilitated (Du Mont, 2009). These drugs are typically mixed into drinks served to the victims. Odourless and tasteless, they loosen inhibitions and cause amnesia for up to 12 hours. Victims often have little or no memory of what's occurred after ingesting the drug, and are therefore unlikely to report the incidents.

In Toronto, a man put a drug into a drink and served it to a couple he was visiting. He then sexually assaulted both the man and the woman. In court, the two victims reported that for brief moments they'd observed the accused sexually assaulting one or both of them, but because of the drug's effects, they couldn't act to stop the assaults. The accused was found guilty of sexual assault and of

A World of Diversity

FEMALE SEX OFFENDERS

It's often assumed that women rarely commit sexual offences, if ever. Using police and court records and victim surveys from Canada and other Western countries, however, researchers estimate that women are responsible for 4% to 5% of all sexual offences (Cortoni, Hanson, & Coache, 2009).

Because there's been less research on female than on male sex offenders, we know relatively little about them. Studies have been limited by very small sample sizes and by the fact that most have included only women who have committed more serious sexual offences. Nevertheless, our knowledge of female sexual offending is growing as more research is done.

Although female sex offenders share some characteristics with male sex offenders (e.g., they're likely to have antisocial attitudes), they also tend to differ from male sex offenders in fundamental ways. In a review of the research, Jill Atkinson (1996) at Queen's University has found that female sex offenders are less likely than males to use violence and to deny their actions once they're caught.

Many female sex offenders have been physically or sexually abused as children and are likely to have problems with alcohol or drugs. Their victims are likely to be relatives or acquaintances under 12 years of age (Vandiver, 2006).

One study found that about half of the women charged with sexual offences have acted in tandem with male co-offenders (Vandiver, 2006). In the majority of cases, the male co-offenders have been husbands or boyfriends.

A substantial number of women who have committed sex offences with male co-offenders have been coerced to do so by the males. They may have been persuaded through intimidation or forced to participate in the sexual abuse of children. According to Atkinson (1996), "They usually resist at first, but eventually become passive partners in the abuse as a result of physical punishment or intimidation. These sex offenders tend to be of low intelligence, under-assertive, dependent on men, desperate to maintain a relationship, and willing to participate in and even initiate sexual relationships to please a male partner" (p. 40).

One subtype of female sexual offender is the so-called teacher/lover.

The teacher/lover uses a position of authority (e.g., as an older family member, teacher, or employer) to initiate sexual activity with an under-aged, usually male youth.

Cases of women charged with teacher/lover sexual offences tend to receive a high degree of media attention, especially if the women are deemed to be attractive. There have been several high-profile cases in Canada and the United States in which attractive female teachers have been prosecuted for having sex with their male students. In some instances, media stories have suggested that the boys in these cases have "gotten lucky."

David Finkelhor (2005a), director of the Crimes Against Children Research Center at the University of New Hampshire, notes that the bringing of these cases to court reflects a decline in the double standard that's applied to men and women. Finkelhor suggests that increasing numbers of female police officers and prosecutors are less likely to buy into the traditional idea that boys who have sex with older women have something to be thankful for (Zernicke, 2005).

administering a noxious substance (Small, 2004). More recently, a Toronto area husband and wife were convicted and sentenced to prison terms of six and four years, respectively, for drugging and sexually assaulting another couple they'd met at a bar (Mitchell, 2010).

Some pharmacies in Quebec have begun selling Drink Detective™ cards that people can use to test their drinks for GHB and several prescription sleep and anti-anxiety drugs (Chung, 2010).

Not all drug-facilitated sexual assaults involve GHB and Rohypnol. Researchers who used toxicology reports to look at suspected drug-facilitated sexual assaults in Ontario found that many of the victims had ingested cannabinoids such as marijuana (40.2%), cocaine (32.2%), or amphetamines (13.8%) (Du Mont et al., 2010). The researchers noted that they were unable to determine the extent to which these drugs were taken voluntarily by the victims, but the findings do suggest that a number of different substances can play a role in drug-facilitated sexual assault.

Types of Sexual Assault

One of the central myths in our culture is that most sexual assaults are perpetrated by strangers lurking in dark alleyways, or by intruders who climb through open windows in the middle of the night. In fact, most women are assaulted by men they know (Perreault & Brennan, 2010)—and often by men they trust.

STRANGER SEXUAL ASSAULT **Stranger sexual assault** is committed by an assailant (or assailants) previously unknown to the victim. The stranger often selects a target who seems vulnerable—a woman who lives alone, is older or mentally challenged, is walking down a deserted street, or is asleep or intoxicated. After choosing a target, the assailant may search for a safe time and place to commit the crime, such as a deserted, rundown part of town, a dark street, or a second-floor apartment without window bars or locks.

Sometimes an assailant will use a phony ploy to get a woman to lower her guard. In Toronto, a man posed as a photographer for a university, and asked women on campus if he could take their pictures for a project. After taking the women to a more secluded area, he assaulted them ("Women warned," 2008).

The police-reported data from the 2007 URC show that the victims and perpetrators were strangers in only 18% of the incidents reported in Canada that year (Brennan & Taylor-Butts, 2008).

ACQUAINTANCE SEXUAL ASSAULT Data from the 2007 URC indicates that 82% of sexual assault victims in 2007 knew their perpetrators in some way (Brennan & Taylor-Butts, 2008). More detailed information from 2002 shows that 51% of victims of sexual offences were sexually assaulted by friends or acquaintances, while 28% were victimized by family members (Statistics Canada, 2003a).

Acquaintance sexual assaults are much less likely to be reported to police than assaults by strangers (Fisher et al., 2003), in part because victims may not perceive being forced into sexual activity by acquaintances as sexual assault.

DATE SEXUAL ASSAULT One of the most common forms of acquaintance sexual assault occurs within the dating context. Studies of college women in the United States indicate that as many as one in four reports having been forced to have sexual intercourse by a date (McAnulty, 2012). Date sexual assault (often called date rape) is more likely to occur when the couple has too much to drink and parks in the man's car or goes back to his residence (Cole, 2006). The man tends to perceive his partner's willingness to return home with him as a signal of sexual interest, even if she resists his advances.

Some men may assume that women who frequent places like singles bars are expressing tacit agreement to have sex with men who show interest in them. Some

Stranger sexual assault A sexual assault committed by an assailant previously unknown to the victim.

Acquaintance sexual assault A sexual assault committed by an acquaintance of the victim.

assailants believe a woman who resists advances is just "protesting too much," so she won't appear "easy." They interpret resistance as coyness—in other words, as a ploy in the cat-and-mouse game that to them typifies the "battle of the sexes." They may believe that when a woman says no she means maybe, and that when she says maybe she means yes, especially when a sexual relationship has already been established (McAnulty, 2012). They may therefore not see themselves as committing sexual assaults—but of course they are.

The issue of consent lies at the heart of whether a sexual act is an assault. Unlike stranger assault, date rape occurs within a context in which sexual relations could occur voluntarily. The issue of consent can become murky. The defendant may concede that sexual intercourse took place but claim it was consensual. Judges and juries face the task of discerning shadings in the meaning of "consent." Lawyers on both sides vie to persuade judges and juries to see things their way.

A sexual assault charge stemming from a dating situation often comes down to his word against hers. Her word often becomes less persuasive in the eyes of the jury if it's clear that she consented to mutual activities before the incident, such as sharing dinner, attending a movie, accompanying her date to his home, sharing a drink, and perhaps kissing or petting.

A Closer Look

ANATOMY OF A DATE RAPE

Her Story

I first met him at a party. He was really good-looking, and he had a great smile. I wanted to meet him, but I wasn't sure how. I didn't want to appear too forward.

Then he came over and introduced himself. We talked, and found we had a lot in common. I really liked him.

When he asked me over to his place for a drink, I thought it would be okay. He was such a good listener, and I wanted him to ask me out again.

When we got to his room, the only place to sit was on the bed. I didn't want him to get the wrong idea, but what else could I do? We talked for a while, and then he made his move. I was so startled. He started by kissing. I really liked him, so the kissing was nice.

But then he pushed me down on the bed. I tried to get up, and I told him to stop. He was so much bigger and stronger. I got scared, and I started to cry. I froze, and he sexually assaulted me.

It took only a couple of minutes, and it was terrible—he was so rough. When it was over, he kept asking me what was wrong, like he didn't know. He had just forced himself on me, and he thought that was okay.

He drove me home and said he wanted to see me again. I'm so afraid to see him. I never thought it would happen to me.

His Story

I first met her at a party. She looked really hot, wearing a sexy dress that showed off her great body. We started talking right away. I knew she liked me by the way she kept smiling and touching my arm while she was speaking.

She seemed pretty relaxed, so I asked her back to my place for a drink. When she said yes, I knew I was going to get lucky!

When we got to my place, we sat on the bed kissing. At first, everything was great. Then, when I started to lay her down on the bed, she started twisting and saying she didn't want to. Most women don't like to appear too easy, so I knew she was just going through the motions. When she stopped struggling, I knew she would have to throw in some tears before we did it.

She was still very upset afterward, and I just don't understand it! If she didn't want to have sex, why did she come back to the room with me? You could tell by the way she dressed and acted that she was no virgin, so why she had to put up such a big struggle, I don't know.

But let's be clear: it doesn't matter whether a woman wears a sexy outfit, is on the pill, or shares a passionate kiss or embrace with a man. If the encounter ends with her being forcibly violated, a sexual assault has taken place. When a woman says no, a man must take no for an answer.

The problem of date rape has been subject to closer public scrutiny in recent years. Take Back the Night marches on university campuses have become a common form of protest against men's sexual misconduct. Many universities have mandated date-rape seminars and workshops.

GANG SEXUAL ASSAULT   Exercise of power appears to be the major motive behind gang assaults, although some attackers may also be expressing anger against women. An American college survey showed that sexual assaults involving groups of assailants tend to be more vicious than individual assaults (Gidycz & Koss, 1990). Relatively few survivors of gang assaults reported the attacks to police or sought support from crisis centres.

SEXUAL ASSAULT AGAINST MALES   Although rates of sexual assault against males are far lower than rates of sexual assault against females, sexual assault of men is more common than many people assume. According to GSS data, an estimated 204 000 incidents of sexual assault were committed against men in Canada in 2009 (Perreault & Brennan, 2010). In a study of university students in New Brunswick, about one-fifth of the men reported that they'd been coerced into having sex during the previous year (O'Sullivan et al., 1998).

Sarrel and Masters (1982) reported 11 cases of men who'd been sexually assaulted by women, including a 37-year-old man who'd been coerced into sexual intercourse by two women who'd accosted him at gunpoint. In another case, a 27-year-old man had fallen asleep in his hotel room with a woman he'd just met in a bar, and awakened to find himself bound to the bed, gagged, and blindfolded. He'd then been forced into sexual intercourse with four different women, who threatened him with castration if he didn't perform satisfactorily.

Despite these examples, most sexual assaults against men are committed by other men. While they often occur in prison settings, some occur outside prison walls. It's not true that men who sexually assault other men are typically gay. Most are heterosexual. Their motives tend to include domination and control, revenge and retaliation, sadism and degradation, and—when the assaults are carried out by gang members—status and affiliation (Peterson et al., 2010). In recent years the media have been full of stories about men in positions of authority, such as teachers and priests, assaulting boys. Male sexual assault survivors may suffer traumatic effects similar to those suffered by female survivors (Peterson et al., 2010).

Males can also be assaulted in college sports hazing rituals. A rookie football player withdrew from McGill University after his teammates forced him down onto all fours and prodded him anally with a broom handle. Other rookies were coerced into simulating oral sex on one another in their boxer shorts (Peritz, 2005).

Combatting Sexual Assault on Campus.
Many Canadian universities and colleges have instituted awareness programs to combat the problem of date rape and other types of sexual assault on campus.

SEXUAL ASSAULT AGAINST GAY AND BISEXUAL MALES   There have been few studies of sexual assault against gay and bisexual men. Researchers in Vancouver (Ratner et al., 2003) asked 358 19- to 35-year-old gay and bisexual men if they'd ever been forced into unwanted sex. Fourteen percent reported that they'd been coerced or forced into sex before the age of 14. Half of the reported incidents involved forced receptive anal intercourse. Men who'd been sexually coerced had lower self-esteem and higher rates of depression. They were more likely to abuse alcohol and to have attempted suicide.

PARTNER OR MARITAL SEXUAL ASSAULT   Although there are many countries where it's legal for a husband to sexually assault his wife, in Canada it's clearly illegal.

Partner sexual assault is probably more common than date rape, because a sexual relationship has already been established (Osman, 2003). A "traditional" man may believe it's his wife's duty to satisfy his sexual needs, even when she's not interested. Men who are better educated and less rigid regarding stereotypes about sexual relationships are less likely to sexually assault their partners (Basile, 2002).

Data from the United States suggests that partner sexual assault is more likely to go unreported—and, often, unrecognized by survivors as actually being sexual assault (Strebeigh, 2009). Women may also fail to report partner sexual assault because of fear that no one will believe them.

Motives for partner sexual assault vary. Some people use sex to dominate their partners. Others use it to degrade their partners, especially after arguments. Sexual coercion often occurs within a pattern of violence and physical intimidation

Innovative Canadian Research

SEXUALLY AGGRESSIVE BEHAVIOUR IN BARS AND CLUBS

Kathryn Graham and colleagues (2014) from the Centre for Addiction and Mental Health in Toronto investigated incidents of sexual aggression observed in 118 Toronto area bars. Drawing on data compiled from a broader survey of over 1000 aggressive incidents in these bars and clubs, this study focused on 258 incidents that involved behaviour with a sexual component. Sexual behaviour was broadly defined to include both verbal and physical incidents that had a likely or obvious intent to cause harm to the target. The study considered only male-initiated incidents towards female targets, since these represented almost 90% of all recorded sexually aggressive incidents.

In considering incidents of sexual aggression in bars, the authors refer to the phenomenon of opportunistic offending. This is the tendency of perpetrators to display sexually aggressive behaviour in settings where it is sometimes more tolerated and overlooked (e.g., bars), and to avoid such behaviour in public settings where it is not socially acceptable. The study notes that the aggressive behaviour of men was not related to their level of intoxication. Rather, the persistence of aggressive men increased with the intoxication levels of their female victims, suggesting that intoxicated women were being targeted. Graham et al. (2014) conclude that most aggressive incidents were intentional and could not be blamed on the effects of alcohol consumption by male initiators. The most common responses to aggression were evasion and avoidance. However, responses from female targets became more forceful as their level of intoxication increased. Third party intervention (i.e., by friends of initiator or target, staff) occurred in only 21% of incidents, and in some cases this intervention took the form of encouragement for the actions of the initiator.

(Johnson, 2003). In some cases, though, violence is limited to the sexual relationship. Some men see sex as the solution to disputes. They think that if they can force their partners into sex, "Everything will be okay."

Victims of partner sexual assault may fear serious injury or death just as much as victims of stranger sexual assault do. The long-term effects of partner sexual assault are also similar to those experienced by survivors of stranger sexual assault, including fear, depression, and sexual dysfunction (Kaczmarek et al., 2006; Polusny & Arbisi, 2006). Moreover, the woman who's sexually assaulted by her husband usually has to live with her assailant, and may fear repeated attacks.

The Complexity of Consent

A central issue in cases of sexual assault is that of sexual consent. As presented in "A Closer Look: Anatomy of a Date Rape," differing perceptions of sexual consent can be problematic in dating situations.

Melanie Beres (2007), a University of Alberta researcher, conducted a comprehensive review and analysis of the research on sexual consent. She found that sexual consent has been conceptualized and defined in numerous ways. Many scholars have discussed sexual consent without defining the term at all, assuming that everyone shares the same understanding of its meaning. Following are some of Beres's key findings from the literature on sexual consent:

- Some researchers argue that a person who says yes to sexual advances is giving consent, even under coercion or force. Others disagree, and state that consent can be given only if there is no coercion.
- Researchers disagree over whether sexual consent must be given verbally. For example, does sexual consent mean a person must say yes to a sexual request, or is it sufficient for the person to refrain from stopping a partner's physical advances, or does sexual consent involve a combination of the two?
- Sexual consent is usually seen as overly simplistic, involving a yes or no response to a sexual request.
- Only a few researchers have studied the ways people actually ask for and give consent.
- Research on—and discussion of—sexual consent has mainly taken place in the context of a heterosexual bias. This perspective mistakenly assumes that sexual consent from men isn't needed, because of the stereotype that men are always willing to have sex.
- Researchers usually assume women seldom initiate sexual encounters.
- Sex educators provide female students with strategies for saying no to sex, but not for saying yes.
- Little research has been done on sexual consent involving gay men and lesbians.
- Most of the research on sexual consent has been related to violent sexual activity. Research about the more common, consensual sexual interactions is limited.

Beres (2007) believes it's essential for researchers to clearly define sexual consent. She also stresses the need to develop interactive models using qualitative research methods. This approach will help us better understand how sexual consent is perceived, and how it's actually communicated within sexual relationships. An example of such research is Beres's study of communicating sexual consent with casual sex partners, which we discussed Chapter 7.

Terry Humphreys (2007; Humphreys & Brousseau, 2010) at Trent University in Peterborough has also researched the complexities of the sexual consent process. He's especially critical of educational programs that assume simply saying no means no.

Humphreys's research indicates that the sexual-consent process involves many factors. One of his main findings is that most women and men have nonverbal means of asking for and giving sexual consent. Typically, people indirectly indicate consent in a number of ways, such as by *not* pulling away from their partners. Most people find it very awkward to make direct, verbal sexual requests. If a person does say no to a sexual request, most men and women believe s/he should give a reason for the refusal. Humphreys's research is discussed in more detail Chapter 7.

With respect to sexual assault prevention education programming on college campuses, Jozkowski and Humphreys (2014) offer a critique of current sexual consent promotion frameworks and provide suggestions for future programs to reduce sexual assault on campus. Many campus-based programs emphasize the need for women to be more clear in their communication of affirmative consent ("Yes means Yes") and refusal ("No means No"). The authors argue that while these types of programs can help to raise awareness, the extent to which they are effective in reducing sexual assault is questionable. Jozkowski and Humphreys endorse a "sociocultural approach" that focuses on the following factors:

- Focusing attention away from the idea that sex necessarily involves an initiator and a recipient of sexual behaviour and instead promotes a more collaborative effort of a couple to ensure positive, consensual sex.
- College and university educational programs, as well as elementary and secondary school programs, should address gender inequality.
- Educational programs at all levels should teach critical awareness of media messages that objectify women and promote violence, discrimination, and sexism.
- Sexual assault prevention education should focus on deconstructing the sociocultural determinants of sexual violence, including institutions of male domination and entitlement.

Social Attitudes and Myths

Many people believe a number of myths about sexual assault, such as that women say no when they mean yes, that women like men who are pushy and forceful, and that women dress in a way that invites assault. Yet another myth is that deep down, women want to be assaulted (Osman, 2003).

Sexual assault myths create a social climate that legitimizes sexual assault. Though both men and women may subscribe to sexual assault myths, researchers at the University of British Columbia have found that male students are more accepting of these myths than female students are (Kennedy & Gorzalka, 2002). There are also ethnic differences; Asian students are more likely to accept these myths than students from Western backgrounds are. The longer the Asian students have been in Canada, the less likely they are to accept such myths.

Men also cling more stubbornly to myths about date sexual assault, even after taking classes designed to challenge these views (Maxwell et al., 2003). Such myths don't occur in a social vacuum. They're related to other social attitudes, including gender-role stereotyping, a perception of sex as adversarial, and acceptance of violence in relationships (Yost & Zurbriggen, 2006).

Many observers contend that our society encourages sexual assault by socializing males into socially and sexually dominant roles. Males are often conditioned from childhood to engage in aggressive and competitive behaviour.

Research with university students supports the connection between stereotypical masculine identification and tendencies to sexual assault. In New Brunswick, researchers compared students who believed in strictly traditional gender roles with students who held less rigid attitudes. Men who engaged in coercive sex were more likely to hold more traditional views of women's roles, and more likely to hold coercion-supportive beliefs (Byers & Eno, 1991). Men with traditional views were more likely to ignore partners who said they didn't want to have sex. The

CRITICAL THINKING QUESTIONS

Images of women and girls in popular media (music videos, advertising) have been said to perpetuate sexual assault myths. Can you think of any images that might support this claim?

Applied Knowledge

THE DATE-RAPE DRUG

Rophies, roofies, R2, roofenol, roachies, la rocha, rope, or whatever you call it, the date-rape drug is easily slipped into the drinks of unsuspecting women. The drug has no taste or odour, so the victims don't realize anything has happened.

It lowers their inhibitions, lessens their ability to resist sexual assault, and, when mixed with alcohol, often causes blackouts that prevent victims from remembering what's happened to them. For this reason, Rohypnol has also been called the forget pill, trip-and-fall, and mind erasers.

Rohypnol is often used with other drugs, such as alcohol, to create a dramatic high. Rohypnol intoxication is generally associated with impaired judgment, memory, and motor skills and can make a victim unable to resist or recall a sexual attack.

About ten minutes after taking it, the victim may feel dizzy and disoriented, simultaneously too hot and too cold, or nauseated. She may have difficulty speaking and moving before she passes out, usually about 30 minutes after ingesting the drug. Effects peak within two hours and can persist for eight to 24 hours. Once she awakens, the victim has little or no memory of what's happened.

Rohypnol is prescribed as a treatment for insomnia and a sedative hypnotic in other countries. It's in the same class of drugs as the tranquillizer Valium, but about ten times stronger.

Here are some tips for avoiding problems with Rohypnol:

- Be wary about accepting drinks from anyone you don't know well or long enough to trust.
- Don't put your drink down and leave it unattended, even to go to the bathroom.
- If you think you've been a victim, notify authorities immediately.

Source: Based on National Institute on Drug Abuse. (2010). Club drugs (GHB, ketamine, and Rohypnol). NIDA infofacts. United States Department of Health and Human Services. Retrieved from www.drugabuse.gov/Infofacts/RohypnolGHB.html

---

traditionalists express a greater likelihood of committing sexual assault, were more accepting of violence against women, were more likely to blame victims for their assaults, and were more aroused by depictions of sexual assault than men who didn't hold traditional views (Raichle & Lambert, 2000).

Young men may come to view dates not as chances to get to know their partners but as opportunities for sexual conquest, in which the object is to overcome their partners' resistance. Sexual behaviour and sports are linked in our culture through common idioms. A young man may be taunted by his friends after a date with such questions as "Did you score?" or, more bluntly, "Did you get in?"

Some researchers, such as Queen's University psychologist Vernon Quinsey, hypothesize that evolutionary psychology can account for the role of male sexual competitiveness in sexual assault. According to this perspective, during the course of human evolution, the main constraint on male reproductive success was the limited number of potential mating partners, and as a result, males were obliged to compete with one another for mating opportunities. To increase their opportunities for successfully perpetuating their genes, some men engaged in sexual coercion (Quinsey, 2002).

Although the evolutionary perspective may view sexual aggressiveness in men, as expressed in the prehistoric environment, as "natural," sexual assault in contemporary society is inexcusable and criminal, and psychologists believe males can *choose* not to be aggressive (Koss, 2003). Perhaps men carry genes that now and then give rise to aggressive impulses, some of which involve sex, but men also carry other genes that enable them to picture themselves in the place of the victim and choose *not* to behave aggressively. Empathy—that is, experiencing the feelings of another person—appears to be more common in women than in men, but it's not absent in men, and it can be cultivated in men, as sexual assault-prevention programs have shown (Foubert & Newberry, 2006).

Sexually Coercive Men

Although sexual aggressiveness may be woven into our social fabric, not all men are equally vulnerable to such cultural influences. Canadian researchers are playing a leading role in identifying factors that predict which men are more likely to be sexually coercive.

Some researchers argue that anger and power are the basic motivations for sexual assault (Groth & Birnbaum, 1979). Those who are motivated by power seek to control and dominate their victims (Mardorossian, 2002). From this perspective, a sexual assault is an attempt "to resolve disturbing doubts about [his] masculine identity and worth, [or] to combat deep-seated feelings of insecurity and vulnerability" (Groth & Hobson, 1983, p. 165). Other researchers believe sexual motivation is an element in at least some sexual assaults (Baumeister et al., 2002; Malamuth et al., 2005).

Much of our knowledge of the psychological characteristics of sexually coercive men derives from studies of incarcerated sex offenders. One conclusion that emerges is that no single type of man commits violent sexual assault. Perpetrators vary in psychological characteristics, family backgrounds, mental health, and criminal histories (Lalumière et al., 2005a). It also appears that most sexually coercive men aren't mentally ill, even though their crimes might strike us as "sick." Generally speaking, sexually coercive men are just as intelligent and just as mentally fit as other people. However, while they don't show deep psychological disturbance, many sexually coercive men do have antisocial personalities that enable them to violate their victims without guilt, shame, anxiety, or empathy (Lalumière et al., 2005a). Some antisocial sex offenders have long histories of violent behavior (Lalumière et al., 2005a, 2005b). Alcohol may also dampen their self-restraint and spur sexual aggressiveness.

For some sexually coercive men, violence and sexual arousal become enmeshed, so they seek to enhance their sexual arousal by combining sex and violence (Lalumière et al., 2005a). Lalumière and his colleagues have found that some sexually coercive men find verbal descriptions, films, and audiotapes that portray rape more sexually arousing (as measured by the sizes of their erections) than other men

Innovative Canadian Research

MALE VERSUS FEMALE VICTIMS OF SEXUAL COERCION

University of Guelph researchers (Hartwick et al., 2007) conducted a study of university students to compare the characteristics of male and female victims of sexual coercion.

More women (48%) than men (39%) in the study had experienced sexual coercion. The main difference between male and female victims was that more women (34%) than men (23%) had experienced coerced kissing and fondling. The rates of coerced sexual intercourse were almost the same (21% for females and 18% for males).

The most common coercive strategies involved getting the person intoxicated and inducing guilt. Men were more likely to be coerced through intoxication, while women were more likely to be pressured into feeling guilty for refusing sex. Strangers tended to use the intoxication strategy, whereas dating partners and friends tended to use the guilt strategy (Hartwick et al., 2007).

do (Lalumière et al., 2005a, 2005b, 2005c). Other researchers, however, have failed to find deviant patterns of arousal in sexually coercive men (Lalumière et al., 2005a, 2005b, 2005c).

Toronto researchers (Langevin et al., 2006) have found that sex offenders tend to come from families with alcohol problems. The researchers have speculated that parental alcohol addiction has often been a factor in the sons' developmental and learning problems. Another Ontario study has found that sexual offenders have significantly greater problems with alcohol abuse than other violent offenders (Looman et al., 2004). The researchers have speculated that something about the combination of alcohol abuse and intimacy problems contributes specifically to sexual offending.

A survey of men from a Canadian city has found that belief in sexual assault myths and hostility are *not* predictive of coercive male behaviour (Senn et al., 2000). The fact that this is one of the few studies on sexual coercion that has attempted to randomly sample men from the community may account for the differences between its findings and those of other studies. The survey did find that men who are sexually coercive are more likely to have experienced childhood abuse, had more sexual partners during adolescence, and lack the ability to express their emotions (Senn et al., 2000). In another study of male sexual aggressors, University of Montreal researchers have reported that male adult sexual aggressors are more likely to have experienced childhood sexual abuse, pornography during childhood or adolescence, and deviant sexual fantasies during childhood or adolescence (Beauregard et al., 2004).

Adjustment of Sexual Assault Survivors

Many people who survive sexual assault by strangers fear for their lives during the attacks (Polusny & Arbisi, 2006). Regardless of whether weapons or threats are used, the experience of being dominated by an unpredictable and threatening assailant is terrifying. The victim doesn't know whether she'll survive and may feel helpless to do anything about it.

Many survivors are in crisis in the days and weeks after the sexual assault (Bryant-Davis, 2011). They have insomnia, and they cry frequently. They tend to report eating problems, cystitis, headaches, irritability, mood changes, anxiety and depression, and menstrual irregularity (Kaczmarek et al., 2006). They may become withdrawn, sullen, and mistrustful. Because some people tend to believe women who are sexually assaulted are at least partly to blame for the assaults (Boros et al., 2005), some survivors experience guilt and shame. Emotional distress tends to peak in severity about three weeks after the assault and generally remains high for a month or two before it begins to abate (Duke et al., 2008; Littleton & Henderson, 2009).

Many survivors encounter more lasting problems. Their feelings of being powerless to affect their own fates can endure, and change their personalities (McEwan et al., 2005). Survivors may encounter problems at work, such as problems with co-workers or bosses, or difficulty concentrating. Relationships with spouses or partners may be impaired. Survivors often report a lack of sexual desire, fear of sex, and difficulty becoming sexually aroused (Beutel et al., 2008; Koss et al., 2003). Sexual assault victims may also suffer physical injury and be exposed to sexually transmitted infections, including HIV.

Many women choose not to report sexual assaults to police. Why? Reasons include fear of retaliation, fear of social stigma, worry that others won't believe them, the feeling that it's hopeless to try to bring charges against the perpetrators, concern about negative publicity, and fear about the emotional distress they'll experience if their cases go to trial (Campbell, 2006; Logan et al., 2006). The GSS survey for 2004 reveals that Canadian sexual assault victims do, however, turn to

Applied Knowledge

IF YOU'RE SEXUALLY ASSAULTED

Here are some suggestions for what to do if you're sexually assaulted.

- Don't change anything about your body—don't wash, don't even comb your hair. Leave your clothes as they are. Otherwise, you could destroy evidence.
- Strongly consider reporting the incident to police. You may prevent another woman from being assaulted, and you'll be taking charge, starting on the path from victim to survivor.
- Ask a relative or friend to take you to a hospital, if you can't get an

ambulance or a police car. If you call the hospital, say why you're requesting an ambulance, in case they're able to send someone trained to deal with sexual assault cases.

- Seek help in an assertive way. Seek medical help. A medical professional may detect injuries you're unaware of. Insist that a written or photographic record be made, to document your condition. If you decide to file charges, the prosecutor may need this evidence to obtain a conviction.
- Question health professionals. Ask about your biological risks. Ask

what treatments are available. Ask about phylactic treatment against HIV infection. Ask for whatever will help make you comfortable. Call the shots. Demand confidentiality, if that's what you want. Refuse what you don't want.

You may also wish to call a sexual assault hotline or sexual assault crisis centre for advice, if one is available in your area. A sexual assault crisis volunteer may be available to accompany you to the hospital and help you through the medical evaluation, and the police investigation, if you report the attack.

---

sources of support such as friends (72%), family (41%), co-workers (33%), and doctors or nurses (13%) (Brennan & Taylor-Butts, 2008).

PSYCHOLOGICAL DISORDERS RESULTING FROM SEXUAL ASSAULT
Sexual assault survivors are at higher than average risk for developing anxiety disorders and depression, and for abusing alcohol and other substances (Littleton & Henderson, 2009). Researchers at Carleton University have found that university women who've experienced sexual coercion in their dating relationships are more likely to have lower levels of self-esteem and sexual self-esteem than women who haven't experienced sexual coercion while dating. They're also more likely to experience depression (Offman & Matheson, 2005).

Post-traumatic stress disorder (PTSD) A type of stress reaction brought on by a traumatic event. It's characterized by flashbacks of the experience, in the form of disturbing dreams or intrusive recollections, a sense of emotional numbing or restricted range of feelings, and heightened body arousal.

Survivors may experience **post-traumatic stress disorder (PTSD)** (Vickerman & Margolina, 2009), a disorder brought on by exposure to a traumatic event. It's often seen among soldiers who've been in combat. Someone with PTSD may have flashbacks to the traumatic experience, disturbing dreams, emotional numbing, and nervousness. PTSD may persist for years. The person may also develop a fear of situations connected with the traumatic event. A woman who's been sexually assaulted in an elevator, for example, may develop a fear of riding in elevators.

Researchers report that women who blame themselves for their sexual assaults tend to suffer more severe depression and adjustment problems, including sexual problems, than women who don't blame themselves (Kaczmarek et al., 2006; Vikerman & Margolina, 2009).

Treatment of Sexual Assault Survivors

Treatment of sexual assault survivors typically involves a two-stage process—helping the victim through the crisis after the attack, then fostering long-term adjustment (Bryant-Davis, 2011). Crisis intervention typically provides survivors with support and information, to help them express their feelings and develop strategies for coping with the trauma.

Psychotherapy, involving a group or individual approach, can help the survivor cope with the emotional consequences of sexual assault, avoid self-blame, improve self-esteem, validate the welter of feelings surrounding the experience, and establish or maintain loving relationships. Therapists also recognize the importance of helping the sexual assault survivor mobilize social support. In major cities and many towns, concerned citizens have formed sexual assault crisis centres and hotlines, peer-counselling groups, and referral agencies geared to assessing and meeting survivors' needs. Some counsellors are specially trained to mediate between survivors and their loved ones. These counsellors help people discuss and work through the often complex emotional legacies of sexual assault. Phone numbers for these services are available from crisis centres, women's shelters, hospital emergency departments, police departments, and telephone directories.

A national survey of rape-crisis and sexual assault centres in Canada has found that many face precarious financial situations because of insufficient government funding (Beres, Crow, & Gotell, 2009). These agencies rely heavily on the unpaid services of volunteers to provide adequate services to sexual assault and abuse survivors. Most of these agencies are also politically active, raising awareness of issues of violence and inequality experienced by Canadian women (Beres, Crow, & Gotell, 2009).

Courtesy of the Take Back the Night Foundation.

Taking Back the Night.
Whose fault is it if a woman is sexually assaulted when she goes out alone at night? Many women—and men who care about women—have marched to demonstrate their disgust with the men who might assault them if they're out walking by themselves, and with a society that too often blames the victim for what happens to her.

Preventing Sexual Assault

Eliminating sexual assault altogether would probably require massive changes in cultural attitudes and socialization processes. However, educational intervention on a smaller scale may reduce its incidence. Many colleges and universities offer educational programs about date sexual assault (Foubert & Newberry, 2006; Potter et al., 2009).

Until the basic cultural attitudes that support sexual assault change, however, preventing sexual assault means women must take a number of precautions. Why should they be advised to do this? Isn't the very listing of such measures a subtle way of blaming women, should they fall prey to attackers? No! Providing information is not blaming the victims. The offenders are *always* responsible for the assaults.

Confronting an Attacker

What if you're accosted by a sexual assailant? Should you try to fight him off, flee, or plead with him to stop? Some women have thwarted attacks by pleading or crying. Screaming may ward off some attacks (Gidycz et al., 2006). Running away sometimes works. No single strategy is likely to be helpful in all cases of sexual assault.

Self-defence training may help you become better prepared to fend off an assailant (Gidycz et al., 2006). Yet physical resistance may spur some assailants to become more aggressive. Effective self-defence is built upon the use of multiple strategies, ranging from attempts to avoid dangerous situations (e.g., installing a home security system and walking only in well-lit areas), to acquiescence when active resistance seems too risky, to more active verbal and physical forms of resistance in low-risk situations (Gidycz et al., 2006).

Coercive Verbal Pressure Tactics

Verbal sexual coercion is persistent verbal pressure or the use of seduction lines to manipulate a person into sexual activity. Verbal coercion is difficult to define precisely. People use a wide spectrum of persuasion, ranging from coaxing to outright bullying and threats. In the middle of the spectrum there's a grey area that might be considered coercive by some but not by others.

Verbal coercion is used far more often than physical coercion. In a study involving students from more than 40 universities and community colleges across

Applied Knowledge

LOWERING YOUR RISK OF SEXUAL ASSAULT

Taking precautions such as these, recommended by the Boston Women's Health Book Collective (2005), may lower your risk for being assaulted:

- Establish a set of signals with other women in the building or neighbourhood.
- List yourself in the phone directory and on the mailbox by your first initials only.
- Use deadbolt locks.
- Keep doorways and entries well lit.
- Keep your keys handy when approaching the car or the front door.
- Avoid deserted areas.
- Don't allow strange men into your house or apartment without first checking their credentials.
- Check out the back seat of your car before getting in.
- Don't give rides to hitchhikers (including female hitchhikers).

Here are some suggestions for avoiding sexual assault by a date:

- Tell your partner how far you're willing to go, so he knows your limits. For example, if your partner starts fondling you in ways that make you uncomfortable, you might say, "I'd prefer if you didn't touch me there. I really like you, but I prefer not getting so intimate at this point in our relationship."
- When meeting a new date, meet at a public place, and arrive and leave in your own car. Don't drive with a stranger or offer a ride to a stranger or a group of people you've just met.
- State your refusal definitively. Be firm in refusing a sexual overture. Look your partner straight in the eye. The more definite you are, the less likely your partner is to misinterpret your wishes.
- Become aware of your fears. Notice any fears about displeasing your partner that might stifle

your assertiveness. If your date is truly respectful, you needn't fear an angry or demeaning response. If your date isn't respectful, it's best to become aware of the fact, and end the relationship right there.

- Pay attention to your vibes. Trust your gut-level feelings. Many victims of sexual assault by acquaintances have said they had strange feelings about the men but failed to pay attention to their feelings.
- Be especially cautious if you're in a new environment, whether it's a university or a foreign country. You may be especially vulnerable to exploitation when you're becoming acquainted with a new environment, different people, and different customs.
- If you've broken off a relationship with someone you don't really like or feel good about, don't let him into your place. Many so-called date rapes are committed by ex-lovers and ex-boyfriends.

Canada, DeKeseredy and Kelly (1993) found that since beginning university, 32% of the women had given in to sex play (not involving intercourse) because they'd been overwhelmed by men's continual arguments and pressure, and 20% had given in to sexual intercourse because of this kind of verbal pressure. In a community survey of men from an Ontario city, 23% reported that they'd used arguments and verbal pressure to try to get women to engage in sex play, and 9% said they'd used this kind of pressure to have sexual intercourse (Senn et al., 2000).

Researchers in Toronto studied young adults who were involved in street life, to find out what strategies they used to coerce dating partners into having sex (Strike et al., 2001). The sample included heterosexuals, gays, lesbians, and bisexuals. Almost all of the men and women had experienced pressure to have sex, and 62% of the men and 42% of the women admitted having pressured dates to have sex. In the Strike et al. study, the tactics used to get sex included the following:

- Using alcohol and drugs to decrease a partner's reluctance to have sex. Some of those who'd been coerced said they'd used alcohol or drugs to loosen their own inhibitions.
- Using obligations, expectations, and guilt. Some coerced their partners by threatening to end the relationships or to get sex elsewhere. Another strategy involved saying how much they were looking forward to having sex. Some made their partners feel obliged to have sex and tried to make them feel guilty for not having it. A commonly held belief was that if a partner paid for date-related expenses such as dinner and drinks, the person was obliged to have sex.
- Exploiting emotional and economic vulnerabilities. People with low self-esteem may be told they're worthless and should consider themselves lucky to be in relationships. Some of the men and women admitted that they'd manipulated people with few or no economic resources by providing food, housing, or money in return for sex. An extreme example of this exploitation occurred when a man provided a woman with shelter and demanded that she provide sex—not only to him, but to his friends as well.

In a community-based survey of men living in Windsor, Senn and her colleagues (2000) found that the most common strategy used to coerce reluctant partners into having sex involved continual arguments and verbal pressure. The second most common strategy involved providing women with alcohol or drugs.

A common sexual stereotype is that women never have to use pressure tactics to engage in sex with male partners. Researchers at the University of Guelph have found that some young women use a diversity of sexual pressure tactics to get reluctant male partners to engage in sex (Parr-LeFeuve & Desmarais, 2005).

Verbal coercion also occurs in same-sex relationships. In a study of these relationships in Canada and the United States, Melanie Beres (2002) has found that 23% of women in lesbian relationships have experienced sexual coercion from other women. The rates for men are somewhat higher; 35% have experienced sexual coercion from other men.

Sexual Abuse of Children

Many view sexual abuse of children as among the most heinous of crimes. Canadians are shocked and horrified when they find out about children being sexually abused. One of the most publicized cases was the sexual abuse of boys by priests at the Mount Cashel Orphanage in Newfoundland. Eleven priests were convicted of those offences, and the Newfoundland government paid $11 million to 40 abuse victims.

Children who are sexually assaulted often suffer social and emotional problems that impair their development and persist into adulthood, affecting their self-esteem and their ability to form intimate relationships.

Data from the 2007 UCR survey of sexual assaults reported to police in Canada show that more than half of all sexual assault victims that year were under age 18, and 25% were under 12 (Brennan & Taylor-Butts, 2008). The UCR data also showed that the vast majority (81%) of sexual assault victims under age 18 were female. Since many cases are never reported, we don't know with certainty how many children have been sexually abused. An analysis of 65 studies in 22 countries has estimated that 7% to 8% of boys and 19% to 20% of girls have been sexually abused (Pereda et al., 2009).

In addition to sexual assaults (levels 1, 2, and 3), which can occur against children or youth, there are also a number of sexual violations within the *Criminal Code* that apply only to victims under the age of 18. These five specific sexual violations are luring a child via a computer, sexual exploitation, sexual interference, invitation to sexual touching, and making sexually explicit material available to a child. These crimes are categorized within the UCR as sexual violations against children. According to UCR data, there were 4 232 police reported incidents of sexual violations against children in Canada in 2013, almost 300 more than in 2012 (Boyce, Cotter, & Perreault, 2014). These figures translate into a rate of 12 sexual violations per 1000 youth under age 18. The rate of luring a child by computer increased by 30% from 2012 to 2013, while the rate of invitation to sexual touching decreased by 5% (Boyce, Cotter, & Perreault, 2014).

Sexual abuse of children can take many forms including exhibitionism, kissing, fondling, sexual touching, oral sex, anal intercourse, and vaginal intercourse. Sexual contact between an adult and a child is abusive, even if the child is willing, because children are legally incapable of consenting to sexual activity. (Acts such as touching children's sexual organs while changing or bathing them, sleeping with children, or appearing nude before them are not usually considered sexual contact. While these acts are open to interpretation, they're often innocent [Haugaard, 2000].)

Voluntary sexual activity *between children* of similar ages is not sexual abuse. Children often engage in consensual sex play with peers or siblings, playing doctor or engaging in mutual masturbation. Although such experiences may be recalled in adulthood with feelings of shame or guilt, they're not typically harmful. When an experience involves coercion, or when one child is significantly older or in a position of power over the younger child, the sexual contact may be considered sexual abuse.

The Canadian Press/Andrew Vaugh

The Mount Cashel Scandal.
One of the most publicized child sex-abuse cases in Canada involved Catholic priests at the Mount Cashel Orphanage in Newfoundland.

In Canada, it's against the law for an adult or a teenager to engage in any type of sexual activity, ranging from kissing to intercourse, with a child under the age of 14. The exception is for sexual activity between a child who's at least 12 years old and someone who's less than two years older.

In 1985, Parliament amended the *Criminal Code* to make it an offence for a person in a position of trust or authority to have any sexual contact, consensual or not, with a person under 18. Under this law, there have been several cases where teachers have been convicted for sexual contact with their students.

To provide greater protection for 14- to 18-year-olds, 2002 legislation created a new category of sexual exploitation for any adult who, because of his or her age and/or position of authority, is able to coerce a young person into having sex. This legislation also makes it illegal for an adult to use the Internet to lure a person s/he believes is under 18 for the purpose of committing a sexual assault, or to entice a child believed to be under 14 into sexual relations.

The first person charged under this law was a 33-year-old Toronto man who arranged a meeting with an 11-year-old girl he'd met on the Internet. He was also charged with sexual assault after spending the night with the girl in a hotel room. The man was convicted of Internet luring, abduction of a person under age 16, and sexual interference (Levy, 2004). Internet luring crosses national borders. A 32-year-old man from Belgium was arrested at a Montreal hotel and charged with sexual offences and Internet luring, when he was found there with a missing 13-year-old girl. The pair had been chatting online for several months (Banerjee, 2008).

To combat Internet luring, police have laid traps by posing as children in chat rooms. In 2005, a Toronto detective posed as a 12-year-old girl on the Yahoo chat room Teen Oh Canada Chat. A man entered the chat room and engaged in casual conversation with her. After a few months, they arranged to meet to have sex. At this meeting, the police arrested a 36-year-old pastor (Naili & Josey, 2005).

In 2008, the Canadian Parliament raised the legal age of consent from 14 to 16, to protect adolescents in that age group from adult sexual exploitation. The new law allowed a close-in-age provision of five years, so it would be legal, for example, for a 19-year-old to have sex with a 15-year-old. Gay-rights organizations claim that the age-of-consent law is discriminatory toward gay males, because it's illegal in Canada to engage in anal sex with someone who's under 18.

In 2011, in order to better protect children from online sexual exploitation, the government of Canada passed legislation making it mandatory for Internet service providers to report instances of child pornography.

In Bountiful, British Columbia, a fundamentalist Mormon sect not only flouts Canadian law with its practice of polygamy but also allegedly forces girls as young as 13 to marry much older men. Winston Blackmore, the bishop of the religious group, has admitted to having married several underage girls (*Vancouver Sun*, 2014). He argues that freedom of religion in Canada prohibits the justice system from interfering with the church's beliefs. In 2014, however, Blackmore was charged by the British Columbia government with engaging in polygamy. In the United States, Warren Jeffs, the leader of the American segment of this Mormon sect, was sentenced in 2011 to life in prison for sexually assaulting underage girls (Associated Press, 2011).

Patterns of Abuse

Children from stable, middle-class families appear to be generally at lower risk for sexual abuse than children from poorer, less cohesive families (Amodeo et al., 2006; Turner et al., 2006). In most cases, children who are sexually abused are not accosted by the proverbial stranger lurking in the schoolyard. According to Canadian police reports, in 2003 half of all victims under the age of six were sexually assaulted by family members, and only 4% were assaulted by strangers. Twenty percent of the 14- to 17-year-old victims were assaulted by family members, and 20% were assaulted by strangers (Statistics Canada, 2005g). In many cases, the molesters are people who are close to their victims—relatives, step-relatives, family friends, and neighbours (Edwards et al., 2003).

Parents who discover that their children have been abused by family members are often reluctant to notify authorities (Finkelhor et al., 2012). The decision to report the abuse to police depends largely on the relationship between the abuser and the person who discovers the abuse (Finkelhor et al., 2012).

Typically, the child initially trusts the abuser. Physical force is seldom needed to gain compliance, largely because of the child's helplessness, gullibility, and submission to adult authority. Whereas most sexually abused children are abused only once, those who are abused by family members are more likely to suffer repeated acts of abuse than those who are abused by strangers.

Genital fondling is the most common type of abuse (Edwards et al., 2003). In one sample of women who'd been molested in childhood, most of the contacts involved genital fondling (38% of the cases) or exhibitionism (20% of the cases). Intercourse is rare. Repeated abuse by a family member, however, commonly follows a pattern that begins with affectionate fondling during the preschool years and progresses to oral sex or mutual masturbation during the early school years, and then to sexual penetration (vaginal or anal intercourse) during preadolescence or adolescence.

Abused children rarely report the abuse, often because they fear retaliation from their abusers, or because they believe they'll be blamed for it. Adults may suspect abuse if a child shows sudden personality changes or develops fears, problems in school, or difficulty eating or sleeping. A pediatrician may discover physical signs of abuse during a medical exam. The average age at which most children are first sexually abused ranges from six to 12 years for girls and seven to ten for boys (Finkelhor et al., 2005b).

ABUSER TYPES   The overwhelming majority of people who sexually abuse children—both boys and girls—are male (Turner et al., 2006). Although most child abusers are adults, some are adolescents. Male adolescent sex offenders are more likely than other adolescents to have been molested themselves as boys. Some adolescent sex offenders may be imitating their own victimization. Adolescent child molesters also tend to feel socially inadequate, and to fear social interactions with same-aged peers.

Although the great majority of sexual abusers are male, the number of female sexual abusers may be greater than we've generally believed (Zernike, 2005). Many female sexual abusers may go undetected, because society accords women a much freer range of physical contact with children than it does men. A study of Canadian police officers and psychiatrists has found among these groups a culture of denial of women as potential sexual aggressors (Denov, 2001).

SEX TOURISM   Some Canadians travel to developing countries to have sex with children, partly because there's less chance of being prosecuted there. In 1997, the Canadian government changed the *Criminal Code* to allow prosecution of Canadians who sexually abuse children while out of the country. A 2002 amendment allows prosecution in Canada even without the agreement of the country in which the offence occurs.

In 2005, the first conviction was obtained under this legislation when a British Columbia man was convicted of having sex with children under the age of 14 in Cambodia (Girard, 2005). In 2008, two Quebec men were charged with sexual abuse of children in an orphanage in Haiti.

Pedophilia

Pedophilia A paraphilia that features sexual attraction to children.

Pedophilia is a paraphilia in which an adult finds children the preferred and sometimes the exclusive objects of sexual desire. According to the *Diagnostic and Statistical Manual of Mental Disorders* (American Psychiatric Association, 2013b), pedophilia involves sexually arousing fantasies, urges, or behaviours that involve sexual activity with a prepubescent child. A clinical diagnosis is given when a person acts on or is distressed by these pedophilic urges.

Not all child molesters are necessarily pedophiles, and not all pedophiles, despite their fantasies and urges, necessarily molest children. The prevalence of pedophilia in the general population is unknown. Based on a few small-sample surveys, it's been estimated that up to 5% of men have sexual fantasies or sexual contact with prepubescent children (Seto, 2009).

Pedophiles are almost exclusively male, although some isolated cases of female pedophiles have been reported (Finkelhor et al., 2005b). Some pedophiles are sexually attracted only to children. Others are sexually attracted to both children and adults. Some pedophiles may never have any sexual contact with children (Seto, 2009). Some pedophiles limit their sexual interest in children to incestuous relationships with family members, while others abuse children they're not related to. Some pedophiles limit their sexual interest in children to looking at or undressing them, while others fondle them or masturbate in their presence. Some manipulate or coerce children into oral, anal, or vaginal intercourse.

Children tend not to be worldly-wise. They can often be taken in by pedophiles who say they want to show them something, teach them something, or do something with them that they'll like. Some pedophiles seek to gain children's affection, and, later, to discourage the children from disclosing the sexual activity by showering them with attention and gifts. Others threaten the children or their families, to prevent disclosure.

Although most pedophiles don't wear trench coats and hang around schoolyards, there's research evidence that many do have personality disorders (Madsen et al., 2006). Research finds them emotionally unstable, disagreeable, angry, impulsive, and mistrustful. A study by Toronto researchers has found that many offenders have grown up in families with insecure attachment experiences (Stripe et al., 2006).

Some pedophiles who lack social skills may turn to children after failing to establish gratifying relationships with adult women. Many pedophiles distort reality in ways that enable them to pursue sexual activity with children (Marziano et al., 2006). Pedophiles often:

- See children as sexual beings who want to have sex with adults.
- Believe sex doesn't harm children, and that it may be beneficial.
- Think themselves so important that they're entitled to have sex with whomever they want.

Ray Blanchard and his colleagues at the Centre for Addiction and Mental Health in Toronto have explored how disturbances in early neurodevelopment are related to pedophilia. They find that pedophiles are more likely to have experienced serious head injuries before age six, and that these injuries are associated with memory loss and lower levels of intelligence. Pedophilia is somewhat related to left-handedness, which may be attributable to altered fetal development (Blanchard & Lippa, 2007; Cantor et al., 2004, 2005a).

A group of Ontario researchers has also found that men with older brothers are more prone to sexually coercing both children and adults, and that male perpetrators with older brothers are more likely to choose male than female victims (Lalumière et al., 1998). In another Ontario study (Cantor et al., 2006), pedophilia has been associated with school failure by one or more years and subsequent enrollment in special education. In a separate study, Cantor et al. (2005b) has found that pedophiles have lower intelligence levels as measured by IQ (intelligence quotient) tests.

In a groundbreaking study, Cantor and his colleagues (2008) have found significant brain differences between pedophiles and other men—differences that may exist at birth. By using magnetic resonance imaging, the researchers have discovered that the wiring that connects the brain regions responsible for sexual response is thinner in

There Really Was a Monster in Her Bedroom.
Not all monsters are make-believe. Some, such as perpetrators of incest, are family members.

pedophiles. This indicates that the part of the brain related to identifying sexual partners may not develop normally in pedophiles.

Using penile tests of sexual arousal, Toronto researchers (Seto et al., 2006) have found that men charged with child pornography offences are highly likely to be aroused by sexual images of children. The researchers have concluded that child pornography offences are stronger than child sexual offences in indicating pedophilia. The researchers have speculated that some men who sexually assault young victims are attracted to those who show some signs of sexual development, rather than to their victims' youth (Seto et al., 2006).

What's the relationship between committing child-porn offences and other sexual offences? In a sample of adult males convicted of child-porn offences, Michael Seto and Angela Eke (2005) found that 24% had committed previous sexual offences involving contact. Child-pornography offenders who had committed prior or concurrent contact offences were most likely to offend again.

Incest

Incest Sexual relations between individuals who are so closely related that sexual relations are prohibited and punishable by law.

Incest involves people who are consanguineous, or related by blood. The law may also proscribe intercourse between, say, a stepfather and a stepdaughter. Although a few societies have permitted incestuous pairings among royalty, all known cultures have some sort of incest taboo. Most of our knowledge of incestuous relationships concerns father–daughter incest. Why? Most identified cases involve fathers who were eventually incarcerated.

About 1% of a sample of women in five American cities reported sexual encounters with fathers or stepfathers (Anderson, 2006). But brother–sister incest, not parent–child incest, is the most common type (Caffaro & Conn-Caffaro, 2005). Brother–sister incest is also believed to be greatly underreported, possibly because it tends to be transient, and because it appears to be less harmful than parent–child incest. Finkelhor (1990) found that 21% of the college men in his sample, and 39% of the college women, reported incestuous relationships with siblings of the other sex. Only 4% reported incestuous relationships with their fathers. Mother–daughter incest is the least common form of incest, but it does occur (Bartolo, 2005; Turton, 2005).

FATHER–DAUGHTER INCEST   Father–daughter incest often begins with affectionate cuddling or embraces, and progresses to teasing sexual play, lengthy caresses, hugs, kisses, and genital contact—even penetration. In some cases, genital contact occurs more abruptly, usually when the father has been drinking or arguing with his wife. Force isn't typically used to gain compliance, but daughters are sometimes physically overcome and injured by their fathers.

BROTHER–SISTER INCEST   In sibling incest, the brother usually initiates the sexual activity and assumes the dominant role. Some brothers and sisters may view their sexual activity as natural, and not know it's taboo.

Evidence on the effects of incest between brothers and sisters is mixed. In one study of university undergraduates, those who reported childhood incest with siblings showed no greater evidence of sexual-adjustment problems than those who didn't report incest experiences (Greenwald & Leitenberg, 1989). Sibling incest is most likely to be harmful when it's recurrent or forced, or when parental response is harsh (Adams, 2007).

MOTHER–SON INCEST   Mother–son incest occurs far less frequently than father–daughter incest. However, it may be that boys who are sexually abused by their mothers are less likely to report it. Nevertheless, these cases do occur.

In an unusual case in Cambridge, Ontario, a mother and her son had three children together. The son was 16 years old when he fathered the first child. In an attempt to cover up the incestuous relationship, the son fabricated identity documents. Both mother and son were found guilty of incest (Wood, 2005).

FAMILY FACTORS   Incest frequently occurs within the context of general family disruption. There may also be spousal abuse, a dysfunctional marriage, or alcoholic or physically abusive parents. Stressful events in the father's life, such as a job loss or work problems, often precede the initiation of incest (Welldon, 2005).

Fathers who abuse their daughters when they're older tend to be domineering and authoritarian with their families (Waterman, 1986). Fathers who abuse pre-school daughters are more likely to be passive, dependent, and low in self-esteem.

Marriages in incestuous families tend to be characterized by uneven power relationships between the spouses. Abusive fathers are usually dominant. Another thread that frequently runs through incestuous families is troubled sexual relationships between the spouses. The wives often rejects the husbands sexually (Waterman, 1986).

Gebhard and his colleagues (1965) found that many fathers who committed incest with their daughters were religiously devout, fundamentalist, and moralistic. Perhaps such men, when sexually frustrated, are less likely to seek extramarital and extra-familial sexual outlets or to turn to masturbation for sexual release. In many cases, the father is under stress but doesn't find adequate emotional and sexual support from his wife (Gagnon, 1977). He turns to a daughter as a wife surrogate, often when he's been drinking alcohol (Gebhard et al., 1965). The daughter may become, in her father's fantasies, the "woman of the house." This fantasy may become his justification for continuing the incestuous relationship. In some incestuous families, a role reversal occurs—the abused daughter assumes many of the mother's responsibilities for managing the household and caring for the younger children.

Incestuous abuse is often repeated from generation to generation. One study found that in 154 cases of sexual abuse within families, more than one-third of the male offenders and about one-half of the mothers had either been abused themselves or been exposed to abuse as children (Faller, 1989).

Australian and Canadian researchers (Greenberg et al., 2005) compared the characteristics of male incest offenders who were biological fathers with those who were stepfathers. Both groups reported serious problems in their own childhoods, including sexual and physical abuse and placement outside of their homes. Their current problems involved alcohol abuse and deviant sexual arousal. Of all the variables analyzed, biological fathers and stepfathers differed statistically only in their sexual arousal to children—biological fathers were less aroused by sexual abuse of children than stepfathers were.

Effects of Sexual Abuse on Children

The effects of sexual abuse are varied, and no single identifiable syndrome emerges from it (Anderson, 2006; Resick, 2003). Children who are sexually abused may suffer from a litany of short- and long-term psychological complaints, including anger, depression, anxiety, eating disorders, inappropriate sexual behaviour, aggressive behaviour, self-destructive behaviour, sexual promiscuity, drug abuse, suicide attempts, post-traumatic stress disorder, low self-esteem, sexual dysfunction, mistrust of others, and feelings of detachment (Edwards et al., 2003). Sexual abuse may also have physical effects, such as genital injuries, and may cause stress-related problems such as stomach aches and headaches.

Abused children often act out. Younger children may have tantrums or display aggressive or antisocial behaviour, while older children may turn to substance abuse (Anderson, 2006). Some abused children become withdrawn, retreating into fantasy or refusing to leave the house. Regressive behaviours, such as thumb sucking, fear of the dark, and fear of strangers, are also common among sexually abused children.

Applied Knowledge

HELPING CHILDREN AVOID SEXUAL ABUSE

Prevention programs can help children understand what sexual abuse is and how they can avoid it (Hébert & Tourigny, 2004). In addition to learning to avoid strangers, children need to recognize the differences between acceptable touching, such as an affectionate embrace or pat on the head, and unacceptable or "bad" touching. Even children of elementary school age can learn the distinction between "good touching" and "bad touching."

Good school-based programs are generally helpful in preparing children to handle actual encounters with potential molesters. Children who receive comprehensive training are more likely to use strategies such as running away, yelling, and saying no when they're threatened by abusers. They're also more likely to report such incidents to adults.

Researchers recognize that children can be easily intimidated and overpowered by adults and older children (Miller, 2005). They may be unable to say no in sexually abusive situations, even though they want to and know it's the right thing to do.

Although children may not always be able to prevent abuse, they can be encouraged to tell someone about it. Most prevention programs emphasize such ideas as "It's not your fault," "Never keep a bad or scary secret," and "Always tell your parents about this, especially if someone says you *shouldn't* tell them."

Children also need to be alerted to the types of threats they might receive for disclosing the abuse. They're more likely to resist threats if they're reassured that they'll be believed if they disclose the abuse, that their parents will continue to love them, and that they and their families will be protected from the molesters.

School-based prevention programs focus on protecting children. In Canada, teachers and helping professionals are required to report suspected abuse to authorities. Administrators and teachers in preschool and daycare facilities need to be taught to recognize the signs of sexual abuse, and to report suspected cases.

On the heels of the assault and in the ensuing years, many survivors of childhood sexual abuse—like many sexual assault survivors—show signs of post-traumatic stress disorder. They suffer flashbacks, nightmares, numbing of emotions, and feelings of estrangement from others (Herrera & McCloskey, 2003).

The sexual development of abused children may also be adversely affected. A survivor may, for example, become prematurely sexually active or promiscuous in adolescence and adulthood (Herrera & McCloskey, 2003). Researchers find that adolescent girls who are sexually abused tend to engage in consensual sex at earlier ages than their peers who are not abused (Herrera & McCloskey, 2003).

Researchers generally find more similarities than differences between the sexes with respect to the effects of sexual abuse in childhood (Edwards et al., 2003). Both boys and girls tend to experience fears and sleep disturbances. There are some sex differences, however. The most consistent is that boys are more likely to externalize their problems (e.g., become more physically aggressive), while girls are more likely to internalize their difficulties (e.g., become depressed) (Anderson, 2006).

Late adolescence and early adulthood seem to be especially difficult for survivors of childhood sexual abuse. Studies of women in these age groups reveal more psychological and social problems in abused than in non-abused women (Anderson, 2006).

Treatment of Childhood Sexual Abuse Survivors

Psychotherapy in adulthood often becomes the first opportunity for survivors to confront residual pain, anger, and misplaced guilt. Group and individual therapy can help improve survivors' self-esteem and ability to develop intimate relationships.

Many therapists recommend a multi-component treatment approach, which may involve individual therapy for the child, mother, and father; group therapy for the adolescent or even the preadolescent survivor; art therapy or play therapy for the younger child (e.g., using drawings or puppets to express feelings); marital counselling for the parents; and family therapy for the entire family.

In 2011, the Ontario government announced $2.2 million in funding to 45 agencies to provide individual and group counselling for male victims of sexual abuse (Wood, 2011).

Treatment of Perpetrators

What does "treatment" mean? When a helping professional treats someone, the goal is usually to help that individual. When we speak of treating a sex offender, the goal is just as likely—or more likely—to be to help society by eliminating the problem behaviour.

A group of Canadian and American researchers has conducted an extensive review of the effectiveness of psychological treatment programs for sex offenders. They've found that treatment programs before 1980 had little effect but that current treatments are somewhat effective in reducing rates of recidivism (Hanson et al., 2002). More recently, Ontario researchers have developed treatment programs that have resulted in re-offences by only 3% of sex offenders (Marshall et al., 2006).

Marshall and his colleagues (2007) emphasize the importance of having offenders take responsibility for their offences. They also teach offenders more effective coping skills for dealing with their relationship problems. With offenders who continue to have deviant patterns of sexual arousal, Marshall and his colleagues use reconditioning strategies to enhance appropriate sexual interests and reduce deviant ones.

Some Canadian communities, including Victoria, Winnipeg, and Kitchener, have volunteer groups known as Circles of Support and Accountability (COSA), which have the twin goals of community protection and offender rehabilitation. These trained volunteer groups help integrate sexual offenders into the community and help them avoid reoffending by meeting their intimacy and relationship needs. This process assumes that offenders needn't be isolated to protect the community (Petrunik, 2003). An evaluation project in Ontario has found that involvement in a COSA can reduce further sexual offending by more than 60% (Wilson, 2005).

In the past, some programs have used extreme measures such as surgical castration to lower offenders' sex drives. Surgical castration raises ethical concerns, because it's invasive and irreversible (Gooren, 2011). Anti-androgen drugs such as Depo-Provera chemically reduce testosterone and sex drive levels but are reversible (Thibaut, 2011).

Pedophilia appears to be linked to prenatal neurological factors. It's therefore unlikely that a sexual preference for children can be changed (Seto, 2009). Psychological and medical interventions are intended to reduce sexual responsiveness to children and increase self-management skills. One study has shown that anti-androgen drugs can decrease pedophilic fantasies and masturbation to pedophilic fantasies in incarcerated sex offenders (Schober et al., 2005). In reviewing the literature, Ontario researcher Michael Seto (2009) has concluded that the effectiveness of psychological interventions to reduce recidivism among pedophilic sex offenders has not been scientifically demonstrated. Nevertheless, he suggests that "learning to control their sexual arousal to children may help motivated individuals to refrain from sexually offending" (Seto, 2009, p. 402).

In 2004, the Canadian federal government responded to pressure from community groups, some provincial governments, and police forces by establishing a national sex-offender registry. Convicted sex offenders must register within 15 days

CRITICAL THINKING QUESTIONS

Agree or disagree with the following statement, and support your answer: We should punish sex offenders and not worry about "treating" them.

of being released from prison, and must reregister annually and within two weeks of moving. Police agencies from across Canada have access to this database, which they believe will help them investigate cases of sexual assault.

By 2010, more than 24 000 names were included in the Canadian sex offender registry. However, an investigation discovered that many offenders were not registered, and that the list of offenders wasn't up to date (Friscolanti, 2008). Since 2011, judges no longer have the discretion to decide whether individuals convicted of sexual offences should be included in the sex-offender registry. In 2014, the federal government introduced legislation to establish a publically accessible database of high risk sexual offenders.

Marshall and his colleagues (2006) have criticized public-notification approaches, in the belief that they're likely to cause stress in offenders that will increase the recidivism rate. The researchers therefore suggest that public notification should be used only in extremely dangerous cases, when alternative containment strategies are unavailable.

Some legal experts have argued that the registry violates the human rights of offenders, who can never have their names removed from the list even after living for many years as model citizens. No other category of offender is required to register with police after being released from prison and no longer on parole (Ward et al., 2007).

Sexual Harassment

Sexual harassment
Deliberate or repeated unsolicited and unwelcome comments, gestures, or physical contact of a sexual nature.

For legal purposes, **sexual harassment** in the workplace is usually defined as deliberate or repeated unwanted comments, gestures, or physical contact (Craig, 2005; Finkelman, 2005). It's forbidden by both federal and provincial human-rights legislation. Sexual harassment makes the workplace and other settings hostile. Examples range from unwelcome sexual jokes and sexual innuendos to outright sexual assaults. Sexual harassment may include such behaviours as the following:

- Verbal harassment.
- Verbal abuse.
- Subtle pressure for sexual activity.
- Remarks about a person's clothing, body, or sexual activities.
- Leering at or ogling of a person's body.
- Unwelcome touching, patting, or pinching.
- Brushing against a person's body.
- Demands for sexual favours, accompanied by implied or overt threats about a person's job or student status.
- Physical assault.

In a national survey of about 2000 Canadian working women, 56% reported that they'd experienced sexual harassment during the previous year, and 77% said they'd experienced sexual harassment during their lifetimes (Crocker & Kalemba, 1999). The three most common types of incidents included staring, jokes, and remarks about women or about the respondents themselves. The least common incidents included physical force, threats, and bribery.

Evidence shows that people subjected to sexual harassment do suffer from it. Some become physically ill (Rospenda et al., 2005). Others report anxiety, irritability, lowered self-esteem, and anger. Some find harassment on the job so unbearable that they resign (Sims et al, 2005). College women's grades suffer (Huerta et al., 2006). College women have dropped courses and switched majors to avoid sexual harassment (Huerta et al., 2006; Stratton et al., 2005).

Sexual harassment may have more to do with abuse of power than with sexual desire (Chaiyavej & Morash, 2009). Relatively few cases of sexual harassment

Sexual Harassment.
Many victims of sexual harassment keep the incidents to themselves, for fear that
they'll be blamed for their own victimization, or that their supervisors will fire them for
complaining. Perpetrators can claim that they've been misunderstood or that the victims are
exaggerating.

involve outright requests for sexual favours. The harasser is usually in a dominant position and abuses that position by exploiting the victim's vulnerability. Sexual harassment may also occur between doctors and patients, and between therapists and clients. Therapists may use their power and influence to pressure clients into sexual relations. In Canada, professional organizations for teachers, doctors, and therapists have strict ethical guidelines that forbid sexual contact between doctors and patients, therapists and clients, and teachers and students.

Minority Groups

A Canadian study has shed light on various experiences of harassment (Berdahl & Moore, 2006). It compared the experiences of white women, black women, and Filipina women. White women with full rights as citizens felt most free to report the harassment to authorities. Black women and Filipinas felt that the term "sexual harassment" didn't fully capture their experience—that their treatment also had to do with the power white men could exercise over blacks and, especially, live-in Filipina caregivers. The study also found that women experienced more sexual harassment than men and, in what the authors call double jeopardy, minority women encountered more harassment than white women.

Workplaces

Harassers in the workplace can be employers, supervisors, co-workers, or clients. If a worker asks a co-worker for a date and is refused, it's not sexual harassment. If the co-worker persists with unwelcome advances and doesn't take no for an answer, the behaviour crosses the line and becomes harassment.

Perhaps the most severe form of sexual harassment, short of outright assault, involves an employer or supervisor who demands sexual favours as a condition of

Innovative Canadian Research

TROUBLE LETTING GO: ONLINE AND OFFLINE POST-RELATIONSHIP CONTACT AND TRACKING AMONG YOUNG ADULTS

The breakup of romantic relationships during young adulthood can be highly traumatic. Many young people struggle to adjust to a breakup, and some have trouble "letting go." People struggling to let their ex-partner go may make efforts to maintain or re-establish contact with an ex-partner or track the ex-partner's activities. When taken to the extreme, these activities can be defined as stalking or cyberstalking and constitute criminal harassment.

Brenda Lee and Lucia O'Sullivan (2014) at the University of New Brunswick conducted a study of post-relationship contact and tracking (PRCT) among a sample of 276 female and male young adults aged 18 to 25 years who had experienced a relationship breakup in the previous year. The study participants completed a survey questionnaire that asked them to indicate which behaviours they and their ex-partners had engaged in post-breakup. Using two parallel versions of the questionnaire, participants answered the following question:

> When someone is having trouble letting go of an ex, they may do certain things to try to get their ex's attention, to get back at their ex, or try to fix the relationship. Which of the following did you/this ex do after your breakup? (p. 98)

The participants were given a list of 22 offline and 12 online behaviours to respond to. Overall, 74% indicated that they had used some form of PRCT to pursue or re-establish contact with their ex-partner or to monitor their whereabouts and activities. In contrast, 68% reported that their ex-partner had engaged in PRCT. Overall, there were few gender differences in the use and experience of PRTC.

Most of the PRCT reported by participants was relatively benign. For example, 42% reported telephoning their ex-partners, 40% "tried to find out what they were up to" (p. 100), and 21% wrote letters or notes. Online PRCT was less common, with 22% sending messages of affection, 21% sending very personal messages, and 9.2% sending sexual messages.

Some respondents did report using or experiencing more extreme forms of PRTC. For example, 8.5% reported that they said things that scared the ex-partner, and 16.2% reported that the ex-partner had said things that scared them. A small number (3%) did report threatening to hurt their ex-partner or someone they were dating and 7% reporting receiving such threats. About 2% reported that they or their ex-partner had gone online to get private information about the ex-partner without permission.

Lee and O'Sullivan's (2014) findings show that many young adults have trouble "letting go" of ex-partners in the aftermath of a relationship breakup. They write that "The adjustment process is known to be a difficult one, often extremely distressing, and as such draws considerably on individuals' coping and mental health resources" (p. 102). As the findings also show, in a minority cases, PRCT among young adults can cross over the line to harassment and stalking.

employment or advancement. In Canada, human rights commissions have expanded the definition of sexual harassment in the workplace to include any behaviour of a sexual nature that interferes with an individual's work performance or creates a hostile, intimidating, or offensive work environment. Canadian legislation recognizes sexual harassment as a form of sex discrimination.

Some organizations have gone a step further, banning their employees from having any sexual contact with other employees, even if it's consensual. In a widely publicized 2005 case, the City of Toronto suspended a female senior manager and her (married) male second-in-command, who admitted that they'd had an affair. Concerns were raised that the male assistant's rapid promotion—from temporary employee to a senior position in only ten months—resulted from favouritism on the part of his boss, who was also his lover.

Employers can be held responsible not only for their own actions, but also for sexual harassment by their employees, when they've actually known or *should have known* harassment was taking place and failed to eliminate it promptly. To protect themselves, many companies and universities have developed programs to educate workers about sexual harassment, established mechanisms for dealing with complaints, and imposed sanctions against harassers.

Campuses

Estimates of the frequency of sexual harassment of college students in the United States vary widely across studies. Overall 25% to 30% of students report that they experienced at least one incident of sexual harassment in college, and males are overwhelmingly more likely than females to commit sexual harassment (Wright & Bonita, 2012).

Kathleen Cairns and Doyle Hatt (1995) of the University of Calgary have found that 9% of the female graduate students and 2% of the male graduate students at a large Canadian university have experienced sexual harassment. The most common form has involved sexist remarks and sexual comments. Very few of the students have experienced sexual coercion. The female students have been harassed mainly by male professors and instructors, but also by other students. The male students have been harassed mainly by female students.

Researchers at the Ontario Institute for Studies in Education surveyed psychologists in Ontario about their sexual-harassment experiences while they were in graduate school (Schneider et al., 2002). The reported incidence of harassment was much higher than that found by Cairns and Hatt, most likely because the Ontario researchers measured a wider scope of harassment experiences. The psychologists reported that by far the most common type of harassment was suggestive jokes or stories told by professors. Very few reported sexual coercion by their professors.

Most forms of harassment involve unequal power relationships between the harassers and their targets. Peer harassment involves people who are equal in power, and includes sexual taunts from fellow employees, students, or colleagues. In some cases, the harassers may have less formal power than the individuals they're harassing. Both female and male professors, for example, have been sexually harassed by students.

Canadian universities have sexual harassment policies in place that include reporting mechanisms for both students and employees. University faculty associations in Canada support policies on sexual harassment. Still, the associations are sometimes concerned that their policies may in some instances limit academic freedom, especially the ability to have open discussions of controversial topics.

Schools

Playful sexual antics are common during adolescence. Unwelcome sexual advances and lewd comments go beyond playfulness, however, and have become a concern for many of Canada's teens.

A research team consisting of Loren McMaster, Jennifer Connolly, and Debra Pepler of York University and Wendy McCraig of Queen's University conducted a study of peer-to-peer sexual harassment among 1213 students in grades six to eight in a large Canadian city (McMaster et al., 2002). The study defined sexual harassment as unwanted sexual attention, and asked students whether they'd perpetrated or experienced any of ten types of sexual harassment. Boys were significantly more likely (36%) than girls (21%) to report perpetration, while both genders were equally likely (42% of boys and 38% of girls) to report victimization. The three behaviours both boys and girls most often experienced were homophobic name-calling, sexual comments or jokes or looks, and flashing or mooning. The boys

CRITICAL THINKING QUESTIONS

What factors within society contribute to sexual harassment? Do some of these factors also explain why men are more likely than women to sexually harass?

CRITICAL THINKING QUESTIONS

Are you aware of any sexual-harassment policies at your school?

perpetrated more same-sex harassment, while the girls perpetrated more cross-sex harassment. The most common form of same-sex harassment among boys was homophobic name-calling.

The researchers found that students who were at more advanced stages of pubertal development both perpetrated and experienced sexual harassment more than other students. McMaster et al. (2002) concluded that for some youth, harassment is a phase of development, while for others it's part of a developmental pattern that includes other forms of aggression, such as bullying, and is a predictor of aggression in future dating relationships.

Higher levels of harassment were found in a study of 565 older adolescents in British Columbia and New Brunswick (Dahinten, 2003). The picture that emerges from this poll of teenagers in grades nine to 11 indicates that sexual taunts and advances have become part of an unwelcome ritual for many students, especially girls, as they try to make their way through high school hallways and stairwells. Almost all of the students reported that they'd experienced at least one form of sexual harassment during the preceding two months, while about two-thirds of the girls and half of the boys reported five or more forms of harassment. The most common forms of harassment for two-thirds of the girls were sexual comments, whistles, sexual gestures, stares, and derogatory comments about females.

The students didn't label most of the behaviours as sexual harassment. Of those who'd experienced at least one of the 19 items measuring sexual harassment, only 35% of the girls and 14% of the boys replied yes to the general question of whether they'd been sexually harassed. This discrepancy in labelling clearly illustrates how the type of measurement a researcher chooses can influence the incidence of harassment reported in the literature. It also raises the important question of whether it's legitimate for researchers to categorize behaviours as harassment when the people experiencing them don't consider them harassment (Dahinten, 2003).

Girls in the study were more likely than boys to report that they'd been upset by the sexual harassment behaviours. For boys, the most upsetting experiences were being targets of sexual rumours and graffiti, and being followed or pestered for dates. For girls, the most upsetting experiences were being forced to do something other than kissing or hugging, and being targets of sexual rumours. Most of the students responded passively to the harassment. Hardly any reported it to a teacher or made a complaint through the school system (Dahinten, 2003).

In a more recent survey of Ontario high school students conducted by the Centre for Addiction and Mental Health, one-third of the students said they'd at times felt unsafe at school. About half of the girls said they'd been subjected to sexual comments or gestures at school, and one-third said they'd been touched in a sexual manner (Rushowy, 2008).

Large-scale studies of youth in both Canada and the United States have found that gays, lesbians, and bisexuals experience more physical and sexual abuse than heterosexuals do (Saewyc et al., 2006a, 2006b). The researchers attribute this to the stigma that's often attached to LGB orientations. They also note that most LGB youth aren't physically or sexually abused.

Cyberbullying

Today, there's considerable concern about sexual harassment through cyberbullying, particularly among youth. Cyberbullying is the use of communication technologies such as the Internet, social networking sites, websites, e-mail text messaging, and instant messaging. One form of this kind of harassment is posting nude photos of a current or former romantic partner without the person's consent. (See "Applied Knowledge: Sexting and Canadian Youth" in Chapter 7.) Repeated tormenting online constitutes criminal harassment, and sharing videos or photos with nudity of people under age 18 is illegal in Canada; teens can be charged for these offenses.

Applied Knowledge

RESISTING SEXUAL HARASSMENT

What would you do if you were sexually harassed by an employer or a professor? How would you handle it? Would you try to ignore it, and hope it would stop? What actions might you take?

We offer some suggestions you may find helpful. Recognize, however, that responsibility for sexual harassment always lies squarely with the perpetrator and with the organization that permits sexual harassment to take place, not with you.

- *Convey a professional attitude.* Harassment may be stopped cold if you respond to the harasser with a businesslike, professional attitude.
- *Discourage harassing behaviour, and encourage appropriate behaviour.* Harassment may also be stopped cold if you shape the harasser's behaviour. Your reactions may encourage businesslike behaviour and discourage flirtatious or suggestive behaviour. If a harassing professor suggests that you come back after school to review your term paper, so the two of you won't be disturbed, set limits assertively. Tell the professor you'd feel more comfortable discussing the paper during regular office hours. Remain task-oriented. Stick to business. The harasser should quickly get the message that you insist on maintaining a strictly professional relationship. If the harasser persists, don't blame yourself—you're responsible only for your own actions. When the harasser persists, a more direct response may be appropriate (e.g., "Dr. Jones, I'd like to keep our relationship on a purely professional basis").

- *Avoid being alone with the harasser.* If you're being harassed by your professor but need advice about your term paper, approach him or her after class, when other students are milling about, not privately, during office hours. Or bring a friend to wait outside the office while you consult the professor.
- *Maintain a record.* Keep a record of all incidents of harassment, to use as documentation in the event that you decide to lodge an official complaint. The record should include where each incident took place, the date and time, what happened (including the exact words used, if you can recall them), how you felt, and the names of witnesses.
- *Talk with the harasser.* It may be uncomfortable to address the issue directly with a harasser, but doing so puts the offender on notice that you're aware of the harassment and want it to stop. It may be helpful to describe the specific offending actions (e.g., "When we were alone in the office, you repeatedly attempted to touch me or brush up against me"), your feelings about the offending behaviour (e.g., "It made me feel like my privacy was being violated"), and what you'd like the offender to do (e.g., "So I'd like you to agree never to attempt to touch me again. Okay?"). Having a talk with the harasser may stop the harassment. If the harasser denies the accusations, you may have to take further action.
- *Write a letter to the harasser.* Set down on paper a record of the offending behaviour, and put the harasser on notice that the harassment must stop. Your letter might describe what happened (e.g., "Several times you've made sexist comments about my body"),

describe how you felt (e.g., "It made me feel like a sexual object when you talked to me that way"), and describe what you'd like the harasser to do (e.g., "I want you to stop making sexist comments to me").
- *Seek support.* Support from people you trust can help you through the often trying process of resisting sexual harassment. Talking with others enables you to express your feelings and receive emotional support, encouragement, and advice. It may also strengthen your case if you have opportunities to identify and talk with other people who've been harassed by the offender.
- *File a complaint.* Organizations are required by law to respond reasonably to complaints of sexual harassment. In large organizations, a designated official (e.g., a human-rights officer) is usually charged with handling such complaints. Set up an appointment with this official to discuss your experiences. The major government agencies that handle charges of sexual harassment are the provincial human-rights offices. Look in the government section of your phone book for the number of the nearest office.
- *Seek legal remedies.* Sexual harassment is illegal and actionable. If you're considering legal action, consult a lawyer familiar with this area of law.

The question isn't what victims of sexual assault, incest, and sexual harassment will do to redress the harm that's been done to them. The question is what we'll all do to reshape society so sex can no longer be used as an instrument of power, coercion, and violence.

In one case, Canadian teen Amanda Todd committed suicide after intimate photos of her were circulated online.

In 2014, the federal government introduced the *Protecting Canadians from Online Crime Act* which, if passed into law, will make it illegal to distribute intimate images without consent, no matter how old the person depicted in the images is. In part, this legislation is designed to prevent so-called "revenge porn" in which a person, usually a male, circulates intimate photos or videos of a former partner online for the purpose of shaming and humiliating that person.

Summing Up

The definition of sexual assault involves more than just sexual intercourse.

Types of sexual assault include stranger sexual assault, acquaintance sexual assault, date sexual assault, and partner sexual assault.

Social attitudes such as gender-role stereotyping, seeing sex as adversarial, and acceptance of violence in interpersonal relationships all help create a climate that encourages sexual assault.

Some sexually coercive men feel socially inadequate, lack social skills, and avoid social interactions with women. Others are basically antisocial, and have long histories of violent behaviour.

Sexual assault survivors often experience post-traumatic stress disorder (PTSD).

Treatment of sexual assault survivors typically involves helping them through the crisis period following the attack, and then fostering long-term adjustment.

Sexual assault prevention involves educating society at large and familiarizing women with a number of precautions they can take.

Verbal sexual coercion involves the use of verbal pressure or seduction lines to manipulate a person into having sexual relations.

Any form of sexual contact between an adult and a child is abusive, even if force or physical threat isn't used, because a child is legally incapable of consenting to sexual activity with an adult.

In most cases of child sexual abuse, the molesters are close to the children they abuse—relatives, step-relatives, family friends, and neighbours.

Pedophilia is a type of paraphilia in which adults are sexually attracted to children.

Incest is sexual relations between people who are closely related.

Children who are sexually abused often suffer social and emotional problems that impair their development and persist into adulthood, affecting their self-esteem and their formation of intimate relationships.

Psychotherapy may help adult survivors of sexual abuse improve their self-esteem and their ability to develop intimate relationships.

The effectiveness of prison-based rehabilitation programs and anti-androgen drugs in curbing repeat offences requires further empirical support.

The definition of sexual harassment in the workplace has been expanded to include any behaviour of a sexual nature that interferes with an individual's work performance or creates a hostile, intimidating, or offensive work environment.

Most incidents of sexual harassment on campus take the form of sexist comments.

Sexual harassment at school has become an unwelcome ritual that many junior and senior high school students are forced to endure.

Test Yourself

Multiple-Choice Questions

1. A sexual assault that wounds, maims, or disfigures the victim would be categorized as _____ under the *Criminal Code of Canada*.
   (a) level 1
   (b) level 2
   (c) level 3
   (d) level 4

2. Sexual assaults are most often committed by:
   (a) Strangers.
   (b) Family members.
   (c) Gangs.
   (d) Acquaintances.

3. According to the General Social Survey, a person is most likely to be sexually assaulted at age:
(a) 15 to 24.
(b) 25 to 34.
(c) 35 to 44.
(d) 45 to 54.

4. Which of the following is not a myth that encourages sexual assault?
(a) In general, women like men to be aggressive, even forceful, when it comes to sex.
(b) When women dress in revealing clothing, they're asking to be sexually assaulted.
(c) Women who say no to sex really mean no.
(d) Women say no to sex when they really mean yes.

5. Which of the following is not a suggestion about what to do if you're sexually assaulted?
(a) Don't wash, change your clothes, or comb your hair.
(b) Seek medical help, and make sure any injuries are documented.
(c) Think about reporting the assault to police.
(d) Don't talk to anyone about the assault.

6. Rohypnol is used as a date-rape drug because it:
(a) Impairs memory.
(b) Enhances sexual response.
(c) Multiplies the effects of testosterone.
(d) Encourages women to recall consensual sex as assaults.

7. Which of the following statements about pedophilia is false?
(a) Many pedophiles have personality disorders.
(b) With proper treatment, it's likely that a sexual preference for children can be changed.
(c) Many pedophiles believe sex with a child isn't harmful.
(d) Researchers have found brain differences that are likely prenatal between pedophiles and other men.

8. The most common type of child sexual abuse is
(a) Genital fondling.
(b) Vaginal intercourse.
(c) Oral sex.
(d) Exhibitionism.

9. The most common type of incest is:
(a) Father–daughter incest.
(b) Stepfather–stepdaughter incest.
(c) Brother–sister incest.
(d) Mother–son incest.

10. According to Wright and Bonita (2012), what percentage of students report that they have experienced at least one incident of sexual harassment in college?
(a) 5% to 10%.
(b) 15% to 20%.
(c) 25% to 30%.
(d) 35% to 40%.

You'll find answers to the "Test Yourself" questions on page 489.

Questions for Critical Thinking

1. Have you ever tried to convince someone to engage in sexual activity even after they've said no? What eventually happened? How do you feel about it now?

2. Has anyone ever tried to convince you to engage in sexual activity even when you haven't wanted to? What happened? How do you feel about it now? How do you feel about the other person? About yourself?

3. A woman goes to a bar, has a few too many drinks, dances suggestively with several men, and goes home with one of them. If she later reports that she's been sexually assaulted, do you think she's to blame? If she'd been assaulted on the street while waiting for a bus at the same time of night, would she be less to blame?

4. Imagine that you are sexually harassed and are considering reporting it to authorities, but a friend advises, "Why make such a fuss? Is it really worth it? After all, complaining could backfire." How would you respond?

CHAPTER EIGHTEEN

Commercial Sex

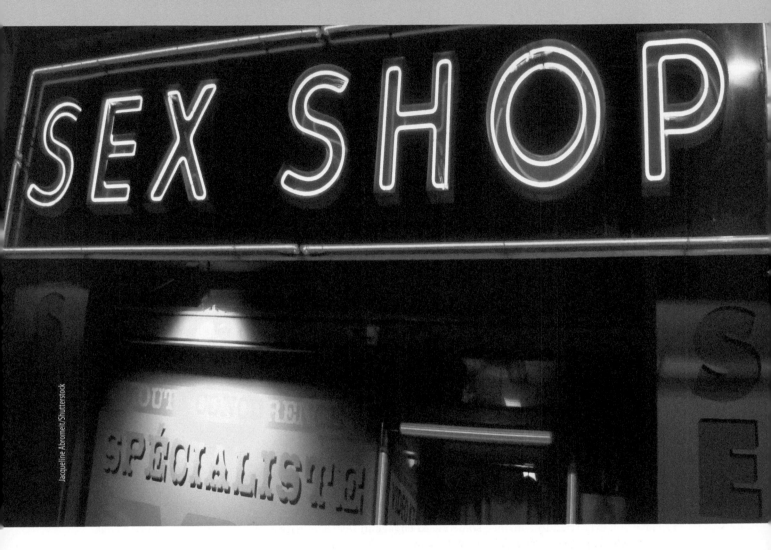

Jacqueline Abromeit/Shutterstock

Sex as commerce runs the gamut from street-based sex work, sexually explicit video, and adult magazines to strip shows, sex-toy shops, escort or outcall services, massage parlours, 1-900 telephone services, cybersex (sex over the Internet), and sexually oriented messages and images in advertisements for a wide range of products. The types of sexual commerce seem unlimited. The annual Everything to Do with Sex Show held in a number of Canadian cities has hundreds of exhibitors, selling all kinds of products and services related to sex. Many thousands of people attend these events.

Prostitution

Prostitution is often called the world's oldest profession—for good reason. It can be traced at least to ancient Mesopotamia, where temple prostitution flourished. Prostitution also thrived in medieval Europe and during the sexually repressive Victorian period.

Prostitution The sale of sexual activity for money or goods of value.

Then, as now, the major motive for becoming a prostitute was economic. Many poor women were drawn to prostitution as a means of survival. In Victorian England, prostitution was widely regarded as a necessary outlet for men's sexual appetites. It was widely held that women didn't enjoy sex, so it was better for a man to visit a prostitute than to "soil" his wife with his carnal passions.

In recent years, "sex worker" has increasingly replaced "prostitute" as the preferred term for a person who engages in sexual activity in exchange for monetary compensation.

Prostitution Law in Canada

Canadian laws governing prostitution have been, and continue to be, confusing. Up until the federal government's introduction of a proposed new set of laws governing prostitution in 2014, under previous laws, while prostitution itself was legal, almost all of the activities involved with it were illegal. The *Criminal Code* prohibited a number of activities related to prostitution, including the following:

- Transporting or directing, or offering to transport or direct, another person to a common bawdy house (establishment within which acts of sex for payment occur).
- Keeping, being an inmate of, being found without lawful excuse in, or allowing a place to be used for the purpose of a common bawdy house.
- Procuring and living off the avails of prostitution.
- Communicating in a public place for the purposes of offering or obtaining the sexual services of a prostitute.

The Everything to Do with Sex Show.
This trade show, held in various cities across Canada, attracts many thousands of people. The exhibitors sell all kinds of erotic products, including toys and videos. The business of sex is booming in Canada.

A World of Diversity

"PROSTITUTION" OR "SEX WORK"?

Many prostitutes have redefined themselves as sex workers, and prostitution as sex work (Lucas, 2005).

The new terms underscore the economic aspects of the work, and are less laden with a history of lewdness and depravity. They've also caught on in the research literature. The Commercial Sex Information Service (CSIS) in Vancouver explains the shift this way:

The terms "sex work" and "sex worker" have been coined by

sex workers themselves to redefine commercial sex, not as the social or psychological characteristic of a class of women, but as an income-generating activity or form of employment for women and men. As such, it can be considered along with other forms of economic activity. An employment or labour perspective is a necessary, if not sufficient, condition for making sex work a part of the mainstream debate on human, women's, and workers' rights at local, national, and international levels.

The lack of international and local protection renders sex workers vulnerable to exploitation in the workplace, and to harassment or violence at the hands of employers, law enforcement officials, clients, and the public.

The need for worker protection, including occupational health and safety provisions, is of particular relevance in the current context of HIV and AIDS.

Source: Bindman, J. (1997). Redefining prostitution as sex work on the international agenda. Vancouver: Commercial Sex Information Service.

In other words, it was against the law to engage in activities that facilitate prostitution, or to be in a house of prostitution.

In 1983, the Canadian minister of justice appointed a special committee (the Fraser Committee) to study pornography and prostitution and make recommendations to Parliament. Although the committee recommended that prostitution offences be removed from the *Criminal Code*, the federal government instead brought in more restrictive legislation, with the aim of decreasing street prostitution. To make it easier for police to prosecute prostitutes as well as their clients, the *Criminal Code* was changed to make it illegal to communicate with or stop a person in a public place (including a motor vehicle) to negotiate sexual services for payment.

The new legislation was soon challenged as being inconsistent with the *Canadian Charter of Rights and Freedoms*. In 1990, however, the Supreme Court ruled that freedom of expression as granted by the Charter could be limited, because street solicitation caused too great a social nuisance. Nonetheless, while the new legislation did facilitate prosecution of both prostitutes and clients, it did not decrease street prostitution (Gemme, 1993).

Police and politicians have been particularly concerned about teen prostitution. In 1988 Parliament significantly increased penalties for clients who attempt to obtain the sexual services of a person under the age of 18 and who procure and live off the avails of prostitutes under the age of 18. Alberta passed the *Protection of Children Involved in Prostitution Act* in 1999 which allows police or social workers to apprehend and detain under-18 prostitutes in safe houses for up to 72 hours.

Police in Canada have often used the strategy of entrapment to obtain convictions against prostitutes and their clients. Male plainclothes officers would pretend they were clients wanting sex (e.g., obtaining topless body rubs at massage studios), to determine whether sex is being sold on the premises. Female police officers would act as decoys by standing in locations frequented by street prostitutes. When men approached and suggested having sex for money, the decoy officers would immediately arrest and charge them with communicating for the purposes of prostitution.

There were a number of grey areas when it came to interpreting laws about prostitution. The laws—and their interpretation—were continually changing. There have also been wide variations across the country in the degree to which prostitution laws are enforced by police.

In recent years, politicians and police forces have targeted the customers of prostitutes. In 2005, for example, the Manitoba government introduced legislation to suspend the drivers' licences of men convicted of soliciting prostitutes.

LEGAL CHALLENGES Attempts over the years to legalize prostitution in Canada have been resisted by government leaders. Because of concern over a high number of deaths among prostitutes in Vancouver and Edmonton, Parliament voted in 2003 to establish a Subcommittee on Solicitation Laws, with a mandate to review and recommend changes to prostitution laws in order to improve the safety of sex workers.

The subcommittee heard from academic researchers, legal experts, and sex workers who presented well-documented examples of how Canadian laws promote unsafe working conditions for sex workers. These delegations proposed several changes to the *Criminal Code* that would give sex workers safer work environments. The subcommittee presented its report, *The Challenge of Change: A Study of Canada's Criminal Prostitution Laws*, in December of 2006. The report acknowledged the analysis of, and recommendations for, greater safety for sex workers presented by numerous witnesses. The subcommittee recommended that the federal government reform the laws so consensual sexual relations between adults, including sex for money, wouldn't be criminalized. However, it didn't offer specific

CRITICAL THINKING QUESTIONS

Should prostitution be decriminalized? What points would you use to support your answer?

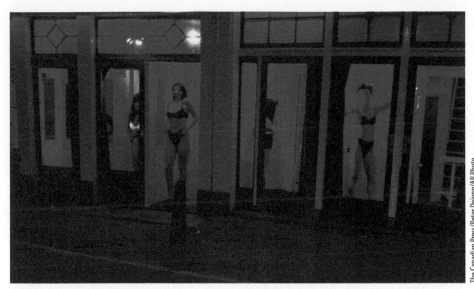

Amsterdam's Red-Light District.
It's one of the city's tourist attractions, where prostitution is legal and regulated. Condoms are a must. Tourists and locals stroll by the canals and window-shop.

recommendations to promote the safety of sex workers. Instead, the subcommittee focused mainly on the sexual exploitation of children and human trafficking.

The Conservative members of the subcommittee disagreed with the idea that prostitution should be decriminalized. Rather, they viewed prostitution as a degrading activity that no one would willingly consent to be involved in. This view suggests that while the Conservative party forms the federal government, efforts to decriminalize prostitution will be resisted.

In 2007, frustrated with federal government inaction, a small group of lawyers in collaboration with sex workers launched constitutional challenges to the prostitution laws. In Ontario, a legal team led by Osgoode Hall Law School professor Alan Young worked with the Toronto-based Sex Professionals of Canada; in British Columbia, a legal team led by Katrina Pacey of the Pivot Legal Society collaborated with the Downtown Eastside Sex Workers United Against Violence Society. The underlying principle of the constitutional challenge was that Canadian prostitution laws contributed to violence against street-based sex workers, and the resulting harm outweighed the laws' benefits to society. Three main sections of the laws were challenged:

- The provision against communication for the purpose of prostitution, because it prevented sex workers from screening potentially violent clients.
- The provision against bawdy houses, because it prohibited sex workers from working in an indoor environment, which is safer than working on the streets.
- The provision against living off the avails of prostitution, because it was too broad, and it prevented sex workers from hiring security personnel. (The constitutional challenge did not, however, aim to stop prosecution of pimps who exploit sex workers.)

As a result of the challenge, in 2010 both the Ontario Superior Court and the British Columbia Court of Appeal issued rulings that effectively struck down Canada's prostitution laws. In response to an application by the Attorney General, the Supreme Court of Canada announced in March of 2011 that it would consider the challenge brought by the Downtown Eastside Sex Workers United Against Violence Society.

In 2013, the Supreme Court of Canada ruled that aspects of the law which related to communicating for the purposes of prostitution, keeping a common bawdy house, and living off the avails of prostitution were unconstitutional in that they violated the charter rights of individuals to "security of person" and to freedom of expression. The ruling was delivered in December 2013 and stipulated that the existing laws would remain in effect for one year, after which time they would be invalid and would need to be replaced with new legislation.

BILL C-36   While many people, including sex worker advocates, hoped that the Supreme Court ruling would lead to the decriminalization of prostitution, the Conservative government introduced Bill C-36, the *Protection of Communities and Exploited Persons Act*, in June 2014 as a replacement for the laws which were struck down. The main feature of Bill C-36 is that it would make the selling of sex legal, with some restrictions, but make the buying of sex illegal. In other words, it would target the customers of sex workers rather than the sex workers themselves. The penalties for being convicted of attempting to purchase sexual services would range from a fine to up to five years in prison. The Bill also includes stiff penalties (up to ten years in prison) for those (e.g., pimps or escort service owners) who receive financial benefit from the sale of sexual services. The new law would also place significant restrictions on how sex workers could advertise.

The main feature of Bill C-36, making the buying of sex illegal but the selling of sex legal, reflects what is known as the *Nordic Model* which refers to countries such as Iceland, Norway, and Sweden which have taken a similar approach to the legal regulation of sex work.

As this book went to press, Bill C-36 had passed two readings in the House of Commons with a third and final reading remaining; then the Bill will proceed to the Senate for approval. Given that the Conservative government which introduced the Bill has a majority in both the House of Commons and the Senate, it is widely expected that Bill C-36 will become law in Canada before the end of 2014. However, it is also widely expected that the new law, once implemented, will also be challenged in the Supreme Court by sex workers who will claim that C-36 is no better than the laws it replaced in protecting their constitutional right to "security of person."

Canadian Attitudes

Public opinion polls measuring attitudes towards prostitution reveal that Canadians have been, and continue to be, divided on whether prostitution should be legal. There also appears to be a gender split with more Canadian men than women believing that the buying and selling of sexual services should be legal.

A 2009 Angus Reid poll found that most Canadians would like to see Canada's prostitution laws modified, though there was considerable disagreement about how. Half (50%) of the poll respondents preferred that some aspects of prostitution that are currently illegal should be decriminalized and that adults should be allowed to engage in consensual prostitution. Twenty-five percent believed prostitution should be prohibited entirely, 16% believed the laws should remain as they were, and 8% weren't sure what they thought (Angus Reid Public Opinion, 2009).

Soon after the federal government introduced Bill C-36 to regulate prostitution, Angus Reid Global (2014) surveyed Canadians on their opinions about the legality of buying and selling sex and their level of support for Bill C-36. Overall, Canadians were evenly split with respect to the buying of sex with 45% saying it should be legal and 45% saying it should be illegal, while 11% were unsure. For selling sex, 51% said it should be legal while 39% said it should be illegal, and 10% were unsure. When the results were broken down by gender, 56% of men of men said buying sex should be legal, while 55% of women said it should be illegal. For selling sex, 62% of men said it should be legal, but 49% of women said it should be illegal. In terms of their support for Bill C-36 which would make the buying of sex illegal but allow the selling of sex under certain circumstances, 35% of Canadians said they supported the Bill, 47% were opposed, and 18% were unsure.

Female Sex Workers

Female sex workers—commonly called hookers, working girls, and escorts—are usually classified according to the settings in which they work. The major types today are street-based sex workers, brothel or house workers (many of whom work in massage parlours), and escorts or call girls.

STREET-BASED SEX WORKERS   **Street-based sex workers** occupy the bottom rung in the hierarchy of sex workers. Although street-based sex workers are most visible to the public, most sex work in Canada takes place off-street (O'Doherty, 2011).

In Canada, about 20% of commercial sex workers negotiate their transactions on the streets (Lowman & Atchison, 2006). They typically earn less than off-street sex workers such as escorts and brothel workers. They also incur a high risk of abuse by customers and **pimps**. Studies of street-based sex workers on Vancouver's Downtown Eastside indicate that up to 98% have experienced violence from clients, pimps, and other sex workers (O'Doherty, 2011). Homeless youth living on the streets are often forced to trade sex for money, food, or shelter, an activity known as survival sex.

Between 1991 and 2004, 171 female sex workers in Canada were murdered, and almost all were streetwalkers. Serial murderers have targeted street-based sex workers. One of the most publicized was British Columbia pig farmer Robert Pickton, who was convicted in 2007 of murdering six streetwalkers and charged with killing 20 more. In Edmonton, where the bodies of 20 sex workers have been found since 1983, police suspect a serial killer is the culprit.

Street-based sex workers tend to operate in the open. This makes them more likely than other sex workers to draw attention to themselves and risk arrest (Kristof, 2009). To avoid arrest, street-based sex workers may be indirect about their services. They may ask passersby if they're interested in a good time or some fun, rather than offering sex, per se.

Prior to the introduction of Bill C-36 in Canada which would make the selling of sex legal, in most locales, penalties for prostitution involved small fines or short jail terms. Many police departments, besieged by drug peddling and violent crime, consider prostitution a minor or nuisance crime. For many sex workers, the criminal justice system has been a revolving door. They pay the fine, they spend a night or two in jail, and they return to the streets.

Some sex workers support pimps, especially those who are younger and have less than high school educations (Shaver, 2005). A pimp acts as lover, father, companion, and master. He provides protection, bail, and sometimes room and board, in exchange for a high percentage of a sex worker's earnings—often more than 90%. Sex workers are often physically abused by their pimps, who may use threats and beatings as a means of control (Nussbaum, 2012).

For many street-based sex workers, life is a round of sex, violence, disease, and substance abuse (Degenhardt et al., 2006; Romero-Daza et al., 2005). Many feel powerless to control their own fates, and are often talked or coerced into oral or vaginal sex without protection. Many die young from drug abuse, disease, suicide, and physical abuse from pimps and customers (Lloyd, 2012). Those who survive become less marketable with age. Researchers find high levels of psychological disturbance among street-based sex workers (Brown, 2005; Farley, 2005), often related to the physical and sexual abuse they've experienced. In a Canadian study of 100 prostitutes, 90% had been physically assaulted on the job, and 78% had been sexually assaulted.

Street-based sex workers Sex workers who solicit customers on the street.

Pimps Men who serve as agents for sex workers and live off their earnings.

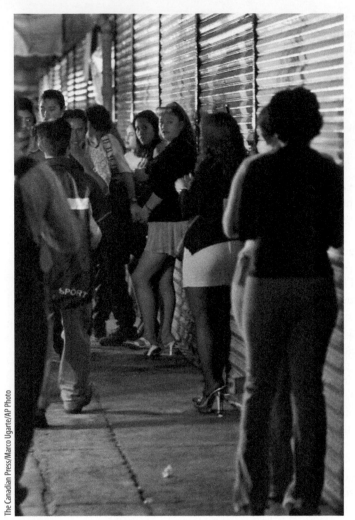

Sex Workers in Mexico City.
Street-based sex workers are most visible to the public, because they work in the open, in diverse places.

Sex workers who work hotels and conventions generally hold a higher status than those who work the streets or bars. Clients are typically convention-eers or businessmen travelling away from home. Hotel sex workers must be skilled in conveying subtle messages to potential clients without attract-ing the attention of hotel management or security. They usually provide sexual services in the clients' hotel rooms. Some hotel managers tolerate known sex workers (usually for a payoff under the table), so long as the women conduct themselves discreetly.

BROTHEL WORKERS   Brothel workers occupy a middle position in the hierarchy of sex work, between street-based sex workers and call girls. They work in brothels or—more commonly, today—massage parlours.

MASSAGE-PARLOUR WORKERS   Many massage parlours provide massage—and only massage—to customers. Masseuses and masseurs are licensed by provincial governments, and laws prohibit them from offering sexual services. Many localities require that masseuses and masseurs keep certain parts of their bodies clothed, and refrain from touching cli-ents' genitals.

Many massage parlours, however, serve as fronts for sex work. In these establishments, clients typically pay fees for standard massages and tip the workers for sexual extras.

To avoid massage-parlour regulations, some owners have obtained licenses by claiming they were holistic health centres or aromatherapy centres. In May of 2005, The *Toronto Star* ran front-page exposés of the holistic health centre industry, with headlines such as "What Can Toronto Do about Sex Dens?" At one of the centres the reporters visited, the manager outlined the additional options available beyond the $40 entrance fee: $20 for a topless massage, $40 for a nude massage, and $60 for a body slide (the nude masseuse slides herself over the naked body of the client). Many places also offer a nude reverse, in which clients can massage the naked masseuse (Cribb & Brazao, 2005). The articles created a furor at City Hall, and Toronto City Council instructed its licensing staff and police to clamp down on agencies that weren't legitimate health centres.

Massage parlours that do offer sexual services generally limit them to mastur-bation of the client (hence the term "rub and tug"). Most don't offer oral sex or penetration ("full service"), in the sometimes mistaken belief that this will protect them from prosecution.

ESCORTS   Conventioneers and businessmen are more likely to check the listings for massage and escort services in telephone directories and newspaper personals columns than to seek hotel prostitutes. Services that provide outcalls send mas-seuses (or masseurs) or escorts to hotel rooms.

Escort services typically (but not always) offer sexual services. Escort services are found in every major Canadian city, where they present themselves as legiti-mate businesses that provide escorts for men. Indeed, unattached men travelling away from home and to corporate functions can find female companionship under "escort services." Many escort services provide only sexual services, however, and others negotiate sexual services after formal escort duties are completed—or in their stead.

Sex workers who work for escort services often come from middle-class backgrounds and are well educated—the better to hold their own in social conversation. Escort services may make arrangements with legitimate companies to provide escorts for visiting customers or potential clients.

CALL GIRLS   So-called **call girls** occupy the highest rungs on the social ladder of female sex work. Many of them overlap with escorts. Call girls tend to be the most attractive and best educated sex workers, and tend to charge more for their services. Many come from middle-class backgrounds. Unlike other types of sex worker, call girls usually work on their own. Because they don't split their incomes with pimps, escort services, or massage parlours, they can earn substantial amounts and can be more selective about the customers they accept.

Call girls may escort their clients to dinners and social functions, providing not only sex, but also charming, gracious conversation (Sanders, 2005). They give clients the feeling that they're important and attractive. They may simulate sexual pleasure and create the illusion that time doesn't matter. It does, of course. To the call girl, as to other entrepreneurs, time is money.

Call girls may receive clients in their apartments (in-calls), or make outcalls to clients' homes and hotels. To protect themselves from police and abusive clients, they may insist on seeing a client's business card or learning his home telephone number before making personal contact. They may investigate whether the customer is in fact the person he purports to be.

> **Call girls** Sex workers who arrange for their sexual contacts by telephone. "Call" refers both to telephone calls and to being on call.

Advocacy for Sex Workers

Sex work can be a dangerous, highly stigmatized occupation. Although the exchange of sex for money doesn't necessarily violate the *Criminal Code* (A noted above, Bill C-36 will make the buying of sex illegal), various aspects of Canadian law related to prostitution push sex workers further to the margins of society. These conditions make it difficult for many sex workers to do their work in a safe, secure manner (Young, 2008).

Meaningful progress toward improving safety and working conditions will likely depend on the impact of Canada's new laws regulating sex work. Francis Shaver of Concordia University and Jacqueline Lewis and Eleanor Maticka-Tyndale of the University of Windsor have conducted studies with sex workers across Canada. They argue that, beyond decriminalization, the safety and well-being of sex workers can be enhanced through policies that focus on occupational health and safety, access to essential services, and rights. They propose an approach to sex work similar to that adopted in New Zealand, which places sex work in a harm-reduction and labour-rights framework (Shaver, Lewis, & Maticka-Tyndale, 2011).

A number of organizations provide support services to sex workers across Canada, such as legal aid offered by the Pivot Legal Society in Vancouver. A major Canadian resource is Maggie's & the Prostitutes' Safe Sex Project of Toronto, the first education project in Canada run by sex workers. The project provides information about health promotion, HIV and STI prevention, Canadian law, and dangerous clients. Maggie's has been a model for international sex-worker peer-education projects.

Human Trafficking

Human trafficking, the forced illegal movement of people, often involves coercing girls and women into prostitution and other sex related work such as working in massage parlours. While attention has been focused primarily on the trafficking of girls and women into Canada from other countries, human trafficking also occurs within Canada. According to research by Diane Redsky, project director of the Canadian Women's Foundation's national task force on human trafficking of women and girls, human trafficking in Canada is underreported with few perpetrators caught by police (Moore & Levasseur, 2014). According to Redsky's research, women trafficked in Canada are often aboriginals or immigrants who live in poverty and are vulnerable to exploitation.

Human trafficking is a major global enterprise that generates US $5 to $7 billion each year, and the trafficking of girls and women for sexual exploitation is the industry's major component (Stewart & Gajie-Veljanoski, 2005). Because it's illegal and underground, accurate information about the numbers of girls and women trafficked to Canada is difficult to obtain. It's estimated that 800 to 16 000 people may be trafficked into Canada each year (Stewart & Gajie-Veljanoski, 2005). The Royal Canadian Mounted Police (RCMP, 2011) has documented cases of girls and women from Eastern Europe, Asia, and Africa being trafficked into Canada, usually by organized crime groups.

Asian and Eastern European women are lured to big cities in developing countries and to the West by promises of the good life (Rubenson et al., 2005). Upon arrival, they find themselves enslaved in brothels—working for tips and not allowed to leave. In a typical scenario, a woman comes to Canada after false promises of a high-paying job as a nanny, housekeeper, or exotic dancer. Upon her arrival in Canada, she's coerced into sex work, to repay the trafficker for her travel costs. The trafficker keeps her working in the sex trade by withholding her passport, isolating her from the wider community, confining her with force, and threatening her with violence (RCMP, 2011). In 2008, six people were arrested in Toronto for trafficking after police were informed that women from Eastern Europe had been lured to Canada with the promise of modelling jobs. Instead, their passports were taken away, and they were confined and forced to work in the sex trade (Piercy, 2008).

Entry into Sex Work

No single factor explains women's entry into sex work. Yet poverty and sexual and/ or physical abuse figure prominently in the backgrounds of a sizable percentage of sex workers (Carter & Dalla, 2006).

In various developing nations, such as Thailand, some rural, impoverished parents sell their daughters to recruiters, who place them in city brothels (Kristof, 2006). Many of the women send home whatever money they can, and work hard to try to pay off their procurers and break free of their financial bonds.

In Canada and the United States, many street-based sex workers are teen runaways. While some come from middle-class or affluent homes, others have been reared in poverty. Family discord and dysfunction frequently set the stage for their entry into street life and sex work (Carter & Dalla, 2006). Many teen runaways perceive life on the street—despite its dangers—as the only possible escape from family strife and conflict, or from the physical, emotional, or sexual abuse they suffer at home. Teen runaways with marginal skills and limited means of support may find few alternatives to sex work.

The great majority of studies of sex workers have focused on those who work on the street. Their findings may not reflect the characteristics of other categories of sex worker, such as those employed by escort services. Shaver (2002) has conducted several field studies of sex workers in Canada and believes much of the material on them overstates the disadvantaged backgrounds they may come from. For example, some university students may engage in some form of sex work, such as stripping, because the pay is better than for many other jobs (Lewis, 1998).

A study that examined predictors of employment in sex work versus employment in the food service industry and in hair styling salons in Victoria, British

Columbia, and Sacramento, California, found that sex workers were more likely than those in the other jobs to have experienced economic insecurity and physical or sexual abuse during their youth (McCarthy, Benoit, & Jansson, 2014). Nevertheless, most of the sex workers did not have these negative experiences in their background. The study also found that lower levels of education and having worked in fewer different occupations were associated with sex work. According to the authors, individuals who don't have a varied set of employment skills may find sex work to be a reasonable alternative to other jobs that are available to them, or to unemployment.

Shaver (1996) argues that researchers who study sex workers from a deviance perspective typically ignore the fact that some of them voluntarily enter this business and don't see themselves as victims. According to Shaver, they feel they have a lot of control over their work, in that "the prostitute sets the price, chooses the client, and has the last say as to when, how, and even if sex takes place" (p. 219). Shaver believes many of the problems associated with sex work would diminish if it were recognized as a legitimate profession.

Male Customers of Female Sex Workers

Many sex workers refer to customers as johns or tricks. Men who pay female sex workers for their services come from all walks of life and represent all socioeconomic and racial groups. Many, perhaps most, are married men of middle-class background (Bennetts, 2011).

A Vancouver survey of 500 men arrested for soliciting found that in many respects they were similar to other Canadian men (Kennedy et al., 2003). They ranged in age from 18 to 92, with an average age of 38. More than half were married or in serious relationships. Their incomes, education levels, and ethnic backgrounds were similar to those of the general Vancouver population. On average, the men had used the services of sex workers 19 times. Seventy percent reported that no one close to them knew they visited sex workers. They didn't differ from a comparison group of university men in sexual attitudes and sex drive (Kennedy et al., 2003).

Most Canadian studies of clients of sex workers have used samples from john schools (i.e., educational sessions for clients who have been charged with prostitution related offences). These samples are biased, since they consist of men arrested for soliciting streetwalkers. Vancouver researchers John Lowman and Chris Atchison (2006) obtained a broader range of sex workers' clients. One-half had regular sex partners or spouses, and two-thirds of these men said they were either satisfied or very happy with their relationships. The most common reason they gave for their first visits to sex workers was availability and visibility. The second reason they gave was that their decisions were spontaneous.

Most patrons are occasional johns. Examples include travelling salesmen and military personnel who stop in town without their regular sex partners. Many men are interested in sexual novelty or variety, which may be a major motive for occasional johns.

Habitual johns use sex workers as their major or exclusive sexual outlets. Some habitual johns have never established intimate sexual relationships. Some wealthy men who wish to avoid intimate relationships habitually patronize call girls.

Some johns employ sex workers to meet psychological or sexual needs they're unable to meet otherwise. Some want to engage in acts of fetishism or transvestism that they're unable to engage in with their wives and girlfriends. Others may have a **whore–madonna complex**. They see women as either sinners or saints. They can permit themselves to enjoy sex only with sex workers, or ask only sex workers to engage in acts such as fellatio. When they have sex with wives and girlfriends (the "saints"), they engage only in conventional sexual activities such as vaginal intercourse.

Whore–madonna complex A rigid stereotyping of women as either sinners or saints.

Innovative Canadian Research

MEDIA STEREOTYPES

University of Victoria researchers Helga Hallgrimsdottir, Rachel Phillips, and Cecilia Benoit (2006) compared media portrayals of sex workers with sex workers' accounts of their personal backgrounds and experiences.

The researchers wanted to demonstrate how media portrayals are often inaccurate, presenting stereotypes that encourage stigmatization of sex workers. They analyzed articles about sex workers in Victoria's *Times Colonist* newspaper for the years 1980 to 2004, to illustrate how media portrayals of sex workers have changed.

In general, the newspaper negatively described sex workers as criminals who were morally lost and the source of major social problems such as drug addiction and violence. They were seen as a bad influence on morality, and as a source of sexually transmitted diseases. Most of the articles focused on streetwalkers, ignoring male sex workers.

There was a change in blame attribution over that time. Whereas sex workers were seen in the early 1980s as wicked women who should be punished for their sexual transgressions, they were presented in 2004 as victims who'd been trapped into sex work by pimps or international sex-slave traders, and who were at the mercy of their clients. In the latter years, the newspaper included more stories about child and adolescent prostitution. For the entire period of the survey, sex workers were presented as emotionally damaged.

The researchers (Hallgrimsdottir et al., 2006) compared a sample of sex workers with these representations.

Contrary to media stereotypes of young girls brought to Canada by international traffickers, the sex workers in the survey averaged 32 years of age, and the great majority were born in Canada. One-quarter were caring for dependent children, a fact not commonly noted in the media. However, many did come from unstable family backgrounds, which does coincide with the media reports.

There were also media distortions about why women entered sex work. The articles said sex workers were either forced into sex work or turned to it to finance drug addictions. Hardly any of the sex workers surveyed said they'd been forced into the occupation, and only a minority said they'd entered it to pay for drug addictions. The majority said they'd voluntarily chosen to become sex workers, for economic reasons and because they'd had the opportunity to do so.

Although the newspaper articles didn't portray sex work as a career choice, most of the workers saw it that way. Like other jobs, it elicited a diversity of feelings among the workers, yet most of those surveyed felt the benefits of sex work outweighed the costs.

Research with sex workers in three Maritime cities (Jeffrey & MacDonald, 2006) supports the findings of Hallgrimsdottir and her colleagues (2006). Most of the Maritime sex workers said they'd carefully decided which economic choices were available, and voluntarily decided sex work was a better choice than such alternatives as living on welfare or working at minimum wage jobs.

MOTIVES FOR BUYING SEX   There appear to be six common motives for hiring a sex worker:

- Sex without negotiation—By turning to a sex worker, a man needn't spend the time, effort, and money involved in dating and getting to know someone for the sake of sexual activity.
- Sex without emotional commitment—A sex worker requires no emotional commitment from the man, other than payment for services rendered. The sex worker won't call him at home or expect to be called in return.
- Sex for eroticism and variety—Many sex workers offer "something extra" in the way of novel or kinky sex, such as oral sex, costumes (e.g., leather attire), and S&M rituals (e.g., bondage and discipline or spanking). A man may desire such activity, but be unable to obtain it with his regular partner. He may even be afraid to mention the idea.

- Prostitution as a social outlet—In the nineteenth and early twentieth centuries, the brothel served not only as a place to obtain sex, but also as a kind of stopping-off place between home and work. Sex was secondary to the companionship and amiable conversation men found in brothels. Similarly, women who attend male strip clubs enjoy bonding with their friends, as well as the stripping itself.
- Sex away from home—Among the most common contemporary reasons is that a man is away from home, such as at a convention or an out-of-town sporting event.
- Difficulty attracting a partner—A man with a physical disability or a disfiguring condition may seek the services of a sex worker because of difficulty attracting other partners, or because of fear of rejection. A lonely man who lacks sex partners may seek sex workers as a substitute.

JOHN SCHOOLS   Some Canadian cities have established john schools for men with no previous criminal records who are charged with communicating for the purpose of prostitution. In return for attending the day-long school, charges against

CRITICAL THINKING QUESTIONS

Why are men so much more likely than women to pay for sex?

A World of Diversity

GIRLS ON THE STREETS OF AMERICAN CITIES

Fourteen-year-old African American Jasmine Caldwell was selling sex on the streets of Atlanta, Georgia, when she thought she saw an opportunity to escape from her pimp: She was picked up by an undercover policeman. Her pimp "ran" 13 girls and took every penny they earned from their customers. If the policeman had taken Jasmine to Covenant House, a shelter for runaway teenagers, or a shelter for women who are victims of violence, perhaps she would have been able to resume her education and get her life back in some kind of order. But he didn't. He showed Jasmine his handcuffs and threatened to put her in prison. She was terrified and begged not to be imprisoned. Then the policeman offered to let her go in exchange for sex. Afterward, her pimp beat her for not collecting any payment.

Now 21, Jasmine said, "That happens a lot" (Kristof, 2009). "The cops sometimes just want to blackmail you into having sex."

Prostitution in the United States may not be as brutal as in India,

Pakistan, Malaysia, and Cambodia, where young girls are frequently kidnapped and tortured by owners of brothels, and sometimes killed if they do not comply. Americans tend to envision forced prostitution as a problem for Asian or Mexican women who are brought into the United States and imprisoned in brothels. A greater scandal involves American teenagers. Streetwalkers in the United States encounter abuse and violence because the authorities seem to care little about 14-year-olds like Jasmine. When the occasional middle-class European American girl is missing, radio stations broadcast alerts, and cable TV broadcasts "missing beauty" updates (Kristof, 2009). But poor early-teen African and Latina American girls vanish every day, and only pimps seem to be paying attention (Hallgrímsdóttir et al., 2008). These minority teens are typically runaways or "throwaways"—girls in conflict with parents or other "caregivers" who get kicked out.

Pimps are not father types or business partners. They exploit the girls they run by taking every cent they

earn. They may force the girls to work seven days a week. Occasionally they tattoo girls like ranchers brand cattle and horses. They beat girls who don't comply readily enough.

"If you don't earn enough money, you get beat," says Jasmine, "If you say something you're not supposed to, you get beat. If you stay too long with a customer, you get beat. And if you try to leave the pimp, you get beat."

Violence alone doesn't keep girls attached to their pimps. Jasmine had run away from a violent home at the age of 13, and she explained that she thought the pimp loved her. Drugs, gifts, a little bit of affection, and lack of an alternative keep most girls working. If a girl rebels, the pimp beats her and threatens to kill her.

According to New York Times columnist Nicholas Kristof (2009), "Solutions are complicated and involve broader efforts to overcome urban poverty, including improving schools and attempting to shore up the family structure. But a first step is to stop treating these teenagers as criminals and focusing instead on arresting the pimps and the customers."

the client are erased from the official court record. Typically, the men listen to presentations from street-based sex workers about the sex trade's negative effects on them. They also receive lectures on sexually transmitted infections, and in some instances they hear community representatives talk about the impact of street prostitution on their communities. The men are expected to provide donations to help support the programs (Fischer et al., 2002).

Male Sex Workers

Male sex work includes both male–male and male–female activities. Male sex workers who service female clients—gigolos—are rare. Gigolos' clients are typically older, relatively wealthy, unattached women. Gigolos may serve as escorts or as surrogate sons for the women, and they may or may not offer sexual services.

An interesting variation of male sex work involves female tourists from developed countries who have sex with local men in the developing countries they travel to. Unlike female sex workers, the beach boys who make money from their relations with female tourists don't openly demand fixed sums of money. Rather, they make requests for money and other goods in a disguised, subtle manner.

The overwhelming majority of male sex workers service gay men. Men who engage in sex work are sometimes called **hustlers**. Their patrons are typically called **scores**. Many male sex workers, like their female counterparts, come from families troubled by conflict, alcoholism, and physical and sexual abuse (Weitzer, 2012a).

Hustler A man who engages in sex work with male customers.

Score A customer of a hustler.

The major motive for male sex work, like female sex work, is money (Weitzer, 2012b). Running away from home typically serves as an entry point. Some males run away because of family problems; others are seeking adventure or independence. Some gay sex workers are literally thrown out because their families cannot accept their sexual orientation.

Most hustlers are part-timers who continue some form of educational or vocational activity as they support themselves through prostitution. Drug dealing and drug use are also common among hustlers (Weitzer, 2012b).

Hustlers may be gay, bisexual, or heterosexual in orientation. In a large-scale Australian survey, half of the male sex workers described themselves as gay, about one-third (31%) said they were bisexual, and 5.5% considered themselves straight (Minichiello et al., 2001).

Hustlers typically aren't attached to pimps. They generally make contact with clients in gay bars and social clubs, or by working the streets in areas frequented by gay men. They typically learn to hustle from watching other hustlers ply their trade.

Various kinds of male sex worker have been identified (Minichiello et al., 2001):

- Strippers—These males dance and strip. Female and male patrons fondle them and sometimes have sex with them.
- Kept boys—These males have relationships with older, economically secure men who keep them in affluent lifestyles. The older males, or "sugar daddies," often assume parental roles.
- Call boys—Like call girls, call boys may work on their own or through agencies or escort services.
- Punks—These are prison inmates who are used sexually by other inmates, in return for protection or goods such as cigarettes and drugs.
- Drag prostitutes—These are transvestites or pre-surgical male-to-female transsexuals who impersonate female prostitutes and have sex with men, who are frequently unaware (at least initially) of their gender. Some drag prostitutes limit themselves to fellatio on their customers, to conceal their gender. Others take the passive role in anal sex.
- Brothel prostitutes—Because fewer houses of male prostitution exist, male brothel prostitutes are rarer than their female counterparts.

- Bar hustlers and street hustlers—Like their female counterparts, these males have the lowest status, and ply their trade in gay bars or on streets frequented by gay passersby. Street hustlers are the most common and typically the youngest subtype. They're also the most visible, and consequently the ones most likely to draw police attention.

Why do men purchase the services of male sex workers? In a British Columbia study, clients of male sex workers generally fell into three categories: men who kept their desire to have sex with other men hidden from others, men who wanted to have sex with younger men, and men who couldn't attract regular male sex partners (Allman, 1999).

STIs and Sex Work

Among the most significant occupational hazards faced by sex workers is the threat of sexually transmitted infections (STIs) including HIV. It has been well-established that high risk for STIs among sex workers is linked to the criminalization of sex work (Krüsi et al., 2014). One of the primary reasons the Supreme Court of Canada cited in striking down the existing prostitution laws in 2013 was that the laws reduced the ability of sex workers to protect themselves from violence, abuse, and STIs. For example, when sex workers are faced with the threat of violence, they are often forced to prioritize their immediate physical safety over insisting on condom use with clients (Shannon & Celeste, 2010).

In a Montreal study in the mid-1990s, about one-third of both male and female sex workers reported that they'd had STIs within the previous two years (Shaver, 1996). All of the women said they always used condoms when engaging in vaginal or anal sex with clients, and 97% always used condoms with oral sex. Ninety percent of the male sex workers reported using condoms with clients during anal sex, but only 50% used condoms during oral sex. Both men and women used condoms far less often with men who weren't clients. A study of Montreal male street youth involved in sex work about ten years later had similar findings—many didn't use condoms, especially when having oral sex (Haley et al., 2004).

In a Vancouver study of female sex workers in massage parlours, 5% reported having had STIs within the previous six months (Johnson et al., 2007). Nine percent of the sex workers reported inconsistent condom use. A key reason was a financial incentive—some clients offered more money to have sex without condoms. Some sex workers gave in to persistent verbal pressure not to use condoms. Some sex workers of Asian background lacked knowledge of proper condom use.

The sex workers were at greater risk of STI transmission from having sex with people who weren't clients; 63% reported inconsistent condom use with their lovers. With non-clients, the sex workers believed they were protected, because they felt that their partners were monogamous. Another reason they gave for not using condoms was the feeling that condoms belonged at work, and not in a relationship.

Sex with sex workers is an important factor in the male–female transmission of HIV in Africa, where the infection is spread predominantly via male–female sexual intercourse.

STRIPPING   Stripping, also known as exotic dancing, is a type of sex work, though women and men who dance in strip clubs typically refer to themselves simply as dancers. Many sex workers in strip clubs limit their activity to dancing and doffing their clothes. Others do lap dances or table dances, making contact with customers as they dance. Customers buy the dances from the club and are expected to tip the strippers (Frank, 2002, 2003). Some strip clubs have private shows, VIP rooms, and the like, where strippers can be alone with their customers. What happens in these private shows may be tightly regulated by the clubs, or may depend on the sizes of the tips.

Many sex workers engage in this work only on a part-time or temporary basis. In a study of female strippers, Jacqueline Lewis (1998) of the University of Windsor distinguished between career and short-term, goal-oriented dancers. The latter group included several university students:

> And I looked at the salaries these people were making, and it was, you know, a thousand dollars a night, some nights, and it was really, really substantially helping with their tuition. And these were people working on master's degrees and doctorates and all kinds of things, and I thought, "Wow, if they can do this, hey, maybe I can." (Lewis, 1998, p. 59)

Research on stripping has focused on both the positive and negative aspects of this form of sex work (Bradley-Engen & Ulmer, 2009). While some strippers are able to earn money in clubs that provide adequate working conditions, others have little control over their work environments and face harassment from both club operators and patrons.

Sexually Explicit Material (SEM)

Sexually explicit material (SEM) is found nearly everywhere. In addition to adult magazines and DVD rentals, millions of people search for pornography on the Internet, and use cable and satellite services to watch sexually explicit content. People also download pornography onto their camera cell phones and video MP3 players.

SEM is typically used to elicit or enhance sexual arousal, often as a masturbation aid (Kingston et al., 2009; Owens et al., 2012). SEM may also be used by couples to enhance sexual arousal during lovemaking. Some sex therapists recommend that couples who are bored with their sexual routines, or experiencing other difficulties with the sexual aspects of their relationships, experiment with SEM, to help them become aroused. Many couples find that sexy videos, DVDs, and cable television movies enliven their sexual appetites and suggest novel techniques.

What's Pornographic?

Pornography Written, visual, or audiotaped material that's sexually explicit and produced to elicit or enhance sexual arousal. It has a negative connotation today and is typically associated with SEM that's violent and/or degrading.

Prurient Tending to excite lust; lewd.

Sexually explicit material (SEM) Written, visual, or audiotaped material that's graphic and produced to elicit or enhance sexual arousal.

Erotica SEM that doesn't involve violence or degradation of women. It may be as sexually explicit as pornography.

Webster's Deluxe Unabridged Dictionary defines **pornography** as "writing, pictures, etc., intended to arouse sexual desire." Inclusion of the word "intended" places the determination of what's pornographic in the mind of the person composing the work. Applying this definition makes it all but impossible to determine what's pornographic. If a filmmaker admits that s/he wants to arouse the audience sexually, we may judge the work to be pornographic even if no naked bodies or explicit sex scenes are shown. On the other hand, explicit representations of people engaged in sexual activity would not be pornographic if the work is intended as an artistic expression, rather than created for its **prurient** value.

Many works that were once prohibited in Canada because of explicit sexual content, such as the novels *Tropic of Cancer* by Henry Miller and *Lady Chatterley's Lover* by D. H. Lawrence, are now generally considered literary works, rather than excursions into pornography.

Let's define **sexually explicit material (SEM)** as written, visual, or audiotaped material that's graphic and produced to elicit or enhance sexual arousal. This has been the traditional definition of pornography.

In the 1980s, feminist groups began to differentiate two types of SEM—pornography and erotica. Pornography was defined as SEM that involves violence and/or degradation of women. **Erotica** was defined as SEM that doesn't involve violence or degradation of women. Erotica may be as sexually explicit as pornography.

SEM is often classified as either hard-core or soft-core. Hard-core SEM includes graphic and sexually explicit depictions of sex organs and sexual acts. Soft-core material, as represented by R-rated films and *Playboy* photo spreads, features more stylized nude photos and suggested (or simulated) rather than explicit sexual acts.

Perspectives on Pornography

There are many different opinions about SEM. These differences of opinion are often characterized as the pornography debates. Let's briefly look at some of the schools of thought that have been advanced in the discussion. Watson (2010) identifies five basic approaches: obscenity-based, conservative, liberal, anti-pornography feminist, and pro-pornography feminist.

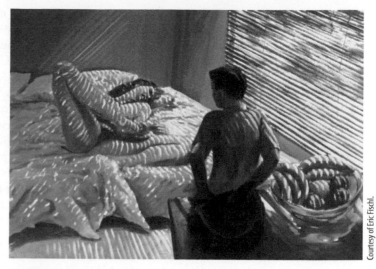

Courtesy of Eric Fischl.

Art or Obscenity?
Eric Fischl is a mainstream artist, yet some of his subject matter has been labelled obscene by some critics.

THE OBSCENITY-BASED APPROACH   Lawmakers in the United States and Canada often consider legal regulation of SEM on the basis of whether certain types of material can be judged obscene. That is, legislative bodies usually write laws about **obscenity**, rather than about pornography.

However, obscenity is difficult to define. In general, an obscenity is something that offends community standards—but determining exactly what the community standards are or should be with respect to SEM is notoriously difficult. United States Supreme Court judge Potter Stewart famously quipped that he couldn't define obscenity or pornography precisely, but "I know it when I see it." The Supreme Court of Canada has also had a difficult time defining obscenity and determining where, if anywhere, laws against obscenity run afoul of the Canadian *Charter of Rights and Freedoms*.

Obscenity SEM that offends community standards.

THE CONSERVATIVE POSITION   The conservative position on pornography holds that SEM is a threat to the "traditional values" of society. The proliferation of pornography is seen as encouraging immoral promiscuity and deemphasizing the importance of confining sexual behaviour to monogamous marriage.

This approach is often taken by conservative religious institutions. In their view, the increasing access to SEM in contemporary society reflects ". . . a declining public morality, a decline which conservatives argue seriously threatens the overall stability of civil society" (Watson, 2010, p. 538).

THE LIBERAL POSITION   The liberal approach to pornography argues that in the absence of clear evidence of harm to others or to the community as a result of SEM consumption, the government shouldn't restrict people's right to access it. Philosopher Ronald Dworkin has championed this point of view, arguing that access to SEM is a matter of individual liberty and free expression (McGlynn & Ward, 2009). In one variant of the liberal approach, legal regulation of SEM is seen as a violation of free speech.

THE ANTI-PORNOGRAPHY FEMINIST APPROACH   As SEM became much more widespread in the United States and Canada during the 1960s and 1970s, some feminists began to object to pornography that portrayed women simply as objects intended to provide sexual pleasure for men. They noted that the vast majority of commercially available pornographic material was produced by men,

CRITICAL THINKING
QUESTIONS

Which of the five perspectives
on pornography described
here best matches your own
perspective?

for men, and claimed that such material often presented women in dehumanized, degrading ways. As a result, they argued, pornography promoted gender inequality and sexual violence against women.

In 1980, feminist activists Catherine MacKinnon and Andrea Dworkin proposed legislation for the city of Minneapolis that defined pornography, in part, as material that presents women as "dehumanized sexual objects," material that presents "women's body parts such that women are reduced to those parts," or material that presents women "in scenarios that are degrading" (MacKinnon, 2007). The legislation, which didn't pass, would have allowed women who were victimized as a result of pornography to sue the producers, distributors, and sellers of pornography.

Nevertheless, some feminists continue to argue that many contemporary forms of pornography promote gender inequality and harm women.

THE PRO-PORNOGRAPHY FEMINIST APPROACH   Pro-pornography feminists believe SEM can promote gender equality. According to this view, pornography can be summarized as ". . . a source of freedom and liberation from dominant and patriarchal notions of sexuality for women (as well as other marginalized groups, including gays, lesbians, and transgendered persons)" (Watson, 2010, pp. 540–541).

The pro-pornography feminist approach is exemplified by Candida Royalle and Tristan Taormino, who make sexually explicit films from a woman's point of view, promoting women's exploration of sexual pleasure on their own terms. Since 2006, the Toronto sex store Good for Her has sponsored the Feminist Porn Awards, celebrating SEM that depicts genuine female sexual pleasure and challenges the sexual and gender stereotypes so often portrayed in many forms of pornography (Walker, 2008).

Canadian Law and SEM

Laws against obscenity provide the legal framework for outlawing the dissemination of pornography. Because the definition of obscenity relies on offending people or running afoul of community standards, what's deemed obscene may vary from person to person and from culture to culture.

The Supreme Court of Canada has been strongly influenced by the feminist argument that pornography exploits and degrades women. For example, the Women's Legal Education and Action Fund has argued that pornography causes violence against women, a view that was used by the Supreme Court to uphold the right of censorship in *Regina v. Butler* (1992). This case concerned the police raid of a Winnipeg store that sold sexually explicit videos. In his appeal to the Supreme Court, store owner Donald Butler argued that according to the *Canadian Charter of Rights and Freedoms*, he had a right to freedom of expression.

In upholding the constitutionality of the federal obscenity law, the Supreme Court argued that for a work to be considered obscene, there must be "undue" exploitation of sex. A "community-standard-of-tolerance" test must be applied, to determine whether undue exploitation has occurred. The courts must consider whether a community is likely to accept or tolerate the exposure of others to these materials, taking into consideration the possibility of harm that may result from such exposure. A key factor is whether the exploitation of sex is seen as degrading or dehumanizing to society in general, and to women in particular.

In *Regina v. Butler*, the Supreme Court devised three categories of obscenity. The first category involves material that mixes sex with violence and/or includes children. The second category includes material that involves sex and degradation, and is therefore seen as encouraging violence or harm to women. Materials that fall into either of these categories are deemed obscene. The third category involves material that's considered nonviolent and not degrading to women, and that doesn't

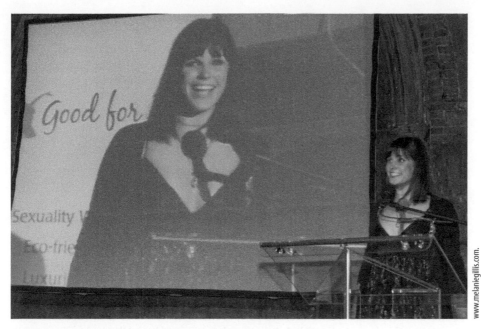

www.melaniegillis.com.

Feminist Porn Awards.
The Toronto women's sex shop Good for Her sponsors an annual event that recognizes the work of Canadian and international pornography producers and actors. One of the event's objectives is to show that pornography and feminism are not mutually exclusive categories. At the sixth annual Feminist Porn Awards show, actor Bobbi Starr accepted the award for Steamiest Romantic Movie for A Little Part of Me.

involve children. Materials that fall into the third category are not seen as involving undue exploitation of sex, and are therefore considered acceptable to Canadian society.

Civil libertarians were strongly opposed to legal changes resulting from the *Butler* decision, and felt the new interpretations were too restrictive. They were also concerned about the potential subjectivity involved in trying to determine which materials are degrading. In some respects, however, the new interpretation of obscenity allowed for greater permissiveness in legalizing previously banned explicit materials.

The Supreme Court decision had a monumental effect on changing the guidelines used by provincial censorship boards. In Canada, censorship and classification of films is a provincial responsibility. Until the 1992 *Butler* decision, some provincial censorship boards, particularly in Ontario, had banned any scenes of hard-core or penetrative sex. The Ontario Film Review Board revised its guidelines after 1992, which resulted in the legitimizing of sexually explicit films and videos and an increase in the number of adult video stores.

All materials such as books and videos that come into Canada can be confiscated by the Canada Border Services Agency if they're deemed to violate Canada's obscenity laws, and video stores can still be charged by police for selling materials that are defined as obscene under the *Criminal Code* (Benzie, 2004).

In many respects, legal efforts to regulate the distribution of obscene SEM in Canada have been thwarted by the fact that an increasing proportion of SEM is accessed from websites in the borderless world of cyberspace. It's difficult, if not impossible, for Canadian law enforcement to regulate obscene material at its source if the material originates outside of Canada.

In recent years, Canadian law enforcement has increasingly focused on identifying and prosecuting Canadians who use the Internet to distribute or download child pornography onto their computers. In 2002, the Canadian child pornography law was amended to include such language as "transmission," "making available," and "accessing," to target the online distribution of child pornography (Casavant & Robertson, 2007). Since 2005, police departments in Canada have begun using Microsoft's Child Exploitation Tracking System, software that enables them to detect computers in Canada that are accessing child pornography (Wilkes, 2011).

Child Pornography

Although many people don't find depictions of consensual sexual activity between adults—however explicit—obscene, Canadians almost universally regard child pornography as obscene and harmful. Canada's first *Criminal Code* law specifically directed toward child pornography was enacted in 1993. It makes it illegal to sell child pornography, as well as to possess anything that depicts people under the age of 18 engaging in real or simulated sexual behaviour. It also forbids visual representations (intended for sexual purposes) of the sex organs of people who are under 18, as well as written materials and pictures that advocate having sex with underaged individuals. The law does allow for exemption from prosecution if the material has artistic merit or an educational, scientific, or medical purpose.

In 2001, the Supreme Court of Canada did uphold the law, although it allowed for minor exceptions. These include private materials, such as drawings and personal journals, that are intended only for the eyes of the individuals who create them, and SEM created by children and adolescents, such as photos of themselves that are meant to be kept strictly private and only for personal use.

Legislation passed in 2005 narrowed the defense allowed individuals accused of possessing child pornography. The accused must prove that s/he was using the material for a legitimate purpose related to the administration of justice, science, medicine, education, or art, and that this purpose doesn't pose undue risk of harm to a child.

To avoid police detection, some people who access child pornography use their laptop computers to tap into other people's wireless networks without their knowledge or permission. This practice is called "war driving." Many people don't turn on the security features of their wireless networks, leaving themselves vulnerable to war drivers who can access their computers and files and do whatever they want online—such as access sexually explicit websites (Millar, 2003).

Convicted users of Internet child porn come from all social classes and are of all ages. In a series of raids in January of 2008, the Ontario Provincial Police arrested 23 people for possession of child pornography. The offenders were from 16 communities, and included a woman and a young offender. The oldest was 65.

Television and SEM

Prior to the 1990s, SEM and nudity were rarely found on broadcast television. With the advent of videocassette recorders in the 1980s, people were able to watch hard-core SEM in the privacy of their own homes. SEM on video proved to be highly popular, and by the 1990s, cable television companies in Canada started offering sexually explicit pay-per-view movies, which have since become a highly profitable aspect of the cable television business. Canadian satellite companies also offer channels that show hard-core material. In 2010, Canada's first adult-oriented television channel, offering locally produced, hard-core SEM, went on air in Quebec (Chung, 2011). Soft-core SEM is readily available on television. Cable television shows such as *Californication* and *Entourage* regularly feature nudity and simulated sexual activity.

The availability and apparent popularity of SEM on television likely reflects a significant change in Canadian attitudes toward SEM, and perhaps toward aspects of sexuality. Some have referred to the increasing consumption of SEM on television and the Internet as the "mainstreaming of porn."

CRITICAL THINKING QUESTIONS

What potentially positive and negative effects on society result from the proliferation of SEM on television and the Internet?

Employers and SEM

Many Canadian employers have policies that forbid the viewing of SEM in the workplace. Some use filtering software to prevent employees from visiting certain websites, and screen e-mail messages for offensive content. Some employees have lost their jobs for looking at Internet SEM at work. In 2003, six employees of the Catholic Children's Aid Society of Toronto were fired after they were discovered exchanging SEM via office email. Contrary to the stereotype that only males engage in this behaviour, four of the six fired employees were women (Brennan, 2004).

The Internet and SEM

People increasingly use the Internet to view SEM. A study of 813 students (mean age = 20) from six colleges across the United States found that about 9 out of 10 (87%) men and one-third (31%) of women reported making use of SEM (Carroll et al., 2008). Viewing SEM wasn't associated with much stigma in this sample. Large percentages—two-thirds (67%) of the men and half (49%) of the women—responded that viewing pornography is acceptable.

Another survey of Canadian university students found higher rates of exposure to online SEM (Byers, 2005). Almost all of the men (95%) and half of the women (53%) had accessed nude pictures online, and three-quarters of the men and half of the women had accessed sexually explicit movies. The men spent more time per week viewing and sending SEM than the women did (2.8 hours for men versus 0.2 hours for women). Yet about the same proportion of women (64%) as men (60%) had sent sexually explicit e-mails. Another major gender difference was that 69% of the men but only 18% of the women had saved SEM on their computer (Byers, 2005).

Repeated exposure to the same pornographic materials progressively lessens the sexual response to them. People may become aroused by the familiar materials again if some time is allowed to go by. Novel materials are also likely to reactivate a sexual response (Hoffman et al., 2012).

Many Canadians are exposed to unsolicited SEM through e-mail messages and pop-ups. Researchers at Wilfrid Laurier University and the University of Guelph studied student reactions to this type of advertising (Nosko, Wood, & Desmarais, 2007). Males were more likely than females to have positive attitudes about these messages, and to follow up by searching online for the explicitly promoted websites. Students who spent more time with computers were more likely to follow through with searches in response to these e-mail messages and pop-ups, and so were students who were more curious about online sexual material.

One of the newer forms of cybersex is virtual sex. On the website "SecondLife .com," the avatars (animated, cartoon-like figures) of residents (players) can engage in any activity they want to, including virtual sex with the avatars of other residents.

Gender Differences in Response to SEM

Researchers have found that both men and women are physiologically sexually aroused by sexually explicit pictures, movies, or audiotaped passages (Chivers & Timmers, 2012; Diamond & Dickenson, 2012). That is, both men and women respond to pornographic stimuli with vasocongestion of the genitals and myotonia (muscle tension). However, there is a difference between physiological response and subjective feelings of arousal in women. Despite what is happening within their bodies, women tend to rate romantic scenes as more sexually arousing than sexually explicit scenes (Chivers & Timmers, 2012). Women are less accepting than men of sex without emotional involvement, and in their choice of erotic materials women are much more likely than men to want the element of romance included (Petersen & Hyde, 2011).

Most erotic visual materials are produced by men, for men. Anthony Bogaert (2001) at Brock University found that the type of film most preferred by men showed women with insatiable sexual desires. Women may read erotic romance novels, but they show relatively less interest in erotic pictures, films, or websites (Petersen & Hyde, 2011). Some women may find SEM a "turn-off" or disgusting, especially when it portrays women in unflattering roles (e.g., as promiscuous and subservient to men's desires).

Could a basic evolutionary process be at work? Did ancestral men who were more sexually aroused by the sight of passing females have reproductive advantages over their less-aroused peers? Women had fewer mating opportunities than men, and had to make the most of any reproductive opportunities, by selecting the best possible mates and providers. Becoming sexually aroused by the sight of male genitalia might have encouraged random matings, which would have undermined women's reproductive success.

Are women really uninterested in viewing SEM? A study of women in Sweden found that almost all (85%) had been exposed to SEM (Rogala & Tydén, 2003). Of those who had viewed the materials, 65% believed the experience had been positive (e.g., making them feel sexy or encouraging them to try new things), while 27% had reacted negatively (e.g., some felt their partners would want to make them engage in sexual behaviours they didn't want to be involved with). And a large-scale study of 18- to 30-year-olds in Denmark found that both men and women reported generally positive effects from viewing hard-core SEM, and few if any negative effects. Men tended to report higher levels of positive effects than women did. Those who reported higher rates of SEM viewing and masturbating saw more positive effects of viewing SEM (Hald & Malmuth, 2008).

More Canadian women are comfortable today than in the past with posing in such SEM as topless and nude photos. Members of the Canadian women's Nordic ski team and the Canadian women's rugby team have posed nude or semi-nude for fundraising calendars. Women of varying ages from across Canada also posed topless in the *Breast of Canada* calendar, which raised awareness of breast health and cancer prevention from 2002 to 2008.

www.melaniegillis.com

Boudoir Photography.
As this photo by Melanie Gillis shows, many Canadian women have seductive pictures of themselves taken by professional photographers as gifts for their boyfriends and husbands.

Innovative Canadian Research

WOMEN WHO VISIT SEX SHOPS

Increasing acceptance of SEM by Canadian women is illustrated by the rise in the number of female-friendly sex shops.

Stacey Jacobs (2007), a graduate student at the University of Guelph, conducted a survey of women who visited female-friendly sex shops in Ontario. Most were single and had higher education. Only 15% had children.

The women were most likely to visit sex shops with their partners and by themselves. The most important reason they gave for making purchases was to increase their own sexual pleasure, and the second most important reason was to increase their partners' pleasure.

The items they most often purchased were (in order of frequency) sex toys, lubricants, novelty items, massage oils, lingerie, condoms, sex manuals, BDSM (bondage, domination, and sado-masochism) equipment, and SEM. Only 19% purchased sex DVDs and videos in the stores, but almost one-half purchased them online.

Although most of the women were comfortable in the sex shops, one-third said they'd at some time wanted to ask the employees questions, but had been too embarrassed or frightened to do so. They asked questions mainly about sex toys such as vibrators and lubricants. Two-thirds were more comfortable asking questions when talking to female than to male employees.

Also on the rise is boudoir photography, in which women have themselves photographed in sexually provocative poses, for their own enjoyment or as gifts for boyfriends and husbands. Photographer Mark Laurie in Calgary has taken pictures of more than 4000 women over 25 years, ranging from seductive poses to completely nude images (Mark, 2003).

Many Canadian couples of all sexual orientations use modern technology such as digital cameras to produce homemade SEM for private consumption. This involves taking nude photographs and videos of their partners or of both of them having sex together. Some couples post these photos on the Internet.

Some young women in North America voluntarily pose for revealing photos for the websites GirlsGoneWild.com and CanadianWildGirls.com. The photos are typically taken at bars and special events, such as spring break in Florida. The women receive hats or T-shirts for this, instead of cash. It seems that posing topless in certain contexts has become more acceptable in Canadian society. The media seem to support this trend, as evidenced by the film *Calendar Girls*, in which a group of older women posed nude for a charity fundraising calendar.

Cybersex Addiction/Compulsivity

The Internet has become the most frequently used way to access pornography. For most people, these ventures into cybersex are harmless enough, but the accessibility and anonymity of sex on the Internet are fuelling what some health professionals call cybersex addiction or compulsivity, which is believed to be spreading rapidly and bringing turmoil to the lives of the afflicted (Ayres & Haddock, 2009; Griffiths, 2012; Wetterneck et al., 2012).

Surveys show that many people, mostly men, now spend dozens of hours each week surfing pornographic and other sex-related websites (Cooper et al., 2004; Daneback et al., 2006). Those most strongly hooked on online sex may

Innovative Canadian Research

AN EDUCATIONAL PROGRAM TO COUNTERACT THE EFFECTS OF INTERNET PORN

University of Western Ontario researchers Corey Isaacs and William Fisher (2008) developed and tested an educational program to counteract the potentially negative effects of watching Internet pornography.

They assigned male participants to three groups. Group 1 viewed violent and degrading pornography accompanied by an educational intervention. Group 2 viewed the same pornography accompanied with a fake intervention that lacked the educational content given to group 1. Group 3 neither viewed pornography nor received an intervention.

The intervention consisted of an interactive computer program designed to sensitize participants to the negative messages portrayed in violent and degrading pornography. Viewers were presented with examples of pornography that had negative messages, as well as the reality of the issue of sexual violence. They were encouraged to evaluate the content of sexual media more critically.

The dependent measures were acceptance of rape myths, attraction to sexual aggression, and opinions of SEM.

Contrary to their expectations, the researchers did not observe any negative effects of viewing pornography for any of the dependent measures. However, the educational intervention did diminish positive reactions to sexual aggression and encouraged participants to become more sensitive to—and to reject—violence in pornography.

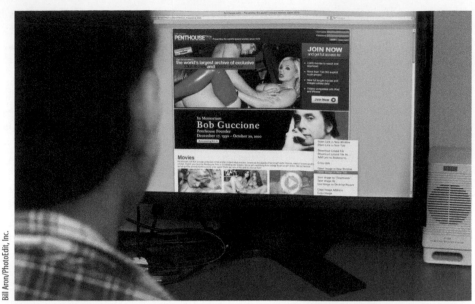

Bill Aron/PhotoEdit, Inc.

Sex in Cyberspace.
One-third of Internet visits are thought to involve sexually oriented websites. Many people, mostly men, spend dozens of hours each week surfing porn sites. Some even have "online sex" with people they contact via chat rooms or webcams.

spend hours a day masturbating to pornographic images or—less often—having "online sex" with people they contact via chat rooms or webcams (Daneback et al., 2006).

Cybersex compulsives are like drug addicts (Ayres & Haddock, 2009). They "use the Internet as an important part of their sexual acting out, much like a drug addict who has a drug of choice. Especially vulnerable are those whose sexuality may have been suppressed and limited all their lives, who suddenly find an infinite supply of sexual opportunities" online (Cooper, cited in Brody, 2000). Although some studies find that men who become addicted to online sex have ample sexual opportunities in the real world, other studies find them to be lonelier than men with those opportunities (Yoder et al., 2005).

Online viewing that begins as a harmless recreation can become all-consuming, and can even lead to real sexual encounters with people the individual meets online. Cybersex compulsives sometimes ignore their partners and children and risk their jobs. Schneider (2005) reports other adverse consequences, including broken relationships. Partners often report feeling betrayed, ignored, and unable to compete with the online fantasies.

Sexual Coercion and SEM

Is SEM a harmless diversion, or an inducement to commit sexual violence and other antisocial acts? Let's consider sources of evidence for this highly charged issue.

SEM AND SEX OFFENDERS   An approach to examining the role of SEM in crimes of sexual violence involves comparing sex offenders' and non-sex offenders' experiences with sexually explicit materials.

In a review of the research literature, Marshall (1989) found little or no difference in levels of SEM exposure between incarcerated sex offenders and comparison groups of felons incarcerated for nonsexual crimes. More recent research, however, has found that sexually aggressive individuals are more likely than others to use pornography (Alexy et al., 2009; Quayle, 2012).

These studies are correlational, not experimental. It may be that a desire to use pornography and to commit sexually aggressive acts are both related to other factors, such as a general tendency to seek out sexual images and experiences that humiliate women.

VIOLENT SEM   Research suggests that it's the violence in violent SEM—not the sexual explicitness—that potentially affects or reinforces the attitudes and behaviours of sex offenders.

In an Ontario study, Kingston and his colleagues (2008) studied the use of pornography among convicted child molesters. Those who viewed deviant (including violent) pornography were more likely to reoffend. Higher frequency of porn use was predictive of recidivism among those who were already considered to be at high risk for reoffending. The researchers speculate that more aggressive men are drawn to images of violent pornography, which reinforces negative attitudes such as hostility toward women. They note that use of deviant pornography is more predictive of violent sexual reoffending than of sexual offending in general.

Research on the effects of violent SEM should be interpreted with caution. While some experimental studies conducted in laboratories (e.g., exposing men to violent sexual images and then measuring their attitudes towards women and the acceptability of sexual aggression) indicates that violent sexual images may have negative effects, other studies have not found these effects (Fisher, Kohut, Di Gioacchino, & Federoff, 2013). We still lack evidence that normal men are spurred to sexually assault women because of exposure to violent SEM or other depictions of violence.

NONVIOLENT SEM   Nonviolent SEM may not contain scenes of sexual violence, but it typically portrays women as sexually promiscuous, insatiable, and subservient (Itzin et al., 2007). Might such portrayals of women reinforce traditional stereotypes of women as sex objects? Might they lead viewers to condone sexual assault by suggesting that women are essentially promiscuous? Might the depiction of women as readily sexually accessible inspire men to refuse to "take no for an answer" on dates?

Michael Seto, Alexandra Maric, and Howard Barbaree (2001) at the Centre for Addiction and Mental Health in Toronto conducted an extensive review of the research and concluded that there's little empirical support for the idea that SEM causes sexual aggression. Rather, they believe men who are predisposed to sexual aggression are more likely to view violent SEM, and therefore likely to show the strongest effects. Men who are not predisposed to sexual violence are unlikely to show any effects.

William Fisher, a psychology professor at the University of Western Ontario, has conducted several experimental studies to measure the effects of SEM. In one study (Barak and Fisher, 1997), he and a colleague explored the effects of computer-based, interactive erotic stimuli on men's attitudes and behaviours toward women. University men who were exposed to computer-based erotic stimuli showed significant increases in sexual arousal, but didn't show negative changes in attitude or behaviour toward women when compared to men who were exposed to control stimuli. Specifically, exposure to interactive erotic stimulation neither resulted in aggressive behaviour toward women nor affected men's attitudes toward women's rights and roles in society. This exposure also didn't change men's perceptions of sexual assault myths.

From a recent review of the research literature on the effects of pornography, Fisher, et al. (2013) note that while use of pornography among individuals predisposed to sexual aggression (e.g., men with hostile masculinity, psychopathy, previous sexual offenses) is a cause for concern, increasing and widespread access to all types of SEM on the Internet has not lead to an increase in reported sex crimes.

Another concern is the potential effect of nonviolent SEM on a viewer's sexual values. Nonviolent SEM typically features impromptu sexual encounters between new acquaintances. Might repeated exposure to such material alter viewers' attitudes toward traditional sexual values? Brown (2003) reports intriguing evidence that repeated exposure to this type of nonviolent SEM loosens traditional sexual and family values. When compared with people who viewed nonsexual films, men and women who were exposed to six weekly, hour-long sessions involving scenes of explicit sexual encounters between new acquaintances showed attitudinal changes, including greater acceptance of premarital and extramarital sex and simultaneous sexual relationships with multiple partners. Prolonged exposure to such SEM may also foster dissatisfaction with the physical appearance and sexual performance of one's intimate partners (Brown, 2003).

Another concern is that SEM doesn't offer realistic presentations of how most people function sexually. While many people in real life experience sexual problems, the people portrayed in the sexual media never have sexual problems. The actors are always able to have sex, any time and any place, for hours at a time. Penises are always erect, vaginas are continuously lubricated, and the women have insatiable desires for sex, as well as orgasms that occur with little effort. Most of the actors don't use condoms, and sexually transmitted infections are never discussed.

In sum, so far research on the effects of nonviolent SEM is inconclusive. Its effects may be more closely connected with whether women are presented in a dehumanizing manner than with sexual explicitness per se. No research has yet linked sexual explicitness itself with undesirable effects.

A group of researchers in Ireland and western Canada (Morrison et al., 2004) criticizes most previous research for being narrowly focused on a harm-based approach to the study of SEM's effects. They're also concerned that almost all of the research has surveyed only men and viewed women as victims.

Morrison and his colleagues (2004) argue that researchers have generally ignored the fact that an increasing amount of sexually explicit material is produced by women, for women and couples, which indicates that many women are willing consumers of these materials. To gain a broader perspective, these researchers surveyed 382 females and 202 males attending a university in western Canada. Among both genders, those with higher sexual self-esteem and lower sexual anxiety had higher levels of exposure to SEM on television and DVDs. Females with more recent experience with vaginal and anal intercourse were also more likely to have seen SEM. Safer sex practices were not related to degree of SEM exposure. Based on these findings, the researchers concluded that exposure to SEM is not related to many of the types of harm that are often discussed in the literature.

Summing Up

Commercial sex runs the gamut from street-based sex work and sexually explicit videos to strip shows, sex-toy shops, brothels, escort services, massage parlours, and "1-900" telephone services.

One view is that prostitution is immoral and exploits women. A contrasting view is that prostitution is a legitimate occupation.

The laws governing prostitution (the exchange of sex for money) in Canada have been confusing, because prostitution itself has been legal, but almost all of the activities that involve prostitution have been illegal.

In 2013, the Supreme Court of Canada struck down the existing laws regulating prostitution on the grounds that they violated the constitutional rights of sex workers.

In 2014, the government introduced Bill C-36 to replace the laws struck down by the Supreme Court. The new laws would make the selling of sexual services legal but make it illegal to buy sex.

The major types of female sex worker are street-based sex workers, brothel workers (many of whom work in massage parlours), escorts, and call girls. No single factor explains entry into female sex work.

Those who pay sex workers for their services are often referred to as "johns" or "tricks." Most patrons are "occasional johns" who have regular sex partners.

Most male sex workers are "hustlers," who service male clients. Hustlers typically begin selling sex in their teens, and may be gay or heterosexual.

The majority of sex workers consistently use condoms with clients. Some are pressured by clients and offered more money to have sex without condoms.

Pornography is "writing, pictures, etc., intended to arouse sexual desire." The judgment of what's pornographic or obscene varies from person to person and from culture to culture.

The feminist movement has had a strong influence on federal laws governing SEM in Canada.

Accessing SEM on the Internet is increasingly common.

Although both genders can become physiologically aroused by erotic materials, men are generally more interested than women in sexually explicit pictures and films.

Some researchers argue that it's the violence in violent SEM, and not the sexual explicitness, that promotes violence against women. The effects of nonviolent SEM on normal populations remain unclear.

Test Yourself

Multiple-Choice Questions

1. The main feature of Bill C-36, making the selling of sex legal but the buying of sex illegal in Canada reflects what is known as the _____ Model adopted in several other countries.
   (a) Caribbean
   (b) South American
   (c) Nordic
   (d) Commonwealth

2. Among sex workers, _____ have the lowest status and earn the lowest wages.
   (a) street-based workers
   (b) brothel workers
   (c) call girls
   (d) massage-parlour workers

3. The majority of studies on sex workers have focused on _____ .
   (a) street-based workers
   (b) brothel workers
   (c) call girls
   (d) massage-parlour workers

4. All of the following are important factors in the backgrounds of many young sex workers except:
   (a) Poverty.
   (b) Sexual addiction.
   (c) Physical abuse.
   (d) Sexual abuse.

5. Shaver, Lewis, and Maticka-Tyndale propose an approach to sex work that emphasizes:
   (a) Penalizing johns rather than sex workers for acts of prostitution.
   (b) Increasing the legal penalties for sex work.
   (c) Financial incentives for sex workers to seek other types of employment.
   (d) Harm reduction and labour rights.

6. Men who engage in sex work with male customers are commonly known as:
   (a) Pimps.
   (b) Gigolos.
   (c) Hustlers.
   (d) Johns.

7. A photograph or video is considered hard-core SEM if it contains:
   (a) Hints or suggestions of sexual acts.
   (b) Explicit depictions of sexual acts.
   (c) Stylized nude photos.
   (d) Non-consensual sexual behaviour.

8. The work of Tristan Taormino reflects which of the following perspectives on pornography?
   (a) The conservative position.
   (b) The liberal position.
   (c) The anti-pornography feminist approach.
   (d) The pro-pornography feminist approach.

9. Most research on the effects of exposure to sexually explicit materials has focused on:
   (a) Violence.
   (b) Orgasm.
   (c) Relationship enhancement.
   (d) Sexual orientation.

10. Which of the following groups was not included in the study that contained the educational intervention to reduce the potential negative effects of pornography?
    (a) A group that viewed violent pornography and received an educational intervention.
    (b) A group that viewed violent pornography and received a fake intervention.
    (c) A group that viewed nonviolent pornography and received an educational intervention.
    (d) A group that neither viewed pornography nor received an educational intervention.

You'll find answers to the "Test Yourself" questions on page 489.

Questions for Critical Thinking

1. Should all aspects of prostitution be legal in Canada? Why or why not?

2. Look at one of your favourite magazines. Do you see advertisers using sex to sell their products? If these images were shown just as pictures, rather than as ads, would you see them as art or as pornography? Explain.

3. Have you ever used sexually explicit material with a sex partner? Has this helped or hurt your relationship?

4. Sexually explicit material is now easily available to anyone on the Internet. Does this concern you? If so, why?

Answer Key

Chapter 1	Chapter 2	Chapter 3	Chapter 4	Chapter 5	Chapter 6
1. b	1. b	1. c	1. a	1. c	1. a
2. a	2. a	2. b	2. c	2. b	2. b
3. b	3. b	3. b	3. b	3. d	3. d
4. a	4. d	4. c	4. c	4. a	4. b
5. d	5. a	5. d	5. a	5. b	5. d
6. d	6. c	6. c	6. a	6. b	6. c
7. b	7. d	7. c	7. d	7. d	7. b
8. a	8. b	8. d	8. a	8. c	8. c
9. c	9. b	9. c	9. c	9. b	9. c
10. b	10. c	10. a	10. a	10. d	10. a

Chapter 7	Chapter 8	Chapter 9	Chapter 10	Chapter 11	Chapter 12
1. c	1. c	1. d	1. c	1. d	1. b
2. b	2. b	2. b	2. a	2. b	2. d
3. d	3. d	3. d	3. c	3. a	3. a
4. d	4. d	4. c	4. d	4. b	4. c
5. a	5. b	5. a	5. b	5. b	5. d
6. a	6. a	6. c	6. d	6. c	6. c
7. b	7. b	7. b	7. c	7. a	7. b
8. c	8. a	8. b	8. b	8. c	8. d
9. a	9. c	9. a	9. d	9. c	9. a
10. a	10. d	10. a	10. d	10. d	10. b

Chapter 13	Chapter 14	Chapter 15	Chapter 16	Chapter 17	Chapter 18
1. c	1. c	1. a	1. b	1. c	1. c
2. b	2. a	2. c	2. c	2. d	2. a
3. d	3. d	3. a	3. b	3. a	3. a
4. a	4. d	4. c	4. d	4. c	4. b
5. c	5. b	5. c	5. c	5. d	5. d
6. b	6. b	6. b	6. b	6. a	6. c
7. a	7. b	7. a	7. a	7. b	7. b
8. d	8. c	8. a	8. d	8. a	8. d
9. a	9. a	9. c	9. c	9. c	9. a
10. b	10. b	10. a	10. b	10. c	10. c

References

Aarts, H., & van Honk, J. (2009). Testosterone and unconscious positive priming increase human motivation separately. *Neuro-Report, 20*(14), 1300–1303.

Abal, Y. N., Mariín, J. A. L., & Sánchez, S. R. (2003). A new paraphilia of the XXI century: Chat-scatophilia. *Archivos Hispano-americanos de Sexologíía, 9*(1), 81–104.

ABC News. (2004). *The American Sex Survey: A Peek Beneath the Sheets.* ABC News Primetime Live Poll. Retrieved from http://abcnews.com/pollvault.html

Abell, J., Locke, A., Condor, S., Gibson, S., & Stevenson, C. (2006). Trying similarity, doing difference: The role of interviewer self-disclosure in interview talk with young people. *Qualitative Research, 6*(2), 221–244.

Adam, B. (2006a.) New gay relations: Relationship innovation in male relationships? *Sexualities, 9*(1), 5–26.

Adam, B. (2006b). Infectious behaviour: Imputing subjectivity to HIV behaviour. *Social Theory and Health, 4,* 168–179.

Adam, B. (2007). Cultural trends in safe and unsafe sex. Paper presented at the annual meeting of the International Academy of Sex Research, Vancouver, BC.

Adam, B., Husbands, W., Murray, J., & Maxwell, J. (2005). AIDS optimism, condom fatigue, or self-esteem? Explaining unsafe sex among gay and bisexual men. *Journal of Sex Research, 42*(3), 238–248.

Adam, B. D. (2000a). Age preferences among gay and bisexual men. *GLQ, 6*(3), 413–414.

Adam, B. D. (2000b). Love and sex in constructing identity among men who have sex with men. *International Journal of Sexuality and Gender Studies, 5*(5), 325–339.

Adam, B. D., Maticka-Tyndale, E., & Cohen, J. J. (2001). *Living with combination therapies.* A report to the Ontario HIV Treatment Network.

Adams, H. E., Wright, L. W., Jr., & Lohr, B. A. (1996). Is homophobia associated with homosexual arousal? *Journal of Abnormal Psychology, 105,* 440–445.

Adams, N. (2006). Systemic therapy techniques for sexual difficulties. In Hiller, J., et al. (Eds.). *Sex, mind, and emotion: Innovation in psychological theory and practice* (pp. 209–227). London, UK: Karnac Books.

Adams, R. A. (2007). College students' attribution of blame in father–daughter incest. *Family and Consumer Sciences Research Journal, 36*(1), 55–62.

Advisory Committee on Family Planning. (2008). *Sexual health education survey: Urban and rural comparative.* Conducted by Fast Consulting, Saskatoon, SK for the Advisory Committee on Family Planning, Saskatoon, Saskatchewan. Retrieved from http://www.skprevention.ca/wp-content/uploads/2013/01/7-504-ACFP-Education-Survey-Report.pdf

Agrawal, A. (1997). Gendered bodies: The case of the "third gender" in India. *Contributions to Indian Sociology, 31,* 273–297.

Ah Shene, D. (2003). Crystal meth. *Developments, 23*(2). Alberta Alcohol and Drug Abuse Commission. [Online]. Retrieved from http://corp.aadac.com/services/developments_newsletter/dev_news_vol23_issue2.asp

Ahrols, T. K., & Meston, C. M. (2010). Ethnic differences in sexual attitudes of U.S. college students: gender, acculturation, and religiosity factors. *Archives of Sexual Behavior, 39*(1), 190–202

Albarracin, D., Gillette, J. C., Earl, A. N., Glasman, L. R., Durantini, M. R., & Ho, M. H. (2005). A test of the major assumptions about behavior change: A comprehensive look at the effects of passive and active HIV-prevention interventions since the beginning of the epidemic. *Psychological Bulletin, 131*(6), 856–897.

Alberta Health Services (2013). *Sexuality and Disability: A Guide for Parents.* Retrieved from http://teachers.teachingsexual health.ca

Alberta Health Services. (2014). *Teachingsexualhealth.ca.* Retrieved from http://www.teachingsexualhealth.ca/

Alcoba, N. (2009). Should the state be funding in vitro fertilization? *National Post,* August 21st, 2009.

Alderson, K. (2007). "What's love got to do with it?" Defining and measuring sexual orientation. Paper presented at the Annual Meeting of the Canadian Sex Research Forum, Banff, Alberta.

Alderson, K. G. (2003). The ecological model of gay male identity. *Canadian Journal of Human Sexuality, 12,* 75–85.

Alexander, G. M., Wilcox, T., & Woods, R. (2009). Sex differences in infants' visual interest in toys. *Archives of Sexual Behavior, 38*(3), 427–433.

Alexy, E. M., Burgess, A. W., & Prentky, R. A. (2009). Pornography use as a risk marker for an aggressive pattern of behavior among sexually reactive children and adolescents. *Journal of the American Psychiatric Nurses Association, 14*(6), 442–453.

Allen, E. S., & Atkins, D. C. (2005). The multidimensional and developmental nature of infidelity: Practical applications. *Journal of Clinical Psychology, 61*(11), 1371–1382.

Allen, T. D., & de Tormes Eby, L. T. (2012). The study of interpersonal relationships: An introduction. In L. T. de Tormes Eby & T. D. Allen (Eds.). *Personal relationships* (pp. 3–14). New York: Routledge.

Allen, W., & Brickman, M. Annie Hall. Hollywood: Metro-Goldwyn-Mayer, 1977.

Allison, C. M., & Hyde, J. S. (2011). Early menarche: Confluence of biological and contextual factors. *Sex Roles.* DOI:10.1007/s11199-011-9993-5.

Allman, D. (1999). *M is for mutual: A is for acts.* Ottawa: Health Canada.

Althof, S. E. (1994). Paper presented at the annual meeting of the American Urological Association, San Francisco, CA.

Althof, S. E. (2010). What's new in sex therapy? *Journal of Sexual Medicine, 7*(1, Pt 1), 5–13. doi:10.1111/j.1743-6109.2009.01433.x.

Althof, S. E. (2012). Psychological interventions for delayed ejaculation/orgasm. *International Journal of Impotence Research, 24*(4), 131–36. doi:10.1038/ijir.2012.2.

Althof, S. E., & Needle, R. B. (2011). Sex therapy in male sexual dysfunction. *Current Clinical Urology, Part 5,* 731–738. doi:10.1007/978-1-60761-916-148

Amankwah, E., Ngwakongnwi, E., & Quan, H. (2009). Why visible minority women in Canada do not participate in cervical cancer screening. *Ethnicity and Health, 14*(4), 337–349.

American Academy of Family Physicians. (2012, June 13). *Family planning and contraception.* Retrieved from http://www.aafp.org/afp/topicModules/viewTopicModule.htm?topicModuleId=71 (Accessed June 23, 2012).

American Academy of Pediatrics. (2005). Breastfeeding and the use of human milk. *Pediatrics, 115,* 496–506.

American Cancer Society. (2009). Cancer facts & figures 2009. Retrieved from http://www.cancer.org/downloads/STT/500809web.pdf

American Cancer Society. (2012a). *Breast cancer.* Retrieved from http://www.cancer.org/Cancer/BreastCancer/index

American Cancer Society. (2012b). *Cervical cancer.* Retrieved from http://www.cancer.org/Cancer/CervicalCancer/index

American Cancer Society. (2012c). *Endometrial cancer.* Retrieved from http://www.cancer.org/Cancer/EndometrialCancer/index

American Cancer Society. (2012d). *Ovarian cancer.* Retrieved from http://www.cancer.org/Cancer/OvarianCancer/index

American Cancer Society. (2012e). *Testicular cancer.* Retrieved from http://www.cancer.org/Cancer/TesticularCancer/index

American Cancer Society. (2012f). *Prostate cancer.* Retrieved from http://www.cancer.org/Cancer/ProstateCancer/OverviewGuide/index

American Fertility Association. (2012). Library: LGBT family building. Retrieved June 1, 2012 from http://www.theafa.org/library/lgbt-family-building/

American Psychiatric Association. (2000). *Diagnostic and statistical manual of mental disorders* (4th ed.). Washington, DC: Author.

American Psychiatric Association. (2012). *DSM-5 development.* Retrieved from http://www.dsm5.org/Pages/Default.aspx

American Psychiatric Association. (2013a). *Gender dysphoria.* Retrieved from http://www.dsm5.org/documents/gender%20dysphoria%20fact%20sheet.pdf

American Psychiatric Association (2013b) *DSM-5: Diagnostic and Statistical Manual for Mental Disorders* (5th ed.). Washington, DC: American Psychiatric Press.

American Psychological Association. (2012). APA on Children Raised by Gay and Lesbian Parents. Retrieved June 11, 2012 from https://www.apa.org/news/press/response/gay-parents.aspx

Amnesty International. (2012). *Violence against women information.* Retrieved from http://www.amnestyusa.org/our-work/issues/women-s-rights/violence-against-women/violence-against-women-information.

Amodeo, M., Griffin, M. K., Fassler, I. R., Clay, C. M., & Ellis, M. A. (2006). Childhood sexual abuse among black women and white women from two-parent families. *Child Maltreatment, 11*(3), 237–246.

Amodio, D. M., & Showers, C. J. (2005). "Similarity breeds liking" revisited: The moderating role of commitment. *Journal of Social and Personal Relationships, 22*(6), 817–836.

Andersen, M. L., & Tufik, S. (2005). Effects of progesterone blockade over cocaine-induced genital reflexes of paradoxical sleep-deprived male rats. *Hormones and Behavior, 47*(4), 477–484.

Anderson Moore, K. (2008). *Teen births: Examining the recent increase.* Washington, DC: The National Campaign to Prevent Teen and Unplanned Pregnancy.

Anderson, J. E. & Mueller, T. E. (2008). Trends in sexual risk behavior and unprotected sex among high school students, 1991–2005: The role of substance use. *Journal of School Health, 78*(11), 575–580.

Anderson, K. M. (2006). Surviving incest: The art of resistance. *Families in Society, 87*(3), 409–416.

Anderson, M., Kunkel, A., & Dennis, M. R. (2011). "Let's (not) talk about that": Bridging the past sexual experiences taboo to build healthy romantic relationships. *Journal of Sex Research, 48*(4), 381–391.

Anderson, S. E., et al. (2003). Relative weight and race influence average age at menarche: Results from two nationally representative surveys of U.S. girls studied 25 years apart. *Pediatrics, 111,* 844–850.

Andriole, G. L., et al. (2009). Mortality results from a randomized prostate-cancer screening trial. *New England Journal of Medicine, 360,* 1310–1319.

Angus Reid. (2010a). Canadians and Britons are More Open on Same-Sex Relations Than Americans. July 26th, 2010. Angus Reid Public Opinion.

Angus Reid. (2010b). Canadians endorse multiculturalism, but pick melting pot over mosaic. Retrieved from http://angus-reid.com

Angus Reid Global. (2013). Canadians have mixed feelings on abortion, but shun a new debate. Retrieved from http://www.angusreidglobal.com/wp-content/uploads/2013/01/2013.01.28_Abortion_CAN.pdf

Angus Reid Global. (2014). Gender split reveals deep divide between men, women on issues surrounding the sex trade. June 10, 2014.

Angus Reid Public Opinion. (2009). *Canadians reject status quo on prostitution.* Angus Reid Public Opinion. Retrieved from www.angus-reid/polls

Angus Reid Public Opinion. (2009). *Gender split reveals deep divide between men, women on issues surrounding the sex trade: But politics drives split in support for Canadian government's proposed new prostitution laws.* Public Opinion Poll. Retrieved from http://www.angusreidglobal.com/wp-content/uploads/2014/06/2014.06.09-Prostitution-Bill-C36.pdf

Ann Johnston Health Station. (Online). People with physical disabilities—SexAbility. Retrieved from www.ajhs.ca

Annon, J. S. (1976). *Behavioral treatment of sexual problems.* New York, NY: Harper & Row.

Aron, A., et al. (2008). Falling in love. In S. Sprecher, A. Wenzel, & J. Harvey (Eds.), *Handbook of relationship initiation* (pp. 315–336). New York: CRC Press.

Associated Press (2008, April 10). Five homosexuals jailed for "debauchery," p. AA2.

Associated Press. (2011, August 4). Polygamist leader Warren Jeffs convicted of child sex abuse in Texas. http://www.cleveland.com/nation/index.ssf/2011/08/polygamist_leader_convicted_of.html

Associated Press. (2011, August 4). Polygamist leader Warren Jeffs convicted of child sex abuse in Texas. *Globe and Mail.*

Associated Press/MTV. (2009). A Thin Line: 2009 AP-MTV Digital Abuse Study. Retrieved from http://www.athinline.org

Astley, S. J., & Clarren, S. K. (2001). Measuring the facial phenotype of individuals with prenatal alcohol exposure: Correlations with brain dysfunction. *Alcohol & Alcoholism, 36*(2), 147–159.

Atchison, C. (2010). Report of the Preliminary Findings for Johns' Voice: A Study of Adult Canadian Sex Buyers. Retrieved from www.johnsvoice.ca/docs/JOHNS_VOICE_GENERAL_RESULTS_EXECUTIVE_SUMMARY_FINAL_DIST.pdf

Atkinson, J. L. (1996). Female sex offenders: A literature review. *Forum on Corrections Research, 8*(2), 39–42.

Aubin, S., Heiman, J. R., Berger, R. E., Murallo, A. V., & Yung-Wen, L. (2009). Comparing sildenafil alone vs. sildenafil plus brief couple sex therapy on erectile dysfunction and couples' sexual and marital quality of life. *Journal of Sex and Marital Therapy, 35*(2), 122–143.

Ayres, M. M., & Haddock, S. A. (2009). Therapists' approaches in working with heterosexual couples struggling with male partners' online *sexual behavior. Sexual Addiction & Compulsivity, 16*(1), 55–78.

Bader, M. (2003). *Arousal: The secret logic of sexual fantasies.* New York: Griffin Trade Paperback.

Bailey, I. (2000, April 26). They are a couple and proud of it. *National Post,* pp. A1, A2.

Bailey, J. M. (1999). Homosexuality and mental illness. *Archives of General Psychiatry, 56*(10), 883–884.

Bailey, J. M. (2003b). *The man who would be queen: The science of gender-bending and transsexualism.* Washington, DC: Joseph Henry Press.

Bailey, J.V., Farquhar, C., Owen, C., & Whittaker, D. (2003). Sexual behaviour of lesbians and bisexual women. *Sexually Transmitted Infections, 79,* 147–150.

Bains, C. (2008, April 2). Canada has global sex abuse problem, expert finds. *Waterloo Region Record,* p. Z5.

Baker, J. L., et al. (2008). Breastfeeding reduces postpartum weight retention. *American Journal of Clinical Nutrition, 88,* 1553–1551.

Baldwin, J. D., & Baldwin, J. I. (1989). The socialization of homosexuality and heterosexuality in a non-Western society. *Archives of Sexual Behavior, 18,* 13–29.

Bancroft, J., Carnes, L., Janssen, E., Goodrich, D., & Long, J. S. (2005b). Erectile and ejaculatory problems in gay and heterosexual men. *Archives of Sexual Behavior, 34*(3), 285–297.

Bandura, A. (2004). Health promotion by social cognitive means. *Health Education & Behavior, 31*(2), 143–164.

Banerjee, S. (2008, June 17). Belgian faces sex-related charges. *Toronto Star,* p. A14.

Banszegi, O., et al. (2010). Testosterone treatment of pregnant rabbits affects sexual development of their daughters. *Physiology and Behavior, 101*(4), 422–427.

Barak, A., & Fisher, W. A. (1997). Effects of interactive computer erotica on men's attitudes and behavior toward women: An experimental study. *Computers in Human Behavior, 13*(3), 353–369.

Barbaree, H. E., & Blanchard, R. (2008). Sexual deviance over the lifespan. In D. R. Laws and W. T. O'Donohue (Eds.), *Sexual deviance: Theory, assessment, and treatment* (2nd ed., pp. 27–60). New York: Guilford Press.

Barrett, M. (1990). Selected observations on sex education in Canada. *SIECCAN Journal, 5*(1), 21–31.

Barrett, M. (1994). Sexuality education in Canadian schools: an overview in 1994. *The Canadian Journal of Human Sexuality, 3*(3), 199–225.

Barrett, M. (2006). What everyone should know about human papillomavirus (HPV): Questions and answers. *The Canadian Journal of Human Sexuality, 15*(3–4), 171–174.

Barrett, M., et al. (2012). Sexual health curriculum and training in Canadian medical schools: A study of family medicine, obstetrics and gynaecology and undergraduate medicine programs in 2011 with comparisons to 1996. *The Canadian Journal of Human Sexuality, 21*(2), 63–73.

Barrett, M. B. (1990). *Invisible lives: The truth about millions of women-loving women.* New York: Harper & Row (Perennial Library).

Barry, K. (1994). *Female sexual slavery.* New York, NY: NYU Press.

Bartels, R. M., & Gannon, T. A. (2011). Understanding the sexual fantasies of sex offenders and their correlates. *Aggression and Violent Behavior, 16*(6), 551–561.

Bartolo, K. C. (2005). Mother–daughter incest: A guide for helping professionals. *Journal of Family Studies, 11*(2), 328–329.

Basile, K. C. (2002). Attitudes toward wife rape: Effects of social background and victim status. *Violence & Victims, 17*(3), 341–354.

Basow, S. A., & Rubenfeld, K. (2003). "Troubles talk": Effects of gender and gender-typing. *Sex Roles, 48*(3–4), 183–187.

Basson, B., Davis, S. R., & Rodenberg, C. (2009). Testosterone for low libido. *New England Journal of Medicine, 360*(7), 728–729.

Basson, R. (2000, May). Paper presented at the annual meeting of the American College of Obstetricians and Gynecologists, San Francisco, CA.

Basson, R. (2002). A model of women's sexual arousal. *Journal of Sex and Marital Therapy, 28,* 1–10.

Basson, R. (2004). Recent advances in women's sexual function and dysfunction. *Menopause, 11*(6 Pt 2), 714–725.

Basson, R. (2008). Women's sexual function and dysfunction: current uncertainties, future directions. *International Journal of Impotence Research, 20,* 466–478.

Basson, R. (2010). Is it time to move on from "hypoactive sexual desire disorder?" *Menopause, 17*(6), 1097–1098.

Bauer, G., Redman, N., Bradley, K. & Scheim, A. (2013). Sexual health of trans men who are gay, bisexual, or who have sex with men: Results from Ontario, Canada. *International Journal of Transgenderism, 14*(2), 66–74.

Bauer, G., et al. (2010). Who are trans people in Ontario? *Trans PULSE e-Bulletin, 1*(1). Retrieved from http://www.transpulseproject.ca

Bauerle, S. Y., Amirkhan J. H., & Hupka, R. B. (2002). An attribution theory analysis of romantic jealousy. *Motivation & Emotion, 26*(4), 297–319.

Baumeister, R. F., Catanese, K. R., & Wallace, H. M. (2002). Conquest by force: A narcissistic reactance theory of rape and sexual coercion. *Review of General Psychology, 6*(1), 92–135.

Baute, N. (2010, January 7). "Sexting" nude photos a teen concern. *Toronto Star.* http://www.thestar.com/life/health_wellness/2010/01/07/sexting_nude_photos_a_teen_concern.html

Beauregard, E., Lussier, P., & Proulx, J. (2004). An exploration of developmental factors related to deviant sexual preferences among adult rapists. *Sexual Abuse: A Journal of Research and Treatment, 16*(2), 151–161.

Becerra, L., Breiter, H. C., Wise, R., Gonzalez, R. G., & Borsook, D. (2001). Reward circuitry activation by noxious thermal stimuli. *Neuron, 32*(5), 927–946.

Behrendt, N., Buhl, N., & Seidl, S. (2002). The lethal paraphiliac syndrome: Accidental auto-erotic deaths in four women and a review of the literature. *International Journal of Legal Medicine, 116*(3), 148–152.

Belden, M. (2011). *Obstetrics & gynecology: A competency-based companion.* Philadelphia: Saunders.

Bell, A. P., & Weinberg, M. S. (1978). *Homosexualities: A study of diversity among men and women.* New York: Simon & Schuster.

Bem, S. L. (1975). Sex role adaptability: One consequence of psychological androgyny. *Journal of Personality and Social Psychology, 31,* 634–643.

Bem, S. L. (1993). *The lenses of gender.* New Haven, CT: Yale University Press.

Bem, S. L., Martyna, W., & Watson, C. (1976). Sex typing and androgyny: Further explorations of the expressive domain. *Journal of Personality and Social Psychology, 34,* 1016–1023.

Bennets, L. (2011, July 18). The growing demand for prostitution. *Newsweek* magazine. http://www.newsweek.com/growing-demand-prostitution-68493

Bennett, S., & Assefi, N. (2005). School-based pregnancy prevention programs: A systematic review of randomized controlled studies. *Journal of Adolescent Health, 36*(1), 72–81.

Benzie, R. (2004, December 10). Film board cut out as censor. *Toronto Star,* p. A4.

Berdahl, J. L., & Moore, C. (2006). Workplace harassment: Double jeopardy for minority women. *Journal of Applied Psychology, 91*(2), 426–436.

Bereket, T., & Adam, B. (2006). The emergence of gay identities in contemporary Turkey. *Sexualities, 9*(2), 131–151.

Beres, M. (2010). Sexual miscommunication? Untangling assumptions about sexual communication between casual sex partners. *Culture, Health & Sexuality, 12*(1), 1–14.

Beres, M. A. (2002). *Sexual consent behaviors in same sex relationships.* Unpublished master's thesis, University of Guelph.

Beres, M. A. (2007). "Spontaneous" sexual consent: An analysis of sexual consent literature. *Feminism & Psychology, 17*(1), 93–108.

Beres, M., Crow, B., & Gotell, L. (2009). The perils of institutionalization in neoliberal times: results of a national survey of Canadian sexual assault and rape crisis centres. *Canadian Journal of Sociology, 34,* (1), 135–164.

Berger, L. (2000, June 25). A racial gap in infant deaths, and a search for reasons. *The New York Times,* p. WH13.

Berger, P. B. (2009). Prosecuting for knowingly transmitting HIV is warranted. *Canadian Medical Association Journal, 180*(13), 1368.

Bergeron, S., Binik, Y. M., Khalife, S., Pagidas, K., Glazer, H. I., Meana, M., & Amsel, R. (2001). A randomized comparison of group cognitive-behavioral therapy, surface electromyographic biofeedback, and vestibulectomy in the treatment of dyspareunia resulting from vulvar vestibulitis. *Pain, 91,* 297–306.

Bergeron, S., Khalifé, S., Glazer, H. I., & Binik, Y. M. (2008). Surgical and behavioral treatments for vestibulodynia: Two-and-one-half-year follow-up and predictors and outcome. *Obstetrics & Gynecology, 111*(1), 159–166.

Bergeron, S., & Lord, M. (2003). The integration of pelvi-perineal re-education and cognitive-behavioural therapy in the multidisciplinary treatment of the sexual pain disorders. *Sexual & Relationship Therapy, 18*(2), 135–141.

Bergner, D. (2009, January 22). What do women want? *The New York Times.* http://www.nytimes.com/2009/01/25/magazine/25desire-t.html?pagewanted=all&_r=0

Bernstein, I. M., et al. (2005). Maternal smoking and its association with birth weight. *Obstetrics & Gynecology, 106,* 986–991.

Berscheid, E. (2003). On stepping on land mines. In Sternberg, R. J. (Ed.), *Psychologists defying the crowd: Stories of those who battled the establishment and won* (pp. 33–44). Washington, DC: American Psychological Association.

Berscheid, E., & Reis, H. T. (1998). Attraction and close relationships. In D. T. Gilbert, S. T. Fiske, et al. (Eds.), *The handbook of social psychology* (Vol. 2) (4th ed., pp. 193–281). New York: McGraw-Hill.

Best Start. (2007). *Update report on teen pregnancy prevention.* Toronto, ON: Best Start: Ontario's Maternal, Newborn and Early Child Development Resource Centre.

Best Start. (2008). *Teen pregnancy prevention: Exploring out-of-school approaches.* Toronto, ON: Best Start: Ontario's Maternal, Newborn and Early Child Development Resource Centre.

Beutel, M. E., Stöbel-Richter, Y., & Brähler, E. (2008). Sexual desire and sexual activity of men and women across their lifespans: Results from a representative German community survey. *BJU International, 101*(1), 76–82.

Beyerlein, A., et al. (2011). The relationship between birth weight, smoking during pregnancy, and maternal weight gain. *American Journal of Epidemiology, 113*(5), 590–595.

Bibby, R. (2002). *Homosexuality in Canada: A national reading.* A Project Canada Research Release. Retrieved May 13, 2002 from http://www.reginaldbibby.com/images/PCReleaseHomosexualityMay02.pdf

Bibby, R. (2006). *The boomer factor: What Canada's most famous generation is leaving behind.* Bastian Books.

Bielay, B., & Herold, E. S. (1995). Popular magazines as a source of sexuality information for university women. *Journal of Canadian Sexuality, 4,* 247–261.

Bimbi, D. S. (2007). Male prostitution: Pathology, paradigms and progress in research. *Journal of Homosexuality, 53(1–2),* 7–35.

Binik, Y. M. (2005). Should dyspareunia be retained as a sexual dysfunction in *DSM-V?* A painful classification decision. *Archives of Sexual Behavior, 34*(1), 11–21.

Binik, Y. M., Reissing, E., Pukall, C., Flory, N., Payne, K. A., & Khalife, S. (2002). The female sexual pain disorders: Genital pain or sexual dysfunction? *Archives of Sexual Behavior, 31,* 425–429.

Bisson, M. A., & Levin, T. R. (2009). Negotiating a friends with benefits relationship. *Archives of Sexual Behavior, 38,* 66–73.

Black, A. et al. (2009). Contraceptive use among Canadian women of reproductive age: Results of a national survey. *Journal of Obstetrics and Gynecology Canada, 31*(7), 627–640.

Blais, K., Collin-Vezina, D., Marcellin, K., & Picard, A. (2004). Current reality of homosexual couples: Clinical implications in the context of partnership counseling. *Canadian Psychology, 45*(2), 174–186.

Blanchard, R. (1989). The concept of autogynephilia and the typology of male gender dysphoria. *Journal of Nervous & Mental Disease, 177*(10), 616–623.

Blanchard, R. (2010). The DSM criteria for transvestic fetishism. *Archives of Sexual Behavior, 39*(2), 363–72. doi:10.1007/s10508-009-9541-3

Blanchard, R., Cantor, J. M., Bogaert, A. F., Breedlove, S. M., & Ellis, L. (2006). Interaction of fraternal birth order and handedness in the development of male homosexuality. *Hormones and Behavior, 49,* 405–414.

Blanchard, R., Christensen, B. K., Strong, S. M., Cantor, J. M., Kuban, M. E., Klassen, P., Dickey, R., & Blak, T. (2002). Retrospective self-reports of childhood accidents causing unconsciousness in phallometrically diagnosed pedophiles. *Archives of Sexual Behaviour, 31*(6), 511–526.

Blanchard, R., & Lippa, R. A. (2007). Birth order, sibling sex ratio, handedness, and sexual orientation of male and female participants in a BBC Internet research project. *Archives of Sexual Behaviour, 36*, 163–176.

Blanchard, R., Steiner, B. W., & Clemmensen, L. H. (1985). Gender dysphoria, gender reorientation, and the clinical management of transsexualism. *Journal of Consulting and Clinical Psychology, 53*, 295–304.

Blaze Carlson, K. (2012). The true north LGBT: New poll reveals landscape of gay Canada. *National Post*, July 6, 2012. Retrieved from http://news.nationalpost.com/2012/07/06/the-true-north-lgbt-new-poll-reveals-landscape-of-gay-canada/

Bloch, M., Rotenberg, N., Koren, D., & Ehud, K. (2006). Risk factors for early postpartum depressive symptoms. *General Hospital Psychiatry, 28*(1), 3–8.

Blow, C. M. (2009, June 27). The prurient trap. *The New York Times*. http://www.nytimes.com/2009/06/27/opinion/27blow.html

Blum, L.D. (2012). Penis size: A consideration of fantasy and reality (with only a few puns). *Psychiatric Times, 29*, 12, 26.

Bockting, W. O., & Fung, L. C. T. (2006). Genital reconstruction and gender identity disorders. In D. B. Sarwer et al. (Eds.), *Psychological aspects of reconstructive and cosmetic plastic surgery: Clinical, empirical, and ethical perspectives* (pp. 207–229). New York: Lippincott Williams & Wilkins.

Bogaert, A. (2012). *Understanding asexuality*. Rowan & Littlefield Publishers.

Bogaert, A. F. (1996). Volunteer bias in human sexuality research: Evidence for both sexuality and personality differences in males. *Archives of Sexual Behavior, 25*(2), 125–140.

Bogaert, A.F. (2001). Personality, individual differences, and preferences for sexual media. *Archives of Sexual Behavior, 30*(1), 29–53.

Bogaert, A. F. (2004). Asexuality: Prevalence and associated factors in a national probability sample. *Journal of Sex Research, 41*, 279–287.

Bogaert, A. F. (2006a). Toward a conceptual understanding of asexuality. *Review of General Psychology, 10*(3), 241–250.

Bogaert, A. F. (2006b). Biological versus nonbiological older brothers and men's sexual orientation. *Proceedings of the National Academy of Sciences of the United States of America, 103*(28), 10771–10774.

Bogaert, A. F., & Jamieson, L. (2008). Justice beliefs and other predictors of the timing of "coming out" in gay and bisexual men. Paper presented at the Guelph Sexuality Conference, Guelph, ON.

Bogin, G. Y. (2006). Out of the darkness: Male adolescents and the experience of sexual victimization. *School Social Work Journal, 30*(2), 1–21.

Boies, S. C. (2002). University students' uses of and reactions to online sexual information and entertainment: Links to online and offline sexual behavior. *Canadian Journal of Human Sexuality, 11*(2), 77–89.

Bolton, J. M., Sareen, J., & Reiss, J. P. (2006). Genital anaesthesia persisting six years after sertraline discontinuation. *Journal of Sex & Marital Therapy, 32*(4), 327–330.

Borisoff, J. J., Elliot, S. L., Hocalski, S., & Birch, G.. E. (2010). The development of a sensory substitution system for the sexual rehabilitation of men with chronic spinal cord injury. *Journal of Sexual Medicine, 7*, 3647–3658.

Born, L., Soares, C. N., Phillips, S., Jung, M., & Steiner, M. (2006). Women and reproductive-related trauma. In Yehuda, R. (Ed.). (2006). *Psychobiology of posttraumatic stress disorders: A decade of progress* (pp. 491–494). Vol. 1071. New York: Blackwell Publishing.

Boros, S., Mateuca, A., & Matus, M. (2005). The role of social identity in attributions—Evaluating the guilt in rape assault. *Cognitie Creier Comportament, 9*(1), 35–57.

Boston Women's Health Book Collective. (2005). *Our bodies, ourselves: A new edition for a new era*. New York: Touchstone.

Boyce, J., Cotter, A., & Perreault, S. (2014). Police reported crime statistics in Canada, 2013. *Juristat*. Statistics Canada catalogue no. 85-002-x. Retrieved from http://www.statcan.gc.ca/pub/85-002-x/2014001/article/14040-eng.pdf

Boyce, W., Doherty, M., & MacKinnon, D. (2003). *Canadian youth, sexual health and HIV/AIDS study*. Council of Ministers of Education, Canada.

Boyce, W. et al. (2006). Sexual health of Canadian youth: Findings from the Canadian Youth, Sexual health and HIV AIDS Study. *The Canadian Journal of Human Sexuality, 15*(2), 59–68.

Boyle, T. (2007, April 30). Pupils punished over Facebook comments. *Toronto Star*, p. E5.

Bradford, J. M. W. (2000). The treatment of sexual deviation using a pharmacological approach. *Journal of Sex Research, 37*, 248–257.

Bradley, S. J., Oliver, G. D., Chernick, A. B., & Zucker, K. J. (1998). Experiment of nurture: Ablatio penis at 2 months, sex reassignment at 7 months, and a psychosexual follow-up in young adulthood. *Pediatrics, 102*(1), e9.

Bradley-Engen, M.S., & Ulmer, J.T. (2009). Social worlds of stripping: The processual orders of exotic dance. *The Sociological Quarterly, 50*(1), 29–60. doi:10.1111/j.1533-8525.2008.01132.x

Brauer, M., ter Kuile, M. M., Laan, E., & Trimbos, B. (2009). Cognitive-affective correlates and predictors of superficial dyspareunia. *Journal of Sex & Marital Therapy, 35*(1), 1–24.

Brennan, R. (2004, July 13). Ontario rehires "smut" traders. *Toronto Star*. P. A 06.

Brennan, S., & Taylor-Butts, A. (2008). *Sexual assaults in Canada 2004 and 2007*. Canadian Centre for Justice Statistics Profile Series. Statistics Canada.

Briken, P., Hill, A., & Berner, W. (2011). Pharmacotherapy of sexual offenders and men who are at risk of sexual offending. In D. P. Boer et al. (Eds.). *International Perspectives on the Assessment and Treatment of Sexual Offenders: Theory, Practice, and Research* (pp. 419–431). Hoboken, NJ: Wiley.

Briken, P., Hill, A., Nika, E., & Berner, W. (2005). Obscene telephone calls—Relations to paraphilias, paraphilia related disorders and stalking. *Psychiatrische Praxis, 32*(6), 304–307.

Brock, G., Moreira, E.D., Glasser, D.B. & Gingell, C. (2006). Sexual disorders and associated help-seeking behaviours in Canada. *The Canadian Journal of Urology, 3*(1), 2953–2961.

Brock, G. et al. (2009). Canadian male sexual health council survey to assess the prevalence and treatment of premature ejaculation in Canada. *The Journal of Sexual Medicine, 6*(8), 2115–2123.

Brody, J. E. (2000, May 16). Cybersex gives birth to a psychological disorder. *The New York Times*, pp. F7, F12.

Bronner, E. (1998, February 1). "Just say maybe. No sexology, please. We're Americans." *The New York Times*, p. WK6.

Brotman, S., Ryan, B., & Cormier, R. (2003). The health and social service needs of gay and lesbian elders and their families in Canada. *The Gerontologist, 43*(2), 192–202.

Brotto, L., Heiman, J., Goff, B., Greer, B., Lentz, G., Swisher, E., et al. (2008). A psychoeducational intervention for sexual dysfunction in women with gynecologic cancer. *Archives of Sexual Behavior, 37*(2), 317–329.

Brotto, L. A. (2010). Asexuality: A mixed methods approach. *Archives of Sexual Behavior, 39*, 599–618).

Brotto, L.A. (2013). Mindful sex. *The Canadian Journal of Human Sexuality, 22*(2), 63–68.

Brotto, L.A. (2010). The DSM diagnostic criteria for hypoactive sexual desire disorder in women. *Archives of Sexual Behavior, 39*(2), 221–239.

Brotto L. A., Bitzer, J., Laan, E., Leiblum, S., & Luria, M. (2010). Women's sexual desire and arousal disorders. *Journal of Sexual Medicine, 7*(1, Pt 2), 586–614.

Brotto, L. A., Chik, H. M., Ryder, A. G., Gorzalka, B. B., & Seal, B. N. (2005). Acculturation and sexual function in Asian women. *Archives of Sexual Behaviour, 34*(6), 613–626.

Brotto, L. A., & Gorzalka, B. B. (2002). Genital and subjective sexual arousal in postmenopausal women: Influence of laboratory-induced hyperventilation. *Journal of Sex & Marital Therapy, 28*(Suppl 1), 39–53.

Brotto, L. A., & Heiman, J. R. (2007). Mindfulness in sex therapy: Applications for women with sexual difficulties following gynecologic cancer. *Sex and Marital Therapy, 22*(1), 3–11.

Brotto, L. A., Woo, J. S., & Ryder, A. G. (2007). Acculturation and sexual function in Canadian East Asian men. *Journal of Sexual Medicine, 4*(1), 72–82

Brotto, L. A., & Yule, M. A. (2011). Physiological and subjective sexual arousal in self-identified asexual women. *Archives of Sexual Behavior, 40*, 699–712.

Brown, D. (2003). Pornography and erotica. In Bryant, J., Roskos–Ewoldsen, D., & Cantor, J. (Eds.). *Communication and emotion: Essays in honor of Dolf Zillmann* (pp. 221–253). LEA's communication series. Hillsdale, NJ: Lawrence Erlbaum.

Brown, G. R., & Haaser, R. C. (2005). Sexual disorders. In Levenson, J. L. (Ed.), *The American psychiatric publishing textbook of psychosomatic medicine* (pp. 359–386). Washington, DC: American Psychiatric Publishing.

Brown, L. M., McNatt, P. S., & Cooper, G. D. (2003). Ingroup romantic preferences among Jewish and non-Jewish white undergraduates. *International Journal of Intercultural Relations, 27*(3), 335–354.

Brown, L. S. (2005). Prostitution, trafficking and traumatic stress. *Journal of Trauma & Dissociation, 6*(3), 143–145.

Brown, R., Balousek, S., Mundt, M., & Fleming, M. (2005). Methadone maintenance and male sexual dysfunction. *Journal of Addictive Diseases, 24*(2), 91–106.

Brown, T. (2002). A proposed model of bisexual identity development that elaborates on experiential differences of women and men. *Journal of Bisexuality, 2*(4), 67–91.

Browning, D. S., et al. (2006). *Sex, marriage, and family in world religions*. New York: Columbia University Press.

Bryant, C. (2010). Adolescence, pornography and harm. *Youth Studies Australia, 29*(1), 18–26

Bryant-Davis, T. (Ed.). (2011). *Surviving sexual violence*. Lanham, MD: Rowman & Littlefield.

Bullough, V. L. (2002). Masturbation: A historical overview. *Journal of Psychology & Human Sexuality, 14*(2–3), 17–33.

Bumpass, L. (1995, July 6). Cited in J. Steinhauer. No marriage, no apologies. *The New York Times*, pp. C1, C7.

Burchell, A. N., Tellier, P. P., Hanley, J., Coutlée, F., & Franco, E. L. (2010). Influence of partner's infection status on prevalent human papillomavirus among persons with a new sex partner. *Sexually Transmitted Diseases, 37*(1), 34–40. doi:10.1097/OLQ.0b013e3181b35693

Burke, T. J., & Young, V. J. (2012). Sexual transformations and intimate behaviors in romantic relationships. *Journal of Sex Research, 49*(5), 454–463.

Bush, K. R., Henderson, E. A., Dunn, J., Read, R. R., & Singh, A. (2008). Mapping the core: chlamydia and gonorrhea infections in Calgary, Alberta. *Sexually Transmitted Diseases, 35*(3), 291–297. doi:10.1097/OLQ.0b013e31815c1edb

Bushnik, T. et al. (2012). Estimating the prevalence of infertility in Canada. *Human Reproduction, 27*(3), 738–746.

Buss, D. M. (1994). *The evolution of desire: Strategies of human mating*. New York: Basic Books.

Buss, D. M. (Ed.). (2005). *The handbook of evolutionary psychology*. Hoboken, NJ: John Wiley & Sons.

Buss, D.M. (2009). An evolutionary formulation of person–situation interactions. *Journal of Research in Personality, 43*(2), 241–242.

Buss, D. M. (2009). The great struggles of life: Darwin and the emergence of evolutionary psychology. *American Psychologist, 64*(2), 140–148.

Buss, D. M., & Schmitt, D. P. (1993). Sexual strategies theory: An evolutionary perspective on human mating. *Psychological Review, 100*(2), 204–232.

Buss, D. M., & Schmitt, D. P. (2011). Evolutionary psychology and feminism. *Sex Roles, 64*(9–10), 768–787.

Butler, J. (1993). *Bodies that matter: On the discursive limits of sex*. New York: Routledge.

Butler, J. (2003). *Kritik der ethischenGewalt*. Adorno lectures. 2002. Frankfurt am Main: Institut fur Sozialforschung an der Johann Wolfgang Goethe-Universitat.

Butler, L. M., Osmond, D. H., Jones, A. G., & Martin, J. N. (2009). Use of saliva as a lubricant in anal sexual practices among homosexual men. *Journal of Acquired Immunodeficiency Syndrome, 50*, 162–167.

Buvat, J., Maggi, M., Gooren, L., Guay, A. T., Kaufman, J., Morgentaler, A., Schulman, C., Tan, H. M., Torres, L. O., Yassin, A., & Zitzmann, M. (2010). Endocrine aspects of male sexual dysfunctions. *Journal of Sexual Medicine, 7*(4, Pt 2), 1627–1656. doi: 10.1111/j.1743-6109.2010.01780.x

Byerly, M. J., et al. (2006). Sexual dysfunction associated with second-generation antipsychotics in outpatients with schizophrenia or schizoaffective disorder: An empirical evaluation of olanzapine, risperidone, and quetiapine. *Schizophrenia Research, 86*(1–3), 244–250.

Byers, E. S. (1996). How well does the traditional sexual script explain sexual coercion? Review of a program of research. *Journal of Psychology & Human Sexuality, 8*, 7–25.

Byers, E. S. (2011). Beyond the birds and the bees and was it good for you?: Thirty years of research on sexual communication. *Canadian Psychology, 52*(1), 20–28.

Byers, E. S., & Demmons, S. (1999). Sexual satisfaction and sexual self-disclosure within dating relationships. *Journal of Sex Research, 36*, 180–189.

Byers, E. S., & Eno, R. (1991). Predicting men's sexual coercion and aggression from attitudes, dating history and sexual response. *Journal of Psychology and Human Sexuality, 4*(3), 55–69.

Byers, E. S., & Grenier, G. (2003). Premature or rapid ejaculation: Heterosexual couples' perceptions of men's ejaculatory behavior. *Archives of Sexual Behavior, 32*(3), 261–270.

Byers, E. S., & Lewis, K. (1988). Dating couples' disagreements over the desired level of sexual intimacy. *Journal of Sex Research, 24*, 15–29.

Byers, E. S. & MacNeil, S. (2006). Further validation of the interpersonal exchange model of sexual satisfaction. *Journal of Sex and Marital Therapy, 32*, 53–69.

Byers, E. S. & Wang, A. (2004). Understanding sexuality in close relationships from the social exchange perspective. In J. H. Harvey, A. Wenzel, & S. Sprecher. (Eds.), *The handbook of sexuality in close relationships* (pp. 203–234). Mahwah, NJ: Lawrence Erlbaum.

Byers, L. (2005). *Gendered use of and exposure to SEMI.* Paper presented at the 2005 Canadian Sociology Association Annual Meeting, London, ON.

Byers, S. (2005). Relationship satisfaction and sexual satisfaction: A longitudinal study of individuals in long-term relationships. *The Journal of Sex Research, 42*(2), 113–118.

Cado, S., & Leitenberg, H. (1990). Guilt reactions to sexual fantasies during intercourse. *Archives of Sexual Behavior, 19*, 49–64.

Caffaro, J. V., & Conn-Caffaro, A. (2005). Treating sibling abuse families. *Aggression and Violent Behavior, 10*(5), 604–623.

Cai, R., Alexander, M., & Marson, L. (2008). Activation of somatosensory afferents elicit changes in vaginal blood flow and the urethrogenital reflex via autonomic efferents. *The Journal of Urology, 180*(3), 1167–1172.

Cairns, K. V. (1997). Counseling the partners of heterosexual male cross-dressers. *Canadian Journal of Human Sexuality, 6*, 297–306.

Cairns, K. V., & Hatt, D. G. (1995). Discrimination and sexual harassment in a graduate student sample. *Canadian Journal of Human Sexuality, 4*, 169–176.

Calzavara, L., Allman, D., Worthington, C., Tyndall, M., & Adrien, A. (2012). HIV and AIDS in Canada: A National Survey summary report. CIHR Social Research Centre in HIV Prevention/Canadian Foundation for AIDS Research. Retrieved from http://www.srchiv.ca/NationalSurvey/wp-content/uploads/2012/04/Attitudinal-Survey-Summary-Report_June15.pdf

Campbell, R. (2006). Rape survivors' experiences with the legal and medical systems: Do rape victim advocates make a difference? *Violence Against Women, 12*(1), 30–45.

Canadian Cancer society. (2009). Hormone replacement therapy. Retrieved from http://www.cancer.ca

Canadian Cancer Society. (2010a). Statistics for cervical cancer. Retrieved from http://www.cancer.ca

Canadian Cancer society. (2010f). Prostate cancer overview. Retrieved from http://www.cancer.ca

Canadian Cancer Society. (2013a). Cervical cancer statistics. Retrieved from http://www.cancer.ca

Canadian Cancer Society. (2013b). Uterine cancer statistics. Retrieved from http://www.cancer.ca

Canadian Cancer Society. (2013c). Ovarian cancer statistics. Retrieved from http://www.cancer.ca

Canadian Cancer Society. (2013d). Breast cancer statistics. Retrieved from http://www.cancer.ca

Canadian Cancer Society. (2013e). Testicular cancer statistics. Retrieved from http://www.cancer.ca

Canadian Cancer Society. (2013f). Prostate cancer statistics. Retrieved from http://www.cancer.ca

Canadian Cancer Society. (2013g). Early detection of prostate cancer. Retrieved from http://www.cancer.ca

Canadian Institute for Health Information. (2007a). *Giving birth in Canada: Regional trends from 2001–2002 to 2005–2006.* Available: http://secure.cihi.ca/cihiweb/en/downloads/Childbirth_AiB_FINAL_E.pdf

Canadian Institute for Health Information. (2007b). Therapeutic abortions data. Retrieved from www.cihi.ca

Canadian Institute for Health Information. (2008). Therapeutic abortions data. Retrieved from www.cihi.ca

Canadian Institute for Health Information. (2011). *Health indicators, 2011.* Retrieved from http://www.cihi.ca/hirpt/SearchServlet

Canadian Liver Foundation. (2010). *A survey of boomers' Sexual behaviours and attitudes: summary of findings.* Leger Marketing.

Canadian Press. (2007, September 10). Importance of marriage strong for individuals. *Toronto Star*, p. A6.

Canadian Press. (2008, July 14). Teachers vote in favour of criminalizing cyberbullying. *Toronto Star*, p. A5.

Canadian Press. (2010, May 17). Poll finds unease at Tory tack on G8 health plan. *Toronto Star*, p. A6.

Canadian Press. (2011). Top court will hear prostitution law challenge. Retrieved from www.cbc.ca. March 31, 2011.

Canadian Women's Health Network. (2010). Too many women getting hysterectomies when less invasive methods exist. Retrieved from http://www.cwhn.ca

Cantor, J. M. (2011). New MRI studies support the Blanchard typology of male-to-female transsexualism. *Archives of Sexual Behavior, 40*(5), 863–864.

Cantor, J. M., Blanchard, R., Christensen, B. K., Dickey, R., Klassen, P. E., Beckstead, A. L., et al. (2004). Intelligence, memory, and handedness in pedophilia. *Neuropsychology, 18*(1), 3–14.

Cantor, J. M., Blanchard, R., Robichaud, L. K., & Christensen, B. K. (2005b). Quantitative reanalysis of aggregate data on IQ in sexual offenders. *Psychological Bulletin, 131*(4), 555–568.

Cantor, J. M., Kabani, N., Christensen, B. K., Zipursky, R. B., Barbaree, H. E., Dickey, R., Klassen, P. E., Mikulis, D. J., Kuban, M. E., Blak, T., Richards, B. A., Hanratty, M. K., & Blanchard, R. (2008). Cerebral white matter deficiencies in pedophilic men. *Journal of Psychiatric Research, 42*(3), 167–183.

Cantor, J. M., Klassen, P. E., Dickey, R., Christensen, B. K., Kuban, M. E., Blak, T., et al. (2005a). Handedness in pedophilia and hebephillia. *Archives of Sexual Behaviour, 34*(4), 447–459.

Cantor, J. M., Kuban, M. E., Blak, T., Klassen, P. E., Dickey, R., & Blanchard, R. (2006). Grade failure and special education placement in sexual offenders' educational histories. *Archives of Sexual Behaviour, 35*(6), 743–751.

Carey, B. (2005, May 31). Watching new love as it sears the brain. *The New York Times*, p. F1

Carmody, J., Reed, G., Kristeller, J., & Merriam, P. (2008). Mindfulness, spirituality, and health-related symptoms. *Journal of Psychosomatic Research, 64*(4), 393–403.

Carrère, S., Buehlman, K. T., Gottman, J. M., Coan, J. A., & Ruckstuhl, L. (2000). Predicting marital stability and divorce in newlywed couples. *Journal of Family Psychology, 14*(1), 42–58.

Carrier, S., Morales, A., & Defoy, I. (2005). Viagra long-term efficacy and quality of life: Results of Canadian long-term study. Paper presented to World Congress of Sexology, Montreal.

Carroll, J. S., et al. (2008). Generation XXX: Pornography acceptance and use among emerging adults. *Journal of Adolescent Research*, 23(1), 6–30.

Carter, D. J., & Dalla, R. L. (2006). Transactional analysis case report: Street-level prostituted women as mental health care clients. *Sexual Addiction & Compulsivity*, 13(1), 95–119.

Carvalho, J., & Nobre, P. (2010). Gender issues and sexual desire: The role of emotional and relationship variables. *Journal of Sexual Medicine*, 7, 2469–2478.

Casavant, L. & Robertson, J. R. (2007). *Evolution of pornography law in Canada. Current Issue Review 84-3E*. Library of Parliament. Ottawa, ON: Government of Canada.

Causarano, N. et al. (2010). Exposure to and desire for sexual health education among urban youth: Associations with religion and other factors. *The Canadian Journal of Human Sexuality*, 19(4), 169–184.

Centers for Disease Control and Prevention. (2007). *Human papillomavirus: HPV information for clinicians*. Atlanta, GA: Department of Health and Human Services.

Centers for Disease Control and Prevention. (2014). *Chlamydia—CDC Fact Sheet*. Retrieved from http://www.cdc.gov/std/chlamydia/STDFact-chlamydia-detailed.htm

Chae, D. H., & Ayala, G. (2010). Sexual orientation and sexual behavior among Latino and Asian Americans: Implications for unfair treatment and psychological distress. *Journal of Sex Research*, 47(5), 451–459.

Chaiyavej, S., & Morash, M. (2009). Reasons for policewomen's assertive and passive reactions to sexual harassment. *Police Quarterly*, 12(1), 63–85.

Chandra, A., et al. (2008). Does watching sex on television predict teen pregnancy? Findings from a national longitudinal survey of youth. *Pediatrics*, 122(5), 1047–1054.

Chandra, A., et al. (2012). HIV risk-related behaviors in the United States household population aged 15–44 years: Data from the National Survey of Family Growth, 2002 and 2006–2110. *National Health Statistics Reports*, January 19, 2012, No. 46.

Chavoshi, N., Waters, S., Moniruzzaman, A., Richardson, C. G., Schechter, M. T., & Spittal, P. M. (2012). The Cedar Project: sexual vulnerabilities among Aboriginal young people involved in illegal drug use in two Canadian cities. *Canadian Journal of Public Health*, 103(6), e413–16.

Chesler, P. (2006, February 24). The failure of feminism. *Chronicle of Higher Education*, 52(25).

Child, T. J., Henderson, A. M., & Tan, S. L. (2004). The desire for multiple pregnancy in male and female infertility patients. *Human Reproduction*, 19(3), 558–561.

Chivers, M., & Bailey, J. M. (2005). A sex difference in features that elicit genital response. *Biological Psychology*, 70(2), 115–120.

Chivers, M., Seto, M., & Blanchard, R. (2007). Gender and sexual orientation differences in sexual response to sexual activities versus gender of actors in sexual films. *Journal of Personality and Social Psychology*, 93(6), 1108–1121.

Chivers, M., Seto, M., Lalumière, M., Laan, E. & Grimbos, T. (2010). Agreement of self-reported and genital measures of sexual arousal among men and women: A meta-analysis. *Archives of Sexual Behavior*, 39, 5–56.

Chivers, M. & Timmers, A. (2012). Effects of gender and relationship context in audio narratives on genital and subjective sexual response in heterosexual women and men. *Archives of Sexual Behavior*, 41(1), 185–197.

Chivers, M. L., & Bailey, J. M. (2007). The sexual physiology of sexual orientation. In E. Janssen (Ed.), T*he psychophysiology of sex*. The Kinsey Institute series (pp. 458–474). Bloomington: Indiana University Press.

Chivers, M. L., Rieger, G., Latty, E., & Bailey, J. M. (2004). A sex difference in the specificity of sexual arousal. *Psychological Science*, 15(11), 736–744.

Chivers, M. L. & Rosen, R. C. (2010). Phosphodiestrase type 5 inhibitors and female sexual response: faulty protocols or paradigms? *Journal of Sexual Medicine*, 7, 858–872.

Cho, S., Park, E. S., Park, C. I., & Na, S. (2004). Characteristics of psychosexual functioning in adults with cerebral palsy. *Clinical Rehabilitation*, 18(4), 423–429.

Christin-Maitre, S., Bouchard, P., & Spitz, I. M. (2000). Drug therapy: Medical termination of pregnancy. *The New England Journal of Medicine* online, 342(13).

Chung, A. (2010, July 21). Simple card detects date-rape drugs. *Toronto Star*, A6.

Chung, A. (2011, March 2). The profits of porn. *Toronto Star*. http://www.thestar.com/news/canada/2011/03/20/quebec_under_covers_the_profits_of_porn.html

Chung, A. (2011, March 2). The profits of porn. *Toronto Star*. www.thestar.com/.../quebec_under_covers_the_profits_of_porn.html

Cleary, J., Barhman, R., MacCormack, T., & Herold, E. (2002). Discussing sexual health with a partner: A qualitative study with young women. *Canadian Journal of Human Sexuality*, 11(3–4), 117–132.

Cleland, K., Zhu, H., Goldstuck, N., Cheng, L., & Trussell, J. (2012). The efficacy of intrauterine devices for emergency contraception: A systematic review of 35 years of experience. *Human Reproduction*, 27(7), 1994–2000.

Cnattingius, S. (2004). The epidemiology of smoking during pregnancy: Smoking prevalence, maternal characteristics, and pregnancy outcomes. *Nicotine & Tobacco Research*, 6(Suppl. 2), S125–S140.

Cnattingius, S., Bergstrom, R., Lipworth, L., & Kramer, M. S. (1998). Prepregnancy weight and the risk of adverse pregnancy outcomes. *The New England Journal of Medicine*, 338, 147–152.

Cohen, A. B., & Tannenbaum, I. J. (2001). Lesbian and bisexual women's judgments of the attractiveness of different body types. *Journal of Sex Research*, 38(3), 226–232.

Cohen, J. N., Byers, E. S., Sears, H. A., & Weaver, A. D. (2004). Sexual health education: Attitudes, knowledge, and comfort of teachers in New Brunswick schools. *Canadian Journal of Human Sexuality*, 13(1), 1–15.

Cohen, L. S., et al. (2006). Relapse of major depression during pregnancy in women who maintain or discontinue antidepressant treatment. *Journal of the American Medical Association*, 295(5), 499–507.

Cohen-Bendahan, C. C. C., van de Beek, C., & Berenbaum, S. A. (2005). Prenatal sex hormone effects on child and adult sex-typed behavior: Methods and findings. *Neuroscience & Biobehavioral Reviews*, 29(2), 353–384.

Coker, A.L. (2007). Does physical intimate partner violence affect sexual health? A systematic review. *Trauma, Violence, and Abuse*, 8(2), 149–177.

Colangelo, J. J., & Keefe-Cooperman, K. (2012). Understanding the impact of childhood sexual abuse on women's sexuality. *Journal of Mental Health Counseling*, 34(1), 14–37.

Cole, F. S. (2000). Extremely preterm birth—Defining the limits of hope. *The New England Journal of Medicine, 343*(6).

Cole, S. S. (1988). Women's sexuality, and disabilities. *Women and Therapy, 7,* 277–294.

Cole, T. B. (2006). Rape at US colleges often fueled by alcohol. *Journal of the American Medical Association, 296*(5), 504–505.

Coleman, E. (2002). Masturbation as a means of achieving sexual health. *Journal of Psychology and Human Sexuality, 14*(1–2), 5–16.

Coleman, E. (2003). Compulsive sexual behavior: What to call it, how to treat it. *SIECUS Report, 31*(5), 12–16.

Coleman, E. (2011). Impulsive/compulsive sexual behavior: Assessment and treatment. *The Oxford Handbook of Impulse Control Disorders.* New York: Oxford University Press.

Coleman, T., et al. (2011). Challenging the binary: Gender characteristics of trans Ontarians. *Trans PULSE e-Bulletin, 2*(2). Retrieved from http://www.transpulseproject.ca

Collins, R. L., et al. (2004). Watching sex on television predicts adolescent initiation of sexual behavior. *Pediatrics,* 114(3), e280–e289.

Compas Inc. (1998). *Modern life survey of the Canadian adult population.* Unpublished raw data. Toronto: Compas Inc.

Connell, E., & Hunt, A. (2006). Sexual ideology and sexual physiology in the discourses of sex advice literature. *The Canadian Journal of Human Sexuality, 15*(1), 23–45.

Connolly, J., Pepler, D., Craig, W., & Taradash, A. (2000). Dating experiences of bullies in early adolescence. *Child Maltreatment, 5*(4), 299–310.

Cook, R. L. & Clark, D. B. (2005). Is there an association between alcohol consumption and sexually transmitted diseases? A systematic review. *Sexually Transmitted Diseases, 32*(3), 156–164.

Cooper, A., Delmonico, D. L., & Burg, R. (2000). Cybersex users, abusers, and compulsives: New findings and implications. *Sexual Addiction & Compulsivity, 7*(1–2), 5–29.

Cooper, A., Delmonico, D. L., Griffin–Shelley, E., & Mathy, R. M. (2004). Online sexual activity: An examination of potentially problematic behaviors. *Sexual Addiction & Compulsivity, 11*(3), 129–143.

Cooper, S. M., Guthrie, B. J., Brown, C., & Metzger, I. (2011). Daily hassles and African American adolescent females' psychological functioning: Direct and interactive associations with gender role orientation. *Sex Roles, 65*(5–6), 397–409.

Cortoni, F., Hanson, R. K., & Coache, M. E. (2009). Les delinquantes sexuelles: Prevalence et recidive [Female sexual offenders: Prevalence and recidivism]. *Revue internationale de criminolgie et de police technique et scientifique, LXII,* 319–336.

Courtois, F. J., Charvier, K. F., Leriche, A., Vézina, J.-G., Côté, M., & Bélanger, M. (2007). Blood pressure changes during sexual stimulation, ejaculation and midodrine treatment in men with spinal cord injury. *British Journal of Urology, 101,* 331–337.

Courtois, F., Charvier, K., Vezine, J., Journel, N., Carrier, S., Jacquemin, G., & Cote, I. (2011). Assessing and conceptualizing orgasm after a spinal cord injury. *BJU International, 108,* 1624–33.

Cox, D. J. (1988). Incidence and nature of male genital exposure behavior as reported by college women. *Journal of Sex Research, 24,* 227–234.

Coyle, J. P. (2006). Treating difficult couples: Helping clients with coexisting mental and relationship disorders. *Family Relations: Interdisciplinary Journal of Applied Family Studies, 55*(1), 146–147.

Crabtree, S., & Pelham, B. (2009). What Alabamians and Iranians Have in Common. Gallup Poll. Retrieved from http://www.gallup.com

Craig, R. J. (2005). Harassment. In R. J. Craig (Ed.), *Personality-guided forensic psychology. Personality-guided psychology* (pp. 155–167). Washington, DC: American Psychological Association.

Crawford, M., & Popp, D. (2003). Sexual double standards: A review and methodological critique of two decades of research. *Journal of Sex Research, 40,* 13–26.

Crawford, T. V., Rawlins, J., McGrowder, D. A., & Adams, R. L. (2011). The Church's response to sexual reproductive health issues. *Journal of Religion and Health, 50*(1), 163–176.

Cribb, R., & Brazao, D. (2005, May 10). What can Toronto do about sex dens? Holistic centres "a never-ending mess" for city: "Holistic" spas upset nearby residents—Police not enforcing "moral offences." *Toronto Star,* p. A01.

Critelli, J. W., & Bivona, J. M. (2008). Women's erotic rape fantasies: An evaluation of theory and research. *Journal of Sex Research, 45*(1), 57–70.

Crocker, D., & Kalemba, V. (1999). The incidence and impact of women's experiences of sexual harassment in Canadian workplaces. *The Canadian Review of Sociology and Anthropology, 36*(4), 541–558.

Crosby, R. A., Sanders, S. A., Yarber, W. L., Graham, C. A., & Dodge, B. (2002). Condom use errors and problems among college men. *Sexually Transmitted Diseases, 29,* 552–557.

Crowley, T., Richardson, D., Goldmeier, D., & BASHH Special Interest Group for Sexual Dysfunction. (2006). Recommendations for the management of vaginismus: BASHH Special Interest Group for Sexual Dysfunction. *International Journal of STD & AIDS, 17*(1), 14–18.

Csoka, A. B., & Shipko, S. (2006). Persistent sexual side effects after SSRI discontinuation. *Psychotherapy and Psychosomatics, 75*(3), 187–188.

Cummings, A., & Leschied, W. (Eds.) (2002). *Violence in the lives of adolescent girls: Implications for educators and counsellors.* New York: Edwin Mellen Press.

Cummings, S. R., et al. (1999). The effect of raloxifene on risk of breast cancer in postmenopausal women: Results from the MORE randomized trial. *Journal of the American Medical Association, 281,* 2189–2197.

Cunningham, M. R., & Barbee, A. P. (2008). Prelude to a kiss: Nonverbal flirting, opening gambits, and other communication dynamics in the initiation of romantic relationships. In S. Sprecher, A. Wenzel, & J. Harvey (Eds.), *Handbook of relationship initiation* (pp. 97–120). New York: CRC Press.

Cutler, W. B. (1999). Human sex-attractant hormones: Discovery, research, development, and application in sex therapy. *Psychiatric Annals, 29*(1), 54–59.

Cuzin, B., et al. (2011). Guidelines for general practitioners for first-line management of erectile dysfunction. *Sexologies, 20*(1), 23–35.

Dahan, R., Feldman, R., & Harmoni, D. (2008). Is patients' sexual orientation a blind spot of family physicians? *Journal of Homosexuality, 55*(3), 524–532

Dahinten, V. S. (2003). Peer sexual harassment in adolescence: The function of gender. *The Canadian Journal of Nursing Research, 35*(2), 56–73.

Dalby, P. (2007, September 17). Cancer's on hold so life can go on. *Toronto Star,* p. X7.

Daley, A. (2009). Exercise and premenstrual symptomatology: A comprehensive review. *Journal of Women's Health, 18*(6), 895–899.

Damon, W. (2002). Dominance, sexism, and inadequacy: Testing a compensatory conceptualization in a sample of heterosexual men involved in SM. *Journal of Psychology & Human Sexuality, 14*(4), 25–45.

Dancer, P. L., Kleinplatz, P. J., & Moser, C. (2006). 24/7 SM slavery. *Journal of Homosexuality, 50*(2–3), 81–101.

Daneback, K., Cooper, A., & Månsoon, S. (2005). An Internet study of cybersex participants. *Archives of Sexual Behavior, 34*(3), 321–328.

Daneback, K., Mansson, S., Ross, M. & Markham, C. M. (2012). The Internet as a source of information about sexuality. *Sex Education, 12*(5), 583–598.

Daneback, K. & Ross, M. W. (2011). The complexity of Internet sexuality. In R. Balon (Ed.). *Advances in Psychosomatic Medicine, 31,* 121–134.

Daneback, K., Ross, M. W., & Månsson, S. (2006). Characteristics and behaviors of sexual compulsives who use the internet for sexual purposes. *Sexual Addition & Compulsivity, 13*(1), 53–67.

Darcangelo, S. (2008). Fetishism: Psychopathology and theory. In D. R. Laws and W. T. O'Donohue (Eds.), *Sexual deviance: Theory, assessment, and treatment* (2nd ed., pp. 76–107). New York: Guilford Press.

Darling, C. A., Davidson, J. K., & Jennings, D. A. (1991). The female sexual response revisited: Understanding the multiorgasmic experience in women. *Archives of Sexual Behavior, 20,* 527–540.

Dauvergne, M., & Turner, J. (2010). Police-reported crime statistics in Canada, 2009. *Juristat, 30*(2).

Davidson, J. K. (2004). *Fearless sex: A babe's guide to overcoming your romantic obsessions and getting the sex life you deserve* (2nd ed.). Gloucester, MA: Fair Winds Press.

Davidson, J. K., & Hoffman, L. E. (1986). Sexual fantasies and sexual satisfaction: An empirical analysis of erotic thought. *Journal of Sex Research, 22*(2), 184–205.

Davies, M. (2004). Correlates of negative attitudes toward gay men: Sexism, male role norms, and male sexuality. *Journal of Sex Research, 41*(3), 259–266.

Davis, D., Shaver, P. R., & Vernon, M. L. (2003). Physical, emotional, and behavioral reactions to breaking up: The roles of gender, age, emotional involvement, and attachment style. *Personality & Social Psychology Bulletin, 29*(7), 871–884.

Davis, R. L. (2010). *More perfect unions: The American search for marital bliss.* Cambridge, MA: Harvard University Press.

Davis, S. R., & Braunstein, G. D. (2012). Efficacy and safety of testosterone in the management of hypoactive sexual desire disorder in menopausal women. *The Journal of Sexual Medicine, 9*(4), 1134–1148.

Davis, S. R., et al. (2008). Testosterone for low libido in postmenopausal women not taking estrogen. *New England Journal of Medicine, 359,* 2005.

Dawson, S. J., Suschinsky, K. D., & Lalumière, M. L. (2012). Sexual fantasies and viewing times across the menstrual cycle: A diary study. *Archives of Sexual Behavior, 41*(1), 173–183.

De Cuyper, M., de Bolle, M., & de Fruyt, F. (2012). Personality similarity, perceptual accuracy, and relationship satisfaction in dating and married couples. *Personal Relationships, 19*(1), 128–145.

De Graaf, H., & Rademakers, J. (2011). The psychological measurement of childhood sexual development in Western societies: Methodological challenges. *Journal of Sex Research, 48*(2–3), 118–129.

De Smet, O., Loeys, T., & Buysse, A. (2012). Post-breakup unwanted pursuit: A refined analysis of the role of romantic relationship characteristics. *Journal of Family Violence, 27*(5), 437–452.

De Vries, G. J., et al. (2002). A model system for study of sex chromosome effects on sexually dimorphic neural and behavioral traits. *Journal of Neuroscience, 22*(20), 9005–9014.

Decaire, B., & Foster, D. (2010). Is being a lesbian a queer thing to do? In L. R. Ross (Ed). *Feminist Counselling: Theory, Issues, and Practice.* Toronto, ON: Canadian Scholars Press.

Degenhardt, L., Day, C., Conroy, E., & Gilmour, S. (2006). Examining links between cocaine use and street-based sex work in New South Wales, Australia. *Journal of Sex Research, 43*(2), 107–114.

DeJesus, E., Rockstroh, J. K., Henry, K., Molina, J. M., Gathe, J., Ramanathan, S., Wei, X., Yale, K., Szwarcberg, J., White, K., Cheng, A. K., Kearney, B. P., & GS-236-0103 Study Team. (2012). Co-formulated elvitegravir, cobicistat, emtricitabine, and tenofovir disoproxil fumarate versus ritonavir-boosted atazanavir plus co-formulated emtricitabine and tenofovir disoproxil fumarate for initial treatment of HIV-1 infection: A randomised, double-blind, phase 3, non-inferiority trial. *The Lancet, 379*(9835), 2429–2438. doi: 10.1016/S0140-6736(12)60918-0

Dekeseredy, W., & Kelly, K. (1993). The incidence and prevalence of woman abuse in Canadian university and college dating relationships. *Canadian Journal of Sociology, 18,* 137–159.

del Busto, E., & Harlow, M. C. (2011). American sex offender castration treatment and legislation. In D. P. Boer et al. (Eds.). *International Perspectives on the Assessment and Treatment of Sexual Offenders: Theory, Practice, and Research* (pp. 543–571). Hoboken, NJ: Wiley.

Delamater, J., & Karraker, A. (2009). Sexual functioning in older adults. *Current Psychiatry Reports, 11,* 6–11

Delamater, J., & Moorman, S. M. (2007). Sexual behavior in later life. *Journal of Aging and Health, 19*(6), 921–945

DeLuzio Chasin, C. J. (2011). Theoretical issues in the study of asexuality. *Archives of Sexual Behavior, 40,* 713–723.

Denmark, F., Paludi, M. A., & Lott, B. (2008). *Psychology of women: A handbook of issues and theories.* Santa Barbara, CA: Greenwood Press.

Denov, M. S. (2001). A culture of denial: Exploring professional perspectives on female sex offending. *Canadian Journal of Criminology, 43*(3), 303–329.

Denzin, N. K., & Lincoln, Y. S. (Eds.). (2005). *The Sage handbook of qualitative research* (3rd ed.). Thousand Oaks, CA: Sage Publications.

Derby, C. A. (2000, October 2). Cited in Study finds exercise reduces the risk of impotence. The Associated Press.

DesChamps, G. (1998). *We are part of a tradition.* Toronto: 2-Spirited People of the 1st Nations.

Devor, H. (2002). Who are "we"? Where sexual orientation meets gender identity. *Journal of Gay & Lesbian Psychotherapy, 6*(2), 5–21.

Devries, K., Free, C., Morison, L., & Saewyc, E. (2009). Factors associated with pregnancy and STI among aboriginal students in British Columbia. *Canadian Journal of Public Health, 100*(3), 226–230.

Dew, J., & Wilcox, W. B. (2011, December 8). Give and you shall receive? Generosity, sacrifice, and marital quality. *National Marriage Project Working Paper*, No. 11-1.

Dharmajah, T. (2008, July 17). No jail after sex-game death. *Guelph Mercury*, p. A1.

Diamond, L. M. (2003a). Was it a phase? Young women's relinquishment of lesbian/bisexual identities over a 5-year period. *Journal of Personality & Social Psychology, 84*(2), 352–364.

Diamond, L. M. (2003b). What does sexual orientation orient? A biobehavioral model distinguishing romantic love and sexual desire. *Psychological Review, 110*(1), 173–192.

Diamond, L. M., & Dickenson, J. A. (2012). The neuroimaging of love and desire: Review and future directions. *Clinical Neuropsychiatry, 9*(1), 39–46. 9E

Diamond, M. (2011). Developmental, sexual and reproductive neuroendocrinology: Historical, clinical and ethical considerations. *Frontiers in Neuroendocrinology, 32*(2), 255–263.

DiDonato, M. D., & Berenbaum, S. A. (2011). The benefits and drawbacks of gender typing: How different dimensions are related to psychological adjustment. *Archives of Sexual Behavior, 40*(2), 457–463.

Dielissen, P. W., Teunissen, D. A., & Laggro-Janssen, T. L. (2013). Chlamydia prevalence in the general population: Is there a sex difference? A systematic review. *BMC Infectious Diseases, 13*, 534. doi:10.1186/1471-2334-13-534. Retrieved from http://www.biomedcentral.com/content/pdf/1471-2334-13-534.pdf

DiGiulio, G. (2003). Sexuality and people living with physical or developmental disabilities: A review of key issues. *The Canadian Journal of Human Sexuality, 12*, 53–68.

Dijkstra, P., & Buunk, B. P. (2002). Sex differences in the jealousy-evoking effect of rival characteristics. *European Journal of Social Psychology, 32*(6), 829–852.

Dindia, K., & Timmermann, L. (2003). Accomplishing romantic relationships. In J. O. Greene & B. R. Burleson (Eds.), *Handbook of communication and social interaction skills* (pp. 685–721). Mahwah, NJ: Erlbaum.

Disney, E. R., Iacono, W., McGue, M., Tully, E., & Legrand, L. (2008). Strengthening the case: Prenatal alcohol exposure is associated with increased risk for conduct disorder. *Pediatrics, 122*(6), e1225–e1230

Dittert, S., Seidl, O., & Soyka, M. (2005). Zoophilia as a special case of paraphilia. Presentation of three case reports and an Internet survey. *Nervenarzt, 76*(1), 61–67.

Dixson, B.J., et al. (2011). Men's preferences for women's breast morphology in New Zealand, Samoa, and Papua New Guinea. *Archives of Sexual Behavior, 40*, 1271–1279.

Do, C., et al. (2009). Statins and erectile dysfunction: Results of a case/non-case study using the French Pharmacovigilance System Database. *Drug Safety, 32*(7), 591–597.

Downing, L., & Gillett, R. (2011). Viewing critical psychology through the lens of queer. *Psychology and Sexuality, 2*(1), 4–15.

Downs, M., & Nazario, B. (2003, February 11). *Aphrodisiacs through the ages.* WebMD Features. [Online].

Dredger, A. (2008). The controversy surrounding *The man who would be queen: A case history of the politics of science, identity, and sex in the Internet Age. Archives of Sexual Behavior*, 37, 366–421.

Drigotas, S. M., Rusbult, C. E., & Verette, J. (1999). Level of commitment, mutuality of commitment, and couple well-being. *Personal Relationships, 6*(3), 389–409.

Drucker, D. J. (2012). A most interesting chapter in the history of science: Intellectual responses to Alfred Kinsey's *Sexual*

behavior in the human male. History of the Human Sciences, 25(1), 75–98.

Du Mont, J. (2009). Factors associated with suspected drug-facilitated sexual assault. *Canadian Medical Association Journal, 180*(5), 513–519.

Du Mont, J., Macdonald, S., Rotbard, N., Bainbridge, D., Asilani, E., Smith, N., & Cohen, M. M. (2010). Drug-facilitated sexual assault in Ontario, Canada: Toxicological and DNA findings. *Journal of Forensic and Legal Medicine, 17*(6), 333–338. doi:10.1016/j.jflm.2010.05.004

Duke, L. A., Allen, D. N., Rozee, P. D., & Bommaritto, M. (2008). The sensitivity and specificity of flashbacks and nightmares to trauma. *Journal of Anxiety Disorders, 22*(2), 319–327.

Duru, C., Jha, S., & Lashen, H. (2012). Urodynamic outcomes after hysterectomy for benign conditions: A systematic review and meta-analysis. *Obstetrical and Gynecological Survey, 67*(1), 45–54.

Dworkin, A. (1987). *Intercourse.* New York, NY: Free Press.

Dworkin, S. L., & O'Sullivan, L. (2005). Actual versus desired initiation patterns among a sample of college men: Tapping disjunctures within traditional male scripts. *Journal of Sex Research, 42*, 150–158.

Dwyer, P. L. (2011). Skene's gland revisited: Function, dysfunction, and the G-spot. *International Urogynecology Journal, 23*(2), 135–137.

Dye, M. L., & Davis, K. E. (2003). Stalking and psychological abuse: Common factors and relationship-specific characteristics. *Violence & Victims, 18*(2), 163–180.

Eardley, I., et al. (2010). Pharmacotherapy for erectile dysfunction. *Journal of Sexual Medicine, 7*(1, Pt 2), 524–540. doi:10.1111/j.1743-6109.2009.01627.x.

East, L., & Orchard, T. (2013). Somebody's else's job: Experiences of sex education among health professionals, parents and adolescents with physical disabilities in southwestern Ontario. *Sexuality and Disability.* Advance publication.

Eastwick, P.W., & Finkel, E.J. (2008). Sex differences in mate preferences revisited: Do people know what they initially desire in a romantic partner? *Journal of Personality and Social Psychology, 94*(2), 245–264.

Edwards, V. J., Holden, G. W., Felitti, V. J., & Anda, R. F. (2003). Relationship between multiple forms of childhood maltreatment and adult mental health in community respondents: Results from the Adverse Childhood Experiences study. *American Journal of Psychiatry, 160*(8), 1453–1460.

Egale Canada. (2009). Youth speak up about homophobia and transphobia. http://egale.ca/extra/CG_Taylor_Climate_Survey_Phase_One_Report.pdf

Eggers, D. (2000, May 7). Intimacies. *The New York Times Magazine*, 76–77.

EKOS Research Associates. (2010). *Canadians decisively pro-choice on abortion.* Retrieved from www.ekospolitics.ca

El-Defrawi, M. H., Lotfy, G., Dandash, K. F., Refaat, A. H., & Eyada, M. (2001). Female genital mutilation and its psychosexual impact. *Journal of Sex & Marital Therapy, 27*(5), 465–473.

Elizabeth, A. (2013). Challenging the binary: Sexual identity that is not duality. *Journal of Bisexuality, 13*, 329–337.

Elliot, A. J., & Niesta, D. (2008). Romantic red: Red enhances men's attraction to women. *Journal of Personality and Social Psychology, 95*(5), 1150–1164.

Elliot, A. J., et al. (2010). Red, rank, and romance in women viewing men. *Journal of Experimental Psychology: General, 139*(3), 399–417.

Elliot, S. (2006). Problems of sexual function after spinal cord injury. In L.C. Weaver & C. Polosa, (Eds.). *Progress in Brain Research*, Vol. 152, Chapter 26, pp. 387–399.

Eltahawy, M. (2008, August 5). Shame on Egypt's sexist bullies. *The Toronto Globe and Mail*, p. A11.

Environics Research Group. (2013). *The Playtex Fresh and Sexy report: A definitve look at what's happening between the sheets in Canada.* Retrieved from http://stream1.newswire.ca/media/2013/02/04/20130204_C2529_DOC_EN_23232.pdf

Epstein, R. (2008). *The Assisted Human Reproduction Act and LGBTQ communities.* A paper submitted by the AHRA/LGBTQ Working Group. Toronto: Sherbourne Health Centre.

Esmail, S., Darry, K., Walter, A., & Knupp, H. (2010). Attitudes and perceptions towards disability and sexuality. *Disability and Rehabilitation, 32*(14), 1148–1155.

Esmail, S., Munro, B., & Gibson, N. (2007). Couple's experience with multiple sclerosis in the context of their sexual relationship. *Sexuality and Disability, 25*(4), 163–177.

Esmail, S., Selman, J., Munro, B., Heather, J., Ponsetti, J., & Knupp, H. (2007). Using theatre to achieve student-centered sexual education. Paper presented at the Annual Conference of the Canadian Sex Research Forum. Banff, AB.

Faller, K. C. (1989). Why sexual abuse? An exploration of the intergenerational hypothesis. *Child Abuse and Neglect, 13,* 543–548.

Fang, L., Oliver, A., Jayaraman, G. C., & Wong, T. (2010). Trends in age disparities between younger and middle-age adults among reported rates of Chlamydia, gonorrhea, and infectious syphilis infections in Canada: Findings from 1997 to 2007. *Sexually Transmitted Infections, 37,* 18–25.

Farley, M., Lynne, J., & Cotton, A. J. (2005). Prostitution in Vancouver: Violence and the colonization of First Nations Women. *Transcultural Psychiatry, 42*(2), 242–271.

Fausto-Sterling, A. (May/April 1993). The five sexes: Why male and female are not enough. *The Sciences,* 20–25.

Federoff, J. P. (1995). Antiandrogens vs. serotonergic medications in the treatment of sex offenders: A preliminary compliance study. *Canadian Journal of Human Sexuality, 4,* 111–123.

Federoff, J. P. (2011). Forensic and diagnostic concerns arising from proposed *DSM-5* criteria for sexual paraphilic disorder. *The Journal of the American Academy of Psychiatry and the Law, 39,* 238–241.

Federoff, J. P., Di Gioacchino, L., & Murphy, L. (2013). Problems with paraphilias in the *DSM-5. Current Psychiatry Reports, 15*(8), 363. doi:10.1007/s11920-013-0363-6.

Fedoroff, J. P., Fishell, A., & Fedoroff, B. (1999). A case series of women evaluated for paraphilic disorders. *The Canadian Journal of Human Sexuality, 8,* 127–140.

Fedoroff, P. (2003). The paraphilic world. In S. B. Levine, C. R. Risen, & S. E. Althof (Eds.), *Handbook of clinical sexuality for mental health professionals* (pp. 333–355). New York: Brunner-Routledge.

Feinberg, D. R., et al. (2006). Menstrual cycle, trait estrogen level, and masculinity preferences in the human voice. *Hormones and Behavior, 49*(2), 215–222.

Fekete, J. (1994). *Moral panic: Biopolitics rising.* Montreal: Robert Davies Publishing.

Ferraro, G. (2004). *Cultural anthropology—An applied perspective* (5th ed.). Belmont, CA: Wadsworth.

Festa, E. D., et al. (2004). Sex differences in cocaine-induced behavioral responses, pharmacokinetics, and monoamine levels. *Neuropharmacology, 46*(5), 672–687.

Fichner-Rathus, L. (2010). *Understanding art* (9th ed.). Belmont, CA: Thomson Learning/Wadsworth.

Finkel, E., Eastwick, P., & Matthews, J. (2007). Speed-dating as an invaluable tool for studying romantic attraction: A methodological primer. *Personal Relationships, 14,* 149–166.

Finkel, E. J., Eastwick, P., Karney, B., Reis, H. T., & Sprecher, S. (2012). Online dating: A critical analysis from the perspective of psychological science. *Psychological Science in the Public Interest,* 1–64. DOI:10.1177/1529100612436522.

Finkelhor, D. (1990). Early and long-term effects of child sexual abuse: An update. *Professional Psychology: Research and Practice, 21,* 325–330.

Finkelhor, D., Cross, T. P., & Cantor, E. N. (2005a). The justice system for juvenile victims: A comprehensive model of case flow. *Trauma, Violence, & Abuse, 6*(2), 83–102.

Finkelhor, D., Ormrod, R., Turner, H., & Hamby, S. (2012). *Child and youth victimization known to police, school, and medical authorities. National Survey of Children's Exposure to Violence.* Juvenile Justice Bulletin. Office of Juvenile Justice and Delinquency Prevention.

Finkelhor, D., Ormrod, R., Turner, H., & Hamby, S. L. (2005b). The victimization of children and youth: A comprehensive, national survey. *Child Maltreatment: Journal of the American Professional Society on the Abuse of Children, 10*(1), 5–25.

Finkelman, J. M. (2005). Sexual harassment: The organizational perspective. In Barnes, A. (Ed.). *The handbook of women, psychology, and the law* (pp. 64–78). New York: John Wiley & Sons.

Firestone, R. W., Firestone, L. A., & Catlett, J. (2006a). *Sex and love in intimate relationships.* Washington, DC: American Psychological Association.

Firestone, R. W., Firestone, L. A., & Catlett, J. (2006b). Sexual withholding. In R. W. Firestone, L. A. Firestone, & J. Catlett (Eds.), *Sex and love in intimate relationships* (pp. 171–195). Washington, DC: American Psychological Association.

Fischer, B., Wortley, S., Webster, C., & Kirst, M. (2002). The socio-legal dynamics and implications of "diversion": The case study of the Toronto "john school" diversion programme for prostitution offenders. *Criminal Justice, 2*(4), 385–410.

Fisher, A. D., Bandini, E., Casale, H., & Maggi, M. (2012). Paraphilic disorders: Diagnosis and treatment. In M. Maggi (Ed.). *Hormonal therapy for male sexual dysfunction* (pp. 94–110). Hoboken, NJ: Wiley.

Fisher, B. S., Daigle, L. E., Cullen, F. T., & Turner, M. G. (2003). Reporting sexual victimization to the police and others: Results from a national-level study of college women. *Criminal Justice & Behavior, 30*(1), 6–38.

Fisher, H. E. (2000). Brains do it: Lust, attraction and attachment. *Cerebrum, 2,* 23–42.

Fisher, J. D., & Fisher, W. A. (1992). Changing AIDS-risk behavior. *Psychological Bulletin, 111,* 455–474.

Fisher, T. D., Moore, Z. T., & Pittenger, M. (2012). Sex on the brain? An examination of frequency of sexual cognitions as a function of gender, erotophilia, and social desirability. *Journal of Sex Research, 49*(1), 69–77.

Fisher, W. (2007). Prevention for positives: Development, implementation and evaluation of a clinician-delivered intervention to promote safer sexual behavior among HIV1 patients in clinical care. Paper presented at the Annual Meeting of the Canadian Sex Research Forum, Banff, Alberta.

Fisher, W., Boroditsky, R., & Morris, B. (2004a). The 2002 Canadian contraception study: Part 1. *Journal of Obstetrics and Gynaecology Canada, 26*(6), 580–590.

Fisher, W., Boroditsky, R., & Morris, B. (2004b). The 2002 Canadian contraception study: Part 2. *Journal of Obstetrics and Gynaecology Canada, 26*(7), 646–656.

Fisher, W., et al. (2005). Association of PDE-5 inhibitor use in men with ED and sexual function of partners. Paper presented at the World Congress of Sexology, Montreal.

Fisher, W. A., & Black, A. (2007). Contraception in Canada: A review of method choices, characteristics, adherence and approaches to counselling. *Canadian Medical Association Journal, 176*(7), 953–961.

Fisher, W. A., & Fisher, J. D. (1998). Understanding and promoting sexual and reproductive health behavior: Theory and method. *Annual Review of Sex Research, 9,* 39–76

Fisher, W. A., Kohut, T., Di Gioacchino, L. A., & Federoff, P. (2013). Pornography, sex crime, and paraphilia. *Current Psychiatry Reports, 15,* 362.

Fitzpatrick, M. (2010). Future of federal agency uncertain after supreme court fertility ruling. *Post Media News.* December 22, 2010.

Flaxman, S. M., & Sherman, P. W. (2000). Morning sickness: A mechanism for protecting mother and embryo. *The Quarterly Review of Biology, 5*(2), 113–148.

Flicker, S., et al. (2009). *Sexpress: The Toronto Teen Survey Report.* Toronto, ON: Planned Parenthood of Toronto. Retrieved from http://www.ppt.on.ca/pdf/reports/TTS_report.pdf

Forbes, A., While, A., Mathes, L., & Griffiths, P. (2006). Health problems and health-related quality of life in people with multiple sclerosis. *Clinical Rehabilitation, 20*(1), 67–78.

Ford, C. S., & Beach, F. A. (1951). *Patterns of sexual behavior.* New York: Harper & Row.

Forte, T., Lockwood, G. A., McLachlin, C. M., Fekete, S., & Bryant, H. E. (2012). A first look at participation rates in cervical cancer screening programs in Canada. *Current Oncology, 19*(5), 269.

Fortenberry, J. D., Schick, V., Herbenick, D., Sanders, S. A., Dodge, B., & Reece, M. (2010). Sexual behaviors and condom use at last vaginal intercourse: a national sample of adolescents ages 14–17 years. *The Journal of Sexual Medicine, 7*(Suppl. 5), 305–314.

Foster, D. (2005a). The formation and continuance of lesbian families in Canada. *Canadian Bulletin of Medical History, 22*(2), 279–295.

Foster, D. (2005b). Why lesbian households are so good for kids! Research on lesbian parenting. *Canadian Women's Studies, 24*(2/3), 51–56.

Foubert, J. D., & Newberry, J. T. (2006). Effects of two versions of an empathy-based rape prevention program on fraternity men's survivor empathy, attitudes, and behavioral intent to commit rape or sexual assault. *Journal of College Student Development, 47*(2), 133–148.

Fox, N. S., et al. (2008). Physical and sexual activity during pregnancy and near delivery. *Journal of Women's Health, 17,* 1431.

Franco, E. L., Schlecht, N. F., & Saslow, D. (2003). The epidemiology of cervical cancer. *Cancer Journal, 9*(5), 348–359.

Frank, K. (2002). *G-strings and sympathy: Strip club regulars and male desire.* Raleigh, NC: Duke University Press.

Frank, K. (2003). Just trying to relax: Masculinity, masculinizing practices, and strip club regulars. *The Journal of Sex Research, 40*(1), 61–75.

Frappier, J-Y., et al. (2008). Sex and sexual health: A survey of Canadian youth and mothers. *Pediatric and Child Health, 13* (1), 25–30.

Frayser, S. (1985). *Varieties of sexual experience: An anthropological perspective on human sexuality.* New Haven, CT: Human Relations Area Files Press.

Freeman, N. (2005, June 16). Blatant objectification: Echo's Hot Summer Issue crossed the line. *Echo,* pp. 10–11.

Freud, S. (1922/1959). Analysis of a phobia in a 5-year-old boy. In A. J. Strachey (Ed. & Trans.). *Collected papers* (Vol. 3). New York: Basic Books. (Original work published 1909.)

Freund, K., Seto, M. C., & Kuban, M. (1997). Frotteurism and the theory of courtship disorder. In D. R. Laws & W. T. O'Donohue (Eds.). *Sexual deviance: Theory, assessment and treatment* (pp. 111–130). New York: Guilford Press.

Freund, K., Watson, R., & Rienzo, D. (1988). The value of self-reports in the study of voyeurism and exhibitionism. *Annals of Sex Research 1,* 243–262.

Friday, N. (2008). *My secret garden: Women's sexual fantasies.* New York: Simon & Schuster.

Fried, P. A., & Smith, A. M. (2001). A literature review of the consequences of prenatal marihuana exposure: An emerging theme of a deficiency in aspects of executive function. *Neurotoxicology & Teratology, 23*(1), 1–11.

Friedman, R. C., & Downey, J. I. (2001). The Oedipus complex and male homosexuality. In P. Hartocollis (Ed.), *Mankind's Oedipal destiny: Libidinal and aggressive aspects of sexuality* (pp. 113–138). Madison, CT: International Universities Press.

Friedman, R. C., & Downey, J. I. (2008). Sexual differentiation of behavior: The foundation of a developmental model of psychosexuality. *Journal of the American Psychoanalytic Association, 56*(1), 147–175.

Friedrich, W. N., & Gerber, P. N. (1994). Autoerotic asphyxia: The development of a paraphilia. *Journal of the American Academy of Child and Adolescent Psychiatry, 33*(7), 970–974.

Frisch, R. E. (2002). *Female fertility and the body fat connection.* Chicago: University of Chicago Press.

Friscolanti, M. (2008, July 29). Taking the handcuffs off to keep track of sex offender. *Maclean's,* 18–21.

Frohlich, P. F., & Meston, C. M. (2005). Tactile sensitivity in women with sexual arousal disorder. *Archives of Sexual Behavior, 34*(2), 207–217.

Frohmader, K. S., Bateman, K. L., Lehman, M. N., & Coolen, L. M. (2010). Effects of methamphetamine on sexual performance and compulsive sex behavior in male rats. *Psychopharmacology, 212*(1), 93–104.

Frohmader, K. S., Pitchers, K. K. Balfour, M. E., & Coolen, L. M. (2010). Mixing pleasures: review of the effects of drugs on sex behavior in humans and animal models. *Hormones and Behavior, 58*(1), 149–162.

Fugl-Meyer, K. S., Öberg, K., Lundberg, P. O., Lewin, B., & Fugl-Meyer, A. (2006). On orgasm, sexual techniques, and erotic perceptions in 18- to 74-year-old Swedish women. *Journal of Sexual Medicine, 3*(1), 56–68.

Fullerton, T., Rye, B. J., Meaney, G. J., & Loomis, C. (2013). Condom and hormonal contraceptive use by young women: An information-motivation-behavioral skills assessment. *Canadian Journal of Behavioural Science, 45*(3), 196–209.

Furnham, A. (2009). Sex differences in mate selection preferences. *Personality and Individual Differences, 47*(4), 262–267.

Gaetz, S. (2004). Safe streets for whom? Homeless youth, social exclusion, and criminal victimization. *Canadian Journal of Criminology & Criminal Justice, 46*(4), 423–455.

Gagnon, J. H. (1977). *Human sexualities.* Glenview, IL: Scott, Foresman.

Gagnon, J. H. (1990). The explicit and implicit use of the scripting perspective in sex research. *Annual Review of Sex Research, 1*, 1–44.

Gagnon, J. H. & Simon, W. (1973). *Sexual conduct: The social origins of human sexuality.* Chicago, IL: Aldine.

Gallo, M. F., Grimes, D. A., Lopez, L. M., & Schulz, K. F. (2006). Non-latex versus latex male condoms for contraception. *Cochrane Database System Reviews,* Jan 25: (1) cd003550

Gallup, O., Boyce, W. F., & Fergus, S. (2009). Non-use of condoms at last sexual intercourse among Canadian youth: Influences of sexual partners and social expectations. *The Canadian Journal of Human Sexuality, 18*(1&2), 27–34.

Gavin, N. I., et al. (2005). Perinatal depression: A systematic review of prevalence and incidence. *Obstetrics & Gynecology, 106*, 1071–1083.

Gay, P. (1984). *The bourgeois experience: Victoria to Freud.* New York: Oxford University Press.

Gebhard, P. H. (1976). The institute. In M. S. Weinberg (Ed.), *Sex research: Studies from the Kinsey Institute.* New York: Oxford University Press.

Gebhard, P. H., et al. (1965). *Sex offenders: An analysis of types.* New York: Harper & Row.

Gemme, R. (1993). Prostitution: A legal, criminological and sexological perspective. *The Canadian Journal of Human Sexuality, 4*, 227–238.

Genier, E. (2012). Gen Y still believes in marriage, kids and retirement, poll finds. *The Huffington Post Canada,* Nov. 12, 2012. Retrieved from http://www.huffingtonpost.ca/2012/12/11/gen-y-marriage-canada-_n_2272281.html?view=print&comm_ref=false

Gerressu, M., Mercer, C., Graham, C., Wellings, K., & Johnson, M. (2008). Prevalence of masturbation and associated factors in a British national probability survey. *Archives of Sexual Behavior, 37*, 266–278.

Gidycz, C. A., & Koss, M. P. (1990). A comparison of group and individual sexual assault victims. *Psychology of Women Quarterly, 14*, 325–342.

Gidycz, C. A., Rich, C. L., Orchowski, L., King, C., & Miller, A. K. (2006). The evaluation of a sexual assault self-defense and risk-reduction program for college women: A prospective study. *Psychology of Women Quarterly, 30*(2), 173–186.

Giguere, B., Lalonde, R., & Lou, E. (2010). Living at the crossroads of cultural worlds: The experience of normative conflicts by second generation immigrant youth. *Social and Personality Psychology Compass, 4*, 14–49.

Gillis, M. (2005, June 16). It's my ass. *Echo,* p. 11.

Gilmore, K. (2008). Birth mother, adoptive mother, dying mother, dead mother. In E. L. Jurist et al. (Eds.), *Mind to mind: Infant research, neuroscience, and psychoanalysis* (pp. 373–397). New York: Other Press.

Gil-Rivas, V. (2012). Sexual risk taking among college students: Correlates and consequences. In R. D. McAnulty (Ed.), *Sex in college: The things they don't write home about.* Santa Barbara, CA: ABC-CLIO, LLC.

Ginzburg, E., et al. (2010). Long-term safety of testosterone and growth hormone supplementation: A retrospective study of metabolic, cardiovascular, and other outcomes. *Journal of Clinical Medicine and Research, 2*(4), 159–166.

Gionet, L. (2013). Breastfeeding trends in Canada. *Health at a Glance.* November. Statistics Canada Catalogue no. 82-624-X. Ottawa: Statistics Canada.

Girard, D. (2005, June 2). First conviction in sex tourism case. *The Toronto Star,* p. A1

Glasser, C., Robnett, B., & Feliciano, C. (2009). Internet daters' body type preferences: Race-ethnic and gender differences. *Sex Roles, 61*(1), 14–33.

Globe & Mail Editorial Board. (2011, June 20). The UN coaxes the world toward universal gay rights. *The Globe & Mail.* http://www.theglobeandmail.com/globe-debate/editorials/the-un-coaxes-the-world-toward-universal-gay-rights/article583850/

Godfrey, T. (2003, December 19). Drifter arrested after cow assault. *The Toronto Sun.*

Goldstein, I. (1998). Cited in Kolata, G. (1998, April 4). Impotence pill: Would it also help women? *The New York Times,* pp. A1, A6.

Goldstein, I., Meston, C., Davis, S., & Traish, A. (Eds.). (2006). *Female sexual dysfunction.* New York: Parthenon.

Golombok, S., et al. (2008). Developmental trajectories of sex-typed behavior in boys and girls: A longitudinal general population study of children aged 2.5–8 years. *Child Development, 79*(5), 1583–1593.

Goodson, P., McCormick, D., & Evans, A. (2001). Searching for sexually explicit materials on the Internet: An exploratory study of college students' behavior and attitudes. *Archives of Sexual Behavior, 30*(2), 101–118.

Goodwin, R. D., Canino, G., Ortega, A. N., & Bird, H. R. (2009). Maternal mental health and childhood asthma among Puerto Rican youth: The role of prenatal smoking. *Journal of Asthma, 46*(7), 726–730.

Gooren, L. J. (2011). Ethical and medical considerations of androgen deprivation treatment of sex offenders. *The Journal of Clinical Endocrinology & Metabolism, 96*(12), 3626–3637.

Gordon, A. E., et al. (2002). Why is smoking a risk factor for sudden infant death syndrome? *Child: Care, Health & Development, 28*(Suppl. 1), 23–25.

Gorzalka, B. B., Hill, M. N., & Chang, S. C. H. (2011), Male–female differences in the effects of cannabinoids on sexual behavior and gonadal hormone function. *Hormones and Behavior, 58*(1), 91–99.

Goulet, J. (2006). The "berdache"/"two-spirit": A comparison of anthropological and native constructions of gendered identities among the Northern Athapaskans. *Journal of the Royal Anthropological Institute, 683*(19).

Gouveia, V. V., et al. (2009). Versão abreviada da Escala Triangular do Amor: Evidências de validade fatorial e consistência interna. *Estudos de Psicologia, 14*(1), 31–39.

Gower, P., & Philp, M. (2002b, November 27). The curse of alcohol and pregnancy. *The Toronto Star,* pp. A1, A16–A17.

Grace, A.P., & Wells, K. (2006). The quest for a queer-inclusive cultural ethics: Setting directions for teachers' preservice and continuing professional development. In R. J. Hill (Ed.), *New Directions for Adult and Continuing Education* (pp. 51–61). San Francisco: Jossey-Bass.

Grady, D. (2012, May 14). Taking Truvada to prevent HIV also comes with risks. *The New York Times,* p. D5.

Graham, C. A. (2010). The *DSM* diagnostic criteria for female sexual arousal disorder. *Archives of Sexual Behavior, 39*(2), 240–255. doi: 10.1007/s10508-009-9535-1

Graham, J. M. (2011). Measuring love in romantic relationships: A meta-analysis. *Journal of Social and Personal Relationships, 28*(6), 748–771.

Graham, K., et al. (2014). "Blurred lines?" Sexual aggression and barroom culture. *Alcoholism: Clinical & Experimental Research, 38*, 1416–1424.

Granata, A. R., et al. (2012). Hormonal regulation of male sexual desire: The role of testosterone, estrogen, prolactin, oxytocin, vasopressin and others. In M. Maggi (Ed.). *Hormonal therapy for male sexual dysfunction* (pp. 72–82). Hoboken, NJ: Wiley.

Graziano, W. G., & Bruce, J. W. (2008). Attraction and the initiation of relationships. In S. Sprecher, A. Wenzel, & J. Harvey (Eds.), *Handbook of relationship initiation* (pp. 269–296). New York: CRC Press.

Graziottin, A., & Althof, S. (2011). What does premature ejaculation mean to the man, the woman, and the couple? *The Journal of Sexual Medicine, 8*(Suppl s4), 304–309.

Green, R. (2008). Childhood cross-gender behavior and adult homosexuality: Why the link? *Journal of Gay & Lesbian Mental Health, 12*(1), 17–28.

Greenberg, D. M., Firestone, P., Nunes, K. L., Bradford, J. M., & Curry, S. (2005). Biological fathers and stepfathers who molest their daughters: Psychological, phallometric and criminal features. *Sexual Abuse: A Journal of Research and Treatment, 17*(1), 39–46.

Greenwald, E., & Leitenberg, H. (1989). Long-term effects of sexual experiences with siblings and non-siblings during childhood. *Archives of Sexual Behavior, 18*, 389–399.

Grenier, G., & Byers, E. S. (2001). Operationalizing premature or rapid ejaculation. *Journal of Sex Research, 38*, 369–378.

Griffith, K. H., & Hebl, M. R. (2002). The disclosure dilemma for gay men and lesbians: "Coming out" at work. *Journal of Applied Psychology, 87*(6), 1191–1199.

Griffiths, M.D. (2012). Internet sex addiction: a review of empirical research. *Addiction Research and Theory, 20*(2), 111–124.

Gross, B. (2006). The pleasure of pain. *Forensic Examiner, 15*(1), 57–61.

Gross, J. (2006, April 20). Learning to savor a full life, love life included. *The New York Times.*

Groth, A. N., & Birnbaum, H. J. (1979). *Men who rape: The psychology of the offender.* New York: Plenum Press.

Groth, A. W., & Hobson, W. (1983). The dynamics of sexual assault. In L. Schlesinger & E. Revitch (Eds.). *Sexual dynamics of antisocial behavior.* Springfield, IL: Thomas.

Grov, C., Bimbi, D. S., Nanin, J. E., & Parsons, J. T. (2006). Race, ethnicity, gender, and generational factors associated with the coming-out process among gay, lesbian, and bisexual individuals. *The Journal of Sex Research, 43*(2), 115–121.

Grover, S. et al. (2006). The prevalence of erectile dysfunction in the primary care setting. *Archives of Internal Medicine, 166*, 213–219.

Grubin, D. (2008). Medical models and interventions in sexual deviance. In D. R. Laws and W. T. O'Donohue (Eds.), *Sexual deviance: Theory, assessment, and treatment* (2nd ed., pp. 594–610). New York: Guilford Press.

Gruszecki, L., Forchuk, C., & Fisher, W. A. (2005). Factors associated with common sexual concerns in women: New findings from the Canadian Contraception Study. *The Canadian Journal of Human Sexuality, 14*(1–2), 1–13.

Gutmann, P. (2006). About confusions of the mind due to abnormal conditions of the sexual organs. *History of Psychiatry, 17*(1), 107–111.

Haake, P., et al. (2003). Acute neuroendocrine response to sexual stimulation in sexual offenders. *Canadian Journal of Psychiatry, 48*(4), 265–271.

Hackett, G. I. (2008). Disorders of male sexual desire. In D. L. Rowland & L. Incrocci (Eds.), *Handbook of sexual and gender identity disorders.* Hoboken, NJ: Wiley.

Hald, G., & Malmuth, N. (2008). Self-perceived effects of pornography consumption. *Archives of Sexual Behavior, 37*, 614–625.

Haley, N., Roy, E., Leclerc, P., Boudreau, J. F., & Boivin, J. F. (2004). HIV risk profile of male street youth involved in survival sex. *Sexually Transmitted Infections, 80*(6), 526–530.

Hallgrimsdottir, H. K., Phillips, R., & Benoit, C. (2006). Fallen women and rescued girls: Social stigma and media narratives of the sex industry in Victoria, B. C., from 1980–2005. *The Canadian Review of Sociology and Anthropology, 43*(3), 265–280.

Hallgrímsdóttir, H. K., Phillips, R., Benoit, C., & Walby, K. (2008). Sporting girls, streetwalkers, and inmates of houses of ill repute. *Sociological Perspectives, 51*(1), 119–138.

Hamer, D. H., et al. (1993, July 16). A linkage between DNA markers on the X chromosome and male sexual orientation. *Science, 261*, 321–327.

Hampton, M. R., Jeffery, B., McWatters, B., & Smith, P. (2005). Influence of teens' perceptions of parental disapproval and peer behaviour on their initiation of sexual intercourse. *The Canadian Journal of Human Sexuality, 14*(3–4), 105–121.

Hanson, R. K., Gordon, A., Harris, A. J. R., et al. (2002). First report of the collaborative outcome data project on the effectiveness of psychological treatment for sex offenders. *Sexual Abuse, 14*, 155–168.

Hardwick, D., & Patychuck, D. (1999). Geographic mapping demonstrates the association between social inequality, teen births, and STDs among youth. *Canadian Journal of Human Sexuality, 8*, 77–89.

Harel, Z. (2008). Dysmenorrhea in adolescents. *Annals of the New York Academy of Sciences, 1135*, 185–195.

Hariri, S., & Warner, L. (2013). Condom use and human papillomavirus in men. *Journal of Infectious Diseases, 208*(3), 367–369.

Harris, M., & Johnson, O. (2000). *Cultural anthropology.* Needham Heights, MA: Allyn & Bacon.

Harte, C. B., Rand, M., Adkins, R., & Meston, C. (2007). Gender-differential subjective sexual arousal patterns to diverse sexual stimuli. Paper presented at the annual meeting of the International Academy of Sex Research, Vancouver, British Columbia.

Hartwick, C., Desmarais, S., & Hennig, K. (2007). Characteristics of male and female victims of sexual coercion. *The Canadian Journal of Human Sexuality, 16*(1–2), 31–44.

Haselton, M. G., Mortezaie, M., Pillsworth, E. G., Bleske-Rechek, A., & Frederick, D. A. (2007). Ovulatory shifts in human female ornamentation: Near ovulation, women dress to impress. *Hormones and Behavior, 51*(1), 40–45.

Hatcher, R. A., Trussell, J., Nelson, A. L., Cates, W., Kowal, D., & Policar, M. (Eds). (2011). *Contraceptive technology: Twentieth revised edition.* New York, NY: Ardent Media.

Hatfield, E., Bensman, L., & Rapson, R. L. (2012). A brief history of social scientists' attempts to measure passionate love. *Journal of Social and Personal Relationships, 29*(2), 143–164.

Hatfield, E., Pillemer, J. T., O'Brien, M. U., & Le, Y-C. L. (2008). The endurance of love: Passionate and companionate love in newlywed and long-term marriages. *Interpersona, 2*(1), 35–64.

Hatfield, E., & Rapson, R. L. (2002). Passionate love and sexual desire: Cultural and historical perspectives. In A. L. Vangelisti,

H. T. Reis, et al. (Eds.), *Stability and change in relationships: Advances in personal relationships* (pp. 306–324). New York: Cambridge University Press.

Hatzichristou, D. G., et al. (2000). Sildenafil versus intracavernous injection therapy: Efficacy and preference in patients on intracavernous injection for more than 1 year. *The Journal of Urology, 164*, 1197–1200.

Hatzichristou, D. G., et al. (2005). Vardenafil improves satisfaction rates, depressive symptomatology, and self-confidence in a broad population of men with erectile dysfunction. *Journal of Sexual Medicine, 2(1)*, 109–116.

Haugaard, J. J. (2000). The challenge of defining child sexual abuse. *American Psychologist, 55*(9), 1036–1039.

Hay, D. F., et al. (2011). The emergence of gender differences in physical aggression in the context of conflict between young peers. *British Journal of Developmental Psychology, 29*(2), 158–175.

Health Canada. (2001). Sexually transmitted diseases data tables. Division of Sexual Health Promotion and STD Prevention and Control, Bureau of HIV/AIDS, STD & TB. Ottawa: Health Canada. [14]

Hébert, A., & Weaver, A. (2014). An examination of personality characteristics associated with BDSM orientations. *The Canadian Journal of Human Sexuality, 23*(2), 106–115.

Hébert, M., & Tourigny, M. (2004). Child sexual abuse prevention: A review of evaluative studies and recommendations for program development. *Advances in Psychology Research, 32*, 109–142.

Hegarty, P. (2011). Becoming curious: An invitation to the special issue on queer theory. *Psychology and Sexuality, 2*(1), 1–3.

Heil, P., & Simons, D. (2008). Multiple paraphilias: Prevalence, etiology, assessment, and treatment. In D. R. Laws and W. T. O'Donohue (Eds.), *Sexual deviance: Theory, assessment, and treatment* (2nd ed., pp. 527–556). New York: Guilford Press.

Heiman, J. R. (2008). Treating low sexual desire—New findings for testosterone in women. *New England Journal of Medicine, 359(19)*, 2047–2049.

Henderson, A. W., Lehavot, K., & Simoni, J. M. (2009). Ecological models of sexual satisfaction among lesbian/bisexual and heterosexual women. *Archives of Sexual Behavior, 38*(1), 50–65.

Hendrick, C., & Hendrick, S. (1986). A theory and method of love. *Journal of Personality and Social Psychology, 50*, 392–402.

Hendrick, C., & Hendrick, S. (Eds.) (2000). *Close relationships: A sourcebook.* Thousand Oaks, CA: Sage.

Hendrick, C., & Hendrick, S. (2003). Romantic love: Measuring Cupid's arrow. In S. Lopez & C. R. Snyder (Eds.), *Positive psychological assessment: A handbook of models and measures* (pp. 235–249). Washington, DC: American Psychological Association.

Hendrick, S. S., & Hendrick, C. (2002). Love. In C. R. Snyder & S. J. Lopez (Eds.). *Handbook of positive psychology* (pp. 472–484). London: Oxford University Press.

Herbenick, D., et al. (2009). Prevalence and characteristics of vibrator use by women in the United States: Results from a nationally representative study. *Journal of Sexual Medicine, 6*, 1857–1866.

Herbenick, D., et al. (2010a). Sexual behavior in the United States: results from a national probability sample of men and women ages 14–94. *Journal of Sexual Medicine, 7*(Suppl. 5), 255–265.

Herbenick, D., et al. (2010b). Sexual behaviors, relationships, and perceived health among adult women in the United States:

Results from a national probability sample. *Journal of Sexual Medicine, 7*(Suppl. 5), 277–290.

Herbenick, D., et al. (2010c). An event-level analysis of the sexual characteristics and composition among adults ages 18 to 59: Results from a national probability sample in the United States. *Journal of Sexual Medicine, 7*(Suppl .5), 346–361.

Herbenick, D., et al. (2011). Beliefs about women's vibrator use: Results from a nationally representative probability survey in the United States. *Journal of Sex & Marital Therapy, 37*(5), 329–345.

Herold, E. S., Corbesi, B., & Collins, J. (1994). Psychosocial aspects of female topless behavior on Australian beaches. *Journal of Sex Research, 31*, 133–142.

Herrera, V. M., & McCloskey, L. A. (2003). Sexual abuse, family violence, and female delinquency: Findings from a longitudinal study. *Violence & Victims, 18*(3), 319–334.

Hess, K. L., Javanbakht, M., Brown, J. M., Weiss, R. E., Hsu, P., & Gorbach, P. M. (2012). Intimate partner violence and sexually transmitted infections among young adult women. *Sexually Transmitted Diseases, 39*(5), 366–371. doi: 10.1097/OLQ.0b013e3182478fa5

Hester, J. D. (2005). Eunuchs and the postgender Jesus: Matthew 19:12 and transgressive sexualities. *Journal for the Study of the New Testament, 28*(1), 13–40.

Hicks, T. V., & Leitenberg, H. (2001). Sexual fantasies about one's partner versus someone else: Gender differences in incidence and frequency. *Journal of Sex Research, 38*(1), 43–50.

Hill, D. B., Menvielle, E., Sica, K. M., & Johnson, A. (2010). An affirmative intervention for families with gender-variant children: Parental ratings of child mental health and gender. *Journal of Sex & Marital Therapy, 36*(1), 6–23.

Hill, R. A., Donovan, S., & Koyama, N. F. (2005). Female sexual advertisement reflects resource availability in twentieth-century UK society. *Human Nature, 16*(3), 266–277.

Hill, T. (2005). *Female sexual frustration.* Unpublished M.A. thesis, University of Guelph.

Hines, M. (2011). Prenatal endocrine influences on sexual orientation and on sexually differentiated childhood behavior. *Frontiers in Neuroendocrinology, 32*(2), 170–182.

Hird, M. J. (2004). Naturally queer. *Feminist Theory, 5*(1), 85–89.

Hird, M. J. (2006). Sex diversity and evolutionary psychology. *The Psychologist, 19*(1), 30–32.

Hoffman, H., Peterson, K., & Garner, H. (2012). Field conditioning of sexual arousal in humans. *Socioaffective Neuroscience & Psychology, 2*, 17336. doi:10.3402/snp.v2i0.17336.

Hogg, R. S., Heath, K., Lima, V. D., Nosyk, B., Kanters, S., Wood, E., Kerr, T., & Montaner, J. S. G. (2012). Disparities in the burden of HIV/AIDS in Canada. *PLoS ONE 7*(11), e47260. doi:10.1371/journal.pone.0047260 [14]

Holmberg, D. Blair, K.L. (2009). Sexual desire, communication, satisfaction, and preferences of men and women in same-sex relationships. *Journal of Sex Research, 46*, 57–66.

Holmberg, D., Blair, K. L., & Phillips, M. (2009). Women's sexual satisfaction as a predictor of well-being in same-sex versus mixed-sex relationships. *Journal of Sex Research, 47*(1), 1–11.

Holmes, S. T., & Holmes, R. M. (2002). *Sex crimes.* Thousand Oaks, CA: Sage.

Holmstrom, A. J. (2009). Sex and gender similarities and differences in communication values in same-sex and cross-sex friendships. *Communication Quarterly, 57*(2), 224–238.

Horowitz, H. L. (2002). *Rereading sex: Battles over sexual knowledge and suppression in nineteenth-century America.* New York: Knopf.

Houts, F. W., Taller, I., Tucker, D. E., & Berlin, F. S. (2011). Sexual dysfunction. In R. Balon (Ed.). *Beyond the brain-body connection. Advances in Psychosomatic Medicine, Vol. 31*, pp. 149–163. Basel: Karger.

Hubbard, T. K. (2009). The paradox of "natural" heterosexuality with "unnatural" women. *Classical World, 102*(3), 249–258.

Huberman, J., Suschinsky, K., Lalumière, M., & Chivers, M. (2013). Relationship between impression management and three measures of women's self-reported sexual arousal. *Canadian Journal of Behavioural Science, 45*, 259–273.

Hucker, S. J. (2008). Sexual masochism: Psychopathology and theory. In D. R. Laws and W. T. O'Donohue (Eds.), *Sexual deviance: Theory, assessment, and treatment* (2nd ed., pp. 250–263). New York: Guilford Press.

Huerta, M., Cortina, L. M., Pang, J. S., Torges, C. M., & Magley, V. J. (2006). Sex and power in the academy: Modeling sexual harassment in the lives of college women. *Personality and Social Psychology Bulletin, 32*(5), 616–628.

Hugh-Jones, S., Gough, B., & Littlewood, A. (2005). Sexual exhibitionism as "sexuality and individuality": A critique of psycho-medical discourse from the perspectives of women who exhibit. *Sexualities, 8*(3), 259–281.

Humphreys, T. (2007a). The complexity of sexual consent negotiations. Paper presented at the Annual Guelph Conference on Human Sexuality, Guelph, Ontario.

Humphreys, T., DeCicco, T., King, D., & Kartes, K. (2007). Sex dreams & waking sexual activity: Is there a connection? Poster session presented at the Annual Meeting of the Society for the Scientific Study of Sexuality. Indianapolis, IN.

Humphreys, T., & Herold, E. (2003). Should universities and colleges mandate sexual behavior: Student perceptions of Antioch college's consent policy. *Journal of Psychology and Human Sexuality, 15*, 35–52.

Humphreys, T., & Herold, E. (2007). Sexual consent in heterosexual relationships: Development of a new measure. *Sex Roles, 57*, 305–315.

Humphreys, T., & Newby, J. (2007). Initiating new sexual behaviours in heterosexual relationships. *The Canadian Journal of Human Sexuality, 16*(3–4), 77–88.

Humphreys, T. P. (2004). Understanding sexual consent: An empirical investigation of the normative script for young heterosexual adults. In M. Cowling & P. Reynolds (Eds.), *Making sense of sexual consent.* Aldershot, UK: Ashgate.

Humphreys, T. P., & Brousseau, M. (2010). The sexual consent scale-revised: Development, reliability, and preliminary validity. *The Journal of Sex Research, 47*(5), 420–428. doi:10.1080/00224490903151358

Hunter, M. S. (2011). Cortisol, hot flashes, and cardiovascular risk. *Menopause, 18*(3), 251–252.

Hussain, A. (2002, June 26). It's official: Men really are afraid of commitment. Reuters.

Hutton, H. E., McCaul, M. E., Santora, P. B., & Erbelding, E. J. (2008). The relationship between recent alcohol use and sexual behaviors: Gender differences among sexually transmitted disease clinic patients. *Alcoholism: Clinical and Experimental Research, 32*(11), 2008–2015. doi:10.1111/j.1530-0277.2008.00788.x

Iemmola, F., & Ciani, A. C. (2009). New evidence of genetic factors influencing sexual orientation in men: Female fecundity

increase in the maternal line. *Archives of Sexual Behavior, 38*(3), 393–399.

Impett, E. A., Muise, A., & Peragine, D. (2013). Sexuality in the context of relationships. In L. Diamond and D. Tolman (Eds.), *APA Handbook of Sexuality and Psychology* (Vol 1, pp. 269–316). Washington DC: American Psychological Association.

Intersex Society of North America. Accessed May 26, 2012. Retrieved from www.isna.org.

Ipsos. (2010). *Ipsos Global@dvisory: Is religion a force for good in the world?* Combined population of 23 major nations evenly divided in advance of Blair, Hitchens. Retrieved from http://www.ip505-na.com

Isaacs, C. R., & Fisher, W. A. (2008). A computer-based educational intervention to address potential negative effects of Internet pornography. *Communication Studies, 59*(1), 1–18.

IsHak, W. W., & Tobia, G. (2013). *DSM-5* changes in diagnostic criteria of sexual dysfunctions. *Reproductive System & Sexual Disorders, 2*(2), 122. doi:10.4172/2161-038X.1000122

Itzin, C., Taket, A., & Kelly, L. (2007). The evidence of harm to adults relating to exposure to extreme pornographic material: A rapid evidence assessment (REA). Ministry of Justice Research Series 11/07. Retrieved from http://webarchive.nationalarchives.gov.uk/+/http://www.justice.gov.uk/docs/280907.pdf

Jacobs, S. (2007). *The characteristics and perceptions of women who visit adult retail stores.* Unpublished master's thesis, University of Guelph.

Jamison, P. L., & Gebhard, P. H. (1988). Penis size increase between flaccid and erect states: An analysis of the Kinsey data. *Journal of Sex Research, 24*(1), 177–183.

Jannini, E. A., Blanchard, R., Camperio-Ciani, A., & Bancroft, J. (2010). Male homosexuality: Nature or culture? *Journal of Sexual Medicine, 7*(10), 3245–3253.

Jannini, E. A., Whipple, B., Kingsberg, S. A., Buisson, O., Foldès, P., & Vardi, Y. (2010). Who's afraid of the G-spot? *Journal of Sexual Medicine, 7*(1), 25–34.

Jansen, E., McBride, K., & Yarber, W. (2008). Factors that influence sexual arousal in men: A focus group study. *Journal of Sex Research, 37*(2), 252–265.

Javed, N. (2008, May 24). GTA's secret world of polygamy. *Toronto Star*, p. A10.

Jayaraman, S., & Mann, M. (2012). Male and female sterilization. *Obstetrics, Gynaecology, & Reproductive Medicine, 22*(4), 85–91.

Jeffrey, L. A., & MacDonald, G. (2006). "It's the money, honey": The economy of sex work in the Maritimes. *Canadian Review of Sociology & Anthropology, 43*(3), 113–327.

Johannes, C. B., et al. (2000). Incidence of erectile dysfunction in men 40 to 69 years old: Longitudinal results from the Massachusetts male aging study. *The Journal of Urology, 163*(2), 460–463.

Johns, A., & Lush, G. (2004). *Adolescent sexual decision-making in Newfoundland and Labrador.* St. Johns, NF: Planned Parenthood Newfoundland and Labrador.

Johnson, C., Remple, V., & Bungay, V. (2007). Inconsistent condom use by indoor commercial sex workers (CSW) in Vancouver, British Columbia: A quantitative and qualitative study. Paper presented at the CAHR Conference, Toronto, Ontario.

Johnson, H. (2003). The cessation of assaults on wives. *Journal of Comparative Family Studies, 34*(1), 75–91.

Johnstone, S. J., et al. (2001). Obstetric risk factors for postnatal depression in urban and rural community samples. *Australian & New Zealand Journal of Psychiatry, 35*(1), 69–74.

Jordan, K., Fromberger, P., Stolpmann, G., & Muller, J. L. (2011). The role of testosterone in sexuality and paraphilia—A neurobiological approach. *Sexual Medicine*, 8(11), 3008–3029.

Jozkowski, K. N., & Humphreys, T. P. (2014). Sexual consent on college campuses: Implications for sexual assault prevention education. *The Health Education Monograph Series*, 31(2), 31–36.

Kaczmarek, P., LeVine, E., & Segal, A. F. (2006). Section 6. Civil and criminal trial matters. In P. Kaczmarek, E. LeVine, & A. F. Segal (Eds.) *Law & mental health professionals: New Mexico* (pp. 269–296). Washington, DC: American Psychological Association.

Kaestle, C. (2007). What's love got to do with it? Sexual behaviors of opposite sex couples through emerging adulthood. *Perspectives on Sexual and Reproductive Health*, 39(3), 134–140.

Kaestle, C. E., & Allen, K. R. (2011). The role of masturbation in healthy sexual development: Perceptions of young adults. *Archives of Sexual Behavior*, 40(5), 983–994.

Kaestle, C. E. & Waller, M. W. (2011). Bacterial STDs and perceived risk among sexual minority young adults. *Perspectives on Sexual and Reproductive Health*, 43(3), 158–163.

Kafka, M. P. (2003). Sex offending and sexual appetite: The clinical and theoretical relevance of hypersexual desire. *International Journal of Offender Therapy & Comparative Criminology*, 47(4), 439–451.

Kafka, M. P. (2010). Hypersexual disorder: A proposed diagnosis for *DSM-V*. *Archives of Sexual Behavior*, 39(2), 377–400.

Kaplan, H. S. (1974). *The new sex therapy: Active treatment of sexual dysfunctions*. New York: Brunner/Mazel.

Kaplan, H. S. (1987). *Sexual aversion, sexual phobias, and panic disorder*. New York: Brunner/Mazel.

Karakiewicz, P. I., Tanguay, S., Kattan, M. W., Elhilali, M. M., & Aprikian, A. G. (2004). Erectile and urinary dysfunction after radical prostatectomy for prostate cancer in Quebec: A population-based study of 2415 men. *European Urology*, 46(2), 188–194.

Katzman, D. K., & Taddeo, D. (2010). Emergency contraception. *Pediatrics and Child Health*, 15(6), 363–367.

Katz-Wise, S. L. & Hyde, J. S. (2012). Victimization experiences of lesbian, gay, and bisexual individuals: A meta-analysis. *Journal of Sex Research*, 49(2–3), 142–167.

Kaufman, A., et al. (1980). Male rape victims: Noninstitutionalized assault. *American Journal of Psychiatry*, 137(2), 221–223.

Kaufman, M., Silverberg, C., & Odette, F. (2007). *The ultimate guide to sex and disability*. San Francisco, CA: Cleis Press.

Kayser, D. N., Elliot, A. J., & Feltman, R. (2010). Red and romantic behavior in men viewing women. *European Journal of Social Psychology*, 40(6), 901–908.

Keller, J. J., Liang, Y., & Lin, H. (2012). Association between multiple sclerosis and erectile dysfunction: A nationwide case-control study. *Journal of Sexual Medicine*, 9(7), 1753–59. doi:10.1111/j.1743-6109.2012.02746.x.

Kellogg, J. H. (1881). *Plain facts for old and young*. Burlington, IA: Segner and Condit.

Kelly, M. B. (2012). Divorce cases in civil court, 2010/2011. *Juristat*. Statistics Canada catalogue no. 85-002-X. Ottawa: Statistics Canada. Retrieved from http://www.statcan.gc.ca/pub/85-002-x/2012001/article/11634-eng.pdf

Kennedy, M. A., & Gorzalka, B. B. (2002). Asian and non-Asian attitudes toward rape, sexual harassment, and sexuality. *Sex Roles*, 46(7–8), 227–238.

Kennedy, M. A., Gorzalka, B. B., & Yuille, J. C. (2003). Prostitution myths held by consumers of the sex trade. Paper presented at annual meeting of American Psychological Association, Toronto.

Kennedy, S. H., & Rizvi, S. (2009). Sexual dysfunction, depression, and the impact of antidepressants. *Journal of Clinical Psychopharmacology*, 29(2), 157–164.

Kiene, S. M., Fisher, W. A., Shuper, P. A., Cornman, D. H., Christie, S., Macdonald, S., Pillay, S., Mahlase, G., & Fisher, J. D. (2013). Understanding HIV transmission risk behavior among HIV-infected South Africans receiving antiretroviral therapy: An information—motivation—behavioral skills model analysis. *Health Psychology*, 32(8), 860–868. doi:10.1037/a0030554.

Kilchevsky, A., Vardi, Y., Lowenstein, L., & Gruenwald, I. (2012). Is the female G-spot truly a distinct anatomic entity? *The Journal of Sexual Medicine*, 9(3), 719–726.

Kimble, D. P. (1992). *Biological psychology* (2nd ed.). Fort Worth, TX: Harcourt.

King, A. J. C., Beazley, R. P., Warren, W. K., Hankins, C. A., Robertson, A. S., & Radford, J. L. (1989). Highlights from the Canada youth and AIDS study. *Journal of School Health*, 59(4), 139–145.

King, D. B., DeCicco, T. L., & Humphreys, T. P. (2009). Investigating sexual dream imagery in relation to daytime sexual behaviours and fantasies among Canadian university students. *The Canadian Journal of Human Sexuality*, 18(3), 135–146.

King, M. (2008). A systematic review of mental disorder, suicide, and deliberate self harm in lesbian, gay and bisexual people. *BMC Psychiatry*, 8, 70. doi:10.1186/1471-244X-8-70. Retrieved from http://www.biomedcentral.com/1471244X/8/70. (Accessed October 15, 2009).

King, R., Belsky, J., Mah, K., & Binik, Y. (2011). Are there different types of female orgasm? *Archives of Sexual Behavior*, 40(5), 865–75. doi: 10.1007/s10508-010-9639-7. Epub 2010 Aug 10.

Kingston, A. (2009, March 12). The sexting scare. *Maclean's*.

Kingston, D. A., Fedoroff, P., Firestone, P., Curry, S., & Bradford, J. M. (2008). Pornography use and sexual aggression: The impact of frequency and type of pornography use on recidivism among sexual offenders. *Aggressive Behavior*, 34(4), 341–351.

Kingston, D. A., Malamuth, N. M., Fedoroff, P., & Marshall, W. L. (2009). The importance of individual differences in pornography use: Theoretical perspectives and implications for treating sexual offenders. *Journal of Sex Research*, 46(2–3), 216–232.

Kinsey, A. C., Pomeroy, W. B., & Martin, C. E. (1948). *Sexual behavior in the human male*. Philadelphia: W. B. Saunders.

Kinsey, A. C., Pomeroy, W. B., Martin, C. E., & Gebhard, P. H. (1953). *Sexual behavior in the human female*. Philadelphia: W. B. Saunders.

Kinsman, G. (1996). *The regulation of desire: Sexuality in Canada*. Montreal: Black Rose Books.

Kippax, S., & Smith, G. (2001). Anal intercourse and power in sex between men. *Sexualities*, 4(4), 413–434.

Kirby, D., Laris, B. A., & Rolleri, L. (2007). Sex and HIV education programs: Their impact on sexual behaviors of young people throughout the world. *Journal of Adolescent Health*, 40(3), 206–217.

Kirenskaya–Berus, A. V., & Tkachenko, A. A. (2003). Characteristic features of EEG spectral characteristics in persons with deviant sexual behavior. *Human Physiology*, 29(3), 278–287.

Kirkpatrick, R. C. (2000). The evolution of human homosexual behavior. *Current Anthropology*, 41(3), 385–413.

Kito, M. (2005). Self-disclosure in romantic relationships and friendships among American and Japanese college students. *Journal of Social Psychology, 145*(2), 127–140.

Klahr, A. M., McGue, M., Iacono, W. G., & Burt, S. A. (2011). The association between parent-child conflict and adolescent conduct problems over time: results from a longitudinal adoption study. *Journal of Abnormal Psychology, 120*(1), 46–56. doi:10.1037/a0021350

Klein, R., & Knäuper, B. (2002). The role of suppression, inquiry, and mental representations of condoms in condom discontinuation. Paper presented at the annual meeting of the Canadian Sex Research Forum, Toronto.

Klein, R., & Knäuper, B. (2003). The role of cognitive avoidance of STIs for discussing safer sex practices and for condom use consistency. *Canadian Journal of Human Sexuality, 12*(3–4), 137.

Kleinplatz, P. J. (2003). What's new in sex therapy? From stagnation to fragmentation. *Sexual & Relationship Therapy, 18*(1), 95–106.

Kleinplatz, P. J. (2012). (Ed.). *New directions in sex therapy: Innovations and alternatives* (2nd ed.). New York, NY: Routledge.

Kleinplatz, P. J., & Krippner, S. (2007). Spirituality and sexuality: Celebrating erotic transcendence and spiritual embodiment. In Kleinplatz, P. J., & Moser, C. (2005). Is SM pathological? *Lesbian & Gay Psychology Review, 6*(3), 255–260.

Kleinplatz, P. J. et al. (2009). The components of optimal sexuality: A portrait of "great sex." *The Canadian Journal of Human Sexuality, 18*(1–2), 1–13.

Klofstad, C. A., McDermott, R., & Hatemi, P. K. (2013). The dating preferences of liberals and conservatives. *Political Behavior, 35*(3), 519–538. DOI:10.1007/s11109-012-9207-z

Klusmann, D. (2002). Sexual motivation and the duration of partnership. *Archives of Sexual Behavior, 31*(3), 275–287.

Klüver, H., & Bucy, P. C. (1939). Preliminary analysis of functions of the temporal lobes in monkeys. *Archives of Neurology and Psychiatry, 42*, 979.

Knaak, S. (2005). Breast-feeding, bottle-feeding and Dr. Spock: The shifting context of choice. *Canadian Review of Sociology and Anthropology, 42*(2), 197–216.

Knapp, M. L., & Vangelisti, A. L. (2000). *Interpersonal communication and human relationships* (4th ed.). Boston: Allyn & Bacon.

Knäuper, B., Aydin, C., Atkinson, K., Guberman, C., & Kornik, R. (2002). Paper presented at the annual meeting of the Canadian Sex Research Forum, Toronto.

Kniffin, K. M., & Wilson, D. S. (2004). The effect of nonphysical traits on the perception of physical attractiveness: Three naturalistic studies. *Evolution and Human Behavior, 25*(2), 88–101.

Knoll, J. L., & Hazelwood, R. R. (2009). Becoming the victim: Beyond sadism in serial sexual murderers. *Aggression and Violent Behavior, 14*(2), 106–114.

Knox, D., Schacht, C., & Zusman, M. E. (1999). Love relationships among college students. *College Student Journal, 31*(4), 445–448.

Koch, P. B., Mansfield, P. K., Thurau, D., & Carey, M. (2005). "Feeling frumpy": The relationships between body image and sexual response changes in midlife women. *The Journal of Sex Research, 42*(3), 215–224.

Koehler, N., et al. (2012). Erectile dysfunction after radical prostatectomy: The impact of nerve-sparing status and surgical approach. *International Journal of Impotence Research, 24*(4), 155–60. doi:10.1038/ijir.2012.8

Kohlberg, L. (1966). A cognitive-developmental analysis of children's sex-role concepts and attitudes. In E. E. Maccoby (Ed.), *The development of sex differences.* Stanford, CA: Stanford University Press.

Kohler, R. K., Manhart, L. E., & Lafferty, W. E. (2008). Abstinence-only and comprehensive sex education and the initiation of sexual activity and teen pregnancy. *Journal of Adolescent Health, 42*(4), 344–351. doi:10.1016/j.jadohealth.2007.08.026

Komisaruk, B. R., & Whipple, B. (2005). Brain activity imaging during sexual response in women with spinal cord injury. In Hyde, J. S. (Ed.), *Biological substrates of human sexuality* (pp. 109–145). Washington, DC: American Psychological Association.

Koren, G., Pastuszak, A., & Ito, S. (1998). Drug therapy: Drugs in pregnancy. *New England Journal of Medicine, 338*, 1128–1137.

Koss, M. P. (2003). Evolutionary models of why men rape: Acknowledging the complexities. In Travis, C. B. (Ed.), *Evolution, gender, and rape* (pp. 191–205). Cambridge, MA: MIT Press.

Koss, M. P., Bailey, J. A., Yuan, N. P., Herrera, V. M., & Lichter, E. L. (2003). Depression and PTSD in survivors of male violence: Research and training initiatives to facilitate recovery. *Psychology of Women Quarterly, 27*(2), 130–142.

Krahe, B., Waizenhofer, E., & Moller, I. (2003). Women's sexual aggression against men: Prevalence and predictors. *Sex Roles, 49*(5–6), 219–232.

Kramer, M. S., et al. (2000). The contribution of mild and moderate preterm birth to infant mortality. *Journal of the American Medical Association, 284*, 843–849.

Kristof, N. D. (2006, January 22). Slavery in our time. *The New York Times*, Section 4, p. 17.

Kristof, N. D. (2009, May 7). Girls on our streets. *The New York Times*, p. A33

Krüsi, A., Pacey, K., Bird, L., Taylor, C., Chettiar, J., Allan, S., Bennett, D., Montaner, J.S., Kerr, T., & Shannon, K. (2014). Criminalisation of clients: Reproducing vulnerabilities for violence and poor health among street-based sex workers in Canada—a qualitative study. *BMJ Open*, 4; e005191. doi:10.1136/bmjopen-2014-005191

Kuhnle, U., Krob, G., & Maier, E. (2003). True hermaphroditism: Presentation, management, outcomes. *Endocrinologist, 13*(3), 214–218.

Kuiper, B., & Cohen-Kettenis, P. (1988). Sex reassignment surgery: A study of 141 Dutch transsexuals. *Archives of Sexual Behavior, 17*(5), 439–457.

Kukkonen, T. M., Binik, Y. M., Amsel, R., & Carrier, S. (2007). Thermography as a physiological measure of sexual arousal in both men and women. *Journal of Sexual Medicine, 4*(1), 93–105.

Kulik, L. (2000). Gender identity, sex typing of occupations, and gender role ideology among adolescents: Are they related? *International Journal for the Advancement of Counselling, 22*(1), 43–56.

Kurdek, L. A. (2005). What do we know about gay and lesbian couples? *Current Directions in Psychological Science, 14*(5), 251–254.

Kurdek, L. A. (2006). Differences between partners from heterosexual, gay, and lesbian cohabiting couples. *Journal of Marriage and Family, 68*(2), 509–528.

Kurzban, R., & Weeden, J. (2005). HurryDate: Mate preferences in action. *Evolution and Human Behavior, 26*(3), 227–244.

La Rose, L. (2008, February 13). Most believe in love at first sight, survey suggests. *Toronto Star.*

Labelle, A., Bourget, D., Bradford, J. M. W., Alda, M., & Tessier, P. (2012). Familial paraphilia: A pilot study with the construction of genograms. *ISRN Psychiatry, 2012*(2012), Article ID 692813, 9 pages. doi:10.5402/2012/692813.

LaGasse, L. L., et al. (2012). Prenatal methamphetamine exposure and childhood behavior problems at 3 and 5 years of age. *Pediatrics, 129*(4), 681–688.

Lalonde, R. N., Hynie, M., Pannu, M., & Tatla, S. (2004). The role of culture in interpersonal relationships: Do second generation South Asian Canadians want a traditional partner? *Journal of Cross-Cultural Psychology, 35*(5), 503–524.

Lalumière, M. L., Blanchard, R., & Zucker, K. J. (2000). Sexual orientation and handedness in men and women: A meta-analysis. *Psychological Bulletin, 126*(4), 575–592.

Lalumière, M. L., Harris, G. T., Quinsey, V. L., & Rice, M. E. (1998). Sexual deviance and number of older brothers among sex offenders. *Sexual Abuse, 10*(1), 5–15.

Lalumière, M. L., Harris, G. T., Quinsey, V. L., & Rice, M. E. (2005a). Introduction. In M. L. Lalumière, G. T. Harris, V. L. Quinsey, & M. E. Rice (Eds.), *The causes of rape: Understanding individual differences in male propensity for sexual aggression* (pp. 3–6). Washington, DC: American Psychological Association.

Lalumière, M. L., Harris, G. T., Quinsey, V. L., & Rice, M. E. (2005b). Antisociality and mating effort. In M. L. Lalumière, G. T. Harris, V. L. Quinsey, & M. E. Rice (Eds.), *The causes of rape: Understanding individual differences in male propensity for sexual aggression* (pp. 61–103). Washington, DC: American Psychological Association.

Lalumière, M. L., Harris, G. T., Quinsey, V. L., & Rice, M. E. (2005c). Sexual interest in rape. In M. L. Lalumière, G. T. Harris, V. L. Quinsey, & M. E. Rice (Eds.), *The causes of rape: Understanding individual differences in male propensity for sexual aggression* (pp. 105–128). Washington, DC: American Psychological Association.

Lamanna, M. A. & Riedmann. (2005). *Marriages and families: Making choices in a diverse society.* Wadsworth Publishing.

LaMarre, A. K., Paterson, L. Q., & Gorzalka, B. B. (2003). Breastfeeding and postpartum maternal sexual functioning: A review. *Canadian Journal of Human Sexuality, 12*(3–4), 151–168.

Lamaze, F. (1981). *Painless childbirth.* New York: Simon & Schuster.

Lambert, B., Bergeron, S., Desrosiers, M., & Lepage, Y. (2012). Introital primary and secondary dyspareunia: Multimodal clinical and surgical control. *Sexologies, 21*(1), 9–12.

Landolt, M. A., Bartholomew, K., Saffrey, C., Oram, D., & Perlman, D. (2004). Gender nonconformity, childhood rejection, and adult attachment: A study of gay men. *Archives of Sexual Behavior, 33*(2), 117–128.

Lane, R., & Thayer, J. (2008). Sexual dysfunction and coronary artery disease. *The American Journal of Medicine, 121*(4), 256–257.

Langevin, R. (2003). A study of the psychosexual characteristics of sex killers: Can we identify them before it is too late? *International Journal of Offender Therapy & Comparative Criminology, 47*(4), 366–382.

Langevin, R. (2006). Acceptance and completion of treatment among sex offenders. *International Journal of Offender Therapy and Comparative Criminology, 50*(4), 402–417.

Langevin, R., Curnoe, S., Federoff, P., Bennett, R., Langevin, R., Peever, C., Pettica, R., & Sandhu, S. (2004). Lifetime sex offender recidivism: A 25-year follow-up study. *Canadian Journal of Criminology and Criminal Justice, 46*(5), 531–552.

Langevin, R., Langevin, M., Curnoe, S., & Bain, J. (2006). Generational substance abuse among male sexual offenders and paraphilics. *Victims & Offenders, 1*(4), 395–409.

Langevin, R., Paitich, D., Ramsay, G., Anderson, C., Kamrad, J., Pope, S., Geller, G., Pearl, L. & Newman, S. (1979). Experimental studies of the etiology of genital exhibitionism. *Archives of Sexual Behavior, 8*(4), 307–332.

Langille, D. B., & Steenbeck, A. (2013). STD risk perception among higher risk university students. *Sexually Transmitted Infections, 89*, A313–A314.

Langille, D. B., Asbridge, M., Azagba, S., Flowerdew, G., Rasic, D., & Cragg, A. (2014). Sex differences in associations of school connectedness with adolescent sexual risk-taking in Nova Scotia, Canada. *Journal of School Health, 84*(6), 387–395. doi: 10.1111/josh.12161

Langlois, J. H., et al. (2000). Maxims or myths of beauty? A meta-analytic and theoretical review. *Psychological Bulletin, 126*(3), 390–423.

Langstaff, A. (2011). A twenty-year survey of Canadian attitudes towards homosexuality and gay rights. In D. M. Rayside & C. Wilcox (Eds.). *Faith, Politics, and Sexual Diversity in Canada and the United States.* Vancouver, BC: University of British Columbia Press (pp. 49–56).

Långström, N. (2010). The *DSM* diagnostic criteria for exhibitionism, voyeurism, and frotteurism. *Archives of Sexual Behavior, 39*(2), 317–24. doi:10.1007/s10508-009-9577-4.

Långström, N., & Seto, M. (2006). Exhibitionistic and voyeuristic behavior in a Swedish national population survey. *Archives of Sexual Behavior, 35*(4), 427–435.

Långström, N., & Zucker, K. J. (2005). Transvestic fetishism in the general population: Prevalence and correlates. *Journal of Sex & Marital Therapy, 31*(2), 87–95.

Laqueur, T. W. (2003). *Solitary sex: A cultural history of masturbation.* Zone Books. Retrieved from www.newzonebooks.com.

Laumann, E. O., Gagnon, J. H., Michael, R. T., & Michaels, S. (1994). *The social organization of sexuality: Sexual practices in the United States.* Chicago: University of Chicago Press.

Laumann, E. O., Nicolosi, A., Glasser, D. B., Paik, A., Gingell, C., Moreira, E., et al. (2005). Sexual problems among women and men aged 40–80: Prevalence and correlates identified in the global study of sexual attitudes and behaviors. *International Journal of Impotence Research, 17*(1), 39.

Laumann, E. O., et al. (2006). A cross-national study of subjective sexual well-being among older women and men: Findings from the global study of sexual attitudes and behaviors. *Archives of Sexual Behavior, 35*(2), 145–161.

Lavin, M. (2008). Voyeurism: Psychopathology and theory. In D. R. Laws and W. T. O'Donohue (Eds.), *Sexual deviance: Theory, assessment, and treatment* (2nd ed., pp. 305–319). New York: Guilford Press.

Lawrance, K., & Byers, E. S. (1995). Sexual satisfaction in long-term heterosexual relationships: The interpersonal exchange model of sexual satisfaction. *Personal Relationships, 2*(4), 267–285. DOI:10.1111/j.1475-6811.1995.tb00092.x

Lawrence, A., Latty, E., Chivers, M., & Bailey, J. M. (2005). Measurement of sexual arousal in postoperative male-to-female transsexuals using vaginal photoplethysmography. *Archives of Sexual Behavior, 34*(2), 135–145.

Lawrence, A. A. (2004). Autogynephilia: A paraphilic model of gender identity disorder. *Journal of Gay & Lesbian Psychotherapy, 8*(1–2), 69–87.

Laws, D. R., & Marshall, W. L. (2003). A brief history of behavioral and cognitive behavioral approaches to sexual offenders: Part 1. Early developments. *Sexual Abuse: Journal of Research & Treatment, 15*(2), 75–92.

Laws, D. R., & O'Donohue, W. T. (2008). Introduction. *Sexual deviance: Theory, assessment, and treatment* (2nd ed., pp. 1–20). New York: Guilford Press.

Lazarus, L, Deering, K., Nabess, R., Gibson, K., Tyndall, M., & Shannon, K. (2012). Occupational stigma as a primary barrier to health care for street-based sex workers in Canada. *Culture, Health & Sexuality, 14*(2), 139–150. doi: 10.1080/13691058.2011.628411

Lederman, M. M., & Valdez, H. (2000). Immune restoration with antiretroviral therapies: Implications for clinical management. *Journal of the American Medical Association, 284*, 223–228.

Lee, B.H., & O'Sullivan, L.F. (2014). The ex-factor: Characteristics of online and offline post-relationship contact and tracking among Canadian emerging adults. *The Canadian Journal of Human Sexuality, 23*(2), 96–104. doi:10.3138/cjhs.2415

Legate, N., Ryan, R. M., & Weinstein, N. (2012). Is coming out always a "good thing"? Exploring the relations of autonomy support, outness, and wellness for lesbian, gay, and bisexual individuals. *Social Psychology and Personality Science, 3*(2), 145–152.

Leger Marketing. (2010). Cialis on Demand Study. www.leger-marketing.com

Lehne, G. K. (2009). Phenomenology of paraphilia: Lovemap theory. In F. M. Saleh et al. (Eds.), *Sex offenders: Identification, risk assessment, treatment, and legal issue* (pp. 12–26). New York: Oxford University Press.

Leiblum, S., & Chivers, M. (2007). Normal and persistent genital arousal in women: New perspectives. *Journal of Sex & Marital Therapy, 33*(4), 357–373.

Leitenberg, H., Detzer, M. J., & Srebnik, D. (1993). Gender differences in masturbation and the relation of masturbation experience in preadolescence and/or early adolescence to sexual behavior and sexual adjustment in young adulthood. *Archives of Sexual Behavior, 22*(2), 87–98.

Leitenberg, H., & Henning, K. (1995). Sexual fantasy. *Psychological Bulletin, 117*, 469–496. p. 470.

Lepischak, B. (2004). Building community for Toronto's lesbian, gay, bisexual, transsexual and transgender youth. *Journal of Gay & Lesbian Social Services: Issues in Practice, Policy & Research, 16*(3–4), 81–98.

Leue, A., Borchard, B., & Hoyer, J. (2004). Mental disorders in a forensic sample of sexual offenders. *European Psychiatry, 19*(3), 123–130.

LeVay, S. (1991). A difference in hypothalamic structure between heterosexual and homosexual men. *Science, 253*, 1034–1037.

Lever, J., Frederick, D., & Peplau, L. A. (2006). Does size matter? Men's and women's views on penis size across the lifespan. *Psychology of Men and Masculinity, 7*(3), 129–134.

Levine, D. (2000). Virtual attraction: What rocks your boat. *CyberPsychology & Behavior 3*(4), 565–573.

Levy, H. (2004, November 25). Internet luring sentence sparks outrage. *Toronto Star.*

Lewis, A. L., & White, J. (2009). The defense mechanisms of homophobia adolescent males. *Journal of Adolescence, 32*(2), 435–41. DOI:10.1016/j.adolescence.2008.04.006

Lewis, J. (1998). Learning to strip: The socialization experiences of exotic dancers. *The Canadian Journal of Human Sexuality, 7*(1), 51–66.

Lewis, R. W., et al. (2010). Definitions/epidemiology/risk factors for sexual dysfunction. *Journal of Sexual Medicine, 7*(4, Pt 2), 1598–1607.

Li, T., Dobinson, C., Scheim, A., & Ross, L. (2013). Unique issues bisexual people face in intimate relationships: A descriptive exploration of lived experience. *Journal of Gay and Lesbian Mental Health, 17*(1), 21–39.

Lindberg, L. D., Jones, R., & Santelli, J. S. (2008). Non-coital sexual activities among adolescents. *Journal of Adolescent Health, 42*(2 Suppl), 44–45. doi:10.1016/j.jadohealth.2007.11.117.

Lippa, R. (2008). The relation between childhood gender non-conformity and adult masculinity–femininity and anxiety in heterosexual and homosexual men and women. *Sex Roles, 59*(9–10), 684–693. doi:10.1007/s11199-008-9476-5

Lippa, R. A. (2012). Effects of sex and sexual orientation on self-reported attraction and viewing times to images of men and women: Testing for category specificity. *Archives of Sexual Behavior, 41*(1), 149–160.

Lippman, A., Melnychuck, R., Shimanin, C., & Boscoe, M. (2007). Human papillomavirus vaccines and women's health: Questions and cautions. *Canadian Medical Association Journal, 177*(5), 484–487.

Little, A. C., Caldwell, C. A., Jones, B. C., & DeBruine, L. M. (2011). Effects of partner beauty on opposite-sex attractiveness judgments. *Archives of Sexual Behavior, 40*(6), 1119–1127.

Littleton, H., & Henderson, C. E. (2009). If she is not a victim, does that mean she was not traumatized? Evaluation of predictors of PTSD symptomatology among college rape victims. *Violence Against Women, 15*(2), 148–167.

Liu, K. E., & Fisher, W. A. (2002). Canadian physicians' role in contraception from the 19th century to now. *Journal of Obstetrics and Gynaecology Canada, 24*(3), 239–244.

Lloyd, R. (2012, April 19). Legality leads to more trafficking. *The New York Times* (Online).

Loder, N. (2000). US science shocked by revelations of sexual discrimination. *Nature, 405*, 713–714.

Logan, C. (2008). Sexual deviance in females. In D. R. Laws and W. T. O'Donohue (Eds.), *Sexual deviance: Theory, assessment, and treatment* (2nd ed., pp. 486–507). New York: Guilford Press.

Logan, T. K., Walker, R., Jordan, C. E., & Leukefeld, C. G. (2006). Justice system options and responses. In T. K. Logan, R. Walker, C. E. Jordan, & C. G. Leukefeld (Eds.), *Women and victimization: Contributing factors, interventions, and implications* (pp. 161–194). Washington, DC: American Psychological Association.

Lohmann, R. I. (2004). Sex and sensibility: Margaret Mead's descriptive and rhetorical ethnography. *Reviews in Anthropology, 33*(2), 111–130.

Longman, M. R. (2013). Experiences of transphobia among trans Ontarians. *Trans PULSE e-Bulletin, 3*(2). Retrieved from http://www.transpulseproject.ca

Looman, J., Abracen, J., DiFazio, R., & Maillet, G. (2004). Alcohol and drug abuse among sexual and nonsexual offenders: Relationship to intimacy deficits and coping strategy. *Sexual Abuse: A Journal of Research and Treatment, 16*(3), 177–189.

Lowman, J., & Atchison, C. (2006). Men who buy sex: A survey in the greater Vancouver regional district. *The Canadian Review of Sociology and Anthropology, 43*(3), 281–296.

Lucas, A. M. (2005). The work of sex work: Elite prostitutes' vocational orientations and experiences. *Deviant Behavior, 26*(6), 513–546.

Lussier, P., & Piché, L. (2008). Frotteurism: Psychopathology and theory. In D. R. Laws and W. T. O'Donohue (Eds.), *Sexual* deviance: Theory, assessment, and treatment (2nd ed., pp. 131–149). New York: Guilford Press.

Lutfey, K., Link, C., Rosen, R., Wiegel, M., & McKinlay, J. (2009). Prevalence and correlates of sexual activity and function in women: Results from the Boston Area Community Health (BACH) Survey. *Archives of Sexual Behavior, 38*(4), 514–27. doi:10.1007/s10508-007-9290-0

MacCulloch, D. (2011). *Christianity: The first three thousand years.* New York: Viking.

MacIntosh, H., Reissing, E. D., & Andruff, H. (2010). Same sex marriage in Canada: The impact of legal marriage on the first cohort of gay and lesbians to wed. *The Canadian Journal of Human Sexuality, 19*(3), 79–90

MacKinnon, C. (1984). *Towards a feminist theory of the state.* Cambridge, MA: Harvard University Press.

MacKinnon, C. A. (2007). *Women's lives, men's laws.* Cambridge, MA: Harvard University Press.

Maclean's magazine (1998, July 20). Findings from the Gold-Parlo Poll. *Maclean's,* 10.

MacNeil, S. (2004). It takes two: Modeling the role of sexual self-disclosure in sexual satisfaction. (Doctoral dissertation, www.il.proquest.com/umi/). *Dissertation Abstracts International: Section B: The Sciences & Engineering, 65* (1-B), 481. (UMI Dissertation Order Number AAINQ87631; Print).

MacNeil, S., & Byers, E. S. (1997). The relationships between sexual problems, communication and sexual satisfaction. *Canadian Journal of Human Sexuality, 6*(4), 277–283.

MacNeil, S., & Byers, E. S. (2005). Dyadic assessment of sexual self-disclosure and sexual satisfaction in heterosexual dating couples. *Journal of Social and Personal Relationships, 22*(2), 169–181.

MacNeil, S., & Byers, E. S. (2009). Role of sexual self-disclosure in the sexual satisfaction of long-term heterosexual couples. *Journal of Sex Research, 46,* 1–12.

Macy, R. J., Nurius, P. S., & Norris, J. (2006). Responding in their best interests: Contextualizing women's coping with acquaintance sexual aggression. *Violence Against Women, 12*(5), 478–500.

Madanikia, Y., Bartholomew, K., & Cytrynbaum, J. (2013). Depiction of masturbation in North American movies. *Canadian Journal of Human Sexuality, 22*(2), 106–111.

Madsen, L., Parsons, S., & Grubin, D. (2006). The relationship between the five-factor model and *DSM* personality disorder in a sample of child molesters. *Personality and Individual Differences, 40*(2), 227–236.

Maggi, M. (2012). *Hormonal therapy for male sexual dysfunction.* Hoboken, NJ: Wiley.

Mah, K., & Binik, Y. (2002). Do all orgasms feel alike? Evaluating a two-dimensional model of the orgasm experience across gender and sexual context. *Journal of Sex Research, 39*(2), 104–114.

Mahoney, A. R., & Knudson-Martin, C. (2009). *Couples, gender, and power.* New York: Springer.

Maisel, L., & Meggers, H. (2007). Now and then: Females learning and practicing masturbation. Poster session presented at the Annual Meeting of the Society for the Scientific Study of Sexuality, Indianapolis, IN.

Major, B., Cozzarelli, C., Cooper, M. L., Zubek, J., Richards, C., et al. (2000). Psychological responses of women after first-trimester abortion. *Archives of General Psychiatry, 57*(8), 777–784.

Major, B., Kaiser, C. R., & McCoy, S. K. (2003). It's not my fault: When and why attributions to prejudice protect self-esteem. *Personality & Social Psychology Bulletin, 29*(6), 772–781.

Malacad, B.L., & Hess, G.C. (2010). Oral sex: Behaviours and feelings of Canadian young women and implications for sex education. *European Journal of Contraception and Reproductive Health Care, 15*(3), 177–185.

Malamuth, N. M., Huppin, M., & Paul, B. (2005). Sexual coercion. In D. M. Buss (Ed.), *The handbook of evolutionary psychology* (pp. 394–418). Hoboken, NJ: Wiley.

Maletzky, B. M. (1980). Self-referred vs. court-referred sexually deviant patients: Success with assisted covert sensitization. *Behavior Therapy, 11,* 306–314.

Man accused of stealing panties agrees to counselling. (2002, April 28). *National Post,* p. A6.

Maniglio, R. (2011). The role of childhood trauma, psychological problems, and coping in the development of deviant sexual fantasies in sexual offenders. *Clinical Psychology Review, 31*(5), 748–756.

Mantovani, F. (2001). Cyber-attraction: The emergence of computer-mediated communication in the development of interpersonal relationships. In L. Anolli, R. Cieri, & G. Riva (eds.), *Say not to say: New perspectives on miscommunication* (pp. 236–252). Amsterdam, Holland: IOS Press.

Maranda, M. J., Han, C., & Rainone, G. A. (2004). Crack cocaine and sex. *Journal of Psychoactive Drugs, 36*(3), 315–322.

Marazziti, D. (2005). The neurobiology of love. *Current Psychiatry Reviews, 1*(3), 331–335.

Marchbanks, P. A., et al. (2002). Oral contraceptives and the risk of breast cancer. *New England Journal of Medicine, 346*(26), 2025–2032.

Marcus, D. K., & Miller, R. S. (2003). Sex differences in judgments of physical attractiveness: A social relations analysis. *Personality & Social Psychology Bulletin, 29*(3), 325–335.

Mardorossian, C. M. (2002). Toward a new feminist theory of rape. *Signs, 27*(3), 743–775.

Mark, M. (2003, October 1). Consenting adults: A look behind closed doors in Calgary. *The Calgary Sun.*

Markman, H. J. (2005). The prevention of extramarital involvement: Steps toward "affair proofing" marriage. *Clinical Psychology: Science and Practice, 12*(2), 134–138.

Marrazzo, J. M. (2005). Sexual practices, risk perception and knowledge of sexually transmitted disease risk among lesbian and bisexual women. *Perspectives on Sexual and Reproductive Health, 37*(1), 6–12.

Marshall, D. S. (1971). Sexual behavior on Mangaia. In D. S. Marshall & R. C. Suggs (Eds.), *Human sexual behavior.* New York: Basic Books.

Marshall, L. E. & Briken, P. (2010). Assessment, diagnosis, and management of hypersexual disorders. *Current Opinion in Psychiatry, 23*(6), 570–573. doi:10.1097/YCO.0b013e32833d15d1

Marshall, W. L. (1989). Pornography and sex offenders. In D. Zillmann & J. Bryant (Eds.), *Pornography: Research advances and policy considerations* (pp. 185–214). Hillsdale, NJ: Lawrence Erlbaum.

Marshall, W. L., Marshall, L. E., & Serran, G. A. (2007). Strategies in the treatment of paraphilias: A critical review. *Annual Review of Sex Research, 17,* 162–182.

Marshall, W. L., Marshall, L. E., Serran, G. A., & Fernandez, Y. M. (2006). *Treating sexual offenders: An integrated approach.* New York: Routledge.

Martin, E. T., et al. (2009). A pooled analysis of the effect of condoms in preventing HSV-2 acquisition. *Archives of Internal Medicine, 163* (13), 1233–1240.

Martinez, G., Copen, C. E., & Abma, J. C. (2011). Teenagers in the United States: Sexual activity, contraceptive use, and child-bearing, 2006–1010 National Survey of Family Growth. National Center for Health Statistics. *Vital Health Statistics, 23*(31).

Martins, Y., Preti, G., Crabtree, C. R., Runyan, T., Vainius, A. A., & Wysocki, C. J. (2005). Preference for human body odors is influenced by gender and sexual orientation. *Psychological Science, 16*(9), 694.

Martins, Y., Tiggemann, M., & Churchett, L. (2008). Hair today, gone tomorrow: A comparison of body hair removal practices in gay and heterosexual men. *Body Image, 5*(3), 312–316.

Marziano, V., Ward, T., Beech, A. R., & Pattison, P. (2006). Identification of five fundamental implicit theories underlying cognitive distortions in child abusers: A preliminary study. *Psychology, Crime & Law, 12*(1), 97–105.

Masters, N. T., Casey, E., Wells, E. A., & Morrison, D. M. (2013). Sexual scripts among young heterosexually active men and women: Continuity and change. *Journal of Sex Research, 50*(5), 409–420.

Masters, W. H., & Johnson, V. E. (1966). *Human sexual response.* Boston: Little, Brown.

Masters, W. H., & Johnson, V. E. (1970). *Human sexual inadequacy.* Boston: Little, Brown.

Maticka-Tyndale, E. (2001). Sexual health and Canadian youth: How do we measure up? *Canadian Journal of Human Sexuality, 10*, 1–17.

Maticka-Tyndale, E. (2010). Sustainability of gains made in a primary school HIV prevention programme in Kenya into the secondary school years. *Journal of Adolescence, 33*, 563–573.

Maticka-Tyndale, E., & Smylie, L. (2008). Sexual rights: Striking a balance. *International Journal of Sexual Health, 20* (1 1 2), 7–24.

Maticka-Tyndale, E., Lewis, J., & Street, M. (2005). Making a place for escort work: A case study. *The Journal of Sex Research, 42*(1), 46–53.

Maticka-Tyndale, E., Shirpak, K. R., & Chinichian, M. (2007). Providing for the sexual health needs of Canadian immigrants. *Canadian Journal of Public Health, 98*(3), 183–186.

Maticka-Tyndale, E., Wildish, J., & Gichuru, M. (2007). Quasi-experimental evaluation of a national primary school HIV intervention in Kenya. *Evaluation and Program Planning, 30*, 172–186.

Maxwell, C. (2007). "Alternative" narratives of young people's heterosexual experiences in the UK. *Sexualities, 10*(5), 539–558.

Maxwell, C. D., Robinson, A. L., & Post, L. A. (2003). The nature and predictors of sexual victimization and offending among adolescents. *Journal of Youth & Adolescence, 32*(6), 465–477.

Maybach, K. L., & Gold, S. R. (1994). Hyperfemininity and attraction to macho and non-macho men. *Journal of Sex Research, 31*(2), 91–98.

Mayo, J., & Sheppard, M. (2012). New social learning from Two Spirit Native Americans. *The Journal of Social Studies Research, 36*(3), 262–282.

Mayo Clinic Staff. (2006, October 10). Vulvodynia. *MayoClinic. com.* Retrieved from http://www.mayoclinic.com/health/vulvodynia/DS00159

Mazur, T. *The infant's developing sexuality.* Accessed February 10, 2006. [Online]. Retrieved from www2.huberlin.de/sexology/gesund/archiv/sen/ch07.htm#b11-children%20and%20sex

McAnulty, R. (2012). *Sex in college: The things they don't write home about.* Santa Barbara, CA: ABC-CLIO, LLC.

McCabe M., Althof, S.E., Assalian, P., Chevret-Measson, M., Leiblum, S. R., Simonelli, C., & Wylie, K. (2010). Psychological and interpersonal dimensions of sexual function and dysfunctions. *Journal of Sexual Medicine, 7*(1, Pt 2), 327–336. doi:10.1111/j.1743-6109.2009.01618.x

McCabe, M. P. (2004). Exacerbation of symptoms among people with multiple sclerosis: Impact on sexuality and relationships over time. *Archives of Sexual Behavior, 33*(6), 593–601.

McCall, D., et al. (1999). *Schools, public health, sexuality and HIV: A status report.* Toronto, ON: Council of Ministers of Education.

McCarthy, B., Benoit, C., & Jansson, M. (2014). Sex work: A comparative study. *Archives of Sexual Behavior.* Advance online publication.

McCarthy, B. W., Bodnar, L. E., & Handal, M. (2004). Integrating sex therapy and couple therapy. In Harvey, J. H., Wenzel, A., & Sprecher, S. (Eds.). *The handbook of sexuality in close relationships* (pp. 573–593). Philadelphia, PA: Lawrence Erlbaum.

McCarthy, B. W., Ginsberg, R. L., & Fucito, L. M. (2006). Resilient sexual desire in heterosexual couples. *Family Journal: Counseling and Therapy for Couples and Families, 14*(1), 59–64.

McCormick, N.B. (2010). Preface to sexual scripts: Social and therapeutic implications. *Sexual and Relationship Therapy, 25*(1), 91–95.

McCoy, N. L., & Pitino, L. (2002). Pheromonal influences on sociosexual behavior in young women. *Physiology & Behavior, 75*(3), 367–375.

McCreary Centre Society. (2007). *Not yet equal: The health of lesbian, gay, & bisexual youth in BC.* Vancouver: Author.

McElroy, W. (1995). *XXX: A woman's right to pornography.* New York: St. Martin's Press.

McEwan, S. L., de Man, A. F., & Simpson-Housley, P. (2005). Acquaintance rape, ego-identity achievement, and locus of control. *Social Behavior and Personality, 33*(6), 587–592.

McGlynn, C & Ward, I. (2009). Pornography, pragmatism, and proscription. *Journal of Law and Society, 36*(3), 327–251.

McGregor, M. J., Ericksen, J., Ronald, L. A., Janssen, P. A., Van Vliet, A., & Schulzer, M. (2004). Rising incidence of hospital-reported drug-facilitated sexual assault in a large urban community in Canada. *Canadian Journal of Public Health, 95*(6), 441–445.

McKay, A. (1998). *Sexual ideology and schooling: Towards democratic sexuality education.* London, ON: The Althouse Press.

McKay, A. (2005). Sexuality and substance use: The impact of tobacco, alcohol, and selected recreational drugs on sexual function. *Canadian Journal of Human Sexuality, 14*(1–2), 47–56.

McKay, A. (2006c). Trends in teen pregnancy in Canada with comparisons to U.S.A. and England/Wales. *The Canadian Journal of Human Sexuality, 15*, (3&4), 157–162.

McKay, A. (2007). The effectiveness of latex condoms for prevention of STI/HIV. *The Canadian Journal of Human Sexuality, 16*(1–2), 57–61.

McKay, A. (2012). Trends in Canadian national and provincial/territorial teen pregnancy rates: 2001–2010. *The Canadian Journal of Human Sexuality, 21*(3–4), 161–175.

McKay, A., & Barrett, B. (2008). Rising reported rates of chlamydia among young women in Canada: What do they tell us about trends in the actual prevalence of the infection? *The Canadian Journal of Human Sexuality, 17*(1), 61–69.

McKay, A. & Barrett, M. (1999). Pre-service sexual health education training of elementary, secondary, and physical education teachers in Canadian faculties of education. *The Canadian Journal of Human Sexuality*, 7, 139–145.

McKay, A., & Holowaty, P. (1997). Sexual health education: A study of adolescents' opinions, self-perceived needs, and current and preferred sources of information. *The Canadian Journal of Human Sexuality*, 6, 29–38.

McKay, A., Pietrusiak, M., & Holowaty, P. (1998). Parents' opinions and attitudes toward sexuality education in the schools. *The Canadian Journal of Human Sexuality*, 7, 139–145.

McKay, A., et al. (In press). Ontario parents' opinions and attitudes towards sexual health education in the schools. *The Canadian Journal of Human Sexuality*.

McMahon, C. G. (2011). Premature ejaculation. *Journal of Sexual Medicine*, Virtual Issue Number 3.

McMaster, L. E., Connolly, J., Pepler, D., & Craig, W. M. (2002). Peer to peer sexual harassment in early adolescence: A developmental perspective. *Development and Psycho-pathology*, 14, 91–105.

McMillen, M. (2011, September 1). Circumcision rates are dropping in the U.S. CDC says circumcision is slightly less common today than a decade ago. *WebMD Health News*. Retrieved from http://www.webmd.com/parenting/baby/news/20110901/circumcision-rates-are-dropping-in-the-us

McNeil, D. G. (2011, July 13). Two studies show pills can prevent HIV infection. *The New York Times (Online)*.

Meaney, G., & Rye, B. (2007). Sex, sexuality and leisure. In R. McCarville & K. MacKay (Eds.), *Leisure for Canadians*. State College, PA: Venture Publishing, pp. 131-140.

Meaney, G., & Rye, B. J. (2008). Portrayals of homosexuality in introductory human sexuality textbooks. Paper presented at the Guelph Sexuality Conference, Guelph, ON.

Meaney, G. J., Rye, B. J., Wood, E., Solovieva, E. (2009). Satisfaction with school-based sexual health education in a sample of university students recently graduated from Ontario high schools. *The Canadian Journal of Human Sexuality*, 18(3), 107–125.

Media Smarts, Canada's Centre for Digital and Media Literacy. (2012). I heard it 'round the Internet: Sexual health education and authenticating online information. Retrieved from http://mediasmarts.ca/lessonplan/i-heard-it-round-internet-sexual-health-education-and-authenticating-online-information

Meininger, E., Saewyc, E. M., Skay, C., Clark, T., Poon, C., Robinson, E., Pettingell, S., & Homma, Y. (2007). Enacted sigma and HIV risk behaviors in sexual minority youth of European heritage across three countries [abstract]. *Journal of Adolescent Health*, 40, S27.

Ménard, F. P. (2011). What makes it fall apart? The determinants of the dissolution of marriages and common-law unions in Canada. *McGill Sociological Review*, 2, 59–76.

Messinger, J. C. (1993). Sex and repression in an Irish folk community. In D. N. Suggs & A. W. Miracle (Eds.), *Culture and human sexuality: A reader*. Pacific Grove, CA: Brooks/Cole.

Meston, C. M., & Frohlich, P. F. (2000). The neurobiology of sexual function. *Archives of General Psychiatry*, 57(11), 1012–1030.

Meston, C. M., Trapnell, P. D., & Gorzalka, B. B. (1996). Ethnic and gender differences in sexuality: Variations in sexual behavior between Asian and non-Asian university students. *Archives of Sexual Behavior*, 25, 33–72.

Meyer-Bahlburg, H., Dolezal, C., & Schober, J. (2007). Self-ratings of genital anatomy and sexual function by women using the Sagasf-F. Paper presented at the annual conference of the International Academy of Sex Research, Vancouver, BC.

Meyer-Cook, F. & Labelle, D. (2004). Namaji: Two-Spirit organizing in Montreal, Canada. *Journal of Gay & Lesbian Social Service*, 16, 29–51.

Michel, A., & Pédinielli, J.-L. (2005). Vers une conceptualisation du transsexualisme. *Annales Médico-Psychologiques*, 163(5), 379–386.

Migliardi, P. (2007). *Unheard voices of ethno-racial minority youth*. Winnipeg: Sexuality Education Resource Centre.

Milan, A. (2013). Fertility: overview, 2009 to 2011. *Report on the Demographic Situation in Canada*. Statistics Canada Catalogue no. 91-209-x. Ottawa: Statistics Canada.

Milan, A., Maheux, H., & Chui, T. (2010). A portrait of couples in mixed unions. *Canadian Social Trends*, No. 89. Ottawa: Statistics Canada. Retrieved from http://www.statcan.gc.ca/pub/11-008-x/2010001/article/11143-eng.htm

Milhausen, R. (2004). Factors that inhibit and enhance sexual arousal in college men and women. Unpublished doctoral dissertation, Indiana University, Indianapolis, Indiana.

Milhausen, R. R. (2000). Double standard or reverse double standard: A comparative analysis of male and female perspectives. Unpublished master's thesis, University of Guelph.

Milhausen, R. R., & Herold, E. S. (1999). Does the sexual double standard still exist? Perceptions of university women. *Journal of Sex Research*, 36(4), 361–368.

Milhausen, R. R., & Herold, E. S. (2001). Reconceptualizing the sexual double standard. *Journal of Psychology and Human Sexuality*, 13, 63–83.

Milhausen, R. R., et al. (2013). Prevalence and predictors of condom use in a national sample of Canadian university students. *The Canadian Journal of Human Sexuality*, 22(3), 142–151.

Mill, J. S. (1983). *Utilitarianism*. Indianapolis: Hackett Publishing.

Millar, C. (2003, November 22). Web porn accessed from car. *The Toronto Star*, p. A22.

Miller, R. (2005). Overcoming violence against women and girls: The international campaign to eradicate a worldwide problem. *Culture, Health & Sexuality*, 7(5), 519–521.

Minichiello, V., et al. (2001). Male sex workers in three Australian cities: Socio-demographic and sex work characteristics. *Journal of Homosexuality*, 42(1), 29–51.

Mitchell, B. (2006, October 16). Sex assault charge for Peel teacher. *Toronto Star*, p. C4.

Mitchell, B. (2010, August 26). Mississauga couple sentenced for sex assault. *Toronto Star*, p. GT2.

Money, J. (2003). History, causality, and sexology. *Journal of Sex Research*, 40(3), 237–239.

Montaner, J. S., et al. (2010). Association of highly active antiretroviral therapy coverage, population viral load, and yearly new HIV diagnosis in British Columbia, Canada: a population-based study. *The Lancet*, Early online publication July 18, 2010.

Montemurro, B., Bloom, C., & Madell, K. (2003). Ladies night out: A typology of women patrons of a male strip club. *Deviant Behavior*, 24(4), 333–352.

Montoya, R. M., Horton, R. S., & Kirchner, J. (2008). Is actual similarity necessary for attraction? A meta-analysis of actual and perceived similarity. *Journal of Social and Personal Relationships*, 25(6), 889–922.

Moore, H., & Levasseur, J. (2014). *Human traffickers going unpunished in Canada, experts say*. CBC News, March 25, 2014.

Retrieved from http://www.cbc.ca/news/canada/manitoba/human-traffickers-going-unpunished-in-canada-experts-say-1.2584944

Moore, S. M., & Rosenthal, D. (1993). *Sexuality in adolescence.* New York, NY: Routledge.

Morris, L. B. (2000, June 25). For the post partum blues, a question of whether to medicate. *The New York Times.* [Online].

Morrison, E. S., et al. (1980). *Growing up sexual.* New York: Van Nostrand Reinhold.

Morrison, G. G., Harriman, R., Morrison, M. A., Bearden, A., & Ellis, S. (2004). Correlates of exposure to sexually explicit material among Canadian post-secondary students. *The Canadian Journal of Human Sexuality, 13*(3–4), 143–157.

Morry, M. M., & Gaines, S. O. (2005). Relationship satisfaction as a predictor of similarity ratings: A test of the attraction-similarity hypothesis. *Journal of Social and Personal Relationships, 22*(4), 561–584.

Morry, M. M., Kito, M., & Ortiz, L. (2011). The attraction-similarity model and dating couples. *Personal Relationships, 18*(1), 125–143.

Moser, C. (2001). Paraphilia: A critique of a confused concept. In P. Kleinplatz (Ed.), *New directions in sex therapy: Innovations and alternatives* (pp. 91–108). New York: Brunner-Routledge.

Moser, C. (2010). Blanchard's autogynephilia theory: A critique. *Journal of Homosexuality, 57*(6), 790–809.

Moser, C., & Kleinplatz, P. J. (2002, Spring). Transvestic fetishism: Psychopathology or iatrogenic artifact? *New Jersey Psychologist,* 16–17.

Moser, C., & Kleinplatz, P. J. (2005a). *DSM-IV-TR* and the paraphilias: An argument for removal. *Journal of Psychology & Human Sexuality, 17*(3–4), 91–109.

Moser, C., & Kleinplatz, P. J. (2005b). Does heterosexuality belong in the *DSM? Lesbian & Gay Psychology Review, 6*(3), 261–267.

Muehlenhard, C. L. (2000). Categories and sexuality. *The Journal of Sex Research, 37*(2), 101–107.

Muise, A. (2006). A discourse analytic study of the discursive management of female sexual desire in online weblogs. Poster session presented at the Annual Guelph Sexuality Conference, Guelph, Ontario.

Muise, A. (2008, September). The discursive management of female sexual desire in online weblogs. Paper presented at the 32nd Annual Meeting of the Canadian Sex Research Forum, Ottawa, Ontario.

Muise, A., Christofides, E., & Desmarais, S. (2008). Who are you "poking"?: Students' experience of jealousy on Facebook. Poster session presented at the Annual Guelph Conference on Human Sexuality, Guelph, Ontario.

Muise, A., & Impett, E. A. (in press). Good, giving and game: The relationship benefits of communal sexual responsiveness. *Social Psychological and Personality Science.*

Muise, A., Impett, E. A., & Desmarais, S., & Kogan, A. (2013). Keeping the spark alive: Being motivated to meet a partner's sexual needs sustains sexual desire in long-term romantic relationships. *Social Psychological and Personality Science, 4*(3), 267–273. DOI:10.1177/1948550612457185

Muise, A., Preyde, M., Maitland, S. B., & Milhausen, R. (2010). Sexual identity and sexual well-being in female heterosexual university students. *Archives of Sexual Behavior, 39,* 915–925.

Mulick, P. S., & Wright, L. W., Jr. (2002). Examining the existence of biphobia in the heterosexual and homosexual populations. *Journal of Bisexuality, 2*(4), 45–64.

Murphy, N., & Young, P. C. (2005). Sexuality in children and adolescents with disabilities. *Developmental Medicine & Child Neurology, 47,* 640–644.

Murphy, W. D., & Page, I. J. (2008). Exhibitionism: Psychopathology and theory. In D. R. Laws and W. T. O'Donohue (Eds.), *Sexual deviance: Theory, assessment, and treatment* (2nd ed., pp. 61–75). New York: Guilford Press.

Murray, J. & Adam, B. (2001). Aging, sexuality, and HIV issues among gay and bisexual men. *Canadian Journal of Human Sexuality, 10*(3/4), 75–90.

Murray, S. H., & Milhausen, R. R. (2012). Sexual desire and relationship duration in young men and women. *Journal of Sex & Marital Therapy, 38*(1), 28–40.

Murray, S. O., & Roscoe, W. (1997). *Islamic homosexualities: Culture, history, and literature.* New York: New York University Press.

Mustanski, B., Chivers, M., & Bailey, M. (2003). A critical review of recent biological research on human sexual orientation. *Annual Review of Sex Research, 13,* 89–140.

Myers, T., Aguinaldo, J. P., Dakers, D., et al. (2004). How drug using men who have sex with men account for substance use during sexual behaviours: Questioning assumptions of HIV prevention and research. *Addiction Research and Theory, 12*(3), 213–229.

Myers, T., & Allman, D. (2004). *Ontario men's survey.* Ottawa: Canadian Public Health Association.

Myers, T., Allman, D., Adam, B., Alexander, S., Blais, M., Calzavara, L.M., Remis, R., Marchand, R., & Maxwell, J. (2013). *Male Call Canada Technical Report.* Retrieved from http://www.malecall.ca/MaleCall/wp-content/uploads/2012/03/Male-Call-Canada-Technical-Report_13April13_DRAFT.pdf

Myers, T., Allman, D., Calzavara, L., Maxwell, J., Remis, R., Swantee, C., & Travers, R. (2004a). Ontario men's survey. Library and Archives Canada Cataloguing in Publication. Available: cbr.cbrc.net/files/1126039797/Ontario%20Mens%20Survey%20Final%20Report.pdf

Myers, T., Bullock, S. L., Calzavara, L. M., Cockerill, R., & Marshall, V. W. (1997). Differences in sexual risk-taking behaviour with state of inebriation in an Aboriginal population in Ontario, Canada. *Journal of Studies in Alcohol, 58,* 312–322.

Naili, H., & Josey, S. (2005, August 11). Pastor faces sex charges. *The Toronto Star.*

Nakhaie, R., & Arnold, R. (2010). A four-year (1996–2000) analysis of social capital and health status of Canadians: The difference love makes. *Social Science and Medicine, 71,* 1037–1044.

Nappi, R. E., & Nappi, G. (2012). Neuroendocrine aspects of migraine in women. *Gynecological Endocrinology, 28*(1), 37–41.

Nappi, R. E., Wawra, K., & Schmitt, S. (2006). Hypoactive sexual desire disorder in postmenopausal women. *Gynecological Endocrinology, 22*(6), 318–323.

Narchi, H. (2003). Infantile masturbation mimicking paroxysmal disorders. *Journal of Pediatric Neurology, 1*(1), 43–45.

National Cancer Institute. (2012). *Breast cancer.* Retrieved from http://www.cancer.gov/cancertopics/types/breast

National Center for Biotechnology Information (NCBI). (2006, February 1). National Institute of Health. [Online]. www.ncbi.nlm.nih.gov/entrez/query.fcgi?=CMD=Search&db=homologene&term=SRY.

National Center for Transgender Equality. (2014). *Transgender terminology: updated January 2014.* Retrieved from http://transequality.org/Resources/TransTerminology_2014.pdf

National Institute of Allergy and Infectious Diseases. (2009). Herpevac trial for women. http://www3.niad.nih.gov/topics/genitalHerpes/research/herpevac/default.htm

Natsuaki, M. N., Leve, L. D., & Mendle, J. (2011). Going through the rites of passage: Timing and transition of menarche, childhood sexual abuse, and anxiety symptoms in girls. *Journal of Youth and Adolescence, 40*(10), 1357–1370.

NCPTUP/Cosmogirl.com. (2008). Sex and tech: Results from a survey of teens and young adults. http://www.thenational-campaign.org

Nelson, L. E., Thach, C. T., & Zhang, N. (2014). Gender equity predicts condom use among adolescent and young adult parents in Toronto, Canada. *The Canadian Journal of Human Sexuality, 23*(1), 19–26.

Netting, N. S., & Burnett, M. L. (2004). Twenty years of student sexual behavior: Subcultural adaptations to a changing health environment. *Adolescence, 39*(153), 19–38.

Newman, L. (2012). Questions about gender: Children with atypical gender development. *Disorders of Sex Development,* 31–39. DOI:10.1007/978-3-642-22964-0_4

Nickel, J. C., Elhilali, M., Vallancien, G., & ALF-ONE Study Group. (2005). Benign prostatic hyperplasia (BPH) and prostatitis: Prevalence of painful ejaculation in men with clinical BPH. *BJU International, 95*(4), 571–574.

Nicolosi, A., Laumann, E., Glasser, D., Moreira, E., & Paik, A. (2004). Sexual behavior and sexual dysfunctions after age 40: The global study of sexual attitudes and behaviors. *Urology, 64,* 991–997.

Ninomiya, M. M. (2010). Sexual health education in Newfoundland and Labrador schools: Junior high school teachers' experiences, coverage of topics, comfort levels and views about professional practice. *The Canadian Journal of Human Sexuality, 19*(1–2), 15–26.

Nobre, P. J., & Pinto-Gouveia, J. (2006). Dysfunctional sexual beliefs as vulnerability factors for sexual dysfunction. *Journal of Sex Research, 43*(1), 68–75.

Norris, S. M., Huss, M. T., & Palarea, R. E. (2011). A pattern of violence: Analyzing the relationship between intimate partner violence and stalking. *Violence and Victims, 26*(1), 103–115.

Norton-Hawk, M. (2004). A comparison of pimp- and non-pimp-controlled women. *Violence Against Women, 10*(2), 189–194.

Nosek, M. A. (2011). The person with a disability. In D. R. Maki & V. M. Tarvydas (Eds.). *The professional practice of rehabilitation counseling* (pp. 111–130). New York: Springer.

Nosko, A., Wood, E., & Desmarais, S. (2007). Unsolicited online sexual material: What affects our attitudes and likelihood to search for more? *Canadian Journal of Human Sexuality, 16*(1–2), 1–10.

Nour, N. W. (2000). Cited in Dreifus, C. (2000, July 11). A conversation with Dr. Nawal M. Nour: A life devoted to stopping the suffering of mutilation. *The New York Times* online.

Nova Scotia Department of Health and Wellness. (2014). *Sex? A healthy sexuality resource.* Retrieved from http://novascotia.ca/dhw/healthy-development/documents/11032_SexBook_En.pdf

Nurnberg, G., Hensley, P., & Heiman, J. (2008). Sildenafil treatment of women with antidepressant-associated sexual dysfunction: A randomized controlled trial. *Journal of the American Medical Association, 300*(4), 395–404.

Nussbaum, M. A. (2012, April 19). Ignore the stigma and focus on the need. *The New York Times* (Online).

Nuttbrock, L., et al. (2011). A further assessment of Blanchard's typology of homosexual versus non-homosexual or autogynephilic gender dysphoria. *Archives of Sexual Behavior, 40*(2), 247–257.

O'Doherty, T.O. (2011). Victimization on off-street sex industry workers. *Violence Against Women, 17*(7), 944–963.

O'Keefe, M. J., et al. (2003). Learning, cognitive, and attentional problems in adolescents born small for gestational age. *Pediatrics, 112*(2), 301–307.

O'Sullivan, L. F. (2003). The development of romantic relationships in adolescence. *Archives of Sexual Behavior, 32*(3), 292–294.

O'Sullivan, L. F., Byers, E. S., & Finkelman, L. (1998). A comparison of male and female college students' experiences of sexual coercion. *Psychology of Women Quarterly, 22*(2), 177–195. doi:10.1111/j.1471-6402.1998.tb00149.x

O'Sullivan, L. F., & Majerovich, J. (2008). Difficulties with sexual functioning in a sample of male and female late adolescent and young adult university students. *The Canadian Journal of Human Sexuality, 17* (3), 109–121.

Oakes, G. (1994, February 4). Lover who removed his condom jailed 45 days for sexual assault. *Toronto Star.*

O'Connor, J., Pisanski, K., Tigue, C., Fraccaro, P., & Feinberg, D. (2014). Perceptions of infidelity risk predict women's preferences for low male voice pitch in short-term over long-term relationship contexts. *Personality and Individual Differences, 56,* 73–77. DOI:10.1016/j.paid.2013.08.029

Offman, A., & Matheson, K. (2005). Sexual compatibility and sexual function in intimate relationships. *The Canadian Journal of Human Sexuality, 14*(1–2), 31–39.

Ogas, I., & Gaddam, S. (2012). *A billion wicked thoughts: What the Internet tells us about sexual relationships.* New York: Penguin Group USA.

Ogden, G., et al. (2007). Spiritual dimensions of sexual health: Broadening clinical perspectives of women's desire. In A. F. Owens & M. S. Tepper (Eds.), *Sexual health, 4* (pp. 131–152). Westport, CT: Praeger.

Ogilvie, M. (2008, June 19). New egg-freezing technique gives women more options. *Toronto Star,* p. A20.

Ohl, L.E. (2007). Essentials of female sexual dysfunctions from a sex therapy perspective. *Urologic Nursing, 27*(1), 57–63.

Olfson, M., Uttaro, T., Carson, W. H., & Tafesse, E. (2005). Male sexual dysfunction and quality of life in schizophrenia. *Journal of Clinical Psychiatry, 66*(3), 331–338.

Oliveira, M. (2010, March 24). When it comes to online dating, Canadians do it more than the rest of the world. Toronto: The Canadian Press.

Ophea, Healthy Schools Healthy Communities. (2013). Sexual health education in schools across Canada. Retrieved from https://www.ophea.net/sites/default/files/pdfs/advocacy/ADV_SexEdReportFINAL_31MY13.pdf

Options for Sexual Health. (2004). *An assessment of the effectiveness of sexual health education in B.C. schools.* Vancouver, BC: Options for Sexual Health.

Orchard, T., Farr, S., Macphail, S., Wender, C. & Young, D. (2012). Sex work in the Forest City: Experiences of sex work beginnings, types and clientele among women in London, Ontario. *Sexuality Research & Social Policy, 9*(4), 350–362. DOI:10.1007/s13178-012-0097-y

Orchowski, L. M., Mastroleo, N. R., & Borsari, B. (2012). Correlates of alcohol-related regretted sex among college students. *Psychology of Addictive Behaviors, 26*(4), 782–90. DOI:10.1037/a0027840

Ortega, V., Ojeda, P., Sutil, F., & Sierra, J. C. (2005). Culpabilidad sexual en adolescentes: Estudio de algunos factores relacionados. *Anales de Psicología, 21*(2), 268–275.

Osman, S. L. (2003). Predicting men's rape perceptions based on the belief that "no" really means "yes." *Journal of Applied Social Psychology, 33*(4), 683–692.

Ott, M. A., & Santelli, J. S. (2007) Abstinence and abstinence-only education. *Current Opinion in Obstetrics & Gynecology, 19*, 446–452.

Overbeek, G., Nelemans, S., Karremans, J., & Engels, R. (2013). The malleability of mate selection in speed-dating events. *Archives of Sexual Behavior, 42*(7), 1163–1171. doi:10.1007/s10508-012-0067-8

Owens, E. W., Behun, R. J., Manning, J. C., & Reid, R. C. (2012). The impact of Internet pornography on adolescents: Review of the research. *Sexual Addiction & Compulsivity: The Journal of Treatment & Prevention, 19*(2), 99–122.

Paintner, A., Williams, A. D., & Burd, L. (2012). Fetal alcohol spectrum disorders—Implications for child neurology, Part 2: Diagnosis and management. *Journal of Child Neurology, 27*(3), 355–362.

Pakhomou, S. M. (2006). Methodological aspects of telephone scatologia: A case study. *International Journal of Law and Psychiatry, 29*(3), 178–185.

Parent, M. C., Moradi, B., Rummell, C. M., & Tokar, D. M. (2011). Evidence of construct distinctiveness for conformity to masculine norms. *Psychology of Men and Masculinity, 12*(4), 354–367.

Park, N., Jin, B., & Jin, S. A. (2011). Effects of self-disclosure on relational intimacy in Facebook. *Computers in Human Behavior, 27*(5), 1974–1983.

Parker-Pope, T. (2008, February 5). No answers for men with prostate cancer. *The New York Times.* http://well.blogs.nytimes.com/2008/02/05/no-answers-for-men-with-prostate-cancer/?_php=true&_type=blogs&_r=0

Parr-LeFeuve, R., & Desmarais, S. (2005). Do young women use sexual pressure to initiate sex? Unpublished paper. University of Guelph, Dept. of Psychology.

Parrott, D., Zeichner, A., & Hoover, R. (2006). Sexual prejudice and anger network activation: Mediating role of negative affect. *Aggressive Behavior, 32*(1), 7–16.

Pasupathy, D., & Smith, G. C. (2005). The analysis of factors predicting antepartum stillbirth. *Minerva Ginecology, 57*(4), 397–410.

Patel, D., Gillespie, B., & Foxman, B. (2003). Sexual behavior of older women: results of a random-digit-dialing survey of 2000 women in the United States. *Sexually Transmitted Diseases, 30*, 216–220

Patriquin, M. (2007, October 22). Canada: A nation of bigots? *Maclean's*, 17–22.

Pauleta, J. R., Pereira, N. M., & Graca, L. M. (2010). Sexuality during pregnancy. *Journal of Sexual Medicine, 7*, 136–142.

Pek, N. K., & Senn, C. Y. (2004). Not wanted in the inbox! Evaluations of unsolicited and harassing e-mail. *Psychology of Women Quarterly, 28*, 204–214.

Peluso, P. R. (Ed.). (2008). *Infidelity.* Danvers, MA: CRC Press.

Penton-Voak, I. S., Jacobson, A., & Trivers, R. (2004). Population differences in attractiveness judgments of male and female faces: Comparing British and Jamaican samples. *Evolution and Human Behavior, 25*, 355–370.

Pereda, N., Guilera, G., Forns, M., & Gómez-Benito, J. (2009). The prevalence of child sexual abuse in community and student samples: A meta-analysis. *Clinical Psychology Review, 29*(4), 328–338. doi:]10.1016/j.cpr.2009.02.007

Perel, E. (2006). *Mating in captivity: Unlocking erotic intelligence.* New York, NY: Harper Collins.

Perez, K., Gadgil, M., & Dizon, D.S. (2009). Sexual ramifications of medical illness. *Clinical Obstetrics and Gynaecology, 52*(4), 691–701.

Peritz, I. (2005, September 23). Student leaves McGill over sports hazing ritual. *The Globe and Mail*, p. A9.

Peritz, I. (2011). Former Canadian general fined, demoted for affair. *Global and Mail*, July 21.

Perlman, D., & Sprecher, S. (2012). Sex, intimacy, and dating. In R. D. McAnulty (Ed.). *Sex in college: The things they don't write home about* (pp. 91–118). Santa Barbara, CA: ABC-CLIO, LLC.

Perreault, H. S., & Brennan, S. (2010). Criminal victimization in Canada 2009. *Juristat, 30*(2).

Perron, L., & Senikas, V. (2012). Female genital cutting/ mutilation: SOGC policy statement. *Journal of Obstetrics and Gynaecology of Canada, 34*, 197–200.

Petersen, J. L., & Shibley Hyde, J. (2011). Gender differences in sexual attitudes and behaviors: A review of meta-analytic results and large datasets. *Journal of Sex Research, 48*(2–3), 149–165.

Peterson, Z. D., Voller, E. K., Polusny, M. A., & Murdoch, M. (2010). Prevalence and consequences of adult sexual assault of men: Review of empirical findings and state of the literature. *Clinical Psychology Review, 31*(1), 1–24. doi:10.1016/j.cpr.2010.08.006

Petrunik, M. (2003). The hare and the tortoise: Dangerousness and sex offender policy in the United States and Canada. *Canadian Journal of Criminology & Criminal Justice, 45*(1), 43–72.

Pew Research Center. (2009). Teens and sexting: How and why minor teens are sending sexually suggestive nude or nearly nude images via text messaging. http://www.pewinternet.org/

Pew Research. (2014). *Global Attitudes Project. Morality interactive topline results.* Retrieved from http://www.pewglobal.org/files/2014/03/Morality-Topline-FINAL.pdf

Philaretou, A. G. (2006). Female exotic dancers: Intrapersonal and interpersonal perspectives. *Sexual Addiction & Compulsivity, 13*(1), 41–52.

Phipps, A. I., et al. (2011). Long-term use of continuous-combined estrogen-progestin hormone therapy and the risk of endometrial cancer. *Cancer Causes and Control, 22*(2), 1639–1646.

Picard, A. (2010, July 20). U.S., Canada lead world in prosecuting those who transmit AIDS virus. *Globe and Mail.* http://www.updatednews.ca/2010/07/21/u-s-canada-lead-world-in-prosecuting-those-who-transmit-aids-virus/

Piercy, J. (2008, January 12). Six charged in human trafficking ring. *The Toronto Star.* www.thestar.com/news/gta/.../six_charged_in_human_trafficking_ring.html

Pike, L. B. (2005, July 1). *Sexuality and your child.* MU Extension, University of Missouri–Columbia.

Pillard, R. C., & Weinrich, J. D. (1986). Evidence of familial nature of male homosexuality. *Archives of Sexual Behavior, 43*, 808–812.

Pinkerton, S. D., Bogart, L. M., Cecil, H., & Abramson, P. R. (2002). Factors associated with masturbation in collegiate sample. *Journal of Psychology & Human Sexuality, 14*(2–3), 103–121.

Pisanski, K., & Feinberg, D. (2013). Cross-cultural variation in mate preferences for averageness, symmetry, body size, and masculinity. *Cross-cultural Research, 47*(2), 162–197.

Planned Parenthood Federation of Canada. (1999). *A history of birth control in Canada.* Brochure. Ottawa: Planned Parenthood Federation of Canada.

Plant, E. A., Hyde, J. S., Keltner, D., & Devine, P. G. (2000). The gender stereotyping of emotions. *Psychology of Women Quarterly, 24*(1), 81–92.

Plaut, S. M. (2006). Consent to sexual relations. *Archives of Sexual Behavior, 35*(1), 101–103.

Plomin, R., & Asbury, K. (2005). Nature and nurture: Genetic and environmental influences on behavior. *Annals of the American Academy of Political and Social Science, 600,* 86–98.

Polansky, D. C. (2006). The big book of masturbation: From angst to zeal. *Journal of Sex & Marital Therapy, 32*(1), 75–78.

Pollack, H. A. (2001). Sudden infant death syndrome, maternal smoking during pregnancy, and the cost-effectiveness of smoking cessation intervention. *American Journal of Public Health, 91*(3), 432–436.

Pollack, L. M., Boyer, C. B., & Weinstein, N. D. (2013). Perceived risk for sexually transmitted infections aligns with sexual risk behavior with the exception of condom nonuse: data from a nonclinical sample of sexually active young adult women. *Sexually Transmitted Diseases, 40*(5), 388–394. doi: 10.1097/ OLQ.0b013e318283d2e5

Polusny, M. A., & Arbisi, P. A. (2006). Assessment of psychological distress and disability after sexual assault in adults. In G. Young, et al. (Eds.), *Psychological knowledge in court: PTSD, pain, and TBI* (pp. 97–125). Berlin, Germany: Springer Science 1 Business Media.

Potter, S. J., Moynihan, M. M., Stapleton, J. G., & Banyard, V. L. (2009). Empowering bystanders to prevent campus violence against women. *Violence Against Women, 15*(1), 106–121. doi:10.1177/1077801208327482

Potter, S. J., et al. (2009). Empowering bystanders to prevent campus violence against women. *Violence Against Women, 15*(1), 106–121.

Prakash, J., et al. (2010). Does androgyny have psychoprotective attributes? A cross-sectional community-based study. *Industrial Psychiatry Journal, 19*(2), 119–124.

Prentice, T. (2005). Alarming rates of HIV/AIDS for Canada's Aboriginal women. *The Canadian Women's Health Network Magazine, 8,* 1–4.

Preti, G., Wysocki, C. J., Barnhart, K. T., Sondheimer, S. J., & Leyden, J. J. (2003). Male axillary extracts contain pheromones that affect pulsatile secretion of luteinizing hormone and mood in women recipients. *Biology of Reproduction, 68*(6), 2107–2113.

Preti, G., et al. (1986). Human axillary secretions influence women's menstrual cycles: The role of donor extract of females. *Hormones and Behavior, 20,* 474–482.

Pron, N. (2007, September 11). Parlour's "manual release" ruled legal; charges thrown out in masturbation case. *Toronto Star,* p. A2.

Protogerou, C., & Johnson, B. T. (2014). Factors underlying the success of behavioral HIV-prevention interventions for adolescents: A meta-review. *AIDS and Behavior.* Published online: 06 June, 2014.

Provost, M. P., Kormos, C., Kosakoski, G., & Quinsey, V. L. (2006). Sociosexuality in women and preference for facial masculinization and somatotype in men. *Archives of Sexual Behaviour, 35*(3), 305–312.

Provost, M. P., Quinsey, V. L., & Troje, N. F. (2008). Differences in gait across the menstrual cycle and their attractiveness to men. *Archives of Sexual Behavior, 37*(4), 598–604.

Psychology Today. (2006, July 25.) www.psychologytoday.com/ images/.PT_MediaKit_Health_2006.pdf

Public Health Agency of Canada. (2008). *Canadian Guidelines for Sexual Health Education.* Catalogue No: HP40-25/2008E. Ottawa: Author. Retrieved from http://www.phac-aspc.gc.ca/ publicat/cgshe-ldnemss/pdf/guidelines-eng.pdf

Public Health Agency of Canada. (2008). *Canadian Perinatal Health Report,* 2008 Edition. Retrieved from http://www.phac-aspc .gc.ca/publicat/2008/cphr-rspc/pdf/cphr-rspc08-eng.pdf

Public Health Agency of Canada. (2008a). *Canadian guidelines for sexual health education.* Ottawa, ON: Public Health Agency of Canada.

Public Health Agency of Canada. (2008c). *Hepatitis B fact sheet.* Available: www.phac-aspc.gc.ca/hcai-iamss/bbp-pts/hepatitis/ hep_b_e.html

Public Health Agency of Canada. (2008d). *Genital human papillomavirus (HPV) infections. Canadian guidelines for sexually transmitted infections.* Ottawa, ON: Public Health Agency of Canada.

Public Health Agency of Canada. (2008e). *Genital herpes simplex virus (HSV) infections. Canadian guidelines on sexually transmitted infections.* Ottawa, ON: Public Health Agency of Canada.

Public Health Agency of Canada. (2008f). *Immigrants and refugees. Canadian guidelines on sexually transmitted infections.* Ottawa, ON: Public Health Agency of Canada.

Public Health Agency of Canada. (2008g). *Vaginal discharge (bacterial vaginosis, vulvovaginal candidiasis, trichomoniasis). Canadian guidelines on sexually transmitted infections.* Ottawa, ON: Public Health Agency of Canada.

Public Health Agency of Canada. (2009). *What mothers say: The Canadian Maternity Experiences Survey.* Ottawa, ON: Public Health Agency of Canada.

Public Health Agency of Canada. (2010). *Questions & answers: Gender identity in schools.* Ottawa, ON: Public Health Agency of Canada.

Public Health Agency of Canada. (2010a). *Pelvic inflammatory disease. Canadian guidelines on sexually transmitted infections.* Ottawa, ON: Public Health Agency of Canada. www.publichealth.gc.ca/sti

Public Health Agency of Canada. (2010b). *Primary care and sexually transmitted infection. Canadian guidelines for sexually transmitted infection.* Ottawa, ON: Public Health Agency of Canada.

Public Health Agency of Canada. (2010c). *The facts on the safety and effectiveness of HPV vaccine.* http://www.phac-aspc.gc.ca/std-mts/hpv-uph/fact-faits-vacc-eng-php

Public Health Agency of Canada. (2010d). *Canadian guidelines on sexually transmitted infections. Chlamydia infections.* Ottawa: Author. Retrieved from http://www.phac-aspc.gc.ca/std-mts/ sti-its/cgsti-ldcits/section-5-2-eng.php

Public Health Agency of Canada (PHAC). (2010a). *Questions & answers: Sexual orientation in schools.* Ottawa: Author. Retrieved from http://www.phac-aspc.gc.ca/std-mts/rp/so-os/index-eng. php

Public Health Agency of Canada (PHAC). (2010b). *Questions & answers: Gender identity in schools.* Ottawa: Author. Retrieved from http://www.phac-aspc.gc.ca/std-mts/rp/gi-is/index-eng.php

Public Health Agency of Canada. (2012a). *Questions and answers—Sexual health education for youth with physical disabilities*. Ottawa, ON: Public Health Agency of Canada.

Public Health Agency of Canada. (2012b). *Canadian hospitals maternity policies and practices survey*. Ottawa, ON: Public Health Agency of Canada.

Public Health Agency of Canada. (2012c). *Report on sexually transmitted infections in Canada: 2010*. Centre for Communicable Diseases and Infection Control.

Public Health Agency of Canada. (2012d). *Summary: Estimates of HIV prevalence and incidence in Canada, 2011*. Centre for Communicable Diseases and Infection Control. Retrieved from http://www.phac-aspc.gc.ca/aids-sida/publication/survreport/estimat2011-eng.php

Public Health Agency of Canada. (2012e). *Human immunodeficiency virus: HIV screening and testing guide*. Centre for Communicable Diseases and Infection Control. Retrieved from http://www.catie.ca/sites/default/files/EN_HIV-Screening-Guide-2013.pdf

Public Health Agency of Canada. (2013). *HIV and AIDS in Canada: Surveillance report to December 31, 2012*. Surveillance and Epidemiology Division, Centre for Communicable Diseases and Infection Control, Public Health Agency of Canada. Retrieved from http://publications.gc.ca/collections/collection_2014/aspc-phac/HP37-2-2012-eng.pdf

Public Health Agency of Canada. (2014a). *Population-specific status report: HIV/AIDS and other sexually transmitted and blood borne infections among youth in Canada*. Ottawa: Author. Retrieved from http://librarypdf.catie.ca/pdf/ATI-20000s/26485.pdf

Public Health Agency of Canada. (2014b). *Questions & answers: Inclusive practice in the prevention of sexually transmitted and blood borne infections among ethnocultural minorities*. Retrieved from http://www.catie.ca/sites/default/files/Inclusive-practice-in-the-prevention-of-STBBIs-among-ethnocultural-minorities.pdf

Pukall, C., Young, R., Roberts, M., Sutton, K., & Smith K. (2007). The vulvalgesiometer as a device to measure genital pressure-pain threshold. *Physiological Measurement, 28*, 1–8.

Pukall, C. F., Payne, K. A., Binik, Y. M., & Khalife, S. (2003). Pain measurement in vulvodynia. *Journal of Sex & Marital Therapy, 29*(s), 111–120.

Purdie, M. P., et al. (2011). The effects of acute alcohol intoxication, partner risk level, and general intention to have unprotected sex on women's sexual decision making with a new partner. *Experimental and Clinical Psychopharmacology, 19*(5), 378–388.

Pyne, J. (2014). Gender independent kids: A paradigm shift in approaches to gender non-conforming children. *The Canadian Journal of Human Sexuality, 23*(1), 1–8.

Quayle, E. (2008). Online sex offending: Psychopathology and theory. In D. R. Laws and W. T. O'Donohue (Eds.), *Sexual deviance: Theory, assessment, and treatment* (2nd ed., pp. 439–458). New York: Guilford Press.

Quayle, E. (2012). Pedophilia, child porn, and cyberpredators. In C. D. Bryant (Ed.). *The Routledge handbook of deviant behavior* (pp. 390–396). New York: Routledge.

Queen, C. (1996). *Real live nude girl: Chronicles of sex-positive culture*. Pittsburgh, PA: Cleis.

Quinsey, V. L. (2002). Evolutionary theory and animal behavior. *Legal and Criminological Psychology, 7*, 1–13.

Rabinowitz, S. R., Firestone, P., Bradford, J. M., & Greenberg, D. M. (2002). Prediction of recidivism in exhibitionists: Psychological, phallometric, and offense factors. *Sexual Abuse: Journal of Research & Treatment, 14*(4), 329–347.

Raichle, K., & Lambert, A. J. (2000). The role of political ideology in mediating judgments of blame in rape victims and their assailants: A test of the just world, personal responsibility, and legitimization hypotheses. *Personality & Social Psychology Bulletin, 26*(7), 853–863.

Raiford, J. L., Seth, P., & DiClemente, R. J. (2013). What girls won't do for love: Human immunodeficiency virus/sexually transmitted infections risk among young African-American women driven by a relationship imperative. *Journal of Adolescent Health, 52*(5), 566–571.

Ralph, D., & McNicholas, T. (2000). UK management guidelines for erectile dysfunction. *British Medical Journal, 321*, 499–503.

Ramsey, S., Sweeny, C., Fraser, M., & Oades, G. (2009). Pubic hair and sexuality: a review. *Journal of Sexual Medicine, 6*(8), 2102–2110. DOI:10.1111/j.1743-6109.2009.01307.x

Randall, H., & Byers, S. (2003). What is sex? Students' definitions of having sex, sexual partner, and unfaithful sexual behaviour. *The Canadian Journal of Human Sexuality, 12*, 87–96.

Rasmussen, P. R., & Kilborne, K. J. (2008). Sex in intimate relationships: Variations and challenges. In P. Peluso (Ed.), *Infidelity: A practitioners guide to working with couples in crisis*. New York: Routledge.

Ratelle, C., Carbonneau, N., Vallerand, R., & Mageau, G. (2013). Passion in the romantic sphere: A look at relational outcomes. *Motive and Emotion, 37*, 106–120. DOI:10.1007/s11031-012-9286-5

Rathus, S. A. (2011). *Childhood and adolescence: Voyages in development* (4th ed.) Belmont, CA: Cengage.

Rathus, S. A. (2014). *Childhood and adolescence: Voyages in development* (5th ed.). Belmont, CA: Cengage.

Ratner, P. A., Johnson, J. L., Shoveller, J. A., Chan, K., Martindale, S. L., Schilder, A. J., et al. (2003). Non-consensual sex experienced by men who have sex with men: Prevalence and association with mental health. *Patient Education and Counseling, 49*(1), 67–74.

Ravindran, L. N. & Stein, M. B. (2010). The pharmacologic treatment of anxiety disorders: A review of progress. *Journal of Clinical Psychiatry, 71*(7), 839–854.

Rawson, R. A., Washton, A., Domier, C. P., & Reiber, C. (2002). Drugs and sexual effects: Role of drug type and gender. *Journal of Substance Abuse Treatment, 22*(2), 103–108.

RCMP. (2011). *Human trafficking in Canada. RCMP Criminal Intelligence*. Ottawa, ON: Royal Canadian Mounted Police.

Reback, C. J., & Larkins, S. (2010). Maintaining a heterosexual identity: sexual meaning among a sample of heterosexually identified men who have sex with men. *Archives of Sexual Behavior, 39*, 766–773.

Rediger, C., & Muller, A. J. (2013). Parents' rationale for male circumcision. *Canadian Family Physician, 59*(2), e110–115.

Reece, M., et al. (2009). Prevalence and characteristics of vibrator use by men in the United States. *Journal of Sexual Medicine, 6*(7), 1867–1874.

Reece, M., Herbenick, D., Schick, V., Sanders, S. A., Dodge, B., & Fortenberry, J. D. (2010). Sexual behaviors, relationships, and perceived health among adult men in the United States: Results from a national probability sample. *Journal of Sexual Medicine, 7*(suppl. 5), 291–304.

Regina v. Butler. (1992). 1 S.C.R. 452.

Reinisch, J. M. (1990). *The Kinsey Institute new report on sex: What you must know to be sexually literate.* New York: St. Martin's Press.

Reis, H. T., & Aron, A. (2008). Love: What is it, why does it matter, and how does it operate? *Perspectives on Psychological Science, 3*(1), 80–86.

Reis, H. T., Maniaci, M. R., Caprariello, P. A., Eastwick, P. W., & Finkel, E. L. (2011). Familiarity does indeed promote attraction in live interaction. *Journal of Personality and Social Psychology, 101*(3), 557–570.

Reiss, I. (1997). *Solving America's sexual crises.* New York, NY: Prometheus Books.

Reissing, E. D. (2012). Consultation and treatment history and causal attributions in an online sample of women with lifelong and acquired vaginismus. *Journal of Sexual Medicine, 9*(1), 251–258.

Reissing, E. K., Binik, Y. M., Khalife, S., Cohen, D., & Amsel, R. (2004). Vaginal spasm, pain, and behavior: An empirical investigation of the diagnosis of vaginismus. *Archives of Sexual Behavior, 33*(1), 5–17.

Rempel, J. K., & Baumgartner, B. (2003). The relationship between attitudes towards menstruation and sexual attitudes, desires, and behavior in women. *Archives of Sexual Behavior, 32*(2), 155–163.

Resick, P. A. (2003). Post hoc reasoning in possible cases of child sexual abuse: Just say no. *Clinical Psychology: Science & Practice, 10*(3), 349–351.

Reuters. (2006, March 17). When it comes to sex and romance. *National Post*, p. A6.

Rhoades, G. K., Kamp Dush, C. M., Atkins, D. C., Stanley, S. M., & Markman, H. J. (2011). Breaking up is hard to do: The impact of unmarried relationship dissolution on mental health and life satisfaction. *Journal of Family Psychology, 25*(3), 366–374.

Ribner, D. S., & Kleinplatz, P. J. (2007). The hole in the sheet and other myths about sexuality and Judaism. *Sexual and Relationship Therapy, 22*(4), 445–456.

Riccardi, R., Szabo, C.M., & Yribarren-Poullos, A. (2007). Sexuality and spinal cord injury. *Nursing Clinics of North America, 42*, 675–684.

Ricci, E., Parazzini, F., & Pardi, G. (2000). Caesarean section and antiretroviral treatment. *The Lancet, 355*(9202), 496–502.

Richardson, H. et al. (2003). The natural history of type specific human papillomavirus infections in female university students. *Cancer Epidemiology, Biomarkers and Prevention, 12*, 485–490.

Richters, J. (2007). Researching sex between women. Paper presented at the Proceedings of the World Association of Sexual Health XVIII Congress, Sydney, Australia.

Richters, J. de Visser, R., Rissel, C. & Smith, A. (2006). Sexual practices at last heterosexual encounter and occurrence of orgasm in a national sample. *Journal of Sex Research, 43*(3), 217–226.

Richters, J., Hendry, O. L., & Kippax, S. (2003). When safe sex isn't safe. *Culture, Health & Sexuality, 5*(1), 37–52.

Richters, J., Smith, A., de Visser, R., Grulich, A., & Rissle, C. (2006). Circumcision in Australia: Prevalence and effects on sexual health. *International Journal of STD, 17*, 547–554.

Richters, J. et al. (2003). Autoerotic, esoteric and other sexual practices engaged in by a representative sample of adults. *Australian and New Zealand Journal of Public Health, 27*(2), 180–190.

Riddell, L., Varto, H., & Hodgson, Z. G. (2010). Smooth talking: The phenomenon of pubic hair removal in women. *The Canadian Journal of Human Sexuality, 19*(3), 121–130.

Riedmann, A., Lamanna, M., & Nelson, A. (2003). *Marriages and families* (1st Canadian ed.). Toronto: Thomson Canada.

Rieger, G., Linsenmeier, J. A. W., Gygax, L., & Bailey, J. M. (2008). Sexual orientation and childhood gender nonconformity: Evidence from home videos. *Developmental Psychology, 44*(1), 46–58.

Riggio, R. E., & Woll, S. B. (1984). The role of nonverbal cues and physical attractiveness in the selection of dating partners. *Journal of Social and Personal Relationships, 1*, 347–357.

Rimm, E. (May 2000). Lifestyle may play role in potential for impotence. Presented at the annual meeting of the American Urological Association, Atlanta, GA.

Robbins, C. L., et al. (2011). Prevalence, frequency, and associations of masturbation with partnered sexual behaviors among U.S. adolescents. *Archives of Pediatrics & Adolescent Medicine, 165*(12), 1087–1093.

Roberts, T. A., Auinger, P., & Klien, J. D. (2005). Intimate partner abuse and the reproductive health of sexually active female adolescents. *Journal of Adolescent Health, 36*(5), 380–385.

Roesler, A., & Witztum, E. (2000). Pharmacotherapy of paraphilias in the next millennium. *Behavioral Sciences & the Law, 18*(1), 43–56.

Rogala, C., & Tydén, T. (2003). Does pornography influence young women's sexual behavior? *Women's Health Issues, 13*(1), 39–43.

Romero-Daza, N., Weeks, M., & Singer, M. (2005). Conceptualizing the impact of indirect violence on HIV risk among women involved in street-level prostitution. *Aggression and Violent Behavior, 10*(2), 153–170.

Ronis, S. T., & Lebouthillier, D. M. (2013). University students' attitudes toward purchasing condoms. *The Canadian Journal of Human Sexuality, 22*(2), 86–94.

Rosario, M., Schrimshaw, E. W., & Hunter, J. (2011). Different patterns of sexual identity development over time: implications for the psychological adjustment of lesbian, gay, and bisexual youth. *Journal of Sex Research, 48*(1), 3–15

Roscoe, W. (2000). *Changing ones: Third and fourth genders in native North America.* New York: Palgrave Macmillan.

Rosky, C. J. (2009). Like father, like son: Homosexuality, parenthood, and the gender of homophobia. *Yale Journal of Law & Feminism, 20*, 257.

Rospenda, K. M., Richman, J. A., Ehmke, J. L. Z., & Zlatoper, K. W. (2005). Is workplace harassment hazardous to your health? *Journal of Business and Psychology, 20*(1), 95–110.

Ross, L. E. (2005). Perinatal mental health in lesbian mothers: A review of potential risk and protective factors. *Women & Health, 41*(3).

Rotermann, M. (2005). Sex, condoms, and STDs among young people. *Health Reports, 16*(3). Statistics Canada: Analytical Studies and Reports. Retrieved from www.statcan.ca/english/ads/82-003-XPE/pdf/16-3-04.pdf

Rotermann, M. (2009). Trends in teen sexual behaviour and condom use. *Health Reports, 19*(3), 1–5.

Rotermann, M. (2012). Sexual behaviour and condom use of 15- to 24-year-olds in 2003 and 2009/2010. *Health Reports, 23*(1), 1–6.

Rotermann, M., Langlois, K. A., Severini, A., & Totten, S. (2013). Prevalence of chlamydia trachomatis and herpes simplex virus type 2: Results from the 2009 to 2011 Canadian Health Measures Survey. *Health Reports, 24*(4), 1–15.

Rotermann, M., & McKay, A. (2009). Condom use at last sexual intercourse among unmarried, not living common-law 20-to-34 year-old Canadian young adults. *Canadian Journal of Human Sexuality, 18*(3), 75–88

Roughgarden, J. (2004). *Evolution's rainbow: Diversity, gender, and sexuality in nature and people.* Berkeley: University of California Press.

Rowland, D. L., & Incrocci, L. (2008). *Handbook of sexual and gender identity disorders.* Hoboken, NJ: Wiley.

Rubenson, B., Hanh, L. T., Höjer, B., & Johansson, E. (2005). Young sex-workers in Ho Chi Minh City telling their life stories. *Childhood: A Global Journal of Child Research, 12*(3), 391–411.

Rubin, H., & Campbell, L. (2012). Day-to-day changes in intimacy predict heightened relationship passion, sexual occurrence, and sexual satisfaction: A dyadic diary analysis. *Social Psychological and Personality Science, 3*(2), 224–231.

Rushowy, K. (2008, February 22). Safe Schools Action Team to advise education ministry. *Toronto Star,* p. A9.

Russell, S. T., Clarke, T. J., & Clary, J. (2009). Are teens "post gay"? Contemporary adolescents' sexual identity labels. *Journal of Youth and Adolescence, 38,* 884–890.

Rye, B. J. (2001, June). Sex differences in sexual attitudes and sexual behaviours of a sample of university students. Poster session presented at the annual Guelph Sexuality Conference, Guelph, ON.

Rye, B. J., Elmslie, P., & Chalmers, A. (2007). Meeting a transsexual person: Experiences within a classroom setting. *Canadian Online Journal of Queer Studies in Education, 3*(1). Retrieved from https://jps.library.utoronto.ca/index.php/jqstudies/article/viewFile/3269/1444

Rye, B. J., & Meaney, G. (2007). Voyeurism: It is good as long as we do not get caught. *International Journal of Sexual Health, 19*(1), 47–56.

Rye, B. J., & Meaney, G. (2008). Self-defence, sexism, and etiological beliefs: Predictors of attitudes toward gay and lesbian adoption. *Journal of GLBT Family Studies, 6*(1), 1–24. DOI:10.1080/15504280903472485

Rye, B. J., Yessis, J., Brunk, T., McKay, A., Morris, S., & Meaney, G. (2008). Outcome evaluation of Girl Time: Grade 7/8 Healthy Sexuality Program. *Canadian Journal of Human Sexuality, 17*(1–2), 15–36.

Sadalla, E. K., Kenrick, D. T., & Vershure, B. (1987). Dominance and heterosexual attraction. *Journal of Personality and Social Psychology, 52,* 730–738.

Sadownik, L.A. (2014). Etiology, diagnosis, and clinical management of vulvodynia. *International Journal of Women's Health, 6,* 437–449. doi:http://dx.doi.org/10.2147/IJWH.S37660

Saewyc, E. M., Poon, C., Wang, N., Homma, Y., Smith, A., & The McCreary Centre Society. (2007). *Not yet equal: The health of lesbian, gay, & bisexual youth in BC.* Vancouver, BC: The McCreary Centre Society.

Saewyc, E. M., Skay, C., Richens, K., Reis, E., Poon, C., & Murphy, A. (2006b). Sexual orientation, sexual abuse, and HIV-risk behaviors among adolescents in the Pacific Northwest. *American Journal of Public Health, 96*(6), 1104–1110.

Saewyc, E. M., Skay, C. L., Pettingell, S. L., Reis, E. A., Bearinger, L., Resnick, M., et al. (2006a). Hazards of stigma: The sexual and physical abuse of gay, lesbian, and bisexual adolescents in the United States and Canada. *Child Welfare, 85*(2), 195–213.

Saewyc, E. M., Taylor, D., Homma, Y., & Ogilvie, G. (2008). Trends in sexual health and risk behaviours among adolescent students in British Columbia. *Canadian Journal of Human Sexuality, 17*(1–2), 1–13.

Saewyc, E., et al. (2009). Protective factors in the lives of bisexual adolescents in North America. *American Journal of Public Health, 94,* 110–117.

Sagan, C., & Dryan, A. (1990, April 22). The question of abortion: A search for answers. *Parade Magazine,* 4–8.

Sagarin, B. J., Becker, D. V., Guadagno, R. E., Nicastle, D., & Millevoi, A. (2003). Sex differences (and similarities) in jealousy. The moderating influence of infidelity experience and sexual orientation of the infidelity. *Evolution & Human Behavior, 24*(1), 17–23.

Sagarin, B. J., et al. (2012). Sex differences in jealousy: A meta-analytic examination. *Evolution and Human Behavior.* Retrieved from http://dx.doi.org/10.1016/j.evolhumbehav.2012.02.006 (Accessed September 15, 2012).

Saigal, S., et al. (2006). Transition of extremely low-birth-weight infants from adolescence to young adulthood. *Journal of the American Medical Association, 295*(6), 667–675.

Sakaluk, J. K., & Milhausen, R. R. (2012). Factors influencing university students' explicit and implicit sexual double standards. *Journal of Sex Research, 49*(5), 464–476.

Saks, B. R. (2008). Common issues in female sexual dysfunction. *Psychiatric Times, 25*(5), 2.

Saleh, F. M. (2009). Pharmacological treatment of paraphilic sex offenders. In F. M. Saleh et al. (Eds.), *Sex offenders: Identification, risk assessment, treatment, and legal issue* (pp. 189–210). New York: Oxford University Press.

Salehi, R. et al., (2010). Predictors of exposure to sexual health education among teens who are newcomers to Canada. *The Canadian Journal of Human Sexuality, 19*(4), 157–167.

Sales, J. M., Lang, D. L., DiClemente, R. J., Latham, T. P., Wingood, G. M., Hardin, J. W., & Rose, E. S. (2012). The mediating role of partner communication frequency on condom use among African American adolescent females participating in an HIV prevention intervention. *Health Psychology, 31*(1), 63–69. doi:10.1037/a0025073

Salisbury, C., & Fisher, W. (2013). "Did you come?" A qualitative exploration of gender differences in beliefs, experiences, and concerns regarding female orgasm occurrence during heterosexual sexual interactions. *Journal of Sex Research,* Advance online. DOI:10.1080/00224499.2013.838934

Salska, I., et al. (2008). Conditional mate preferences: Factors influencing preferences for height. *Personality and Individual Differences, 44*(1), 203–215.

Sand, M., & Fisher, W. A. (2007). Women's endorsement of models of female sexual response: the nurse's sexuality study. *Journal of Sexual Medicine, 4,* 708–719.

Sanders, S. A., Yarber, W. L., Kaufman, E. L., Crosby, R. A., Graham, C. A., & Milhausen, R. R. (2012). Condom use errors and problems: A global view. *Sexual Health, 9*(1), 81–95.

Sanders, T. (2005). "It's just acting": Sex workers' strategies for capitalizing on sexuality. *Gender, Work & Organization, 12*(4), 319–342.

Sangrador, J. L., & Yela, C. (2000). "What is beautiful is loved": Physical attractiveness in love relationships in a representative sample. *Social Behavior & Personality, 28*(3), 207–218.

Santtila, P., Sandnabba, N. K., Alison, L., & Nordling, N. (2002). Investigating the underlying structure in sadomasochistically oriented behavior. *Archives of Sexual Behavior, 31*(2), 185–196.

Sarrel, P., & Masters, W. (1982). Sexual molestation of men by women. *Archives of Sexual Behavior, 11,* 117–131.

Satterwhite, C., & Douglas, J. (2013). Epidemiology and prevention and control programs for chlamydia. In Black, C. (Ed.), *Chlamydial infections: A clinical and public health perspective. Issues in infectious diseases, 7*, (pp. 9–24).

Savage, L. (2008, August 4). Stifling free speech globally. *Maclean's*, 26–29.

Save the Children. (2011). *State of the world's mothers 2011.* Westport, CT: Save the Children. Retrieved from www.savethechildren.org

Savic, I., Garcia-Falgueras, A., & Swaab, D. F. (2010). Sexual differentiation of the human brain in relation to gender identity and sexual orientation. In I. Savic (Ed.), *Sex differences in the human brain, Their underpinnings and implications. Progress in brain research, 186* (pp. 41–64). New York: Elsevier.

Savic, I., & Lindstrom, P. (2008). PET and MRI show differences in cerebral asymmetry and functional connectivity between homo- and heterosexual subjects. *Proceedings of the National Academy of Sciences, 105*(27), 9403–9408.

Savin-Williams, R. C. (2005). *The new gay teenager.* Cambridge, MA: Harvard University Press.

Savin-Williams, R. C. (2006). Who's gay? Does it matter? *Current Directions in Psychological Science, 15*(1), 40–44.

Savin-Williams, R. C., & Diamond, L. M. (2000). Sexual identity trajectories among sexual-minority youths: Gender comparisons. *Archives of Sexual Behavior, 29*(6), 607–627.

Savin-Williams, R., Joyner, K., & Rieger, G. (2012). Prevalence and stability of self-reported sexual orientation identity during young adulthood. *Archives of Sexual Behavior, 41*(1), 103–110.

Schlichter, A. (2004). *Contesting "straights," "lesbians," "queer heterosexuals," and the critique of heteronormativity.* Binghamton, NY: The Haworth Press.

Schmidt, S. R., Bonner, B. L., & Chaffin, M. (2012). Understanding and treating adolescents with illegal sexual behavior. In P. Goodyear-Brown (Ed.). *Handbook of child sexual abuse: Identification, assessment, and treatment* (pp. 469–485). Hoboken, NJ: Wiley.

Schmitt, D., Jonason, P. K., Byerley, G. J., Flores, S. D., Illbeck, B. E., O'Leary, K. N., & Qudrat, A. (2012). A reexamination of sex differences in sexuality: New studies reveal old truths. *Current Directions in Psychological Science, 21*(2), 135–139.

Schmitt, D., Shackelford, T., Duntley, J., et al. (2002). Is there an early-30s peak in female sexual desire? Cross-sectional evidence from the United States and Canada. *The Canadian Journal of Human Sexuality, 11*, 1–18.

Schmitt, D. P. (2003). Universal sex differences in the desire for sexual variety: Tests from 52 nations, 6 continents, and 13 islands. *Journal of Personality and Social Psychology, 85*(1), 85–104.

Schmitt, M. T., Branscombe, N. R., & Postmes, T. (2003). Women's emotional responses to the pervasiveness of gender discrimination. *European Journal of Social Psychology, 33*(3), 297–312.

Schneider, J. P. (2005). Addiction is addiction is addiction. *Sexual Addiction & Compulsivity, 12*(2/3), 75–77.

Schneider, J.P. & Irons, R.R. (2001). Assessment and treatment of addictive sexual disorders: relevance of chemical dependency relapse. *Substance Use and Misuse, 36*, 1795–1820.

Schneider, M., Baker, S., & Stermac, L. (2002). Sexual harassment experiences of psychologists and psychological associates during their graduate school training. *The Canadian Journal of Human Sexuality, 11*, 159–170.

Schneidewind-Skibbe, A., Hayes, R. D., Koochaki, P. E., Meyer, J., & Dennerstein, L. (2007). The frequency of sexual intercourse reported by women: A review of community-based studies and factors limiting their conclusions. *Journal of Sexual Medicine, 5*(2), 301–335.

Schober, J. M., et al. (2005). Leuprolide acetate suppresses pedophilic urges and arousability. *Archives of Sexual Behavior, 34*(6), 691–705.

Schover, L. R., Fouladi, R. T., Warneke, C. L., Neese, L., Klein, E. A., Zippe, C., et al. (2004). Seeking help for erectile dysfunction after treatment for prostate cancer. *Archives of Sexual Behavior, 33*(5), 443–454.

Schrader, A. M., & Wells, K. (2007). *Challenging silence, challenging censorship: Inclusive resources, strategies and policy directives for addressing bisexual, gay, lesbian, trans-identified, and two-spirited realities in school and public libraries.* Ottawa: Canadian Teachers' Federation.

Schröder, F. H., et al. (2009). Screening and prostate-cancer mortality in a randomized European study. *New England Journal of Medicine, 360*, 1320–1328.

Schrut, A. (2005). A psychodynamic (nonoedipal) and brain function hypothesis regarding a type of male sexual masochism. *Journal of the American Academy of Psychoanalysis and Dynamic Psychiatry, 33*(2), 333–349.

Schultheiss, D., & Glina, S. (2010). Highlights from the history of sexual medicine. *Journal of Sexual Medicine, 7*(6), 2031–2043. doi:10.1111/j.1743-6109.2010.01866.x

Schwartz, P., & Young, L. (2009). Sexuality and sexual satisfaction in committed relationships. *Research and Social Policy: Journal of NSRC, 6*(1), 1–17.

Sciolino, E., & Mekhennet, S. (2008, June 11). In Europe, debate over Islam and virginity. *The New York Times.* http://www.nytimes.com/2008/06/11/world/europe/11virgin.html?pagewanted=all

Scott, J., & Humphreys, T. P. (2007, June). Parents as a source of sexual education for their physically disabled children. Poster presentation at the annual Guelph Sexuality Conference, Guelph, Ontario.

Seligman, L., & Hardenburg, S. A. (2000). Assessment and treatment of paraphilias. *Journal of Counseling & Development, 78*(1), 107–113.

Semans, J. (1956). Premature ejaculation: A new approach. *Southern Medical Journal, 49*, 353–358.

Semp, D. (2011). Questioning heteronormativity: Using queer theory to inform research and practice with mental health services. *Psychology and Sexuality, 2*(1), 69–86.

Senn, C. Y., & Desmarais, S. (2001). Are our recruitment practices for sex studies working across gender? The effect of topic and gender of recruiter on participation rates of university men and women. *Journal of Sex Research, 38*(2), 111–117.

Senn, C. Y., & Desmarais, S. (2006). A new wrinkle on an old concern: Are the new ethics review requirements for explicit warnings in consent forms affecting the results of sexuality research? *The Canadian Journal of Human Sexuality, 15*(3–4), 123–132.

Senn, C. Y., Desmarais, S., Verberg, N., & Wood, E. (2000). Predicting coercive sexual behavior across the lifespan in a random sample of Canadian men. *Journal of Social & Personal Relationships, 17*(1), 93–115. doi:10.1177/0265407500171005

Servais, L. (2006). Sexual health care in persons with intellectual disabilities. *Mental Retardation and Developmental Disabilities Research Reviews, 12*(1), 48–56.

Seth, P., Wingood, G. M., DiClemente, R. J., & Robinson, L. S. (2011). Alcohol use as a marker for risky sexual behaviors and biologically confirmed sexually transmitted infections among young adult African American women. *Women's Health Issues, 21*(2), 130–135. doi: 10.1016/j.whi.2010.10.005

Sethna, C. (1994). Nature, natural, naturalist: Nature study and the teaching of biological reproduction in Ontario, 1900–1930. *Canadian Journal of Human Sexuality, 3*(3), 191–98.

Sethna, C. (2010). Animal sex: Purity education and the naturalization of the abstinence agenda. *Sex Education, 10*(3), 267–279.

Seto, M. C. (2009). Pedophilia. *The Annual Review of Clinical Psychology, 5*, 391–407.

Seto, M. C., & Barbaree, H. E. (2001). Paraphilias. In V. B. Van Hasseit & M. Hersen (Eds.), *Aggression & violence: An introductory text* (pp. 198–213). New York: Allyn & Bacon.

Seto, M. C., Cantor, J. M., & Blanchard, R. (2006). Child pornography offenses are a valid diagnostic indicator of pedophilia. *Journal of Abnormal Psychology, 115*(3), 610–615.

Seto, M. C., & Eke, A. W. (2005). The criminal histories and later offending of child pornography offenders. *Sexual Abuse: A Journal of Research and Treatment, 17*(2), 201–210.

Seto, M. C., Maric, A., & Barbaree, H. E. (2000). The role of pornography in the etiology of sexual aggression. *Aggression and Violent Behavior, 6*, 35–53.

Seto, M. C., Maric, A., & Barbaree, H. E. (2001). The role of pornography in the etiology of sexual aggression. *Aggression and Violent Behavior, 6*, 35–53.

Sex Information and Education Council of Canada (SIEC-CAN). (2010). *Sexual health education in the schools: Questions and answers* (3rd ed.). Toronto: SIECCAN.

Sexual assault plea shortens sentence. (1994, June 1). *The Guelph Mercury.*

Seymour, A. (2008, August 29). Teacher found guilty of sexual assault low risk to re-offend, psychiatrist says. *The Ottawa Citizen.*

Shackelford, T. K., Goetz, A. T., Buss, D. M., Euler, H. A., & Hoier, S. (2005). When we hurt the ones we love: Predicting violence against women from men's mate retention. *Personal Relationships, 12*(4), 447–463.

Shakespeare, T. (2000). Disabled sexuality: towards rights and recognition. *Sexuality and Disability, 18*, 159–166.

Shamloul, R. (2010). Natural aphrodisiacs. *Journal of Sexual Medicine, 7*, 39–49.

Shannon, K., & Celeste, J. (2010). Violence, condom negotiation, and HIV/STI risk among sex workers. *Journal of the American Medical Association, 304*(5), 573–574.

Shannon, K., Kerr, T., Strathdee, S. A., Shovellor, J., Montaner, J. S., & Tyndall, M. W. (2009). Prevalence and structural correlates of gender based violence among a prospective cohort of female sex workers. *BMJ: British Medical Journal, 339*, b2939. doi:10.1136/bmj.b2939.

Sharlip, I. (2005). Diagnosis and treatment of premature ejaculation: The physician's perspective. *Journal of Sexual Medicine, Supple. 2*, 103–109.

Shaughnessy, K., Byers, E. S., & Walsh, L. (2011). Online sexual activity experience of heterosexual students: Gender similarities and differences. *Archives of Sexual Behavior, 40*(2), 419–427. doi:10.1007/s10508-010-9629-9.

Shaver, F. M. (1996a). Prostitution: On the dark side of the service industry. In T. Fleming (Ed.), *Post critical criminology* (pp. 42–45). Scarborough, ON: Prentice Hall.

Shaver, F. M. (1996b). The regulation of prostitution: Setting the morality trap. In B. Schissel & L. Mahood, *Social control in Canada* (pp. 204–226). Toronto: Oxford University Press.

Shaver, F. M. (2002, November). Prostitution portraits: A cautionary tale. Paper presented at the Annual Meeting of the Society for the Scientific Study of Sexuality, Montreal.

Shaver, F. M. (2005). Sex work research: Methodological and ethical challenges. *Journal of Interpersonal Violence, 20*(3), 296–319.

Shaver, F. M., Lewis, J. & Maticka-Tyndale, E. (2011). Rising to the challenge: Addressing the concerns of people working in the sex industry. *Canadian Review of Sociology, 48*(1), 47–65.

Shaw, J. (2007). Look in the phonebook under "A": Women's experiences in attempting to access abortion services in Canadian hospitals. Paper presented at the Guelph Sexuality Conference, Guelph, Ontario.

Sherer, R. (2012). The future of HIV care in the USA. *Sexually Transmitted Infections, 88*, 106–111.

Sherwin, B. B., Gelfand, M. M., & Brender, W. (1985). Androgen enhances sexual motivation in females: A prospective, crossover study of sex steroid administration in the surgical menopause. *Psychosomatic Medicine, 47*, 339–351.

Shibley Hyde, J., & Durik, A. M. (2000). Gender differences in erotic plasticity—Evolutionary or sociocultural forces? Comment on Baumeister (2000). *Psychological Bulletin, 126*, 375–379.

Shields, S. A., & Dicicco, E. C. (2011). The social psychology of sex and gender. *Psychology of Women Quarterly, 35*(3), 491–499.

Shields, S. A., Wong, T., Mann, J., et al. (2004). Prevalence and correlates of chlamydia infection in Canadian street youth. *Journal of Adolescent Health, 34*(5), 384–390.

Shifren, J. L., et al. (2000). Transdermal testosterone treatment in women with impaired sexual function after oophorectomy. *New England Journal of Medicine, 343*(10), 682–688.

Shirpak, K. R., Maticka-Tyndale, E., & Chinichian. (2007). Iranian immigrants' perceptions of sexuality in Canada: A symbolic interactionist approach. *The Canadian Journal of Human Sexuality, 16*, 113–128.

Shorter, E. (2005). *Written in the flesh: A history of desire.* Toronto: University of Toronto Press.

Shoveller, J. A., Johnson, J. L., Langille, D. B., & Mitchell, T. (2004). Socio-cultural influences on young people's sexual development. *Social Science & Medicine, 59*(3), 473–487.

SIECUS. (2014). *Support comprehensive sex education & adolescent sexual health promotion.* New York: Author. Retrieved from http://siecus.org/_data/n_0001/resources/live/CSEFactsheet.pdf

Siegfried, N., Muller, M., Deeks, J., Volmink, T. (2009). Male circumcision for prevention of heterosexual acquisition in men. *Cochrane Database System Review.* April 15, (2): cdoo3362

Silverthorne, Z. A., & Quinsey, V. L. (2000). Sexual partner age preferences of homosexual and heterosexual men and women. *Archives of Sexual Behavior, 29*, 67–76.

Sims, C. S., Drasgow, F., & Fitzgerald, L. F. (2005). The effects of sexual harassment on turnover in the military: Time-dependent modeling. *Journal of Applied Psychology, 90*(6), 1141–1152.

Singh, D., Vidaurri, M., Zambarano, R. J., & Dabbs, J. M., Jr. (1999). Lesbian erotic role identification: Behavioral, morphological, and hormonal correlates. *Journal of Personality and Social Psychology, 76*(6), 1035–1049.

Sinha, M. (2013). Measuring violence against women. *Juristat.* Statistics Canada catalogue no. 85-002-x. Retrieved from http://www.statcan.gc.ca/pub/85-002-x/2013001/article/11766-eng.pdf

Sipski, M. L., Alexander, C. J., & Rosen, R. (2001). Sexual arousal and orgasm in women. *Annals of Neurology, 49*(1), 35–44.

Slane, A. (2009). Sexting, teens, and a proposed offense of invasion of privacy. Iposgoode: Intellectual Property Law and Technology Program. Retrieved from http://www.iposgoode.ca

Small, P. (2004, June 30). Used drug for sex assault. *The Toronto Star*, p. B7.

Small, P. (2007, December 28). Teacher scarred by charges. *Toronto Star*, p. A10.

Smith, A., Saewyc, E., Albert, M., MacKay, L., Northcott, M., and The McCreary Centre Society. (2007). *Against the odds: A profile of marginalized and street-involved youth in BC*. Vancouver, BC: The McCreary Centre Society.

Smith, A., Stewart D., Peled, M., Poon, C., Saewyc, E. and the McCreary Centre Society (2009). *A picture of health: Highlights from the 2008 BC Adolescent Health Survey*. Vancouver, BC: McCreary Centre Society.

Smith, D. K., et al. (2010). Male circumcision in the United States for the prevention of HIV infection and other adverse health outcomes: Report from a CDC consultation. *Public Health Reports, 125*(Suppl. 1), 72–82.

Smith, Y. L. S., Van Goozen, S. H. M., Kuiper, A. J., & Cohen-Kettenis, P. T. (2005). Sex reassignment: Outcomes and predictors of treatment for adolescent and adult transsexuals. *Psychological Medicine, 35*(1), 89–99.

Smoak, L., & Murnen, S. (2011). Gender, self-objectification and pubic hair removal. *Sex Roles, 65*(6/7), 506–517.

Smylie, L., Medaglia, S., & Maticka-Tyndale, E. (2006). The effect of social capital and socio-demographics on adolescent risk and sexual health behaviours. *The Canadian Journal of Human Sexuality, 15*(2), 95–112.

Smylie, L., et al. (2011). Pilot-test and validation of a set of indicators of sexual health among young people in Canada. Abstract presented at the 20th World Congress of Sexual Health, Glasgow, United Kingdom, June 12–16, 2011.

Soble, A. (2009). A history of erotic philosophy. *Journal of Sex Research, 46*(2), 104–120.

Social Security Administration USA. (n.d.). Separate program for abstinence education. *Social Security Act*, Section 5.10. Retrieved from http://www.ssa.gov/OP_Home/ssact/title05/0510.htm#ft23

Society of Obstetricians and Gynaecologists of Canada. (2006). Sexuality and child development. SexualityAndU.ca. Ottawa: Society of Obstetricians and Gynaecologists of Canada. Retrieved from http://www.sexualityandu.ca/health-care-professionals/sexuality-and-child-development

Society of Obstetricians and Gynaecologists of Canada. (2008, June 25). Media advisories: Rising C-section rates add risks during childbirth and place excess strain on the healthcare system, warn. *Canadian obstetricians*. Retrieved from www.sogc.org/media/advisories-20080625_e.asp

SOGC. (2006). Canadian consensus conference on menopause, 2006 update. *Journal of Obstetrics and Gynaecology Canada: JOGC, 171*, 57–59.

Solursh, D. S., et al. (2003). The human sexuality education of physicians in North American medical schools. *Journal of Impotence Research, 15*(suppl), 541–545.

Special, W. P., & Li-Barber, K. T. (2012). Self-disclosure and student satisfaction with Facebook. *Computers in Human Behavior, 28*(2), 624–630.

Spencer, A. L., & Bonnema, R. (2011). Health issues in oral contraception: Risks, side effects, and health benefits. *Expert Review of Obstetrics & Gynecology, 6*(5), 551–557.

Spencer, N. (2006). Explaining the social gradient in smoking in pregnancy: Early life course accumulation and cross-sectional clustering of social risk exposures in the 1958 British national cohort. *Social Science & Medicine, 62*(5), 1250–1259.

Spitzer, R. L., et al. (1989). *DSM-III-R casebook*. Washington, DC: American Psychiatric Press.

Sprecher, S. (1998). Insiders' perspectives on reasons for attraction to a close other. *Social Psychology Quarterly, 61*(4), 287–300.

Sprecher, S. (1998). Social exchange theories and sexuality. *Journal of Sex Research, 35*(1), 32–43.

Sprecher, S. (2009). Relationship initiation and formation on the Internet. *Marriage and Family Review, 45*, 761–782.

Sprecher, S., & Fehr, B. (2011). Dispositional attachment and relationship-specific attachment as predictors of compassionate love for a partner. *Journal of Social and Personal Relationships, 28*(4), 558–574.

Sprecher, S., Sullivan, Q., & Hatfield, E. (1994). Mate selection preferences: Gender differences examined in a national sample. *Journal of Personality and Social Psychology, 66*(6), 1074–1080.

Statistics Canada. (2002c). General social survey—Cycle 15: Changing conjugal life in Canada. [Catalogue No. 89-576-XIE].

Statistics Canada (2002d). Crime statistics in Canada, 2001. *Juristat, 22*(b). [Catalogue. No. 85-002-XIE].

Statistics Canada (2003a). Sexual offences. *The Daily*, July 25. [online]. Retrieved from www.statcan.ca/daily/English/050420/d050420a.htm

Statistics Canada. (2004a). *The Daily*, June 15. Canadian Community Health Survey. [online]. Retrieved from www.statcan.ca/Daily/English/040615/d040615b.htm

Statistics Canada. (2004b). *Spotlight: Mixed unions*. [online]. Retrieved from www.statcan.ca/english/freepub/11-002-XIE/2004/06/17404/17404_04p.htm

Statistics Canada. (2005g). Children and youth as victims of violent crime. *The Daily*, April 20. [online]. Retrieved from www.statcan.ca/daily/English/050420/d050420a.htm

Statistics Canada. (2007g). Table 106-9002—Pregnancy outcomes by age group, Canada, provinces and territories, annual, CANSIM (database).

Statistics Canada. (2008d). Teen sexual behaviour and condom use 1996/1997 to 2005. *The Daily*, August 20. [online]. Retrieved from www.statisticscanada.com/Daily/English/080820/d080820c.htm

Statistics Canada. (2009a). 2006 Census Analysis Series. Retrieved from http://www.statscan.ca

Statistics Canada. (2009b). Visible minority population by age group. (2006 Census). Retrieved from http://www.statscan.ca

Statistics Canada. (2010). Breast feeding, 2009. Retrieved from http://www.statscan.gc.ca

Statistics Canada. (2010). University enrolment. *The Daily*, July, 14. www.statcan.gc.ca

Statistics Canada. (2011). 2006 Census: Portrait of the Canadian population in 2006. Retrieved from http://www.statscan.ca

Statistics Canada. (2012). *Portrait of families and living arrangements in Canada. Families, households and marital status, 2011 census of population*. Retrieved from http://www12.statcan.gc.ca/census-recensement/2011/as-sa/98-312-x/98-312-x2011001-eng.pdf

Statistics Canada. (2012). *Table 102-0512—Life expectancy, at birth and at age 65, by sex, Canada, provinces and territories, annual (years)*, CANSIM (database). Retrieved from http://www5.statcan.gc.ca/cansim/a26

Statistics Canada. (2013). CANSIM Table 102-4505—Crude birth rate, age-specific and total fertility rates (live births), Canada, provinces and territories, annual (rate).

Statistics Canada. (2013). *Table 051-0001—Estimates of population, by age group and sex for July 1, Canada, provinces and territories, annual (persons unless otherwise noted)*, CANSIM (database). Retrieved from http://www5.statcan.gc.ca/cansim/a26

Statistics Canada. (2013a). *National Household Survey, 2011: Immigration and ethnocultural diversity in Canada*. (Catalogue No. 99-010-X2011001). Retrieved from http://www12.statcan.gc.ca/nhs-enm/2011/as-sa/99-010-x/99-010-x2011001-eng.pdf

Steinemann, S., & Steinemann, M. (2005). Retroelements: Tools for sex chromosome evolution. *Cytogenetic and Genome Research, 110*, 134–143.

Stephenson, J. (2000). Widely used spermicide may increase, not decrease, risk of HIV transmission. *Journal of the American Medical Association, 284*(8). (Online).

Stephenson, K. R., & Sullivan, K. T. (2009). Social norms and general sexual satisfaction: The cost of misperceived descriptive norms. *Canadian Journal of Human Sexuality, 18*(3), 89–105.

Sternberg, R. J. (1986). A triangular theory of love. *Psychological Review, 93*, 119–135.

Sternberg, R. J. (1988). *The triangle of love: Intimacy, passion, commitment.* New York: Basic Books.

Stewart, D. F. & Gajic-Veljanoski, O. (2005). Trafficking in women: The Canadian perspective. *Canadian Medical Association Journal, 173*(1), 25–26.

Stockett, M. K. (2005). On the importance of difference: Re-envisioning sex and gender in ancient Mesoamerica. *World Archaeology, 37*(4), 566–578.

Storms, M. D. (1980). Theories of sexual orientation. *Journal of Personality and Social Psychology, 38*, 783–792.

Strager, S. (2003). What men watch when they watch pornography. *Sexuality & Culture: An Interdisciplinary Quarterly, 7*(1), 50–61.

Strassberg, D. S., & Holty, S. (2003). An experimental study of women's internet personal ads. *Archives of Sexual Behavior, 32*(3), 253–260.

Stratton, T. D., McLaughlin, M. A., Witte, F. M., Fosson, S. E., & Nora, L. M. (2005). Does students' exposure to gender discrimination and sexual harassment in medical school affect specialty choice and residency program selection? *Academic Medicine, 80*(4), 400–408.

Strebeigh, F. (2009). *Equal: Women reshape American law.* New York: Norton.

Strike, C., Myers, T., Calzavara, L., & Haubrich, D. (2001). Sexual coercion among young street involved adults: Perpetrators and victims' perspectives. *Violence and Victims, 16*, 537–551.

Stripe, T., Abracen, J., Stermac, L., & Wilson, R. (2006). Sexual offenders' state-of-mind regarding childhood attachment: A controlled investigation. *Sexual Abuse: A Journal of Research and Treatment, 18*, 289–302.

Studd, J., & Nappi, R. E. (2012). Reproductive depression. *Gynecological Endocrinology, 28*(S1), 42–45.

Sun, A., & Ren, J. (2012). Estrogen replacement therapy and cardiac function under metabolic syndrome. *Hypertension, 59*, 552–554.

Suschinsky, K., & Lalumière, M. (2012). Is sexual concordance related to awareness of physiological states? *Archives of Sexual Behavior, 41*(1), 199–208. doi:10.1007/s10508-012-9931-9

Swami, V., & Tovée, M.J. (2013). Men's oppressive beliefs predict their breast size preferences in women. *Archives of Sexual Behavior, 42*(7), 1199–1207. doi: 10.1007/s10508-013-0081-5

Symonds, D. (1979). *The evolution of human sexuality.* New York, NY: Oxford University Press.

Symons, D. (1995, Cited in Goleman, D., June 14). Sex fantasy research said to neglect women. *The New York Times*, p. C14.

Tafoya, T. (1997). Native gay and lesbian issues: The two-spirited. In B. Green (Ed.), *Ethnic and cultural diversity among lesbian and fay men. Psychological Perspectives on lesbian and gay issues.* Thousand Oaks, CA: Sage (pp. 1–10).

Tan, H. M., Tong, S. F., & Ho, C. C. K. (2012). Men's health: Sexual dysfunction, physical, and psychological health—Is there a link? *Journal of Sexual Medicine, 9*(3), 663–671.

Tang, C. S., Yeung, D. Y., & Lee, A. M. (2003). Psychosocial correlates of emotional responses to menarche among Chinese adolescent girls. *Journal of Adolescent Health, 33*(3), 193–201.

Taylor, C. et al. (2011). *Every class in every school. The First National Climate Survey on Homophobia, Biphobia, and Transphobia in Canadian Schools. Final report.* Toronto, ON: Egale Canada Human Rights Trust.

Taylor, M. J., Rudkin, L., & Hawton, K. (2005). Strategies for managing antidepressant-induced sexual dysfunction: Systematic review of randomised controlled trials. *Journal of Affective Disorders, 88*(3), 241–254.

Taylor, V., & Rupp, L. J. (2004). Chicks with dicks, men in dresses: What it means to be a drag queen. *Journal of Homosexuality, 46*(3–4), 113–133.

Ter Kuile, M. M., et al. (2009). Therapist-aided exposure for women with lifelong vaginismus: A replicated single-case design. *Journal of Consulting and Clinical Psychology, 77*, 149–159.

Tessler Lindau, S., Schumm, L., Laumann, E., & Levinson, W. (2007). A study of sexuality and health among older adults in the United States. *New England Journal of Medicine, 357*(8), 51–67.

The Globe and Mail. (2013, February 8). We asked. You more than answered. Results of the Globe's sex survey. *The Globe and Mail*. Retrieved from http://www.theglobeandmail.com/life/relationships/valentines-day/we-asked-you-more-than-answered-results-of-the-globes-sex-survey/article8288541/#

Thibaut, F. (2011). Pharmacological treatment of sex offenders. *Sexologies, 20*(3),166–168.

Thigpen, T. W. (2009). Early sexual behavior in a sample of low income, African American children. *Journal of Sex Research, 46*(1), 67–79.

Thomas, R. M., & Murray, T. R. (2009). Sex and the American teenager: Seeing through the myths and confronting the issues. Lanham, MD: L & R Publishers.

Thomas, W., & Jacobs, S. (1999). "...And we are still here": From Berdache to Two-Spirit people. *American Indian Culture and Research Journal, 23*, 91–107.

Thompson, A. E., & O'Sullivan, L. F. (2011). Gender differences in associations of sexual and romantic stimuli: Do young men really prefer sex over romance? *Archives of Sexual Behavior, 41*(4), 949–957. DOI:10.1007/s10508-011-9794-5

Thompson, E. M., & Morgan, E. M. (2008). "Mostly straight" young women: Variations in sexual behavior and identity. *Developmental Psychology, 44*(1), 15–21.

Thompson, J. K., & Tantleff, S. (1992). Female and male ratings of upper torso: Actual, ideal, and stereotypical conceptions. *Journal of Social Behavior and Personality*, 7, 345–354.

Tiefer, L. (1996). The medicalization of sexuality: conceptual, normative, and professional issues. *Annual Review of Sex Research*, 7, 252–282.

Tiefer, L. (2001). A new view of women's sexual problems: Why new? Why now? *The Journal of Sex Research*, 38, 89–96.

Tiggemann, M., & Hodgson, S. (2008). The hairlessness norm extended: Reasons for and predictors of women's body hair removal at different body sites. *Sex Roles*, 59(11), 889–897. DOI:10.1007/s11199-008-9494-3

Timm, T.M. (2009). "Do I really have to talk about sex?" Encouraging beginning therapists to integrate sexuality into couples therapy. *Journal of Couple and Relationship Therapy*, 8, 15–33.

Tobian, A. A. R., & Gray, R. H. (2011). The medical benefits of male circumcision. *Journal of the American Medical Association*, 306(13), 1479–1480.

Totman, R. (2004). *The third sex: Kathoey: Thailand's ladyboys.* London: Souvenir Press.

Touhara, K., & Vosshall, L. B. (2009). Sensing odorants and pheromones with chemosensory receptors. *Annual Review of Physiology*, 71, 307–332. doi:10.1146/annurev.physiol.010908.163209.

Tracey, S. (2007, September 12). Man died during sex act. *Guelph Mercury*, p. A1.

Travers, R., Newton, H., & Monro, L. (2011). "Because it was expected": Heterosexism as a determinant of pregnancy among sexually diverse youth. *Canadian Journal of Community Mental Health*, 30(2), 65–79.

Trenholm, C. et al. (2007). *Impact of four Title V, Section 510 abstinence education programs, final report.* Mathematica Policy Research Inc. Submitted to U.S. Department of Health and Human Services.

Trivedi, D., Kirby, M., Wellsted, D.M., Ali, S., Hackett, G., O'Connor, B., & van Os, S. (2012). Can simvastatin improve erectile function and health-related quality of life in men aged ≥40 years with erectile dysfunction? Results of the Erectile Dysfunction and Statins Trial. *British Journal of Urology International*, 111(2), 324–33. doi:10.1111/j.1464-410X.2012.11241.x.

Trotter, E. C., & Alderson, K. G. (2007). University students' definitions of having sex, sexual partner, and virginity loss: The influence of participant gender, sexual experience, and contextual factors. *The Canadian Journal of Human Sexuality*, 16(1–2), 11–29.

Trulsson, O., & Rådestad, I. (2004). The silent child—Mothers' experiences before, during, and after stillbirth. *Birth: Issues in Perinatal Care*, 31(3), 189–195.

Trussler, T. et al. (2010). *MaCount sizes-up the gaps: A sexual health survey of gay men in Vancouver.* Vancouver Coastal Health: Vancouver, B.C.

Tullis, C. A., & Zangrillo, A. N. (2013). Sexuality education for adolescents and adults with autism spectrum disorders. *Psychology in the Schools*, 50(9), 866–875.

Tunariu, A. D., & Reavey, R. (2003). Men in love: Living with sexual boredom. *Sexual and Relationship Therapy*, 13(1), 63–94.

Turner, H. A., Finkelhor, D., & Ormrod, R. (2006). The effect of lifetime victimization on the mental health of children and adolescents. *Social Science & Medicine*, 62(1), 13–27.

Turton, J. (2005). Perspectives on female sex offending: A culture of denial. *Sexualities*, 8(5), 632–633.

Twist, M. (2005). Relationship therapy with same-sex couples. *Journal of Marital & Family Therapy*, 31(4), 413.

Udry, J. R. (2001). Feminist critics uncover determinism, positivism, and antiquated theory. *American Sociological Review*, 66(4), 611–618.

UNAIDS. (2006). Report on the global AIDS epidemic: Executive summary. Joint United nations Programme on HIV/AIDS (UNAIDS). Geneva: UNAIDS

UNAIDS. (2013). *Global Report: UNAIDS report on the global AIDS epidemic 2013.* Joint United Nations Programme on HIV/AIDS (UNAIDS). Retrieved from http://www.unaids.org/en/media/unaids/contentassets/documents/epidemiology/2013/gr2013/UNAIDS_Global_Report_2013_en.pdf

UNICEF. (2007). Child poverty in perspective: An overview of child well-being in rich countries. *Innocenti Report Card 7.* Florence: Innocenti Research Centre.

UNICEF. (2012). *HIV and infant feeding.* Retrieved September 12, 2012 from http://www.unicef.org/programme/breastfeeding/hiv.htm

Utian, W. H. (2012). Recent developments in pharmacotherapy for vasomotor symptoms. *Current Obstetrics and Gynecology Reports*, DOI:10.1007/s13669-012-0009-4

Uysal., A., Lin, H. L., Knee, C. R., & Bush, A. L. (2012). The association between self-concealment from one's partner and relationship well-being. *Personality and Social Psychology Bulletin*, 38(1), 39–51.

Vaculík, M., & Hudecek, T. (2005). Development of close relationships in the Internet environment. *Ceskoslovenská Psychologie*, 49(2), 157–174.

Vallerand, R. J. (2008). On the psychology of passion: In search of what makes people's lives most worth living. *Canadian Psychology*, 49(1), 1–13. DOI:10.1037/0708-5591.49.1.1

Vallerand, R. J., et al. (2003). Les passions de l'âme: On obsessive and harmonious passion. *Journal of Personality and Social Psychology*, 85(4), 756–767.

van der Made, F., et al. (2008). Childhood sexual abuse, selective attention for sexual cues and the effects of testosterone with or without vardenafil on physiological sexual arousal in women with sexual dysfunction: A pilot study. *Journal of Sexual Medicine*, 6(2), 429–439.

van Lankveld, J. J. D. M., et al. (2010). Women's sexual pain disorders. *Journal of Sexual Medicine*, 7(1, Pt 2), 615–631. doi:10.1111/j.1743-6109.2009.01631.x.

van Straaten, I., Engels, R. C. M. E., Finkenauer, C., & Holland, R. W. (2009). Meeting your match: How attractiveness similarity affects approach behavior in mixed-sex dyads. *Personality and Social Psychology Bulletin*, 35(6), 685–697.

Vance, C.S. (Ed.). (1984). *Pleasure and danger: Exploring female sexuality.* Boston, MA: Routledge & Kegan Paul.

Vancouver Sun. (2014). Bountiful timeline: A chronology from 1843 to present day. *Vancouver Sun.* August 13, 2014. Retrieved from http://www.vancouversun.com/life/Bountiful+timeline+chronology+from+1843+present/2132938/story.html

VanderLaan, D. P., & Vasey, P. L. (2008). Mate retention behavior of men and women in heterosexual and homosexual relationships. *Archives of Sexual Behavior*, 37, 572–585.

Vandiver, D. M. (2006). Female sex offenders: A comparison of solo offenders and co-offenders. *Violence and Victims*, 21(3), 339–354.

Vanier Institute of the Family. (2010). *Families count: Profiling Canada's families.* Ottawa, ON: Vanier Institute of the Family.

Vannier, S. A., & O'Sullivan, L. F. (2010). Communicating interest in sex: Verbal and non-verbal initiation of sexual activity in young adults romantic dating relationships. *Archives of Sexual Behavior*, doi 10.1007/s/0508-010-9663-7.

Vannier, S.A., & O'Sullivan, L.F. (2012). Who gives and who gets: Why, when, and with whom young people engage in oral sex. *Journal of Youth and Adolescence*, *41*(5), 572–582. doi:10.1007/s10964-012-9745-z.

Vasey, P. L. (2002). Sexual partner preference in female Japanese macaques. *Archives of Sexual Behavior*, *31*(1), 51–62.

Vasey, P. L., & Bartlett, N. H. (2007). What can the Samoan "fa'afafine" teach us about the Western concept of gender identity disorder in childhood. *Perspectives in Biology and Medicine*, *50*(4), 481–490.

Vasey, P. L., Foroud, A., Duckworth, N., & Kovacovsky, S. D. (2006). Male-female and female-female mounting in Japanese macaques: A comparative study of posture and movement. *Archives of Sexual Behavior*, *35*(2), 117–129.

Vickerman, K. A., & Margolina, G. (2009). Rape treatment outcome research: Empirical findings and state of the literature. *Clinical Psychology Review*, *29*, 431–448.

Villar, F., Villamizar, D. J., & López–Chivrall, S. (2005). Components of loving experience in old age: Older people and long-term relationships. *Revista Espanola de Geriatria y Gerontologia*, *40*(3), 166–177.

Voeller, B. (1991). AIDS and heterosexual anal intercourse. *Archives of Sexual Behavior*, *20*, 233–276.

Vrangalova, Z., & Savin-Williams, R. (2012). Mostly heterosexual and mostly gay/lesbian: Evidence for new sexual orientation identities. *Archives of Sexual Behavior*, *41*(1), 85–101.

Wade, T. J., Butrie, L. K., & Hoffman, K. M. (2009). Women's direct opening lines are perceived as most effective. *Personality and Individual Differences*, *47*(2), 145–149.

Wainberg, M. A. (2009). Criminalizing HIV transmission may be a mistake. *Canadian Medical Association Journal*, *180*(6), 688.

Waismann, R., Fenwick, P. B. C., Wilson, G. D., Hewett, T. D., & Lumsden, J. (2003). EEG responses to visual erotic stimuli in men with normal and paraphilic interests. *Archives of Sexual Behavior*, *32*(2), 135–144.

Waldinger, M. D. (2011). The management of premature ejaculation. *Current Clinical Urology, Part 5*, 709–720.

Walker, S. (2008, April 4). Women behind the camera for new breed of adult film. *Toronto Star*, p. E6.

Ward, T., Gannon, T. A., & Birgden, A. (2007). Human rights and the treatment of sex offenders. *Sexual Abuse*, *19*, 195–216.

Waterman, J. (1986). Overview of treatment issues. In K. McFarlane et al. (Eds.), *Sexual abuse of young children: Evaluation and treatment* (pp. 197–203). New York: Guilford.

Watson, L. (2010). Pornography. *Philosophy Compass, 5/7*, 535–550.

Weaver, A. D., et al. (2002). Sexual health education at school and at home: Attitudes and experiences of New Brunswick parents. *Canadian Journal of Human Sexuality*, *11*, 19–31.

Weber, B. (2001, January 10). No sex please, we're in the army. *Toronto Star*, p. A3.

Weinberg, T. S. (1987). Sadomasochism in the United States: A review of recent sociological literature. *Journal of Sex Research*, *23*, 50–69.

Weitzer, R. (2012a). *Legalizing prostitution: From illicit vice to lawful business*. New York: New York University Press.

Weitzer, R. (2012b). Male prostitution. In C. D. Bryant (Ed.). *The Routledge handbook of deviant behavior* (pp. 378–382). New York: Routledge.

Welldon, E. V. (2005). Incest: A therapeutic challenge. In Ambrosio, G. (Ed.), *On incest: Psychoanalytic perspectives* (pp. 81–100). London: Karnac Books.

Wells, C. (2009). Research exploring the health, wellness, and safety concerns of sexual minority youth. *The Canadian Journal of Human Sexuality*, *18* (4), 221–229.

Wells, K. (2006). *Gay–straight student alliances in Alberta schools: A guide for teachers*. Edmonton, AB: Alberta Teachers Federation.

Wells, K. (2008). Generation queer: Sexual minority youth and Canadian schools. *Education Canada*, *48*(1), 18–23.

Wentland, J. (2006). Sexual pleasure orientation in heterosexual women. Unpublished master's thesis, University of Guelph.

Wentland, J. J., Herold, E. S., Desmarais, S., & Milhausen, R. R. (2009). Differentiating highly sexual women from less sexual women. *The Canadian Journal of Human Sexuality*, *18*(4), 169–182.

Wentland, J. J., & Reissing, E. D. (2011). Taking casual sex not too casually: Exploring definitions of casual sexual relationships. *The Canadian Journal of Human Sexuality*, *20*(3), 75–91.

Wentland, L., Muise, A., & Desmarais, S. (2010). Out with the old, in with the new: The new technologized dating script. Poster Presented at the 53rd Annual Meeting of the Society for the Scientific Study of Sexuality, Las Vegas, Nevada.

West, S. L., et al. (2008). Prevalence of low sexual desire and hypoactive sexual desire disorder in a nationally representative sample of US women. *Archives of Internal Medicine*, *168*(13), 1441–1449.

Wetterneck, C. T., Burgess, A. J., Short, M. B., Smith, A. H., & Cervantes, M. E. (2012). The role of sexual compulsivity, impulsivity, and experiential avoidance in Internet pornography use. *The Psychological Record*, *62*(1), 3–18.

Wheeler, J., Newring, K. A. B., & Draper, C. (2008). Transvestic fetishism: Psychopathology and theory. In D. R. Laws and W. T. O'Donohue (Eds.), *Sexual deviance: Theory, assessment, and treatment* (2nd ed., pp. 272–284). New York: Guilford Press.

Whelan, A., Langille, D., & Hurst, E. (2013). Nova Scotia pharmacists' knowledge of, experiences with and perception of factors interfering with their ability to provide emergency contraceptive pill consultations. *International Journal of Pharmacy Practice*, *21*(5), 314–321. doi: 10.1111/ijpp.12017

Whisman, M. A., & Snyder, D. K. (2007). Sexual infidelity in a national survey of American women: Differences in prevalence and correlates as a function of method of assessment. *The Journal of Family Psychology*, *21*(2),147–154.

Widman, L., Welsh, D. P., McNulty, J. K., & Little, K. C. (2006). Sexual communication and contraceptive use in adolescent dating couples. *Journal of Adolescent Health*, *39*, 893–899.

Wierman, M. E., et al. (2010). Endocrine aspects of women's sexual function. *Journal of Sexual Medicine*, *7*(1, Pt 2), 561–585. doi:10.1111/j.1743-6109.2009.01629.x.

Wilbur, C. J., & Campbell, L. (2010). What do women want? An interactionist account of women's mate preferences. *Personality and Individual Differences*, *49*, 749–754.

Wilcox, W. B., & Marquardt, E. (Eds.). (2011). *The state of our unions: Marriage in America 2011*. Charlottesville, VA: The National Marriage Project/Institute for American Values.

Wilkes, J. (2011, March 9). Police can detect computers accessing child porn. *Toronto Star* p. GT. 4.

Williams, C. (2010). Economic well-being. *Women in Canada: A gender-based statistical report.* (6th ed.). Retrieved from www.statcan.gc.ca

Williams, M. E. (Ed.). (2001). *Abortion: Opposing viewpoints.* Farmington Hills, MI: Greenhaven Press.

Wilson, J. M. B., Tripp, D. A., & Boland, F. J. (2005). The relative contributions of waist-to-hip ratio and body mass index to judgments of attractiveness. *Sexualities, Evolution & Gender, 7*(3), 245–267.

Wilson, R. J. (2005). Circles of support and accountability: 10 years and counting. Paper presented at World Congress of Sexology, Montreal.

Winer, R., Hughes, J., Feng, Q., O'Reilly, S., Kiviat, N., Holmes, K., & Koutsky, L. (2006). Condom use and the risk of genital human papillomavirus infection in young women. *New England Journal of Medicine, 354,* 2645–2654.

Winter, S. (2003). Research and discussion paper: Language and identity in transgender: Gender wars and the case of the Thai kathoey. Paper presented at the Hawaii conference on Social Sciences, Waikiki, HI.

Wittenberg, A., & Gerber, J. (2009). Recommendations for improving sexual health curricula in medical schools: Results from a two-arm study collecting data from patients and medical students. *Journal of Sexual Medicine, 6*(2), 362–368. doi:10.1111/j.1743-6109.2008.01046.x.

Women warned about potential sex offender. (2008, August 3). *Toronto Star,* p. A3.

Wong, D. (2012). Doing gender, doing culture: Division of labour among lesbians in Hong Kong. *Women's Studies International Forum, 35*(4), 266–275.

Woo, J. S. T., & Brotto, L. A. (2008). Age of first intercourse and acculturation: Effects on adult sexual responding. *Journal of Sexual Medicine, 5*(3), 571–582.

Woo, J. S. T., Brotto, L. A., & Gorzalka, B. B. (2011). The role of sex guilt in the relationship between culture and women's sexual desire. *Archives of Sexual Behavior, 40*(2), 385–394.

Woo, J., Morshedian, N., Brotto, L. & Gorzalka, B. (2012). Sex guilt mediates the relationship between religiosity and sexual desire in East Asian and Euro-Canadian college-aged women. *Archives of Sexual Behavior, 41*(6), 1485–1495.

Wood, D. (2005, August 18). Cambridge mother and son guilty of incest. *The Record,* p. A4.

Wood, E. (2011, April 16). Government funds services for male victims of sexual abuse. *Guelph Mercury,* A6.

Wood, J., Milhausen, R.R., & Maitland, S. (2013). Why have sex? An investigation of the reported reasons for sex among sexual minority women. Poster presented at the *Canadian Sex Research Forum.* Charlottetown, PEI., October 3-5, 2013.

Woods, A. (2000, October 7). Lesbian bathhouse organizers charged. *The Toronto Star,* p. B1.

Wooten, J. M. (2008). Drug-induced sexual problems. *Southern Medical Journal, 101*(11), 1092–1093.

World Association for Sexual Health. (2008). *Sexual health for the millennium: A declaration and technical document.* Minneapolis, MN: World Association for Sexual Health http://www.worldsexology.org/sites/default/files/Millennium%20Declaration%20(English).pdf

World Health Organization (WHO). (2006). *Defining sexual health: Report of a technical consultation on sexual health, 28–31 January 2002.* Geneva: World Health Organization. Retrieved

from http://www.who.int/reproductivehealth/publications/sexual_health/defining_sexual_health.pdf

World Health Organization. (2012, February). *Female genital mutilation. Fact sheet N 241.* Retrieved from http://www.who.int/mediacentre/factsheets/fs241/en/

World Health Organization. (2013). *Sexually transmitted infections (STIs).* Fact sheet N. 110. Updated November, 2013. Retrieved from http://www.who.int/mediacentre/factsheets/fs110/en/

World Professional Association for Transgender Health (WPATH). (2012). *Standards of care: For the health of transsexual, transgender and gender non-conforming people* (7th Version). Minneapolis, MN: World Professional Association for Transgender Health.

Worthy, R., & Smallbone, S. (2012). *Internet child pornography: Causes, investigations, and prevention.* New York: Praeger.

Wright, J. L., Lin, D. W., & Stanford, J. L. (2012). Circumcision and the risk of prostate cancer. *Cancer, 118*(18), 4437–4443. DOI:10.1002/cncr.26653

Wright, L. W., & Bonita, A. G. (2012). A negative campus climate: Sexual harassment and homophobia. In R. D. McAnulty (Ed.). *Sex in college: The things they don't write home about* (pp. 189–210). Santa Barbara, CA: ABC-CLIO.

Wright, T. C. (2009). Natural history of HPV infections. *The Journal of Family Practice, 58*(9), 53–57.

Wyatt, T. D. (2009). Fifty years of pheromones. *Nature, 457,* 262–263. doi:10.1038/457262a

Wylie, K., & Eardley, I. (2007). Penile size and the small penis syndrome. *BJU International, 99*(6), 1449–1455.

Wynne, A., & Currie, C. (2011). Social exclusion as an underlying determinant of sexually transmitted infections among Canadian aboriginals. *Pimatisiwin: A Journal of Aboriginal and Indigenous Community Health, 9,* 113–127.

Yates, P. M., Hucker, S. J., & Kingston, D. A. (2008). Sexual sadism: Psychopathology and theory. In D. R. Laws and W. T. O'Donohue (Eds.), *Sexual deviance: Theory, assessment, and treatment* (2nd ed., pp. 213–230). New York: Guilford Press.

Yeh, K-Y., Pu, H-F., Wu, C-H., Tai, M-Y., & Tsai, Y-F. (2009). Different subregions of the medial preoptic area are separately involved in the regulation of copulation and sexual incentive motivation in male rats: A behavioral and morphological study. *Behavioural Brain Research, 205*(1), 219–225.

Yoder, V. C., Virden, T. B., III, & Amin, K. (2005). Internet pornography and loneliness: An association? *Sexual Addiction & Compulsivity, 12*(1), 19–44.

Yost, M. R., & Thomas, G. D. (2011). Gender and binegativity: Men's and women's attitudes toward male and female bisexuals. *Archives of Sexual Behavior, 41*(3), 691–702. doi:10.1007/s10508-011-9767-8

Yost, M. R., & Zurbriggen, E. L. (2006). Gender differences in the enactment of sociosexuality: An examination of implicit social motives, sexual fantasies, coercive sexual attitudes, and aggressive sexual behavior. *The Journal of Sex Research, 43*(2), 163–173.

Young, A. (2008). The state is still in the bedrooms of the nation. *The Canadian Journal of Human Sexuality, 17*(4), 203–209.

Youngman, Henry. 2014. Take My Wife, Please!: Henny Youngman's Giant Book of Jokes. Skyhorse Publishing.

Youthography Ping Survey. (February 2004). Canadian Youth (13–29). 1358 respondents.

Zalenskaya, I. A., Cerocchi, O. G., Joseph, T., Donaghay, M. A., Schriver, S. D., & Doncel, G. F. (2011). Increased COX-2 expression in human vaginal epithelial cells exposed to non-oxynol-9, a vaginal contraceptive microbicide that failed to protect women from HIV-1 infection. *American Journal of Reproductive Immunology, 65*(6), 569–77. doi:10.1111/j.1600-0897.2010.00964.x.

Zaviacic, M., & Whipple, B. (1993). Update on the female prostate and the phenomenon of female ejaculation. *Journal of Sex Research, 30,* 148–151.

Zaviacic, M., et al. (1988a). Concentrations of fructose in female ejaculate and urine: A comparative biochemical study. *Journal of Sex Research, 24,* 319–325.

Zaviacic, M., et al. (1988b). Female urethral expulsions evoked by local digital stimulation of the G-spot: Differences in the response patterns. *Journal of Sex Research, 24,* 311–318.

Zernike, K. (2005, December 11). The siren song of sex with boys. *The New York Times.* [Online].

Zerubavel, E. (2006). *The elephant in the room: Silence and denial in everyday life.* New York: Oxford University Press.

Zezima, K. (2006, February 3). Teenager attacks three men at gay bar in Massachusetts. *The New York Times* (Online).

Zhou, Y. R. (2012). Changing behaviours and continuing silence: Sex in the post-immigration lives of mainland Chinese immigrants in Canada. *Culture, Health & Sexuality, 14*(1), 87–100. doi:10.1080/13691058.2011.626454

Zhu, B., et al. (2011). Transition from paroxysmal disorder in infancy to the masturbatory orgasm in childhood. *International Journal of Sexual Health, 23*(4), 278–281.

Zielbauer, P. (2000, May 22). Sex offender listings on Web set off debate. *The New York Times* online.

Zosuls, K. M., et al. (2009). The acquisition of gender labels in infancy: Implications for gender-typed play. *Developmental Psychology, 45*(3), 688–701.

Zucker, K. J. (2005a). Gender identity disorder in children and adolescents. *Annual Review of Clinical Psychology, 1*(1), 467–492.

Zucker, K. J. (2005b). Gender identity disorder in girls. In D. J. Bell, S. L. Foster, & E. J. Mash (Eds.). *Handbook of behavioral and emotional problems in girls. Issues in clinical child psychology* (pp. 285–319). Kluwer Academic/Plenum Publishers.

Zucker, K. J., Wood, H., Singh, D., & Bradley, S. J. (2012). A developmental, biopsychosocial model for the treatment of children with gender identity disorder. *Journal of Homosexuality, 59*(3), 369–397.

Name Index

A

Aarts, H., 223
Abal, Y. N., 411
Abell, J., 175
Adam, B. D., 155, 213, 221, 235, 323, 378
Adams, H. E., 228
Adams, N., 340
Adams, R. A., 450
Advisory Committee on Family Planning, 396
Agrawal, A., 136
Ahrols, T. K., 402
Ah Shene, D., 104
Albarracin, D., 391, 392
Alberta Health Services, 119, 399
Alcoba, N., 240
Alderson, K. G., 5, 213, 231
Alexander, G. M., 140
Alexy, E. M., 484
Allen, E. S., 315, 317
Allen, K. R., 300
Allen, T. D., 169
Allison, C. M., 298
Allman, D., 475
Althof, S., 332, 336, 340, 342, 349, 350
Amankwah, E., 65
American Academy of Family Physicians, 270
American Cancer Society, 65, 67, 69, 86
American Fertility Association, 240, 242, 243, 245
American Psychiatric Association, 258, 328, 332, 333, 346, 406, 410, 411, 417, 418, 448
Amnesty International, 60
Amodeo, M., 447
Amodio, D. M., 153
Andersen, M. L., 104
Anderson, J. E., 378
Anderson, K. M., 450, 451, 452
Anderson, M., 175, 181
Anderson Moore, K., 261
Andriole, G. L., 87
Andruff, H., 310
Angus Reid Global, 10, 11, 227, 286, 466
Angus Reid Public Opinion, 466
Annon, J.S., 340, 341
Arbisi, P. A., 437, 441
Arnold, R., 160
Aron, A., 161, 162
Assefi, N., 394
Associated Press, 172, 220, 447
Astley, S. J., 253
Atchison, C., 47, 467, 471
Atkins, D. C., 315, 317
Atkinson, J. L., 432
Aubin, S., 329, 337, 341

Auinger, P., 379
Ayala, G., 214
Ayres, M. M., 483, 484

B

Bader, M., 191
Bailey, J. M., 49, 110, 221, 222, 233, 409
Bailey, J. V., 200, 201, 205, 223
Bailey, M., 223
Baldwin, J. D., 221
Baldwin, J. I., 221
Bandura, A., 391
Banerjee, S., 447
Banszegi, O., 106
Barak, A., 485
Barbaree, H. E., 106, 407, 418, 423, 485
Barbee, A. P., 173
Barrett, B., 357
Barrett, M. B., 232, 233, 373, 387, 402
Barry, K., 39
Bartels, R. M., 191
Bartholomew, K., 195
Bartlett, N. H., 133
Bartolo, K. C., 450
Basile, K. C., 436
Basow, S. A., 176
Basson, B., 102
Basson, R., 113, 115, 329, 331, 333
Bauer, G., 46, 137
Bauerle, S. Y., 180
Baumeister, R. F., 440
Baumgartner, B., 74
Baute, N., 172
Beach, F. A., 198, 220, 312
Beauregard, E., 441
Becerra, L., 420
Behrendt, N., 415
Belden, M., 66
Bell, A. P., 234
Belsky, J., 115
Bem, S. L., 142
Bennett, S., 394
Benoit, C., 471
Benzie, R., 479
Berdahl, J. L., 455
Bereket, T., 221
Berenbaum, S. A., 148, 149
Beres, M. A., 178, 437, 443, 445
Berger, L., 256
Berger, P. B., 377
Bergeron, S., 334, 351
Bergner, D., 49
Bernstein, I. M., 253
Berscheid, E., 162
Beutel, M. E., 441
Bibby, R., 11, 226, 227
Binik, Y. M., 115, 333, 334

Birnbaum, H. J., 440
Bisson, M. A., 302
Bivona, J. M., 190
Black, A., 274, 278, 280, 306, 377
Blair, K. L., 338
Blais, K., 232
Blanchard, R., 106, 134, 135, 224, 408, 418, 423, 449
Blaze Carlson, K., 216
Bloch, M., 258
Blow, C. M., 316
Blum, L.D., 81
Bockting, W. O., 134
Bogaert, A., 217
Bogaert, A. F., 44, 217, 218, 224, 232, 482
Boies, S. C., 398
Bolton, J. M., 337
Bonita, A. G., 457
Bonnema, R., 271
Borisoff, J. J., 121
Born, L., 258
Boroditsky, R., 327, 401
Boros, S., 441
Boyce, J., 431, 446
Boyce, W., 397
Boyer, C. B., 376
Bradford, J. M. W., 425, 426
Bradley, K., 46
Bradley, S. J., 131
Bradley-Engen, M.S., 476
Brauer, M., 334
Braunstein, G. D., 108
Brazao, D., 468
Brennan, R., 481
Brennan, S., 431, 433, 435, 442, 446
Briken, P., 411, 425, 427
Brock, G., 327, 333
Brody, J. E., 484
Brotman, S., 324
Brotto, L. A., 6, 46, 66, 218, 328, 336, 353, 402
Brousseau, M., 437
Brown, D., 486
Brown, G. R., 334
Brown, L. M., 153
Brown, L. S., 467
Brown, R., 336
Browning, D. S., 17, 21
Bruce, J. W., 156
Bryant, C., 398
Bryant-Davis, T., 441, 442
Bucy, P. C., 105
Bullough, V. L., 193
Bumpass, L., 309
Burchell, A.N., 372
Burke, T. J., 180
Burnett, M. L., 377

Bush, K. R., 379
Bushnik, T., 240
Buss, D. M., 34, 35, 139, 158, 159, 177, 179, 192, 312
Butler, J., 38
Butler, L.M., 205
Buunk, B. P., 156
Buvat, J., 335, 343
Byerly, M. J., 335
Byers, E. S., 37, 38, 176, 306, 314, 332, 338, 396, 397, 438
Byers, L., 176, 306, 481
Byers, S., 5, 176, 306, 481

C

Cado, S., 191
Caffaro, J. V., 450
Cai, R., 118
Cairns, K. V., 409, 457
Calzavara, L., 368
Campbell, L., 157, 180, 181
Campbell, R., 441
Canadian Cancer Society, 64, 65, 67, 69, 70, 75, 85, 86, 88
Canadian Institute for Health Information, 256
Canadian Liver Foundation, 324
Canadian Press, 287, 311
Canadian Women's Health Network, 66
Cantor, J. M., 134, 449
Carbonneau, N., 163
Carmody, J., 353
Carrère, S., 318, 319
Carrier, S., 346
Carroll, J. S., 481
Carter, D. J., 470
Carvalho, J., 108, 342
Casavant, L., 480
Casey, E., 37
Causarano, N., 396
Celeste, J., 475
Centers for Disease Control and Prevention, 360, 372
Chae, D. H., 214
Chaiyavej, S., 454
Chandra, A., 303, 368
Chang, S. C. H., 104
Chavoshi, N., 378
Chesler, P., 38
Chivers, M. L., 49, 110, 191, 223, 347, 481
Cho, S., 120
Chui, T., 153, 312
Chung, A., 433, 480
Ciani, A. C., 222
Clark, D. B., 378
Clarke, T. J., 218
Clarren, S. K., 253
Clary, J., 218
Cleary, J., 182, 377
Cleland, K., 270
Cnattingius, S., 251, 253
Cohen, A. B., 155
Cohen, J. N., 392
Cohen, L. S., 258
Cohen-Bendahan, C. C. C., 139

Cohen-Kettenis, P., 135
Coker, A.L., 379
Colangelo, J. J., 329, 331, 337
Cole, F. S., 257
Cole, S. S., 119
Cole, T. B., 433
Coleman, E., 137, 193, 426
Collins, J., 9
Collins, R. L., 303
Compas Inc., 314, 315
Conn-Caffaro, A., 450
Connell, E., 147
Connolly, J., 138
Cook, R.L., 378
Cooper, A., 149, 483, 484
Corbesi, B., 9
Cortoni, F., 432
Cotter, A., 431, 446
Cotton, A. J., 47
Courtois, F. J., 121
Coyle, J. P., 342
Crabtree, S., 10
Craig, R. J., 454
Craig, W., 138
Crawford, M., 146
Crawford, T. V., 22
Cribb, R., 468
Critelli, J. W., 190
Crocker, D., 454
Crosby, R. A., 278
Crow, B., 443
Crowley, T., 351
Csoka, A. B., 337
Cummings, A., 138
Cummings, S. R., 70
Cunningham, M. R., 173
Currie, C., 382
Cutler, W. B., 99
Cuzin, B., 89
Cytrynbaum, J., 195

D

Dahan, R., 402
Dahinten, V. S., 458
Dalby, P., 88
Daley, A., 77
Dalla, R. L., 470
Damon, W., 422
Dancer, P. L., 416
Daneback, K., 26, 27, 397, 484
Darcangelo, S., 408
Darling, C. A., 117
Darry, K., 118
Davidson, J. K., 147, 191
Davies, M., 228
Davis, D., 180
Davis, K. E., 180
Davis, R. L., 103
Davis, S. R., 102, 108, 343
Dawson, S. J., 190
Decaire, B., 210
DeCicco, T. L., 192
Degenhardt, L., 467
De Graaf, H., 295
DeJesus, E., 368

Dekeseredy, W., 445
Delamater, J., 320
del Busto, E., 425
DeLuzio Chasin, C. J., 218
Demmons, S., 176
Denmark, F., 149
Denov, M. S., 448
Denzin, N. K., 51
Derby, C. A., 336
DesChamps, G., 29
Desmarais, S., 44, 52, 184, 445, 481
De Smet, O., 180
Desrosiers, M., 351
de Tormes Eby, L. T., 169
Devor, H., 219
De Vries, G. J., 127
Devries, K., 383
Dew, J., 313
Diamond, L. M., 214, 215, 225, 231, 481
Diamond, M., 131
Dicicco, E. C., 38
Dickenson, J. A., 481
DiClemente, R. J., 379
DiDonato, M. D., 148, 149
Dielissen, P.W., 358
Di Gioacchino, L., 407, 427
Dijkstra, P., 156
Dindia, K., 169
Disney, E. R., 252
Dittert, S., 419
Dixson, B.J., 155
Dizon, D. S., 336
Do, C., 336
Dobinson, C., 217
Douglas, J., 358
Downey, J. I., 223, 421
Downing, L., 39
Downs, M., 101
Dredger, A., 134
Drigotas, S. M., 164
Drucker, D. J., 43
Dryan, A., 285
Duke, L. A., 441
Du Mont, J., 432, 433
Duru, C., 66
Dworkin, A., 39
Dworkin, S. L., 37
Dwyer, P. L., 64
Dye, M. L., 180

E

Eardley, I., 81, 335
East, L., 401
Eastwick, P. W., 160, 161
Edwards, V. J., 447, 448, 451, 452
Egale Canada, 304
Eggers, D., 190
Eke, A. W., 450
EKOS Research Associates, 286
El-Defrawi, M. H., 61
Elizabeth, A., 218
Elliot, A. J., 97
Elliot, S., 121
Engels, R., 160

Eno, R., 438
Environics Research Group, 313
Epstein, R., 245
Esmail, S., 118, 119, 120, 399

F

Faller, K. C., 451
Fang, L., 324, 358, 359
Farley, M., 47
Fausto-Sterling, A., 136
Federoff, J. P., 407, 427
Fehr, B., 153, 156
Feinberg, D. R., 154, 156
Festa, E. D., 104
Fichner-Rathus, L., 17
Finkel, E. J., 160, 161, 171
Finkelhor, D., 432, 447, 448, 449, 450
Finkelman, J. M., 454
Firestone, R. W., 339, 410
Fischer, B., 474
Fisher, A. D., 45, 142, 190
Fisher, B. S., 278, 433
Fisher, H. E., 105
Fisher, J. D., 392
Fisher, T. D., 45, 142, 190
Fisher, W. A., 115, 116, 268, 278, 327,
    346, 392, 401, 483, 485
Fitzpatrick, M., 246
Flaxman, S. M., 247
Flicker, S., 263, 402
Forbes, A., 120
Ford, C. S., 198, 220, 312
Forte, T., 65
Fortenberry, J. D., 300
Foster, D., 210, 236
Foubert, J. D., 439, 443
Fox, N. S., 248
Foxman, B., 323
Frank, K., 46, 475
Frappier, J-Y., 397
Fraser, M., 58
Frayser, S., 312
Frederick, D., 81
Free, C., 383
Freud, S., 224
Freund, K., 413
Fried, P. A., 252
Friedman, R. C., 223, 421
Friedrich, W. N., 421
Frisch, R. E., 243
Friscolanti, M., 454
Frohlich, P. F., 331
Frohmader, K. S., 104
Fugl-Meyer, K. S., 337
Fullerton, T., 392
Fung, L. C. T., 134
Furnham, A., 154

G

Gaddam, S., 26
Gadgil, M., 336
Gaetz, S., 431
Gagnon, J. H., 37, 451
Gaines, S. O., 153
Gallo, M. F., 277

Gannon, T. A., 191
Gavin, N. I., 258
Gay, P., 23
Gebhard, P. H., 24, 81, 451
Gemme, R., 464
Gerber, J., 401
Gerber, P. N., 421
Gerressu, M., 194
Gidycz, C. A., 435, 443, 444
Giguere, B., 8
Gillespie, B., 323
Gillett, R., 39
Gilmore, K., 244
Gil-Rivas, V., 103
Ginzburg, E., 84
Gionet, L., 259
Girard, D., 448
Glasser, C., 154, 155
Glina, S., 402
Gold, S. R., 156
Goldstein, I., 340, 346
Golombok, S., 140
Goodwin, R. D., 253
Gooren, L. J., 453
Gordon, A. E., 253
Gorzalka, B. B., 46, 104, 438
Gotell, L., 443
Goulet, J., 136
Gouveia, V. V., 164
Gower, P., 253
Grace, A. P., 399
Grady, D., 369
Graham, C. A., 328
Graham, J. M., 163
Graham, K., 436
Granata, A. R., 346
Gray, R. H., 80
Graziano, W. G., 156
Graziottin, A., 332
Green, R., 225, 226
Greenberg, D. M., 451
Greenwald, E., 450
Grenier, G., 332, 396, 397
Griffith, K. H., 232
Griffiths, M. D., 27, 483
Grimes, D. A., 277
Gross, B., 122, 417
Gross, J., 122, 417
Groth, A. N., 440
Groth, A. W., 440
Grov, C., 230, 231
Grover, S., 327, 330
Grubin, D., 425
Gruszecki, L., 340

H

Haake, P., 411, 420
Haaser, R. C., 334
Hackett, G. I., 329, 335
Haddock, S. A., 483, 484
Hald, G., 482
Haley, N., 475
Hallgrimsdottir, H. K., 472, 473
Hamer, D. H., 222
Hampton, M. R., 302, 397

Hanson, R. K., 453
Hardenburg, S. A., 422
Hardwick, D., 379
Harel, Z., 298
Hariri, S., 373
Harlow, M. C., 425
Harris, M., 312
Hartwick, C., 431, 440
Haselton, M. G., 97
Hatcher, R. A., 270, 271, 272, 274, 275,
    276, 277, 278, 279, 283, 284, 359,
    360, 361, 363, 364, 371, 372, 373
Hatemi, P.K., 153
Hatfield, E., 161, 162, 165
Hatt, D. G., 457
Hatzichristou, D. G., 346
Haugaard, J. J., 446
Hay, D. F., 138
Hazelwood, R. R., 415
Hébert, A., 418
Hébert, M., 452
Hebl, M. R., 232
Hegarty, P., 39
Heil, P., 412, 417
Heiman, J. R., 329, 353
Henderson, A. W., 234, 235
Henderson, C. E., 441, 442
Hendrick, C., 164, 165, 169
Hendrick, S. S., 164, 165, 169
Herbenick, D., 194, 197, 200, 216,
    301
Herold, E. S., 9, 146, 178
Herrera, V. M., 452
Hess, G. C., 201
Hess, K. L., 379
Hester, J. D., 136
Hicks, T. V., 190
Hill, D. B., 132
Hill, M. N., 104
Hill, T., 201, 206, 327
Hines, M., 222
Hird, M. J., 221
Hobson, W., 440
Hodgson, S., 58
Hodgson, Z. G., 58
Hoffman, H., 481
Hoffman, L. E., 191
Hogg, R.S., 368, 369
Holmberg, D., 181, 338
Holmes, R. M., 419
Holmes, S. T., 419
Holmstrom, A. J., 181
Holowaty, P., 396
Homma, Y., 262, 296
Horowitz, H. L., 22
Houts, F. W., 425
Hubbard, T. K., 298
Huberman, J., 113
Hucker, S. J., 408, 414, 415
Hudecek, T., 180
Huerta, M., 454
Hugh-Jones, S., 410, 411
Humphreys, T. P., 118, 176, 178, 192,
    300, 437, 438

Hunt, A., 147
Hunter, J., 299
Hunter, M. S., 74, 75, 299
Hussain, A., 177
Hutton, H. E., 378
Hyde, J. S., 97, 108, 143, 231, 296, 298, 315, 329, 481, 482

I

Iemmola, F., 222
Impett, E. A., 184
Incrocci, L., 329
Irons, R. R., 426
Isaacs, C. R., 483
IsHak, W. W., 328
Itzin, C., 485

J

Jacobs, S., 29, 482
Jacobson, A., 154
Jamieson, L., 232
Jamison, P. L., 81
Jannini, E. A., 64, 222
Jansen, E., 330
Jansson, M., 471
Javed, N., 312
Jayaraman, S., 282
Jeffrey, L. A., 472
Johannes, C. B., 336
Johns, A., 396
Johnson, B.T., 394, 395
Johnson, C., 475
Johnson, H., 437
Johnson, O., 312
Johnson, V. E., 92, 109, 117, 118, 341
Johnstone, S. J., 258
Jones, R., 301
Jordan, K., 420
Josey, S., 447
Jozkowski, K.N., 438

K

Kaczmarek, P., 437, 441, 442
Kaestle, C., 206
Kaestle, C. E., 300, 376
Kafka, M. P., 408, 427
Kalemba, V., 454
Kaplan, H. S., 333, 342
Karakiewicz, P. I., 88
Karraker, A., 320
Karremans, J., 160
Katzman, D. K., 272, 273
Katz-Wise, S.L., 231
Kaufman, M., 123
Kayser, D. N., 97
Keefe-Cooperman, K., 329, 331, 337
Keller, J. J., 336
Kellogg, J. H., 192
Kelly, K., 445
Kelly, M. B., 318
Kennedy, M. A., 438, 471
Kennedy, S. H., 102
Kiene, S. M., 392
Kilborne, K. J., 317
Kilchevsky, A., 64

Kimble, D. P., 105
King, D. B., 192
King, M., 233
King, R., 115
Kingston, A., 172
Kingston, D. A., 476, 485
Kinsey, A. C., 43, 117, 214, 296, 415, 419, 421
Kinsman, G., 230
Kippax, S., 206
Kirby, D., 392, 395
Kirkpatrick, R. C., 221
Kito, M., 180
Klahr, A.M., 245
Klein, R., 378
Kleinplatz, P. J., 15, 19, 51, 208, 340, 347, 352, 406, 407, 418
Klien, J. D., 379
Klofstad, C.A., 153
Klusmann, D., 144
Klüver, H., 105
Knaak, S., 259
Knapp, M. L., 173
Knäuper, B., 378
Knoll, J. L., 415
Knox, D., 160
Knudson-Martin, C., 318
Knupp, H., 118
Koch, P. B., 323
Koehler, N., 336
Kogan, A., 184
Kohlberg, L., 141
Kohler, R. K., 394
Komisaruk, B. R., 121
Koren, G., 252
Koss, M. P., 435, 439, 441
Kramer, M. S., 256
Krippner, S., 15
Kristof, N. D., 467, 470, 473
Krüsi, A., 475
Kuhnle, U., 130
Kuiper, B., 135
Kukkonen, T. M., 50
Kulik, L., 149
Kurdek, L. A., 181, 234, 314
Kurzban, R., 154

L

Labelle, A., 420
Labelle, D., 29
LaGasse, L.L., 252
Laggro-Janssen, T.L., 358
Lalonde, R. N., 8, 155, 158
Lalumière, M. L., 113, 190, 224, 408, 413, 440, 441, 449
Lamanna, M. A., 153, 315
LaMarre, A. K., 259
Lamaze, F., 255
Lambert, A. J., 439
Lambert, B., 351
Landolt, M. A., 226
Lane, R., 335
Langevin, R., 410, 411, 413, 423, 441
Langille, D. B., 376, 379
Langstaff, A., 226

Långström, N., 408, 409, 413
Laqueur, T. W., 22
Laris, B. A., 392, 395
Larkins, S., 214
La Rose, L., 161
Latty, E., 110
Laumann, E. O., 8, 14, 37, 143, 146, 194, 206, 216, 322, 353
Lavin, M., 413
Lawrence, A. A., 110, 133, 409
Laws, D. R., 405, 411, 414, 423
Lazarus, L., 47
Lebouthillier, D. M., 378
Lederman, M. M., 368
Lee, B.H., 456
Legate, N., 230, 232
Lehne, G. K., 407, 423
Leitenberg, H., 190, 191, 301, 450
Lepage, Y., 351
Lepischak, B., 135
Leschied, W., 138
Leue, A., 410, 411, 412, 422
Levasseur, J., 470
LeVay, S., 511
Lever, J., 81
Levin, T. R., 302
Levine, D., 154, 302
Levy, H., 447
Lewis, A. L., 227, 228
Lewis, J., 470, 476
Lewis, R. W., 327, 332
Li, T., 217
Li-Barber, K. T., 175
Lincoln, Y. S., 51
Lindberg, L. D., 301
Lindstrom, P., 223
Lippa, R. A., 154, 225, 226, 449
Lippman, A., 373
Little, A. C., 154
Littleton, H., 441, 442
Liu, K. E., 268
Lloyd, R., 467
Loder, N., 138
Logan, C., 408, 414
Logan, T. K., 441
Lohmann, R. I., 298
Longman, M. R., 137
Looman, J., 441
Lopez, L. M., 277
Lord, M., 334
Lou, E., 8
Lowman, J., 467, 471
Lucas, A. M., 463
Lush, G., 396
Lussier, P., 418
Lutfey, K., 353
Lynne, J., 47

M

MacCulloch, D., 20
MacDonald, G., 472
MacIntosh, H., 310
MacKinnon, C. A., 478
MacNeil, S., 38, 176, 306, 314, 338
Madanikia, Y., 195

Madsen, L., 449
Mageau, G., 163
Maggi, M., 106, 107
Mah, K., 115
Maheux, H., 153, 312
Mahoney, A. R., 318
Maisel, L., 196
Maitland, S. B., 299
Majerovich, J., 300
Major, B., 138, 289
Malacad, B. L., 201
Malamuth, N. M., 440
Maletzky, B. M., 424
Malmuth, N., 482
Maniglio, R., 191
Mann, M., 282
Mansson, S., 27
Maranda, M. J., 104
Marazziti, D., 162
Marchbanks, P. A., 271
Marcus, D. K., 155
Mardorossian, C. M., 440
Margolina, G., 442
Mark, M., 483
Markham, C.M., 27
Markman, H. J., 315
Marquardt, E., 313
Marrazzo, J. M., 382
Marshall, D. S., 2
Marshall, L. E., 427
Marshall, W. L., 423, 453, 454, 484
Martin, E. T., 370
Martinez, G., 296
Martins, Y., 98, 99
Marziano, V., 449
Masters, N. T., 37
Masters, W., 435
Masters, W. H., 92, 109, 117, 118, 341
Matheson, K., 442
Maticka-Tyndale, E., 7, 8, 10, 14, 296, 374
Matthews, J., 160
Maxwell, C. D., 37, 438
Maybach, K. L., 156
Mayo, J., 29
Mayo Clinic Staff, 334
Mazur, T., 294
McAnulty, R., 433, 434
McCabe, M. P., 120, 331, 336, 337
McCarthy, B. W., 337, 339, 342, 471
McCloskey, L. A., 452
McCormick, N. B., 37
McCoy, N. L., 98
McCreary Centre Society, 233, 263
McDermott, R., 153
McElroy, W., 39
McEwan, S. L., 441
McGlynn, C., 477
McGregor, M. J., 432
McKay, A., 10, 102, 104, 261, 262, 277, 306, 337, 357, 395, 396
McMahon, C. G., 350
McMaster, L. E., 457, 458
McMillen, M., 79

McNeil, D. G., 369
McNicholas, T., 336
Meaney, G. J., 4, 13, 14, 245, 397, 413
Meggers, H., 196
Meininger, F., 234, 379
Mekhennet, S., 59
Ménard, F. P., 309
Messinger, J.C., 2
Meston, C. M., 206, 331, 402
Meyer-Bahlburg, H., 57
Meyer-Cook, F., 29
Michel, A., 132
Migliardi, P., 8
Milan, A., 153, 260, 312
Milhausen, R. R., 108, 146, 191, 267, 278, 299, 377
Mill, J. S., 14
Millar, C., 480
Miller, R. S., 155, 452
Minichiello, V., 474
Mitchell, B., 433
Money, J., 422
Montaner, J. S., 369
Montoya, R. M., 153
Moore, C., 455
Moore, H., 470
Moore, S. M., 299
Moorman, S. M., 320
Morash, M., 454
Morgan, E. M., 214
Morison, L., 383
Morris, B., 327, 401
Morris, L. B., 258
Morrison, D.M., 37
Morrison, E. S., 68
Morrison, G. G., 486
Morry, M. M., 153, 156
Moser, C., 134, 406, 407, 418
MTV, 172
Muehlenhard, C. L., 143
Mueller, T.E., 378
Muise, A., 175, 179, 184, 299, 417
Mulick, P. S., 217
Muller, A. J., 80
Murphy, L., 407, 427
Murphy, N., 400
Murphy, W. D., 410, 411
Murray, J., 323
Murray, S. H., 191
Murray, S. O., 136
Murray, T. R., 193
Mustanski, B., 223
Myers, T., 201, 206, 207, 214, 376, 382

N

Naili, H., 447
Nakhaie, R., 160
Nappi, G., 75
Nappi, R. E., 75
Narchi, H., 294
National Cancer Institute, 70
National Center for Biotechnology Information, 126, 127

National Center for Transgender Equality, 132
National Institute of Allergy and Infectious Diseases, 371
Natsuaki, M. N., 297
Nazario, B., 101
Needle, R. B., 340
Nelemans, S., 160
Nelson, A., 153
Nelson, L. E., 379
Netting, N. S., 377
Newberry, J. T., 439, 443
Newby, J., 176
Newman, L., 131
Ngwakongnwi, E., 65
Nickel, J. C., 88
Niesta, D., 97
Nobre, P., 108, 342
Nobre, P. J., 337
Norris, S. M., 180
Nosek, M. A., 119
Nosko, A., 481
Nour, N. W., 60, 61
Nova Scotia Department of Health and Wellness, 399
Nurnberg, G., 347
Nussbaum, M. A., 467
Nuttbrock, L., 134

O

Oades, G., 58
Oakes, G., 430
O'Connor, J., 157
O'Doherty, T.O., 467
O'Donohue, W. T., 405, 411, 414
Offman, A., 442
Ogas, I., 26
Ogden, G., 353
Ogilvie, G., 262, 296
Ogilvie, M., 244, 262, 296
Ohl, L.E., 341
Olfson, M., 335, 336
Oliveira, M., 26
Orchard, T., 401
Orchowski, L. M., 104
Ortega, V., 193
Osman, S. L., 436, 438
O'Sullivan, L. F., 37, 148, 176–177, 201, 300, 435, 456
Ott, M.A., 394
Overbeek, G., 160
Owens, E. W., 476

P

Page, I. J., 410, 411
Paintner, A., 252
Pakhomou, S. M., 411
Parent, M. C., 149
Park, N., 171, 175
Parker-Pope, T., 316
Parr-LeFeuve, R., 445
Pasupathy, D., 257
Patel, D., 323
Patriquin, M., 11
Patychuck, D., 379

Pauleta, J. R., 247
Pédinielli, J.-L., 132
Pelham, B., 10
Peluso, P. R., 177, 315, 316, 317
Penton-Voak, I. S., 154
Peplau, L.A., 81
Pepler, D., 138
Peragine, D., 184
Pereda, N., 446
Perel, E., 316
Perez, K., 336
Peritz, I., 435
Perlman, D., 180, 181
Perreault, H. S., 431, 433, 435
Perreault, S., 431, 446
Perron, L., 61
Petersen, J. L., 97, 108, 143, 296, 315, 329, 481, 482
Peterson, Z. D., 435
Petrunik, M., 453
Pew Research Center, 172
Philaretou, A. G., 411
Philp, M., 253
Phipps, A. I., 270
Picard, A., 377
Piché, L., 418
Piercy, J., 470
Pietrusiak, M., 396
Pike, L. B., 295, 388
Pillard, R. C., 222
Pinkerton, S. D., 296
Pinto-Gouveia, J., 337
Pisanski, K., 154
Pitino, L., 98
Plant, E. A., 137
Plaut, S. M., 122
Polansky, D. C., 193
Pollack, H. A., 253
Pollack, L. M., 376
Polusny, M. A., 437, 441
Popp, D., 146
Potter, S. J., 443
Prakash, J., 149
Prentice, T., 382
Preti, G., 99
Preyde, M., 299
Protogerou, C., 394, 395
Provost, M. P., 157
Public Health Agency of Canada, 79, 119, 254, 357, 358, 359, 360, 365, 367, 368, 370, 372, 373, 378, 379, 382, 383, 390, 400
Pukall, C. F., 333
Purdie, M. P., 104
Pyne, J., 132

Q

Quan, H., 65
Quayle, E., 411, 484
Queen, C., 39
Quinsey, V. L., 155, 439

R

Rabinowitz, S. R., 410
Rademakers, J., 295

Rådestad, I., 258
Raichle, K., 439
Raiford, J. L., 379
Ralph, D., 336
Ramsey, S., 58
Randall, H., 5
Rasmussen, P. R., 317
Ratelle, C., 163
Rathus, S. A., 130, 138, 140
Ratner, P. A., 436
Ravindran, L. N., 426
Rawson, R. A., 336–337
Reavey, R., 177
Reback, C. J., 214
Rediger, C., 80
Redman, N., 46
Reece, M., 197, 216
Reinisch, J. M., 294, 295
Reis, H. T., 156, 161
Reiss, I., 14
Reissing, E. D., 46, 302, 310, 351
Reissing, E. K., 334
Rempel, J. K., 74
Ren, J., 271
Resick, P. A., 451
Rhoades, G. K., 170
Ribner, D. S., 19
Riccardi, R., 120
Ricci, E., 369
Richardson, H., 372
Richters, J., 81, 200, 205, 208, 209
Riddell, L., 58
Riedmann, A., 153, 315
Rieger, G., 225
Riggio, R. E., 156
Rimm, E., 336
Rizvi, S., 102
Robbins, C. L., 296
Roberts, T. A., 379
Robertson, J.R., 480
Rodenberg, C., 102
Roesler, A., 103, 425
Rogala, C., 482
Rolleri, L., 392, 395
Romero-Daza, N., 467
Ronis, S. T., 378
Rosario, M., 299
Roscoe, W., 136
Rosen, R.C., 347
Rosenthal, D., 299
Rosky, C. J., 227, 228
Rospenda, K. M., 454
Ross, L., 217
Ross, L. E., 258
Ross, M.W., 26, 27
Rotermann, M., 143, 262, 296, 301, 304, 306, 370
Roughgarden, J., 136
Rowland, D. L., 329
Rubenfeld, K., 176
Rubenson, B., 470
Rubin, H., 180, 181
Rupp, L. J., 408
Rushowy, K., 458
Russell, S. T., 218

Ryder, A. G., 402
Rye, B. J., 4, 13, 14, 135, 195, 199, 206, 227, 245, 314, 332, 397, 399, 413, 431

S

Sadalla, E. K., 156
Sadownik, L. A., 334
Saewyc, E. M., 229, 234, 262, 263, 296, 304, 458
Sagan, C., 285
Sagarin, B. J., 179
Saigal, S., 256
Sakaluk, J. K., 146
Saks, B. R., 102
Saleh, F. M., 425
Salehi, R., 396
Sales, J. M., 376
Salisbury, C., 115
Salska, I., 154
Sand, M., 116
Sanders, S. A., 279
Sanders, T., 469
Santelli, J. S., 301, 394
Santtila, P., 415, 422
Sarrel, P., 435
Satterwhite, C., 358
Savage, L., 220
Savic, I., 131, 223
Savin-Williams, R. C., 213, 214–215, 217, 219, 225, 231
Scheim, A., 46, 217
Schmidt, S. R., 191
Schmitt, D. P., 34, 35, 142, 143, 144, 158, 300–301
Schmitt, M. T., 138
Schneider, J. P., 426, 484
Schneider, M., 457
Schneidewind-Skibbe, A., 74
Schober, J. M., 453
Schover, L. R., 88
Schrader, A. M., 400
Schrimshaw, E. W., 299
Schröder, F. H., 87
Schrut, A., 421
Schultheiss, D., 402
Schulz, K. F., 277
Schwartz, P., 182
Sciolino, E., 59
Scott, J., 118
Seligman, L., 422
Semans, J., 350
Semp, D., 39
Senikas, V., 61
Senn, C. Y., 44, 52, 441, 445
Servais, L., 122
Seth, P., 378, 379
Sethna, C., 387
Seto, M. C., 407, 408, 413, 448–449, 450, 453, 485
Shackelford, T. K., 179
Shakespeare, T., 123
Shamloul, R., 102
Shannon, K., 47, 475
Sharlip, I., 350

Shaughnessy, K., 193, 397, 398
Shaver, F. M., 467, 469, 470, 471, 475
Shaw, J., 287
Sheppard, M., 29
Sherer, R., 368
Sherman, P. W., 247
Shibley Hyde, J., 143
Shields, S. A., 38, 379
Shifren, J. L., 190
Shipko, S., 337
Shirpak, 7, 402
Shorter, E., 25
Shoveller, J. A., 302, 396
Showers, C. J., 153
Siegfried, N., 369
Silverthorne, Z. A., 155
Simon, W., 37
Simons, D., 412, 417
Sims, C. S., 454
Singh, D., 136, 226
Sinha, 431
Sipski, M. L., 121
Slane, A., 172
Small, P., 431, 433
Smallbone, S., 27
Smith, A. M., 88, 252, 267, 301
Smith, D. K., 81
Smith, G. C., 206, 257
Smith, Y. L. S., 135, 257
Smoak, L., 58
Smylie, L., 14, 379
Snyder, D. K., 316
Soble, A., 193
Solovieva, E., 397
Solursh, D. S., 401
Special, W. P., 175
Spencer, A. L., 271
Spencer, N., 253, 271
Spitzer, R. L., 416
Sprecher, S., 38, 153, 154, 156, 180, 181, 308
Steenbeck, A., 376
Stein, M. B., 426
Steinemann, M., 127
Steinemann, S., 127
Stephenson, J., 276
Stephenson, K. R., 300
Sternberg, R. J., 164, 165, 166
Stewart, D. F., 470
Stockett, M. K., 136
Storms, M. D., 215
Strebeigh, F., 436
Strike, C., 445
Stripe, T., 449
Studd, J., 75
Sullivan, K. T., 300
Sun, A., 271
Suschinsky, K. D., 113, 190
Swami, V., 155
Sweeny, C., 58
Symons, D., 34, 192
Szabo, C. M., 120

T

Taddco, D., 272, 273
Tafoya, T., 219

Tan, H. M., 335
Tang, C. S., 298
Tannenbaum, I. J., 155
Taradash, A., 138
Taylor, C., 229
Taylor, D., 262, 296
Taylor, M. J., 336
Taylor, V., 408
Taylor-Butts, A., 431, 433, 442, 446
Ter Kuile, M. M., 334
Tessler Lindau, S., 322
Teunissen, D.A., 358
Thach, C.T., 379
Thayer, J., 335
Thibaut, F., 453
Thigpen, T. W., 292
Thomas, G. D., 35
Thomas, R. M., 193
Thomas, W., 29
Thompson, A. E., 97, 148
Thompson, E. M., 217
Tiggermann, M., 58
Timm, T. M., 341
Timmermann, L., 169
Timmers, A., 110, 191, 481
Tobia, G., 328
Tobian, A. A. R., 80
Totman, R., 136
Touhara, K., 98
Tourigny, M., 452
Tovée, M. J., 155
Travers, R., 263
Trenholm, C., 394
Trivedi, D., 336
Trivers, R., 154
Trulsson, O., 258
Trussler, T., 206
Tufik, S., 104
Tullis, C. A., 400
Tunariu, A. D., 177
Turner, H. A., 447, 448
Turton, J., 450
Twist, M., 315
Tydén, T., 482

U

Udry, J. R., 107
Ulmer, J.T., 476
Uysal., A., 175

V

Vaculík, M., 180
Valdez, H., 368
Vallerand, R. J., 163
Vance, C. S., 39
VanderLaan, D. P., 235
Vandiver, D. M., 432
Vangelisti, A. L., 173
van Honk, J., 223
van Lankveld, J. J. D. M., 335, 336, 351
Vannier, S. A., 176–177, 201
van Straaten, I., 153
Varto, H., 58
Vasey, P. L., 133, 221, 235
Vickerman, K. A., 442

Villar, F., 180
Voeller, B., 207
Vosshall, L. B., 98
Vrangalova, Z., 214–215

W

Wade, T. J., 174
Wainberg, M. A., 377
Waismann, R., 420
Waldinger, M. D., 350
Walker, S., 478
Waller, M.W., 376
Walter, A., 118
Wang, A., 38
Ward, I., 477
Ward, T., 454
Warner, L., 373
Waterman, J., 451
Watson, J. B., 36
Watson (2010), 477, 478
Weaver, A. D., 396, 418
Weeden, J., 154
Weinberg, M. S., 234, 422
Weinrich, J. D., 222
Weinstein, N. D., 376
Weitzer, R., 474
Welldon, E. V., 451
Wells, C., 303
Wells, E.A., 37
Wells, K., 216, 219, 229, 234, 399, 400
Wentland, J. J., 46, 147, 302
Wentland, L., 174
West, S. L., 329
Wetterneck, C.T., 483
Wheeler, J., 408
Whipple, B., 121
Whisman, M. A., 316
White, J., 227, 228
Widman, L., 300
Wierman, M. E., 335, 336
Wilbur, C. J., 157
Wilcox, W. B., 313
Wilkes, J., 480
Williams, C., 138
Williams, M. E., 289
Wilson, J. M. B., 154
Wilson, R. J., 453
Winer, R., 373
Winter, S., 136
Wittenberg, A., 401
Witztum, E., 103, 425
Woll, S. B., 156
Wong, D., 181, 324
Woo, J., 46
Woo, J. S., 402
Woo, J. S. T., 6, 337
Wood, D., 451
Wood, E., 397, 453, 481
Wood, J., 100
Woods, A., 256
Wooten, J. M., 335
World Health Organization, 60, 61, 357, 386
Worthy, R., 27
Wright, J. L., 80

Wright, L. W., 457
Wright, L. W., Jr., 217
Wright, T. C., 373
Wyatt, T. D., 98
Wylie, K., 81
Wynne, A., 382

Y

Yates, P. M., 415–416
Yeh, K-Y., 223
Yoder, V. C., 484

Yost, M. R., 35, 438
Young, A., 469
Young, L., 182
Young, P. C., 400
Young, V. J., 180
Yribarren-Poullos, A., 120
Yule, M. A., 218

Z

Zalenskaya, I. A., 276
Zangrillo, A. N., 400

Zernike, K., 448
Zezima, K., 228
Zhang, N., 379
Zhou, Y. R., 6–7
Zhu, B., 294
Zosuls, K. M., 140
Zucker, K. J., 130, 132, 134, 408, 409
Zurbriggen, E. L., 438

Subject Index

A

ABCDE model of romantic relationships, 169–182
Abortion
    in Canada, 286–288, 289
    history and legal perspectives on, 285–286
    induced, 284
    methods for, 288
    psychological consequences of, 289
    repeated, 289
Abortion drugs, 288
Abstinence, 380
Acquaintance sexual assault, 433
Acquired immune deficiency syndrome (AIDS), 6, 80, 364–365. *See also* Human immunodeficiency virus
    Canadian trends with, 365–366
    diagnosis of, 368
    pregnancy and, 251
    prevention of, 368–369
    progression of, 366–367
    risk reduction for, 380–381
    transmission of, 367–368
    treatment of, 368
Activating effects, 223
Adolescent sexuality
    casual sex and, 302
    coitus in, 301–302
    contraception and, 304
    developmental tasks of, 296
    LGBTQ youth, 299, 303–304
    masturbation and, 300–301
    oral-genital sex and, 301
    puberty, 296, 297–300
    sexual touching and, 301
    virginity and, 300
Adoption, 244–245
Adult sexuality. *See also* Marriage
    cohabitation and, 308–309
    developmental tasks of, 305–307
    sexual health education and, 401–402
    singlehood in, 307–308
After the Affair: Healing the Pain and Rebuilding Trust When a Partner Has Been Unfaithful (Spring), 315
Agape, 160
Age of viability, 251
AIDS. *See* Acquired immune deficiency syndrome
Alcohol, 103–104
    pregnancy and, 252–253
    STIs and, 378
Amenorrhea, 76
Amniotic fluid, 250
Amniotic sac, 250
Amphetamines, 104
Ampulla, 92

Amyl nitrate (poppers), 101
Analogous, 57
Analogues, 27
Anal sex, 205–207
    gay men and, 207
    HIV and, 207
    STIs and, 207
    surveys on, 206
Anaphrodisiacs, 102–103
Ancient Greek peoples, 19–20
Ancient Hebrew peoples, 17–19
Ancient Roman peoples, 20
Androgen insensitivity syndrome, 131
Androgens, 83, 108
Andropause, 84
Anilingus, 206
Anorgasmic, 332
Anovulatory, 297
ANS. *See* Autonomic nervous system
Antiandrogen, 103, 425
Antibodies, 366
Antigens, 366
Aphrodisiac, 19, 97, 101–102
Areola, 68
Are We There Yet?, 399
Arginine, 101
Arranged marriage, 312
Arthritis, 122
Artificial contraception, 268
Artificial insemination, 242–243
Asexuality, 217–218
Ashley Madison, online site, 318
Asian-Canadians, 46
Assigned sex, 129
Assisted Human Reproduction Act, 245–246
Atripla, 368
Attraction. *See also* Physical attractiveness
    cross-cultural, 159
    gender roles expectations of, 156
    inherited preferences in, 158–159
    non-physical traits in, 156
    opposites and, 153
    reciprocity and, 154
Attraction-similarity hypothesis, 153
Australia, sexual behavior in, 208
Auto-erotic asphyxia, 415
Autogynephilic, 134
Autoimmune responses, 242
Autonomic nervous system (ANS), 91
Aversion therapy, 424

B

Bacteria, 359
Bacterial vaginosis (BV), 363
Bartholin's glands, 62
Basal body temperature (BBT), 241, 280–281

BBT. *See* Basal body temperature
B&D. *See* Bondage and discipline
BDSM. *See* Bondage, domination, and sado-masochism
Behaviourists, 36–37
Benign prostatic hyperplasia (BPH), 86
Benign tumours, 70
Berdache (two-spirits), 136
Bias, volunteer, 42
Bill C-36, 466
Biopsychosocial model, for sexual dysfunction, 334
Biphobia, 216
Birth control pill
    advantages and disadvantages of, 269–272
    combination, 268–269
    effectiveness of, 269
    fertility and, 269
    mini, 269
    workings of, 269
Birth rates, in Canada, 260–261
Bisexuality, 19, 216–217
    intimate relationships and, 217
    sexual assault against men and, 436
Bisexual orientation, 212
Blastocyst, 249
Bondage, 415
Bondage and discipline (B&D), 416, 417
Bondage, domination, and sado-masochism (BDSM), 418
Booty calls, 302
Boston Women's Health Book Collective, 444
BPH. *See* Benign prostatic hyperplasia
Brain
    sexual arousal and, 105
    sexual differentiation and, 139–140
    sexual orientation, 223
Braxton Hicks contractions, 254
Breast cancer
    in Canada, 69
    risk factors of, 70
Breastfeeding, 258–259
Breasts, 68–70
    development of, 297
    stimulation of, 199
Brokeback Mountain, 213
Brothel workers, 468
Bullying, 138
Butch, 226
BV. *See* Bacterial vaginosis

C

Caesarean section (C-section), 255–256
CAH. *See* Congenital adrenal hyperplasia

Calendar month, 280
Californication, 480
Call girls, 469
Canada
  abortion in, 286–288
  adoption in, 244–245
  AIDS trends in, 365–366
  Bill C-36 in, 466
  birth rates in, 9–10, 260–261
  breast cancer in, 69
  condom use in, 304, 377–378
  contraception in, 266–268, 306–307
  episiotomy in, 254
  ethnocultural factors in, 382–383
  gay activism in, 230
  gender roles double standard in, 146
  HIV trends in, 365
  human sexuality and demographic
    variables in, 30
  human sexuality in, 5–12
  human sexuality in United States
    compared to, 9–11
  immigrants in, 7–8
  LGBTQ youth harassment in, 229
  loss of virginity, 300
  marital satisfaction in, 313–314
  oral–genital sex in, 201
  prostitution attitudes in, 466–467
  prostitution laws in, 463–466
  repeat abortion in, 289
  reproductive technology legislation in,
    245–246
  rubella in, 251
  same-sex marriage and, 227
  SEM and laws of, 478–480
  sex education in United States
    compared to, 11
  sexual abuse of children in, 445–447
  sexual assault in, 430–433
  sexual dysfunction in, 326
  sexual health education curricula and
    resources in, 398–399
  sexual health education guidelines for,
    390
  sexual orientation and law in, 229–230
  singlehood in, 307–308
  teen pregnancy in, 261, 304
  voyeurism in, 413–414
Canada Border Services Agency, 479
Canada Youth and AIDS Survey, 397
Canadian Charter of Rights and Freedoms,
  11–12, 464, 477
Canadian Contraception Study, 327
*Canadian Guidelines for Sexual Health
  Education*, 387, 389–391
Canadian Human Rights Act, 229
Canadian Institute for Health Information
  (CIHI), 287–288
Canadian Sex Research Forum (CSRF), 5
Cancer
  breast cancer in, 69
  detection and treatment for, 70
Candida albicans, 363
Candidiasis, 363–364
Case study method, 42
Castration, 106

Castration anxiety, 225
Casual sex
  adolescent sexuality and, 302
  new terms for, 302
Celibacy, 308
Cerebral cortex, 105
Cerebral palsy, 120
Cervical cancer, 64–65
Cervical cap, 275–276
Cervicitis, 361
Cervix, 64–65, 254
Chancre, 362
Child abuse. *See* Sexual abuse of children
Childbirth. *See also* Pregnancy
  difficulties with, 256–258
  labor and, 253–254
  methods of, 255–256
  stages of, 254–255
Childhood sexuality
  development of, 293
  early (two to five years), 294–295
  infancy, 294
  middle (five to eight years), 295
  preadolescence (nine to twelve years),
    295–296
  reproduction questions and, 295
Child pornography, 480
Chlamydia, 359–360
  diagnosis and treatment of, 360
  symptoms of, 359–360
  transmission of, 359
Chlamydia trachomatis, 359
Christianity, 20–21
  in Middle Ages, 22
Chromosomes, 127–128, 239
  abnormalities, 253
  abnormalities of, 128–129
Cialis (tadalafil), 102, 344–345
Cigarette smoke, pregnancy and, 253
CIHI. *See* Canadian Institute for Health
  Information
Circles of Support and Accountability
  (COSA), 453
Circumcision, 79–81, 369
Cisgender, 129
Climacteric, 74
Clitoral orgasm, 117
Clitoridectomies, 60
Clitoridectomy, 60
Clitoris, 56–58
Clomiphene, 243
Clomipramine, 350
Cocaine, 104
Coercion. *See* Sexual coercion
Cognitive-behavioural theory, 421–422
Cognitive-behaviour therapy, 423–424
Cognitive-developmental theory, 141–142
Cohabitation, 308–309
Coitus (sexual intercourse), 36
  adolescent sexuality and, 301–302
  early age at first, 302
  techniques/positions for, 203–207
Comarital sex, 316
Combination pill, 268–269
Coming out (of the closet)
  family reaction to, 232–233

  to others, 231–233
  self-acceptance and, 231
Commercial Sex Information Service
  (CSIS), 463
Commitment, in relationships, 177
Common-law relationship, 309
Communication skills
  in adulthood, 306
  getting started with, 183–184
  HIV and, 376–377
  irrational beliefs and, 183
  listening effectively for, 186
  obstacles to, 182–183
  relationships and importance of, 182
  sexual dysfunction and, 338–339
  sexual needs and, 185
  STIs and, 376–377
  vulgarity and, 182–183
Communication technology, Internet and,
  26–27
Complete hysterectomy, 66
Compulsive sexual behavior, 426
Conception, 239–240. *See also* Pregnancy
  optimizing chances of, 241
Concubines, 20
Condoms, 3, 266, 380
  advantages and disadvantages of,
    277–278
  applying, 277, 278
  in Canada, 304, 377–378
  effectiveness of, 277
  errors in using, 279
  female, 278
  HIV and, 278
  psychological obstacles to using,
    377–378
  STIs and, 278
  workings of, 277
Congenital adrenal hyperplasia (CAH),
  130–131
Congenital syphilis, 362
Consensual adultery, 315–316
Consent
  complexity of, 437–444
  research on, 437
  sexual behavior and, 430
Contraception, 3. *See also* Condoms
  adolescent sexuality and, 304
  artificial, 268
  in Canada, 266–268, 306–307
  cervical cap, 275–276
  contraceptive patch, 373
  diaphragm, 274–275
  douche as idea of, 278–279
  emergency, 272–273
  fertility-awareness methods for, 280–281
  injectable, 274
  IUDs, 274
  oral, 268–273
  ovulation-prediction kits, 281
  selecting, 285
  spermicides, 276
  sponge, 276–277
  sterilization, 281–284
  vaginal ring, 273
  withdrawal and, 279–280

Contraceptive patch, 373
Contraceptive sponge, 276–277
Control groups, 50–51
Conventional adultery, 315
Coprophilia, 419
Copulation, 27
Corona, 79
Corpora cavernosa, 57, 79
Corpus luteum, 71
Corpus spongiosum, 79
Correlation, 48
COSA. *See* Circles of Support and
    Accountability
Courtesans, 20
Covert sensitization, 424
Cowper's glands, 85, 110–111
Cremaster muscle, 82
Crimes Against Children Research Center,
    432
Criminal Code of Canada, 229, 268, 286,
    317, 430, 463–464, 469, 479
Critical periods of vulnerability, pregnancy
    and, 251
Crura, 62
Cryptorchidism, 86
Crystal methamphetamine, 104
CSIS. *See* Commercial Sex Information
    Service
CSRF. *See* Canadian Sex Research Forum
Culpotomy, 283
Cunnilingus, 200
    techniques, 202–203
Cybersex addiction, 483–484
Cystitis, 59
Cysts, 70

D

Date rape, 433–435
Date-rape drug, 439
Date sexual assault, 433–435
Decision making, 3–4
Deep Throat, 24
Defense mechanisms, 35
Delayed ejaculation, treating, 349
Demographics, 40
Dependent variable, 50
Depo-Provera, 425
Deviance, 405
*Diagnostic and Statistical Manual of Mental
    Disorders* (DSM), 131
Diaphragm, 274–275
Dilate, cervix, 254
Dilation and evacuation (D&E), 288
Disability
    intellectual and developmental, 122
    physical, 119–122
    sex and, 118–123
    sex education for youth with, 400–401
Divorce, 318–319
Divorce Act of 1985, 318
Dizygotic twins (DZ), 222
Dominican Republic syndrome, 131
Donor IVF, 244
Douche, 63
    as contraceptive idea, 278–279
Drink Detective™ cards, 433

Dysmenorrhea, 75–76
Dyspareunia, 328, 333–334
    treating, 351

E

Ectoparasites, 373–375
Ectopic pregnancy, 66, 252
Efface, cervix, 254
EGALE. *See* Equality for Gays and
    Lesbians Everywhere
Ejaculation
    delayed, 332
    nocturnal emissions, 298
    premature, 91, 332–333, 349–350
    rapid, 91
    retrograde, 93
    spinal-cord injuries and, 120–121
    stages of, 92–93
Ejaculatory ducts, 83
Elavil, 102
ELISA. *See* Enzyme-linked immunosorb-
    ent assay
Embryo, 127
Embryonic stage, of prenatal development,
    249–250
Embryonic transfer, 244
Emergency contraception (EC), 272–273
Emission stage, 92
Empirical approach, 39
Endocrine gland, 71
Endometrial cancer, 65
Endometriosis, 65, 243
Endometrium, 65
Enigmatic orgasm, 116–118
Entourage, 480
Enzyme-linked immunosorbent assay
    (ELISA), 368
Epididymis, 83
Epididymitis, 361
Episiotomy, in Canada, 254
Equality for Gays and Lesbians
    Everywhere (EGALE), 229
Erectile abnormalities, 92, 329–330
Erection, 89
Erogenous zones, 35
Eros, 160, 164
Erotica, 476
Erotic plasticity, 35
Escorts, 468–469
Estrogen, 297
Estrogen replacement therapy (ERT), 108
Estrus (in heat), 107
Ethics
    human sexuality and, 13–14
    in research, 51–52
    sexual rights and, 14
Ethnocultural Communities Facing AIDS
    study, 6
Ethnographic observation, 45
Euro-Canadians, 46
Evolution, 34
Evolutionary psychology
    on gay men and lesbians, 221–222
    gender typing and, 139
    human sexuality and, 34–35
    jealousy and, 179

    sexual fantasies and, 192
The Evolution of Human Sexuality (Symons),
    34
Exchanging information, 173–174
Excitement phase, of sexual response cycle,
    109–110
Exhibitionism, 409–411
Experimental groups, 50–51
Experimental method of research, 48–51
Experiments, 48–51
Expulsion stage, 92
External female sex organs
    clitoris, 56–58
    development of, 128
    hair removal in, 58
    labia majora, 56
    labia minora, 56
    mons veneris, 56
    structures underlying, 61–62
    urethral opening, 58–59
    vaginal opening, 59–61
    vestibule, 58
    vulva, 56
External male sex organs
    development of, 128
    penis, 78–81
    scrotum, 81–82
Extramarital sex, 315
    effects of, 317
    motives for, 315
    patterns of, 315–317
    polyamory and, 317
    swinging, 316, 317

F

Facebook, jealousy and, 179
Fallopian tubes, 66
Family Life Education (FLE), 387
FAS. *See* Fetal alcohol syndrome
Father–daughter incest, 450
*Fearless Sex: A Babe's Guide to Overpowering
    Your Romantic Obsessions and
    Getting the Sex Life You Deserve*
    (Davidson), 147
Fellatio, 200
    techniques, 201–202
Female condoms, 278
Female fertility, 243–245
Female orgasmic disorder, 331–332
    treating, 347–349
Female sex offenders, 432
Female sexual interest/arousal disorder,
    330–331
    treating, 346–347
Female-superior position, 204
Feminism, 25
    pornography approaches of, 477–478
Feminist theory, human sexuality and,
    38–39
Femme, 226
Fertility, 242–243
    birth control pill and, 269
    female issues with, 243–245
    methods assisting, 243–244
Fertility-awareness methods, 280–281
Fetal alcohol syndrome (FAS), 252

Fetal stage, of prenatal development, 250–251
Fetishism, 408
Fifty Shades of Grey, 418
First Nations people
  STIs and, 358
  third gender of, 136
Fisting, 199–200
"Flashers," 409–410
Focus group, 46–47
Follicle, 66
  Graafian, 72–73
Foreplay, 197–198
  desired duration of, 198
Foreskin, 79
Fraser Committee Report, 464
Frenulum, 79
Friendship
  in adulthood, 306
  love and, 165–166
Friends with benefits, 302
Frotteurism, 418–419
Fuck buddies, 302

G

Gamma-hydroxybutyric acid (GHB), 432, 433
Gang sexual assault, 435
Gardnerella vaginalis, 363
Gay activism, 25–26
  in Canada, 230
Gay bashing, 227
Gay, lesbian, bisexual, or transgender (GLBT), 216
Gay men. *See also* Coming out; Lesbian, gay, bisexual, transgendered, and queer
  anal sex and, 207
  biological perspectives on, 221–223
  breast stimulation in, 199
  counseling, 232
  cross-cultural perspectives on, 220–221
  cross-species perspectives on, 221
  current attitudes on, 226–230
  evolutionary psychology on, 221–222
  high school prom and, 305
  historical perspective on, 220
  learning theory on, 225
  lifestyles of, 235–237
  parenting, 236–237
  psychoanalytic theory on, 223–225
  psychological perspectives on, 223–226
  relationships of, 234–235
  religious perspective on, 220
  sexual assault against, 436
  sexual behavior of, 207–209
  STI stereotypes with, 207
Gay–Straight Student Alliance Handbook (Wells), 400
Gender, 4, 30, 126
  in aboriginal culture, 29
  pedophiles and, 448–449
  self-disclosure and differences by, 175–176
  SEM responses differing by, 481–483
  sex-advice literature and, 147

sexual arousal and, 109
sexual orientation and, 29, 219
STIs and, 376, 379
third, 136
Gender binary, 130
Gender constancy, 141
Gender dysphoria, 131–132
Gender identity
  sexual orientation and, 213
  types of, 130–131
Gender non-conforming children, 132
Gender nonconformity, 225–226
Gender reassignment surgery, 134–135
Gender roles, 4
  aggression and, 138
  attraction and expectations of, 156
  Canada double standard with, 146
  in internet dating, 174–175
  sexual behavior and, 142–143, 146–147
  stereotypes and, 137, 142–143
Gender schemas, 142
Gender stability, 141
Gender typing, 126
  biological perspectives on, 139–140
  cognitive-developmental theory and, 141–142
  evolutionary psychology and, 139
  gender schemas and, 141
  prenatal brain organization and, 139–140
  psychoanalytic theory and, 140
  psychological perspectives on, 140–142
  social-cognitive theory and, 140–141
Generalize, 41
General Social Survey (GSS), 430, 431, 435, 441
Genetics, sexual orientation and, 222
Genital herpes, 369–371. *See also* Herpes (HSV)
Genital warts, 372
Germ cells, 82
Germinal stage, of prenatal development, 249, 250
GHB. *See* Gamma-hydroxybutyric acid
Gigolos, 474
Girl Time: Grade 7/8 Healthy Sexuality Program, 399
Global Study of Sexual Attitudes and Behaviors, 353
Gonads, 71
Gonorrhea, 358, 360–361
  diagnosis and treatment of, 361
  symptoms of, 361
  transmission of, 360
Graafian follicle, 72–73
Gräfenberg spot (G spot), 63–64
"Great sex," 352
GSS. *See* General Social Survey

H

HAART. *See* Highly active antiretroviral therapy
Hearing, sexual arousal and, 101
Hepatitis, 372
Hepatitis A, 372
Hepatitis B, 372

Hepatitis C, 372
Hepatitis D, 372
Hermaphrodites, 130
Herpes (HSV), 369–371
  coping with, 371
  diagnosis and treatment, 371
  symptoms of, 370–371
  transmission of, 370
Herpes simplex virus, type 1 (HSV-1), 369
Herpes simplex virus, type 2 (HSV-2), 369–370
Heteroerotic interests, 214
Heterosexism, 229
Heterosexuality, heterosexual relationships compared to, 181
Heterosexual orientation, 212
Highly active antiretroviral therapy (HAART), 368
Hijras, 136
Hindus, 21
HIV. *See* Human immunodeficiency virus
Homoerotic interests, 214
Homogamy, 312
Homologous, 57
Homophobia, 39
  forms of, 227
  roots of, 227–228
Homosexuality, 6
  stereotypes and sexual behavior with, 230
Homosexual orientation, 212
Hormone replacement therapy (HRT), 75
Hormones, 71
  activating effects of, 223
  female sexual behavior and, 107–108
  male sexual behavior and, 106–107
  organizing and activating influences of, 106
  sex drive and, 106
  sexual arousal and, 105–108
  sexual orientation and, 222–223
Hot flashes, 74
HPV. *See* Human papillomavirus
HRT. *See* Hormone replacement therapy
HSV-1. *See* Herpes simplex virus, type 1
HSV-2. *See* Herpes simplex virus, type 2
Human chronic gonadotropin (hCG), 247
Human growth hormone (HGH), 84
Human immunodeficiency virus (HIV), 3, 6, 80, 182, 234, 256, 324, 364–365. *See also* Acquired immune deficiency syndrome
  anal sex and, 207
  biological factors with, 375–376
  breastfeeding and, 259
  Canadian trends with, 365
  communication skills for, 376–377
  condoms and, 278
  diagnosis of, 368
  education and prevention of, 383
  infection of, 366
  Kenya educational program for, 374
  pregnancy and, 251
  prevention of, 368–369
  progression of, 366–367

psychological factors and, 376–378
risk reduction for, 380–381
sexual assault and, 430
sexual health education reducing, 401–402
testing for, 380
transmission of, 367–368
treatment of, 368
Human papillomavirus (HPV), 372–373
Human sexuality. *See also* Adult sexuality;
    Senior sexuality
anthropological perspective on, 27–28
biological perspective on, 27
in Canada compared to United States,
    9–11
Canadian demographic variables in, 30
in Canadian society, 5–12
critical thinking for, 15–16
cross-species perspective on, 27
ethics and, 13–14
evolutionary theory on, 34–35
feminist theory and, 38–39
forms of, 4
historical perspective on, 17, 19–27
in Kenya, 10–11
multiple perspectives on, 28–30
normal *vs.* deviant, 405–406
queer theory and, 39
scientific method for, 40–41
scientific study of, 23–24
sociological perspective on, 27–28
spirituality and, 15
study of, 4–5
terminology for, 4
theoretical approaches to, 33–34
values and, 12–13
Human Sexual Response (Masters and
    Johnson), 47
Human trafficking, 469–470
Hustlers, 474–475
Hyaluronidase, 240
Hymen, 59
Hypersexuality, 426–427
Hypogonadism, 107, 335
Hypothalamus, 71
Hypothesis, 40
Hypoxyphilia, 415
Hysterectomy, 66, 283

I

Ibuprofen, 77
Immune system, 366
Impotence (erectile dysfunction), 329–330
    treating, 344–346
Incest, 450–451
Incest taboo, 17, 450
Incidence, 44
Independent variable, 50
Induced abortion, 284
Infatuation, 162
Infertility, 240, 242–246
Information–motivation–behavioural skills
    (IMB) model, 391, 392
Informed consent, 52
In gamete intrafallopian transfer (GIFT),
    244
Injectable contraception, 274

Internal female sex organs
cervix, 64–65
fallopian tubes, 66
G spot, 63–64
ovaries, 66–67
uterus, 65–66
vagina, 62–63
Internal male sex organs
Cowper's glands, 85
prostate gland, 84
seminal vesicles, 83–84
testes, 82–83
vas deferens, 83
Internet
anonymity of, 175
child pornography and, 480
communication technology and,
    26–27
critical thinking for information found
    in, 18
cybersex addiction and, 483–484
drug purchasing on, 345
masturbation and, 193
pornography and, 398, 483–484
SEM and, 481
sexual abuse of children and, 447
sexual health education and, 397–398
S&M and, 417
Internet dating, 308
acceptability of, 174
gender roles in, 174–175
marriage from, 308
in matchmaking, 171
physical attractiveness and, 155
self-disclosure in, 175–176
Intersexuality, 131
Intersexuals, 129–131
Intimacy, 164, 166
in relationships, 180–181, 316
sex and, 316
Intracytoplasmic sperm injection (ICSI),
    244
Intrauterine devices (IUDs), 274
Introitus, 59
In vitro fertilization (IVF), 243–244
Irrational beliefs, 183

J

Jaundice, 372
Jealousy
cognitive-developmental theory and,
    179–180
evolutionary psychology and, 179
Facebook and, 179
in relationships, 177, 179
same-sex affairs and, 179
Johns (clients of prostitutes)
habitual, 471
motives of, 471
occasional, 471
schools, 473–474

K

Kama Sutra, 21, 353
Kegel exercises, 62
Kenya

HIV education in, 374
human sexuality in, 10–11
Kinsey, 44
Kinsey continuum, 214–215
Kinsey reports, 43–44
Kissing, 28, 198, 295, 370
Klinefelter's syndrome, 129
Klismaphilia, 419

L

Labia majora, 56
Labia minora, 56
Laboratory observation, 47
Ladyboys, 136
Lady Chatterley's Lover (Lawrence), 476
Lamaze method, 255
Laparoscopy, 283
Larynx, 298
Lateral-entry position, 204–205
Lavalife, 308
L-dopa, 102
Learning theory, 36–37
on gay men and lesbians, 225
Lesbian, gay, and bisexual (LGB) youth,
    STIs and, 379–382
Lesbian, gay, bisexual, transgendered, and
    queer (LGBTQ), 218–219
adjustments by, 233–235
adolescent sexuality and, 299
adolescent sexuality obstacles for,
    303–304
Canada and youth harassment of, 229
resilence among, 234
school problems facing, 304
senior sexuality and, 323–324
sexual health education needs for,
    399–400
youth, 233–234
Lesbians. *See also* Coming out
adjustments by, 233–235
biological perspectives on, 221–223
butch, 226
counseling, 232
cross-cultural perspectives on,
    220–221
current attitudes on, 226–230
evolutionary psychology on, 221–222
femme, 226
historical perspective on, 220
learning theory on, 225
lifestyles of, 235–237
as mothers, 258
parenting, 236–237
psychoanalytic theory on, 223–225
psychological perspectives on,
    223–226
relationships of, 234–235
religious perspective on, 220
sexual behavior of, 208–209
Leukocytes, 366
Levitra (vardenafil), 344, 345
LHRH. *See* Luteinizing-hormone-
    releasing-hormone
Limbic system, 105
Listening effectively, 186
Lochia, 259

Love
  companionate, 164
  consummate, 164
  contemporary models of, 162–166
  empty, 164–166
  fatuous, 165, 166
  friendship and, 165–166
  Greek heritage of, 160–161
  idealizing, 160
  infatuation and, 162
  romantic, 161–162, 164–166
  Sternberg's triangular theory of,
    164–166
  styles of, 164
Lubricants, 346
Ludus, 164
Lumpectomy, 70
Luteinizing hormone (LH), 241
Luteinizing-hormone-releasing-hormone
  (LHRH), 425

M

Male Call Canada survey, 382
Male erectile disorder, 329–330
Male fertility, 242–243
Male menopause, 84
Male orgasmic disorder, 332
Male sexual functions, 88–93
  ANS in, 91
  brain's role in, 90–91
  ejaculation, 91–93
  erectile abnormalities and, 92
  erection, 89
  spinal reflexes and sexual response in,
    89–92
Male-superior position, 203–204
Malignant tumours, 70
Mammary glands, 68
Mammography, 70
Marijuana (Cannabis), 104
  pregnancy and, 252
Marital sexuality. *See* Marriage
Marriage. *See also* Extramarital sex
  arranged, 312
  cohabitation before, 309
  divorce and, 318–319
  homogamy and, 312
  from internet dating, 308
  marital satisfaction in, 313–314
  polyamory and, 317
  reasons for, 310–311
  same-sex, 12, 220, 227, 309–310
  sexual assault and, 436–437
  sexual conflict in, 314
  types of, 311–312
Massage-parlor workers, 468
Mastalgia, 76
Mastectomy, 70
Masturbation, 293
  adolescent sexuality and, 300–301
  condemnation of, 193
  female techniques for, 196–197
  in history, 192–193
  internet and, 193
  male techniques for, 195–196
  in North America, 195

  orgasm and, 195–196
  in preadolescence, 296
  sex therapy focus on, 349
  surveys on, 193–195
*Mating in Captivity: Reconciling the Erotic
  and the Domestic* (Perel), 316
Medroxyprogesterone acetate (MPA), 425
Menarche, 71, 297, 298
Menopause, 74–75
  male, 84
Menstrual cramps, 76
  treating, 77
Menstrual cycle
  amenorrhea and, 76
  dysmenorrhea and, 75–76
  menstrual phase of, 72–73
  ovulatory phase of, 72–73
  PMS and, 76
  proliferative phase of, 72
  regulation of, 71
  secretory phase of, 73
  treating discomforts in, 77
Menstrual phase, of menstrual cycle,
  72–73
Menstrual synchrony, 98–99
Menstruation
  historical and cross-cultural
    perspectives on, 72
  pregnancy and resumption of, 259–260
  sex during, 74
Midodrine, 121
Mindfulness meditation, 353
Minilaparotomy, 283
Mini pill, 269
Miscarriage, 247
Missionary position, 203–204
Monogamy, 17, 311
  serial, 308
Monozygotic twins (MZ), 222
Mons veneris, 56
Mormonism, sexual abuse of children in
  sect of, 447
Morning sickness, 247
Mother–son incest, 450–451
Motility, 242
Multiple orgasms, 117
Multiple sclerosis (MS), 120, 336
Muslims, 21
Mutual cyclical growth, 181
My Fair Lady, 137
Myotonia, 109

N

Naturalistic observation, 45
Natural selection, 34
Necrophilia, 419
Neisseria gonorrhoeae, 360
*New Directions in Sex Therapy: Innovations
  and Alternatives* (Kleinplatz), 347
The New Gay Teenager (Savin-Williams),
  219
Nicotine, 102
Nocturnal emissions, 298
Nordic Model, 466
North America, masturbation in, 195
Nudity, privacy and, 172

O

Obscene telephone calling, 411–412
Obscenity, 477
Ocular herpes, 370
Oedipus complex, 36, 140, 421
Oestrogen, 66
One-night stands, 302
Online dating, 171
Opening lines, 173
Opportunistic diseases, 367
Oral contraceptives, 268–273
Oral-genital sex, 143
  abstaining from, 201
  adolescent sexuality and, 301
  in Canada, 201
  cunnilingus, 200, 202–203
  fellatio, 200, 201–202
  69 position, 203
  survey data on, 200–201
  techniques for, 201–203
Orgasm, 23, 92
  clitoral, 117
  enigmatic, 116–118
  masturbation and, 195–196
  multiple, 117
  myth and misunderstanding of,
    116–117
  subjective feelings on, 115
  vaginal, 117
Orgasmic disorders, 331–333
  treating, 347–350
Orgasmic phase, of sexual response cycle,
  111–113
Orgasmic platform, 111
Orgasmic reconditioning, 424
Os, 64
Outercourse, 381
*Out of the Shadows: Understanding Sexual
  Addiction* (Carnes), 426
Ovarian cancer, 67
Ovariectomy, 108
Ovaries, 66
Ovulation, 71, 243, 259–260
Ovulation method, 281
Ovulation-prediction kits, 281
Ovulatory phase, of menstrual cycle, 72–73
Ovum, 65, 239–240
  period of the, 249

P

"Pansexuals," 219
Pap test, 7, 65, 67
Paraphilias, 406
  biological perspectives on, 420
  cognitive-behavioural perspectives on,
    421–422
  coprophilia, 419
  exhibitionism, 409–411
  fetishism, 408
  frotteurism, 418–419
  integrated perspective on, 422–423
  klismaphilia, 419
  necrophilia, 419
  partialism, 408
  psychoanalytic perspectives on, 421

severity of, 407
sexual masochism, 414–415
sexual sadism, 415–418
sociological perspectives on, 422
telephone scatologia, 411–412
toucherism, 418
transvestism, 408–409
treating, 423–426
urophilia, 420
voyeurism, 413–414
zoophilia, 419
Paraplegic, 92
Parasympathetic nervous system, 91
Parkinson's disease, 102
Partialism, 408
Participant observation, 45–46
Partner sexual assault, 436–437
Passion, 166, 305–306
Pathogens, 366
Peak days, 281
Pederasty, 19
Pediculosis, 374
Pedophiles, 424
    gender and, 448–449
    research on, 448–450
Pedophilia, 448–450
    origins of, 453
Pelvic examination, 67–68
Pelvic inflammatory disease (PID),
    269, 274, 333, 360
Penicillin, 360, 361, 362–363
Penile strain gauge, 49
Penis, 78–79
    circumcision of, 79–81, 369
    size of, 81
    variations of, 80
Penis envy, 225
Performance anxiety, 89, 330, 340
Pergonal, 243
Perimenopause, 74
Perineum, 60–61
    tearing of, 254
Period of the ovum, 249
Petting, 301
Peyronie's disease, 92
Phallic symbols, 17, 78
Phallic worship, 17
Phalloplasty, 135
Pharyngeal gonorrhea, 360
Pheromones, 98
Philia, 160, 164
Phimosis, 81
Physical attractiveness
    determinants of, 154–156
    importance of, 154
    internet dating and, 155
Pimps, 467
Pituitary gland, 71
Pivot Legal Society, 469
Placebo effect, 101
Placenta, 250
Plateau phase, of sexual response cycle,
    110–111
PLISSIT model, for sexual dysfunction
    treatment, 341
Polyamory, 317

Polyandry, 312
Polygamy, 17, 311
Polygyny, 312
Populations, 41
Pornography
    child, 480
    conservative position on, 477
    defining, 476
    feminism approaches to, 477–478
    internet and, 398, 483–484
    liberal position on, 477
    obscenity and, 477
    perspectives on, 477–478
69 position, 203
Postpartum depression (PPD), 258
Postpartum period, 258–260
Post-relationship contact and tracking
    (PRCT), 456
Post-traumatic stress disorder (PTSD),
    442
Potency, 84
Pragma, 164
Preadolescence, 295–296
Pre-eclampsia, 252
Pregnancy. *See also* Childbirth; Fertility;
    Prenatal development
    alcohol and, 252–253
    cigarette smoke and, 253
    critical periods of vulnerability and,
        251
    diet during, 251
    diseases and disorders in, 251
    drug use during, 252
    early effects of, 247
    early signs of, 246
    ectopic, 252
    HIV/AIDS and, 251
    infertility and, 240, 242
    marijuana and, 252
    menstruation resumption after,
        259–260
    miscarriage and, 247
    narcotics and, 252
    psychological changes during, 248
    puberty and, 297
    rubella and, 251
    sex after, 260
    sex during, 247–248
    syphilis and, 251
    teen, 260–264, 303, 304
    tests for, 246–247
    vitamins and, 252
Pregnancy-induced hypertension, 252
Premature ejaculation, 91, 332–333,
    349–350
Premenstrual syndrome (PMS), 76
Prenatal development
    age of viability in, 251
    delivery date calculation and, 248–253
    embryonic stage of, 249–250
    environmental influences on, 251–253
    fetal stage of, 250–251
    germinal stage of, 249, 250
Prepuce, 57
Preterm birth, 256–257
Priapism, 92

Primary amenorrhea, 76
Primary dysmenorrhoea, 76
Primary erogenous zones, 99
Primary sex characteristics, 297
Prodromal symptoms, 370
Progesterone, 66
Proliferative phase, of menstrual cycle, 72
Propinquity, 153
Prostaglandins, 76
Prostate cancer, 86–88
Prostate gland, 84
    disorders of, 86–88
Prostate-specific antigen (PSA), 87
Prostate surgery, 88
Prostatitis, 88
Prostitution, 23, 462
    Canadian attitudes on, 466–467
    Canadian laws on, 463–466
    female, 467–469
    legal challenges to legalize, 464–466
    police entrapment and, 464
    as sex work, 463
*Protecting Canadians from Online Crime
    Act*, 460
*Protection of Children Involved in Prostitution
    Act* (1999), 464
*Protection of Communities and Exploited
    Persons Act*, 466
Protestant reformers, 22
Prozac, 102
Prurient, 476
Psychoactive drugs
    alcohol, 103–104, 252–253
    stimulants, 104
Psychoanalysis, 35, 423
Psychoanalytic theory, 35–36
    on gay men and lesbians, 223–225
    gender typing and, 140
    paraphilias and, 421
Psychological androgyny, 148–149
Psychosexual development, 36
Psychosexual trauma, 337–338
Psychotherapy, 342
PTSD. *See* Post-traumatic stress disorder
Puberty, 297
    female changes in, 297
    male changes in, 297–299
    preadolescence preparing for, 296
    pregnancy and, 297
    romantic and sexual relationships in,
        299–300
    self-acceptance in, 299
Pubococcygeal muscle, 62

Q

Qualitative methodology, 51
Quantitative methodology, 41–42, 51
Queer theory, human sexuality and, 39
Questionnaires, 43

R

Radiotherapy, 65
Random sample, 41
Rapid ejaculation (RE), 91, 332–333,
    349–350
Rear-entry position, 205

Reciprocity, 154
Regina v. Butler, 478–479
Reliability, of data, 44
Repression, 35
Reproductive technology legislation, in
    Canada, 245–246
Research, 6–7, 30
    case study method for, 42
    on consent, 437
    ethics in, 51–52
    experimental method of, 48–51
    focus group method for, 46–47
    informed consent impact on, 52
    laboratory observation method for, 47
    on pedophiles, 448–450
    qualitative methodology for, 51
    quantitative methodology for,
        41–42, 51
    on senior sexuality, 320, 322
    on sexual arousal, 49
    on sexual consent, 178
    on sexual fantasies, 190–191, 190–197
    on sexual harassment, 457–458
    survey method for, 43–45
    on voyeurism, 413
Resilence, among lesbian, gay, bisexual,
    transgendered, and queer, 234
Resolution phase, of sexual response cycle,
    111–112, 114
Retrograde ejaculation, 93
Rh incompatibility, 252
Rhythm methods, 280–281
Rohypnol, 432, 433, 439
Root, 79
Rubella, 251

S

Sacrum, 90
Sado-masochism (S&M),
    internet and, 417
    popular forms of, 416
    sociological perspective on, 422
    stereotypes with, 417–418
    subculture of, 416–417
Same-sex marriage, 12, 220, 309–310
    adjustments by, 233–235
    benefits of, 310
    Canada and, 227
Sample, random, 41
Save the Children, 257
Scabies, 374–375
Schemas, 141
Scores, 474
Scrotum, 82–83
Secondary amenorrhea, 76
Secondary dysmenorrhoea, 76
Secondary erogenous zones, 99
Secondary sex characteristics, 68, 83,
    105, 297
Secretory phase, of menstrual cycle, 73
Selection factor, 50
Selective serotonin reuptake inhibitors
    (SSRIs), 337, 424–425
Self-disclosure, 175
    gender differences in, 175–176
    importance of, 175

    in internet dating, 175
    sex and, 176
    stereotypes with, 176
Self-examination, of testes, 87
SEM. *See* Sexually explicit material
Semen, 85
Seminal vesicles, 83–84
Seminiferous tubules, 83
Senior sexuality
    death of partner and, 323
    female physical changes in, 320–321
    impotence and, 330
    LGBTQ and, 323–324
    male physical changes in, 321–322
    research on, 320, 322
    sex patterns of, 322–323
    sexual arousal and, 321
    stereotypes of, 319–320
    STIs and, 324
Sensate-focus exercises, 342
Sensory disabilities, 121–122
Serial monogamy, 308
Seronegative, 368
Seropositive, 368
Sex. *See also* Coitus
    after pregnancy, 260
    anal, 205–207
    casual, 302
    definitions of, 5
    disability and, 118–123
    "great," 352
    initiating, 176–177
    intimacy and, 316
    as leisure, 4
    menstruation and, 74
    over romance, men prefer, 148
    parents discussing with children, 388
    during pregnancy, 247–248
    self-disclosure and, 176
    senior sexuality patterns in, 322–323
SexAbility, 119
Sex-advice literature, 147, 209
Sex? A Healthy Sexuality Resource, 399
*Sex and Temperament in Three Primitive
    Societies* (Mead), 28
Sex drive, hormones activating, 106
Sex education, in Canada compared to
    United States, 11
Sex flush, 110
Sex Information and Education Council of
    Canada (SIECCAN), 5, 104
Sexism, 137–138
Sexologist, 23
Sex skin, 111
Sex talk, 182–183
Sex therapy, 340–341
    eroticism promoted in, 347
    integrating, 342
    masturbation and, 349
    qualified professionals for, 343
    SEM promoted in, 476
Sexting, 172
Sex tourism, 448
Sexual abuse of children
    abuser types in, 448
    in Canada, 445–447

    effects of, 451–452
    incest and, 450–451
    internet and, 447
    legislation against, 446
    patterns in, 447–448
    pedophilia and, 448–450, 453
    perpetrator treatment for, 453–454
    prevention programs for, 452
    sex tourism and, 448
    treatment for survivors of, 452–453
Sexual addiction, 426
Sexual arousal
    brain and, 105
    factors influencing, 108
    gender and, 109
    genital compared to subjective, 113
    hearing and, 101
    hormones and, 105–108
    research on, 49
    senior sexuality and, 321
    senses and, 96–101
    sexual orientation and, 110
    sexual response cycle and levels of, 109
    smell and, 97–99
    taste and, 100–101
    thermographic camera measuring, 50
    touch and, 98–99
    vision and, 96–97
Sexual arousal-related disorders, 329–331
    treatments for, 344–347
Sexual assault
    acquaintance, 433
    bisexual men and, 436
    in Canada, 430–433
    date, 433–435
    drugs and, 432–433
    female sex offenders and, 432
    gang, 435
    against gay men, 436
    HIV and, 430
    levels of, 430
    lowering risk of, 444
    male competitiveness and, 439
    marriage and, 436–437
    against men, 435
    myths about, 438–439
    partner, 436–437
    perpetrator treatment for, 453–454
    preventing, 443
    psychological disorders resulting from,
        442
    PTSD from, 442
    self-defense against, 443–444
    social attitudes and, 438–439
    stereotypes with, 436, 438–439
    stranger, 433
    suggestions for victims of, 442
    survivors, 441–443
    treatment for, 442–443
    types of, 433–437
Sexual-aversion disorder, 343
Sexual behavior
    alcohol and, 103–104
    in Australia, 208
    breastfeeding and, 259
    compulsive, 426

consent and, 430
of gay men, 207–209
gender roles and, 142–143, 146–147
of lesbians, 207–209
solitary, 193–195
stereotypes with homosexuality and, 230
Sexual Behavior in the Human Female (Kinsey), 23
Sexual Behavior in the Human Male (Kinsey), 23
Sexual behaviors of diverse populations, 46–47
Sexual coercion
common strategies of, 440
male *vs.* female victims of, 440
men and, 440–441
SEM and, 484–486
verbal pressure tactics in, 444–445
Sexual consent, 178
Sexual desire-related disorders, 328–329
treatments for, 342–343
Sexual differentiation
brain and, 139–140
prenatal, 126–129
Sexual dreams, 192
Sexual dysfunction
aging and, 336
biological causes of, 334–337
biopsychosocial model for, 334
boredom and routine, 338
in Canada, 326
communication skills and, 338–339
cultural influences on, 337
drugs and, 336–337
emotional factors and, 338
health problems and, 335–336
ineffective sexual techniques, 338
Masters and Johnson approach to treating, 341–342
myths and misinformation, 338
origins of, 334–340
performance anxiety and, 89, 330, 340
PLISSIT model treating, 341
prevalence of, 327
psychosexual trauma and, 337–338
psychosocial causes of, 337–340
relationship problems and, 339–340
treating, 340–353
types of, 328–334
Sexual fantasies
evolutionary psychology and, 192
LGB peoples and, 191–192
research on, 190–191
stereotypes with, 190
Sexual Fluidity: Understanding Women's Love and Desire (Diamond), 49
Sexual harassment
behaviors indicating, 454
on campuses, 457
common types of, 454
cyberbullying and, 458–460
cyberstalking and, 456
of minority groups, 455
research on, 457–458
resisting, 459

in schools, 457–458
in workplace, 455–457
Sexual health, definition of, 386
Sexual health education
abstinence-only programs, 393–394
adult sexuality needs and, 401–402
broadly based programs, 394–395
Canada curricula and resources for, 398–399
for disabled youth, 400–401
effective, 392
goals of, 387
information–motivation–behavioural skills (IMB) model, 391, 392
information sources for, 397–398
internet and, 397–398
key ingredients for, 392, 393
LGBTQ needs for, 399–400
in multicultural society, 402
parental attitudes, 396
professionals, sexuality training, 392–393
in schools, brief history, 387–390
youth attitudes, 396–397
Sexual horizons, expanding, 122–123
Sexually explicit material (SEM). *See also* Pornography
Canadian law and, 478–480
censorship and, 478
employers and, 481
erotica, 476
gender differences in response to, 481–483
internet and, 481
nonviolent, 485–486
purposes of, 476
sex offenders and, 484–485
sex therapy promoting, 476
sexual coercion and, 484–486
on television, 480
violent, 485
Sexually transmitted infections (STIs), 3, 304, 333, 356
alcohol and drug abuse and, 378
anal sex and, 207
bacterial infections, 359–363
biological factors with, 375–376
BV, 363
in Canada, 357–359
candidiasis, 363–364
chlamydia, 359–360
communication skills and, 376–377
condoms and, 278
ectoparasites, 373–375
education and prevention of, 383
ethnocultural factors and, 382–383
First Nations people and, 358
gay men stereotypes with, 207
gender and, 376, 379
genital warts, 372
gonorrhea, 358, 360–361
hepatitis, 372
herpes, 369–371
HPV, 372–373
LGB youth, 379–382
pediculosis, 374

psychological factors and, 376–378
risk reduction for, 380–381
scabies, 374–375
senior sexuality and, 324
sexual health education reducing, 401–402
sexual orientation and, 379–382
sex workers and, 475–476
social capital and, 379
social factors with, 378–382
socio-economic status and, 379
syphilis, 251, 358, 361–363
testing for, 380
trichomoniasis, 364
vaginal infections, 363–364
viral infections, 364–373
Sexual masochism, 414–415
Sexual masochists, 414
Sexual needs, 185
Sexual objectification, 39
Sexual orientation
in aboriginal culture, 29
birth order and, 224
body odors and, 99
brain structure and, 223
Canadian law and, 229–230
classifying, 213–216
estimates of, 216
gender and, 29, 219
gender identity and, 213
genetics and, 222
hormonal influences on, 222–223
Kinsey continuum of, 214–215
psychological perspectives on, 223–226
relationship satisfaction and, 314–315
sexual arousal and, 110
STIs and, 379–382
teen pregnancy and, 263
traditional concepts of, 219
Sexual pain-related disorders, 333–334
treating, 351–353
Sexual response cycle
Basson's model of, 115–116
excitement phase of, 109–110
Kaplan's stages of, 114–115
Masters and Johnson's four-phase, 109–114
orgasmic phase of, 111–113
plateau phase of, 110–111
resolution phase of, 111–112, 114
sexual arousal levels during, 109
Sexual revolution, 24–25, 147
Sexual rights, and ethics, 14
Sexual sadism, 415–418
Sexual sadists, 415
Sexual script theory, 37
Sexual self-acceptance, 299
Sexual strategies theory, 144–145
Sexual touching (petting), 301
Sex workers. *See also* Prostitution
advocacy for, 469
entry into life as, 470–471
female types of, 467–469
human trafficking and, 469–470
male, 474–475
male customers for female, 471–474

Sex workers *(Continued)*
  motives for hiring, 472–473
  prostitutes as, 463
  stereotypes with, 472
  STIs and, 475–476
  stripping and, 475–476
  survey of, 46–47
  survey of clients of, 47
Shaft, 79
Sibling incest, 450
Singlehood, 307–308
S&M. *See* Sado-masochism
Small talk, 170, 172–173
Smell, sexual arousal and, 97–99
Social-cognitive theory, 37
  gender typing and, 140–141
Social desirability, 44
Social exchange theory, 38, 169
Socialization, 140
Social skills training, 424
Society for the Scientific Study of Sexuality (SSSS), 5
Society of Obstetricians and Gynecologists (SOGC), 256
Sociobiology, 34
Socio-economic status (SES), 379
Sodomy, 220
SOGC. *See* Society of Obstetricians and Gynecologists
Somatic nervous system, 91
Spark alive in romantic relationships, 184
Speed-dating phenomenon, 160–161
Sperm, 83, 239–240
  motility, 242
Spermatogenesis, 83
Spermatozoa, 83
Spermicides, 276
Sphincters, 61
Spinal-cord injuries, 120–121
Spirituality, human sexuality and, 15
Squeeze technique, 349–350
SSRIs. *See* Selective serotonin reuptake inhibitors
Stalking, 180
Stereotypes
  double standard, 146
  of gay men and STIs, 207
  gender roles and, 137, 142–143
  with homosexuality and sexual behavior, 230
  self-disclosure and, 176
  senior sexuality and, 319–320
  sexual assault and, 436, 438–439
  with sexual fantasies, 190
  sex workers and, 472
  S&M, 417–418
  undersexed women, 146
Sterilization
  advantages and disadvantages of, 284
  defined, 281
  female, 283–284
  male, 282–283
Stillbirth, 251, 257–258
Stimulants, 104
Stimulation, breast, 199
STIs. *See* Sexually transmitted infections

Stone Age, 17
Stop-start technique, 350
Storge, 160, 164
Stranger sexual assault, 433
Stratified random samples, 41
Street-based sex workers, 467–468
Stripping, 475–476
The Strong Breast Revolution, 69
Studies in the Psychology of Sex (Ellis), 23
Sudden infant death syndrome (SIDS), 256
Surrogate motherhood, 244
Survey method, 43–45
Surveys, 43–45
  on anal sex, 206
  limitations of, 44–45
  on masturbation, 193–195
  on oral–genital sex, 200–201
  of sex workers and clients, 47
Swinging, 316, 317
Sympathetic nervous system, 91
Syphilis, 358, 361–363
  diagnosis and treatment of, 362–363
  pregnancy and, 251
  symptoms of, 362
  transmission of, 361–362
Systematic desensitization, 424

T

Take Back the Night, 435, 443
Tampons, 73
Tantric sex, 15, 198
Taoists, 21–22
Taste, sexual arousal and, 100–101
Teachingsexualhealth.ca, 399
Teen motherhood, 263–264
Teen pregnancy
  in Canada, 261, 304
  factors influencing, 261–262
  life after, 263–264
  sexual orientation and, 263
  television exposure and, 303
Telephone scatologia, 411–412
Teratogens, 251
Testes (testicles), 71, 78, 82–83
  descent of, 129
  self-examination of, 87
Testicular cancer, 85–86
Testosterone, 71, 83, 102, 128, 298, 321
Thailand, ladyboys of, 136
Theory, 33
Thermographic camera, 50
Third gender, 136
Tofranil, 102
Toplessness, 7
Toucherism, 418
Touching, 198
Touch, sexual arousal and, 99–100
Toxic shock syndrome (TSS), 73
Traditional sexual script, 37
Transexuals
  gender reassignment surgery for, 134–135
  surgical outcomes for, 135
Transgenderism, 218–219
Transgender/trans, 132
Transition, childbirth stage, 254

Transitioning, 132
Transphobia, 137
Trans Pulse Project, 137
Transsexualism, 132–137
Transverse position, childbirth, 256
Transvestism, 408–409
Treatment, 48
Treponema pallidum (T. pallidum), 361
Trichomonas vaginalis, 364
Trichomoniasis, 364
Tropic of Cancer (Miller), 476
Tubal sterilization, 283
Tumescence, 335
Turner's syndrome, 129
"Two-Spirited," 219

U

UCR. *See* Uniform Crime Reporting Survey
The Ultimate Guide to Sex and Disability, 123
Umbilical cord, 250
Unconscious mind, 35
Uniform Crime Reporting Survey (UCR), 430, 431, 446
United States
  birth rate in, 9–10
  education in, 10
  human sexuality in Canada compared to, 9–11
  sex education in Canada compared to, 11
Urethral bulb, 92
Urethral opening, 58–59
Urethritis, 85
Urogenital system diseases, 85–88
Urologist, 85
Urophilia, 420
Uterine cancer, 65
Uterus, 65–66

V

Vacuum aspiration, 288
Vagina, 62
Vaginal mucus, 241
Vaginal opening, 59–61
Vaginal orgasm, 117
Vaginal photoplethysmograph, 47
Vaginal ring, 273
Vaginismus, 328, 334
  treating, 351
Vaginitis, 63, 363
Validity, of data, 44
Values, 5
  human sexuality and, 12–13
Variables, 40
  dependent, 50
  independent, 50
Vas deferens, 83
Vasectomy, 83, 282–283
Vasocongestion, 47, 109, 113, 329
Vasovasotomy, 283
Verbal coercion tactics, 444–445
Vestibular bulbs, 62
Vestibule, 58
Viagra, 102
Viagra (sildenafil), 344–345, 347

Vibrators, 197
Victorian period, 22–23
Vietnam War, 24
Viral hepatitis. *See* Hepatitis
Virginity, 20
    adolescent sexuality and, 300
    Canadians, losing, 300
Viscosity, 281
Vision, sexual arousal and, 96–97
Volunteer bias, 42
Vomeronasal organ (VNO), 98

Voyeurism, 413–414
    in Canada, 413–414
    normal, 413
    research on, 413
Vulgarity, 182–183
Vulva, 56
Vulvodynia, 334

W

"War driving," 480
Whore-madonna complex, 471

World Association for Sexual Health
    (WAS), 5
    global community goals of, 14
Written in the Flesh: A History of Desire, 25

Z

ZIFT. *See* Zygote intrafallopian transfer
Zona pellucida, 240
Zoophilia, 419
Zygote intrafallopian transfer (ZIFT), 244
Zygotes, 73, 127